A COURSE OF
MODERN ANALYSIS

A COURSE OF
MODERN ANALYSIS

AN INTRODUCTION TO THE GENERAL THEORY OF INFINITE PROCESSES AND OF ANALYTIC FUNCTIONS; WITH AN ACCOUNT OF THE PRINCIPAL TRANSCENDENTAL FUNCTIONS

by

E. T. WHITTAKER

and

G. N. WATSON

FOURTH EDITION
Reprinted

CAMBRIDGE
AT THE UNIVERSITY PRESS
1958

PUBLISHED BY
THE SYNDICS OF THE CAMBRIDGE UNIVERSITY PRESS

Bentley House, 200 Euston Road, London, N.W. I
American Branch: 32 East 57th Street, New York 22, N.Y.

First Edition 1902
Second Edition 1915
Third Edition 1920
Fourth Edition 1927
Reprinted 1935
Reprinted 1940
Reprinted 1946
Reprinted 1950
Reprinted 1952
Reprinted 1958

First printed in Great Britain at the University Press, Cambridge
Reprinted by offset-litho
by Bradford & Dickens

PREFACE

TO THE FOURTH EDITION

ADVANTAGE has been taken of the preparation of the fourth edition of this work to add a few additional references and to make a number of corrections of minor errors.

Our thanks are due to a number of our readers for pointing out errors and misprints, and in particular we are grateful to Mr E. T. Copson, Lecturer in Mathematics in the University of Edinburgh, for the trouble which he has taken in supplying us with a somewhat lengthy list.

E. T. W.
G. N. W.

June 18, 1927.

CONTENTS

PART I. THE PROCESSES OF ANALYSIS

PART II. THE TRANSCENDENTAL FUNCTIONS

[NOTE. The decimal system of paragraphing, introduced by Peano, is adopted in this work. The integral part of the decimal represents the number of the chapter and the fractional parts are arranged in each chapter in order of magnitude. Thus, e.g., on pp. 187, 188, § 9·632 precedes § 9·7 because 9·632 < 9·7.]

CONTENTS

PART I

THE PROCESSES OF ANALYSIS

CHAPTER I

COMPLEX NUMBERS

1·1. *Rational numbers.*

The idea of a set of numbers is derived in the first instance from the consideration of the set of *positive* integral numbers*, or *positive integers*; that is to say, the numbers 1, 2, 3, 4, ... Positive integers have many properties, which will be found in treatises on the Theory of Integral Numbers; but at a very early stage in the development of mathematics it was found that the operations of Subtraction and Division could only be performed among them subject to inconvenient restrictions; and consequently, in elementary Arithmetic, classes of numbers are constructed such that the operations of subtraction and division can always be performed among them.

To obtain a class of numbers among which the operation of subtraction can be performed without restraint we construct the class of *integers*, which consists of the class of positive† integers $(+1, +2, +3, ...)$ and of the class of negative integers $(-1, -2, -3, ...)$ and the number 0.

To obtain a class of numbers among which the operations both of subtraction and of division can be performed freely‡, we construct the class of *rational numbers*. Symbols which denote members of this class are $\frac{1}{2}$, 3, $0, -\frac{15}{7}$.

We have thus introduced three classes of numbers, (i) the *signless integers*, (ii) the *integers*, (iii) the *rational numbers*.

It is not part of the scheme of this work to discuss the construction of the class of integers or the logical foundations of the theory of rational numbers§.

The extension of the idea of number, which has just been described, was not effected without some opposition from the more conservative mathematicians. In the latter half of the eighteenth century, Maseres (1731–1824) and Frend (1757–1841) published works on Algebra, Trigonometry, etc., in which the use of negative numbers was disallowed, although Descartes had used them unrestrictedly more than a hundred years before.

---

* Strictly speaking, a more appropriate epithet would be, not *positive*, but *signless*.

† In the strict sense.

‡ With the exception of division by the rational number 0.

§ Such a discussion, defining a rational number as an ordered number-pair of integers in a similar manner to that in which a complex number is defined in § 1·3 as an ordered number-pair of real numbers, will be found in Hobson's *Functions of a Real Variable*, §§ 1–12.

A rational number x may be represented to the eye in the following manner:

If, on a straight line, we take an origin O and a fixed segment OP_1 (P_1 being on the right of O), we can measure from O a length OP_x such that the ratio OP_x/OP_1 is equal to x; the point P_x is taken on the right or left of O according as the number x is positive or negative. We may regard either the *point* P_x or the *displacement* OP_x (which will be written $\overline{OP_x}$) as representing the number x.

All the rational numbers can thus be represented by points on the line, but the converse is not true. For if we measure off on the line a length OQ equal to the diagonal of a square of which OP_1 is one side, it can be proved that Q does not correspond to any rational number.

Points on the line which do not represent rational numbers may be said to represent irrational numbers; thus the point Q is said to represent the irrational number $\sqrt{2} = 1.414213....$ But while such an explanation of the existence of irrational numbers satisfied the mathematicians of the eighteenth century and may still be sufficient for those whose interest lies in the applications of mathematics rather than in the logical upbuilding of the theory, yet from the logical standpoint it is improper to introduce geometrical intuitions to supply deficiencies in arithmetical arguments; and it was shewn by Dedekind in 1858 that the theory of irrational numbers can be established on a purely arithmetical basis without any appeal to geometry.

1·2. *Dedekind's* theory of irrational numbers.*

The geometrical property of points on a line which suggested the starting point of the arithmetical theory of irrationals was that, if all points of a line are separated into two classes such that every point of the first class is on the right of every point of the second class, there exists one and only one point at which the line is thus severed.

Following up this idea, Dedekind considered rules by which a separation† or *section* of *all* rational numbers into two classes can be made, these classes (which will be called the L-class and the R-class, or the left class and the right class) being such that they possess the following properties:

(i) At least one member of each class exists.

(ii) Every member of the L-class is less than every member of the R-class.

It is obvious that such a section is made by any rational number x; and x is either the greatest number of the L-class or the least number of the

---

* The theory, though elaborated in 1858, was not published before the appearance of Dedekind's tract, *Stetigkeit und irrationale Zahlen*, Brunswick, 1872. Other theories are due to Weierstrass [see von Dantscher, *Die Weierstrass'sche Theorie der irrationalen Zahlen* (Leipzig, 1908)] and Cantor, *Math. Ann.* v. (1872), pp. 123-130.

† This procedure formed the basis of the treatment of irrational numbers by the Greek mathematicians in the sixth and fifth centuries B.C. The advance made by Dedekind consisted in observing that a purely *arithmetical* theory could be built up on it.

R-class. But sections can be made in which no rational number x plays this part. Thus, since there is no rational number* whose square is 2, it is easy to see that we may form a section in which the R-class consists of the positive rational numbers whose squares exceed 2, and the L-class consists of all other rational numbers.

Then this section is such that the R-class has no least member and the L-class has no greatest member; for, if x be any positive rational fraction, and $y = \dfrac{x(x^2+6)}{3x^2+2}$, then $y - x = \dfrac{2x(2-x^2)}{3x^2+2}$ and $y^2 - 2 = \dfrac{(x^2-2)^3}{(3x^2+2)^2}$, so x^2, y^2 and 2 are in order of magnitude; and therefore given any member x of the L-class, we can always find a greater member of the L-class, or given any member x' of the R-class, we can always find a smaller member of the R-class, such numbers being, for instance, y and y', where y' is the same function of x' as y of x.

If a section is made in which the R-class has a least member A_2, or if the L-class has a greatest member A_1, the section determines a *rational-real* number, which it is convenient to denote by the *same*† symbol A_2 or A_1.

If a section is made, such that the R-class has no least member and the L-class has no greatest member, *the section determines an irrational-real number*‡.

If x, y are real numbers (defined by sections) we say that x is greater than y if the L-class defining x contains at least two§ members of the R-class defining y.

Let α, β, ... be real numbers and let A_1, B_1, ... be any members of the corresponding L-classes while A_2, B_2, ... are any members of the corresponding R-classes. The classes of which A_1, A_2, ... are respectively members will be denoted by the symbols (A_1), (A_2), ...

Then the *sum* (written $\alpha + \beta$) of two real numbers α and β is defined as the real number (rational or irrational) which is determined by the L-class $(A_1 + B_1)$ and the R-class $(A_2 + B_2)$.

It is, of course, necessary to prove that these classes determine a section of the rational numbers. It is evident that $A_1 + B_1 < A_2 + B_2$ and that at least one member of each of the classes $(A_1 + B_1)$, $(A_2 + B_2)$ exists. It remains to prove that there is, at most, *one* rational

---

* For if p/q be such a number, this fraction being in its lowest terms, it may be seen that $(2q - p)/(p - q)$ is another such number, and $0 < p - q < q$, so that p/q is not in its lowest terms. The contradiction implies that such a rational number does not exist.

† This causes no confusion in practice.

‡ B. A. W. Russell defines the class of real numbers as *actually being* the class of all L-classes; the class of real numbers whose L-classes have a greatest member corresponds to the class of rational numbers, and though the rational-real number x which corresponds to a rational number x is conceptually distinct from it, no confusion arises from denoting both by the same symbol.

§ If the classes had only one member in common, that member might be the greatest member of the L-class of x and the least member of the R-class of y.

number which is greater than every $A_1 + B_1$ and less than every $A_2 + B_2$; suppose, if possible, that there are two, x and y $(y > x)$. Let a_1 be a member of (A_1) and let a_2 be a member of (A_2); and let N be the integer next greater than $(a_2 - a_1)/\{\frac{1}{2}(y - x)\}$. Take the last of the numbers $a_1 + \dfrac{m}{N}(a_2 - a_1)$, (where $m = 0, 1, \dots N$), which belongs to (A_1) and the first of them which belongs to (A_2); let these two numbers be c_1, c_2. Then

$$c_2 - c_1 = \frac{1}{N}(a_2 - a_1) < \tfrac{1}{2}(y - x).$$

Choose d_1, d_2 in a similar manner from the classes defining β; then

$$c_2 + d_2 - c_1 - d_1 < y - x.$$

But $c_2 + d_2 \geqslant y$, $c_1 + d_1 \leqslant x$, and therefore $c_2 + d_2 - c_1 - d_1 \geqslant y - x$; we have therefore arrived at a contradiction by supposing that two rational numbers x, y exist belonging neither to $(A_1 + B_1)$ nor to $(A_2 + B_2)$.

If every rational number belongs either to the class $(A_1 + B_1)$ or to the class $(A_2 + B_2)$, then the classes $(A_1 + B_1)$, $(A_2 + B_2)$ define an irrational number. If one rational number x exists belonging to neither class, then the L-class formed by x and $(A_1 + B_1)$ and the R-class $(A_2 + B_2)$ define the rational-real number x. In either case, the number defined is called the sum $a + \beta$.

The difference $a - \beta$ of two real numbers is defined by the L-class $(A_1 - B_2)$ and the R-class $(A_2 - B_1)$.

The product of two positive real numbers a, β is defined by the R-class $(A_2 B_2)$ and the L-class of all other rational numbers.

The reader will see without difficulty how to define the product of negative real numbers and the quotient of two real numbers; and further, it may be shewn that real numbers may be combined in accordance with the associative, distributive and commutative laws.

The aggregate of rational-real and irrational-real numbers is called the aggregate of real numbers; for brevity, rational-real numbers and irrational-real numbers are called rational and irrational numbers respectively.

1·3. *Complex numbers.*

We have seen that a real number may be visualised as a displacement along a definite straight line. If, however, P and Q are any two points in a plane, the displacement $\overline{PQ}$ needs two real numbers for its specification; for instance, the differences of the coordinates of P and Q referred to fixed rectangular axes. If the coordinates of P be (ξ, η) and those of Q $(\xi + x, \eta + y)$, the displacement $\overline{PQ}$ may be described by the symbol $[x, y]$. We are thus led to consider the association of real numbers in ordered* pairs. The natural definition of the sum of two displacements $[x, y]$, $[x', y']$ is the displacement which is the result of the successive applications of the two displacements; it is therefore convenient to define the sum of two number-pairs by the equation

$$[x, y] + [x', y'] = [x + x', y + y'].$$

---

* The order of the two terms distinguishes the ordered number-pair $[x, y]$ from the ordered number-pair $[y, x]$.

The product of a number-pair and a real number x' is then naturally defined by the equation

$$x' \times [x,\, y] = [x'x,\, x'y].$$

We are at liberty to define the *product* of two number-pairs in any convenient manner; but the only definition, which does not give rise to results that are merely trivial, is that symbolised by the equation

$$[x,\, y] \times [x',\, y'] = [xx' - yy',\, xy' + x'y].$$

It is then evident that

$$[x,\, 0] \times [x',\, y'] = [xx',\, xy'] = x \times [x',\, y']$$

and
$$[0,\, y] \times [x',\, y'] = [-yy',\, x'y] = y \times [-y',\, x'].$$

The geometrical interpretation of these results is that the effect of multiplying by the displacement $[x,\, 0]$ is the same as that of multiplying by the real number x; but the effect of multiplying a displacement by $[0,\, y]$ is to multiply it by a real number y and turn it through a right angle.

It is convenient to denote the number-pair $[x,\, y]$ by the compound symbol $x + iy$; and a number-pair is now conveniently called (after Gauss) a *complex number*; in the fundamental operations of Arithmetic, the complex number $x + i0$ may be replaced by the real number x and, defining i to mean $0 + i1$, we have $i^2 = [0,\, 1] \times [0,\, 1] = [-1,\, 0]$; and so i^2 may be replaced by -1.

The reader will easily convince himself that the definitions of addition and multiplication of number-pairs have been so framed that we may perform the ordinary operations of algebra with complex numbers in exactly the same way as with real numbers, treating the symbol i as a number and replacing the product ii by -1 wherever it occurs.

Thus he will verify that, if a, b, c are complex numbers, we have

$$a + b = b + a,$$
$$ab = ba,$$
$$(a + b) + c = a + (b + c),$$
$$ab \cdot c = a \cdot bc,$$
$$a\,(b + c) = ab + ac,$$

and if ab is zero, then either a or b is zero.

It is found that algebraical operations, direct or inverse, when applied to complex numbers, do not suggest numbers of any fresh type; the complex number will therefore for our purposes be taken as the most general type of number.

The introduction of the complex number has led to many important developments in mathematics. Functions which, when real variables only are considered, appear as essentially distinct, are seen to be connected when complex variables are introduced:

thus the circular functions are found to be expressible in terms of exponential functions of a complex argument, by the equations

$$\cos x = \frac{1}{2}(e^{ix} + e^{-ix}), \quad \sin x = \frac{1}{2i}(e^{ix} - e^{-ix}).$$

Again, many of the most important theorems of modern analysis are not true if the numbers concerned are restricted to be real; thus, the theorem that every algebraic equation of degree n has n roots is true in general only when regarded as a theorem concerning complex numbers.

Hamilton's quaternions furnish an example of a still further extension of the idea of number. A quaternion

$$w + xi + yj + zk$$

is formed from four real numbers w, x, y, z, and four number-units 1, i, j, k, in the same way that the ordinary complex number $x + iy$ might be regarded as being formed from two real numbers x, y, and two number-units 1, i. Quaternions however do not obey the commutative law of multiplication.

1·4. *The modulus of a complex number.*

Let $x + iy$ be a complex number, x and y being real numbers. Then the positive square root of $x^2 + y^2$ is called the *modulus* of $(x + iy)$, and is written

$$|x + iy|.$$

Let us consider the complex number which is the sum of two given complex numbers, $x + iy$ and $u + iv$. We have

$$(x + iy) + (u + iv) = (x + u) + i(y + v).$$

The modulus of the sum of the two numbers is therefore

$$\{(x + u)^2 + (y + v)^2\}^{\frac{1}{2}},$$

or

$$\{(x^2 + y^2) + (u^2 + v^2) + 2(xu + yv)\}^{\frac{1}{2}}.$$

But

$$\{|x + iy| + |u + iv|\}^2 = \{(x^2 + y^2)^{\frac{1}{2}} + (u^2 + v^2)^{\frac{1}{2}}\}^2$$

$$= (x^2 + y^2) + (u^2 + v^2) + 2(x^2 + y^2)^{\frac{1}{2}}(u^2 + v^2)^{\frac{1}{2}}$$

$$= (x^2 + y^2) + (u^2 + v^2) + 2\{(xu + yv)^2 + (xv - yu)^2\}^{\frac{1}{2}},$$

and this latter expression is greater than (or at least equal to)

$$(x^2 + y^2) + (u^2 + v^2) + 2(xu + yv).$$

We have therefore

$$|x + iy| + |u + iv| \geqslant |(x + iy) + (u + iv)|,$$

i.e. *the modulus of the sum of two complex numbers cannot be greater than the sum of their moduli*; and it follows by induction that the **modulus** of the sum of any number of complex numbers cannot be greater than the sum of their moduli.

Let us consider next the complex number which is the product of two given complex numbers, $x + iy$ and $u + iv$; we have

$$(x + iy)(u + iv) = (xu - yv) + i(xv + yu),$$

and so

$$\begin{aligned}
\mid (x + iy)(u + iv) \mid &= \{(xu - yv)^2 + (xv + yu)^2\}^{\frac{1}{2}} \\
&= \{(x^2 + y^2)(u^2 + v^2)\}^{\frac{1}{2}} \\
&= \mid x + iy \mid \mid u + iv \mid.
\end{aligned}$$

The modulus of the product of two complex numbers (and hence, by induction, of any number of complex numbers) *is therefore equal to the product of their moduli.*

1·5. *The Argand diagram.*

We have seen that complex numbers may be represented in a geometrical diagram by taking rectangular axes Ox, Oy in a plane. Then a point P whose coordinates referred to these axes are x, y may be regarded as representing the complex number $x + iy$. In this way, to every point of the plane there corresponds some one complex number; and, conversely, to every possible complex number there corresponds one, and only one, point of the plane. The complex number $x + iy$ may be denoted by a single letter* z. The point P is then called the *representative point* of the number z; we shall also speak of the number z as being the *affix* of the point P.

If we denote $(x^2 + y^2)^{\frac{1}{2}}$ by r and choose θ so that $r \cos \theta = x$, $r \sin \theta = y$, then r and θ are clearly the radius vector and vectorial angle of the point P, referred to the origin O and axis Ox.

The representation of complex numbers thus afforded is often called the *Argand diagram*†.

By the definition already given, it is evident that r is the modulus of z. The angle θ is called the *argument*, or *amplitude*, or *phase*, of z.

We write $\qquad\qquad \theta = \arg z.$

From geometrical considerations, it appears that (although the modulus of a complex number is unique) the argument is not unique‡; if θ be a value of the argument, the other values of the argument are comprised in the expression $2n\pi + \theta$ where n is any integer, not zero. The *principal* value of $\arg z$ is that which satisfies the inequality $-\pi < \arg z \leqq \pi$.

---

* It is convenient to call x and y the *real* and *imaginary* parts of z respectively. We frequently write $x = R(z)$, $y = I(z)$.

† It was published by J. R. Argand, *Essai sur une manière de représenter les quantités imaginaires dans les constructions géométriques* (1806); it had however previously been used by Gauss, in his Helmstedt dissertation, 1799 (*Werke*, III. pp. 20–23), who had discovered it in Oct. 1797 (*Math. Ann.* LVII. p. 18); and Caspar Wessel had discussed it in a memoir presented to the Danish Academy in 1797 and published by that Society in 1798–9. The phrase *complex number* first occurs in 1831, Gauss, *Werke*, II. p. 102.

‡ See the *Appendix*, § A·521.

If P_1 and P_2 are the representative points corresponding to values z_1 and z_2 respectively of z, then the point which represents the value $z_1 + z_2$ is clearly the terminus of a line drawn from P_1, equal and parallel to that which joins the origin to P_2.

To find the point which represents the complex number $z_1 z_2$, where z_1 and z_2 are two given complex numbers, we notice that if

$$z_1 = r_1 (\cos \theta_1 + i \sin \theta_1),$$
$$z_2 = r_2 (\cos \theta_2 + i \sin \theta_2)$$

then, by multiplication,

$$z_1 z_2 = r_1 r_2 \{\cos (\theta_1 + \theta_2) + i \sin (\theta_1 + \theta_2)\}.$$

The point which represents the number $z_1 z_2$ has therefore a radius vector measured by the product of the radii vectores of P_1 and P_2, and a vectorial angle equal to the sum of the vectorial angles of P_1 and P_2.

REFERENCES.

The logical foundations of the theory of number.

A. N. WHITEHEAD AND B. A. W. RUSSELL, *Principia Mathematica* (1910–1913).

B. A. W. RUSSELL, *Introduction to Mathematical Philosophy* (1919).

On irrational numbers.

R. DEDEKIND, *Stetigkeit und irrationale Zahlen.* (Brunswick, 1872.)

V. VON DANTSCHER, *Vorlesungen ueber die Weierstrass'sche Theorie der irrationalen Zahlen.* (Leipzig, 1908.)

E. W. HOBSON, *Functions of a Real Variable* (1907), Ch. I.

T. J. I'A. BROMWICH, *Theory of Infinite Series* (1908), Appendix I.

On complex numbers.

H. HANKEL, *Theorie der complexen Zahlen-systeme.* (Leipzig, 1867.)

O. STOLZ, *Vorlesungen über allgemeine Arithmetik*, II. (Leipzig, 1886.)

G. H. HARDY, *A course of Pure Mathematics* (1914), Ch. III.

MISCELLANEOUS EXAMPLES.

1. Shew that the representative points of the complex numbers $1 + 4i$, $2 + 7i$, $3 + 10i$, are collinear.

2. Shew that a parabola can be drawn to pass through the representative points of the complex numbers

$$2 + i, \quad 4 + 4i, \quad 6 + 9i, \quad 8 + 16i, \quad 10 + 25i.$$

3. Determine the nth roots of unity by aid of the Argand diagram; and shew that the number of primitive roots (roots the powers of each of which give all the roots) is the number of integers (including unity) less than n and prime to it.

Prove that if $\theta_1, \theta_2, \theta_3, \ldots$ be the arguments of the primitive roots, $\Sigma \cos p\theta = 0$ when p is a positive integer less than $\dfrac{n}{abc \ldots k}$, where $a, b, c, \ldots k$ are the different constituent primes of n; and that, when $p = \dfrac{n}{abc \ldots k}$, $\Sigma \cos p\theta = \dfrac{(-)^\mu n}{abc \ldots k}$, where μ is the number of the constituent primes. (Math. Trip. 1895.)

CHAPTER II

THE THEORY OF CONVERGENCE

2·1. *The definition* of the limit of a sequence.*

Let $z_1, z_2, z_3, \ldots$ be an unending sequence of numbers, real or complex. Then, if a number l exists such that, corresponding to every positive† number ϵ, no matter how small, a number n_0 can be found, such that

$$|z_n - l| < \epsilon$$

for all values of n greater than n_0, *the sequence (z_n) is said to tend to the limit l as n tends to infinity.*

Symbolic forms of the statement‡ 'the limit of the sequence (z_n), as n tends to infinity, is l' are:

$$\lim_{n \to \infty} z_n = l, \quad \lim z_n = l, \quad z_n \to l \ \text{as} \ n \to \infty.$$

If the sequence be such that, given an arbitrary number N (no matter how large), we can find n_0 such that $|z_n| > N$ for all values of n greater than n_0, we say that '$|z_n|$ tends to infinity as n tends to infinity,' and we write

$$|z_n| \to \infty.$$

In the corresponding case when $-x_n > N$ when $n > n_0$ we say that $x_n \to -\infty$.

If a sequence of real numbers does not tend to a limit or to ∞ or to $-\infty$, the sequence is said to *oscillate*.

2·11. *Definition of the phrase 'of the order of.'*

If (ζ_n) and (z_n) are two sequences such that a number n_0 exists such that $|(\zeta_n/z_n)| < K$ whenever $n > n_0$, where K is *independent of* n, we say that ζ_n is 'of the order of' z_n, and we write§

$$\zeta_n = O(z_n);$$

thus
$$\frac{15n + 19}{1 + n^3} = O\left(\frac{1}{n^2}\right).$$

If $\lim (\zeta_n/z_n) = 0$, we write $\zeta_n = o(z_n)$.

---

* A definition equivalent to this was first given by John Wallis in 1655. [*Opera*, I. (1695), p. 382.]

† The number zero is excluded from the class of positive numbers.

‡ The arrow notation is due to Leathem, *Camb. Math. Tracts*, No. 1.

§ This notation is due to Bachmann, *Zahlentheorie* (1894), p. 401, and Landau, *Primzahlen*, I. (1909), p. 61.

2·2. *The limit of an increasing sequence.*

Let (x_n) be a sequence of real numbers such that $x_{n+1} \geqslant x_n$ for all values of n; then *the sequence tends to a limit or else tends to infinity* (and so it does not oscillate).

Let x be any rational-real number; then either:

(i) $x_n \geqslant x$ for all values of n greater than some number n_0 depending on the value of x.

Or (ii) $x_n < x$ for every value of n.

If (ii) is not the case for *any* value of x (no matter how large), then $x_n \to \infty$.

But if values of x exist for which (ii) holds, we can divide the rational numbers into two classes, the L-class consisting of those rational numbers x for which (i) holds and the R-class of those rational numbers x for which (ii) holds. This section defines a real number α, rational or irrational.

And if ϵ be an arbitrary positive number, $\alpha - \frac{1}{2}\epsilon$ belongs to the L-class which defines α, and so we can find n_1 such that $x_n \geqslant \alpha - \frac{1}{2}\epsilon$ whenever $n > n_1$; and $\alpha + \frac{1}{2}\epsilon$ is a member of the R-class and so $x_n < \alpha + \frac{1}{2}\epsilon$. Therefore, whenever $n > n_1$,

$$|\alpha - x_n| < \epsilon.$$

Therefore $x_n \to \alpha$.

Corollary. A decreasing sequence tends to a limit or to $-\infty$.

Example 1.   If $\lim z_m = l$, $\lim z_m' = l'$, then $\lim (z_m + z_m') = l + l'$.

For, given ϵ, we can find n and n' such that

(i) when $m > n$, $|z_m - l| < \frac{1}{2}\epsilon$,   (ii) when $m > n'$, $|z_m' - l'| < \frac{1}{2}\epsilon$.

Let n_1 be the greater of n and n'; then, when $m > n_1$,

$$|(z_m + z_m') - (l + l')| \leqslant |(z_m - l)| + |(z_m' - l')|,$$
$$< \epsilon;$$

and this is the condition that $\lim (z_m + z_m') = l + l'$.

Example 2.   Prove similarly that $\lim (z_m - z_m') = l - l'$, $\lim (z_m z_m') = ll'$, and, if $l' \neq 0$, $\lim (z_m / z_m') = l/l'$.

Example 3.   If $0 < x < 1$, $x^n \to 0$.

For if $x = (1+a)^{-1}$, $a > 0$ and

$$0 < x^n = \frac{1}{(1+a)^n} < \frac{1}{1+na},$$

by the binomial theorem for a positive integral index. And it is obvious that, given a positive number ϵ, we can choose n_0 such that $(1+na)^{-1} < \epsilon$ when $n > n_0$; and so $x^n \to 0$.

2·21. *Limit-points and the Bolzano-Weierstrass* theorem.*

Let (x_n) be a sequence of real numbers. If any number G exists such

---

* This theorem, frequently ascribed to Weierstrass, was proved by Bolzano, *Abh. der k. böhmischen Ges. der Wiss.* v. (1817). [Reprinted in *Klassiker der Exakten Wiss.*, No. 153.] It seems to have been known to Cauchy.

that, for every positive value of ϵ, no matter how small, an unlimited number of terms of the sequence can be found such that

$$G - \epsilon < x_n < G + \epsilon,$$

then G is called a *limit-point*, or *cluster-point*, of the sequence.

Bolzano's theorem is that, *if* $\lambda \leqslant x_n \leqslant \rho$, *where* λ, ρ *are independent of* n, *then the sequence* (x_n) *has at least one limit-point*.

To prove the theorem, choose a section in which (i) the R-class consists of all the rational numbers which are such that, if A be any one of them, there are only a limited number of terms x_n satisfying $x_n > A$; and (ii) the L-class is such that there are an unlimited number of terms x_n such that $x_n \geqslant a$ for all members a of the L-class.

This section defines a real number G; and, if ϵ be an arbitrary positive number, $G - \tfrac{1}{2}\epsilon$ and $G + \tfrac{1}{2}\epsilon$ are members of the L and R classes respectively, and so there are an unlimited number of terms of the sequence satisfying

$$G - \epsilon < G - \tfrac{1}{2}\epsilon \leqslant x_n \leqslant G + \tfrac{1}{2}\epsilon < G + \epsilon,$$

and so G satisfies the condition that it should be a limit-point.

2·211. *Definition of 'the greatest of the limits.'*

The number G obtained in § 2·21 is called 'the greatest of the limits of the sequence (x_n).' The sequence (x_n) cannot have a limit-point greater than G; for if G' were such a limit-point, and $\epsilon = \tfrac{1}{2}(G' - G)$, $G' - \epsilon$ is a member of the R-class defining G, so that there are only a limited number of terms of the sequence which satisfy $x_n > G' - \epsilon$. This condition is inconsistent with G' being a limit-point. We write

$$G = \varlimsup_{n \to \infty} x_n.$$

The 'least of the limits,' L, of the sequence (written $\varliminf_{n \to \infty} x_n$) is defined to be

$$- \varlimsup_{n \to \infty} (- x_n).$$

2·22. CAUCHY'S[*] THEOREM ON THE NECESSARY AND SUFFICIENT CONDITION FOR THE EXISTENCE OF A LIMIT.

We shall now shew that the necessary and sufficient condition for the existence of a limiting value of a sequence of numbers $z_1, z_2, z_3, \ldots$ is that, *corresponding to any given positive number* ϵ, *however small, it shall be possible to find a number* n *such that*

$$|z_{n+p} - z_n| < \epsilon$$

for all positive integral values of p. This result is one of the most important and fundamental theorems of analysis. It is sometimes called the *Principle of Convergence*.

[*] *Analyse Algébrique* (1821), p. 125.

First, we have to shew that this condition is *necessary*, i.e. that it is satisfied whenever a limit exists. Suppose then that a limit l exists; then (§ 2·1) corresponding to any positive number ϵ, however small, an integer n can be chosen such that

$$|z_n - l| < \tfrac{1}{2}\epsilon, \quad |z_{n+p} - l| < \tfrac{1}{2}\epsilon,$$

for all positive values of p; therefore

$$|z_{n+p} - z_n| = |(z_{n+p} - l) - (z_n - l)|$$

$$\leqslant |z_{n+p} - l| + |z_n - l| < \epsilon,$$

which shews the *necessity* of the condition

$$|z_{n+p} - z_n| < \epsilon,$$

and thus establishes the first half of the theorem.

Secondly, we have to prove[*] that this condition is *sufficient*, i.e. that if it is satisfied, then a limit exists.

(I) Suppose that the sequence of *real* numbers (x_n) satisfies Cauchy's condition; that is to say that, corresponding to any positive number ϵ, an integer n can be chosen such that

$$|x_{n+p} - x_n| < \epsilon$$

for all positive integral values of p.

Let the value of n, corresponding to the value 1 of ϵ, be m.

Let λ_1, ρ_1 be the least and greatest of x_1, x_2, ... x_m; then

$$\lambda_1 - 1 < x_n < \rho_1 + 1,$$

for all values of n; write $\lambda_1 - 1 = \lambda$, $\rho_1 + 1 = \rho$.

Then, for all values of n, $\lambda < x_n < \rho$. *Therefore by the theorem of* § 2·21, *the sequence (x_n) has at least one limit-point G.*

Further, there cannot be more than one limit-point; for if there were two, G and H $(H < G)$, take $\epsilon < \tfrac{1}{4}(G - H)$. Then, by hypothesis, a number n exists such that $|x_{n+p} - x_n| < \epsilon$ for every positive value of p. But since G and H are limit-points, positive numbers q and r exist such that

$$|G - x_{n+q}| < \epsilon, \quad |H - x_{n+r}| < \epsilon.$$

Then $|G - x_{n+q}| + |x_{n+q} - x_n| + |x_n - x_{n+r}| + |x_{n+r} - H| < 4\epsilon.$

But, by § 1·4, the sum on the left is greater than or equal to $|G - H|$.

Therefore $G - H < 4\epsilon$, which is contrary to hypothesis; so there is only one limit-point. Hence there are only a finite number of terms of the sequence outside the interval $(G - \delta, G + \delta)$, where δ is an arbitrary positive number;

---

[*] This proof is given by Stolz and Gmeiner, *Theoretische Arithmetik*, II. (1902), p. 144.

for, if there were an unlimited number of such terms, these would have a limit-point which would be a limit-point of the given sequence and which would not coincide with G; *and therefore G is the limit of (x_n).*

(II) Now let the sequence (z_n) of real or complex numbers satisfy Cauchy's condition; and let $z_n = x_n + iy_n$, where x_n and y_n are real; then for all values of n and p

$$|x_{n+p} - x_n| \leqslant |z_{n+p} - z_n|, \quad |y_{n+p} - y_n| \leqslant |z_{n+p} - z_n|.$$

Therefore the sequences of real numbers (x_n) and (y_n) satisfy Cauchy's condition; and so, by (I), the limits of (x_n) and (y_n) exist. Therefore, by § 2·2 example 1, the limit of (z_n) exists. The result is therefore established.

2·3. *Convergence of an infinite series.*

Let $u_1, u_2, u_3, \dots u_n, \dots$ be a sequence of numbers, real or complex. Let the sum

$$u_1 + u_2 + \dots + u_n$$

be denoted by S_n.

Then, if S_n tends to a limit S as n tends to infinity, the infinite series

$$u_1 + u_2 + u_3 + u_4 + \dots$$

is said to *be convergent,* or to *converge to the sum S.* In other cases, the infinite series is said to be *divergent.* When the series converges, the expression $S - S_n$, which is the sum of the series

$$u_{n+1} + u_{n+2} + u_{n+3} + \dots,$$

is called the *remainder after n terms,* and is frequently denoted by the symbol R_n.

The sum $$u_{n+1} + u_{n+2} + \dots + u_{n+p}$$

will be denoted by $S_{n,p}$.

It follows at once, by combining the above definition with the results of the last paragraph, that the necessary and sufficient condition for the convergence of an infinite series is that, given an arbitrary positive number ϵ, we can find n such that $|S_{n,p}| < \epsilon$ for every positive value of p.

Since $u_{n+1} = S_{n,1}$, it follows as a particular case that $\lim u_{n+1} = 0$—in other words, the nth term of a convergent series must tend to zero as n tends to infinity. But this last condition, though necessary, is not sufficient in itself to ensure the convergence of the series, as appears from a study of the series

$$\frac{1}{1} + \frac{1}{2} + \frac{1}{3} + \frac{1}{4} + \frac{1}{5} + \dots.$$

In this series, $$S_{n,n} = \frac{1}{n+1} + \frac{1}{n+2} + \frac{1}{n+3} + \dots + \frac{1}{2n}.$$

The expression on the right is diminished by writing $(2n)^{-1}$ in place of each term, and so $S_{n,n} > \frac{1}{2}$.

Therefore $\quad S_{2^{n+1}} = 1 + S_{1,1} + S_{2,2} + S_{4,4} + S_{8,8} + S_{16,16} + \ldots + S_{2^n,2^n}$

$$> \frac{1}{2}(n+3) \to \infty ;$$

so the series is divergent; this result was noticed by Leibniz in 1673.

There are two general classes of problems which we are called upon to investigate in connexion with the convergence of series:

(i) We may arrive at a series by some formal process, e.g. that of solving a linear differential equation by a series, and then to justify the process it will usually have to be proved that the series thus formally obtained is convergent. Simple conditions for establishing convergence in such circumstances are obtained in §§ 2·31–2·61.

(ii) Given an expression S, it may be possible to obtain a development $S = \sum\limits_{m=1}^{n} u_m + R_n$, valid for all values of n; and, from the definition of a limit, it follows that, if we can prove that $R_n \to 0$, then the series $\sum\limits_{m=1}^{\infty} u_m$ converges and its sum is S. An example of this problem occurs in § 5·4.

Infinite series were used[*] by Lord Brouncker in *Phil. Trans.* II. (1668), pp. 645–649, and the term convergent was introduced by James Gregory, Professor of Mathematics at Edinburgh, in the same year; the term divergent was introduced by N. Bernoulli in 1713. Infinite series were used systematically by Newton in 1669, *De analysi per aequat. num. term. inf.*, and he investigated the convergence of hypergeometric series (§ 14·1) in 1704. But the great mathematicians of the eighteenth century used infinite series freely without, for the most part, examining their convergence. Thus Euler gave the sum of the series

$$\ldots + \frac{1}{z^3} + \frac{1}{z^2} + \frac{1}{z} + 1 + z + z^2 + z^3 + \ldots \quad \ldots\ldots\ldots\ldots\ldots\ldots\ldots\ldots\ldots(a)$$

as zero, on the ground that

$$z + z^2 + z^3 + \ldots = \frac{z}{1-z} \quad \ldots\ldots\ldots\ldots\ldots\ldots\ldots\ldots\ldots(b)$$

and

$$1 + \frac{1}{z} + \frac{1}{z^2} + \ldots = \frac{z}{z-1} \quad \ldots\ldots\ldots\ldots\ldots\ldots\ldots\ldots\ldots(c).$$

The error of course arises from the fact that the series (b) converges only when $|z| < 1$, and the series (c) converges only when $|z| > 1$, so the series (a) never converges.

For the history of researches on convergence, see Pringsheim and Molk, *Encyclopédie des Sci. Math.*, I. (1) and Reiff, *Geschichte der unendlichen Reihen* (Tübingen, 1889).

2·301. *Abel's inequality*[†].

Let $f_n \geqslant f_{n+1} > 0$ for all integer values of n. Then $\left| \sum\limits_{n=1}^{m} a_n f_n \right| \leqslant A f_1$, where A is the greatest of the sums

$$|a_1|, \ |a_1 + a_2|, \ |a_1 + a_2 + a_3|, \ \ldots, \ |a_1 + a_2 + \ldots + a_m|.$$

---

[*] See also the note to § 2·7.

[†] *Journal für Math.* I. (1826), pp. 311–339. A particular case of the theorem of § 2·31, Corollary (i), also appears in that memoir.

For, writing $a_1 + a_2 + \ldots + a_n = s_n$, we have

$$\sum_{n=1}^{m} a_n f_n = s_1 f_1 + (s_2 - s_1) f_2 + (s_3 - s_2) f_3 + \ldots + (s_m - s_{m-1}) f_m$$

$$= s_1 (f_1 - f_2) + s_2 (f_2 - f_3) + \ldots + s_{m-1} (f_{m-1} - f_m) + s_m f_m.$$

Since $f_1 - f_2, f_2 - f_3, \ldots$ are not negative, we have, when $n = 2, 3, \ldots m$,

$$|s_{n-1}|(f_{n-1} - f_n) \leqslant A(f_{n-1} - f_n); \text{ also } |s_m| f_m \leqslant A f_m,$$

and so, summing and using § $1\cdot4$, we get

$$\left| \sum_{n=1}^{m} a_n f_n \right| \leqslant A f_1.$$

Corollary. If $a_1, a_2, \ldots w_1, w_2, \ldots$ are any numbers, real or complex,

$$\left| \sum_{n=1}^{m} a_n w_n \right| \leqslant A \left\{ \sum_{n=1}^{m-1} |w_{n+1} - w_n| + |w_m| \right\},$$

where A is the greatest of the sums $\left| \sum_{n=1}^{p} a_n \right|$, $(p = 1, 2, \ldots m)$.   (Hardy.)

$2\cdot31$. *Dirichlet's* test for convergence.*

Let $\left| \sum_{n=1}^{p} a_n \right| < K$, *where* K *is independent of* p. *Then, if* $f_n \geqslant f_{n+1} > 0$ *and* $\lim f_n = 0\dagger$, $\sum_{n=1}^{\infty} a_n f_n$ *converges.*

For, since $\lim f_n = 0$, given an arbitrary positive number ϵ, we can find m such that $f_{m+1} < \epsilon/2K$.

Then $\left| \sum_{n=m+1}^{m+q} a_n \right| \leqslant \left| \sum_{n=1}^{m+q} a_n \right| + \left| \sum_{n=1}^{m} a_n \right| < 2K$, for all positive values of q; so that, by Abel's inequality, we have, for all positive values of p,

$$\left| \sum_{n=m+1}^{m+p} a_n f_n \right| \leqslant A f_{m+1},$$

where $A < 2K$.

Therefore $\left| \sum_{n=m+1}^{m+p} a_n f_n \right| < 2K f_{m+1} < \epsilon$; and so, by § $2\cdot3$, $\sum_{n=1}^{\infty} a_n f_n$ converges.

Corollary (i). *Abel's test for convergence.* If $\sum_{n=1}^{\infty} a_n$ converges and the sequence (u_n) is monotonic (i.e. $u_n \geqslant u_{n+1}$ always or else $u_n \leqslant u_{n+1}$ always) and $|u_n| < \kappa$, where κ is independent of n, then $\sum_{n=1}^{\infty} a_n u_n$ converges.

For, by § $2\cdot2$, u_n tends to a limit u; let $|u - u_n| = f_n$. Then $f_n \to 0$ steadily; and therefore $\sum_{n=1}^{\infty} a_n f_n$ converges. But, if (u_n) is an increasing sequence, $f_n = u - u_n$, and so $\sum_{n=1}^{\infty} (u - u_n) a_n$ converges; therefore since $\sum_{n=1}^{\infty} u a_n$ converges, $\sum_{n=1}^{\infty} u_n a_n$ converges. If (u_n) is a decreasing sequence $f_n = u_n - u$, and a similar proof holds.

---

* *Journal de Math.* (2), VII. (1862), pp. 253–255. Before the publication of the 2nd edition of Jordan's *Cours d'Analyse* (1893), Dirichlet's test and Abel's test were frequently jointly described as the Dirichlet-Abel test, see e.g. Pringsheim, *Math. Ann.* XXV. (1885), p. 423.

† In these circumstances, we say $f_n \to 0$ *steadily.*

Corollary (ii). Taking $a_n = (-)^{n-1}$ in Dirichlet's test, it follows that, if $f_n \geqslant f_{n+1}$ and $\lim f_n = 0$, $f_1 - f_2 + f_3 - f_4 + \ldots$ converges.

Example 1. Shew that if $0 < \theta < 2\pi$, $\left| \sum\limits_{n=1}^{p} \sin n\theta \right| < \operatorname{cosec} \tfrac{1}{2}\theta$; and deduce that, if $f_n \rightarrow 0$ steadily, $\sum\limits_{n=1}^{\infty} f_n \sin n\theta$ converges for all real values of θ, and that $\sum\limits_{n=1}^{\infty} f_n \cos n\theta$ converges if θ is not an even multiple of π.

Example 2. Shew that, if $f_n \rightarrow 0$ steadily, $\sum\limits_{n=1}^{\infty} (-)^n f_n \cos n\theta$ converges if θ is real and not an odd multiple of π and $\sum\limits_{n=1}^{\infty} (-)^n f_n \sin n\theta$ converges for all real values of θ. [Write $\pi + \theta$ for θ in example 1.]

2·32. *Absolute and conditional convergence.*

In order that a series $\sum\limits_{n=1}^{\infty} u_n$ of real or complex terms may converge, it is *sufficient* (but not necessary) that the series of moduli $\sum\limits_{n=1}^{\infty} |u_n|$ should converge. For, if $\sigma_{n,p} = |u_{n+1}| + |u_{n+2}| + \ldots + |u_{n+p}|$ and if $\sum\limits_{n=1}^{\infty} |u_n|$ converges, we can find n, corresponding to a given number ϵ, such that $\sigma_{n,p} < \epsilon$ for all values of p. But $|S_{n,p}| \leqslant \sigma_{n,p} < \epsilon$, and so $\sum\limits_{n=1}^{\infty} u_n$ converges.

The condition is not necessary ; for, writing $f_n = 1/n$ in § 2·31, corollary (ii), we see that $\frac{1}{1} - \frac{1}{2} + \frac{1}{3} - \frac{1}{4} + \ldots$ converges, though (§ 2·3) the series of moduli $\frac{1}{1} + \frac{1}{2} + \frac{1}{3} + \frac{1}{4} + \ldots$ is known to diverge.

In this case, therefore, the divergence of the series of moduli does not entail the divergence of the series itself.

Series, which are such that the series formed by the moduli of their terms are convergent, possess special properties of great importance, and are called *absolutely convergent* series. Series which though convergent are not absolutely convergent (i.e. the series themselves converge, but the series of moduli diverge) are said to be *conditionally convergent*.

2·33. *The geometric series, and the series* $\sum\limits_{n=1}^{\infty} \dfrac{1}{n^s}$.

The convergence of a particular series is in most cases investigated, not by the direct consideration of the sum $S_{n,p}$, but (as will appear from the following articles) by a comparison of the given series with some other series which is known to be convergent or divergent. We shall now investigate the convergence of two of the series which are most frequently used as standards for comparison.

(I) *The geometric series.*

The geometric series is defined to be the series

$$1 + z + z^2 + z^3 + z^4 + \dots.$$

Consider the series of moduli

$$1 + |z| + |z|^2 + |z|^3 + \dots;$$

for this series $S_{n,p} = |z|^{n+1} + |z|^{n+2} + \dots + |z|^{n+p}$

$$= |z|^{n+1} \frac{1 - |z|^p}{1 - |z|}.$$

Hence, if $|z| < 1$, then $S_{n,p} < \dfrac{|z|^{n+1}}{1 - |z|}$ for all values of p, and, by § 2·2, example 3, given any positive number ϵ, we can find n such that

$$|z|^{n+1} \{1 - |z|\}^{-1} < \epsilon.$$

Thus, given ϵ, we can find n such that, for all values of p, $S_{n,p} < \epsilon$. Hence, by § 2·22, the series

$$1 + |z| + |z|^2 + \dots$$

is convergent so long as $|z| < 1$, and therefore *the geometric series is absolutely convergent if* $|z| < 1$.

When $|z| \geqslant 1$, the terms of the geometric series do not tend to zero as n tends to infinity, and the series is therefore divergent.

(II) *The series* $\dfrac{1}{1^s} + \dfrac{1}{2^s} + \dfrac{1}{3^s} + \dfrac{1}{4^s} + \dfrac{1}{5^s} + \dots.$

Consider now the series $S_n = \sum\limits_{m=1}^{n} \dfrac{1}{m^s}$, where s is greater than 1.

We have

$$\frac{1}{2^s} + \frac{1}{3^s} < \frac{2}{2^s} = \frac{1}{2^{s-1}},$$

$$\frac{1}{4^s} + \frac{1}{5^s} + \frac{1}{6^s} + \frac{1}{7^s} < \frac{4}{4^s} = \frac{1}{4^{s-1}},$$

and so on. Thus the sum of $2^p - 1$ terms of the series is less than

$$\frac{1}{1^{s-1}} + \frac{1}{2^{s-1}} + \frac{1}{4^{s-1}} + \frac{1}{8^{s-1}} + \dots + \frac{1}{2^{(p-1)\,(s-1)}} < \frac{1}{1 - 2^{1-s}},$$

and so the sum of *any* number of terms is less than $(1 - 2^{1-s})^{-1}$. Therefore the increasing sequence $\sum\limits_{m=1}^{n} m^{-s}$ cannot tend to infinity; *therefore, by* § 2·2, *the series* $\sum\limits_{n=1}^{\infty} \dfrac{1}{n^s}$ *is convergent if* $s > 1$; and since its terms are all real and positive, they are equal to their own moduli, and so the series of moduli of the terms is convergent; that is, *the convergence is absolute.*

If $s = 1$, the series becomes

$$\frac{1}{1} + \frac{1}{2} + \frac{1}{3} + \frac{1}{4} + \dots,$$

which we have already shewn to be divergent; and when $s < 1$, it is *a fortiori* divergent, since the effect of diminishing s is to increase the terms of the series. *The series* $\sum\limits_{n=1}^{\infty} \dfrac{1}{n^s}$ *is therefore divergent if* $s \leqslant 1$.

2·34. *The Comparison Theorem.*

We shall now shew that *a series* $u_1 + u_2 + u_3 + \dots$ *is absolutely convergent, provided that* $|u_n|$ *is always less than* $C|v_n|$, *where* C *is some number independent of* n, *and* v_n *is the nth term of another series which is known to be absolutely convergent.*

For, under these conditions, we have

$$|u_{n+1}| + |u_{n+2}| + \dots + |u_{n+p}| < C\{|v_{n+1}| + |v_{n+2}| + \dots + |v_{n+p}|\},$$

where n and p are any integers. But since the series Σv_n is absolutely convergent, the series $\Sigma|v_n|$ is convergent, and so, given ϵ, we can find n such that

$$|v_{n+1}| + |v_{n+2}| + \dots + |v_{n+p}| < \epsilon/C,$$

for all values of p. It follows therefore that we can find n such that

$$|u_{n+1}| + |u_{n+2}| + \dots + |u_{n+p}| < \epsilon,$$

for all values of p, i.e. the series $\Sigma|u_n|$ is convergent. The series Σu_n is therefore absolutely convergent.

Corollary. A series is absolutely convergent if the ratio of its nth term to the nth term of a series which is known to be absolutely convergent is less than some number independent of n.

Example 1. Shew that the series

$$\cos z + \frac{1}{2^2} \cos 2z + \frac{1}{3^2} \cos 3z + \frac{1}{4^2} \cos 4z + \dots$$

is absolutely convergent for all real values of z.

When z is real, we have $|\cos nz| \leqslant 1$, and therefore $\left|\dfrac{\cos nz}{n^2}\right| \leqslant \dfrac{1}{n^2}$. The moduli of the terms of the given series are therefore less than, or at most equal to, the corresponding terms of the series

$$1 + \frac{1}{2^2} + \frac{1}{3^2} + \frac{1}{4^2} + \dots,$$

which by § 2·33 is absolutely convergent. The given series is therefore absolutely convergent.

Example 2. Shew that the series

$$\frac{1}{1^2(z - z_1)} + \frac{1}{2^2(z - z_2)} + \frac{1}{3^2(z - z_3)} + \frac{1}{4^2(z - z_4)} + \dots,$$

where $\qquad\qquad\qquad\qquad z_n = e^{ni}, \qquad (n = 1, 2, 3, \dots)$

is convergent for all values of z, which are not on the circle $|z| = 1$.

The geometric representation of complex numbers is helpful in discussing a question of this kind. Let values of the complex number z be represented on a plane; then the numbers $z_1, z_2, z_3, \ldots$ will give a sequence of points which lie on the circumference of the circle whose centre is the origin and whose radius is unity; and it can be shewn that every point on the circle is a limit-point (§ 2·21) of the points z_n.

For these special values z_n of z, the given series does not exist, since the denominator of the nth term vanishes when $z = z_n$. For simplicity we do not discuss the series for any point z situated on the circumference of the circle of radius unity.

Suppose now that $|z| \neq 1$. Then for all values of n, $|z - z_n| \geqslant |\{1 - |z|\}| > c^{-1}$, for some value of c; so the moduli of the terms of the given series are less than the corresponding terms of the series

$$\frac{c}{1^2} + \frac{c}{2^2} + \frac{c}{3^2} + \frac{c}{4^2} + \ldots,$$

which is known to be absolutely convergent. The given series is therefore absolutely convergent for all values of z, except those which are on the circle $|z| = 1$.

It is interesting to notice that the area in the z-plane over which the series converges is divided into two parts, between which there is no intercommunication, by the circle $|z| = 1$.

Example 3. Shew that the series

$$2 \sin \frac{z}{3} + 4 \sin \frac{z}{9} + 8 \sin \frac{z}{27} + \ldots + 2^n \sin \frac{z}{3^n} + \ldots$$

converges absolutely for all values of z.

Since* $\lim_{n \to \infty} 3^n \sin (z/3^n) = z$, we can find a number k, *independent* of n (but depending on z), such that $|3^n \sin (z/3^n)| < k$; and therefore

$$\left| 2^n \sin \frac{z}{3^n} \right| < k \left(\frac{2}{3} \right)^n.$$

Since $\sum_{n=1}^{\infty} k \left(\frac{2}{3} \right)^n$ converges, the given series converges absolutely.

2·35. *Cauchy's test for absolute convergence†.*

If $\overline{\lim_{n \to \infty}} | u_n |^{1/n} < 1$, $\sum_{n=1}^{\infty} u_n$ *converges absolutely.*

For we can find m such that, when $n \geqslant m$, $| u_n |^{1/n} \leqslant \rho < 1$, where ρ is independent of n. Then, when $n > m$, $| u_n | < \rho^n$; and since $\sum_{n=m+1}^{\infty} \rho^n$ converges, it follows from § 2·34 that $\sum_{n=m+1}^{\infty} u_n$ $\left(\text{and therefore } \sum_{n=1}^{\infty} u_n \right)$ converges absolutely.

[NOTE. If $\overline{\lim} | u_n |^{1/n} > 1$, u_n does not tend to zero, and, by § 2·3, $\sum_{n=1}^{\infty} u_n$ does not converge.]

---

* This is evident from results proved in the *Appendix.*

† *Analyse Algébrique*, pp. 132–135.

2·36. *D'Alembert's* ratio test for absolute convergence.*

We shall now shew that *a series*

$$u_1 + u_2 + u_3 + u_4 + \dots$$

is absolutely convergent, provided that for all values of n greater than some fixed value r, the ratio $\left| \dfrac{u_{n+1}}{u_n} \right|$ *is less than* ρ, *where* ρ *is a positive number independent of n and less than unity.*

For the terms of the series

$$|u_{r+1}| + |u_{r+2}| + |u_{r+3}| + \dots$$

are respectively less than the corresponding terms of the series

$$|u_{r+1}|(1 + \rho + \rho^2 + \rho^3 + \dots),$$

which is absolutely convergent when $\rho < 1$; therefore $\sum\limits_{n=r+1}^{\infty} u_n$ (and hence the given series) is absolutely convergent.

A particular case of this theorem is that if $\lim\limits_{n \to \infty} |(u_{n+1}/u_n)| = l < 1$, the series is absolutely convergent.

For, by the definition of a limit, we can find r such that

$$\left| \left\{ \left| \frac{u_{n+1}}{u_n} \right| - l \right\} \right| < \tfrac{1}{2}(1 - l), \text{ when } n > r,$$

and then

$$\left| \frac{u_{n+1}}{u_n} \right| < \tfrac{1}{2}(1 + l) < 1,$$

when $n > r$.

[NOTE. If $\lim |u_{n+1} \div u_n| > 1$, u_n does not tend to zero, and, by § 2·3, $\sum\limits_{n=1}^{\infty} u_n$ does not converge.]

Example 1. If $|c| < 1$, shew that the series

$$\sum_{n=1}^{\infty} c^{n^2} e^{nz}$$

converges absolutely for all values of z.

[For $u_{n+1}/u_n = c^{(n+1)^2 - n^2} e^z = c^{2n+1} e^z \to 0$, as $n \to \infty$, if $|c| < 1$.]

Example 2. Shew that the series

$$z + \frac{a-b}{2!} z^2 + \frac{(a-b)(a-2b)}{3!} z^3 + \frac{(a-b)(a-2b)(a-3b)}{4!} z^4 + \dots$$

converges absolutely if $|z| < |b|^{-1}$.

[For $\dfrac{u_{n+1}}{u_n} = \dfrac{a - nb}{n+1} z \to -bz$, as $n \to \infty$; so the condition for absolute convergence is $|bz| < 1$, i.e. $|z| < |b|^{-1}$.]

* *Opuscules*, t. v. (1768), pp. 171–182.

Example 3. Shew that the series $\sum\limits_{n=1}^{\infty} \dfrac{nz^{n-1}}{z^n - (1+n^{-1})^n}$ converges absolutely if $|z| < 1$.

[For, when $|z| < 1$, $|z^n - (1+n^{-1})^n| \geqslant (1+n^{-1})^n - |z^n| \geqslant 1 + 1 + \dfrac{n-1}{2n} + \ldots - 1 > 1$, so the moduli of the terms of the series are less than the corresponding terms of the series $\sum\limits_{n=1}^{\infty} n\,|z^{n-1}|$; but this latter series is absolutely convergent, and so the given series converges absolutely.]

2·37. *A general theorem on series for which* $\lim\limits_{n \to \infty} \left| \dfrac{u_{n+1}}{u_n} \right| = 1$.

It is obvious that if, for all values of n greater than some fixed value r, $|u_{n+1}|$ is greater than $|u_n|$, then the terms of the series do not tend to zero as $n \to \infty$, and the series is therefore divergent. On the other hand, if $\left| \dfrac{u_{n+1}}{u_n} \right|$ is less than some number which is itself less than unity and independent of n (when $n > r$), we have shewn in § 2·36 that the series is absolutely convergent. The critical case is that in which, as n increases, $\left| \dfrac{u_{n+1}}{u_n} \right|$ tends to the value unity. In this case a further investigation is necessary.

We shall now shew that* *a series* $u_1 + u_2 + u_3 + \ldots$, *in which* $\lim\limits_{n \to \infty} \left| \dfrac{u_{n+1}}{u_n} \right| = 1$ *will be absolutely convergent if a* positive *number c exists such that*

$$\overline{\lim\limits_{n \to \infty}}\, n \left\{ \left| \dfrac{u_{n+1}}{u_n} \right| - 1 \right\} = -1 - c.$$

For, compare the series $\Sigma\,|u_n|$ with the convergent series Σv_n, where

$$v_n = A n^{-1-\frac{1}{2}c}$$

and A is a constant; we have

$$\dfrac{v_{n+1}}{v_n} = \left(\dfrac{n}{n+1} \right)^{1+\frac{1}{2}c} = \left(1 + \dfrac{1}{n} \right)^{-(1+\frac{1}{2}c)} = 1 - \dfrac{1 + \frac{1}{2}c}{n} + O\left(\dfrac{1}{n^2} \right).$$

As $n \to \infty$, $n \left\{ \dfrac{v_{n+1}}{v_n} - 1 \right\} \to -1 - \tfrac{1}{2}c,$

and hence we can find m such that, when $n > m$,

$$\left| \dfrac{u_{n+1}}{u_n} \right| \leqslant \dfrac{v_{n+1}}{v_n}.$$

By a suitable choice of the constant A, we can therefore secure that for all values of n we shall have

$$|u_n| < v_n.$$

As Σv_n is convergent, $\Sigma\,|u_n|$ is also convergent, and so Σu_n is absolutely convergent.

---

* This is the second (D'Alembert's theorem given in § 2·36 being the first) of a hierarchy of theorems due to De Morgan. See Chrystal, *Algebra*, Ch. xxvi. for an historical account of these theorems.

Corollary. If $\left|\dfrac{u_{n+1}}{u_n}\right| = 1 + \dfrac{A_1}{n} + O\left(\dfrac{1}{n^2}\right)$, where A_1 is independent of n, then the series is absolutely convergent if $A_1 < -1$.

Example. Investigate the convergence of $\sum\limits_{n=1}^{\infty} n^r \exp\left(-k\sum\limits_{1}^{n}\dfrac{1}{m}\right)$, when $r > k$ and when $r < k$.

2·38. *Convergence of the hypergeometric series.*

The theorems which have been given may be illustrated by a discussion of the convergence of the *hypergeometric series*

$$1 + \frac{a \cdot b}{1 \cdot c}z + \frac{a(a+1)b(b+1)}{1 \cdot 2 \cdot c(c+1)}z^2 + \frac{a(a+1)(a+2)b(b+1)(b+2)}{1 \cdot 2 \cdot 3 \cdot c(c+1)(c+2)}z^3 + \ldots,$$

which is generally denoted (see Chapter XIV) by $F(a, b; c; z)$.

If c is a negative integer, all the terms after the $(1-c)$th have zero denominators; and if either a or b is a negative integer the series will terminate at the $(1-a)$th or $(1-b)$th term as the case may be. We shall suppose these cases set aside, so that a, b, and c are assumed not to be negative integers.

In this series

$$\left|\frac{u_{n+1}}{u_n}\right| = \left|\frac{(a+n-1)(b+n-1)}{n(c+n-1)}z\right| \to |z|,$$

as $n \to \infty$.

We see therefore, by § 2·36, that *the series is absolutely convergent when $|z| < 1$, and divergent when $|z| > 1$.*

When $|z| = 1$, we have*

$$\left|\frac{u_{n+1}}{u_n}\right| = \left|1 + \frac{a-1}{n}\right|\left|1 + \frac{b-1}{n}\right|\left|1 - \frac{c-1}{n} + O\left(\frac{1}{n^2}\right)\right|$$

$$= \left|1 + \frac{a+b-c-1}{n} + O\left(\frac{1}{n^2}\right)\right|.$$

Let a, b, c be complex numbers, and let them be given in terms of their real and imaginary parts by the equations

$$a = a' + ia'', \quad b = b' + ib'', \quad c = c' + ic''.$$

Then we have

$$\left|\frac{u_{n+1}}{u_n}\right| = \left|1 + \frac{a'+b'-c'-1 + i(a''+b''-c'')}{n} + O\left(\frac{1}{n^2}\right)\right|$$

$$= \left\{\left(1 + \frac{a'+b'-c'-1}{n}\right)^2 + \left(\frac{a''+b''-c''}{n}\right)^2 + O\left(\frac{1}{n^2}\right)\right\}^{\frac{1}{2}}$$

$$= 1 + \frac{a'+b'-c'-1}{n} + O\left(\frac{1}{n^2}\right).$$

By § 2·37, Corollary, a condition for absolute convergence is

$$a' + b' - c' < 0.$$

---

* The symbol $O(1/n^2)$ does not denote the same function of n throughout. See § 2·11.

Hence *when* $|z| = 1$, *a sufficient condition** *for the absolute convergence of the hypergeometric series is that the real part of* $a + b - c$ *shall be negative.*

2·4.   *Effect of changing the order of the terms in a series.*

In an ordinary sum the order of the terms is of no importance, for it can be varied without affecting the result of the addition. In an infinite series, however, this is no longer the case†, as will appear from the following example.

Let
$$\Sigma = 1 + \tfrac{1}{3} - \tfrac{1}{2} + \tfrac{1}{5} + \tfrac{1}{7} - \tfrac{1}{4} + \tfrac{1}{9} + \tfrac{1}{11} - \tfrac{1}{6} + \ldots,$$

and
$$S = 1 - \tfrac{1}{2} + \tfrac{1}{3} - \tfrac{1}{4} + \tfrac{1}{5} - \tfrac{1}{6} + \ldots,$$

and let Σ_n and S_n denote the sums of their first n terms. These infinite series are formed of the same terms, but the order of the terms is different, and so Σ_n and S_n are quite distinct functions of n.

Let
$$\sigma_n = \tfrac{1}{1} + \tfrac{1}{2} + \ldots + \tfrac{1}{n}, \text{ so that } S_{2n} = \sigma_{2n} - \sigma_n.$$

Then
$$\Sigma_{3n} = \tfrac{1}{1} + \tfrac{1}{3} + \ldots + \frac{1}{4n-1} - \tfrac{1}{2} - \tfrac{1}{4} - \ldots - \frac{1}{2n}$$

$$= \sigma_{4n} - \tfrac{1}{2}\sigma_{2n} - \tfrac{1}{2}\sigma_n$$

$$= (\sigma_{4n} - \sigma_{2n}) + \tfrac{1}{2}(\sigma_{2n} - \sigma_n)$$

$$= S_{4n} + \tfrac{1}{2}S_{2n}.$$

Making $n \to \infty$, we see that

$$\Sigma = S + \tfrac{1}{2}S;$$

and so the derangement of the terms of S has altered its sum.

Example.   If in the series

$$1 - \tfrac{1}{2} + \tfrac{1}{3} - \tfrac{1}{4} + \ldots$$

the order of the terms be altered, so that the ratio of the number of positive terms to the number of negative terms in the first n terms is ultimately a^2, shew that the sum of the series will become $\log(2a)$.   (Manning.)

2·41.   *The fundamental property of absolutely convergent series.*

We shall shew that the sum of an absolutely convergent series is *not* affected by changing the order in which the terms occur.

Let
$$S = u_1 + u_2 + u_3 + \ldots$$

---

* The condition is also necessary. See Bromwich, *Infinite Series*, pp. 202–204.

† We say that the series $\overset{\infty}{\underset{n=1}{\Sigma}} v_n$ consists of the terms of $\overset{\infty}{\underset{n=1}{\Sigma}} u_n$ in a different order if a law is given by which corresponding to each positive integer p we can find one (and only one) integer q and *vice versa*, and v_q is taken equal to u_p. The result of this section was noticed by Dirichlet, *Berliner Abh.* (1837), p. 48, *Journal de Math.* IV. (1839), p. 397. See also Cauchy, *Résumés analytiques* (Turin, 1833), p. 57.

be an absolutely convergent series, and let S' be a series formed by the same terms in a different order.

Let ϵ be an arbitrary positive number, and let n be chosen so that

$$|u_{n+1}| + |u_{n+2}| + \ldots + |u_{n+p}| < \tfrac{1}{2}\epsilon$$

for all values of p.

Suppose that in order to obtain the first n terms of S we have to take m terms of S'; then if $k > m$,

$$S_k' = S_n + \text{terms of } S \text{ with suffices greater than } n,$$

so that

$$S_k' - S = S_n - S + \text{terms of } S \text{ with suffices greater than } n.$$

Now the modulus of the sum of any number of terms of S with suffices greater than n does not exceed the sum of their moduli, and therefore is less than $\tfrac{1}{2}\epsilon$.

Therefore $\qquad\qquad |S_k' - S| < |S_n - S| + \tfrac{1}{2}\epsilon$.

But $\qquad\qquad |S_n - S| \leqslant \lim_{p \to \infty} \{|u_{n+1}| + |u_{n+2}| + \ldots + |u_{n+p}|\}$

$$\leqslant \tfrac{1}{2}\epsilon.$$

Therefore given ϵ we can find m such that

$$|S_k' - S| < \epsilon$$

when $k > m$; therefore $S_m' \to S$, which is the required result.

If a series of real terms converges, but not absolutely, and if S_p be the sum of the first p positive terms, and if σ_n be the sum of the first n negative terms, then $S_p \to \infty$, $\sigma_n \to -\infty$; and $\lim(S_p + \sigma_n)$ does not exist unless we are given some relation between p and n. It has, in fact, been shewn by Riemann that it is possible, by choosing a suitable relation, to make $\lim(S_p + \sigma_n)$ equal to *any* given real number[*].

2·5. *Double series*[†].

Let $u_{m,n}$ be a number determinate for all positive integral values of m and n; consider the array

$$
\begin{array}{llll}
u_{1,1}, & u_{1,2}, & u_{1,3}, & \ldots \\
u_{2,1}, & u_{2,2}, & u_{2,3}, & \ldots \\
u_{3,1}, & u_{3,2}, & u_{3,3}, & \ldots \\
\multicolumn{4}{c}{\ldots\ldots\ldots\ldots\ldots}
\end{array}
$$

[*] *Ges. Werke*, p. 221.

[†] A complete theory of double series, on which this account is based, is given by Pringsheim, *Münchener Sitzungsberichte*, XXVII. (1897), pp. 101–152. See further memoirs by that writer, *Math. Ann.* LIII. (1900), pp. 289–321 and by London, *ibid.* pp. 322–370, and also Bromwich, *Infinite Series*, which, in addition to an account of Pringsheim's theory, contains many developments of the subject. Other important theorems are given by Bromwich, *Proc. London Math. Soc.* (2), I. (1904), pp. 176–201.

Let the sum of the terms inside the rectangle, formed by the first m rows of the first n columns of this array of terms, be denoted by $S_{m,n}$.

If a number S exists such that, given any arbitrary positive number ϵ, it is possible to find integers m and n such that

$$|S_{\mu,\nu} - S| < \epsilon$$

whenever both $\mu > m$ and $\nu > n$, we say* that the *double series of which the general element is $u_{\mu,\nu}$ converges to the sum S*, and we write

$$\lim_{\mu \to \infty, \nu \to \infty} S_{\mu,\nu} = S.$$

If the double series, of which the general element is $|u_{\mu,\nu}|$, is convergent, we say that the given double series is *absolutely convergent*.

Since $u_{\mu,\nu} = (S_{\mu,\nu} - S_{\mu,\nu-1}) - (S_{\mu-1,\nu} - S_{\mu-1,\nu-1})$, it is easily seen that, if the double series is convergent, then

$$\lim_{\mu \to \infty, \nu \to \infty} u_{\mu,\nu} = 0.$$

Stolz' necessary and sufficient† condition for convergence. A condition for convergence which is obviously necessary (see § 2.22) is that, given ϵ, we can find m and n such that $|S_{\mu+\rho, \nu+\sigma} - S_{\mu,\nu}| < \epsilon$ whenever $\mu > m$ and $\nu > n$ and ρ, σ may take *any* of the values $0, 1, 2, \ldots$. The condition is also sufficient; for, suppose it satisfied; then, when $\mu > m + n$, $|S_{\mu+\rho, \mu+\rho} - S_{\mu,\mu}| < \epsilon$.

Therefore, by § 2.22, $S_{\mu,\mu}$ has a limit S; and then making ρ and σ tend to infinity in such a way that $\mu + \rho = \nu + \sigma$, we see that $|S - S_{\mu,\nu}| \leqslant \epsilon$ whenever $\mu > m$ and $\nu > n$; that is to say, the double series converges.

Corollary. An absolutely convergent double series is convergent. For if the double series converges absolutely and if $t_{m,n}$ be the sum of m rows of n columns of the series of moduli, then, given ϵ, we can find μ such that, when $p > m > \mu$ and $q > n > \mu$, $t_{p,q} - t_{m,n} < \epsilon$. But $|S_{p,q} - S_{m,n}| \leqslant t_{p,q} - t_{m,n}$ and so $|S_{p,q} - S_{m,n}| < \epsilon$ when $p > m > \mu$, $q > n > \mu$; and this is the condition that the double series should converge.

2.51. *Methods‡ of summing double series.*

Let us suppose that $\sum_{\nu=1}^{\infty} u_{\mu,\nu}$ converges to the sum S_{μ}. Then $\sum_{\mu=1}^{\infty} S_{\mu}$ is called the *sum by rows* of the double series; that is to say, the sum by rows is $\sum_{\mu=1}^{\infty} \left(\sum_{\nu=1}^{\infty} u_{\mu,\nu} \right)$. Similarly, the *sum by columns* is defined as $\sum_{\nu=1}^{\infty} \left(\sum_{\mu=1}^{\infty} u_{\mu,\nu} \right)$. That these two sums are not necessarily the same is shewn by the example $S_{\mu,\nu} = \dfrac{\mu - \nu}{\mu + \nu}$, in which the sum by rows is -1, the sum by columns is $+1$; and S does not exist.

---

* This definition is practically due to Cauchy, *Analyse Algébrique*, p. 540.

† This condition, stated by Stolz, *Math. Ann.* xxiv. (1884), pp. 157-171, appears to have been first proved by Pringsheim.

‡ These methods are due to Cauchy.

PRINGSHEIM'S THEOREM*: *If S exists and the sums by rows and columns exist, then each of these sums is equal to S.*

For since S exists, then we can find m such that

$$| S_{\mu, \nu} - S | < \epsilon, \text{ if } \mu > m, \ \nu > m.$$

And therefore, since $\lim\limits_{\nu \to \infty} S_{\mu, \nu}$ exists, $| (\lim\limits_{\nu \to \infty} S_{\mu, \nu}) - S | \leqslant \epsilon$; that is to say, $\left| \sum\limits_{p=1}^{\mu} S_p - S \right| \leqslant \epsilon$ when $\mu > m$, and so (§ 2·22) the sum by rows converges to S. In like manner the sum by columns converges to S.

2·52. *Absolutely convergent double series.*

We can prove the analogue of § 2·41 for double series, namely that *if the terms of an absolutely convergent double series are taken in any order as a simple series, their sum tends to the same limit, provided that every term occurs in the summation.*

Let $\sigma_{\mu, \nu}$ be the sum of the rectangle of μ rows and ν columns of the double series whose general element is $| u_{\mu, \nu} |$; and let the sum of this double series be σ. Then given ϵ we can find m and n such that $\sigma - \sigma_{\mu, \nu} < \epsilon$ whenever both $\mu > m$ and $\nu > n$.

Now suppose that it is necessary to take N terms of the deranged series (in the order in which the terms are taken) in order to include all the terms of $S_{M+1, M+1}$, and let the sum of these terms be t_N.

Then $t_N - S_{M+1, M+1}$ consists of a sum of terms of the type $u_{p, q}$ in which $p > m, q > n$ whenever $M > m$ and $M > n$; and therefore

$$| t_N - S_{M+1, M+1} | \leqslant \sigma - \sigma_{M+1, M+1} < \tfrac{1}{2} \epsilon.$$

Also, $S - S_{M+1, M+1}$ consists of terms $u_{p, q}$ in which $p > m, q > n$; therefore $| S - S_{M+1, M+1} | \leqslant \sigma - \sigma_{M+1, M+1} < \tfrac{1}{2} \epsilon$; therefore $| S - t_N | < \epsilon$; and, corresponding to any given number ϵ, we can find N; and therefore $t_N \to S$.

Example 1. Prove that in an absolutely convergent double series, $\sum\limits_{n=1}^{\infty} u_{m, n}$ exists, and thence that the sums by rows and columns respectively converge to S.

[Let the sum of μ rows of ν columns of the series of moduli be $t_{\mu, \nu}$, and let t be the sum of the series of moduli.

Then $\sum\limits_{\nu=1}^{\infty} | u_{\mu, \nu} | < t$, and so $\sum\limits_{\nu=1}^{\infty} u_{\mu, \nu}$ converges; let its sum be b_μ; then

$$| b_1 | + | b_2 | + \ldots + | b_\mu | \leqslant \lim\limits_{\nu \to \infty} t_{\mu, \nu} \leqslant t,$$

and so $\sum\limits_{\mu=1}^{\infty} b_\mu$ converges absolutely. Therefore the sum by rows of the double series exists, and similarly the sum by columns exists; and the required result then follows from Pringsheim's theorem.]

Example 2.   Shew from first principles that if the terms of an absolutely convergent double series be arranged in the order

$$u_{1,1} + (u_{2,1} + u_{1,2}) + (u_{3,1} + u_{2,2} + u_{1,3}) + (u_{4,1} + \ldots + u_{1,4}) + \ldots,$$

this series converges to S.

2·53.   *Cauchy's theorem** on the multiplication of absolutely convergent series.*

We shall now shew that *if two series*

$$S = u_1 + u_2 + u_3 + \ldots$$

and $\qquad\qquad T = v_1 + v_2 + v_3 + \ldots$

are absolutely convergent, then the series

$$P = u_1 v_1 + u_2 v_1 + u_1 v_2 + \ldots,$$

formed by the products of their terms, written in any order, is absolutely convergent, and has for sum ST.

Let $\qquad\qquad S_n = u_1 + u_2 + \ldots + u_n,$

$$T_n = v_1 + v_2 + \ldots + v_n.$$

Then $\qquad ST = \lim S_n \lim T_n = \lim (S_n T_n)$

by example 2 of § 2·2.   Now

$$
\begin{aligned}
S_n T_n = \ & u_1 v_1 + u_2 v_1 + \ldots + u_n v_1 \\
& + u_1 v_2 + u_2 v_2 + \ldots + u_n v_2 \\
& + \ldots\ldots\ldots\ldots\ldots\ldots\ldots \\
& + u_1 v_n + u_2 v_n + \ldots + u_n v_n.
\end{aligned}
$$

But this double series is absolutely convergent; for if these terms are replaced by their moduli, the result is $\sigma_n \tau_n$, where

$$\sigma_n = |\,u_1\,| + |\,u_2\,| + \ldots + |\,u_n\,|,$$

$$\tau_n = |\,v_1\,| + |\,v_2\,| + \ldots + |\,v_n\,|,$$

and $\sigma_n \tau_n$ is known to have a limit.   Therefore, by § 2·52, if the elements of the double series, of which the general term is $u_m v_n$, be taken in any order, their sum converges to ST.

Example.   Shew that the series obtained by multiplying the two series

$$1 + \frac{z}{2} + \frac{z^2}{2^2} + \frac{z^3}{2^3} + \frac{z^4}{2^4} + \ldots, \quad 1 + \frac{1}{2} + \frac{1}{z^2} + \frac{1}{z^3} + \ldots,$$

and rearranging according to powers of z, converges so long as the representative point of z lies in the ring-shaped region bounded by the circles $|z| = 1$ and $|z| = 2$.

2·6.   *Power-Series*†.

A series of the type

$$a_0 + a_1 z + a_2 z^2 + a_3 z^3 + \ldots,$$

in which the coefficients $a_0, a_1, a_2, a_3, \ldots$ are independent of z, is called a *series proceeding according to ascending powers of z*, or briefly a *power-series*.

---

* *Analyse Algébrique*, Note VII.

† The results of this section are due to Cauchy, *Analyse Algébrique*, Ch. IX.

We shall now shew that *if a power-series converges for any value z_0 of z, it will be absolutely convergent for all values of z whose representative points are within a circle which passes through z_0 and has its centre at the origin.*

For, if z be such a point, we have $|z| < |z_0|$. Now, since $\sum\limits_{n=0}^{\infty} a_n z_0{}^n$ converges, $a_n z_0{}^n$ must tend to zero as $n \to \infty$, and so we can find M (independent of n) such that

$$|a_n z_0{}^n| < M.$$

Thus
$$|a_n z^n| < M \left| \frac{z}{z_0} \right|^n.$$

Therefore every term in the series $\sum\limits_{n=0}^{\infty} |a_n z^n|$ is less than the corresponding term in the convergent geometric series

$$\sum_{n=0}^{\infty} M \left| \frac{z}{z_0} \right|^n;$$

the series is therefore convergent; and so the power-series is *absolutely* convergent, as the series of moduli of its terms is a convergent series; the result stated is therefore established.

Let $\underline{\lim} |a_n|^{-1/n} = r$; then, from § 2·35, $\sum\limits_{n=0}^{\infty} a_n z^n$ converges absolutely when $|z| < r$; if $|z| > r$, $a_n z^n$ does not tend to zero and so $\sum\limits_{n=0}^{\infty} a_n z^n$ diverges (§ 2·3).

The circle $|z| = r$, which includes all the values of z for which the power-series

$$a_0 + a_1 z + a_2 z^2 + a_3 z^3 + \dots$$

converges, is called the *circle of convergence* of the series. The radius of the circle is called the *radius of convergence*.

In practice there is usually a simpler way of finding r, derived from d'Alembert's test (§ 2·36); r is $\lim (a_n/a_{n+1})$ if this limit exists.

A power-series may converge for all values of the variable, as happens, for instance, in the case of the series*

$$z - \frac{z^3}{3!} + \frac{z^5}{5!} - \dots,$$

which represents the function $\sin z$; in this case the series converges over the whole z-plane.

On the other hand, the radius of convergence of a power-series may be zero; thus in the case of the series

$$1 + 1! \, z + 2! \, z^2 + 3! \, z^3 + 4! \, z^4 + \dots$$

we have
$$\left| \frac{u_{n+1}}{u_n} \right| = n \, |z|,$$

---

* The series for e^z, $\sin z$, $\cos z$ and the fundamental properties of these functions and of $\log z$ will be assumed throughout. A brief account of the theory of the functions is given in the *Appendix*.

which, for all values of n after some fixed value, is greater than unity when z has any value different from zero. The series converges therefore only at the point $z = 0$, and the radius of its circle of convergence vanishes.

A power-series may or may not converge for points which are actually *on* the periphery of the circle; thus the series

$$1 + \frac{z}{1^s} + \frac{z^2}{2^s} + \frac{z^3}{3^s} + \frac{z^4}{4^s} + \ldots,$$

whose radius of convergence is unity, converges or diverges at the point $z = 1$ according as s is greater or not greater than unity, as was seen in § 2·33.

Corollary. If (a_n) be a sequence of positive terms such that $\lim (a_{n+1}/a_n)$ exists, this limit is equal to $\underline{\lim}\, a_n^{1/n}$.

2·61. *Convergence of series derived from a power-series.*

Let

$$a_0 + a_1 z + a_2 z^2 + a_3 z^3 + a_4 z^4 + \ldots$$

be a power-series, and consider the series

$$a_1 + 2a_2 z + 3a_3 z^2 + 4a_4 z^3 + \ldots,$$

which is obtained by differentiating the power-series term by term. We shall now shew that *the derived series has the same circle of convergence as the original series.*

For let z be a point within the circle of convergence of the power-series; and choose a positive number r_1, intermediate in value between $|z|$ and r the radius of convergence. Then, since the series $\sum\limits_{n=0}^{\infty} a_n r_1^n$ converges absolutely, its terms must tend to zero as $n \to \infty$; and it must therefore be possible to find a positive number M, independent of n, such that $|a_n| < M r_1^{-n}$ for all values of n.

Then the terms of the series $\sum\limits_{n=1}^{\infty} n |a_n| |z|^{n-1}$ are less than the corresponding terms of the series

$$\frac{M}{r_1} \sum_{n=1}^{\infty} \frac{n |z|^{n-1}}{r_1^{n-1}}.$$

But this series converges, by § 2·36, since $|z| < r_1$. Therefore, by § 2·34, the series

$$\sum_{n=1}^{\infty} n |a_n| |z|^{n-1}$$

converges; that is, the series $\sum\limits_{n=1}^{\infty} n a_n z^{n-1}$ converges absolutely for all points z situated within the circle of convergence of the original series $\sum\limits_{n=0}^{\infty} a_n z^n$. When $|z| > r$, $a_n z^n$ does not tend to zero, and *a fortiori* $n a_n z^n$ does not tend to zero; and so the two series have the same circle of convergence.

Corollary. The series $\sum\limits_{n=0}^{\infty} \dfrac{a_n z^{n+1}}{n+1}$, obtained by integrating the original power-series

term by term, has the same circle of convergence as $\sum\limits_{n=0}^{\infty} a_n z^n$.

2·7. *Infinite Products.*

We next consider a class of limits, known as *infinite products.*

Let $1 + a_1,\ 1 + a_2,\ 1 + a_3,\ \ldots$ be a sequence such that none of its members vanish. If, as $n \to \infty$, the product

$$(1 + a_1)(1 + a_2)(1 + a_3) \ldots (1 + a_n)$$

(which we denote by Π_n) tends to a definite limit other than zero, this limit is called the value of the infinite product

$$\Pi = (1 + a_1)(1 + a_2)(1 + a_3) \ldots,$$

and the product is said to be *convergent**. It is almost obvious that a *necessary* condition for convergence is that $\lim a_n = 0$, since $\lim \Pi_{n-1} = \lim \Pi_n \neq 0$.

The limit of the product is written $\prod\limits_{n=1}^{\infty} (1 + a_n)$.

Now
$$\prod_{n=1}^{m} (1 + a_n) = \exp\left\{ \sum_{n=1}^{m} \log(1 + a_n) \right\},$$

and†
$$\exp\left\{ \lim_{m \to \infty} u_m \right\} = \lim_{m \to \infty} \left\{ \exp u_m \right\}$$

if the former limit exists; hence a sufficient condition that the product should converge is that $\sum\limits_{n=1}^{\infty} \log(1 + a_n)$ should converge when the logarithms have their principal values. If this series of logarithms converges absolutely, the convergence of the product is said to be *absolute.*

The condition for absolute convergence is given by the following theorem: *in order that the infinite product*

$$(1 + a_1)(1 + a_2)(1 + a_3) \ldots$$

may be absolutely convergent, it is necessary and sufficient that the series

$$a_1 + a_2 + a_3 + \ldots$$

should be absolutely convergent.

For, by definition, Π is absolutely convergent or not according as the series

$$\log(1 + a_1) + \log(1 + a_2) + \log(1 + a_3) + \ldots$$

is absolutely convergent or not.

---

* The convergence of the product in which $a_{n-1} = -1/n^2$ was investigated by Wallis as early as 1655.

† See the *Appendix*, § A·2.

Now, since $\lim a_n = 0$, we can find m such that, when $n > m$, $|a_n| < \frac{1}{2}$; and then

$$|a_n^{-1} \log(1 + a_n) - 1| = \left| -\frac{a_n}{2} + \frac{a_n^2}{3} - \frac{a_n^3}{4} + \ldots \right|$$

$$< \frac{1}{2^2} + \frac{1}{2^3} + \ldots = \frac{1}{2}.$$

And thence, when $n > m$, $\frac{1}{2} \leqslant \left| \dfrac{\log(1 + a_n)}{a_n} \right| \leqslant \frac{3}{2}$; therefore, by the comparison theorem, the absolute convergence of $\Sigma \log(1 + a_n)$ entails that of Σa_n and conversely, provided that $a_n \neq -1$ for any value of n.

This establishes the result[*].

If, in a product, a finite number of factors vanish, and if, when these are suppressed, the resulting product converges, the original product is said to *converge* to zero. But such a product as $\prod\limits_{n=2}^{\infty} (1 - n^{-1})$ is said to *diverge* to zero.

Corollary. Since, if $S_n \to l$, $\exp(S_n) \to \exp l$, it follows from § 2·41 that the factors of an absolutely convergent product can be deranged without affecting the value of the product.

Example 1. Shew that if $\prod\limits_{n=1}^{\infty} (1 + a_n)$ converges, so does $\sum\limits_{n=1}^{\infty} \log(1 + a_n)$, if the logarithms have their principal values.

Example 2. Shew that the infinite product

$$\frac{\sin z}{z} \cdot \frac{\sin \frac{1}{2}z}{\frac{1}{2}z} \cdot \frac{\sin \frac{1}{3}z}{\frac{1}{3}z} \cdot \frac{\sin \frac{1}{4}z}{\frac{1}{4}z} \ldots$$

is absolutely convergent for all values of z.

[For $\left(\sin \dfrac{z}{n}\right) / \left(\dfrac{z}{n}\right)$ can be written in the form $1 - \dfrac{\lambda_n}{n^2}$, where $|\lambda_n| < k$ and k is independent of n; and the series $\sum\limits_{n=1}^{\infty} \dfrac{\lambda_n}{n^2}$ is absolutely convergent, as is seen on comparing it with $\sum\limits_{n=1}^{\infty} \dfrac{1}{n^2}$. The infinite product is therefore absolutely convergent.]

2·71. *Some examples of infinite products.*

Consider the infinite product

$$\left(1 - \frac{z^2}{\pi^2}\right) \left(1 - \frac{z^2}{2^2 \pi^2}\right) \left(1 - \frac{z^2}{3^2 \pi^2}\right) \ldots,$$

which, as will be proved later (§ 7·5), represents the function $z^{-1} \sin z$.

In order to find whether it is absolutely convergent, we must consider the series $\sum\limits_{n=1}^{\infty} \dfrac{z^2}{n^2 \pi^2}$, or $\dfrac{z^2}{\pi^2} \sum\limits_{n=1}^{\infty} \dfrac{1}{n^2}$; this series is absolutely convergent, and so the product is absolutely convergent for all values of z.

Now let the product be written in the form

$$\left(1 - \frac{z}{\pi}\right) \left(1 + \frac{z}{\pi}\right) \left(1 - \frac{z}{2\pi}\right) \left(1 + \frac{z}{2\pi}\right) \ldots.$$

---

[*] A discussion of the convergence of infinite products, in which the results are obtained without making use of the logarithmic function, is given by Pringsheim, *Math. Ann.* XXXIII. (1889), pp. 119–154, and also by Bromwich, *Infinite Series*, Ch. VI.

The absolute convergence of this product depends on that of the series

$$-\frac{z}{\pi}+\frac{z}{\pi}-\frac{z}{2\pi}+\frac{z}{2\pi}-\ldots.$$

But this series is only conditionally convergent, since its series of moduli

$$\frac{|z|}{\pi}+\frac{|z|}{\pi}+\frac{|z|}{2\pi}+\frac{|z|}{2\pi}+\ldots$$

is divergent. In this form therefore the infinite product is not absolutely convergent, and so, if the order of the factors $\left(1\pm\dfrac{z}{n\pi}\right)$ is deranged, there is a risk of altering the value of the product.

Lastly, let the same product be written in the form

$$\left\{\left(1-\frac{z}{\pi}\right)e^{\frac{z}{\pi}}\right\}\left\{\left(1+\frac{z}{\pi}\right)e^{-\frac{z}{\pi}}\right\}\left\{\left(1-\frac{z}{2\pi}\right)e^{\frac{z}{2\pi}}\right\}\left\{\left(1+\frac{z}{2\pi}\right)e^{-\frac{z}{2\pi}}\right\}\ldots,$$

in which each of the expressions

$$\left(1\pm\frac{z}{m\pi}\right)e^{\mp\frac{z}{m\pi}}$$

is counted as a single factor of the infinite product. The absolute convergence of this product depends on that of the series of which the $(2m-1)$th and $(2m)$th terms are

$$\left(1\mp\frac{z}{m\pi}\right)e^{\pm\frac{z}{m\pi}}-1.$$

But it is easy to verify that

$$\left(1\mp\frac{z}{m\pi}\right)e^{\pm\frac{z}{m\pi}}=1+O\left(\frac{1}{m^2}\right),$$

and so the absolute convergence of the series in question follows by comparison with the series

$$1+1+\frac{1}{2^2}+\frac{1}{2^2}+\frac{1}{3^2}+\frac{1}{3^2}+\frac{1}{4^2}+\frac{1}{4^2}+\ldots.$$

The infinite product in this last form is therefore again absolutely convergent, the adjunction of the factors $e^{\pm\frac{z}{n\pi}}$ having changed the convergence from conditional to absolute. This result is a particular case of the first part of the factor theorem of Weierstrass (§ 7·6).

Example 1. Prove that $\prod\limits_{n=1}^{\infty}\left\{\left(1-\dfrac{z}{c+n}\right)e^{\frac{z}{n}}\right\}$ is absolutely convergent for all values of z, if c is a constant other than a negative integer.

For the infinite product converges absolutely with the series

$$\sum_{n=1}^{\infty}\left\{\left(1-\frac{z}{c+n}\right)e^{\frac{z}{n}}-1\right\}.$$

Now the general term of this series is

$$\left(1-\frac{z}{c+n}\right)\left\{1+\frac{z}{n}+\frac{z^2}{2n^2}+O\left(\frac{1}{n^3}\right)\right\}-1=\frac{zc-\frac{1}{2}z^2}{n^2}+O\left(\frac{1}{n^3}\right)=O\left(\frac{1}{n^2}\right).$$

But $\sum_{n=1}^{\infty}\dfrac{1}{n^2}$ converges, and so, by § 2·34, $\sum_{n=1}^{\infty}\left\{\left(1-\dfrac{z}{c+n}\right)e^{\frac{z}{n}}-1\right\}$ converges absolutely, and therefore the product converges absolutely.

Example 2. Shew that $\prod_{n=2}^{\infty}\left\{1-\left(1-\dfrac{1}{n}\right)^{-n}z^{-n}\right\}$ converges for all points z situated outside a circle whose centre is the origin and radius unity.

For the infinite product is absolutely convergent provided that the series

$$\sum_{n=2}^{\infty}\left(1-\frac{1}{n}\right)^{-n}z^{-n}$$

is absolutely convergent. But $\lim\limits_{n\to\infty}\left(1-\dfrac{1}{n}\right)^{-n}=e$, so the limit of the ratio of the $(n+1)$th term of the series to the nth term is $\dfrac{1}{z}$; there is therefore absolute convergence when

$$\left|\frac{1}{z}\right|<1,\ \text{i.e. when } |z|>1.$$

Example 3. Shew that

$$\frac{1.2.3\ldots(m-1)}{(z+1)(z+2)\ldots(z+m-1)}m^z$$

tends to a finite limit as $m\to\infty$, unless z is a negative integer.

For the expression can be written as a product of which the nth factor is

$$\frac{n}{z+n}\left(\frac{n+1}{n}\right)^z=\left(1+\frac{1}{n}\right)^z\left(1+\frac{z}{n}\right)^{-1}=\left\{1+\frac{z(z-1)}{2n^2}+O\left(\frac{1}{n^3}\right)\right\}.$$

This product is therefore absolutely convergent, provided the series

$$\sum_{n=1}^{\infty}\left\{\frac{z(z-1)}{2n^2}+O\left(\frac{1}{n^3}\right)\right\}$$

is absolutely convergent; and a comparison with the convergent series $\sum_{n=1}^{\infty}\dfrac{1}{n^2}$ shews that this is the case. When z is a negative integer the expression does not exist because one of the factors in the denominator vanishes.

Example 4. Prove that

$$z\left(1-\frac{z}{\pi}\right)\left(1-\frac{z}{2\pi}\right)\left(1+\frac{z}{\pi}\right)\left(1-\frac{z}{3\pi}\right)\left(1-\frac{z}{4\pi}\right)\left(1+\frac{z}{2\pi}\right)\ldots=e^{-\frac{z}{\pi}\log 2}\sin z.$$

For the given product

$$\lim_{k\to\infty}z\left(1-\frac{z}{\pi}\right)\left(1-\frac{z}{2\pi}\right)\left(1+\frac{z}{\pi}\right)\ldots\left(1-\frac{z}{(2k-1)\pi}\right)\left(1-\frac{z}{2k\pi}\right)\left(1+\frac{z}{k\pi}\right)$$

$$=\lim_{k\to\infty}\left[\begin{array}{l}e^{\frac{z}{\pi}\left(-1-\frac{1}{2}+1-\frac{1}{3}-\frac{1}{4}+\frac{1}{2}-\ldots-\frac{1}{2k-1}-\frac{1}{2k}+\frac{1}{k}\right)}\\[2mm]\times z\left(1-\dfrac{z}{\pi}\right)e^{\frac{z}{\pi}}.\left(1-\dfrac{z}{2\pi}\right)e^{\frac{z}{2\pi}}\ldots\left(1-\dfrac{z}{2k\pi}\right)e^{\frac{z}{2k\pi}}.\left(1+\dfrac{z}{k\pi}\right)e^{-\frac{z}{k\pi}}\end{array}\right]$$

$$=\lim_{k\to\infty}e^{-\frac{z}{\pi}\left(1-\frac{1}{2}+\frac{1}{3}-\ldots+\frac{1}{2k-1}-\frac{1}{2k}\right)}z\left(1-\frac{z}{\pi}\right)e^{\frac{z}{\pi}}\left(1+\frac{z}{\pi}\right)e^{-\frac{z}{\pi}}\left(1-\frac{z}{2\pi}\right)e^{\frac{z}{2\pi}}\left(1+\frac{z}{2\pi}\right)e^{-\frac{z}{2\pi}}\ldots,$$

since the product whose factors are

$$\left(1 - \frac{z}{r\pi}\right) e^{r\pi}$$

is *absolutely* convergent, and so the order of its factors can be altered.

Since $$\log 2 = 1 - \tfrac{1}{2} + \tfrac{1}{3} - \tfrac{1}{4} + \tfrac{1}{5} - \dots ,$$

this shews that the given product is equal to

$$e^{-\frac{z}{\pi} \log 2} \sin z.$$

2·8. *Infinite Determinants.*

Infinite series and infinite products are not by any means the only known cases of limiting processes which can lead to intelligible results. The researches of G. W. Hill in the Lunar Theory* brought into notice the possibilities of *infinite determinants*.

The actual investigation of the convergence is due not to Hill but to Poincaré, *Bull. de la Soc. Math. de France*, xiv. (1886), p. 87. We shall follow the exposition given by H. von Koch, *Acta Math.* xvi. (1892), p. 217.

Let A_{ik} be defined for all integer values (positive and negative) of i, k, and denote by

$$D_m = [A_{ik}]_{i, k = -m, \dots + m}$$

the determinant formed of the numbers $A_{ik}\,(i,\, k = -m,\, \dots + m)$; then if, as $m \to \infty$, the expression D_m tends to a determinate limit D, we shall say that the infinite determinant

$$[A_{ik}]_{i,\, k = -\infty \dots +\infty}$$

is *convergent* and has the value D. If the limit D does not exist, the determinant in question will be said to be *divergent*.

The elements A_{ii}, (where i takes all values), are said to form the *principal diagonal* of the determinant D; the elements A_{ik}, (where i is fixed and k takes all values), are said to form the *row* i; and the elements A_{ik}, (where k is fixed and i takes all values), are said to form the *column* k. Any element A_{ik} is called a *diagonal* or a *non-diagonal* element, according as $i = k$ or $i \lessgtr k$. The element $A_{0,0}$ is called the *origin* of the determinant.

2·81. *Convergence of an infinite determinant.*

We shall now shew that *an infinite determinant converges, provided the product of the diagonal elements converges absolutely, and the sum of the non-diagonal elements converges absolutely*.

For let the diagonal elements of an infinite determinant D be denoted by $1 + a_{ii}$, and let the non-diagonal elements be denoted by a_{ik}, $(i \neq k)$, so that the determinant is

---

* Reprinted in *Acta Mathematica*, viii. (1886), pp. 1–36. Infinite determinants had previously occurred in the researches of Fürstenau on the algebraic equation of the nth degree, *Darstellung der reellen Wurzeln algebraischer Gleichungen durch Determinanten der Coeffizienten* (Marburg, 1860). Special types of infinite determinants (known as *continuants*) occur in the theory of infinite continued fractions; see Sylvester, *Math. Papers*, i, p. 504 and iii, p. 249

$$\left| \begin{array}{cccc} \cdots \cdots \cdots \cdots \cdots \cdots \cdots \cdots \cdots \cdots \cdots \cdots \cdots \cdots \cdots \\ \cdots 1 + a_{-1-1} & a_{-10} & a_{-11} \cdots \\ \cdots \quad a_{0-1} & 1 + a_{00} & a_{01} \quad \cdots \\ \cdots \quad a_{1-1} & a_{10} & 1 + a_{11} \quad \cdots \\ \cdots \cdots \cdots \cdots \cdots \cdots \cdots \cdots \cdots \cdots \cdots \cdots \cdots \cdots \cdots \end{array} \right|.$$

Then, since the series $\sum\limits_{i,\,k=-\infty}^{\infty} |a_{ik}|$ is convergent, the product

$$\bar{P} = \prod_{i=-\infty}^{\infty} \left(1 + \sum_{k=-\infty}^{\infty} |a_{ik}| \right)$$

is convergent.

Now form the products

$$P_m = \prod_{i=-m}^{m} \left(1 + \sum_{k=-m}^{m} a_{ik} \right), \quad \bar{P}_m = \prod_{i=-m}^{m} \left(1 + \sum_{k=-m}^{m} |a_{ik}| \right);$$

then if, in the expansion of P_m, certain terms are replaced by zero and certain other terms have their signs changed, we shall obtain D_m; thus, to each term in the expansion of D_m there corresponds, in the expansion of $\bar{P}_m$, a term of equal or greater modulus. Now $D_{m+p} - D_m$ represents the sum of those terms in the determinant D_{m+p} which vanish when the numbers $a_{ik} \{i, k = \pm(m+1) \ldots \pm(m+p)\}$ are replaced by zero; and to each of these terms there corresponds a term of equal or greater modulus in $\bar{P}_{m+p} - \bar{P}_m$.

Hence
$$|D_{m+p} - D_m| \leqslant \bar{P}_{m+p} - \bar{P}_m.$$

Therefore, since P_m tends to a limit as $m \to \infty$, so also D_m tends to a limit. This establishes the proposition.

2·82. *The rearrangement Theorem for convergent infinite determinants.*

We shall now shew that *a determinant, of the convergent form already considered, remains convergent when the elements of any row are replaced by any set of elements whose moduli are all less than some fixed positive number.*

Replace, for example, the elements
$$\ldots A_{0,\,-m}, \ldots \quad A_0 \ldots A_{0,\,m} \ldots$$
of the row through the origin by the elements
$$\ldots \mu_{-m}, \ldots \quad \mu_0 \ldots \mu_m \ldots$$
which satisfy the inequality
$$|\mu_r| < \mu,$$
where μ is a positive number; and let the new values of D_m and D be denoted by D_m' and D'. Moreover, denote by $\bar{P}_m'$ and $\bar{P}'$ the products obtained by suppressing in $\bar{P}_m$ and $\bar{P}$ the factor corresponding to the index zero; we see that no terms of D_m' can have a greater modulus than the corresponding term in the expansion of $\mu \bar{P}_m'$; and consequently, reasoning as in the last article, we have

$$|D'_{m+p} - D_m'| < \mu \bar{P}'_{m+p} - \mu \bar{P}_m',$$

which is sufficient to establish the result stated.

Example. Shew that the necessary and sufficient condition for the absolute convergence of the infinite determinant

$$\lim_{m \to \infty} \left| \begin{array}{cccccc} 1 & a_1 & 0 & 0 & \ldots & 0 \\ \beta_1 & 1 & a_2 & 0 & \ldots & 0 \\ 0 & \beta_2 & 1 & a_3 & \ldots & 0 \\ \cdots \cdots \cdots \cdots \cdots \cdots \cdots \cdots \cdots \cdots \cdots \\ 0 & \ldots & 0 & \beta_m & & 1 \end{array} \right|$$

is that the series

$$a_1 \beta_1 + a_2 \beta_2 + a_3 \beta_3 + \ldots$$

shall be absolutely convergent.

(von Koch.)

REFERENCES.

Convergent series.

    A. PRINGSHEIM, *Math. Ann.* XXXV. (1890), pp. 297–394.

    T. J. I'A. BROMWICH, *Theory of Infinite Series* (1908), Chs. II, III, IV.

Conditionally convergent series.

    G. F. B. RIEMANN, *Ges. Math. Werke*, pp. 221–225.

    A. PRINGSHEIM, *Math. Ann.* XXII. (1883), pp. 455–503.

Double series.

    A. PRINGSHEIM, *Münchener Sitzungsberichte*, XXVII. (1897), pp. 101–152.

       „   „   *Math. Ann.* LIII. (1900), pp. 289–321.

    G. H. HARDY, *Proc. London Math. Soc.* (2) I. (1904), pp. 124–128.

MISCELLANEOUS EXAMPLES.

1.   Evaluate $\lim\limits_{n\to\infty} (e^{-na}\,n^b)$, $\lim\limits_{n\to\infty} (n^{-a}\log n)$ when $a>0$, $b>0$.

2.   Investigate the convergence of

$$\sum_{n=1}^{\infty} \left\{1-n\log\frac{2n+1}{2n-1}\right\}. \qquad\qquad \text{(Trinity, 1904.)}$$

3.   Investigate the convergence of

$$\sum_{n=1}^{\infty} \left\{\frac{1.3\ldots 2n-1}{2.4\ldots 2n}\cdot\frac{4n+3}{2n+2}\right\}^2. \qquad \text{(Peterhouse, 1906.)}$$

4.   Find the range of values of z for which the series

$$2\sin^2 z - 4\sin^4 z + 8\sin^6 z - \ldots + (-)^{n+1} 2^n \sin^{2n} z + \ldots$$

is convergent.

5.   Shew that the series

$$\frac{1}{z} - \frac{1}{z+1} + \frac{1}{z+2} - \frac{1}{z+3} + \ldots$$

is conditionally convergent, except for certain exceptional values of z; but that the series

$$\frac{1}{z} + \frac{1}{z+1} + \ldots + \frac{1}{z+p-1} - \frac{1}{z+p} - \frac{1}{z+p+1} - \ldots - \frac{1}{z+2p+q-1} + \frac{1}{z+2p+q} + \ldots,$$

in which $(p+q)$ negative terms always follow p positive terms, is divergent.   (Simon.)

6.   Shew that

$$1 - \tfrac{1}{2} - \tfrac{1}{4} + \tfrac{1}{3} - \tfrac{1}{6} - \tfrac{1}{8} + \tfrac{1}{5} - \ldots = \tfrac{1}{2}\log 2. \qquad \text{(Trinity, 1908.)}$$

7.   Shew that the series

$$\frac{1}{1^a} + \frac{1}{2^\beta} + \frac{1}{3^a} + \frac{1}{4^\beta} + \ldots \qquad\qquad (1<a<\beta)$$

is convergent, although

$$u_{2n+1}/u_{2n} \to \infty. \qquad\qquad \text{(Cesàro.)}$$

8.   Shew that the series

$$a + \beta^2 + a^3 + \beta^4 + \ldots \qquad\qquad (0<a<\beta<1)$$

is convergent although

$$u_{2n}/u_{2n-1} \to \infty. \qquad\qquad \text{(Cesàro.)}$$

9. Shew that the series

$$\sum_{n=1}^{\infty} \frac{nz^{n-1}\{(1+n^{-1})^n-1\}}{(z^n-1)\{z^n-(1+n^{-1})^n\}}$$

converges absolutely for all values of z, except the values

$$z=\left(1+\frac{a}{m}\right)e^{2k\pi i/m}$$

$$(a=0,1;\ k=0,1,\dots m-1;\ m=1,2,3,\dots).$$

10. Shew that, when $s>1$,

$$\sum_{n=1}^{\infty}\frac{1}{n^s}=\frac{1}{s-1}+\sum_{n=1}^{\infty}\left[\frac{1}{n^s}+\frac{1}{s-1}\left\{\frac{1}{(n+1)^{s-1}}-\frac{1}{n^{s-1}}\right\}\right],$$

and shew that the series on the right converges when $0<s<1$.

(de la Vallée Poussin, *Mém. de l'Acad. de Belgique*, LIII. (1896), no. 6.)

11. In the series whose general term is

$$u_n=q^{n-\nu}x^{\frac{1}{2}\nu(\nu+1)},\qquad (0<q<1<x)$$

where ν denotes the number of digits in the expression of n in the ordinary decimal scale of notation, shew that

$$\lim_{n\to\infty}u_n^{1/n}=q,$$

and that the series is convergent, although $\overline{\lim_{n\to\infty}}\ u_{n+1}/u_n=\infty$.

12. Shew that the series

$$q_1+q_1{}^2+q_2{}^3+q_1{}^4+q_2{}^5+q_3{}^6+q_1{}^7+\dots,$$

where $$q_n=q^{1+(4/n)},\qquad (0<q<1)$$

is convergent, although the ratio of the $(n+1)$th term to the nth is greater than unity when n is not a triangular number. (Cesàro.)

13. Shew that the series

$$\sum_{n=0}^{\infty}\frac{e^{2n\pi ix}}{(w+n)^s},$$

where w is real, and where $(w+n)^s$ is understood to mean $e^{s\log(w+n)}$, the logarithm being taken in its arithmetic sense, is convergent for all values of s, when $I(x)$ is positive, and is convergent for values of s whose real part is positive, when x is real and not an integer.

14. If $u_n>0$, shew that if Σu_n converges, then $\underline{\lim_{n\to\infty}}(nu_n)=0$, and that, if in addition $u_n\geqslant u_{n+1}$, then $\lim_{n\to\infty}(nu_n)=0$.

15. If $$a_{m,n}=\frac{m-n}{2^{m+n}}\frac{(m+n-1)!}{m!\,n!},\qquad (m,n>0)$$

$$a_{m,0}=2^{-m},\quad a_{0,n}=-2^{-n},\quad a_{0,0}=0,$$

shew that

$$\sum_{m=0}^{\infty}\left(\sum_{n=0}^{\infty}a_{m,n}\right)=-1,\quad \sum_{n=0}^{\infty}\left(\sum_{m=0}^{\infty}a_{m,n}\right)=1.\qquad\text{(Trinity, 1904.)}$$

16. By converting the series

$$1+\frac{8q}{1-q}+\frac{16q^2}{1+q^2}+\frac{24q^3}{1-q^3}+\dots,$$

(in which $|q|<1$), into a double series, shew that it is equal to

$$1+\frac{8q}{(1-q)^2}+\frac{8q^2}{(1+q^2)^2}+\frac{8q^3}{(1-q^3)^2}+\dots.\qquad\text{(Jacobi.)}$$

17. Assuming that $\qquad \sin z = z \prod_{r=1}^{\infty} \left(1 - \dfrac{z^2}{r^2\pi^2}\right),$

shew that if $m \to \infty$ and $n \to \infty$ in such a way that $\lim (m/n) = k$, where k is finite, then

$$\lim_{} {\prod_{r=-n}^{m}}' \left(1 + \frac{z}{r\pi}\right) = k^{z/\pi} \frac{\sin z}{z},$$

the prime indicating that the factor for which $r = 0$ is omitted.   (Math. Trip., 1904.)

18. If $u_0 = u_1 = u_2 = 0$, and if, when $n > 1$,

$$u_{2n-1} = -\frac{1}{\sqrt{n}}, \quad u_{2n} = \frac{1}{\sqrt{n}} + \frac{1}{n} + \frac{1}{n\sqrt{n}},$$

then $\prod\limits_{n=0}^{\infty} (1 + u_n)$ converges, though $\sum\limits_{n=0}^{\infty} u_n$ and $\sum\limits_{n=0}^{\infty} u_n^2$ are divergent.

(Math. Trip., 1906.)

19. Prove that

$$\prod_{n=1}^{\infty} \left\{ \left(1 - \frac{z}{n}\right)^{n^k} \exp\left(\sum_{m=1}^{k+1} \frac{n^{k-m} z^m}{m}\right) \right\},$$

where k is any positive integer, converges absolutely for all values of z.

20. If $\sum\limits_{n=1}^{\infty} a_n$ be a conditionally convergent series of real terms, then $\prod\limits_{n=1}^{\infty} (1 + a_n)$ converges (but not absolutely) or diverges to zero according as $\sum\limits_{n=1}^{\infty} a_n^2$ converges or diverges.

(Cauchy.)

21. Let $\sum\limits_{n=1}^{\infty} \theta_n$ be an absolutely convergent series. Shew that the infinite determinant

$$\Delta(c) = \begin{vmatrix} \cdots & \cdots & \cdots & \cdots & \cdots \\ \cdots & \dfrac{(c-4)^2 - \theta_0}{4^2 - \theta_0} & \dfrac{-\theta_1}{4^2 - \theta_0} & \dfrac{-\theta_2}{4^2 - \theta_0} & \dfrac{-\theta_3}{4^2 - \theta_0} & \dfrac{-\theta_4}{4^2 - \theta_0} & \cdots \\ \cdots & \dfrac{-\theta_1}{2^2 - \theta_0} & \dfrac{(c-2)^2 - \theta_0}{2^2 - \theta_0} & \dfrac{-\theta_1}{2^2 - \theta_0} & \dfrac{-\theta_2}{2^2 - \theta_0} & \dfrac{-\theta_3}{2^2 - \theta_0} & \cdots \\ \cdots & \dfrac{-\theta_2}{0^2 - \theta_0} & \dfrac{-\theta_1}{0^2 - \theta_0} & \dfrac{c^2 - \theta_0}{0^2 - \theta_0} & \dfrac{-\theta_1}{0^2 - \theta_0} & \dfrac{-\theta_2}{0^2 - \theta_0} & \cdots \\ \cdots & \dfrac{-\theta_3}{2^2 - \theta_0} & \dfrac{-\theta_2}{2^2 - \theta_0} & \dfrac{-\theta_1}{2^2 - \theta_0} & \dfrac{(c+2)^2 - \theta_0}{2^2 - \theta_0} & \dfrac{-\theta_1}{2^2 - \theta_0} & \cdots \\ \cdots & \dfrac{-\theta_4}{4^2 - \theta_0} & \dfrac{-\theta_3}{4^2 - \theta_0} & \dfrac{-\theta_2}{4^2 - \theta_0} & \dfrac{-\theta_1}{4^2 - \theta_0} & \dfrac{(c+4)^2 - \theta_0}{4^2 - \theta_0} & \cdots \\ \cdots & \cdots & \cdots & \cdots & \cdots \end{vmatrix}$$

converges ; and shew that the equation

$$\Delta(c) = 0$$

is equivalent to the equation

$$\sin^2 \tfrac{1}{2}\pi c = \Delta(0) \sin^2 \tfrac{1}{2}\pi \theta_0^{\frac{1}{2}}.$$ (Hill ; see § 19·42.)

CHAPTER III

CONTINUOUS FUNCTIONS AND UNIFORM CONVERGENCE

3·1. *The dependence of one complex number on another.*

The problems with which Analysis is mainly occupied relate to the *dependence* of one complex number on another. If z and ζ are two complex numbers, so connected that, if z is given any one of a certain set of values, corresponding values of ζ can be determined, e.g. if ζ is the square of z, or if $\zeta = 1$ when z is real and $\zeta = 0$ for all other values of z, then ζ is said to be a function of z.

This dependence must not be confused with the most important case of it, which will be explained later under the title of *analytic functionality*.

If ζ is a real function of a real variable z, then the relation between ζ and z, which may be written

$$\zeta = f(z),$$

can be visualised by a curve in a plane, namely the locus of a point whose coordinates referred to rectangular axes in the plane are (z, ζ). No such simple and convenient geometrical method can be found for visualising an equation

$$\zeta = f(z),$$

considered as defining the dependence of one complex number $\zeta = \xi + i\eta$ on another complex number $z = x + iy$. A representation strictly analogous to the one already given for real variables would require four-dimensional space, since the number of variables ξ, η, x, y is now four.

One suggestion (made by Lie and Weierstrass) is to use a doubly-manifold system of lines in the quadruply-manifold totality of lines in three-dimensional space.

Another suggestion is to represent ξ and η separately by means of surfaces

$$\xi = \xi(x, y), \quad \eta = \eta(x, y).$$

A third suggestion, due to Heffter*, is to write

$$\zeta = re^{i\theta},$$

then draw the surface $r = r(x, y)$—which may be called the *modular-surface* of the function—and on it to express the values of θ by surface-markings. It might be possible to modify this suggestion in various ways by representing θ by curves drawn on the surface $r = r(x, y)$.

3·2. *Continuity of functions of real variables.*

The reader will have a general idea (derived from the graphical representation of functions of a real variable) as to what is meant by continuity.

---

* *Zeitschrift für Math. und Phys.* XLIX. (1899), p. 235.

We now have to give a precise definition which shall embody this vague idea.

Let $f(x)$ be a function of x defined when $a \leqslant x \leqslant b$.

Let x_1 be such that $a \leqslant x_1 \leqslant b$. If there exists a number l such that, corresponding to an arbitrary positive number ϵ, we can find a positive number η such that

$$|f(x) - l| < \epsilon,$$

whenever $|x - x_1| < \eta$, $x \neq x_1$, and $a \leqslant x \leqslant b$, then l is called the limit of $f(x)$ as $x \to x_1$.

It may happen that we can find a number l_+ (even when l does not exist) such that $|f(x) - l_+| < \epsilon$ when $x_1 < x < x_1 + \eta$. We call l_+ the limit of $f(x)$ when x approaches x_1 from the right and denote it by $f(x_1 + 0)$; in a similar manner we define $f(x_1 - 0)$ if it exists.

If $f(x_1 + 0)$, $f(x_1)$, $f(x_1 - 0)$ all exist and are equal, we say that $f(x)$ is *continuous* at x_1; so that if $f(x)$ is continuous at x_1, then, given ϵ, we can find η such that

$$|f(x) - f(x_1)| < \epsilon,$$

whenever $|x - x_1| < \eta$ and $a \leqslant x \leqslant b$.

If l_+ and l_- exist but are unequal, $f(x)$ is said to have an *ordinary discontinuity** at x_1; and if $l_+ = l_- \neq f(x_1)$, $f(x)$ is said to have a *removable discontinuity* at x_1.

If $f(x)$ is a complex function of a real variable, and if $f(x) = g(x) + i h(x)$ where $g(x)$ and $h(x)$ are real, the continuity of $f(x)$ at x_1 implies the continuity of $g(x)$ and of $h(x)$. For when $|f(x) - f(x_1)| < \epsilon$, then $|g(x) - g(x_1)| < \epsilon$ and $|h(x) - h(x_1)| < \epsilon$; and the result stated is obvious.

Example. From § 2·2 examples 1 and 2 deduce that if $f(x)$ and $\phi(x)$ are continuous at x_1, so are $f(x) \pm \phi(x)$, $f(x) \times \phi(x)$ and, if $\phi(x_1) \neq 0$, $f(x)/\phi(x)$.

The popular idea of continuity, so far as it relates to a real variable $f(x)$ depending on another real variable x, is somewhat different from that just considered, and may perhaps best be expressed by the statement "The function $f(x)$ is said to depend continuously on x if, as x passes through the set of all values intermediate between any two adjacent values x_1 and x_2, $f(x)$ passes through the set of all values intermediate between the corresponding values $f(x_1)$ and $f(x_2)$."

The question thus arises, how far this popular definition is equivalent to the precise definition given above.

Cauchy shewed that if a real function $f(x)$, of a real variable x, satisfies the precise definition, then it also satisfies what we have called the popular definition; this result

---

* If a function is said to have ordinary discontinuities at certain points of an interval it is implied that it is continuous at all other points of the interval.

will be proved in § 3·63. But the converse is not true, as was shewn by Darboux. This fact may be illustrated by the following example*.

Between $x = -1$ and $x = +1$ (except at $x = 0$), let $f(x) = \sin \dfrac{\pi}{2x}$; and let $f(0) = 0$.

It can then be proved that $f(x)$ depends continuously on x near $x = 0$, in the sense of the popular definition, but is not continuous at $x = 0$ in the sense of the precise definition.

Example. If $f(x)$ be defined and be an increasing function in the range (a, b), the limits $f(x \pm 0)$ exist at all points in the interior of the range.

[If $f(x)$ be an increasing function, a section of rational numbers can be found such that, if a, A be any members of its L-class and its R-class, $a < f(x + h)$ for every positive value of h and $A \geqslant f(x + h)$ for some positive value of h. The number defined by this section is $f(x + 0)$.]

3·21. *Simple curves. Continua.*

Let x and y be two real functions of a real variable t which are continuous for every value of t such that $a \leqslant t \leqslant b$. We denote the dependence of x and y on t by writing

$$x = x(t), \quad y = y(t). \qquad\qquad (a \leqslant t \leqslant b)$$

The functions $x(t)$, $y(t)$ are supposed to be such that they do not assume the same pair of values for any two different values of t in the range $a < t < b$.

Then the set of points with coordinates (x, y) corresponding to these values of t is called a *simple curve*. If

$$x(a) = x(b), \quad y(a) = y(b),$$

the simple curve is said to be *closed*.

Example. The circle $x^2 + y^2 = 1$ is a simple closed curve; for we may write†

$$x = \cos t, \quad y = \sin t. \qquad\qquad (0 \leqslant t \leqslant 2\pi)$$

A *two-dimensional continuum* is a set of points in a plane possessing the following two properties:

(i) If (x, y) be the Cartesian coordinates of any point of it, a *positive* number δ (depending on x and y) can be found such that every point whose distance from (x, y) is less than δ belongs to the set.

(ii) Any two points of the set can be joined by a simple curve consisting entirely of points of the set.

Example. The points for which $x^2 + y^2 < 1$ form a continuum. For if P be any point inside the unit circle such that $OP = r < 1$, we may take $\delta = 1 - r$; and any two points inside the circle may be joined by a straight line lying wholly inside the circle.

The following two theorems‡ will be assumed in this work; simple cases of them appear obvious from geometrical intuitions and, generally, theorems of a similar nature will be taken for granted, as formal proofs are usually extremely long and difficult.

---

* Due to Mansion, *Mathesis*, (2) xix. (1899), pp. 129–131.

† For a proof that the sine and cosine are continuous functions, see the *Appendix*, § A·41.

‡ Formal proofs will be found in Watson's *Complex Integration and Cauchy's Theorem.* (Cambridge Math. Tracts, No. 15.)

(I) A simple closed curve divides the plane into two continua (the 'interior' and the 'exterior').

(II) If P be a point on the curve and Q be a point not on the curve, the angle between QP and Ox increases by $\pm 2\pi$ or by zero, as P describes the curve, according as Q is an interior point or an exterior point. If the increase is $+ 2\pi$, P is said to describe the curve 'counterclockwise.'

A continuum formed by the interior of a simple curve is sometimes called *an open two-dimensional region*, or briefly an *open region*, and the curve is called its *boundary*; such a continuum with its boundary is then called *a closed two-dimensional region*, or briefly a *closed region* or *domain*.

A simple curve is sometimes called *a closed one-dimensional region*; a simple curve *with its end-points omitted* is then called an *open one-dimensional region*.

3·22. *Continuous functions of complex variables.*

Let $f(z)$ be a function of z defined at all points of a closed region (one- or two-dimensional) in the Argand diagram, and let z_1 be a point of the region.

Then $f(z)$ is said to be continuous at z_1, if given any positive number ϵ, we can find a corresponding positive number η such that

$$|f(z) - f(z_1)| < \epsilon,$$

whenever $|z - z_1| < \eta$ and z is a point of the region.

3·3. *Series of variable terms. Uniformity of convergence.*

Consider the series

$$x^2 + \frac{x^2}{1 + x^2} + \frac{x^2}{(1 + x^2)^2} + \dots + \frac{x^2}{(1 + x^2)^n} + \dots.$$

This series converges absolutely (§ 2·33) for all real values of x.

If $S_n(x)$ be the sum of n terms, then

$$S_n(x) = 1 + x^2 - \frac{1}{(1 + x^2)^{n-1}};$$

and so

$$\lim_{n \to \infty} S_n(x) = 1 + x^2; \qquad (x \neq 0)$$

but $S_n(0) = 0$, and therefore $\lim_{n \to \infty} S_n(0) = 0$.

Consequently, although the series is an absolutely convergent series of continuous functions of x, the sum is a discontinuous function of x. We naturally enquire the reason of this rather remarkable phenomenon, which was investigated in 1841–1848 by Stokes[*], Seidel[†] and Weierstrass[‡], who shewed that it cannot occur except in connexion with another phenomenon, that of *non-uniform* convergence, which will now be explained.

[*] *Camb. Phil. Trans.* VIII. (1847), pp. 533–583. [*Collected Papers*, I. pp. 236–313.]
[†] *Münchener Abhandlungen*, v. (1848), p. 381.
[‡] *Ges. Math. Werke*, I. pp. 67, 75.

Let the functions $u_1(z)$, $u_2(z)$, ... be defined at all points of a closed region of the Argand diagram.   Let

$$S_n(z) = u_1(z) + u_2(z) + \ldots + u_n(z).$$

The condition that the series $\overset{\infty}{\underset{n=1}{\Sigma}} u_n(z)$ should *converge* for any particular value of z is that, given ϵ, a number n should exist such that

$$|S_{n+p}(z) - S_n(z)| < \epsilon$$

for *all* positive values of p, the value of n of course depending on ϵ.

Let n have the smallest integer value for which the condition is satisfied. This integer will *in general* depend on the particular value of z which has been selected for consideration.   We denote this dependence by writing $n(z)$ in place of n.   Now it *may happen* that we can find a number N, INDEPENDENT OF z, such that

$$n(z) < N$$

for all values of z in the region under consideration.

If this number N exists, the series is said to CONVERGE UNIFORMLY throughout the region.

If no such number N exists, the convergence is said to be non-uniform*.

Uniformity of convergence is thus a property depending on a whole *set* of values of z, whereas previously we have considered the convergence of a series for various particular values of z, the convergence for each value being considered *without reference to the other values*.

We define the phrase 'uniformity of convergence *near* a point z' to mean that there is a definite positive number δ such that the series converges uniformly in the domain common to the circle $|z - z_1| \leqslant \delta$ and the region in which the series converges.

3·31.   *On the condition for uniformity of convergence†.*

If $R_{n,p}(z) = u_{n+1}(z) + u_{n+2}(z) + \ldots + u_{n+p}(z)$, we have seen that the necessary and sufficient condition that $\overset{\infty}{\underset{n=1}{\Sigma}} u_n(z)$ should converge uniformly in a region is that, given any positive number ϵ, it should be possible to choose N INDEPENDENT OF z (but depending on ϵ) such that

$$|R_{N,p}(z)| < \epsilon$$

for ALL positive integral values of p.

*. The reader who is unacquainted with the concept of uniformity of convergence will find it made much clearer by consulting Bromwich, *Infinite Series*, Ch. VII, where an illuminating account of Osgood's graphical investigation is given.

† This section shews that it is indifferent whether uniformity of convergence is defined by means of the partial remainder $R_{n,p}(z)$ or by $R_n(z)$.   Writers differ in the definition taken as fundamental.

If the condition is satisfied, by § 2·22, $S_n(z)$ tends to a limit, $S(z)$, say for each value of z under consideration; and then, since ϵ is *independent of* p,

$$|\{\lim_{p \to \infty} R_{N,p}(z)\}| \leqslant \epsilon,$$

and therefore, when $n > N$,

$$S(z) - S_n(z) = \{\lim_{p \to \infty} R_{N,p}(z)\} - R_{N,\,n-N}(z),$$

and so

$$|S(z) - S_n(z)| < 2\epsilon.$$

Thus (writing $\tfrac{1}{2}\epsilon$ for ϵ) a *necessary* condition for uniformity of convergence is that $|S(z) - S_n(z)| < \epsilon$, whenever $n > N$ and N is *independent of* z; the condition is also *sufficient*; for if it is satisfied it follows as in § 2·22 (I) that $|R_{N,p}(z)| < 2\epsilon$, which, by definition, is the condition for uniformity.

Example 1. Shew that, if x be real, the sum of the series

$$\frac{x}{1(x+1)} + \frac{x}{(x+1)(2x+1)} + \dots + \frac{x}{\{(n-1)x+1\}\{nx+1\}} + \dots$$

is discontinuous at $x=0$ and the series is non-uniformly convergent near $x=0$.

The sum of the first n terms is easily seen to be $1 - \dfrac{1}{nx+1}$; so when $x=0$ the sum is 0; when $x \neq 0$, the sum is 1.

The value of $R_n(x) = S(x) - S_n(x)$ is $\dfrac{1}{nx+1}$ if $x \neq 0$; so when x is small, say $x =$ one-hundred-millionth, the remainder after a million terms is $\dfrac{1}{\frac{1}{100}+1}$ or $1 - \dfrac{1}{101}$, so the first million terms of the series do not contribute one per cent. of the sum. And in general, to make $\dfrac{1}{nx+1} < \epsilon$, it is necessary to take

$$n > \frac{1}{x}\left(\frac{1}{\epsilon}-1\right).$$

Corresponding to a given ϵ, no number N exists, independent of x, such that $n < N$ for all values of x in any interval including $x=0$; for by taking x sufficiently small we can make n greater than any number N which is independent of x. There is therefore non-uniform convergence near $x=0$.

Example 2. Discuss the series

$$\sum_{n=1}^{\infty} \frac{x\{n(n+1)x^2-1\}}{\{1+n^2x^2\}\{1+(n+1)^2x^2\}},$$

in which x is real.

The nth term can be written $\dfrac{nx}{1+n^2x^2} - \dfrac{(n+1)x}{1+(n+1)^2x^2}$, so $S(x) = \dfrac{x}{1+x^2}$, and

$$R_n(x) = \frac{(n+1)x}{1+(n+1)^2x^2}.$$

[NOTE. In this example the sum of the series is not discontinuous at $x=0$.]

But (taking $\epsilon < \tfrac{1}{2}$, and $x \neq 0$), $|R_n(x)| < \epsilon$ if $\epsilon^{-1}(n+1)|x| < 1+(n+1)^2x^2$; i.e. if

$$n+1 > \tfrac{1}{2}\{\epsilon^{-1} + \sqrt{\epsilon^{-2}-4}\}|x|^{-1} \text{ or } n+1 < \tfrac{1}{2}\{\epsilon^{-1} - \sqrt{\epsilon^{-2}-4}\}|x|^{-1}.$$

Now it is not the case that the second inequality is satisfied for all values of n *greater* than a certain value and for all values of x; and the first inequality gives a value of $n(x)$ which tends to infinity as $x \to 0$; so that, corresponding to any interval containing the point $x=0$, there is no number N *independent of x*. The series, therefore, is non-uniformly convergent near $x=0$.

The reader will observe that $n(x)$ is discontinuous at $x=0$; for $n(x) \to \infty$ as $x \to 0$, but $n(0)=0$.

3·32. *Connexion of discontinuity with non-uniform convergence.*

We shall now shew that *if a series of continuous functions of z is uniformly convergent for all values of z in a given closed domain, the sum is a continuous function of z at all points of the domain.*

For let the series be $f(z) = u_1(z) + u_2(z) + \ldots + u_n(z) + \ldots = S_n(z) + R_n(z)$, where $R_n(z)$ is the remainder after n terms.

Since the series is uniformly convergent, given any positive number ϵ, we can find a corresponding integer n *independent of z*, such that $|R_n(z)| < \frac{1}{3}\epsilon$ for *all* values of z within the domain.

Now n and ϵ being thus fixed, we can, on account of the continuity of $S_n(z)$, find a positive number η such that

$$|S_n(z) - S_n(z')| < \frac{1}{3}\epsilon,$$

whenever $|z - z'| < \eta$.

We have then

$$|f(z) - f(z')| = |S_n(z) - S_n(z') + R_n(z) - R_n(z')|$$
$$< |S_n(z) - S_n(z')| + |R_n(z)| + |R_n(z')|$$
$$< \epsilon,$$

which is the condition for continuity at z.

Example 1.   Shew that near $x=0$ the series

$$u_1(x) + u_2(x) + u_3(x) + \ldots,$$

where $\qquad u_1(x) = x, \quad u_n(x) = x^{\frac{1}{2n-1}} - x^{\frac{1}{2n-3}},$

and real values of x are concerned, is discontinuous and non-uniformly convergent.

In this example it is convenient to take a slightly different form of the test; we shall shew that, given an arbitrarily small number ϵ, it is possible to choose values of x, as small as we please, depending on n in such a way that $|R_n(x)|$ is *not* less than ϵ for any value of n, no matter how large. The reader will easily see that the existence of such values of x is inconsistent with the condition for uniformity of convergence.

The value of $S_n(x)$ is $x^{\frac{1}{2n-1}}$; as n tends to infinity, $S_n(x)$ tends to 1, 0, or -1, according as x is positive, zero, or negative. The series is therefore absolutely convergent for all values of x, and has a discontinuity at $x=0$.

In this series $R_n(x) = 1 - x^{\frac{1}{2n-1}}, (x > 0)$; however great n may be, by taking* $x = e^{-(2n-1)}$ we can cause this remainder to take the value $1 - e^{-1}$, which is not arbitrarily small. The series is therefore non-uniformly convergent near $x = 0$.

Example 2. Shew that near $z = 0$ the series

$$\sum_{n=1}^{\infty} \frac{-2z(1+z)^{n-1}}{\{1 + (1+z)^{n-1}\}\{1 + (1+z)^n\}}$$

is non-uniformly convergent and its sum is discontinuous.

The nth term can be written

$$\frac{1 - (1+z)^n}{1 + (1+z)^n} - \frac{1 - (1+z)^{n-1}}{1 + (1+z)^{n-1}},$$

so the sum of the first n terms is $\dfrac{1 - (1+z)^n}{1 + (1+z)^n}$. Thus, considering real values of z greater than -1, it is seen that the sum to infinity is 1, 0, or -1, according as z is negative, zero, or positive. There is thus a discontinuity at $z = 0$. This discontinuity is explained by the fact that the series is non-uniformly convergent near $z = 0$; for the remainder after n terms in the series when z is positive is

$$\frac{-2}{1 + (1+z)^n},$$

and, however great n may be, by taking $z = \dfrac{1}{n}$, this can be made numerically greater than $\dfrac{2}{1+e}$, which is not arbitrarily small. The series is therefore non-uniformly convergent near $z = 0$.

3·33. *The distinction between absolute and uniform convergence.*

The *uniform* convergence of a series in a domain does not necessitate its *absolute* convergence at any points of the domain, nor conversely. Thus the series $\sum \dfrac{z^2}{(1 + z^2)^n}$ converges *absolutely*, but (near $z = 0$) not *uniformly*; while in the case of the series

$$\sum_{n=1}^{\infty} \frac{(-)^{n-1}}{z^2 + n},$$

the series of moduli is

$$\sum_{n=1}^{\infty} \frac{1}{|n + z^2|},$$

which is divergent, so the series is only *conditionally convergent*; but for all real values of z, the terms of the series are alternately positive and negative and numerically decreasing, so the sum of the series lies between the sum of its first n terms and of its first $(n + 1)$ terms, and so the remainder after n terms is numerically less than the nth term. Thus we only need take a finite number (independent of z) of terms in order to ensure that for all real values of z the remainder is less than any assigned number ϵ, and so the series is *uniformly* convergent.

Absolutely convergent series behave like series with a finite number of terms in that we can multiply them together and transpose their terms.

---

* This value of x satisfies the condition $|x| < \delta$ whenever $2n - 1 > \log \delta^{-1}$.

Uniformly convergent series behave like series with a finite number of terms in that they are continuous if each term in the series is continuous and (as we shall see) the series can then be integrated term by term.

3·34. *A condition, due to Weierstrass*, for uniform convergence.*

A sufficient, though not *necessary*, condition for the uniform convergence of a series may be enunciated as follows:—

If, for all values of z within a domain, the moduli of the terms of a series

$$S = u_1(z) + u_2(z) + u_3(z) + \ldots$$

are respectively less than the corresponding terms in a convergent series of positive terms

$$T = M_1 + M_2 + M_3 + \ldots,$$

where M_n is INDEPENDENT OF z, then the series S is uniformly convergent in this region. This follows from the fact that, the series T being convergent, it is always possible to choose n so that the remainder after the first n terms of T, and therefore the modulus of the remainder after the first n terms of S, is less than an assigned positive number ϵ; and since the value of n thus found is independent of z, it follows (§ 3·31) that the series S is uniformly convergent; by § 2·34, the series S also converges absolutely.

Example. The series

$$\cos z + \frac{1}{2^2}\cos^2 z + \frac{1}{3^2}\cos^3 z + \ldots$$

is uniformly convergent for all real values of z, because the moduli of its terms are not greater than the corresponding terms of the convergent series

$$1 + \frac{1}{2^2} + \frac{1}{3^2} + \ldots,$$

whose terms are positive constants.

3·341. *Uniformity of convergence of infinite products†.*

A convergent product $\prod\limits_{n=1}^{\infty} \{1 + u_n(z)\}$ is said to converge uniformly in a domain of values of z if, given ϵ, we can find m *independent of z* such that

$$\left| \prod_{n=1}^{m+p} \{1 + u_n(z)\} - \prod_{n=1}^{m} \{1 + u_n(z)\} \right| < \epsilon$$

for all positive integral values of p.

The only condition for uniformity of convergence which will be used in this work is that the product converges uniformly if $|u_n(z)| < M_n$ where M_n is independent of z and $\sum\limits_{n=1}^{\infty} M_n$ converges.

---

* *Abhandlungen aus der Funktionenlehre*, p. 70. The test given by this condition is usually described (e.g. by Osgood, *Annals of Mathematics*, III. (1889), p. 130) as the M-test.

† The definition is, effectively, that given by Osgood, *Funktionentheorie*, p. 462. The condition here given for uniformity of convergence is also established in that work.

To prove the validity of the condition we observe that $\prod\limits_{n=1}^{\infty} (1+M_n)$ converges (§ 2·7), and so we can choose m such that

$$\prod_{n=1}^{m+p} \{1+M_n\} - \prod_{n=1}^{m} \{1+M_n\} < \epsilon\,;$$

and then we have

$$\left| \prod_{n=1}^{m+p} \{1+u_n(z)\} - \prod_{n=1}^{m} \{1+u_n(z)\} \right| = \left| \prod_{n=1}^{m} \{1+u_n(z)\} \left[\prod_{n=m+1}^{m+p} \{1+u_n(z)\} - 1 \right] \right|$$

$$\leqslant \prod_{n=1}^{m} (1+M_n) \left[\prod_{n=m+1}^{m+p} \{1+M_n\} - 1 \right]$$

$$< \epsilon,$$

and the choice of m is independent of z.

3·35. *Hardy's tests for uniform convergence*.*

The reader will see, from § 2·31, that if, in a given domain, $\left| \sum\limits_{n=1}^{p} a_n(z) \right| \leqslant k$ where $a_n(z)$ is real and k is finite and independent of p and z, and if $f_n(z) \geqslant f_{n+1}(z)$ and $f_n(z) \to 0$ uniformly as $n \to \infty$, then $\sum\limits_{n=1}^{\infty} a_n(z) f_n(z)$ converges uniformly.

Also that if

$$k \geqslant u_n(z) \geqslant u_{n+1}(z) \geqslant 0,$$

where k is *independent of z* and $\sum\limits_{n=1}^{\infty} a_n(z)$ converges uniformly, then $\sum\limits_{n=1}^{\infty} a_n(z) u_n(z)$ converges uniformly. [To prove the latter, observe that m can be found such that

$$a_{m+1}(z),\ a_{m+1}(z)+a_{m+2}(z),\ ...,\ a_{m+1}(z)+a_{m+2}(z)+...+a_{m+p}(z)$$

are numerically less than ϵ/k; and therefore (§ 2·301)

$$\left| \sum_{n=m+1}^{m+p} a_n(z) u_n(z) \right| < \epsilon u_{m+1}(z)/k < \epsilon,$$

and the choice of ϵ and m is *independent of z*.]

Example 1. Shew that, if $\delta > 0$, the series

$$\sum_{n=1}^{\infty} \frac{\cos n\theta}{n}, \quad \sum_{n=1}^{\infty} \frac{\sin n\theta}{n}$$

converge uniformly in the range

$$\delta \leqslant \theta \leqslant 2\pi - \delta.$$

Obtain the corresponding result for the series

$$\sum_{n=1}^{\infty} \frac{(-)^n \cos n\theta}{n}, \quad \sum_{n=1}^{\infty} \frac{(-)^n \sin n\theta}{n},$$

by writing $\theta + \pi$ for θ.

Example 2. If, when $a \leqslant x \leqslant b$, $|\omega_n(x)| < k_1$ and $\sum\limits_{n=1}^{\infty} |\omega_{n+1}(x) - \omega_n(x)| < k_2$, where k_1, k_2 are independent of n and x, and if $\sum\limits_{n=1}^{\infty} a_n$ is a convergent series independent of x, then $\sum\limits_{n=1}^{\infty} a_n \omega_n(x)$ converges uniformly when $a \leqslant x \leqslant b$. (Hardy.)

---

* *Proc. London Math. Soc.* (2) IV. (1907), pp. 247–265. These results, which are generalisations of Abel's theorem (§ 3·71, below), though well known, do not appear to have been published before 1907. From their resemblance to the tests of Dirichlet and Abel for convergence, Bromwich proposes to call them Dirichlet's and Abel's tests respectively.

[For we can choose m, independent of x, such that $\left| \sum\limits_{n=m+1}^{m+p} a_n \right| < \epsilon$, and then, by § 2·301 corollary, we have $\left| \sum\limits_{n=m+1}^{m+p} a_n \omega_n(x) \right| < (k_1 + k_2)\,\epsilon.$]

3·4. *Discussion of a particular double series.*

Let ω_1 and ω_2 be any constants whose ratio is not purely real; and let α be positive.

The series $\sum\limits_{m,\,n} \dfrac{1}{(z + 2m\omega_1 + 2n\omega_2)^\alpha}$, in which the summation extends over all positive and negative integral and zero values of m and n, is of great importance in the theory of Elliptic Functions. At each of the points $z = -2m\omega_1 - 2n\omega_2$ the series does not exist. It can be shewn that the series converges absolutely for all other values of z if $\alpha > 2$, and the convergence is uniform for those values of z such that $|z + 2m\omega_1 + 2n\omega_2| \geqslant \delta$ for all integral values of m and n, where δ is an arbitrary positive number.

Let Σ' denote a summation for all integral values of m and n, the term for which $m = n = 0$ being omitted.

Now, if m and n are not both zero, and if $|z + 2m\omega_1 + 2n\omega_2| \geqslant \delta > 0$ for all integral values of m and n, then we can find a positive number C, depending on δ but not on z, such that

$$\left| \frac{1}{(z + 2m\omega_1 + 2n\omega_2)^\alpha} \right| < C \left| \frac{1}{(2m\omega_1 + 2n\omega_2)^\alpha} \right|.$$

Consequently, by § 3·34, the given series is absolutely and uniformly* convergent in the domain considered if

$$\Sigma' \frac{1}{|m\omega_1 + n\omega_2|^\alpha}$$

converges.

To discuss the convergence of the latter series, let

$$\omega_1 = \alpha_1 + i\beta_1, \quad \omega_2 = \alpha_2 + i\beta_2,$$

where $\alpha_1, \alpha_2, \beta_1, \beta_2$ are real. Since ω_2/ω_1 is not real, $\alpha_1\beta_2 - \alpha_2\beta_1 \neq 0$. Then the series is

$$\Sigma' \frac{1}{\{(\alpha_1 m + \alpha_2 n)^2 + (\beta_1 m + \beta_2 n)^2\}^{\frac{1}{2}\alpha}}.$$

This converges (§ 2·5 corollary) if the series

$$S = \Sigma' \frac{1}{(m^2 + n^2)^{\frac{1}{2}\alpha}}$$

converges; for the quotient of corresponding terms is

$$\left\{ \frac{(\alpha_1 + \alpha_2\mu)^2 + (\beta_1 + \beta_2\mu)^2}{1 + \mu^2} \right\}^{\frac{1}{2}\alpha},$$

* The reader will easily define uniformity of convergence of double series (see § 3·5).

4—2

where $\mu = n/m$. This expression, *qua* function of a continuous real variable μ, can be proved to have a positive minimum* (not zero) since $\alpha_1\beta_2 - \alpha_2\beta_1 \neq 0$; and so the quotient is always greater than a *positive* number K (independent of μ).

We have therefore only to study the convergence of the series S. Let

$$S_{p,q} = \sum_{m=-p}^{p} \sideset{}{'}\sum_{n=-q}^{q} \frac{1}{(m^2 + n^2)^{\frac{1}{2}a}},$$

$$\leqslant 4 \sum_{m=0}^{\infty} \sideset{}{'}\sum_{n=0}^{\infty} \frac{1}{(m^2 + n^2)^{\frac{1}{2}a}}.$$

Separating $S_{p,q}$ into the terms for which $m = n$, $m > n$, and $m < n$, respectively, we have

$$\tfrac{1}{4}S_{p,q} = \sum_{m=1}^{p} \frac{1}{(2m^2)^{\frac{1}{2}a}} + \sum_{m=1}^{p}\sum_{n=0}^{m-1} \frac{1}{(m^2 + n^2)^{\frac{1}{2}a}} + \sum_{n=1}^{q}\sum_{m=0}^{n-1} \frac{1}{(m^2 + n^2)^{\frac{1}{2}a}}.$$

But
$$\sum_{n=0}^{m-1} \frac{1}{(m^2 + n^2)^{\frac{1}{2}a}} < \frac{m}{(m^2)^{\frac{1}{2}a}} = \frac{1}{m^{a-1}}.$$

Therefore
$$\tfrac{1}{4}S \leqslant \sum_{m=1}^{\infty} \frac{1}{2^{\frac{1}{2}a}\,m^a} + \sum_{m=1}^{\infty} \frac{1}{m^{a-1}} + \sum_{n=1}^{\infty} \frac{1}{n^{a-1}}.$$

But these last series are known to be convergent if $a - 1 > 1$. So the series S is convergent if $a > 2$. The original series is therefore absolutely and uniformly convergent, when $a > 2$, for the specified range of values of z.

Example. Prove that the series

$$\Sigma \frac{1}{(m_1^2 + m_2^2 + \ldots + m_r^2)^\mu},$$

in which the summation extends over all positive and negative integral values and zero values of $m_1, m_2, \ldots m_r$, except the set of simultaneous zero values, is absolutely convergent if $\mu > \tfrac{1}{2}r$. (Eisenstein, *Journal für Math.* XXXV.)

3·5. *The concept of uniformity.*

There are processes other than that of summing a series in which the idea of uniformity is of importance.

Let ϵ be an arbitrary positive number; and let $f(z, \zeta)$ be a function of two variables z and ζ, which, for each point z of a closed region, satisfies the inequality $|f(z, \zeta)| < \epsilon$ when ζ is given any one of a certain set of values which will be denoted by (ζ_z); the particular set of values of course depends on the particular value of z under consideration. If a set $(\zeta)_0$ can be found such that every member of the set $(\zeta)_0$ is a member of *all* the sets (ζ_z), the function $f(z, \zeta)$ is said to satisfy the inequality *uniformly* for all points z of

---

* The reader will find no difficulty in verifying this statement; the minimum value in question is given by

$$K^{2/a} = \tfrac{1}{2}\,[\alpha_1{}^2 + \alpha_2{}^2 + \beta_1{}^2 + \beta_2{}^2 - \{(\alpha_1 - \beta_2)^2 + (\alpha_2 + \beta_1)^2\}^{\frac{1}{2}} \{(\alpha_1 + \beta_2)^2 + (\alpha_2 - \beta_1)^2\}^{\frac{1}{2}}].$$

the region. And if a function $\phi(z)$ possesses some property, for every positive value of ϵ, in virtue of the inequality $|f(z, \zeta)| < \epsilon$, $\phi(z)$ is then said to *possess the property uniformly*.

In addition to the uniformity of convergence of series and products, we shall have to consider uniformity of convergence of integrals and also uniformity of continuity ; thus a series is uniformly convergent when $|R_n(z)| < \epsilon$, $\zeta (=n)$ assuming integer values independent of z only.

Further, a function $f(z)$ is continuous in a closed region if, given ϵ, we can find a positive number η_z such that $|f(z+\zeta_z)-f(z)| < \epsilon$ whenever

$$0 < |\zeta_z| < \eta_z$$

and $z+\zeta$ is a point of the region.

The function will be *uniformly* continuous if we can find a positive number η *independent of z*, such that $\eta < \eta_z$ and $|f(z+\zeta)-f(z)| < \epsilon$ whenever

$$0 < |\zeta| < \eta$$

and $z+\zeta$ is a point of the region, (in this case the set $(\zeta)_0$ is the set of points whose moduli are less than η).

We shall find later (§ $3\cdot61$) that continuity involves uniformity of continuity ; this is in marked contradistinction to the fact that convergence does not involve uniformity of convergence.

$3\cdot6$. *The modified Heine-Borel theorem.*

The following theorem is of great importance in connexion with properties of uniformity ; we give a proof for a one-dimensional closed region*.

Given (i) *a straight line CD and* (ii) *a law by which, corresponding to each point† P of CD, we can determine a closed interval I(P) of CD, P being an interior‡ point of I(P).*

Then the line CD can be divided into a finite *number of closed intervals $J_1, J_2, \ldots J_k$, such that each interval J_r contains at least one point (not an end point) P_r, such that no point of J_r lies outside the interval $I(P_r)$ associated (by means of the given law) with that point P_r§.*

A closed interval of the nature just described will be called a *suitable* interval, and will be said to satisfy condition (A).

If CD satisfies condition (A), what is required is proved. If not, bisect CD ; if either or both of the intervals into which CD is divided is not suitable, bisect it or them‖.

---

* A formal proof of the theorem for a two-dimensional region will be found in Watson's *Complex Integration and Cauchy's Theorem* (Camb. Math. Tracts, No. 15).

† Examples of such laws associating intervals with points will be found in §§ $3\cdot61$, $5\cdot13$.

‡ Except when P is at C or D, when it is an end point.

§ This statement of the Heine-Borel theorem (which is sometimes called the Borel-Lebesgue theorem) is due to Baker, *Proc. London Math. Soc.* (2) I. (1904), p. 24. Hobson, *The Theory of Functions of a Real Variable* (1907), p. 87, points out that the theorem is practically given in Goursat's proof of Cauchy's theorem (*Trans. American Math. Soc.* I. (1900), p. 14) ; the ordinary form of the Heine-Borel theorem will be found in the treatise cited.

‖ A suitable interval is not to be bisected ; for one of the parts into which it is divided might not be suitable.

This process of bisecting intervals which are not suitable either will terminate or it will not. If it does terminate, the theorem is proved, for CD will have been divided into suitable intervals.

Suppose that the process does not terminate; and let an interval, which *can* be divided into suitable intervals by the process of bisection just described, be said to satisfy condition (B).

Then, by hypothesis, CD does not satisfy condition (B); therefore at least one of the bisected portions of CD does not satisfy condition (B). Take that one which does not (if neither satisfies condition (B) take the left-hand one); bisect it and select that bisected part which does not satisfy condition (B). This process of bisection and selection gives an unending sequence of intervals $s_0, s_1, s_2, \ldots$ such that:

(i)   The length of s_n is $2^{-n}CD$.

(ii) No point of s_{n+1} is outside s_n.

(iii) The interval s_n does not satisfy condition (A).

Let the distances of the end points of s_n from C be x_n, y_n; then $x_n \leqslant x_{n+1} < y_{n+1} \leqslant y_n$. Therefore, by § 2·2, x_n and y_n have limits; and, by the condition (i) above, these limits are the same, say ξ; let Q be the point whose distance from C is ξ. But, by hypothesis, there is a number δ_Q such that every point of CD, whose distance from Q is less than δ_Q, is a point of the associated interval $I(Q)$. Choose n so large that $2^{-n}CD < \delta_Q$; then Q is an internal point or end point of s_n and the distance of every point of s_n from Q is less than δ_Q. And therefore the interval s_n satisfies condition (A), which is contrary to condition (iii) above. The hypothesis that the process of bisecting intervals does not terminate therefore involves a contradiction; therefore the process does terminate and the theorem is proved.

In the two-dimensional form of the theorem*, the interval CD is replaced by a closed two-dimensional region, the interval $I(P)$ by a circle† with centre P, and the interval J_r by a square with sides parallel to the axes.

3·61.   *Uniformity of continuity.*

From the theorem just proved, it follows without difficulty that if a function $f(x)$ of a real variable x is continuous when $a \leqslant x \leqslant b$, then $f(x)$ is *uniformly* continuous‡ throughout the range $a \leqslant x \leqslant b$.

For let ϵ be an arbitrary positive number; then, in virtue of the continuity of $f(x)$, corresponding to any value of x, we can find a positive number δ_x, depending on x, such that

$$| f(x') - f(x) | < \tfrac{1}{4}\epsilon$$

for all values of x' such that $| x' - x | < \delta_x$.

---

* The reader will see that a proof may be constructed on similar lines by drawing a square circumscribing the region and carrying out a process of dividing squares into four equal squares.

† Or the portion of the circle which lies inside the region.

‡ This result is due to Heine; see *Journal für Math.* LXXI. (1870), p. 361, and LXXIV. (1872), p. 188.

Then by § 3·6 we can divide the range (a, b) into a *finite* number of closed intervals with the property that in each interval there is a number x_1 such that $|f(x') - f(x_1)| < \frac{1}{4}\epsilon$, whenever x' lies in the interval in which x_1 lies.

Let δ_0 be the length of the smallest of these intervals; and let ξ, ξ' be *any* two numbers in the closed range (a, b) such that $|\xi - \xi'| < \delta_0$. Then ξ, ξ' lie in the same or in adjacent intervals; if they lie in adjacent intervals let ξ_0 be the common end point. Then we can find numbers x_1, x_2, one in each interval, such that

$$|f(\xi) - f(x_1)| < \tfrac{1}{4}\epsilon, \qquad |f(\xi_0) - f(x_1)| < \tfrac{1}{4}\epsilon,$$

$$|f(\xi') - f(x_2)| < \tfrac{1}{4}\epsilon, \qquad |f(\xi_0) - f(x_2)| < \tfrac{1}{4}\epsilon,$$

so that

$$\begin{aligned}
|f(\xi) - f(\xi')| = |\,\{f(\xi) - f(x_1)\} - \{f(\xi_0) - f(x_1)\} \\
- \{f(\xi') - f(x_2)\} + \{f(\xi_0) - f(x_2)\}\,| \\
< \epsilon.
\end{aligned}$$

If ξ, ξ' lie in the same interval, we can prove similarly that

$$|f(\xi) - f(\xi')| < \tfrac{1}{2}\epsilon.$$

In either case we have shewn that, for *any* number ξ in the range, we have

$$|f(\xi) - f(\xi + \zeta)| < \epsilon$$

whenever $\xi + \zeta$ is in the range and $-\delta_0 < \zeta < \delta_0$, where δ_0 is *independent of* ξ. The *uniformity* of the continuity is therefore established.

Corollary (i). From the two-dimensional form of the theorem of § 3·6 we can prove that a function of a complex variable, continuous at all points of a closed region of the Argand diagram, is uniformly continuous throughout that region.

Corollary (ii). A function $f(x)$ which is continuous throughout the range $a \leqslant x \leqslant b$ is *bounded* in the range; that is to say we can find a number κ independent of x such that $|f(x)| < \kappa$ for all points x in the range.

[Let n be the number of parts into which the range is divided.

Let a, ξ_1, ξ_2, ... ξ_{n-1}, b be their end points; then if x be any point of the rth interval we can find numbers x_1, x_2, ... x_n such that

$$|f(a) - f(x_1)| < \tfrac{1}{4}\epsilon, \quad |f(x_1) - f(\xi_1)| < \tfrac{1}{4}\epsilon, \quad |f(\xi_1) - f(x_2)| < \tfrac{1}{4}\epsilon, \quad |f(x_2) - f(\xi_2)| < \tfrac{1}{4}\epsilon, \ldots$$

$$\ldots |f(x_{r-1}) - f(x)| < \tfrac{1}{4}\epsilon.$$

Therefore $|f(a) - f(x)| < \tfrac{1}{2}r\epsilon$, and so

$$|f(x)| < |f(a)| + \tfrac{1}{2}n\epsilon,$$

which is the required result, since the right-hand side is independent of x.]

The corresponding theorem for functions of complex variables is left to the reader.

3·62. *A real function, of a real variable, continuous in a closed interval, attains its upper bound.*

Let $f(x)$ be a real continuous function of x when $a \leqslant x \leqslant b$. Form a section in which the R-class consists of those numbers r such that $r > f(x)$

for all values of x in the range (a, b), and the L-class of all other numbers. This section defines a number α such that $f(x) \leqslant \alpha$, but, if δ be *any* positive number, values of x in the range exist such that $f(x) > \alpha - \delta$. Then α is called the *upper bound* of $f(x)$; and the theorem states that a number x' in the range can be found such that $f(x') = \alpha$.

For, no matter how small δ may be, we can find values of x for which $|f(x) - \alpha|^{-1} > \delta^{-1}$; therefore $|\{f(x) - \alpha\}|^{-1}$ is not bounded in the range; therefore (§ 3·61 cor. (ii)) it is not continuous at some point or points of the range; but since $|f(x) - \alpha|$ is continuous at all points of the range, its reciprocal is continuous at all points of the range (§ 3·2 example) except those points at which $f(x) = \alpha$; therefore $f(x) = \alpha$ at some point of the range; the theorem is therefore proved.

Corollary (i). The lower bound of a continuous function may be defined in a similar manner; and a continuous function attains its lower bound.

Corollary (ii). If $f(z)$ be a function of a complex variable continuous in a closed region, $|f(z)|$ attains its upper bound.

3·63. *A real function, of a real variable, continuous in a closed interval, attains all values between its upper and lower bounds.*

Let M, m be the upper and lower bounds of $f(x)$; then we can find numbers $\bar{x}, \underline{x}$, by § 3·62, such that $f(\bar{x}) = M, f(\underline{x}) = m$; let μ be any number such that $m < \mu < M$. Given any positive number ϵ, we can (by § 3·61) divide the range $(\bar{x}, \underline{x})$ into a *finite* number, r, of closed intervals such that

$$|f(x_1^{(r)}) - f(x_2^{(r)})| < \epsilon,$$

where $x_1^{(r)}, x_2^{(r)}$ are any points of the rth interval; take $x_1^{(r)}, x_2^{(r)}$ to be the end points of the interval; then there is at least one of the intervals for which $f(x_1^{(r)}) - \mu, f(x_2^{(r)}) - \mu$ have opposite signs; and since

$$|\{f(x_1^{(r)}) - \mu\} - \{f(x_2^{(r)}) - \mu\}| < \epsilon,$$

it follows that $\qquad |f(x_1^{(r)}) - \mu| < \epsilon.$

Since we can find a number $x_1^{(r)}$ to satisfy this inequality for all values of ϵ, no matter how small, the lower bound of the function $|f(x) - \mu|$ is zero; since this is a continuous function of x, it follows from § 3·62 cor. (i) that $f(x) - \mu$ vanishes for some value of x.

3·64. *The fluctuation of a function of a real variable*[*].

Let $f(x)$ be a real bounded function, defined when $a \leqslant x \leqslant b$. Let

$$a \leqslant x_1 \leqslant x_2 \leqslant \ldots \leqslant x_n \leqslant b.$$

Then $|f(a) - f(x_1)| + |f(x_1) - f(x_2)| + \ldots + |f(x_n) - f(b)|$ is called the *fluctuation* of $f(x)$ in the range (a, b) for the set of subdivisions $x_1, x_2, \ldots x_n$.

---

[*] The terminology of this section is partly that of Hobson, *The Theory of Functions of a Real Variable* (1907) and partly that of Young, *The Theory of Sets of Points* (1906).

If the fluctuation have an upper bound $F_a{}^b$, independent of n, for all choices of $x_1, x_2, \ldots x_n$, then $f(x)$ is said to have *limited* total *fluctuation* in the range (a, b). $F_a{}^b$ is called the *total fluctuation* in the range.

Example 1.   If $f(x)$ be monotonic* in the range (a, b), its total fluctuation in the range is $|f(a) - f(b)|$.

Example 2.   A function with limited total fluctuation can be expressed as the difference of two positive increasing monotonic functions.

[These functions may be taken to be $\frac{1}{2}\{F_a{}^x + f(x)\}$, $\frac{1}{2}\{F_a{}^x - f(x)\}$.]

Example 3.   If $f(x)$ have limited total fluctuation in the range (a, b), then the limits $f(x \pm 0)$ exist at all points in the interior of the range.   [See § 3·2 example.]

Example 4.   If $f(x)$, $g(x)$ have limited total fluctuation in the range (a, b) so has $f(x) g(x)$.

[For $\qquad |f(x') g(x') - f(x) g(x)| \leqslant |f(x')| \cdot |g(x') - g(x)| + |g(x)| \cdot |f(x') - f(x)|$,
and so the total fluctuation of $f(x) g(x)$ cannot exceed $g \cdot F_a{}^b + f \cdot G_a{}^b$, where f, g are the upper bounds of $|f(x)|$, $|g(x)|$.]

3·7. *Uniformity of convergence of power series.*

Let the power series

$$a_0 + a_1 z + \ldots + a_n z^n + \ldots$$

converge absolutely when $z = z_0$.

Then, if $|z| \leqslant |z_0|$, $\qquad |a_n z^n| \leqslant |a_n z_0{}^n|$.

But since $\sum\limits_{n=0}^{\infty} |a_n z_0{}^n|$ converges, it follows, by § 3·34, that $\sum\limits_{n=0}^{\infty} a_n z^n$ converges uniformly with regard to the variable z when $|z| \leqslant |z_0|$.

Hence, by § 3·32, a power series is a continuous function of the variable throughout the closed region formed by the interior and boundary of any circle concentric with the circle of convergence and of smaller radius (§ 2·6).

3·71. *Abel's theorem† on continuity up to the circle of convergence.*

Let $\sum\limits_{n=0}^{\infty} a_n z^n$ be a power series, whose radius of convergence is unity, and let it be such that $\sum\limits_{n=0}^{\infty} a_n$ converges; and let $0 \leqslant x \leqslant 1$; then Abel's theorem asserts that $\lim\limits_{x \to 1} \left(\sum\limits_{n=0}^{\infty} a_n x^n \right) = \sum\limits_{n=0}^{\infty} a_n$.

For, with the notation of § 3·35, the function x^n satisfies the conditions laid on $u_n(x)$, when $0 \leqslant x \leqslant 1$; consequently $f(x) = \sum\limits_{n=0}^{\infty} a_n x^n$ converges *uni-*

* The function is monotonic if $\{f(x) - f(x')\}/(x - x')$ is one-signed or zero for all pairs of different values of x and x'.

† *Journal für Math.* I. (1826), pp. 311–339, Theorem IV.   Abel's proof employs directly the arguments by which the theorems of § 3·32 and § 3·35 are proved.   In the case when $\Sigma |a_n|$ converges, the theorem is obvious from § 3·7.

formly throughout the range $0 \leqslant x \leqslant 1$; it is therefore, by § 3·32, a continuous function of x throughout the range, and so $\lim\limits_{x \to 1-0} f(x) = f(1)$, which is the theorem stated.

3·72. *Abel's theorem* on multiplication of series.*

This is a modification of the theorem of § 2·53 for absolutely convergent series.

Let $$c_n = a_0 b_n + a_1 b_{n-1} + \ldots + a_n b_0.$$

Then the convergence of $\sum\limits_{n=0}^{\infty} a_n, \sum\limits_{n=0}^{\infty} b_n$ *and* $\sum\limits_{n=0}^{\infty} c_n$ *is a sufficient condition that*

$$\left(\sum_{n=0}^{\infty} a_n \right) \left(\sum_{n=0}^{\infty} b_n \right) = \sum_{n=0}^{\infty} c_n.$$

For, let

$$A(x) = \sum_{n=0}^{\infty} a_n x^n, \quad B(x) = \sum_{n=0}^{\infty} b_n x^n, \quad C(x) = \sum_{n=0}^{\infty} c_n x^n.$$

Then the series for $A(x)$, $B(x)$, $C(x)$ are absolutely convergent when $|x| < 1$, (§ 2·6); and consequently, by § 2·53,

$$A(x) B(x) = C(x)$$

when $0 < x < 1$; therefore, by § 2·2 example 2,

$$\{ \lim_{x \to 1-0} A(x) \} \{ \lim_{x \to 1-0} B(x) \} = \{ \lim_{x \to 1-0} C(x) \}$$

provided that these three limits exist; but, by § 3·71, these three limits are $\sum\limits_{n=0}^{\infty} a_n, \sum\limits_{n=0}^{\infty} b_n, \sum\limits_{n=0}^{\infty} c_n$; and the theorem is proved.

3·73. *Power series which vanish identically.*

If a convergent power series vanishes for all values of z such that $|z| \leqslant r_1$, where $r_1 > 0$, then all the coefficients in the power series vanish.

For, if not, let a_m be the first coefficient which does not vanish.

Then $a_m + a_{m+1} z + a_{m+2} z^2 + \ldots$ vanishes for all values of z (zero excepted) and converges absolutely when $|z| \leqslant r < r_1$; hence, if $s = a_{m+1} + a_{m+2} z + \ldots$, we have

$$|s| \leqslant \sum_{n=1}^{\infty} |a_{m+n}| r^{n-1},$$

and so we can find† *a positive number* $\delta \leqslant r$ such that, whenever $|z| \leqslant \delta$,

$$|a_{m+1} z + a_{m+2} z^2 + \ldots| \leqslant \tfrac{1}{2} |a_m|;$$

and then $|a_m + s| \geqslant |a_m| - |s| > \tfrac{1}{2} |a_m|$, and so $|a_m + s| \neq 0$ when $|z| < \delta$.

---

* *Journal für Math.* I. (1826), pp. 311–339, Theorem VI. This is Abel's original proof. In some text-books a more elaborate proof, by the use of Cesàro's sums (§ 8·43), is given.

† It is sufficient to take δ to be the smaller of the numbers r and $\tfrac{1}{2} |a_m| \div \sum\limits_{n=1}^{\infty} |a_{m+n}| r^{n-1}$.

We have therefore arrived at a contradiction by supposing that some coefficient does not vanish. Therefore all the coefficients vanish.

Corollary 1. We may 'equate corresponding coefficients' in two power series whose sums are equal throughout the region $|z| < \delta$, where $\delta > 0$.

Corollary 2. We may also equate coefficients in two power series which are proved equal only when z is real.

REFERENCES.

T. J. I'A. BROMWICH, *Theory of Infinite Series* (1908), Ch. VII.

E. GOURSAT, *Cours d'Analyse* (Paris, 1910, 1911), Chs. I, XIV.

C. J. DE LA VALLÉE POUSSIN (Louvain and Paris, 1914), *Cours d'Analyse Infinitésimale*, Introduction and Ch. VIII.

G. H. HARDY, *A course of Pure Mathematics* (1914), Ch. V.

W. F. OSGOOD, *Lehrbuch der Funktionentheorie* (Leipzig, 1912), Chs. II, III.

G. N. WATSON, *Complex Integration and Cauchy's Theorem* (Camb. Math. Tracts, No. 15), (1914), Chs. I, II.

MISCELLANEOUS EXAMPLES.

1. Shew that the series

$$\sum_{n=1}^{\infty} \frac{z^{n-1}}{(1-z^n)(1-z^{n+1})}$$

is equal to $\dfrac{1}{(1-z)^2}$ when $|z| < 1$ and is equal to $\dfrac{1}{z(1-z)^2}$ when $|z| > 1$.

Is this fact connected with the theory of uniform convergence?

2. Shew that the series

$$2 \sin \frac{1}{3z} + 4 \sin \frac{1}{9z} + \ldots + 2^n \sin \frac{1}{3^n z} + \ldots$$

converges absolutely for all values of z ($z=0$ excepted), but does not converge uniformly near $z=0$.

3. If $\qquad u_n(x) = -2(n-1)^2 xe^{-(n-1)^2 x^2} + 2n^2 xe^{-n^2 x^2}$,

shew that $\sum\limits_{n=1}^{\infty} u_n(x)$ does not converge uniformly near $x=0$. (Math. Trip., 1907.)

4. Shew that the series $\dfrac{1}{\sqrt{1}} - \dfrac{1}{\sqrt{2}} + \dfrac{1}{\sqrt{3}} - \ldots$ is convergent, but that its square (formed by Abel's rule)

$$\frac{1}{1} - \frac{2}{\sqrt{2}} + \left(\frac{2}{\sqrt{3}} + \frac{1}{2}\right) - \left(\frac{2}{\sqrt{4}} + \frac{2}{\sqrt{6}}\right) - \ldots$$

is divergent.

5. If the convergent series $s = \dfrac{1}{1^r} - \dfrac{1}{2^r} + \dfrac{1}{3^r} - \dfrac{1}{4^r} + \ldots$ $(r > 0)$ be multiplied by itself the terms of the product being arranged as in Abel's result, shew that the resulting series diverges if $r \leqslant \frac{1}{2}$ but converges to the sum s^2 if $r > \frac{1}{2}$. (Cauchy and Cajori.)

6. If the two conditionally convergent series

$$\sum_{n=1}^{\infty} \frac{(-)^{n+1}}{n^r} \quad \text{and} \quad \sum_{n=1}^{\infty} \frac{(-)^{n+1}}{n^s},$$

where r and s lie between 0 and 1, be multiplied together, and the product arranged as in Abel's result, shew that the necessary and sufficient condition for the convergence of the resulting series is $r+s>1$.   (Cajori.)

7. Shew that if the series $1 - \frac{1}{3} + \frac{1}{5} - \frac{1}{7} + \dots$

be multiplied by itself any number of times, the terms of the product being arranged as in Abel's result, the resulting series converges.   (Cajori.)

8. Shew that the qth power of the series

$$a_1 \sin \theta + a_2 \sin 2\theta + \dots + a_n \sin n\theta + \dots$$

is convergent whenever $q(1-r)<1$, r being the greatest number satisfying the relation

$$a_n \leqslant n^{-r}$$

for all values of n.

9. Shew that if θ is not equal to 0 or a multiple of 2π, and if $u_0, u_1, u_2, \dots$ be a sequence such that $u_n \to 0$ steadily, then the series $\Sigma u_n \cos(n\theta + a)$ is convergent.

Shew also that, if the limit of u_n is not zero, but u_n is still monotonic, the sum of the series is oscillatory if $\frac{\theta}{\pi}$ is rational, but that, if $\frac{\theta}{\pi}$ is irrational, the sum may have any value between certain bounds whose difference is $a \operatorname{cosec} \frac{1}{2}\theta$, where $a = \lim_{n \to \infty} u_n$.

(Math. Trip., 1896.)

CHAPTER IV

THE THEORY OF RIEMANN INTEGRATION

4·1. *The concept of integration.*

The reader is doubtless familiar with the idea of integration as the operation inverse to that of differentiation; and he is equally well aware that the integral (in this sense) of a given elementary function is not always expressible in terms of elementary functions. In order therefore to give a definition of the integral of a function which shall be always available, even though it is not practicable to obtain a function of which the given function is the differential coefficient, we have recourse to the result that the integral* of $f(x)$ between the limits a and b is the area bounded by the curve $y = f(x)$, the axis of x and the ordinates $x = a$, $x = b$. We proceed to frame a formal definition of integration with this idea as the starting-point.

4·11. *Upper and lower integrals†.*

Let $f(x)$ be a bounded function of x in the range (a, b). Divide the interval at the points $x_1, x_2, \ldots x_{n-1}$ $(a \leqslant x_1 \leqslant x_2 \leqslant \ldots \leqslant x_{n-1} \leqslant b)$. Let U, L be the bounds of $f(x)$ in the range (a, b), and let U_r, L_r be the bounds of $f(x)$ in the range (x_{r-1}, x_r), where $x_0 = a$, $x_n = b$.

Consider the sums‡

$$S_n = U_1(x_1 - a) + U_2(x_2 - x_1) + \ldots + U_n(b - x_{n-1}),$$

$$s_n = L_1(x_1 - a) + L_2(x_2 - x_1) + \ldots + L_n(b - x_{n-1}).$$

Then
$$U(b - a) \geqslant S_n \geqslant s_n \geqslant L(b - a).$$

For a given n, S_n and s_n are bounded functions of $x_1, x_2, \ldots x_{n-1}$. Let their lower and upper bounds§ respectively be $\underline{S}_n$, $\bar{s}_n$, so that $\underline{S}_n$, $\bar{s}_n$ depend only on n and on the form of $f(x)$, and not on the particular way of dividing the interval into n parts.

---

* Defined as the (elementary) function whose differential coefficient is $f(x)$.

† The following procedure for establishing existence theorems concerning integrals is based on that given by Goursat, *Cours d'Analyse*, I. Ch. IV. The concepts of upper and lower integrals are due to Darboux, *Ann. de l'École norm. sup.* (2) IV. (1875), p. 64.

‡ The reader will find a figure of great assistance in following the argument of this section. S_n and s_n represent the sums of the areas of a number of rectangles which are respectively greater and less than the area bounded by $y = f(x)$, $x = a$, $x = b$ and $y = 0$, if this area be assumed to exist.

§ The bounds of a function of n variables are defined in just the same manner as the bounds of a function of a single variable (§ 3·62).

Let the lower and upper bounds of these functions of n be S, s. Then

$$S_n \geqslant S, \quad s_n \leqslant s.$$

We proceed to shew that s is *at most* equal to S; i.e. $S \geqslant s$.

Let the intervals (a, x_1), (x_1, x_2), ... be divided into smaller intervals by new points of subdivision, and let

$$a, y_1, y_2, \dots y_{k-1}, y_k (= x_1), y_{k+1}, \dots y_{l-1}, y_l (= x_2), y_{l+1}, \dots y_{m-1}, b$$

be the end points of the smaller intervals; let U_r', L_r' be the bounds of $f(x)$ in the interval (y_{r-1}, y_r).

Let $$T_m = \sum_{r=1}^{m} (y_r - y_{r-1}) U_r', \quad t_m = \sum_{r=1}^{m} (y_r - y_{r-1}) L_r'.$$

Since U_1', U_2', ... U_k' do not exceed U_1, it follows without difficulty that $S_n \geqslant T_m \geqslant t_m \geqslant s_n$.

Now consider the subdivision of (a, b) into intervals by the points x_1, x_2, ... x_{n-1}, and also the subdivision by a different set of points x_1', x_2', ... $x'_{n'-1}$. Let $S'_{n'}$, $s'_{n'}$ be the sums for the second kind of subdivision which correspond to the sums S_n, s_n for the first kind of subdivision. Take *all* the points x_1, ... x_{n-1}; x_1', ... $x'_{n'-1}$ as the points y_1, y_2, ... y_m.

Then $$S_n \geqslant T_m \geqslant t_m \geqslant s_n,$$

and $$S'_{n'} \geqslant T_m \geqslant t_m \geqslant s'_{n'}.$$

Hence every expression of the type S_n *exceeds* (or at least equals) every expression of the type $s'_{n'}$; and therefore S cannot be less than s.

[For if $S < s$ and $s - S = 2\eta$ we could find an S_n and an $s'_{n'}$ such that $S_n - S < \eta$, $s - s'_{n'} < \eta$ and so $s'_{n'} > S_n$, which is impossible.]

The bound S is called the *upper* integral of $f(x)$, and is written $\int_a^b f(x)\, dx$;

s is called the *lower* integral, and written $\int_a^b f(x)\, dx$.

If $S = s$, their common value is called the *integral* of $f(x)$ taken between the limits[*] of integration a and b.

The integral is written $\int_a^b f(x)\, dx.$

We define $\int_b^a f(x)\, dx$, when $a < b$, to mean $-\int_a^b f(x)\, dx$.

Example 1. $\int_a^b \{f(x) + \phi(x)\}\, dx = \int_a^b f(x)\, dx + \int_a^b \phi(x)\, dx.$

Example 2. By means of example 1, define the integral of a continuous complex function of a real variable.

---

* 'Extreme values' would be a more appropriate term but 'limits' has the sanction of custom. 'Termini' has been suggested by Lamb, *Infinitesimal Calculus* (1897), p. 207.

4·12. *Riemann's condition of integrability**.

A function is said to be 'integrable in the sense of Riemann' if (with the notation of § 4·11) S_n and s_n have a common limit (called the *Riemann integral* of the function) when the number of intervals (x_{r-1}, x_r) tends to infinity in such a way that the length of the longest of them tends to zero.

The necessary and sufficient condition that a bounded function should be integrable is that $S_n - s_n$ should tend to zero when the number of intervals (x_{r-1}, x_r) tends to infinity in such a way that the length of the longest tends to zero.

The condition is obviously necessary, for if S_n and s_n have a common limit $S_n - s_n \to 0$ as $n \to \infty$. And it is sufficient; for, since $S_n \geqslant S \geqslant s \geqslant s_n$, it follows that if $\lim (S_n - s_n) = 0$, then

$$\lim S_n = \lim s_n = S = s.$$

NOTE. A continuous function $f(x)$ is 'integrable.' For, given ϵ, we can find δ such that $|f(x') - f(x'')| < \epsilon/(b-a)$ whenever $|x' - x''| < \delta$. Take all the intervals (x_{s-1}, x_s) less than δ, and then $U_s - L_s < \epsilon/(b-a)$ and so $S_n - s_n < \epsilon$; therefore $S_n - s_n \to 0$ under the circumstances specified in the condition of integrability.

Corollary. If S_n and s_n have the same limit S for one mode of subdivision of (a, b) into intervals of the specified kind, the limits of S_n and of s_n for any other such mode of subdivision are both S.

Example 1. The product of two integrable functions is an integrable function.

Example 2. A function which is continuous except at a finite number of ordinary discontinuities is integrable.

[If $f(x)$ have an ordinary discontinuity at c, enclose c in an interval of length δ_1; given ϵ, we can find δ so that $|f(x') - f(x)| < \epsilon$ when $|x' - x| < \delta$ and x, x' are not in this interval.

Then $S_n - s_n \leqslant \epsilon (b - a - \delta_1) + k\delta_1$, where k is the greatest value of $|f(x') - f(x)|$, when x, x' lie in the interval.

When $\delta_1 \to 0$, $k \to |f(c+0) - f(c-0)|$, and hence $\lim_{n \to \infty} (S_n - s_n) = 0$.]

Example 3. A function with limited total fluctuation and a finite number of ordinary discontinuities is integrable. (See § 3·64 example 2.)

4·13. *A general theorem on integration.*

Let $f(x)$ be integrable, and let ϵ be any positive number. Then it is possible to choose δ so that

$$\left| \sum_{p=1}^{n} (x_p - x_{p-1}) f(x'_{p-1}) - \int_a^b f(x)\, dx \right| < \epsilon,$$

provided that $x_p - x_{p-1} \leqslant \delta, \quad x_{p-1} \leqslant x'_{p-1} \leqslant x_p.$

---

* Riemann (*Ges. Math. Werke*, p. 239) bases his definition of an integral on the limit of the sum occurring in § 4·13; but it is then difficult to prove the uniqueness of the limit. A more general definition of integration (which is of very great importance in the modern theory of Functions of Real Variables) has been given by Lebesgue, *Annali di Mat.* (3) VII. (1902), pp. 231–359. See also his *Leçons sur l'intégration* (Paris, 1904).

To prove the theorem we observe that, given ϵ, we can choose the length of the longest interval, δ, so small that $S_n - s_n < \epsilon$.

Also
$$S_n \geqslant \sum_{p=1}^{n} (x_p - x_{p-1}) f(x'_{p-1}) \geqslant s_n,$$

$$S_n \geqslant \int_a^b f(x)\, dx \geqslant s_n.$$

Therefore
$$\left| \sum_{p=1}^{n} (x_p - x_{p-1}) f(x'_{p-1}) - \int_a^b f(x)\, dx \right| \leqslant S_n - s_n$$
$$< \epsilon.$$

As an example* of the evaluation of a definite integral directly from the theorem of this section consider $\int_0^X \dfrac{dx}{(1-x^2)^{\frac{1}{2}}}$, where $X < 1$.

Take $\delta = \dfrac{1}{p}$ arc sin X and let $x_s = \sin s\delta$, $(0 < s\delta < \tfrac{1}{2}\pi)$, so that
$$x_{s+1} - x_s = 2 \sin \tfrac{1}{2}\delta \cos (s + \tfrac{1}{2})\,\delta < \delta\,;$$

also let
$$x_s' = \sin (s + \tfrac{1}{2})\,\delta.$$

Then
$$\sum_{s=1}^{p} \frac{x_s - x_{s-1}}{(1 - x'^2_{s-1})^{\frac{1}{2}}} = \sum_{s=1}^{p} \frac{\sin s\delta - \sin (s-1)\,\delta}{\cos (s - \tfrac{1}{2})\,\delta}$$
$$= 2p \sin \tfrac{1}{2}\delta$$
$$= \text{arc sin } X \,.\, \{\sin \tfrac{1}{2}\delta / (\tfrac{1}{2}\delta)\}.$$

By taking p sufficiently large we can make
$$\left| \int_0^X \frac{dx}{(1-x^2)^{\frac{1}{2}}} - \sum_{s=1}^{p} \frac{x_s - x_{s-1}}{(1 - x'^2_{s-1})^{\frac{1}{2}}} \right|$$

arbitrarily small.

We can also make
$$\text{arc sin } X \,.\, \left\{ \frac{\sin \tfrac{1}{2}\delta}{\tfrac{1}{2}\delta} - 1 \right\}$$

arbitrarily small.

That is, given an arbitrary number ϵ, we can make
$$\left| \int_0^X \frac{dx}{(1-x^2)^{\frac{1}{2}}} - \text{arc sin } X \right| < \epsilon$$

by taking p sufficiently large. But the expression now under consideration *does not depend on* p; and therefore it must be zero; for if not we could take ϵ to be less than it, and we should have a contradiction.

That is to say
$$\int_0^X \frac{dx}{(1-x^2)^{\frac{1}{2}}} = \text{arc sin } X.$$

Example 1. Shew that
$$\lim_{n \to \infty} \frac{1 + \cos \dfrac{x}{n} + \cos \dfrac{2x}{n} + \ldots + \cos \dfrac{(n-1)\,x}{n}}{n} = \frac{\sin x}{x}.$$

Example 2. If $f(x)$ has ordinary discontinuities at the points $a_1, a_2, \ldots a_\kappa$, then
$$\int_a^b f(x)\, dx = \lim \left\{ \int_a^{a_1 - \delta_1} + \int_{a_1 + \epsilon_1}^{a_2 - \delta_2} + \ldots + \int_{a_\kappa + \epsilon_\kappa}^{b} f(x)\, dx \right\},$$

where the limit is taken by making $\delta_1, \delta_2, \ldots \delta_\kappa, \epsilon_1, \epsilon_2, \ldots \epsilon_\kappa$ tend to $+0$ independently.

* Netto, *Zeitschrift für Math. und Phys.* XL. (1895).

Example 3. If $f(x)$ is integrable when $a_1 \leqslant x \leqslant b_1$ and if, when $a_1 \leqslant a < b < b_1$, we write

$$\int_a^b f(x)\, dx = \phi(a, b),$$

and if $f(b+0)$ exists, then

$$\lim_{\delta \to +0} \frac{\phi(a, b+\delta) - \phi(a, b)}{\delta} = f(b+0).$$

Deduce that, if $f(x)$ is continuous at a and b,

$$\frac{d}{da} \int_a^b f(x)\, dx = -f(a), \qquad \frac{d}{db} \int_a^b f(x)\, dx = f(b).$$

Example 4. Prove by differentiation that, if $\phi(x)$ is a continuous function of x and $\dfrac{dx}{dt}$ a continuous function of t, then

$$\int_{x_0}^{x_1} \phi(x)\, dx = \int_{t_0}^{t_1} \phi(x) \frac{dx}{dt}\, dt.$$

Example 5. If $f'(x)$ and $\phi'(x)$ are continuous when $a \leqslant x \leqslant b$, shew from example 3 that

$$\int_a^b f'(x)\, \phi(x)\, dx + \int_a^b \phi'(x) f(x)\, dx = f(b)\, \phi(b) - f(a)\, \phi(a).$$

Example 6. If $f(x)$ is integrable in the range (a, c) and $a \leqslant b \leqslant c$, shew that $\displaystyle\int_a^b f(x)\, dx$ is a continuous function of b.

4·14. *Mean Value Theorems.*

The two following general theorems are frequently useful.

(I) Let U and L be the upper and lower bounds of the integrable function $f(x)$ in the range (a, b).

Then from the definition of an integral it is obvious that

$$\int_a^b \{U - f(x)\}\, dx, \qquad \int_a^b \{f(x) - L\}\, dx$$

are not negative; and so

$$U(b-a) \geqslant \int_a^b f(x)\, dx \geqslant L(b-a).$$

This is known as the *First Mean Value Theorem.*

If $f(x)$ is *continuous* we can find a number ξ such that $a \leqslant \xi \leqslant b$ and such that $f(\xi)$ has any given value lying between U and L (§ 3·63). Therefore we can find ξ such that

$$\int_a^b f(x)\, dx = (b-a)f(\xi).$$

If $F(x)$ has a continuous differential coefficient $F'(x)$ in the range (a, b), we have, on writing $F'(x)$ for $f(x)$,

$$F(b) - F(a) = (b-a) F'(\xi)$$

for some value of ξ such that $a \leqslant \xi \leqslant b$.

Example. If $f(x)$ is continuous and $\phi(x) \geqslant 0$, shew that ξ can be found such that

$$\int_a^b f(x)\, \phi(x)\, dx = f(\xi) \int_a^b \phi(x)\, dx.$$

(11) Let $f(x)$ and $\phi(x)$ be integrable in the range (a, b) and let $\phi(x)$ be a *positive decreasing* function of x. Then *Bonnet's* form of the Second Mean Value Theorem* is that a number ξ exists such that $a \leqslant \xi \leqslant b$, and

$$\int_a^b f(x)\,\phi(x)\,dx = \phi(a)\int_a^\xi f(x)\,dx.$$

For, with the notation of §§ 4·1–4·13, consider the sum

$$S = \sum_{s=1}^p (x_s - x_{s-1})\,f(x_{s-1})\,\phi(x_{s-1}).$$

Writing $(x_s - x_{s-1})\,f(x_{s-1}) = a_{s-1}$, $\phi(x_{s-1}) = \phi_{s-1}$, $a_0 + a_1 + \ldots + a_s = b_s$, we have

$$S = \sum_{s=1}^{p-1} b_{s-1}(\phi_{s-1} - \phi_s) + b_{p-1}\,\phi_{p-1}.$$

Each term in the summation is increased by writing $\bar{b}$ for b_{s-1} and decreased by writing $\underline{b}$ for b_{s-1}, if $\bar{b}$, $\underline{b}$ be the greatest and least of $b_0, b_1, \ldots b_{p-1}$; and so $\underline{b}\phi_0 \leqslant S \leqslant \bar{b}\phi_0$. Therefore S lies between the greatest and least of the sums $\phi(x_0) \sum_{s=1}^m (x_s - x_{s-1})\,f(x_{s-1})$ where $m = 1, 2, 3, \ldots p$. But, given ϵ, we can find δ such that, when $x_s - x_{s-1} < \delta$,

$$\left| \sum_{s=1}^p (x_s - x_{s-1})\,f(x_{s-1})\,\phi(x_{s-1}) - \int_{x_0}^{x_p} f(x)\,\phi(x)\,dx \right| < \epsilon,$$

$$\left| \phi(x_0) \sum_{s=1}^m (x_s - x_{s-1})\,f(x_{s-1}) - \phi(x_0)\int_{x_0}^{x_m} f(x)\,dx \right| < \epsilon,$$

and so, writing a, b for x_0, x_p, we find that $\int_a^b f(x)\,\phi(x)\,dx$ lies between the upper and lower bounds of † $\phi(a)\int_a^{\xi_1} f(x)\,dx \pm 2\epsilon$, where ξ_1 may take all values between a and b. Let U and L be the upper and lower bounds of $\phi(a)\int_a^{\xi_1} f(x)\,dx$.

Then $U + 2\epsilon \geqslant \int_a^b f(x)\,\phi(x)\,dx \geqslant L - 2\epsilon$ for *all* positive values of ϵ; therefore

$$U \geqslant \int_a^b f(x)\,\phi(x)\,dx \geqslant L.$$

Since $\phi(a)\int_a^{\xi_1} f(x)\,dx$ *qua* function of ξ_1 takes all values between its upper and lower bounds, there is some value ξ, say, of ξ_1 for which it is equal to $\int_a^b f(x)\,\phi(x)\,dx$. This proves the Second Mean Value Theorem.

Example. By writing $|\phi(x) - \phi(b)|$ in place of $\phi(x)$ in Bonnet's form of the mean value theorem, shew that if $\phi(x)$ is a monotonic function, then a number ξ exists such that $a \leqslant \xi \leqslant b$ and

$$\int_a^b f(x)\,\phi(x)\,dx = \phi(a)\int_a^\xi f(x)\,dx + \phi(b)\int_\xi^b f(x)\,dx.$$

(Du Bois Reymond.)

---

* *Journal de Math.* XIV. (1849), p. 249. The proof given is a modified form of an investigation due to Hölder, *Gött. Nach.* (1889), pp. 38–47.

† By § 4·13 example 6, since $f(x)$ is bounded, $\int_a^{\xi_1} f(x)\,dx$ is a continuous function of ξ_1.

4·2. *Differentiation of integrals containing a parameter.*

The equation* $\dfrac{d}{d\alpha}\displaystyle\int_a^b f(x,\alpha)\,dx = \int_a^b \dfrac{\partial f}{\partial \alpha}\,dx$ is true *if $f(x,\alpha)$ possesses a*

Riemann integral with respect to x and $f_\alpha\left(=\dfrac{\partial f}{\partial \alpha}\right)$ is a continuous function of

both† the variables x and α.

For $\qquad \dfrac{d}{d\alpha}\displaystyle\int_a^b f(x,\alpha)\,dx = \lim_{h\to 0}\int_a^b \dfrac{f(x,\alpha+h)-f(x,\alpha)}{h}\,dx$

if this limit exists. But, by the first mean value theorem, since f_α is a continuous function of α, the second integrand is $f_\alpha(x,\alpha+\theta h)$, where $0 \leqslant \theta \leqslant 1$.

But, for any given ϵ, a number δ *independent* of x exists (since the continuity of f_α is uniform‡ with respect to the variable x) such that

$$|f_\alpha(x,\alpha')-f_\alpha(x,\alpha)| < \epsilon/(b-a),$$

whenever $|\alpha'-\alpha| < \delta$.

Taking $|h| < \delta$ we see that $|\theta h| < \delta$, and so *whenever* $|h| < \delta$,

$$\left|\int_a^b \frac{f(x,\alpha+h)-f(x,\alpha)}{h}\,dx - \int_a^b f_\alpha(x,\alpha)\,dx\right| \leqslant \int_a^b |f_\alpha(x,\alpha+\theta h)-f_\alpha(x,\alpha)|\,dx$$
$$< \epsilon.$$

Therefore by the definition of a limit of a function (§ 3·2),

$$\lim_{h\to 0}\int_a^b \frac{f(x,\alpha+h)-f(x,\alpha)}{h}\,dx$$

exists and is equal to $\displaystyle\int_a^b f_\alpha\,dx$.

Example 1. If a,b be not constants but functions of α with continuous differential coefficients, shew that

$$\frac{d}{d\alpha}\int_a^b f(x,\alpha)\,dx = f(b,\alpha)\frac{db}{d\alpha} - f(a,\alpha)\frac{da}{d\alpha} + \int_a^b \frac{\partial f}{\partial \alpha}\,dx.$$

Example 2. If $f(x,\alpha)$ is a continuous function of both variables, $\displaystyle\int_a^b f(x,\alpha)\,dx$ is a continuous function of α.

* This formula was given by Leibniz, without specifying the restrictions laid on $f(x,\alpha)$.

† $\phi(x,y)$ is defined to be a continuous function of *both* variables if, given ϵ, we can find δ such that $|\phi(x',y')-\phi(x,y)| < \epsilon$ whenever $\{(x'-x)^2+(y'-y)^2\}^{\frac{1}{2}} < \delta$. It can be shewn by § 3·6 that if $\phi(x,y)$ is a continuous function of both variables at all points of a closed region in a Cartesian diagram, it is *uniformly* continuous throughout the region (the proof is almost identical with that of § 3·61). It should be noticed that, if $\phi(x,y)$ is a continuous function of *each* variable, it is *not* necessarily a continuous function of both; as an example take

$$\phi(x,y) = \frac{(x+y)^2}{x^2+y^2}, \quad \phi(0,0) = 1;$$

this is a continuous function of x and of y at $(0,0)$, but not of both x and y.

‡ It is obvious that it would have been sufficient to assume that f_α had a Riemann integral and was a continuous function of α (the continuity being uniform with respect to x), instead of assuming that f_α was a continuous function of both variables. This is actually done by Hobson, *Functions of a Real Variable*, p. 599.

4·3. *Double integrals and repeated integrals.*

Let $f(x, y)$ be a function which is continuous with regard to both of the variables x and y, when $a \leqslant x \leqslant b$, $\alpha \leqslant y \leqslant \beta$.

By § 4·2 example 2 it is clear that

$$\int_a^b \left\{ \int_\alpha^\beta f(x, y)\, dy \right\} dx, \qquad \int_\alpha^\beta \left\{ \int_a^b f(x, y)\, dx \right\} dy$$

both exist. These are called *repeated integrals.*

Also, as in § 3·62, $f(x, y)$, being a continuous function of both variables, attains its upper and lower bounds.

Consider the range of values of x and y to be the points inside and on a rectangle in a Cartesian diagram; divide it into $n\nu$ rectangles by lines parallel to the axes.

Let $U_{m, \mu}$, $L_{m, \mu}$ be the upper and lower bounds of $f(x, y)$ in one of the smaller rectangles whose area is, say, $A_{m, \mu}$; and let

$$\sum_{m=1}^n \sum_{\mu=1}^\nu U_{m, \mu} A_{m, \mu} = S_{n, \nu}, \qquad \sum_{m=1}^n \sum_{\mu=1}^\nu L_{m, \mu} A_{m, \mu} = s_{n, \nu}.$$

Then $S_{n, \nu} > s_{n, \nu}$, and, as in § 4·11, we can find numbers $\underline{S}_{n, \nu}$, $\bar{s}_{n, \nu}$ which are the lower and upper bounds of $S_{n, \nu}$, $s_{n, \nu}$ respectively, the values of $\underline{S}_{n, \nu}$, $\bar{s}_{n, \nu}$ depending only on the number of the rectangles and not on their shapes; and $\underline{S}_{n, \nu} \geqslant \bar{s}_{n, \nu}$. We then find the lower and upper bounds (S and s) respectively of $\underline{S}_{n, \nu}$, $\bar{s}_{n, \nu}$ *qua* functions of n and ν; and $S_{n, \nu} \geqslant S \geqslant s \geqslant s_{n, \nu}$, as in § 4·11.

Also, from the uniformity of the continuity of $f(x, y)$, given ϵ, we can find δ such that

$$U_{m, \mu} - L_{m, \mu} < \epsilon,$$

(for all values of m and μ) whenever the sides of all the small rectangles are less than the number δ which depends only on the form of the function $f(x, y)$ and on ϵ.

And then $\qquad\qquad S_{n, \nu} - s_{n, \nu} < \epsilon (b - a) (\beta - \alpha),$

and so $\qquad\qquad\qquad S - s < \epsilon (b - a) (\beta - \alpha).$

But S and s are *independent* of ϵ, and so $S = s$.

The common value of S and s is called the *double integral* of $f(x, y)$ and is written

$$\int_a^b \int_\alpha^\beta f(x, y)\, (dx\, dy).$$

It is easy to shew that the repeated integrals and the double integral are all equal when $f(x, y)$ is a continuous function of both variables.

For let Υ_m, Λ_m be the upper and lower bounds of

$$\int_\alpha^\beta f(x, y)\, dy$$

as x varies between x_{m-1} and x_m.

Then
$$\sum_{m=1}^n \Upsilon_m (x_m - x_{m-1}) \geqslant \int_a^b \left\{ \int_\alpha^\beta f(x, y)\, dy \right\} dx \geqslant \sum_{m=1}^n \Lambda_m (x_m - x_{m-1}).$$

But*
$$\sum_{\mu=1}^\nu U_{m,\mu} (y_\mu - y_{\mu-1}) \geqslant \Upsilon_m \geqslant \Lambda_m \geqslant \sum_{\mu=1}^\nu L_{m,\mu} (y_\mu - y_{\mu-1}).$$

Multiplying these last inequalities by $x_m - x_{m-1}$, using the preceding inequalities and summing, we get

$$\sum_{m=1}^n \sum_{\mu=1}^\nu U_{m,\mu} A_{m,\mu} \geqslant \int_a^b \left\{ \int_\alpha^\beta f(x, y)\, dy \right\} dx \geqslant \sum_{m=1}^n \sum_{\mu=1}^\nu L_{m,\mu} A_{m,\mu};$$

and so, proceeding to the limit,

$$S \geqslant \int_a^b \left\{ \int_\alpha^\beta f(x, y)\, dy \right\} dx \geqslant s.$$

But
$$S = s = \int_a^b \int_\alpha^\beta f(x, y)\, (dx\, dy),$$

and so one of the repeated integrals is equal to the double integral. Similarly the other repeated integral is equal to the double integral.

Corollary. If $f(x, y)$ be a continuous function of both variables,

$$\int_0^1 dx \left\{ \int_0^{1-x} f(x, y)\, dy \right\} = \int_0^1 dy \left\{ \int_0^{1-y} f(x, y)\, dx \right\}.$$

$4\cdot4$. *Infinite integrals.*

If $\lim\limits_{b \to \infty} \left(\int_a^b f(x)\, dx \right)$ exists, we denote it by $\int_a^\infty f(x)\, dx$; and the limit in question is called an *infinite integral* †.

Examples.

(1) $\displaystyle\int_a^\infty \frac{dx}{x^2} = \lim_{b \to \infty} \left(\frac{1}{a} - \frac{1}{b} \right) = \frac{1}{a}.$

(2) $\displaystyle\int_0^\infty \frac{x\, dx}{(x^2 + a^2)^2} = \lim_{b \to \infty} \left(-\frac{1}{2(b^2 + a^2)} + \frac{1}{2a^2} \right) = \frac{1}{2a^2}.$

(3) By integrating by parts, shew that $\displaystyle\int_0^\infty t^n e^{-t}\, dt = n\,!.$ (Euler.)

Similarly we define $\displaystyle\int_{-\infty}^b f(x)\, dx$ to mean $\lim\limits_{a \to -\infty} \int_a^b f(x)\, dx$, if this limit exists; and $\displaystyle\int_{-\infty}^\infty f(x)\, dx$ is defined as $\displaystyle\int_{-\infty}^a f(x)\, dx + \int_a^\infty f(x)\, dx$. In this last definition the choice of a is a matter of indifference.

* The upper bound of $f(x, y)$ in the rectangle $A_{m,\mu}$ is not less than the upper bound of $f(x, y)$ on that portion of the line $x = \xi$ which lies in the rectangle.

† This phrase, due to Hardy, *Proc. London Math. Soc.* xxxiv. (1902), p. 16, suggests the analogy between an infinite integral and an infinite series.

4·41. *Infinite integrals of continuous functions. Conditions for convergence.*

A necessary and sufficient condition for the convergence of $\int_a^\infty f(x)\,dx$ is that, corresponding to any positive number ϵ, a positive number X should exist such that $\left| \int_{x'}^{x''} f(x)\,dx \right| < \epsilon$ whenever

$$x'' \geqslant x' \geqslant X.$$

The condition is obviously necessary; to prove that it is sufficient, suppose it is satisfied; then, if $n \geqslant X - a$ and n be a positive integer and $S_n = \int_a^{a+n} f(x)\,dx$, we have

$$|S_{n+p} - S_n| < \epsilon.$$

Hence, by § 2·22, S_n tends to a limit, S; and then, if $\xi > a + n$,

$$\left| S - \int_a^\xi f(x)\,dx \right| \leqslant \left| S - \int_a^{a+n} f(x)\,dx \right| + \left| \int_{a+n}^\xi f(x)\,dx \right|$$

$$< 2\epsilon;$$

and so $\lim_{\xi \to \infty} \int_a^\xi f(x)\,dx = S$; so that the condition is sufficient.

4·42. *Uniformity of convergence of an infinite integral.*

The integral $\int_a^\infty f(x, \alpha)\,dx$ is said to converge uniformly with regard to α in a given domain of values of α if, corresponding to an arbitrary positive number ϵ, there exists a number X *independent* of α such that

$$\left| \int_{x'}^\infty f(x, \alpha)\,dx \right| < \epsilon$$

for all values of α in the domain and all values of $x' \geqslant X$.

The reader will see without difficulty on comparing §§ 2·22 and 3·31 with § 4·41 that a necessary and sufficient condition that $\int_a^\infty f(x, \alpha)\,dx$ should converge uniformly in a given domain is that, corresponding to any positive number ϵ, there exists a number X independent of α such that

$$\left| \int_{x'}^{x''} f(x, \alpha)\,dx \right| < \epsilon$$

for all values of α in the domain whenever $x'' \geqslant x' \geqslant X$.

4·43. *Tests for the convergence of an infinite integral.*

There are conditions for the convergence of an infinite integral analogous to those given in Chapter II for the convergence of an infinite series.

The following tests are of special importance.

(I) *Absolutely convergent integrals.* It may be shewn that $\int_a^\infty f(x)\,dx$ certainly converges if $\int_a^\infty |f(x)|\,dx$ does so; and the former integral is then said to be absolutely convergent. The proof is similar to that of § 2·32.

Example. The comparison test. If $|f(x)| \leqslant g(x)$ and $\int_a^\infty g(x)\,dx$ converges, then $\int_a^\infty f(x)\,dx$ converges absolutely.

[NOTE. It was observed by Dirichlet* that it is *not necessary* for the convergence of $\int_a^\infty f(x)\,dx$ that $f(x) \to 0$ as $x \to \infty$: the reader may see this by considering the function

$$f(x) = 0 \qquad\qquad (n \leqslant x \leqslant n+1-(n+1)^{-2}),$$
$$f(x) = (n+1)^4 (n+1-x)\{x-(n+1)+(n+1)^{-2}\} \qquad (n+1-(n+1)^{-2} \leqslant x \leqslant n+1),$$

where n takes all integral values.

For $\int_0^\xi f(x)\,dx$ increases with ξ and $\int_n^{n+1} f(x)\,dx = \frac{1}{6}(n+1)^{-2}$; whence it follows without difficulty that $\int_a^\infty f(x)\,dx$ converges. But when $x = n+1-\frac{1}{2}(n+1)^{-2}$, $f(x) = \frac{1}{4}$; and so $f(x)$ does *not* tend to zero.]

(II) *The Maclaurin-Cauchy† test.* If $f(x) > 0$ and $f(x) \to 0$ steadily, $\int_1^\infty f(x)\,dx$ and $\sum\limits_{n=1}^\infty f(n)$ converge or diverge together.

For
$$f(m) \geqslant \int_m^{m+1} f(x)\,dx \geqslant f(m+1),$$

and so
$$\sum_{m=1}^n f(m) \geqslant \int_1^{n+1} f(x)\,dx \geqslant \sum_{m=2}^{n+1} f(m).$$

The first inequality shews that, if the series converges, the increasing sequence $\int_1^{n+1} f(x)\,dx$ converges (§ 2·2) when $n \to \infty$ through integral values, and hence it follows without difficulty that $\int_1^{x'} f(x)\,dx$ converges when $x' \to \infty$; also if the integral diverges, so does the series.

The second shews that if the series diverges so does the integral, and if the integral converges so does the series (§ 2·2).

(III) *Bertrand's‡ test.* If $f(x) = O(x^{\lambda-1})$, $\int_a^\infty f(x)\,dx$ converges when $\lambda < 0$; and if $f(x) = O(x^{-1}\{\log x\}^{\lambda-1})$, $\int_a^\infty f(x)\,dx$ converges when $\lambda < 0$.

These results are particular cases of the comparison test given in (I).

---

* Dirichlet's example was $f(x) = \sin x^2$; *Journal für Math.* XVII. (1837), p. 60.

† Maclaurin (*Fluxions*, I. pp. 289, 290) makes a verbal statement practically equivalent to this result. Cauchy's result is given in his *Oeuvres* (2), VII. p. 269.

‡ *Journal de Math.* VII. (1842), pp. 38, 39.

(IV) *Chartier's test* for integrals involving periodic functions.*

If $f(x) \to 0$ steadily as $x \to \infty$ and if $\left| \int_a^x \phi(x)\, dx \right|$ is bounded as $x \to \infty$,

then $\int_a^\infty f(x)\, \phi(x)\, dx$ is convergent.

For if the upper bound of $\left| \int_a^x \phi(x)\, dx \right|$ be A, we can choose X such that $f(x) < \epsilon/2A$

when $x \geqslant X$; and then by the second mean value theorem, when $x'' \geqslant x' \geqslant X$, we have

$$\left| \int_{x'}^{x''} f(x)\, \phi(x)\, dx \right| = \left| f(x') \int_{x'}^{\xi} \phi(x)\, dx \right| = f(x') \left| \int_a^\xi \phi(x)\, dx - \int_a^{x'} \phi(x)\, dx \right| \leqslant 2A f(x') < \epsilon,$$

which is the condition for convergence.

Example 1. $\int_0^\infty \dfrac{\sin x}{x}\, dx$ converges.

Example 2. $\int_0^\infty x^{-1} \sin(x^3 - ax)\, dx$ converges.

4·431. *Tests for uniformity of convergence of an infinite integral†.*

(I) *De la Vallée Poussin's test‡.* The reader will easily see by using the reasoning of § 3·34 that $\int_a^\infty f(x, \alpha)\, dx$ converges uniformly with regard to α in a domain of values of α if $|f(x, \alpha)| < \mu(x)$, where $\mu(x)$ is independent of α and $\int_a^\infty \mu(x)\, dx$ converges. [For, choosing X so that $\int_{x'}^{x''} \mu(x)\, dx < \epsilon$ when $x'' \geqslant x' \geqslant X$, we have $\left| \int_{x'}^{x''} f(x, \alpha)\, dx \right| < \epsilon$, and the choice of X is independent of α.]

Example. $\int_0^\infty x^{a-1} e^{-x}\, dx$ converges uniformly in any interval (A, B) such that $1 \leqslant A \leqslant B$.

(II) *The method of change of variable.*

This may be illustrated by an example.

Consider $\int_0^\infty \dfrac{\sin ax}{x}\, dx$ where a is real.

We have $\displaystyle \int_{x'}^{x''} \frac{\sin ax}{x}\, dx = \int_{ax'}^{ax''} \frac{\sin y}{y}\, dy.$

Since $\int_0^\infty \dfrac{\sin y}{y}\, dy$ converges we can find Y such that $\left| \int_{y'}^{y''} \dfrac{\sin y}{y}\, dy \right| < \epsilon$ when $y'' \geqslant y' \geqslant Y$.

So $\left| \int_{x'}^{x''} \dfrac{\sin ax}{x}\, dx \right| < \epsilon$ whenever $|ax'| \geqslant Y$; if $|a| \geqslant \delta > 0$, we therefore get

$$\left| \int_{x'}^{x''} \frac{\sin ax}{x}\, dx \right| < \epsilon$$

---

* *Journal de Math.* XVIII. (1853), pp. 201–212. It is remarkable that this test for *conditionally* convergent integrals should have been given some years before formal definitions of absolutely convergent integrals.

† The results of this section and of § 4·44 are due to de la Vallée Poussin, *Ann. de la Soc. Scientifique de Bruxelles*, XVI. (1892), pp. 150–180.

‡ This name is due to Osgood.

when $x'' \geqslant x' \geqslant X = Y/\delta$; and this choice of X is independent of a. So the convergence is uniform when $a \geqslant \delta > 0$ and when $a \leqslant -\delta < 0$.

Example. $\displaystyle\int_1^\infty \left\{ \int_0^a \sin(\beta^2 x^3)\, d\beta \right\} dx$ is uniformly convergent in any range of real values of a.   (de la Vallée Poussin.)

[Write $\beta^2 x^3 = z$, and observe that $\left| \displaystyle\int_0^{a^2 x^3} z^{-\frac{1}{2}} \sin z\, dz \right|$ does not exceed a constant independent of a and x since $\displaystyle\int_0^\infty z^{-\frac{1}{2}} \sin z\, dz$ converges.]

(III) *The method of integration by parts.*

If $\displaystyle\int f(x, a)\, dx = \phi(x, a) + \int \chi(x, a)\, dx$

and if $\phi(x, a) \to 0$ uniformly as $x \to \infty$ and $\displaystyle\int_a^\infty \chi(x, a)\, dx$ converges uniformly with regard to a, then obviously $\displaystyle\int_a^\infty f(x, a)\, dx$ converges uniformly with regard to a.

(IV) *The method of decomposition.*

Example. $\displaystyle\int_0^\infty \frac{\cos x \sin ax}{x}\, dx = \tfrac{1}{2}\int_0^\infty \frac{\sin(a+1)x}{x}\, dx + \tfrac{1}{2}\int_0^\infty \frac{\sin(a-1)x}{x}\, dx\,;$

both of the latter integrals converge uniformly in any closed domain of real values of a from which the points $a = \pm 1$ are excluded.

4·44. *Theorems concerning uniformly convergent infinite integrals.*

(I) *Let $\displaystyle\int_a^\infty f(x, a)\, dx$ converge uniformly when α lies in a domain S.*

Then, if $f(x, \alpha)$ is a continuous function of both variables when $x \geqslant a$ and α lies in S, $\displaystyle\int_a^\infty f(x, \alpha)\, dx$ is a continuous function* of α.

For, given ϵ, we can find X independent of α, such that $\left| \displaystyle\int_\xi^\infty f(x, \alpha)\, dx \right| < \epsilon$ whenever $\xi \geqslant X$.

Also we can find δ *independent of x and α*, such that

$$|f(x, \alpha) - f(x, \alpha')| < \epsilon/(X - a)$$

whenever $|\alpha - \alpha'| < \delta$.

That is to say, given ϵ, we can find δ independent of α, such that

$$\left| \int_a^\infty f(x, \alpha')\, dx - \int_a^\infty f(x, \alpha)\, dx \right| \leqslant \left| \int_a^X \{ f(x, \alpha) - f(x, \alpha') \}\, dx \right|$$

$$+ \left| \int_X^\infty f(x, \alpha')\, dx \right| + \left| \int_X^\infty f(x, \alpha)\, dx \right|$$

$$< 3\epsilon,$$

whenever $|\alpha' - \alpha| < \delta$; and this is the condition for continuity.

---

* This result is due to Stokes. His statement is that the integral is a continuous function of α if it does not 'converge infinitely slowly.'

(II) *If $f(x, \alpha)$ satisfies the same conditions as in* (I), *and if α lies in S when $A \leqslant \alpha \leqslant B$, then*

$$\int_A^B \left\{ \int_a^\infty f(x, \alpha)\, dx \right\} d\alpha = \int_a^\infty \left\{ \int_A^B f(x, \alpha)\, d\alpha \right\} dx.$$

For, by § 4·3,

$$\int_A^B \left\{ \int_a^\xi f(x, \alpha)\, dx \right\} d\alpha = \int_a^\xi \left\{ \int_A^B f(x, \alpha)\, d\alpha \right\} dx.$$

Therefore

$$\left| \int_A^B \left\{ \int_a^\infty f(x, \alpha)\, dx \right\} d\alpha - \int_a^\xi \left\{ \int_A^B f(x, \alpha)\, d\alpha \right\} dx \right|$$

$$= \left| \int_A^B \left\{ \int_\xi^\infty f(x, \alpha)\, dx \right\} d\alpha \right|$$

$$< \int_A^B \epsilon\, d\alpha < \epsilon (B - A),$$

for all sufficiently large values of ξ.

But, from §§ 2·1 and 4·41, this is the condition that

$$\lim_{\xi \to \infty} \int_a^\xi \left\{ \int_A^B f(x, \alpha)\, d\alpha \right\} dx$$

should exist, and be equal to

$$\int_A^B \left\{ \int_a^\infty f(x, \alpha)\, dx \right\} d\alpha.$$

Corollary. The equation $\dfrac{d}{d\alpha} \displaystyle\int_a^\infty \phi(x, \alpha)\, dx = \int_a^\infty \dfrac{\partial \phi}{\partial \alpha}\, dx$ is true if the integral on the right converges uniformly and the integrand is a continuous function of both variables, when $x \geqslant a$ and α lies in a domain S, and if the integral on the left is convergent.

Let A be a point of S, and let $\dfrac{\partial \phi}{\partial \alpha} = f(x, \alpha)$, so that, by § 4·13 example 3,

$$\int_A^\alpha f(x, \alpha)\, d\alpha = \phi(x, \alpha) - \phi(x, A).$$

Then $\displaystyle\int_a^\infty \left\{ \int_A^\alpha f(x, \alpha)\, d\alpha \right\} dx$ converges, that is $\displaystyle\int_a^\infty \{\phi(x, \alpha) - \phi(x, A)\}\, dx$ converges, and therefore, since $\displaystyle\int_a^\infty \phi(x, \alpha)\, dx$ converges, so does $\displaystyle\int_a^\infty \phi(x, A)\, dx$.

Then

$$\frac{d}{d\alpha} \left[\int_a^\infty \phi(x, \alpha)\, dx \right] = \frac{d}{d\alpha} \left[\int_a^\infty \{\phi(x, \alpha) - \phi(x, A)\}\, dx \right]$$

$$= \frac{d}{d\alpha} \left[\int_a^\infty \left\{ \int_A^\alpha f(x, \alpha)\, d\alpha \right\} dx \right]$$

$$= \frac{d}{d\alpha} \int_A^\alpha \left\{ \int_a^\infty f(x, \alpha)\, dx \right\} d\alpha$$

$$= \int_a^\infty f(x, \alpha)\, dx = \int_a^\infty \frac{\partial \phi}{\partial \alpha}\, dx,$$

which is the required result; the change of the order of the integrations has been justified above, and the differentiation of $\displaystyle\int_A^\alpha$ with regard to α is justified by § 4·44 (I) and § 4·13 example 3.

4·5.   *Improper integrals.   Principal values.*

If $|f(x)| \to \infty$ as $x \to a + 0$, then $\lim\limits_{\delta \to +0} \int_{a+\delta}^{b} f(x)\,dx$ may exist, and is written simply $\int_{a}^{b} f(x)\,dx$; this limit is called an *improper integral*.

If $|f(x)| \to \infty$ as $x \to c$, where $a < c < b$, then

$$\lim_{\delta \to +0} \int_{a}^{c-\delta} f(x)\,dx + \lim_{\delta' \to +0} \int_{c+\delta'}^{b} f(x)\,dx$$

may exist; this is also written $\int_{a}^{b} f(x)\,dx$, and is also called an improper integral; it might however happen that neither of these limits exists when $\delta,\ \delta' \to 0$ independently, but

$$\lim_{\delta \to +0} \left\{ \int_{a}^{c-\delta} f(x)\,dx + \int_{c+\delta}^{b} f(x)\,dx \right\}$$

exists; this is called 'Cauchy's principal value of $\int_{a}^{b} f(x)\,dx$' and is written for brevity $P \int_{a}^{b} f(x)\,dx$.

Results similar to those of §§ 4·4–4·44 may be obtained for improper integrals. But all that is required in practice is (i) the idea of absolute convergence, (ii) the analogue of Bertrand's test for convergence, (iii) the analogue of de la Vallée Poussin's test for uniformity of convergence. The construction of these is left to the reader, as is also the consideration of integrals in which the integrand has an infinite limit at more than one point of the range of integration*.

Examples.   (1) $\int_{0}^{\pi} x^{-\frac{1}{2}} \cos x\,dx$ is an improper integral.

(2) $\int_{0}^{1} x^{\lambda-1} (1-x)^{\mu-1}\,dx$ is an improper integral if $0 < \lambda < 1,\ 0 < \mu < 1$. It does not converge for negative values of λ and μ.

(3) $P \int_{0}^{2} \dfrac{x^{a-1}}{1-x}\,dx$ is the principal value of an improper integral when $0 < a < 1$.

4·51.   *The inversion of the order of integration of a certain repeated integral.*

General conditions for the legitimacy of inverting the order of integration when the integrand is not continuous are difficult to obtain.

The following is a good example of the difficulties to be overcome in inverting the order of integration in a repeated improper integral.

---

* For a detailed discussion of improper integrals, the reader is referred either to Hobson's or to Pierpont's *Functions of a Real Variable*. The connexion between infinite integrals and improper integrals is exhibited by Bromwich, *Infinite Series*, § 164.

Let $f(x, y)$ be a continuous function of both variables, and let $0 < \lambda \leqslant 1,\ 0 < \mu \leqslant 1,$
$0 < \nu \leqslant 1$; then

$$\int_0^1 dx \left\{ \int_0^{1-x} x^{\lambda-1} y^{\mu-1} (1-x-y)^{\nu-1} f(x, y)\, dy \right\}$$
$$= \int_0^1 dy \left\{ \int_0^{1-y} x^{\lambda-1} y^{\mu-1} (1-x-y)^{\nu-1} f(x, y)\, dx \right\}.$$

This integral, which was first employed by Dirichlet, is of importance in the theory of integral equations; the investigation which we shall give is due to W. A. Hurwitz[*].

Let $x^{\lambda-1} y^{\mu-1} (1-x-y)^{\nu-1} f(x, y) = \phi(x, y)$; and let M be the upper bound of $|f(x, y)|$.

Let δ be any positive number less than $\tfrac{1}{3}$.

Draw the triangle whose sides are $x = \delta,\ y = \delta,\ x + y = 1 - \delta$; at all points on and inside this triangle $\phi(x, y)$ is continuous, and hence, by § 4·3 corollary,

$$\int_\delta^{1-2\delta} dx \left\{ \int_\delta^{1-x-\delta} \phi(x, y)\, dy \right\} = \int_\delta^{1-2\delta} dy \left\{ \int_\delta^{1-y-\delta} \phi(x, y)\, dx \right\}.$$

Now

$$\int_\delta^{1-2\delta} dx \left\{ \int_0^{1-x} \phi(x, y)\, dy \right\} = \int_\delta^{1-2\delta} dx \left\{ \int_\delta^{1-x-\delta} \phi(x, y)\, dy \right\} + \int_\delta^{1-2\delta} I_1\, dx + \int_\delta^{1-2\delta} I_2\, dx,$$

where

$$I_1 = \int_0^\delta \phi(x, y)\, dy, \quad I_2 = \int_{1-x-\delta}^{1-x} \phi(x, y)\, dy.$$

But

$$|I_1| \leqslant \int_0^\delta M x^{\lambda-1} y^{\mu-1} (1-x-y)^{\nu-1}\, dy$$
$$\leqslant M x^{\lambda-1} (1-x-\delta)^{\nu-1} \int_0^\delta y^{\mu-1}\, dy,$$

since

$$(1-x-y)^{\nu-1} \leqslant (1-x-\delta)^{\nu-1}.$$

Therefore, writing $x = (1-\delta) x_1$, we have[†]

$$\left| \int_\delta^{1-2\delta} I_1\, dx \right| \leqslant M \delta^\mu\, \mu^{-1} \int_0^{1-\delta} x^{\lambda-1} (1-x-\delta)^{\nu-1}\, dx$$
$$\leqslant M \delta^\mu\, \mu^{-1} (1-\delta)^{\lambda+\nu-1} \int_0^1 x_1^{\lambda-1} (1-x_1)^{\nu-1}\, dx_1$$
$$< M \delta^\mu\, \mu^{-1} (1-\delta)^{\lambda+\nu-1} B(\lambda, \nu) \to 0 \text{ as } \delta \to 0.$$

The reader will prove similarly that $I_n\, dx \to 0$ as $\delta \to 0$.

Hence[‡]
$$\int_0^1 dx \left\{ \int_0^{1-x} \phi(x, y)\, dy \right\} = \lim_{\delta \to 0} \int_\delta^{1-2\delta} dx \left\{ \int_0^{1-x} \phi(x, y)\, dy \right\}$$
$$= \lim_{\delta \to 0} \int_\delta^{1-2\delta} dx \left\{ \int_\delta^{1-x-\delta} \phi(x, y)\, dy \right\}$$
$$= \lim_{\delta \to 0} \int_\delta^{1-2\delta} dy \left\{ \int_\delta^{1-y-\delta} \phi(x, y)\, dx \right\},$$

[*] *Annals of Mathematics*, IX. (1908), p. 183.

[†] $\int_0^1 x_1^{\lambda-1} (1-x_1)^{\nu-1}\, dx_1 = B(\lambda, \nu)$ exists if $\lambda > 0,\ \nu > 0$ (§ 4·5 example 2).

[‡] The repeated integral exists, and is, in fact, absolutely convergent; for
$$\int_0^{1-x} |x^{\lambda-1} y^{\mu-1} (1-x-y)^{\nu-1} f(x, y)\, dy| < M x^{\lambda-1} (1-x)^{\mu+\nu-1} \int_0^1 s^{\mu-1} (1-s)^{\nu-1}\, ds,$$
writing $y = (1-x)s$; and $\int_0^1 M x^{\lambda-1} (1-x)^{\mu+\nu-1}\, dx \cdot \int_0^1 s^{\mu-1} (1-s)^{\nu-1}\, ds$ exists. And since the integral exists, its value which is $\lim\limits_{\delta,\,\epsilon \to 0} \int_\delta^{1-\epsilon}$ may be written $\lim\limits_{\delta \to 0} \int_\delta^{1-2\delta}$.

by what has been already proved; but, by a precisely similar piece of work, the last integral is

$$\int_0^1 dy \left\{ \int_0^{1-y} \phi(x, y)\, dx \right\}.$$

We have consequently proved the theorem in question.

Corollary. Writing $\xi = a + (b-a)x$, $\eta = b - (b-a)y$, we see that, if $\phi(\xi, \eta)$ is continuous,

$$\int_a^b d\xi \left\{ \int_\xi^b (\xi-a)^{\lambda-1} (b-\eta)^{\mu-1} (\eta-\xi)^{\nu-1} \phi(\xi, \eta)\, d\eta \right\}$$
$$= \int_a^b d\eta \left\{ \int_a^\eta (\xi-a)^{\lambda-1} (b-\eta)^{\mu-1} (\eta-\xi)^{\nu-1} \phi(\xi, \eta)\, d\xi \right\}.$$

This is called Dirichlet's formula.

[NOTE. What are now called infinite and improper integrals were defined by Cauchy, *Leçons sur le calc. inf.* 1823, though the idea of infinite integrals seems to date from Maclaurin (1742). The test for convergence was employed by Chartier (1853). Stokes (1847) distinguished between 'essentially' (absolutely) and non-essentially convergent integrals though he did not give a formal definition. Such a definition was given by Dirichlet in 1854 and 1858 (see his *Vorlesungen*, 1904, p. 39). In the early part of the nineteenth century improper integrals received more attention than infinite integrals, probably because it was not fully realised that an infinite integral is really the *limit* of an integral.]

4·6.   *Complex integration**.

Integration with regard to a real variable x may be regarded as integration along a particular path (namely part of the real axis) in the Argand diagram. Let $f(z)$, $(= P + iQ)$, be a function of a complex variable z, which is continuous along a simple curve AB in the Argand diagram.

Let the equations of the curve be

$$x = x(t), \quad y = y(t) \qquad (a \leqslant t \leqslant b).$$

Let $x(a) + iy(a) = z_0, \quad x(b) + iy(b) = Z.$

Then if† $x(t)$, $y(t)$ have continuous differential coefficients‡ we *define* $\int_{z_0}^{Z} f(z)\, dz$ taken along the simple curve AB to mean

$$\int_a^b (P + iQ) \left(\frac{dx}{dt} + i \frac{dy}{dt} \right) dt.$$

The 'length' of the curve AB will be defined as $\int_a^b \sqrt{\left(\frac{dx}{dt} \right)^2 + \left(\frac{dy}{dt} \right)^2}\, dt$. It obviously exists if $\frac{dx}{dt}$, $\frac{dy}{dt}$ are continuous; we have thus reduced the discussion of a complex integral to the discussion of four real integrals, viz.

$$\int_a^b P \frac{dx}{dt}\, dt, \quad \int_a^b P \frac{dy}{dt}\, dt, \quad \int_a^b Q \frac{dx}{dt}\, dt, \quad \int_a^b Q \frac{dy}{dt}\, dt.$$

---

* A treatment of complex integration based on a different set of ideas and not making so many assumptions concerning the curve AB will be found in Watson's *Complex Integration and Cauchy's Theorem.*

† This assumption will be made throughout the subsequent work.

‡ Cp. § 4·13 example 4.

By § 4·13 example 4, this definition is consistent with the definition of an integral when AB happens to be part of the real axis.

Examples. $\int_{z_0}^{Z} f(z)\, dz = -\int_{Z}^{z_0} f(z)\, dz$, the paths of integration being the same (but in opposite directions) in each integral.

$$\int_{z_0}^{Z} dz = Z - z_0. \quad \int_{z_0}^{Z} z\, dz = \int_a^b \left\{ x\, \frac{dx}{dt} - y\, \frac{dy}{dt} + i \left(x\, \frac{dy}{dt} + y\, \frac{dx}{dt} \right) \right\} dt$$
$$= \left[\tfrac{1}{2} x^2 - \tfrac{1}{2} y^2 + ixy \right]_{t=a}^{t=b} = \tfrac{1}{2} (Z^2 - z_0^2).$$

4·61. *The fundamental theorem of complex integration.*

From § 4·13, the reader will easily deduce the following theorem:

Let a sequence of points be taken on a simple curve $z_0 Z$; and let the first n of them, rearranged in order of magnitude of their parameters, be called $z_1^{(n)}, z_2^{(n)}, \ldots z_n^{(n)}$ $(z_0^{(n)} = z_0, z_{n+1}^{(n)} = Z)$; let their parameters be $t_1^{(n)}, t_2^{(n)}, \ldots t_n^{(n)}$, and let the sequence be such that, given any number δ, we can find N such that, when $n > N$, $t_{r+1}^{(n)} - t_r^{(n)} < \delta$, for $r = 0, 1, 2, \ldots, n$; let $\zeta_r^{(n)}$ be any point whose parameter lies between $t_r^{(n)}, t_{r+1}^{(n)}$; then we can make

$$\left| \sum_{r=0}^{n} (z_{r+1}^{(n)} - z_r^{(n)}) f(\zeta_r^{(n)}) - \int_{z_0}^{Z} f(z)\, dz \right|$$

arbitrarily small by taking n sufficiently large.

4·62. *An upper limit to the value of a complex integral.*

Let M be the upper bound of the continuous function $|f(z)|$.

Then
$$\left| \int_{z_0}^{Z} f(z)\, dz \right| \leqslant \int_a^b |f(z)| \left| \left(\frac{dx}{dt} + i\, \frac{dy}{dt} \right) \right| dt$$
$$\leqslant \int_a^b M \left\{ \left(\frac{dx}{dt} \right)^2 + \left(\frac{dy}{dt} \right)^2 \right\}^{\frac{1}{2}} dt$$
$$\leqslant Ml,$$

where l is the 'length' of the curve $z_0 Z$.

That is to say, $\left| \int_{z_0}^{Z} f(z)\, dz \right|$ cannot exceed Ml.

4·7. *Integration of infinite series.*

We shall now shew that if $S(z) = u_1(z) + u_2(z) + \ldots$ is a uniformly convergent series of continuous functions of z, for values of z contained within some region, then the series

$$\int_C u_1(z)\, dz + \int_C u_2(z)\, dz + \ldots,$$

(where all the integrals are taken along some path C in the region) is convergent, and has for sum $\int_C S(z)\, dz$.

For, writing

$$S(z) = u_1(z) + u_2(z) + \ldots + u_n(z) + R_n(z),$$

we have

$$\int_C S(z)\, dz = \int_C u_1(z)\, dz + \ldots + \int_C u_n(z)\, dz + \int_C R_n(z)\, dz.$$

Now since the series is uniformly convergent, to every positive number ϵ there corresponds a number r *independent* of z, such that when $n \geqslant r$ we have $|R_n(z)| < \epsilon$, for all values of z in the region considered.

Therefore if l be the length of the path of integration, we have (§ 4·62)

$$\left| \int_C R_n(z)\, dz \right| < \epsilon l.$$

Therefore the modulus of the difference between $\int_C S(z)\, dz$ and $\sum\limits_{m=1}^{n} \int_C u_m(z)\, dz$ can be made less than any positive number, by giving n any sufficiently large value. This proves both that the series $\sum\limits_{m=1}^{\infty} \int_C u_m(z)\, dz$ is convergent, and that its sum is $\int_C S(z)\, dz$.

Corollary. As in § 4·44 corollary, it may be shewn that[*]

$$\frac{d}{dz} \sum_{n=0}^{\infty} u_n(z) = \sum_{n=0}^{\infty} \frac{d}{dz} u_n(z)$$

if the series on the right converges uniformly and the series on the left is convergent.

Example 1.   Consider the series

$$\sum_{n=1}^{\infty} \frac{2x \{n(n+1) \sin^2 x^2 - 1\} \cos x^2}{\{1 + n^2 \sin^2 x^2\} \{1 + (n+1)^2 \sin^2 x^2\}},$$

in which x is real.

The nth term is

$$\frac{2xn \cos x^2}{1 + n^2 \sin^2 x^2} - \frac{2x(n+1) \cos x^2}{1 + (n+1)^2 \sin^2 x^2},$$

and the sum of n terms is therefore

$$\frac{2x \cos x^2}{1 + \sin^2 x^2} - \frac{2x(n+1) \cos x^2}{1 + (n+1)^2 \sin^2 x^2}.$$

Hence the series is absolutely convergent for all real values of x except $\pm \sqrt{(m\pi)}$ where $m = 1, 2, \ldots$; but

$$R_n(x) = \frac{2x(n+1) \cos x^2}{1 + (n+1)^2 \sin^2 x^2},$$

and if n be any integer, by taking $x = (n+1)^{-1}$ this has the limit 2 as $n \to \infty$. The series is therefore non-uniformly convergent near $x = 0$.

[*] $\dfrac{df(z)}{dz}$ means $\lim\limits_{h \to 0} \dfrac{f(z+h) - f(z)}{h}$ where $h \to 0$ along a definite simple curve; this definition is modified slightly in § 5·12 in the case when $f(z)$ is an *analytic* function.

Now the sum to infinity of the series is $\dfrac{2x \cos x^2}{1 + \sin^2 x^2}$, and so the integral from 0 to x of the sum of the series is arc tan $\{\sin x^2\}$. On the other hand, the sum of the integrals from 0 to x of the first n terms of the series is

$$\text{arc tan } \{\sin x^2\} - \text{arc tan } \{(n+1) \sin x^2\},$$

and as $n \to \infty$ this tends to arc tan $\{\sin x^2\} - \tfrac{1}{2}\pi$.

Therefore the integral of the sum of the series differs from the sum of the integrals of the terms by $\tfrac{1}{2}\pi$.

Example 2. Discuss, in a similar manner, the series

$$\sum_{n=1}^{\infty} \frac{2 e^n . x \{1 - n(e-1) + e^{n+1} x^2\}}{n(n+1)(1 + e^n x^2)(1 + e^{n+1} x^2)}$$

for real values of x.

Example 3. Discuss the series

$$u_1 + u_2 + u_3 + \ldots,$$

where

$$u_1 = z e^{-z^2}, \quad u_n = n z e^{-n z^2} - (n-1) z e^{-(n-1) z^2},$$

for real values of z.

The sum of the first n terms is $n z e^{-n z^2}$, so the sum to infinity is 0 for all real values of z. Since the terms u_n are real and ultimately all of the same sign, the convergence is absolute.

In the series

$$\int_0^z u_1 dz + \int_0^z u_2 dz + \int_0^z u_3 dz + \ldots,$$

the sum of n terms is $\tfrac{1}{2}(1 - e^{-n z^2})$, and this tends to the limit $\tfrac{1}{2}$ as n tends to infinity; this is not equal to the integral from 0 to z of the sum of the series Σu_n.

The explanation of this discrepancy is to be found in the non-uniformity of the convergence near $z = 0$, for the remainder after n terms in the series $u_1 + u_2 + \ldots$ is $- n z e^{-n z^2}$; and by taking $z = n^{-1}$ we can make this equal to $e^{-1/n}$, which is not arbitrarily small; the series is therefore non-uniformly convergent near $z = 0$.

Example 4. Compare the values of

$$\int_0^z \left\{ \sum_{n=1}^{\infty} u_n \right\} dz \quad \text{and} \quad \sum_{n=1}^{\infty} \int_0^z u_n dz,$$

where

$$u_n = \frac{2 n^2 z}{(1 + n^2 z^2) \log(n+1)} - \frac{2(n+1)^2 z}{\{1 + (n+1)^2 z^2\} \log(n+2)}.$$

(Trinity, 1903.)

REFERENCES.

G. F. B. Riemann, *Ges. Math. Werke*, pp. 239–241.

P. G. Lejeune-Dirichlet, *Vorlesungen.* (Brunswick, 1904.)

F. G. Meyer, *Bestimmte Integrale.* (Leipzig, 1871.)

E. Goursat, *Cours d'Analyse* (Paris, 1910, 1911), Chs. IV, XIV.

C. J. de la Vallée Poussin, *Cours d'Analyse Infinitésimale* (Paris and Louvain, 1914), Ch. VI.

E. W. Hobson, *Functions of a Real Variable* (1907), Ch. V.

T. J. I'A. Bromwich, *Theory of Infinite Series* (1908), Appendix III.

MISCELLANEOUS EXAMPLES.

1. Shew that the integrals

$$\int_0^\infty \sin(x^2)\, dx, \qquad \int_0^\infty \cos(x^2)\, dx, \qquad \int_0^\infty x \exp(-x^6 \sin^2 x)\, dx$$

converge.

(Dirichlet and Du Bois Reymond.)

2. If a be real, the integral

$$\int_0^\infty \frac{\cos(ax)}{1+x^2}\, dx$$

is a continuous function of a.

(Stokes.)

3. Discuss the uniformity of the convergence of $\int_0^\infty x \sin(x^3 - ax)\, dx$.

$$\left[3 \int x \sin(x^3 - ax)\, dx = -\left(\frac{1}{x} + \frac{a}{3x^3}\right) \cos(x^3 - ax) \right.$$

$$\left. -\int \left(\frac{1}{x^2} + \frac{a}{x^4}\right) \cos(x^3 - ax)\, dx + \frac{1}{3} a^2 \int \frac{\sin(x^3 - ax)}{x^3}\, dx. \right]$$

(de la Vallée Poussin.)

4. Shew that $\int_0^\infty \exp[-e^{ia}(x^3 - nx)]\, dx$ converges uniformly in the range $(-\tfrac{1}{2}\pi, \tfrac{1}{2}\pi)$ of values of a.

(Stokes.)

5. Discuss the convergence of $\int_0^\infty \dfrac{x^\mu\, dx}{1 + x^\nu |\sin x|^p}$ when μ, ν, p are positive.

(Hardy, *Messenger*, XXXI. (1902), p. 177.)

6. Examine the convergence of the integrals

$$\int_0^\infty \left(\frac{1}{x} - \frac{1}{2} e^{-x} + \frac{1}{1-e^x}\right) \frac{dx}{x}, \qquad \int_0^\infty \frac{\sin(x+x^2)}{x^n}\, dx.$$

(Math. Trip. 1914.)

7. Shew that $\int_\pi^\infty \dfrac{dx}{x^2 (\sin x)^{\frac{2}{3}}}$ exists.

8. Shew that $\int_a^\infty x^{-n} e^{\sin x} \sin 2x\, dx$ converges if $a > 0$, $n > 0$.   (Math. Trip. 1908.)

9. If a series $g(z) = \sum\limits_{\nu=0}^\infty (c_\nu - c_{\nu+1}) \sin(2\nu+1)\pi z$, (in which $c_0 = 0$), converges uniformly in an interval, shew that $g(z) \dfrac{\pi}{\sin \pi z}$ is the derivative of the series $f(z) = \sum\limits_{\nu=1}^\infty \dfrac{c_\nu}{\nu} \sin 2\nu\pi z$.

(Lerch, *Ann. de l'Éc. norm. sup.* (3) XII. (1895), p. 351.)

10. Shew that $\displaystyle\int^\infty \int^\infty \cdots \int^\infty \frac{dx_1\, dx_2 \ldots dx_n}{(x_1^2 + x_2^2 + \ldots + x_n^2)^a}$ and $\displaystyle\int^\infty \int^\infty \cdots \int^\infty \frac{dx_1\, dx_2 \ldots dv_n}{x_1^a + x_2^\beta + \ldots + x_n^\lambda}$ converge when $a > \tfrac{1}{2}n$ and $a^{-1} + \beta^{-1} + \ldots + \lambda^{-1} < 1$ respectively.   (Math. Trip. 1904.)

11. If $f(x, y)$ be a continuous function of both x and y in the ranges $(a \leqslant x \leqslant b)$, $(a \leqslant y \leqslant b)$ except that it has ordinary discontinuities at points on a finite number of curves, with continuously turning tangents, each of which meets any line parallel to the coordinate axes only a finite number of times, then $\int_a^b f(x, y)\, dx$ is a continuous function of y.

[Consider $\displaystyle\int_a^{a_1 - \delta_1} + \int_{a_1 + \epsilon_1}^{a_2 - \delta_2} + \ldots + \int_{a_n + \epsilon_n}^b \{f(x, y+h) - f(x, y)\}\, dx$, where the numbers $\delta_1, \delta_2, \ldots \epsilon_1, \epsilon_2, \ldots$ are so chosen as to exclude the discontinuities of $f(x, y+h)$ from the range of integration; $a_1, a_2, \ldots$ being the discontinuities of $f(x, y)$.]   (Bôcher.)

CHAPTER V

THE FUNDAMENTAL PROPERTIES OF ANALYTIC FUNCTIONS;
TAYLOR'S, LAURENT'S AND LIOUVILLE'S THEOREMS

5·1. *Property of the elementary functions.*

The reader will be already familiar with the term *elementary function*, as used (in text-books on Algebra, Trigonometry, and the Differential Calculus) to denote certain analytical expressions* depending on a variable z, the symbols involved therein being those of elementary algebra together with exponentials, logarithms and the trigonometrical functions; examples of such expressions are

$$z^2, \quad e^z, \quad \log z, \quad \arcsin z^{\frac{3}{2}}.$$

Such combinations of the elementary functions of analysis have in common a remarkable property, which will now be investigated.

Take as an example the function e^z.

Write $$e^z = f(z).$$

Then, if z be a fixed point and if z' be any other point, we have

$$\frac{f(z') - f(z)}{z' - z} = \frac{e^{z'} - e^z}{z' - z} = e^z \cdot \frac{e^{(z'-z)} - 1}{z' - z}$$

$$= e^z \left\{ 1 + \frac{z' - z}{2!} + \frac{(z' - z)^2}{3!} + \dots \right\};$$

and since the last series in brackets is uniformly convergent for all values of z', it follows (§ 3·7) that, as $z' \to z$, the quotient

$$\frac{f(z') - f(z)}{z' - z}$$

tends to the limit e^z, uniformly for all values of $\arg(z' - z)$.

This shews that *the limit of*

$$\frac{f(z') - f(z)}{z' - z}$$

is in this case independent of the path by which the point z' tends towards coincidence with z.

It will be found that this property is shared by many of the well-known elementary functions; namely, that if $f(z)$ be one of these functions and h be

---

* The reader will observe that this is not the sense in which the term function is defined (§ 3·1) in this work. Thus e.g. $x - iy$ and $|z|$ are *functions* of $z (= x + iy)$ in the sense of § 3·1, but are not elementary functions of the type under consideration.

any complex number, the limiting value of

$$\frac{1}{h}\{f(z+h)-f(z)\}$$

exists and is independent of the mode in which h tends to zero.

The reader will, however, easily prove that, if $f(z) = x - iy$, where $z = x + iy$, then $\lim \dfrac{f(z+h)-f(z)}{h}$ is *not* independent of the mode in which $h \to 0$.

5·11. *Occasional failure of the property.*

For each of the elementary functions, however, there will be certain points z at which this property will cease to hold good. Thus it does not hold for the function $1/(z-a)$ at the point $z = a$, since

$$\lim_{h\to 0}\frac{1}{h}\left\{\frac{1}{z-a+h}-\frac{1}{z-a}\right\}$$

does not exist when $z = a$. Similarly it does not hold for the functions $\log z$ and $z^{\frac{1}{2}}$ at the point $z = 0$.

These exceptional points are called *singular points* or *singularities* of the function $f(z)$ under consideration; at other points $f(z)$ is said to be *analytic*.

The property does not hold good at *any* point for the function $|z|$.

5·12. *Cauchy's* definition of an analytic function of a complex variable.*

The property considered in § 5·11 will be taken as the basis of the definition of an *analytic function*, which may be stated as follows.

Let a two-dimensional region in the z-plane be given; and let u be a function of z defined uniquely at all points of the region. Let z, $z + \delta z$ be values of the variable z at two points, and u, $u + \delta u$ the corresponding values of u. Then, if, at any point z within the area, $\dfrac{\delta u}{\delta z}$ tends to a limit when $\delta x \to 0$, $\delta y \to 0$, independently (where $\delta z = \delta x + i\,\delta y$), u is said to be a function of z, which is *monogenic* or *analytic*† at the point. If the function is analytic and *one-valued* at all points of the region, we say that the function is *analytic throughout the region*‡.

We shall frequently use the word 'function' alone to denote an analytic function, as the functions studied in this work will be almost exclusively analytic functions.

---

* See the memoir cited in § 5·2.

† The words 'regular' and 'holomorphic' are sometimes used. A distinction has been made by Borel between 'monogenic' and 'analytic' functions in the case of functions with an infinite number of singularities. See § 5·51.

‡ See § 5·2 cor. 2, footnote.

In the foregoing definition, the function u has been defined only within a certain region in the z-plane. As will be seen subsequently, however, the function u can generally be defined for other values of z not included in this region; and (as in the case of the elementary functions already discussed) may have *singularities*, for which the fundamental property no longer holds, at certain points outside the limits of the region.

We shall now state the definition of analytic functionality in a more arithmetical form.

Let $f(z)$ be analytic at z, and let ϵ be an arbitrary positive number; then we can find numbers l and δ, (δ depending on ϵ) such that

$$\left| \frac{f(z') - f(z)}{z' - z} - l \right| < \epsilon$$

whenever $|z' - z| < \delta$.

If $f(z)$ is analytic at all points z of a region, l obviously depends on z; we consequently write $l = f'(z)$.

Hence
$$f(z') = f(z) + (z' - z) f'(z) + v(z' - z),$$

where v is a function of z and z' such that $|v| < \epsilon$ when $|z' - z| < \delta$.

Example 1.   Find the points at which the following functions are not analytic :

(i) z^2.   (ii) $\operatorname{cosec} z$ $(z = n\pi,\ n$ any integer).   (iii) $\dfrac{z-1}{z^2 - 5z + 6}$ $(z = 2, 3)$.

(iv) $e^{\frac{1}{z}}$ $(z = 0)$.   (v) $\{(z-1)z\}^{\frac{1}{3}}$ $(z = 0, 1)$.

Example 2.   If $z = x + iy$, $f(z) = u + iv$, where u, v, x, y are real and f is an analytic function, shew that

$$\frac{\partial u}{\partial x} = \frac{\partial v}{\partial y}, \quad \frac{\partial u}{\partial y} = -\frac{\partial v}{\partial x}.$$

(Riemann.)

5·13.   *An application of the modified Heine-Borel theorem.*

Let $f(z)$ be analytic at all points of a continuum; and on any point z of the boundary of the continuum let numbers $f_1(z)$, δ (δ depending on z) exist such that

$$|f(z') - f(z) - (z' - z) f_1(z)| < \epsilon |z' - z|$$

whenever $|z' - z| < \delta$ and z' is a point of the continuum or its boundary.

[We write $f_1(z)$ instead of $f'(z)$ as the differential coefficient might not exist when z' approaches z from outside the boundary so that $f_1(z)$ is not necessarily a unique derivate.]

The above inequality is obviously satisfied for all points z of the continuum as well as boundary points.

Applying the two-dimensional form of the theorem of § 3·6, we see that the region formed by the continuum and its boundary can be divided into a *finite* number of parts (squares with sides parallel to the axes and their interiors, or portions of such squares) such that *inside* or on the boundary of any part there is one point z_1 such that the inequality

$$|f(z') - f(z_1) - (z' - z_1)f_1(z_1)| < \epsilon \,|\, z' - z_1 \,|$$

is satisfied by all points z' inside or on the boundary of that part.

5·2. CAUCHY'S THEOREM* ON THE INTEGRAL OF A FUNCTION ROUND A CONTOUR.

A simple closed curve C in the plane of the variable z is often called a *contour*; if A, B, D be points taken in order in the counter-clockwise sense along the arc of the contour, and if $f(z)$ be a one-valued continuous† function of z (not necessarily analytic) at all points on the arc, then the integral

$$\int_{ABDA} f(z)\,dz \quad \text{or} \quad \int_{(C)} f(z)\,dz$$

taken round the contour, starting from the point A and returning to A again, is called *the integral of $f(z)$ taken along the contour*. Clearly the value of the integral taken along the contour is unaltered if some point in the contour other than A is taken as the starting-point.

We shall now prove a result due to Cauchy, which may be stated as follows. *If $f(z)$ is a function of z, analytic at all points on‡ and inside a contour C, then*

$$\int_{(C)} f(z)\,dz = 0.$$

For divide up the interior of C by lines parallel to the real and imaginary axes in the manner of § 5·13; then the interior of C is divided into a number of regions whose boundaries are squares $C_1, C_2, \ldots C_M$ and other regions whose boundaries $D_1, D_2, \ldots D_N$ are portions of sides of squares and parts of C; consider

$$\sum_{n=1}^{M} \int_{(C_n)} f(z)\,dz + \sum_{n=1}^{N} \int_{(D_n)} f(z)\,dz,$$

each of the paths of integration being taken counter-clockwise; in the complete sum each side of each square appears twice as a path of integration, and the integrals along it are taken in opposite directions and consequently cancel§; the only parts of the sum which survive are the integrals of $f(z)$

---

* *Mémoire sur les intégrales définies prises entre des limites imaginaires* (1825). The proof here given is that due to Goursat, *Trans. American Math. Soc.* I. (1900), p. 14.

† It is sufficient for $f(z)$ to be continuous when variations of z *along the arc only* are considered.

‡ It is not necessary that $f(z)$ should be analytic *on* C (it is sufficient that it be continuous on and inside C), but if $f(z)$ is not analytic on C, the theorem is much harder to prove. This proof merely assumes that $f'(z)$ *exists* at all points on and inside C. Earlier proofs made more extended assumptions; thus Cauchy's proof assumed the *continuity* of $f'(z)$. Riemann's proof made an equivalent assumption. Goursat's first proof assumed that $f(z)$ was *uniformly differentiable* throughout C.

§ See § 4·6, example.

taken along a number of arcs which together make up C, each arc being taken in the same sense as in $\int_{(C)} f(z)\,dz$; these integrals therefore just make up $\int_{(C)} f(z)\,dz$.

Now consider $\int_{(C_n)} f(z)\,dz$. With the notation of § 5·12,

$$\int_{(C_n)} f(z)\,dz = \int_{(C_n)} \{f(z_1) + (z - z_1) f'(z_1) + (z - z_1) v\}\,dz$$

$$= \{f(z_1) - z_1 f'(z_1)\} \int_{(C_n)} dz + f'(z_1) \int_{(C_n)} z\,dz + \int_{(C_n)} (z - z_1) v\,dz.$$

But $$\int_{(C_n)} dz = [z]_{C_n} = 0, \quad \int_{(C_n)} z\,dz = \left[\tfrac{1}{2} z^2\right]_{C_n} = 0,$$

by the examples of § 4·6, since the end points of C_n coincide.

Now let l_n be the side of C_n and A_n the area of C_n.

Then, using § 4·62,

$$\left| \int_{(C_n)} f(z)\,dz \right| = \left| \int_{(C_n)} (z - z_1) v\,dz \right| \leqslant \int_{(C_n)} |(z - z_1)\,v\,dz|$$

$$< \epsilon l_n \sqrt{2} . \int_{C_n} |dz| = \epsilon l_n \sqrt{2} . 4 l_n = 4 \epsilon A_n \sqrt{2}.$$

In like manner

$$\left| \int_{(D_n)} f(z)\,dz \right| \leqslant \int_{(D_n)} |(z - z_1)\,v\,dz|$$

$$\leqslant 4\epsilon \left(A_n' + l_n' \lambda_n \right) \sqrt{2},$$

where A_n' is the area of the complete square of which D_n is part, l_n' is the side of this square and λ_n is the length of the part of C which lies inside this square. Hence, if λ be the whole length of C, while l is the side of a square which encloses all the squares C_n and D_n,

$$\left| \int_{(C)} f(z)\,dz \right| \leqslant \sum_{n=1}^{M} \left| \int_{(C_n)} f(z)\,dz \right| + \sum_{n=1}^{N} \left| \int_{(D_n)} f(z)\,dz \right|$$

$$< 4\epsilon \sqrt{2} \left\{ \sum_{n=1}^{M} A_n + \sum_{n=1}^{N} A_n' + l \sum_{n=1}^{N} \lambda_n \right\}$$

$$< 4\epsilon \sqrt{2} . (l^2 + l\lambda).$$

Now ϵ is arbitrarily small, and l, λ and $\int_{(C)} f(z)\,dz$ are *independent of* ϵ. It therefore follows from this inequality that the only value which $\int_{C} f(z)\,dz$ can have is zero; and this is Cauchy's result.

Corollary 1.   If there are two paths z_0AZ and z_0BZ from z_0 to Z, and if $f(z)$ is a function of z analytic at all points on these curves and throughout the domain enclosed by these two paths, then $\int_{z_0}^{Z} f(z)\,dz$ has the same value whether the path of integration is z_0AZ or z_0BZ.   This follows from the fact that z_0AZBz_0 is a contour, and so the integral taken round it (which is the difference of the integrals along z_0AZ and z_0BZ) is zero. Thus, if $f(z)$ be an analytic function of z, the value of $\int_{AB} f(z)\,dz$ is to a certain extent independent of the choice of the arc AB, and depends only on the terminal points A and B. It must be borne in mind that *this is only the case when $f(z)$ is an analytic function* in the sense of § 5·12.

Corollary 2.   Suppose that two simple closed curves C_0 and C_1 are given, such that C_0 completely encloses C_1, as e.g. would be the case if C_0 and C_1 were confocal ellipses.

Suppose moreover that $f(z)$ is a function which is analytic* at all points on C_0 and C_1 and throughout the ring-shaped region contained between C_0 and C_1.   Then by drawing a network of intersecting lines in this ring-shaped space, we can shew, exactly as in the theorem just proved, that *the integral*

$$\int f(z)\,dz$$

is zero, where the integration is taken round the whole boundary of the ring-shaped space; this boundary consisting of two curves C_0 and C_1, the one described in the counter-clockwise direction and the other described in the clockwise direction.

Corollary 3.   In general, if any connected region be given in the z-plane, bounded by any number of simple closed curves C_0, C_1, C_2, ..., and if $f(z)$ be any function of z which is analytic and one-valued everywhere in this region, *then*

$$\int f(z)\,dz$$

is zero, where the integral is taken round the whole boundary of the region; this boundary consisting of the curves C_0, C_1, ..., each described in such a sense that the region is kept either always on the right or always on the left of a person walking in the sense in question round the boundary.

An extension of Cauchy's theorem $\int f(z)\,dz = 0$, to curves lying on a cone whose vertex is at the origin, has been made by Ravut (*Nouv. Annales de Math* (3) XVI. (1897), pp. 365–7).   Morera, *Rend. del Ist. Lombardo*, XXII. (1889), p. 191, and Osgood, *Bull. Amer. Math. Soc.* II. (1896), pp. 296–302, have shewn that the property $\int f(z)\,dz = 0$ may be taken as the property defining an analytic function, the other properties being deducible from it.   (See p. 110, example 16.)

Example.   A ring-shaped region is bounded by the two circles $|z| = 1$ and $|z| = 2$ in the z-plane.   Verify that the value of $\int \dfrac{dz}{z}$, where the integral is taken round the boundary of this region, is zero.

* The phrase 'analytic throughout a region' implies one-valuedness (§ 5·12); that is to say that after z has described a closed path surrounding C_0, $f(z)$ has returned to its initial value.   A function such as $\log z$ considered in the region $1 \leqslant |z| \leqslant 2$ will be said to be 'analytic at all points of the region.'

For the boundary consists of the circumference $|z|=1$, described in the clockwise direction, together with the circumference $|z|=2$, described in the counter-clockwise direction. Thus, if for points on the first circumference we write $z=e^{i\theta}$, and for points on the second circumference we write $z=2e^{i\phi}$, then θ and ϕ are real, and the integral becomes

$$\int_0^{-2\pi} \frac{i \cdot e^{i\theta}\, d\theta}{e^{i\theta}} + \int_0^{2\pi} \frac{i \cdot 2e^{i\phi}\, d\phi}{2e^{i\phi}} = -2\pi i + 2\pi i = 0.$$

5·21. *The value of an analytic function at a point, expressed as an integral taken round a contour enclosing the point.*

Let C be a contour within and on which $f(z)$ is an analytic function of z.

Then, if a be any point within the contour,

$$\frac{f(z)}{z-a}$$

is a function of z, which is analytic at all points within the contour C except the point $z=a$.

Now, given ϵ, we can find δ such that

$$|f(z) - f(a) - (z-a)f'(a)| \leqslant \epsilon |z-a|$$

whenever $|z-a| < \delta$; with the point a as centre describe a circle γ of radius $r < \delta$, r being so small that γ lies wholly inside C.

Then in the space between γ and C $f(z)/(z-a)$ is analytic, and so, by § 5·2 corollary 2, we have

$$\int_C \frac{f(z)\, dz}{z-a} = \int_\gamma \frac{f(z)\, dz}{z-a},$$

where $\int_C$ and $\int_\gamma$ denote integrals taken counter-clockwise along the curves C and γ respectively.

But, since $|z-a| < \delta$ on γ, we have

$$\int_\gamma \frac{f(z)\, dz}{z-a} = \int_\gamma \frac{f(a) + (z-a)f'(a) + v(z-a)}{z-a}\, dz,$$

where $|v| < \epsilon$; and so

$$\int_C \frac{f(z)\, dz}{z-a} = f(a) \int_\gamma \frac{dz}{z-a} + f'(a) \int_\gamma dz + \int_\gamma v\, dz.$$

Now, if z be on γ, we may write

$$z - a = re^{i\theta},$$

where r is the radius of the circle γ, and consequently

$$\int_\gamma \frac{dz}{z-a} = \int_0^{2\pi} \frac{ire^{i\theta}\, d\theta}{re^{i\theta}} = i \int_0^{2\pi} d\theta = 2\pi i,$$

and

$$\int_\gamma dz = \int_0^{2\pi} ire^{i\theta}\, d\theta = 0;$$

also, by § 4·62,

$$\left| \int_\gamma v\, dz \right| \leqslant \epsilon \cdot 2\pi r.$$

Thus $$\left| \int_C \frac{f(z)\,dz}{z-a} - 2\pi i f(a) \right| = \left| \int_\gamma v\,dz \right| \leqslant 2\pi r\epsilon.$$

But the left-hand side is independent of ϵ, and so it must be zero, since ϵ is arbitrary; that is to say

$$f(a) = \frac{1}{2\pi i} \int_C \frac{f(z)\,dz}{z-a}.$$

This remarkable result expresses the value of a function $f(z)$, (which is *analytic* on and inside C) at any point a *within* a contour C, in terms of an integral which depends only on the value of $f(z)$ at points *on* the contour itself.

Corollary. If $f(z)$ is an analytic one-valued function of z in a ring-shaped region bounded by two curves C and C', and a is a point in the region, then

$$f(a) = \frac{1}{2\pi i} \int_C \frac{f(z)}{z-a}\,dz - \frac{1}{2\pi i} \int_{C'} \frac{f(z)}{z-a}\,dz,$$

where C is the outer of the curves and the integrals are taken counter-clockwise.

5·22.   *The derivates of an analytic function $f(z)$.*

The function $f'(z)$, which is the limit of

$$\frac{f(z+h)-f(z)}{h}$$

as h tends to zero, is called the *derivate* of $f(z)$. We shall now shew that $f'(z)$ *is itself an analytic function of z, and consequently itself possesses a derivate.*

For if C be a contour surrounding the point a, and situated entirely within the region in which $f(z)$ is analytic, we have

$$f'(a) = \lim_{h \to 0} \frac{f(a+h)-f(a)}{h}$$

$$= \lim_{h \to 0} \frac{1}{2\pi i h} \left\{ \int_C \frac{f(z)\,dz}{z-a-h} - \int_C \frac{f(z)\,dz}{z-a} \right\}$$

$$= \lim_{h \to 0} \frac{1}{2\pi i} \int_C \frac{f(z)\,dz}{(z-a)(z-a-h)}$$

$$= \frac{1}{2\pi i} \int_C \frac{f(z)\,dz}{(z-a)^2} + \lim_{h \to 0} \frac{h}{2\pi i} \int_C \frac{f(z)\,dz}{(z-a)^2(z-a-h)}.$$

Now, on C, $f(z)$ is continuous and therefore bounded, and so is $(z-a)^{-2}$; while we can take $|h|$ less than the lower bound of $\frac{1}{2}|z-a|$.

Therefore $\left| \dfrac{f(z)}{(z-a)^2(z-a-h)} \right|$ is bounded; let its upper bound be K. Then, if l be the length of C,

$$\left| \lim_{h \to 0} \frac{h}{2\pi i} \int_C \frac{f(z)\,dz}{(z-a)^2(z-a-h)} \right| \leqslant \lim_{h \to 0} |h|\,(2\pi)^{-1} Kl = 0,$$

and consequently

$$f'(a) = \frac{1}{2\pi i} \int_C \frac{f(z)\,dz}{(z-a)^2},$$

a formula which expresses the value of the derivate of a function at a point as an integral taken along a contour enclosing the point.

From this formula we have, if the points a and $a+h$ are inside C,

$$\frac{f'(a+h) - f'(a)}{h} = \frac{1}{2\pi i} \int_C \frac{f(z)\,dz}{h} \left\{ \frac{1}{(z-a-h)^2} - \frac{1}{(z-a)^2} \right\}$$

$$= \frac{1}{2\pi i} \int_C f(z)\,dz \cdot \frac{2\left(z-a-\tfrac{1}{2}h\right)}{(z-a-h)^2(z-a)^2}$$

$$= \frac{2}{2\pi i} \int_C \frac{f(z)\,dz}{(z-a)^3} + hA_h,$$

and it is easily seen that A_h is a bounded function of z when $|h| < \tfrac{1}{2}|z-a|$.

Therefore, as h tends to zero, $h^{-1}\{f'(a+h) - f'(a)\}$ tends to a limit, namely

$$\frac{2}{2\pi i} \int_C \frac{f(z)\,dz}{(z-a)^3}.$$

Since $f'(a)$ has a unique differential coefficient, it is an analytic function of a; its derivate, which is represented by the expression just given, is denoted by $f''(a)$, and is called the *second derivate* of $f(a)$.

Similarly it can be shewn that $f''(a)$ is an analytic function of a, possessing a derivate equal to

$$\frac{2 \cdot 3}{2\pi i} \int_C \frac{f(z)\,dz}{(z-a)^4};$$

this is denoted by $f'''(a)$, and is called the *third derivate* of $f(a)$. And in general an nth derivate $f^{(n)}(a)$ of $f(a)$ exists, expressible by the integral

$$\frac{n!}{2\pi i} \int_C \frac{f(z)\,dz}{(z-a)^{n+1}},$$

and having itself a derivate of the form

$$\frac{(n+1)!}{2\pi i} \int_C \frac{f(z)\,dz}{(z-a)^{n+2}};$$

the reader will see that this can be proved by induction without difficulty.

A function which possesses a first derivate with respect to the *complex* variable z at all points of a closed two-dimensional region in the z-plane therefore possesses derivates of all orders at all points *inside* the region.

5·23. *Cauchy's inequality for $f^{(n)}(a)$.*

Let $f(z)$ be analytic on and inside a circle C with centre a and radius r. Let M be the upper bound of $f(z)$ on the circle. Then, by § 4·62,

$$|f^{(n)}(a)| \leqslant \frac{n!}{2\pi} \int_C \frac{M}{r^{n+1}} |dz|$$

$$\leqslant \frac{M.n!}{r^n}.$$

Example. If $f(z)$ is analytic, $z = x + iy$ and $\nabla^2 = \dfrac{\partial^2}{\partial x^2} + \dfrac{\partial^2}{\partial y^2}$, shew that

$$\nabla^2 \log |f(z)| = 0 ; \text{ and } \nabla^2 |f(z)| > 0$$

unless $f(z) = 0$ or $f'(z) = 0$.   (Trinity, 1910.)

5·3. *Analytic functions represented by uniformly convergent series.*

Let $\overset{\infty}{\underset{n=0}{\Sigma}} f_n(z)$ be a series such that (i) it converges uniformly along a contour C, (ii) $f_n(z)$ is analytic throughout C and its interior.

Then $\overset{\infty}{\underset{n=0}{\Sigma}} f_n(z)$ converges, and the sum of the series is an analytic function throughout C and its interior.

For let a be any point inside C; on C, let $\overset{\infty}{\underset{n=0}{\Sigma}} f_n(z) = \Phi(z)$.

Then

$$\frac{1}{2\pi i} \int_C \frac{\Phi(z)}{z-a} dz = \frac{1}{2\pi i} \int_C \left\{ \overset{\infty}{\underset{n=0}{\Sigma}} f_n(z) \right\} \frac{dz}{z-a}$$

$$= \overset{\infty}{\underset{n=0}{\Sigma}} \left\{ \frac{1}{2\pi i} \int_C \frac{f_n(z)}{z-a} dz \right\},$$

by* § 4·7. But this last series, by § 5·21, is $\overset{\infty}{\underset{n=0}{\Sigma}} f_n(a)$; the series under consideration therefore converges at all points inside C; let its sum inside C (as well as on C) be called $\Phi(z)$. Then the function is analytic if it has a unique differential coefficient at all points inside C.

But if a and $a + h$ be inside C,

$$\frac{\Phi(a+h) - \Phi(a)}{h} = \frac{1}{2\pi i} \int_C \frac{\Phi(z) dz}{(z-a)(z-a-h)},$$

and hence, as in § 5·22, $\lim_{h \to 0} [\{\Phi(a+h) - \Phi(a)\} h^{-1}]$ exists and is equal to

---

* Since $|z-a|^{-1}$ is bounded when a is fixed and z is on C, the uniformity of the convergence of $\overset{\infty}{\underset{n=0}{\Sigma}} f_n(z)/(z-a)$ follows from that of $\overset{\infty}{\underset{n=0}{\Sigma}} f_n(z)$.

$\frac{1}{2\pi i}\int_C \frac{\Phi(z)}{(z-a)^2}\,dz$; and therefore $\Phi(z)$ is analytic inside C. Further, by transforming the last integral in the same way as we transformed the first one, we see that $\Phi'(a) = \sum_{n=0}^{\infty} f_n{}'(a)$, so that $\sum_{n=0}^{\infty} f_n(a)$ may be 'differentiated term by term.'

If a series of analytic functions converges only at points of a curve which is *not* closed nothing can be inferred as to the convergence of the derived series*.

Thus $\sum_{n=1}^{\infty} (-)^n \frac{\cos nx}{n^2}$ converges uniformly for real values of x (§ 3·34). But the derived series $\sum_{n=1}^{\infty} (-)^{n-1} \frac{\sin nx}{n}$ converges non-uniformly near $x=(2m+1)\pi$, (m any integer); and the derived series of this, viz. $\sum_{n=1}^{\infty} (-)^{n-1} \cos nx$, does not converge at all.

Corollary. By § 3·7, the sum of a power series is analytic inside its circle of convergence.

5·31. *Analytic functions represented by integrals.*

Let $f(t, z)$ satisfy the following conditions when t lies on a certain path of integration (a, b) and z is any point of a region S:

(i) f and $\frac{\partial f}{\partial z}$ are continuous functions of t.

(ii) f is an analytic function of z.

(iii) The continuity of $\frac{\partial f}{\partial z}$ *qua* function of z is uniform with respect to the variable t.

Then $\int_a^b f(t, z)\,dt$ is an analytic function of z. For, by § 4·2, it has the unique derivate $\int_a^b \frac{\partial f(t, z)}{\partial z}\,dt$.

5·32. *Analytic functions represented by infinite integrals.*

From § 4·44 (II) corollary, it follows that $\int_a^{\infty} f(t, z)\,dt$ is an analytic function of z at all points of a region S if (i) the integral converges, (ii) $f(t, z)$ is an analytic function of z when t is on the path of integration and z is on S, (iii) $\frac{\partial f(t, z)}{\partial z}$ is a continuous function of both variables, (iv) $\int_a^{\infty} \frac{\partial f(t, z)}{\partial z}\,dt$ converges uniformly throughout S.

For if these conditions are satisfied $\int_a^{\infty} f(t, z)\,dt$ has the unique derivate $\int_a^{\infty} \frac{\partial f(t, z)}{\partial z}\,dt$.

* This might have been anticipated as the main theorem of this section deals with uniformity of convergence over a *two-dimensional* region.

A case of very great importance is afforded by the integral $\int_0^\infty e^{-tz} f(t)\, dt$, where $f(t)$ is continuous and $|f(t)| < Ke^{rt}$ where K, r are independent of t; it is obvious from the conditions stated that the integral is an analytic function of z when $R(z) \geqslant r_1 > r$. [Condition (iv) is satisfied, by § 4·431 (I), since $\int_0^\infty te^{(r-r_1)\,t}\, dt$ converges.]

5·4. TAYLOR'S THEOREM*.

Consider a function $f(z)$, which is analytic in the neighbourhood of a point $z = a$. Let C be a circle with a as centre in the z-plane, which does not have any singular point of the function $f(z)$ on or inside it; so that $f(z)$ is analytic at all points on and inside C. Let $z = a + h$ be any point inside the circle C. Then, by § 5·21, we have

$$f(a+h) = \frac{1}{2\pi i} \int_C \frac{f(z)\, dz}{z-a-h}$$

$$= \frac{1}{2\pi i} \int_C f(z)\, dz \left\{ \frac{1}{z-a} + \frac{h}{(z-a)^2} + \ldots + \frac{h^n}{(z-a)^{n+1}} + \frac{h^{n+1}}{(z-a)^{n+1}(z-a-h)} \right\}$$

$$= f(a) + hf'(a) + \frac{h^2}{2!} f''(a) + \ldots + \frac{h^n}{n!} f^{(n)}(a) + \frac{1}{2\pi i} \int_C \frac{f(z)\, dz \cdot h^{n+1}}{(z-a)^{n+1}(z-a-h)}.$$

But when z is on C, the modulus of $\dfrac{f(z)}{z-a-h}$ is continuous, and so, by § 3·61 cor. (ii), will not exceed some finite number M.

Therefore, by § 4·62,

$$\left| \frac{1}{2\pi i} \int_C \frac{f(z)\, dz \cdot h^{n+1}}{(z-a)^{n+1}(z-a-h)} \right| \leqslant \frac{M \cdot 2\pi R}{2\pi} \left(\frac{|h|}{R} \right)^{n+1},$$

where R is the radius of the circle C, so that $2\pi R$ is the length of the path of integration in the last integral, and $R = |z-a|$ for points z on the circumference of C.

The right-hand side of the last inequality tends to zero as $n \to \infty$. We have therefore

$$f(a+h) = f(a) + hf'(a) + \frac{h^2}{2!} f''(a) + \ldots + \frac{h^n}{n!} f^{(n)}(a) + \ldots,$$

which we can write

$$f(z) = f(a) + (z-a) f'(a) + \frac{(z-a)^2}{2!} f''(a) + \ldots + \frac{(z-a)^n}{n!} f^{(n)}(a) + \ldots.$$

This result is known as *Taylor's Theorem*; and the proof given is due to Cauchy. It follows that *the radius of convergence of a power series is always*

---

* The formal expansion was first published by Dr Brook Taylor (1715) in his *Methodus Incrementorum*.

at least so large as only just to exclude from the interior of the circle of convergence the nearest singularity of the function represented by the series. And by § 5·3 corollary, it follows that the radius of convergence is *not larger than the number just specified.* Hence the radius of convergence is just such as to exclude from the interior of the circle that singularity of the function which is nearest to a.

At this stage we may introduce some terms which will be frequently used.

If $f(a) = 0$, the function $f(z)$ is said to have a *zero* at the point $z = a$. If at such a point $f'(a)$ is different from zero, the zero of $f(a)$ is said to be *simple*; if, however, $f'(a), f''(a), \ldots f^{(n-1)}(a)$ are all zero, so that the Taylor's expansion of $f(z)$ at $z = a$ begins with a term in $(z - a)^n$, then the function $f(z)$ is said to have a *zero of the nth order* at the point $z = a$.

Example 1.   Find the function $f(z)$, which is analytic throughout the circle C and its interior, whose centre is at the origin and whose radius is unity, and has the value

$$\frac{a - \cos\theta}{a^2 - 2a\cos\theta + 1} + i\,\frac{\sin\theta}{a^2 - 2a\cos\theta + 1}$$

(where $a > 1$ and θ is the vectorial angle) at points on the circumference of C.

[We have

$$f^{(n)}(0) = \frac{n!}{2\pi i}\int_C \frac{f(z)\,dz}{z^{n+1}}$$

$$= \frac{n!}{2\pi i}\int_0^{2\pi} e^{-ni\theta}.i d\theta.\frac{a - \cos\theta + i\sin\theta}{a^2 - 2a\cos\theta + 1}, \quad (\text{putting } z = e^{i\theta})$$

$$= \frac{n!}{2\pi}\int_0^{2\pi} \frac{e^{-ni\theta}\,d\theta}{a - e^{i\theta}} = \frac{n!}{2\pi i}\int_C \frac{dz}{z^{n+1}(a-z)} = \left\lfloor\frac{d^n}{dz^n}\frac{1}{a-z}\right\rfloor_{z=0}$$

$$= \frac{n!}{a^{n+1}}.$$

Therefore by Maclaurin's Theorem*,

$$f(z) = \sum_{n=0}^{\infty} \frac{z^n}{a^{n+1}},$$

or $f(z) = (a - z)^{-1}$ for all points within the circle.

This example raises the interesting question, Will it still be convenient to define $f(z)$ as $(a-z)^{-1}$ at points outside the circle? This will be discussed in § 5·51.]

Example 2.   Prove that the arithmetic mean of all values of $z^{-n}\sum_{\nu=0}^{\infty} a_\nu z^\nu$, for points z on the circumference of the circle $|z| = 1$, is a_n, if $\Sigma a_\nu z^\nu$ is analytic throughout the circle and its interior.

[Let $\sum_{\nu=0}^{\infty} a_\nu z^\nu = f(z)$, so that $a_\nu = \frac{f^{(\nu)}(0)}{\nu!}$. Then, writing $z = e^{i\theta}$, and calling C the circle $|z| = 1$,

$$\frac{1}{2\pi}\int_0^{2\pi} \frac{f(z)\,d\theta}{z^n} = \frac{1}{2\pi i}\int_C \frac{f(z)\,dz}{z^{n+1}} = \frac{f^{(n)}(0)}{n!} = a_n.]$$

* The result $f(z) = f(0) + zf'(0) + \frac{z^2}{2}f''(0) + \ldots$, obtained by putting $a = 0$ in Taylor's Theorem, is usually called *Maclaurin's Theorem*; it was discovered by Stirling (1717) and published by Maclaurin (1742) in his *Fluxions*.

Example 3.   Let $f(z) = z^r$; then $f(z+h)$ is an analytic function of h when $|h| < |z|$ for all values of r; and so $(z+h)^r = z^r + rz^{r-1}h + \dfrac{r(r-1)}{2} z^{r-2}h^2 + \dots$, this series converging when $|h| < |z|$.   This is the binomial theorem.

Example 4.   Prove that if h is a positive constant, and $(1 - 2zh + h^2)^{-\frac{1}{2}}$ is expanded in the form

$$1 + hP_1(z) + h^2P_2(z) + h^3P_3(z) + \dots \quad \dots\dots\dots\dots\dots\dots\dots(A),$$

(where $P_n(z)$ is easily seen to be a polynomial of degree n in z), then this series converges so long as z is in the interior of an ellipse whose foci are the points $z = 1$ and $z = -1$, and whose semi-major axis is $\frac{1}{2}(h + h^{-1})$.

Let the series be first regarded as a function of h.   It is a power series in h, and therefore converges so long as the point h lies within a circle in the h-plane.   The centre of this circle is the point $h = 0$, and its circumference will be such as to pass through that singularity of $(1 - 2zh + h^2)^{-\frac{1}{2}}$ which is nearest to $h = 0$.

But $\qquad\qquad 1 - 2zh + h^2 = \{h - z + (z^2 - 1)^{\frac{1}{2}}\}\{h - z - (z^2 - 1)^{\frac{1}{2}}\},$

so the singularities of $(1 - 2zh + h^2)^{-\frac{1}{2}}$ are the points $h = z - (z^2 - 1)^{\frac{1}{2}}$ and $h = z + (z^2 - 1)^{\frac{1}{2}}$. [These singularities are branch points (see § 5·7).]

Thus the series (A) converges so long as $|h|$ is less than both

$$|z - (z^2 - 1)^{\frac{1}{2}}| \text{ and } |z + (z^2 - 1)^{\frac{1}{2}}|.$$

Draw an ellipse in the z-plane passing through the point z and having its foci at ± 1. Let a be its semi-major axis, and θ the eccentric angle of z on it.

Then $\qquad\qquad\qquad\qquad z = a\cos\theta + i(a^2 - 1)^{\frac{1}{2}}\sin\theta,$

which gives $\qquad\qquad z \pm (z^2 - 1)^{\frac{1}{2}} = \{a \pm (a^2 - 1)^{\frac{1}{2}}\}(\cos\theta \pm i\sin\theta),$

so $\qquad\qquad\qquad\qquad |z \pm (z^2 - 1)^{\frac{1}{2}}| = a \pm (a^2 - 1)^{\frac{1}{2}}.$

Thus the series (A) converges so long as h is less than the smaller of the numbers $a + (a^2 - 1)^{\frac{1}{2}}$ and $a - (a^2 - 1)^{\frac{1}{2}}$, i.e. so long as h is less than $a - (a^2 - 1)^{\frac{1}{2}}$.   But $h = a - (a^2 - 1)^{\frac{1}{2}}$ when $a = \frac{1}{2}(h + h^{-1})$.

Therefore the series (A) converges so long as z is within an ellipse whose foci are 1 and -1, and whose semi-major axis is $\frac{1}{2}(h + h^{-1})$.

5·41.   *Forms of the remainder in Taylor's series.*

Let $f(x)$ be a *real* function of a *real* variable; and let it have continuous differential coefficients of the first n orders when $a \leqslant x \leqslant a + h$.

If $0 \leqslant t \leqslant 1$, we have

$$\frac{d}{dt}\left\{ \sum_{m=1}^{n-1} \frac{h^m}{m!}(1-t)^m f^{(m)}(a + th) \right\} = \frac{h^n(1-t)^{n-1}}{(n-1)!} f^{(n)}(a + th) - hf'(a + th).$$

Integrating this between the limits 0 and 1, we have

$$f(a + h) = f(a) + \sum_{m=1}^{n-1} \frac{h^m}{m!} f^{(m)}(a) + \int_0^1 \frac{h^n(1-t)^{n-1}}{(n-1)!} f^{(n)}(a + th)\,dt.$$

Let $\qquad\qquad R_n = \frac{h^n}{(n-1)!}\int_0^1 (1-t)^{n-1}f^{(n)}(a + th)\,dt;$

and let p be a positive integer such that $p \leqslant n$.

Then $\qquad R_n = \dfrac{h^n}{(n-1)!} \displaystyle\int_0^1 (1-t)^{p-1} \cdot (1-t)^{n-p} f^{(n)}(a+th)\, dt.$

Let U, L be the upper and lower bounds of $(1-t)^{n-p} f^{(n)}(a+th)$.

Then

$$\int_0^1 L(1-t)^{p-1}\, dt < \int_0^1 (1-t)^{p-1} \cdot (1-t)^{n-p} f^{(n)}(a+th)\, dt < \int_0^1 U(1-t)^{p-1}\, dt.$$

Since $(1-t)^{n-p} f^{(n)}(a+th)$ is a continuous function it passes through all values between U and L, and hence we can find θ such that $0 \leqslant \theta \leqslant 1$, and

$$\int_0^1 (1-t)^{n-1} f^{(n)}(a+th)\, dt = p^{-1}(1-\theta)^{n-p} f^{(n)}(a+\theta h).$$

Therefore $\qquad R_n = \dfrac{h^n}{(n-1)!\,p}(1-\theta)^{n-p} f^{(n)}(a+\theta h).$

Writing $p=n$, we get $R_n = \dfrac{h^n}{n!} f^{(n)}(a+\theta h)$, which is *Lagrange's form for the remainder*; and writing $p=1$, we get $R_n = \dfrac{h^n}{(n-1)!}(1-\theta)^{n-1} f^{(n)}(a+\theta h)$, which is *Cauchy's form for the remainder*.

Taking $n=1$ in this result, we get

$$f(a+h) - f(a) = hf'(a+\theta h)$$

if $f'(x)$ is continuous when $a \leqslant x \leqslant a+h$; this result is usually known as the *First Mean Value Theorem* (see also § 4·14).

Darboux gave in 1876 (*Journal de Math.* (3) II. p. 291) a form for the remainder in Taylor's Series, which is applicable to complex variables and resembles the above form given by Lagrange for the case of real variables.

5·5. *The Process of Continuation.*

Near every point P, z_0, in the neighbourhood of which a function $f(z)$ is analytic, we have seen that an expansion exists for the function as a series of ascending positive integral powers of $(z - z_0)$, the coefficients in which involve the successive derivates of the function at z_0.

Now let A be the singularity of $f(z)$ which is nearest to P. Then the circle within which this expansion is valid has P for centre and PA for radius.

Suppose that we are merely given the values of a function at all points of the circumference of a circle slightly smaller than the circle of convergence and concentric with it together with the condition that the function is to be analytic throughout the interior of the larger circle. Then the preceding theorems enable us to find its value at all points *within* the smaller circle and to determine the coefficients in the Taylor series proceeding in powers of $z - z_0$. The question arises, Is it possible to define the function at points *outside* the circle in such a way that the function is analytic throughout a larger domain than the interior of the circle?

In other words, *given a power series which converges and represents a function only at points within a circle, to define by means of it the values of the function at points outside the circle.*

For this purpose choose any point P_1 within the circle, not on the line PA. We know the value of the function and all its derivates at P_1, from the series, and so we can form the Taylor series (for the same function) with P_1 as origin, which will define a function analytic throughout some circle of centre P_1. Now this circle will extend as far as the singularity* which is nearest to P_1, which may or may not be A; but in either case, this new circle will usually† lie partly outside the old circle of convergence, and *for points in the region which is included in the new circle but not in the old circle, the new series may be used to define the values of the function, although the old series failed to do so.*

Similarly we can take any other point P_2, in the region for which the values of the function are now known, and form the Taylor series with P_2 as origin, which will in general enable us to define the function at other points, at which its values were not previously known; and so on.

This process is called *continuation*‡. By means of it, starting from a representation of a function by any one power series we can find any number of other power series, which between them define the value of the function at all points of a domain, any point of which can be reached from P without passing through a singularity of the function; and the aggregate§ of all the power series thus obtained constitutes the analytical expression of the function.

It is important to know whether continuation by two different paths PBQ, $PB'Q$ will give the same final power series; it will be seen that this is the case, if the function have no singularity inside the closed curve $PBQB'P$, in the following way: Let P_1 be any point on PBQ, inside the circle C with centre P; obtain the continuation of the function with P_1 as origin, and let it converge inside a circle C_1; let P_1' be any point inside both circles and also inside the curve $PBQB'P$; let S, S_1, S_1' be the power series with P, P_1, P_1' as origins; then|| $S_1 \equiv S_1'$ over a certain domain which will contain P_1, if P_1' be taken sufficiently near P_1; and hence S_1 will be the continuation of S_1'; for if T_1 were the continuation of S_1', we have $T_1 \equiv S_1$ over a domain containing P_1, and so (§ 3·73) corresponding coefficients in S_1 and T_1 are the same. By carrying out such a process a sufficient number of times, we deform the path PBQ into the path $PB'Q$ if no singular point is inside $PBQB'P$. The reader will convince himself by drawing a figure that the process can be carried out in a finite number of steps.

---

* Of the function defined by the new series.

† The word 'usually' must be taken as referring to the cases which are likely to come under the reader's notice while studying the less advanced parts of the subject.

‡ French, *prolongement*; German, *Fortsetzung*.

§ Such an aggregate of power series has been obtained for various functions by M. J. M. Hill, by purely algebraical processes, *Proc. London Math. Soc.* xxxv. (1903), pp. 388–416.

‖ Since each is equal to S.

Example. The series

$$\frac{1}{a} + \frac{z}{a^2} + \frac{z^2}{a^3} + \frac{z^3}{a^4} + \dots$$

represents the function

$$f(z) = \frac{1}{a-z}$$

only for points z within the circle $|z| = |a|$.

But any number of other power series exist, of the type

$$\frac{1}{a-b} + \frac{z-b}{(a-b)^2} + \frac{(z-b)^2}{(a-b)^3} + \frac{(z-b)^3}{(a-b)^4} + \dots;$$

if b/a is not real and positive these converge at points inside a circle which is partly inside and partly outside $|z| = |a|$; these series represent this same function at points outside this circle.

5·501. *On functions to which the continuation-process cannot be applied.*

It is not always possible to carry out the process of continuation. Take as an example the function $f(z)$ defined by the power series

$$f(z) = 1 + z^2 + z^4 + z^8 + z^{16} + \dots + z^{2^n} + \dots,$$

which clearly converges in the interior of a circle whose radius is unity and whose centre is at the origin.

Now it is obvious that, as $z \to 1 - 0$, $f(z) \to +\infty$; the point $+1$ is therefore a singularity of $f(z)$.

But

$$f(z) = z^2 + f(z^2),$$

and if $z^2 \to 1 - 0$, $f(z^2) \to \infty$ and so $f(z) \to \infty$, and hence the points for which $z^2 = 1$ are singularities of $f(z)$; the point $z = -1$ is therefore also a singularity of $f(z)$.

Similarly since

$$f(z) = z^2 + z^4 + f(z^4),$$

we see that if z is such that $z^4 = 1$, then z is a singularity of $f(z)$; and, in general, any root of any of the equations

$$z^2 = 1, \quad z^4 = 1, \quad z^8 = 1, \quad z^{16} = 1, \quad \dots,$$

is a singularity of $f(z)$. But these points all lie on the circle $|z| = 1$; and in any arc of this circle, however small, there are an unlimited number of them. The attempt to carry out the process of continuation will therefore be frustrated by the existence of this unbroken front of singularities, beyond which it is impossible to pass.

In such a case the function $f(z)$ *cannot be continued at all* to points z situated outside the circle $|z| = 1$; such a function is called a *lacunary function*, and the circle is said to be a *limiting circle* for the function.

5·51. *The identity of two functions.*

The two series

$$1 + z + z^2 + z^3 + \dots$$

and

$$-1 + (z-2) - (z-2)^2 + (z-2)^3 - (z-2)^4 + \dots$$

do not both converge for any value of z, and are distinct expansions. Nevertheless, we generally say that they represent *the same function*, on the strength of the fact that they can both be represented by the same rational expression $\frac{1}{1-z}$.

This raises the question of the *identity* of two functions. When can two *different* expansions be said to represent the *same* function?

We might define a function (after Weierstrass), by means of the last article, as consisting of one power series together with all the other power series which can be derived from it by the process of continuation. Two different analytical expressions will then define the same function, if they represent power series derivable from each other by continuation.

Since if a function is analytic (in the sense of Cauchy, § 5·12) at and near a point it can be expanded into a Taylor's series, and since a convergent power series has a unique differential coefficient (§ 5·3), it follows that the definition of Weierstrass is really equivalent to that of Cauchy.

It is important to observe that *the limit of a combination of analytic functions can represent different analytic functions in different parts of the plane.* This can be seen by considering the series

$$\frac{1}{2}\left(z + \frac{1}{z}\right) + \sum_{n=1}^{\infty} \left(z - \frac{1}{z}\right)\left(\frac{1}{1+z^n} - \frac{1}{1+z^{n-1}}\right).$$

The sum of the first $n+1$ terms of this series is

$$\frac{1}{z} + \left(z - \frac{1}{z}\right) \cdot \frac{1}{1+z^n}.$$

The series therefore converges for all values of z (zero excepted) not on the circle $|z| = 1$. But, as $n \to \infty$, $|z^n| \to 0$ or $|z^n| \to \infty$ according as $|z|$ is less or greater than unity; hence we see that the sum to infinity of the series is z when $|z| < 1$, and $\frac{1}{z}$ when $|z| > 1$. *This series therefore represents one function at points in the interior of the circle $|z| = 1$, and an entirely different function at points outside the same circle.* The reader will see from § 5·3 that this result is connected with the non-uniformity of the convergence of the series near $|z| = 1$.

It has been shewn by Borel* that if a region C is taken and a set of points S such that points of the set S are arbitrarily near every point of C, it may be possible to define a function which has a unique differential coefficient (i.e. is monogenic) at all points of C which do not belong to S; but the function is not analytic in C in the sense of Weierstrass.

Such a function is

$$f(z) \equiv \sum_{n=1}^{\infty} \sum_{p=0}^{n} \sum_{q=0}^{n} \frac{\exp(-\exp n^4)}{z - (p+qi)/n}.$$

* *Proc. Math. Congress*, Cambridge (1912), I. pp. 137–138. *Leçons sur les fonctions monogènes* (1917). The functions are not monogenic strictly in the sense of § 5·1 because, in the example quoted, in working out $\{f(z+h) - f(z)\}/h$, it must be supposed that $R(z+h)$ and $I(z+h)$ are not both rational fractions.

5·6. LAURENT'S THEOREM.

A very important theorem was published in 1843 by Laurent[*]; it relates to expansions of functions to which Taylor's Theorem cannot be applied.

Let C and C' be two concentric circles of centre a, of which C' is the inner; and let $f(z)$ be a function which is analytic[†] at all points on C and C' and throughout the annulus between C and C'. Let $a + h$ be any point in this ring-shaped space. Then we have (§ 5·21 corollary)

$$f(a + h) = \frac{1}{2\pi i} \int_C \frac{f(z)}{z - a - h}\, dz - \frac{1}{2\pi i} \int_{C'} \frac{f(z)}{z - a - h}\, dz,$$

where the integrals are supposed taken in the positive or counter-clockwise direction round the circles.

This can be written

$$f(a+h) = \frac{1}{2\pi i} \int_C f(z) \left\{ \frac{1}{z-a} + \frac{h}{(z-a)^2} + \dots + \frac{h^n}{(z-a)^{n+1}} + \frac{h^{n+1}}{(z-a)^{n+1}(z-a-h)} \right\} dz$$

$$+ \frac{1}{2\pi i} \int_{C'} f(z) \left\{ \frac{1}{h} + \frac{z-a}{h^2} + \dots + \frac{(z-a)^n}{h^{n+1}} - \frac{(z-a)^{n+1}}{h^{n+1}(z-a-h)} \right\} dz.$$

We find, as in the proof of Taylor's Theorem, that

$$\int_C \frac{f(z)\, dz \cdot h^{n+1}}{(z-a)^{n+1}(z-a-h)} \text{ and } \int_{C'} \frac{f(z)\, dz\, (z-a)^{n+1}}{(z-a-h)\, h^{n+1}}$$

tend to zero as $n \to \infty$; and thus we have

$$f(a + h) = a_0 + a_1 h + a_2 h^2 + \dots + \frac{b_1}{h} + \frac{b_2}{h^2} + \dots,$$

where[‡] $a_n = \dfrac{1}{2\pi i} \displaystyle\int_C \frac{f(z)\, dz}{(z-a)^{n+1}}$ and $b_n = \dfrac{1}{2\pi i} \displaystyle\int_{C'} (z-a)^{n-1} f(z)\, dz.$

This result is *Laurent's Theorem*; changing the notation, it can be expressed in the following form: *If $f(z)$ be analytic on the concentric circles C and C' of centre a, and throughout the annulus between them, then at any point z of the annulus $f(z)$ can be expanded in the form*

$$f(z) = a_0 + a_1 (z - a) + a_2 (z - a)^2 + \dots + \frac{b_1}{(z-a)} + \frac{b_2}{(z-a)^2} + \dots,$$

where $a_n = \dfrac{1}{2\pi i} \displaystyle\int_C \frac{f(t)\, dt}{(t-a)^{n+1}}$ *and* $b_n = \dfrac{1}{2\pi i} \displaystyle\int_{C'} (t-a)^{n-1} f(t)\, dt.$

An important case of Laurent's Theorem arises when there is only one singularity within the inner circle C', namely at the centre a. In this case the circle C' can be taken as small as we please, and so Laurent's expansion is valid for all points in the interior of the circle C, except the centre a.

---

[*] *Comptes Rendus*, XVII. (1843), pp. 348–349. The theorem is contained in a paper which was written by Weierstrass in 1841, but apparently not published before 1894, *Werke*, I. pp. 51–66.

[†] See § 5·2 corollary 2, footnote.

[‡] We cannot write $a_n = f^{(n)}(a)/n!$ as in Taylor's Theorem since $f(z)$ is not necessarily analytic inside C'.

Example 1. Prove that

$$e^{\frac{x}{2}\left(z-\frac{1}{z}\right)}=J_0\left(x\right)+zJ_1\left(x\right)+z^2J_2\left(x\right)+\ldots+z^nJ_n\left(x\right)+\ldots$$
$$-\frac{1}{z}J_1\left(x\right)+\frac{1}{z^2}J_2\left(x\right)-\ldots+\frac{(-)^n}{z^n}J_n\left(x\right)+\ldots,$$

where

$$J_n\left(x\right)=\frac{1}{2\pi}\int_0^{2\pi}\cos\left(n\theta-x\sin\theta\right)d\theta.$$

[For the function of z under consideration is analytic in any domain which does not include the point $z=0$; and so by Laurent's Theorem,

$$e^{\frac{x}{2}\left(z-\frac{1}{z}\right)}=a_0+a_1z+a_2z^2+\ldots+\frac{b_1}{z}+\frac{b_2}{z^2}+\ldots,$$

where

$$a_n=\frac{1}{2\pi i}\int_C e^{\frac{x}{2}\left(z-\frac{1}{z}\right)}\frac{dz}{z^{n+1}}\text{ and }b_n=\frac{1}{2\pi i}\int_{C'} e^{\frac{x}{2}\left(z-\frac{1}{z}\right)}z^{n-1}dz,$$

and where C and C' are any circles with the origin as centre. Taking C to be the circle of radius unity, and writing $z=e^{i\theta}$, we have

$$a_n=\frac{1}{2\pi i}\int_0^{2\pi} e^{ix\sin\theta}\cdot e^{-ni\theta}i\,d\theta=\frac{1}{2\pi}\int_0^{2\pi}\cos\left(n\theta-x\sin\theta\right)d\theta,$$

since $\int_0^{2\pi}\sin\left(n\theta-x\sin\theta\right)d\theta$ vanishes, as may be seen by writing $2\pi-\phi$ for θ. Thus $a_n=J_n\left(x\right)$, and $b_n=(-)^n a_n$, since the function expanded is unaltered if $-z^{-1}$ be written for z, so that $b_n=(-)^n J_n\left(x\right)$, and the proof is complete.]

Example 2. Shew that, in the annulus defined by $|a|<|z|<|b|$, the function

$$\left\{\frac{bz}{(z-a)(b-z)}\right\}^{\frac{1}{2}}$$

can be expanded in the form

$$S_0+\sum_{n=1}^{\infty}S_n\left(\frac{a^n}{z^n}+\frac{z^n}{b^n}\right),$$

where

$$S_n=\sum_{l=0}^{\infty}\frac{1.3\ldots(2l-1).1.3\ldots(2l+2n-1)}{2^{2l+n}.l!\,(l+n)!}\left(\frac{a}{b}\right)^l.$$

The function is one-valued and analytic in the annulus (see § 5·7), for the branch-points 0, a neutralise each other, and so, by Laurent's Theorem, if C denote the circle $|z|=r$, where $|a|<r<|b|$, the coefficient of z^n in the required expansion is

$$\frac{1}{2\pi i}\int_C\frac{dz}{z^{n+1}}\left\{\frac{bz}{(z-a)(b-z)}\right\}^{\frac{1}{2}}.$$

Putting $z=re^{i\theta}$, this becomes

$$\frac{1}{2\pi}\int_0^{2\pi} e^{-ni\theta}\,r^{-n}\,d\theta\left(1-\frac{r}{b}e^{i\theta}\right)^{-\frac{1}{2}}\left(1-\frac{a}{r}e^{-i\theta}\right)^{-\frac{1}{2}},$$

or

$$\frac{1}{2\pi}\int_0^{2\pi} e^{-ni\theta}r^{-n}\,d\theta\sum_{k=0}^{\infty}\frac{1.3\ldots(2k-1)}{2^k.k!}\frac{r^ke^{ki\theta}}{b^k}\sum_{l=0}^{\infty}\frac{1.3\ldots(2l-1)}{2^l.l!}\frac{a^le^{-li\theta}}{r^l},$$

the series being absolutely convergent and uniformly convergent with regard to θ.

The only terms which give integrals different from zero are those for which $k=l+n$. So the coefficient of z^n is

$$\frac{1}{2\pi}\int_0^{2\pi}d\theta\sum_{l=0}^{\infty}\frac{1.3\ldots(2l-1)}{2^l.l!}\frac{1.3\ldots(2l+2n-1)}{2^{l+n}.(l+n)!}\frac{a^l}{b^{l+n}}=\frac{S_n}{b^n}.$$

Similarly it can be shewn that the coefficient of $\frac{1}{z^n}$ is $S_n a^n$.

Example 3. Shew that

$$e^{uz + v/z} = a_0 + a_1 z + a_2 z^2 + \dots + \frac{b_1}{z} + \frac{b_2}{z^2} + \dots,$$

where

$$a_n = \frac{1}{2\pi} \int_0^{2\pi} e^{(u+v)\cos\theta} \cos\{(u-v)\sin\theta - n\theta\}\, d\theta,$$

and

$$b_n = \frac{1}{2\pi} \int_0^{2\pi} e^{(u+v)\cos\theta} \cos\{(v-u)\sin\theta - n\theta\}\, d\theta.$$

5·61. *The nature of the singularities of one-valued functions.*

Consider first a function $f(z)$ which is analytic throughout a closed region S, except at a single point a inside the region.

Let it be possible to define a function $\phi(z)$ such that

(i) $\phi(z)$ is analytic throughout S,

(ii)   when $z \neq a$, $f(z) = \phi(z) + \dfrac{B_1}{z-a} + \dfrac{B_2}{(z-a)^2} + \dots + \dfrac{B_n}{(z-a)^n}$.

Then $f(z)$ is said to have a '*pole of order n at a*'; and the terms $\dfrac{B_1}{z-a} + \dfrac{B_2}{(z-a)^2} + \dots + \dfrac{B_n}{(z-a)^n}$ are called the *principal part* of $f(z)$ near a. By the definition of a singularity (§ 5·12) a pole is a singularity. If $n = 1$, the singularity is called a *simple* pole.

Any singularity of a one-valued function other than a pole is called an *essential singularity*.

If the essential singularity, a, is isolated (i.e. if a region, of which a is an interior point, can be found containing no singularities other than a), then a Laurent expansion can be found, in ascending and descending powers of $(z - a)$ valid when $\Delta > |z - a| > \delta$, where Δ depends on the other singularities of the function, and δ is arbitrarily small. Hence the 'principal part' of a function near an isolated essential singularity consists of an infinite series.

It should be noted that a pole is, by definition, an isolated singularity, so that all singularities which are not isolated (e.g. the limiting point of a sequence of poles) are essential singularities.

There does not exist, in general, an expansion of a function valid near a non-isolated singularity in the way that Laurent's expansion is valid near an isolated singularity.

Corollary. If $f(z)$ has a pole of order n at a, and $\psi(z) = (z-a)^n f(z)$ $(z \neq a)$, $\psi(a) = \lim_{z \to a} (z-a)^n f(z)$, then $\psi(z)$ is analytic at a.

Example 1. A function is not bounded near an isolated essential singularity.

[Prove that if the function were bounded near $z = a$, the coefficients of negative powers of $z - a$ would all vanish.]

Example 2.   Find the singularities of the function $e^{\frac{c}{z-a}}/\{e^{\frac{z}{a}}-1\}$.

At $z=0$, the numerator is analytic, and the denominator has a simple zero.   Hence the function has a simple pole at $z=0$.

Similarly there is a simple pole at each of the points $2n\pi i a\,(n=\pm1,\,\pm2,\,\pm3,\,...)$; the denominator is analytic and does not vanish for other values of z.

At $z=a$, the numerator has an isolated singularity, so Laurent's Theorem is applicable, and the coefficients in the Laurent expansion may be obtained from the quotient

$$\frac{1+\dfrac{c}{z-a}+\dfrac{c^2}{2\,!\,(z-a)^2}+...}{e\left(1+\dfrac{z-a}{a}+...\right)-1},$$

which gives an expansion involving all positive and negative powers of $(z-a)$.   So there is an essential singularity·at $z=a$.

Example 3.   Shew that the function defined by the series

$$\sum_{n=1}^{\infty}\frac{nz^{n-1}\{(1+n^{-1})^n-1\}}{(z^n-1)\{z^n-(1+n^{-1})^n\}}$$

has simple poles at the points $z=(1+n^{-1})\,e^{2ki\pi/n}$, $(k=0,\,1,\,2,\,...\,n-1\,;\,n=1,\,2,\,3,\,...)$.

(Math. Trip. 1899.)

5·62.   *The 'point at infinity.'*

The behaviour of a function $f(z)$ as $|z|\to\infty$ can be treated in a similar way to its behaviour as z tends to a finite limit.

If we write $z=\dfrac{1}{z'}$, so that large values of z are represented by small values of z' in the z'-plane, there is a one-one correspondence between z and z', provided that neither is zero; and to make the correspondence complete it is sometimes convenient to say that when z' is the origin, z is the 'point at infinity.'   But the reader must be careful to observe that this is *not* a definite point, and any proposition about it is really a proposition concerning the point $z'=0$.

Let $f(z)=\phi(z')$.   Then $\phi(z')$ is not defined *at* $z'=0$, but its behaviour near $z'=0$ is determined by its Taylor (or Laurent) expansion in powers of z'; and we define $\phi(0)$ as $\lim\limits_{z'\to0}\phi(z')$ if that limit exists.   For instance the function $\phi(z')$ may have a zero of order m at the point $z'=0$; in this case the Taylor expansion of $\phi(z')$ will be of the form

$$Az'^m+Bz'^{m+1}+Cz'^{m+2}+...,$$

and so the expansion of $f(z)$ valid for sufficiently large values of $|z|$ will be of the form

$$f(z)=\frac{A}{z^m}+\frac{B}{z^{m+1}}+\frac{C}{z^{m+2}}+....$$

In this case, $f(z)$ is said to have a *zero of order m at 'infinity.'*

Again, the function $\phi(z')$ may have a pole of order m at the point $z' = 0$; in this case

$$\phi(z') = \frac{A}{z'^m} + \frac{B}{z'^{m-1}} + \frac{C}{z'^{m-2}} + \ldots + \frac{L}{z'} + M + Nz' + Pz'^2 + \ldots;$$

and so, for sufficiently large values of $|z|$, $f(z)$ can be expanded in the form

$$f(z) = Az^m + Bz^{m-1} + Cz^{m-2} + \ldots + Lz + M + \frac{N}{z} + \frac{P}{z^2} + \ldots.$$

In this case, $f(z)$ is said to have a *pole of order m at 'infinity.'*

Similarly $f(z)$ is said to have an *essential singularity* at infinity, if $\phi(z')$ has an essential singularity at the point $z' = 0$. Thus the function e^z has an essential singularity at infinity, since the function $e^{\frac{1}{z'}}$ or

$$1 + \frac{1}{z'} + \frac{1}{2! \, z'^2} + \frac{1}{3! \, z'^3} + \ldots$$

has an essential singularity at $z' = 0$.

Example. Discuss the function represented by the series

$$\sum_{n=0}^{\infty} \frac{1}{n!} \frac{1}{1 + a^{2n} z^2}, \qquad (a > 1).$$

The function represented by this series has singularities at $z = \frac{i}{a^n}$ and $z = -\frac{i}{a^n}$, $(n = 1, 2, 3, \ldots)$, since at each of these points the denominator of one of the terms in the series is zero. These singularities are on the imaginary axis, and have $z = 0$ as a limiting point; so no Taylor or Laurent expansion can be formed for the function valid throughout any region of which the origin is an interior point.

For values of z, other than these singularities, the series converges absolutely, since the limit of the ratio of the $(n+1)$th term to the nth is $\lim_{n \to \infty} (n+1)^{-1} a^{-2} = 0$. The function is an even function of z (i.e. is unchanged if the sign of z be changed), tends to zero as $|z| \to \infty$, and is analytic on and outside a circle C of radius greater than unity and centre at the origin. So, for points outside this circle, it can be expanded in the form

$$\frac{b_2}{z^2} + \frac{b_4}{z^4} + \frac{b_6}{z^6} + \ldots,$$

where, by Laurent's Theorem,

$$b_{2k} = \frac{1}{2\pi i} \int_C z^{2k-1} \sum_{n=0}^{\infty} \frac{1}{n!} \frac{a^{-2n}}{a^{-2n} + z^2} \, dz.$$

Now
$$\sum_{n=0}^{\infty} \frac{a^{-2n} z^{2k-1}}{n! \, (a^{-2n} + z^2)} = \sum_{n=0}^{\infty} \sum_{m=0}^{\infty} \frac{z^{2k-3}}{n!} \frac{a^{-2n}}{} (-)^m a^{-2nm} z^{-2m}.$$

This double series converges absolutely when $|z| > 1$, and if it be rearranged in powers of z it converges uniformly.

Since the coefficient of z^{-1} is $\sum_{n=0}^{\infty} \frac{(-)^{k-1} a^{-2kn}}{n!}$ and the only term which furnishes a non-zero integral is the term in z^{-1}, we have

$$b_{2k} = \frac{1}{2\pi i} \int_C \sum_{n=0}^{\infty} \frac{(-)^{k-1} a^{-2kn}}{n!} \frac{dz}{z}$$

$$= \sum_{n=0}^{\infty} \frac{(-)^{k-1}}{n! \, a^{2kn}}$$

$$= (-)^{k-1} e^{\frac{1}{a^{2k}}}.$$

Therefore, when $|z| > 1$, the function can be expanded in the form

$$\frac{e^{\frac{1}{a^2}}}{z^2} - \frac{e^{\frac{1}{a^4}}}{z^4} + \frac{e^{\frac{1}{a^6}}}{z^6} - \dots$$

The function has a zero of the second order at infinity, since the expansion begins with a term in z^{-2}.

5·63.   LIOUVILLE'S THEOREM*.

Let $f(z)$ be analytic for all values of z and let $|f(z)| < K$ for all values of z, where K is a constant (so that $|f(z)|$ is bounded as $|z| \to \infty$). Then $f(z)$ is a constant.

Let z, z' be any two points and let C be a contour such that z, z' are inside it. Then, by § 5·21,

$$f(z') - f(z) = \frac{1}{2\pi i} \int_C \left\{ \frac{1}{\zeta - z'} - \frac{1}{\zeta - z} \right\} f(\zeta)\, d\zeta;$$

take C to be a circle whose centre is z and whose radius is $\rho \geqslant 2|z' - z|$; on C write $\zeta = z + \rho e^{i\theta}$; since $|\zeta - z'| \geqslant \frac{1}{2}\rho$ when ζ is on C it follows from § 4·62 that

$$\begin{aligned}
|f(z') - f(z)| &= \left| \frac{1}{2\pi} \int_C \frac{z' - z}{(\zeta - z')(\zeta - z)} f(\zeta)\, d\zeta \right| \\
&< \frac{1}{2\pi} \int_0^{2\pi} \frac{|z' - z| \cdot K}{\frac{1}{2}\rho}\, d\theta \\
&= 2|z' - z| K\rho^{-1}.
\end{aligned}$$

Make $\rho \to \infty$, keeping z and z' fixed; then it is obvious that $f(z') - f(z) = 0$; that is to say, $f(z)$ is constant.

As will be seen in the next article, and again frequently in the latter half of this volume (Chapters XX, XXI and XXII), Liouville's theorem furnishes short and convenient proofs of some of the most important results in Analysis.

5·64.   *Functions with no essential singularities.*

We shall now shew that *the only one-valued functions which have no singularities, except poles, at any point (including ∞) are rational functions.*

For let $f(z)$ be such a function; let its singularities in the finite part of the plane be at the points $c_1, c_2, \dots c_k$: and let the principal part (§ 5·61) of its expansion at the pole c_r be

$$\frac{a_{r,1}}{z - c_r} + \frac{a_{r,2}}{(z - c_r)^2} + \dots + \frac{a_{r,n_r}}{(z - c_r)^{n_r}}.$$

Let the principal part of its expansion at the pole at infinity be

$$a_1 z + a_2 z^2 + \dots + a_n z^n;$$

if there is not a pole at infinity, then all the coefficients in this expansion will be zero.

---

* This theorem, which is really due to Cauchy, *Comptes Rendus*, XIX. (1844), pp. 1377, 1378, was given this name by Borchardt, *Journal für Math.* LXXXVIII. (1880), pp. 277–310, who heard it in Liouville's lectures in 1847.

Now the function

$$f(z) - \sum_{r=1}^{k} \left\{ \frac{a_{r,1}}{z-c_r} + \frac{a_{r,2}}{(z-c_r)^2} + \ldots + \frac{a_{r,n_r}}{(z-c_r)^{n_r}} \right\} - a_1 z - a_2 z^2 - \ldots - a_n z^n$$

has clearly no singularities at the points c_1, c_2, ... c_k, or at infinity; it is therefore analytic everywhere and is bounded as $|z| \to \infty$, and so, by Liouville's Theorem, is a constant; that is,

$$f(z) = C + a_1 z + a_2 z^2 + \ldots + a_n z^n + \sum_{r=1}^{k} \left\{ \frac{a_{r,1}}{z-c_r} + \frac{a_{r,2}}{(z-c_r)^2} + \ldots + \frac{a_{r,n_r}}{(z-c_r)^{n_r}} \right\},$$

where C is constant; $f(z)$ is therefore a rational function, and the theorem is established.

It is evident from Liouville's theorem (combined with § 3·61 corollary (ii)) that a function which is analytic everywhere (including ∞) is merely a constant. Functions which are analytic everywhere *except at* ∞ are of considerable importance; they are known as *integral functions*[*]. Examples of such functions are e^z, $\sin z$, e^{e^z}. From § 5·4 it is apparent that there is no finite radius of convergence of a Taylor's series which represents an integral function; and from the result of this section it is evident that all integral functions (except mere polynomials) have essential singularities at ∞.

5·7. *Many-valued functions.*

In all the previous work, the functions under consideration have had a unique value (or limit) corresponding to each value (other than singularities) of z.

But functions may be defined which have more than one value for each value of z; thus if $z = r(\cos\theta + i\sin\theta)$, the function $z^{\frac{1}{2}}$ has the two values

$$r^{\frac{1}{2}}\left(\cos\frac{1}{2}\theta + i\sin\frac{1}{2}\theta\right), \quad r^{\frac{1}{2}}\left\{\cos\frac{1}{2}(\theta+2\pi) + i\sin\frac{1}{2}(\theta+2\pi)\right\};$$

and the function arc tan x (x real) has an unlimited number of values, viz. Arc tan $x + n\pi$, where $-\frac{1}{2}\pi < \text{Arc tan } x < \frac{1}{2}\pi$ and n is any integer; further examples of many-valued functions are $\log z$, $z^{-\frac{4}{3}}$, $\sin(z^{\frac{1}{2}})$.

Either of the two functions which $z^{\frac{1}{2}}$ represents is, however, analytic except at $z = 0$, and we can apply to them the theorems of this chapter; and the two functions are called '*branches* of the many-valued function $z^{\frac{1}{2}}$.' There will be certain points in general at which two or more branches coincide or at which one branch has an infinite limit; these points are called 'branch-points.' Thus $z^{\frac{1}{2}}$ has a branch-point at O; and, if we consider the change in $z^{\frac{1}{2}}$ as z describes a circle counter-clockwise round O, we see that θ

---

[*] French, *fonction entière*; German, *ganze Funktion*.

increases by 2π, r remains unchanged, and *either branch of the function passes over into the other branch.* This will be found to be a general characteristic of branch-points. It is not the purpose of this book to give a full discussion of the properties of many-valued functions, as we shall always have to consider particular branches of functions in regions not containing branch-points, so that there will be comparatively little difficulty in seeing whether or not Cauchy's Theorem may be applied.

Thus we cannot apply Cauchy's Theorem to such a function as $z^{\frac{3}{2}}$ when the path of integration is a circle surrounding the origin; but it is permissible to apply it to one of the branches of $z^{\frac{3}{2}}$ when the path of integration is like that shewn in § 6·24, for throughout the contour and its interior the function has a single definite value.

Example. Prove that if the different values of a^z, corresponding to a given value of z, are represented on an Argand diagram, the representative points will be the vertices of an equiangular polygon inscribed in an equiangular spiral, the angle of the spiral being independent of a.

(Math. Trip. 1899.)

The idea of the different *branches* of a function helps us to understand such a paradox as the following.

Consider the function
$$y = x^x,$$

for which
$$\frac{dy}{dx} = x^x (1 + \log x).$$

When x is negative and real, $\frac{dy}{dx}$ is not real. But if x is negative and of the form $\frac{p}{2q+1}$ (where p and q are positive or negative integers), y is real.

If therefore we draw the real curve
$$y = x^x,$$

we have for negative values of x a set of conjugate points, one point corresponding to each rational value of x with an odd denominator; and then we might think of proceeding to form the tangent as the limit of the chord, just as if the curve were continuous; and thus $\frac{dy}{dx}$, when derived from the inclination of the tangent to the axis of x, would appear to be real. The question thus arises, Why does the ordinary process of differentiation give a non-real value for $\frac{dy}{dx}$? The explanation is, that these conjugate points do not all arise from the same *branch* of the function $y = x^x$. We have in fact
$$y = e^{x \log x + 2k\pi i x},$$

where k is any integer. To each value of k corresponds one branch of the function y. Now in order to get a real value of y when x is negative, we have to choose a suitable value for k: and *this value of k varies as we go from one conjugate point to an adjacent one.* So the conjugate points do not represent values of y arising from the same branch of the function $y = x^x$, and consequently we cannot expect the value of $\frac{dy}{dx}$ when evaluated for a definite branch to be given by the tangent of the inclination to the axis of x of the line joining two arbitrarily close members of the series of conjugate points.

REFERENCES.

E. Goursat, *Cours d'Analyse*, II. (Paris, 1911), Chs. XIV and XVI.

J. Hadamard, *La Série de Taylor et son prolongement analytique* (Scientia, 1901).

E. Lindelöf, *Le Calcul des Résidus* (Paris, 1905).

C. J. de la Vallée Poussin, *Cours d'Analyse Infinitésimale*, I. (Paris and Louvain, 1914), Ch. X.

E. Borel, *Leçons sur les Fonctions Entières* (Paris, 1900).

G. N. Watson, *Complex Integration and Cauchy's Theorem* (Camb. Math. Tracts, no. 15, 1914).

MISCELLANEOUS EXAMPLES.

1. Obtain the expansion

$$f(z) = f(a) + 2\left\{ \frac{z-a}{2} f'\left(\frac{z+a}{2}\right) + \frac{(z-a)^3}{2^3 \cdot 3!} f'''\left(\frac{z+a}{2}\right) + \frac{(z-a)^5}{2^5 \cdot 5!} f^{(5)}\left(\frac{z+a}{2}\right) + \dots \right\},$$

and determine the circumstances and range of its validity.

2. Obtain, under suitable circumstances, the expansion

$$f(z) = f(a) + \frac{z-a}{m}\left[f'\left(a + \frac{z-a}{2m}\right) + f'\left\{a + \frac{3(z-a)}{2m}\right\} + \dots + f'\left\{a + \frac{(2m-1)(z-a)}{2m}\right\} \right]$$

$$+ \frac{2}{3!}\left(\frac{z-a}{2m}\right)^3 \left[f'''\left(a + \frac{z-a}{2m}\right) + f'''\left\{a + \frac{3(z-a)}{2m}\right\} + \dots + f'''\left\{a + \frac{(2m-1)(z-a)}{2m}\right\} \right]$$

$$+ \frac{2}{5!}\left(\frac{z-a}{2m}\right)^5 \left[f^{(5)}\left(a + \frac{z-a}{2m}\right) + f^{(5)}\left\{a + \frac{3(z-a)}{2m}\right\} + \dots + f^{(5)}\left\{a + \frac{(2m-1)(z-a)}{2m}\right\} \right]$$

$$+ \dots. \qquad \text{(Corey, *Ann. of Math.* (2), I. (1900), p. 77.)}$$

3. Shew that for the series

$$\sum_{n=0}^{\infty} \frac{1}{z^n + z^{-n}},$$

the region of convergence consists of two distinct areas, namely outside and inside a circle of radius unity, and that in each of these the series represents one function and represents it completely.

(Weierstrass, *Berliner Monatsberichte*, 1880, p. 731; *Ges. Werke*, II. (1895), p. 227.)

4. Shew that the function

$$\sum_{n=0}^{\infty} z^{n!}$$

tends to infinity as $z \to \exp(2\pi i p/m!)$ along the radius through the point; where m is any integer and p takes the values $0, 1, 2, \dots (m!-1)$.

Deduce that the function cannot be continued beyond the unit circle.

(Lerch, *Sitz. Böhm. Acad.*, 1885–6, pp. 571–582.)

5. Shew that, if $z^2 - 1$ is not a positive real number, then

$$(1-z^2)^{-\frac{1}{2}} = 1 + \frac{1}{2} z^2 + \frac{1 \cdot 3}{2 \cdot 4} z^4 + \dots + \frac{1 \cdot 3 \dots (2n-1)}{2 \cdot 4 \dots 2n} z^{2n}$$

$$+ \frac{3 \cdot 5 \dots (2n+1)}{2 \cdot 4 \dots (2n)} (1-z^2)^{-\frac{1}{2}} \int_0^z t^{2n+1} (1-t^2)^{-\frac{1}{2}} dt.$$

(Jacobi and Scheibner.)

6.   Shew that, if $z-1$ is not a positive real number, then

$$(1-z)^{-m} = 1 + \frac{m}{1}z + \frac{m(m+1)}{2!}z^2 + \ldots + \frac{m(m+1)\ldots(m+n-1)}{n!}z^n$$

$$+ \frac{m(m+1)\ldots(m+n)}{n!}(1-z)^{-m}\int_0^z t^n(1-t)^{m-1}\,dt.$$

(Jacobi and Scheibner.)

7.   Shew that, if z and $1-z$ are not negative real numbers, then

$$(1-z^2)^{-\frac{1}{2}}\int_0^z t^m(1-t^2)^{-\frac{1}{2}}\,dt = \frac{z^{m+1}}{m+1}\left\{1 + \frac{m+2}{m+3}z^2 + \ldots + \frac{(m+2)\ldots(m+2n-2)}{(m+3)\ldots(m+2n-1)}z^{2n-2}\right\}$$

$$+ (1-z^2)^{-\frac{1}{2}}\frac{(m+2)(m+4)\ldots(m+2n)}{(m+1)(m+3)\ldots(m+2n-1)}\int_0^z t^{m+2n}(1-t^2)^{-\frac{1}{2}}\,dt.$$

(Jacobi and Scheibner.)

8.   If, in the expansion of $(a+a_1z+a_2z^2)^m$ by the multinomial theorem, the remainder after n terms be denoted by $R_n(z)$, so that

$$(a+a_1z+a_2z^2)^m = A_0 + A_1z + A_2z^2 + \ldots + A_{n-1}z^{n-1} + R_n(z),$$

shew that

$$R_n(z) = (a+a_1z+a_2z^2)^m\int_0^z \frac{naA_nt^{n-1} + (2m-n+1)a_2A_{n-1}t^n}{(a+a_1t+a_2t^2)^{m+1}}\,dt.$$

(Scheibner.)

9.   If

$$(a_0+a_1z+a_2z^2)^{-m-1}\int_0^z (a_0+a_1t+a_2t^2)^m\,dt$$

be expanded in ascending powers of z in the form

$$A_1z + A_2z^2 + \ldots,$$

shew that the remainder after $n-1$ terms is

$$(a_0+a_1z+a_2z^2)^{-m-1}\int_0^z (a_0+a_1t+a_2t^2)^m\{na_0A_n - (2m+n+1)a_2A_{n-1}t\}\,t^{n-1}\,dt.$$

(Scheibner*.)

10.   Shew that the series

$$\sum_{n=0}^\infty \{1+\lambda_n(z)e^z\}\frac{d^n\phi(z)}{dz^n},$$

where

$$\lambda_n(z) = -1 + z - \frac{z^2}{2!} + \frac{z^3}{3!} - \ldots + (-)^n\frac{z^n}{n!},$$

and where $\phi(z)$ is analytic near $z=0$, is convergent near the point $z=0$; and shew that if the sum of the series be denoted by $f(z)$, then $f(z)$ satisfies the differential equation

$$f'(z) = f(z) - \phi(z).$$

(Pincherle, *Rend. dei Lincei* (5), v. (1896), p. 27.)

11.   Shew that the arithmetic mean of the squares of the moduli of all the values of the series $\sum_{n=0}^\infty a_nz^n$ on a circle $|z|=r$, situated within its circle of convergence, is equal to the sum of the squares of the moduli of the separate terms.

(Gutzmer, *Math. Ann.* XXXII. (1888), pp. 596–600.)

* The results of examples 5, 6 and 7 are special cases of formulae contained in Jacobi's dissertation (Berlin, 1825) published in his *Ges. Werke*, III. (1884), pp. 1–44. Jacobi's formulae were generalised by Scheibner, *Leipziger Berichte*, XLV. (1893), pp. 432–443.

12.   Shew that the series

$$\sum_{m=1}^{\infty} e^{-2(am)^{\frac{1}{2}}} z^{m-1}$$

converges when $|z|<1$; and that, when $a>0$, the function which it represents can also be represented when $|z|<1$ by the integral

$$\left(\frac{a}{\pi}\right)^{\frac{1}{2}} \int_0^\infty \frac{e^{-a/x}}{e^x - z} \frac{dx}{x^{\frac{3}{2}}},$$

and that it has no singularities except at the point $z=1$.

(Lerch, *Monatshefte für Math. und Phys.* VIII.)

13.   Shew that the series

$$\frac{2}{\pi}(z+z^{-1}) + \frac{2}{\pi} \Sigma \left\{ \frac{z}{(1-2\nu - 2\nu'zi)(2\nu + 2\nu'zi)^2} + \frac{z^{-1}}{(1-2\nu - 2\nu'z^{-1} i)(2\nu + 2\nu'z^{-1}i)^2} \right\},$$

in which the summation extends over all integral values of ν, ν', except the combination $(\nu=0, \nu'=0)$, converges absolutely for all values of z except purely imaginary values; and that its sum is $+1$ or -1, according as the real part of z is positive or negative.

(Weierstrass, *Berliner Monatsberichte*, 1880, p. 735.)

14.   Shew that $\sin\left\{u\left(z+\frac{1}{z}\right)\right\}$ can be expanded in a series of the type

$$a_0 + a_1 z + a_2 z^2 + \dots + \frac{b_1}{z} + \frac{b_2}{z^2} + \dots,$$

in which the coefficients, both of z^n and of z^{-n}, are

$$\frac{1}{2\pi} \int_0^{2\pi} \sin(2u \cos\theta) \cos n\theta \, d\theta.$$

15.   If

$$f(z) = \sum_{n=1}^{\infty} \frac{z^2}{n^2 z^2 + a^2},$$

shew that $f(z)$ is finite and continuous for all real values of z, but cannot be expanded as a Maclaurin's series in ascending powers of z; and explain this apparent anomaly.

[For other cases of failure of Maclaurin's theorem, see a posthumous memoir by Cellérier, *Bull. des Sci. Math.* (2), XIV. (1890), pp. 145–599; Lerch, *Journal für Math.* CIII. (1888), pp. 126–138; Pringsheim, *Math. Ann.* XLII. (1893), pp. 153–184; and Du Bois Reymond, *Münchener Sitzungsberichte*, VI. (1876), p. 235.]

16.   If $f(z)$ be a *continuous* one-valued function of z throughout a two-dimensional region, and if

$$\int_C f(z)\, dz = 0$$

for all closed contours C lying inside the region, then $f(z)$ is an analytic function of z throughout the interior of the region.

[Let a be any point of the region and let

$$F(z) = \int_a^z f(z)\, dz.$$

It follows from the data that $F(z)$ has the unique derivate $f(z)$. Hence $F(z)$ is analytic (§ 5·1) and so (§ 5·22) its derivate $f(z)$ is also analytic. This important converse of Cauchy's theorem is due to Morera, *Rendiconti del R. Ist. Lombardo (Milano)*, XXII. (1889), p. 191.]

CHAPTER VI

THE THEORY OF RESIDUES; APPLICATION TO THE EVALUATION OF DEFINITE INTEGRALS

6·1. *Residues.*

If the function $f(z)$ has a pole of order m at $z = a$, then, by the definition of a pole, an equation of the form

$$f(z) = \frac{a_{-m}}{(z-a)^m} + \frac{a_{-m+1}}{(z-a)^{m-1}} + \ldots + \frac{a_{-1}}{z-a} + \phi(z),$$

where $\phi(z)$ is analytic near and at a, is true near a.

The coefficient a_{-1} in this expansion is called the *residue* of the function $f(z)$ relative to the pole a.

Consider now the value of the integral $\int_a f(z) \, dz$, where the path of integration is a circle* α, whose centre is the point a and whose radius ρ is so small that $\phi(z)$ is analytic inside and on the circle.

We have
$$\int_a f(z) \, dz = \sum_{r=1}^{m} a_{-r} \int_a \frac{dz}{(z-a)^r} + \int_a \phi(z) \, dz.$$

Now $\int_a \phi(z) \, dz = 0$ by § 5·2; and (putting $z - a = \rho e^{i\theta}$) we have, if $r \neq 1$,

$$\int_a \frac{dz}{(z-a)^r} = \int_0^{2\pi} \frac{\rho e^{i\theta} i \, d\theta}{\rho^r e^{ri\theta}} = \rho^{-r+1} \int_0^{2\pi} e^{(1-r)\,i\theta}\, i \, d\theta = \rho^{-r+1} \left[\frac{e^{(1-r)\,i\theta}}{1-r} \right]_0^{2\pi} = 0.$$

But, when $r = 1$, we have

$$\int_a \frac{dz}{z-a} = \int_0^{2\pi} i \, d\theta = 2\pi i.$$

Hence finally
$$\int_a f(z) \, dz = 2\pi i a_{-1}.$$

Now let C be any contour, containing in the region interior to it a number of poles $a, b, c, \ldots$ of a function $f(z)$, with residues $a_{-1}, b_{-1}, c_{-1}, \ldots$ respectively: and suppose that the function $f(z)$ is analytic throughout C and its interior, except at these poles.

Surround the points $a, b, c, \ldots$ by circles $\alpha, \beta, \gamma, \ldots$ so small that their respective centres are the only singularities inside or on each circle; then the function $f(z)$ is analytic in the closed region bounded by $C, \alpha, \beta, \gamma, \ldots.$

---

* The existence of such a circle is implied in the definition of a pole as an isolated singularity.

Hence, by § 5·2 corollary 3,

$$\int_C f(z)\,dz = \int_\alpha f(z)\,dz + \int_\beta f(z)\,dz + \dots$$

$$= 2\pi i a_{-1} + 2\pi i b_{-1} + \dots.$$

Thus we have the *theorem of residues*, namely that *if $f(z)$ be analytic throughout a contour C and its interior except at a number of poles inside the contour, then*

$$\int_C f(z)\,dz = 2\pi i \Sigma R,$$

where ΣR denotes the sum of the residues of the function $f(z)$ at those of its poles which are situated within the contour C.

This is an extension of the theorem of § 5·21.

NOTE. If a is a *simple* pole of $f(z)$ the residue of $f(z)$ at that pole is $\lim\limits_{z\to a}\{(z-a)f(z)\}$.

6·2. *The evaluation of definite integrals.*

We shall now apply the result of § 6·1 to evaluating various classes of definite integrals; the methods to be employed in any particular case may usually be seen from the following typical examples.

6·21. *The evaluation of the integrals of certain periodic functions taken between the limits 0 and 2π.*

An integral of the type

$$\int_0^{2\pi} R(\cos\theta,\sin\theta)\,d\theta,$$

where the integrand is a rational function of $\cos\theta$ and $\sin\theta$ finite on the range of integration, can be evaluated by writing $e^{i\theta} = z$; since

$$\cos\theta = \tfrac{1}{2}(z+z^{-1}), \quad \sin\theta = \frac{1}{2i}(z-z^{-1}),$$

the integral takes the form $\int_C S(z)\,dz$, where $S(z)$ is a rational function of z finite on the path of integration C, the circle of radius unity whose centre is the origin.

Therefore, by § 6·1, *the integral is equal to $2\pi i$ times the sum of the residues of $S(z)$ at those of its poles which are inside that circle.*

Example 1. If $0 < p < 1$,

$$\int_0^{2\pi} \frac{d\theta}{1-2p\cos\theta + p^2} = \int_C \frac{dz}{i(1-pz)(z-p)}.$$

The only pole of the integrand inside the circle is a simple pole at p; and the residue there is

$$\lim_{z\to p} \frac{z-p}{i(1-pz)(z-p)} = \frac{1}{i(1-p^2)}.$$

Hence
$$\int_0^{2\pi} \frac{d\theta}{1-2p\cos\theta+p^2} = \frac{2\pi}{1-p^2}.$$

Example 2. If $0 < p < 1$,
$$\int_0^{2\pi} \frac{\cos^2 3\theta}{1-2p\cos 2\theta+p^2}\, d\theta = \int_C \frac{dz}{iz}\left(\frac{1}{2}z^3+\frac{1}{2}z^{-3}\right)^2 \frac{1}{(1-pz^2)(1-pz^{-2})}$$
$$= 2\pi\Sigma R,$$

where ΣR denotes the sum of the residues of $\dfrac{(z^6+1)^2}{4z^5(1-pz^2)(z^2-p)}$ at its poles inside C; these

poles are 0, $-p^{\frac{1}{2}}$, $p^{\frac{1}{2}}$; and the residues at them are $-\dfrac{1+p^2+p^4}{4p^3}$, $\dfrac{(p^3+1)^2}{8p^3(1-p^2)}$, $\dfrac{(p^3+1)^2}{8p^3(1-p^2)}$;

and hence the integral is equal to
$$\frac{\pi(1-p+p^2)}{1-p}.$$

Example 3. If n be a positive integer,
$$\int_0^{2\pi} e^{\cos\theta} \cos(n\theta-\sin\theta)\, d\theta = \frac{2\pi}{n!}, \qquad \int_0^{2\pi} e^{\cos\theta}\sin(n\theta-\sin\theta)\, d\theta = 0.$$

Example 4. If $a > b > 0$,
$$\int_0^{2\pi} \frac{d\theta}{(a+b\cos\theta)^2} = \frac{2\pi a}{(a^2-b^2)^{\frac{3}{2}}}, \qquad \int_0^{2\pi} \frac{d\theta}{(a+b\cos^2\theta)^2} = \frac{\pi(2a+b)}{a^{\frac{3}{2}}(a+b)^{\frac{3}{2}}}.$$

6·22. *The evaluation of certain types of integrals taken between the limits $-\infty$ and $+\infty$.*

We shall now evaluate $\displaystyle\int_{-\infty}^{\infty} Q(x)\, dx$, where $Q(z)$ is a function such that (i) it is analytic when the imaginary part of z is positive or zero (except at a finite number of poles), (ii) it has no poles on the real axis and (iii) as $|z|\to\infty$, $zQ(z)\to 0$ uniformly for all values of $\arg z$ such that $0\leqslant\arg z\leqslant\pi$; provided that (iv) when x is real, $xQ(x)\to 0$, as $x\to\pm\infty$, in such a way* that $\displaystyle\int_0^{\infty} Q(x)\, dx$ and $\displaystyle\int_{-\infty}^0 Q(x)\, dx$ both converge.

Given ϵ, we can choose ρ_0 (independent of $\arg z$) such that $|zQ(z)| < \epsilon/\pi$ whenever $|z| > \rho_0$ and $0\leqslant\arg z\leqslant\pi$.

Consider $\displaystyle\int_C Q(z)\, dz$ taken round a contour C consisting of the part of the real axis joining the points $\pm\rho$ (where $\rho > \rho_0$) and a semicircle Γ, of radius ρ, having its centre at the origin, above the real axis.

Then, by § 6·1, $\displaystyle\int_C Q(z)\, dz = 2\pi i\Sigma R$, where ΣR denotes the sum of the residues of $Q(z)$ at its poles above the real axis†.

---

* The condition $xQ(x)\to 0$ is not in itself sufficient to secure the convergence of $\displaystyle\int_0^{\infty} Q(x)\, dx$; consider $Q(x) = (x\log x)^{-1}$.

† $Q(z)$ has no poles above the real axis outside the contour.

Therefore
$$\left| \int_{-\rho}^{\rho} Q(z)\,dz - 2\pi i \Sigma R \right| = \left| \int_{\Gamma} Q(z)\,dz \right|.$$

In the last integral write $z = \rho e^{i\theta}$, and then

$$\left| \int_{\Gamma} Q(z)\,dz \right| = \left| \int_{0}^{\pi} Q(\rho e^{i\theta})\, \rho e^{i\theta} i\, d\theta \right|$$

$$< \int_{0}^{\pi} (\epsilon/\pi)\, d\theta$$

$$= \epsilon,$$

by § 4·62.

Hence
$$\lim_{\rho \to \infty} \int_{-\rho}^{\rho} Q(z)\,dz = 2\pi i \Sigma R.$$

But the meaning of $\displaystyle\int_{-\infty}^{\infty} Q(x)\,dx$ is $\displaystyle\lim_{\rho,\,\sigma \to \infty} \int_{-\rho}^{\sigma} Q(x)\,dx$; and since $\displaystyle\lim_{\sigma \to \infty} \int_{0}^{\sigma} Q(x)\,dx$ and $\displaystyle\lim_{\rho \to \infty} \int_{-\rho}^{0} Q(x)\,dx$ both exist, this double limit is the same as $\displaystyle\lim_{\rho \to \infty} \int_{-\rho}^{\rho} Q(x)\,dx$.

Hence we have proved that
$$\int_{-\infty}^{\infty} Q(x)\,dx = 2\pi i \Sigma R.$$

This theorem is particularly useful in the special case when $Q(x)$ is a rational function.

[Note.　Even if condition (iv) is not satisfied, we still have
$$\int_{0}^{\infty} \{Q(x) + Q(-x)\}\,dx = \lim_{\rho \to \infty} \int_{-\rho}^{\rho} Q(x)\,dx = 2\pi i \Sigma R.]$$

Example 1.　The only pole of $(z^2+1)^{-3}$ in the upper half plane is a pole at $z = i$ with residue there $-\dfrac{3}{16}i$.　Therefore
$$\int_{-\infty}^{\infty} \frac{dx}{(x^2+1)^3} = \frac{3}{8}\pi.$$

Example 2.　If $a > 0$, $b > 0$, shew that.
$$\int_{-\infty}^{\infty} \frac{x^4\, dx}{(a+bx^2)^4} = \frac{\pi}{16 a^{\frac{3}{2}} b^{\frac{5}{2}}}.$$

Example 3.　By integrating $\int e^{-\lambda z^2}\,dz$ round a parallelogram whose corners are $-R,\ R,\ R+ai,\ -R+ai$ and making $R \to \infty$, shew that, if $\lambda > 0$, then
$$\int_{-\infty}^{\infty} e^{-\lambda x^2} \cos(2\lambda a x)\,dx = e^{-\lambda a^2} \int_{-\infty}^{\infty} e^{-\lambda x^2}\,dx = 2\lambda^{-\frac{1}{2}} e^{-\lambda a^2} \int_{0}^{\infty} e^{-x^2}\,dx.$$

6·221.　*Certain infinite integrals involving sines and cosines.*

If $Q(z)$ satisfies the conditions (i), (ii) and (iii) of § 6·22, and $m > 0$, then $Q(z)\, e^{miz}$ also·satisfies those conditions.

Hence $\int_0^\infty \{Q(x)\,e^{mix} + Q(-x)\,e^{-mix}\}\,dx$ is equal to $2\pi i \Sigma R'$, where $\Sigma R'$ means the sum of the residues of $Q(z)\,e^{miz}$ at its poles in the upper half plane; and so

(i)   If $Q(x)$ is an even function, i.e. if $Q(-x) = Q(x)$,

$$\int_0^\infty Q(x) \cos(mx)\,dx = \pi i \Sigma R'.$$

(ii)   If $Q(x)$ is an odd function,

$$\int_0^\infty Q(x) \sin(mx)\,dx = \pi \Sigma R'.$$

6·222.   *Jordan's lemma*.

The results of § 6·221 are true if $Q(z)$ be subject to the less stringent condition $Q(z) \to 0$ uniformly when $0 \leqslant \arg z \leqslant \pi$ as $|z| \to \infty$ in place of the condition $zQ(z) \to 0$ uniformly.

To prove this we require a theorem known as Jordan's lemma, viz.

If $Q(z) \to 0$ uniformly with regard to $\arg z$ as $|z| \to \infty$ when $0 \leqslant \arg z \leqslant \pi$, and if $Q(z)$ is analytic when both $|z| > c$ (a constant) and $0 \leqslant \arg z \leqslant \pi$, then

$$\lim_{\rho \to \infty} \left(\int_\Gamma e^{miz} Q(z)\,dz \right) = 0,$$

where Γ is a semicircle of radius ρ above the real axis with centre at the origin.

Given ϵ, choose ρ_0 so that $|Q(z)| < \epsilon/\pi$ when $|z| > \rho_0$ and $0 \leqslant \arg z \leqslant \pi$; then, if $\rho > \rho_0$,

$$\left| \int_\Gamma e^{miz} Q(z)\,dz \right| = \left| \int_0^\pi e^{mi(\rho\cos\theta + i\rho\sin\theta)} Q(\rho e^{i\theta}) \rho e^{i\theta} i\,d\theta \right|.$$

But $|e^{mi\rho\cos\theta}| = 1$, and so

$$\left| \int_\Gamma e^{miz} Q(z)\,dz \right| < \int_0^\pi (\epsilon/\pi) \rho e^{-m\rho\sin\theta}\,d\theta$$

$$= (2\epsilon/\pi) \int_0^{\frac{1}{2}\pi} \rho e^{-m\rho\sin\theta}\,d\theta.$$

Now $\sin\theta \geqslant 2\theta/\pi$, when† $0 \leqslant \theta \leqslant \tfrac{1}{2}\pi$, and so

$$\left| \int_\Gamma e^{miz} Q(z)\,dz \right| < (2\epsilon/\pi) \int_0^{\frac{1}{2}\pi} \rho e^{-2m\rho\theta/\pi}\,d\theta$$

$$= (2\epsilon/\pi).(\pi/2m) \left[-e^{-2m\rho\theta/\pi} \right]_0^{\frac{1}{2}\pi}$$

$$< \epsilon/m.$$

---

* Jordan, *Cours d'Analyse*, ii. (1894), pp. 285, 286.

† This inequality appears obvious when we draw the graphs $y = \sin x$, $y = 2x/\pi$; it may be proved by shewing that $(\sin\theta)/\theta$ decreases as θ increases from 0 to $\tfrac{1}{2}\pi$.

Hence
$$\lim_{\rho \to \infty} \int_\Gamma e^{miz} Q(z)\, dz = 0.$$

This result is Jordan's lemma.

Now
$$\int_0^\rho \{e^{mix} Q(x) + e^{-mix} Q(-x)\}\, dx = 2\pi i \Sigma R' - \int_\Gamma e^{miz} Q(z)\, dz,$$

and, making $\rho \to \infty$, we see at once that
$$\int_0^\infty \{e^{mix} Q(x) + e^{-mix} Q(-x)\}\, dx = 2\pi i \Sigma R',$$

which is the result corresponding to the result of § 6·221.

Example 1. Shew that, if $a > 0$, then
$$\int_0^\infty \frac{\cos x}{x^2 + a^2}\, dx = \frac{\pi}{2a} e^{-a}.$$

Example 2. Shew that, if $a \geqslant 0$, $b \geqslant 0$, then
$$\int_0^\infty \frac{\cos 2ax - \cos 2bx}{x^2}\, dx = \pi (b - a).$$

(Take a contour consisting of a large semicircle of radius ρ, a small semicircle of radius δ, both having their centres at the origin, and the parts of the real axis joining their ends ; then make $\rho \to \infty$, $\delta \to 0$.)

Example 3. Shew that, if $b > 0$, $m \geqslant 0$, then
$$\int_0^\infty \frac{3x^2 - a^2}{(x^2 + b^2)^2} \cos mx\, dx = \frac{\pi e^{-mb}}{4b^3} \{3b^2 - a^2 - mb\,(3b^2 + a^2)\}.$$

Example 4. Shew that, if $k > 0$, $a > 0$, then
$$\int_0^\infty \frac{x \sin ax}{x^2 + k^2}\, dx = \tfrac{1}{2} \pi e^{-ka}.$$

Example 5. Shew that, if $m \geqslant 0$, $a > 0$, then
$$\int_0^\infty \frac{\sin mx}{x\,(x^2 + a^2)^2}\, dx = \frac{\pi}{2a^4} - \frac{\pi e^{-ma}}{4a^3}\left(m + \frac{2}{a}\right).$$

(Take the contour of example 2.)

Example 6. Shew that, if the real part of z be positive,
$$\int_0^\infty (e^{-t} - e^{-tz}) \frac{dt}{t} = \log z.$$

[We have
$$\int_0^\infty (e^{-t} - e^{-tz}) \frac{dt}{t} = \lim_{\delta \to 0,\, \rho \to \infty} \left\{ \int_\delta^\rho \frac{e^{-t}}{t}\, dt - \int_\delta^\rho \frac{e^{-tz}}{t}\, dt \right\}$$
$$= \lim_{\delta \to 0,\, \rho \to \infty} \left\{ \int_\delta^\rho \frac{e^{-t}}{t}\, dt - \int_{\delta z}^{\rho z} \frac{e^{-u}}{u}\, du \right\}$$
$$= \lim_{\delta \to 0,\, \rho \to \infty} \left\{ \int_\delta^{\delta z} \frac{e^{-t}}{t}\, dt - \int_\rho^{\rho z} \frac{e^{-t}}{t}\, dt \right\},$$

since $t^{-1} e^{-t}$ is analytic inside the quadrilateral whose corners are δ, δz, ρz, ρ.

Now $\int_\rho^{\rho z} t^{-1} e^{-t}\, dt \to 0$ as $\rho \to \infty$ when $R(z) > 0$; and

$$\int_\delta^{\delta z} t^{-1} e^{-t}\, dt = \log z - \int_\delta^{\delta z} t^{-1}(1 - e^{-t})\, dt \to \log z,$$

since $\qquad\qquad\qquad t^{-1}(1 - e^{-t}) \to 1$ as $t \to 0.$]

6·23. *Principal values of integrals.*

It was assumed in §§ 6·22, 6·221, 6·222 that the function $Q(x)$ had no poles on the real axis; if the function has a finite number of *simple* poles on the real axis, we can obtain theorems corresponding to those already obtained, except that the integrals are all principal values (§ 4·5) and ΣR has to be replaced by $\Sigma R + \frac{1}{2}\Sigma R_0$, where ΣR_0 means the sum of the residues at the poles on the real axis. To obtain this result we see that, instead of the former contour, we have to take as contour a circle of radius ρ and the portions of the real axis joining the points

$$-\rho,\ a - \delta_1;\quad a + \delta_1,\ b - \delta_2;\quad b + \delta_2,\ c - \delta_3, \dots$$

and small semicircles above the real axis of radii $\delta_1, \delta_2, \dots$ with centres $a, b, c, \dots$, where $a, b, c, \dots$ are the poles of $Q(z)$ on the real axis; and then we have to make $\delta_1, \delta_2, \dots \to 0$; call these semicircles $\gamma_1, \gamma_2, \dots$. Then instead of the equation

$$\int_{-\rho}^{\rho} Q(z)\, dz + \int_\Gamma Q(z)\, dz = 2\pi i \Sigma R,$$

we get $\qquad P \int_{-\rho}^{\rho} Q(z)\, dz + \Sigma \lim_{n\ \delta_n \to 0} \int_{\gamma_n} Q(z)\, dz + \int_\Gamma Q(z)\, dz = 2\pi i \Sigma R.$

Let a' be the residue of $Q(z)$ at a; then writing $z = a + \delta_1 e^{i\theta}$ on γ_1 we get

$$\int_{\gamma_r} Q(z)\, dz = \int_\pi^0 Q(a + \delta_1 e^{i\theta}) \delta_1 e^{i\theta} i\, d\theta.$$

But $Q(a + \delta_1 e^{i\theta}) \delta_1 e^{i\theta} \to a'$ uniformly as $\delta_1 \to 0$; and therefore $\lim\limits_{\delta_1 \to 0} \int_{\gamma_1} Q(z)\, dz = -\pi i a'$; we thus get

$$P \int_{-\rho}^{\rho} Q(z)\, dz + \int_\Gamma Q(z)\, dz = 2\pi i \Sigma R + \pi i \Sigma R_0,$$

and hence, using the arguments of § 6·22, we get

$$P \int_{-\infty}^{\infty} Q(x)\, dx = 2\pi i\, (\Sigma R + \tfrac{1}{2}\Sigma R_0).$$

The reader will see at once that the theorems of §§ 6·221, 6·222 have precisely similar generalisations.

The process employed above of inserting arcs of small circles so as to diminish the area of the contour is called *indenting* the contour.

6·24. *Evaluation of integrals of the form* $\int_0^\infty x^{a-1} Q(x)\, dx.$

Let $Q(x)$ be a rational function of x such that it has no poles on the positive part of the real axis and $x^a Q(x) \to 0$ both when $x \to 0$ and when $x \to \infty$.

Consider $\int (-z)^{a-1} Q(z)\, dz$ taken round the contour C shewn in the figure, consisting of the arcs of circles of radii ρ, δ and the straight lines joining their end points; $(-z)^{a-1}$ is to be interpreted as

$$\exp\{(a-1)\log(-z)\}$$

and

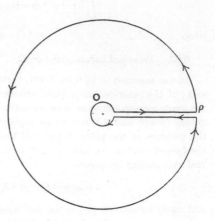

$$\log(-z) = \log|z| + i\arg(-z),$$

where $-\pi \leqslant \arg(-z) \leqslant \pi$;

with these conventions the integrand is one-valued and analytic on and within the contour save at the poles of $Q(z)$.

Hence, if Σr denote the sum of the residues of $(-z)^{a-1} Q(z)$ at all its poles,

$$\int_C (-z)^{a-1} Q(z)\, dz = 2\pi i \Sigma r.$$

On the small circle write $-z = \delta e^{i\theta}$, and the integral along it becomes $-\int_\pi^{-\pi} (-z)^a Q(z)\, i\, d\theta$, which tends to zero as $\delta \to 0$.

On the large semicircle write $-z = \rho e^{i\theta}$, and the integral along it becomes $-\int_{-\pi}^{\pi} (-z)^a Q(z)\, i\, d\theta$, which tends to zero as $\rho \to \infty$.

On one of the lines we write $-z = xe^{\pi i}$, on the other $-z = xe^{-\pi i}$ and $(-z)^{a-1}$ becomes $x^{a-1} e^{\pm(a-1)\pi i}$.

Hence

$$\lim_{(\delta \to 0,\, \rho \to \infty)} \int_\delta^\rho \{x^{a-1} e^{-(a-1)\pi i} Q(x) - x^{a-1} e^{(a-1)\pi i} Q(x)\}\, dx = 2\pi i \Sigma r\,;$$

and therefore $\int_0^\infty x^{a-1} Q(x)\, dx = \pi \operatorname{cosec}(a\pi)\, \Sigma r.$

Corollary. If $Q(x)$ have a number of simple poles on the positive part of the real axis, it may be shewn by indenting the contour that

$$P \int_0^\infty x^{a-1} Q(x)\, dx = \pi \operatorname{cosec}(a\pi)\, \Sigma r - \pi \cot(a\pi)\, \Sigma r',$$

where $\Sigma r'$ is the sum of the residues of $z^{a-1} Q(z)$ at these poles.

Example 1. If $0 < a < 1$,

$$\int_0^\infty \frac{x^{a-1}}{1+x}\, dx = \pi \operatorname{cosec} a\pi, \qquad P \int_0^\infty \frac{x^{a-1}}{1-x}\, dx = \pi \cot a\pi.$$

Example 2.   If $0 < z < 1$ and $-\pi < a < \pi$,

$$\int_0^\infty \frac{t^{z-1}}{t + e^{ia}} dt = \frac{\pi e^{i(z-1)a}}{\sin \pi z}.$$ (Minding.)

Example 3.   Shew that, if $-1 < z < 3$, then

$$\int_0^\infty \frac{x^z}{(1+x^2)^2} dx = \frac{\pi(1-z)}{4 \cos \frac{1}{2}\pi z}.$$

Example 4.   Shew that, if $-1 < p < 1$ and $-\pi < \lambda < \pi$, then

$$\int_0^\infty \frac{x^{-p}\, dx}{1 + 2x \cos \lambda + x^2} = \frac{\pi}{\sin p\pi} \frac{\sin p\lambda}{\sin \lambda}.$$ (Euler.)

6·3.   *Cauchy's integral.*

We shall next discuss a class of contour-integrals which are sometimes found useful in analytical investigations.

Let C be a contour in the z-plane, and let $f(z)$ be a function analytic inside and on C. Let $\phi(z)$ be another function which is analytic inside and on C except at a finite number of poles; let the zeros of $\phi(z)$ in the interior* of C be $a_1, a_2, \ldots$, and let their degrees of multiplicity be $r_1, r_2, \ldots$; and let its poles in the interior of C be $b_1, b_2, \ldots$, and let their degrees of multiplicity be $s_1, s_2, \ldots$.

Then, by the fundamental theorem of residues, $\dfrac{1}{2\pi i} \displaystyle\int_C f(z) \dfrac{\phi'(z)}{\phi(z)} dz$ is equal to the sum of the residues of $\dfrac{f(z)\,\phi'(z)}{\phi(z)}$ at its poles inside C.

Now $\dfrac{f(z)\,\phi'(z)}{\phi(z)}$ can have singularities only at the poles and zeros of $\phi(z)$. Near one of the zeros, say a_1, we have

$$\phi(z) = A(z-a_1)^{r_1} + B(z-a_1)^{r_1+1} + \ldots.$$

Therefore

$$\phi'(z) = Ar_1(z-a_1)^{r_1-1} + B(r_1+1)(z-a_1)^{r_1} + \ldots,$$

and

$$f(z) = f(a_1) + (z-a_1)f'(a_1) + \ldots.$$

Therefore $\left\{ \dfrac{f(z)\,\phi'(z)}{\phi(z)} - \dfrac{r_1 f(a_1)}{z-a_1} \right\}$ is analytic at a_1.

Thus the residue of $\dfrac{f(z)\,\phi'(z)}{\phi(z)}$, at the point $z = a_1$, is $r_1 f(a_1)$.

Similarly the residue at $z = b_1$ is $-s_1 f(b_1)$; for near $z = b_1$, we have

$$\phi(z) = C(z-b_1)^{-s_1} + D(z-b_1)^{-s_1+1} + \ldots,$$

and

$$f(z) = f(b_1) + (z-b_1)\overline{f'}(b_1) + \ldots,$$

so $\dfrac{f(z)\,\phi'(z)}{\phi(z)} + \dfrac{s_1 f(b_1)}{z-b_1}$ is analytic at b_1.

Hence

$$\frac{1}{2\pi i}\int_C f(z)\frac{\phi'(z)}{\phi(z)} dz = \Sigma r_1 f(a_1) - \Sigma s_1 f(b_1),$$

the summations being extended over all the zeros and poles of $\phi(z)$.

6·31.   *The number of roots of an equation contained within a contour.*

The result of the preceding paragraph can be at once applied to find how many roots of an equation $\phi(z) = 0$ lie within a contour C.

For, on putting $f(z) = 1$ in the preceding result, we obtain the result that

$$\frac{1}{2\pi i}\int_C \frac{\phi'(z)}{\phi(z)} dz$$

is equal to the excess of the number of zeros over the number of poles of $\phi(z)$ contained in the interior of C, each pole and zero being reckoned according to its degree of multiplicity.

* $\phi(z)$ must not have any zeros or poles on C.

Example 1. Shew that a polynomial $\phi(z)$ of degree m has m roots.

Let

$$\phi(z) = a_0 z^m + a_1 z^{m-1} + \ldots + a_m, \quad (a_0 \neq 0).$$

Then

$$\frac{\phi'(z)}{\phi(z)} = \frac{m a_0 z^{m-1} + \ldots + a_{m-1}}{a_0 z^m + \ldots + a_m}.$$

Consequently, for large values of $|z|$,

$$\frac{\phi'(z)}{\phi(z)} = \frac{m}{z} + O\left(\frac{1}{z^2}\right).$$

Thus, if C be a circle of radius ρ whose centre is at the origin, we have

$$\frac{1}{2\pi i} \int_C \frac{\phi'(z)}{\phi(z)} dz = \frac{m}{2\pi i} \int_C \frac{dz}{z} + \frac{1}{2\pi i} \int_C O\left(\frac{1}{z^2}\right) dz = m + \frac{1}{2\pi i} \int_C O\left(\frac{1}{z^2}\right) dz.$$

But, as in § 6·22,

$$\int_C O\left(\frac{1}{z^2}\right) dz \to 0$$

as $\rho \to \infty$; and hence as $\phi(z)$ has no poles in the interior of C, the total number of zeros of $\phi(z)$ is

$$\lim_{\rho \to \infty} \frac{1}{2\pi i} \int_C \frac{\phi'(z)}{\phi(z)} dz = m.$$

Example 2. If at all points of a contour C the inequality

$$|a_k z^k| > |a_0 + a_1 z + \ldots + a_{k-1} z^{k-1} + a_{k+1} z^{k+1} + \ldots + a_m z^m|$$

is satisfied, then the contour contains k roots of the equation

$$a_m z^m + a_{m-1} z^{m-1} + \ldots + a_1 z + a_0 = 0.$$

For write

$$f(z) = a_m z^m + a_{m-1} z^{m-1} + \ldots + a_1 z + a_0.$$

Then

$$f(z) = a_k z^k \left(1 + \frac{a_m z^m + \ldots + a_{k+1} z^{k+1} + a_{k-1} z^{k-1} + \ldots + a_0}{a_k z^k}\right)$$

$$= a_k z^k (1 + U),$$

where $|U| \leqslant a < 1$ on the contour, a being independent* of z.

Therefore the number of roots of $f(z)$ contained in C

$$= \frac{1}{2\pi i} \int_C \frac{f'(z)}{f(z)} dz = \frac{1}{2\pi i} \int_C \left(\frac{k}{z} + \frac{1}{1+U}\frac{dU}{dz}\right) dz.$$

But $\int_C \frac{dz}{z} = 2\pi i$; and, since $|U| < 1$, we can expand $(1+U)^{-1}$ in the uniformly convergent series

$$1 - U + U^2 - U^3 + \ldots,$$

so

$$\int_C \frac{1}{1+U}\frac{dU}{dz} dz = [U - \tfrac{1}{2}U^2 + \tfrac{1}{3}U^3 - \ldots]_C = 0.$$

Therefore the number of roots contained in C is equal to k.

Example 3. Find how many roots of the equation

$$z^6 + 6z + 10 = 0$$

lie in each quadrant of the Argand diagram. (Clare, 1900.)

---

* $|U|$ is a continuous function of z on C, and so *attains* its upper bound (§ 3·62). Hence its upper bound a must be less than 1.

6·4. *Connexion between the zeros of a function and the zeros of its derivate.*

Macdonald * has shewn that *if $f(z)$ be a function of z analytic throughout the interior of a single closed contour C, defined by the equation $|f(z)| = M$, where M is a constant, then the number of zeros of $f(z)$ in this region exceeds the number of zeros of the derived function $f'(z)$ in the same region by unity.*

On C let $f(z) = Me^{i\theta}$; then at points on C

$$f'(z) = Me^{i\theta} i \frac{d\theta}{dz}, \quad f''(z) = Me^{i\theta} \left\{ i \frac{d^2\theta}{dz^2} - \left(\frac{d\theta}{dz} \right)^2 \right\}.$$

Hence, by § 6·31, the excess of the number of zeros of $f(z)$ over the number of zeros of $f'(z)$ inside† C is

$$\frac{1}{2\pi i} \int_C \frac{f'(z)}{f(z)} dz - \frac{1}{2\pi i} \int_C \frac{f''(z)}{f'(z)} dz = -\frac{1}{2\pi i} \int_C \left(\frac{d^2\theta}{dz^2} \Big/ \frac{d\theta}{dz} \right) dz.$$

Let s be the arc of C measured from a fixed point and let ψ be the angle the tangent to C makes with Ox; then

$$-\frac{1}{2\pi i} \int_C \left(\frac{d^2\theta}{dz^2} \Big/ \frac{d\theta}{dz} \right) dz = -\frac{1}{2\pi i} \left[\log \frac{d\theta}{dz} \right]_C$$

$$= -\frac{1}{2\pi i} \left[\log \frac{d\theta}{ds} - \log \frac{dz}{ds} \right]_C.$$

Now $\log \dfrac{d\theta}{ds}$ is purely real and its initial value is the same as its final value; and $\log \dfrac{dz}{ds} = i\psi$; hence the excess of the number of zeros of $f(z)$ over the number of zeros of $f'(z)$ is the change in $\psi/2\pi$ in describing the curve C; and it is obvious ‡ that if C is any ordinary curve, ψ increases by 2π as the point of contact of the tangent describes the curve C; this gives the required result.

Example 1. Deduce from Macdonald's result the theorem that a polynomial of degree n has n zeros.

Example 2. Prove that, if a polynomial $f(z)$ has real coefficients and if its zeros are all real and different, then between two consecutive zeros of $f(z)$ there is one zero and one only of $f'(z)$.

[Dr Pólya has pointed out that this result is not necessarily true for functions other than polynomials, as may be seen by considering the function $(z^2 - 4) \exp(z^2/3)$.]

REFERENCES.

M. C. JORDAN, *Cours d'Analyse*, II. (Paris, 1894), Ch. VI.

E. GOURSAT, *Cours d'Analyse* (Paris, 1911), Ch. XIV.

E. LINDELÖF, *Le Calcul des Résidus* (Paris, 1905), Ch. II.

* *Proc. London Math. Soc.* XXIX. (1898), pp. 576, 577.

† $f'(z)$ does not vanish on C unless C has a node or other singular point; for, if $f = \phi + i\psi$, where ϕ and ψ are real, since $i\dfrac{\partial f}{\partial x} = \dfrac{\partial f}{\partial y}$, it follows that if $f'(z) = 0$ at any point, then $\dfrac{\partial \phi}{\partial x}$, $\dfrac{\partial \phi}{\partial y}$, $\dfrac{\partial \psi}{\partial x}$, $\dfrac{\partial \psi}{\partial y}$ all vanish; and these are sufficient conditions for a singular point on $\phi^2 + \psi^2 = M^2$.

‡ For a formal proof, see *Proc. London Math. Soc.* (2), XV. (1916), pp. 227–242.

MISCELLANEOUS EXAMPLES.

1.   A function $\phi(z)$ is zero when $z=0$, and is real when z is real, and is analytic when $|z| \leqslant 1$; if $f(x, y)$ is the coefficient of i in $\phi(x+iy)$, prove that if $-1 < x < 1$,

$$\int_0^{2\pi} \frac{x \sin \theta}{1 - 2x \cos \theta + x^2} f(\cos \theta, \sin \theta)\, d\theta = \pi \phi(x).$$

(Trinity, 1898.)

2.   By integrating $\dfrac{e^{\pm aiz}}{e^{2\pi z} - 1}$ round a contour formed by the rectangle whose corners are $0, R, R+i, i$ (the rectangle being indented at 0 and i) and making $R \to \infty$, shew that

$$\int_0^\infty \frac{\sin ax}{e^{2\pi x} - 1}\, dx = \frac{1}{4} \frac{e^a + 1}{e^a - 1} - \frac{1}{2a}.$$

(Legendre.)

3.   By integrating $\log(-z)\, Q(z)$ round the contour of § 6·24, where $Q(z)$ is a rational function such that $zQ(z) \to 0$ as $|z| \to 0$ and as $|z| \to \infty$, shew that if $Q(z)$ has no poles on the positive part of the real axis, $\displaystyle\int_0^\infty Q(x)\, dx$ is equal to minus the sum of the residues of $\log(-z)\, Q(z)$ at the poles of $Q(z)$; where the imaginary part of $\log(-z)$ lies between $\pm \pi$.

4.   Shew that, if $a > 0$, $b > 0$,

$$\int_0^\infty e^{a \cos bx} \sin(a \sin bx) \frac{dx}{x} = \frac{1}{2}\pi (e^a - 1).$$

5.   Shew that

$$\left. \begin{aligned} \int_0^{\frac{1}{2}\pi} \frac{a \sin 2x}{1 - 2a \cos 2x + a^2} x\, dx &= \frac{1}{4}\pi \log(1+a), \quad (-1 < a < 1) \\ &= \frac{1}{4}\pi \log(1 + a^{-1}), \quad (a^2 > 1) \end{aligned} \right\}.$$

(Cauchy.)

6.   Shew that

$$\int_0^\infty \frac{\sin \phi_1 x}{x} \frac{\sin \phi_2 x}{x} \cdots \frac{\sin \phi_n x}{x} \cos a_1 x \cdots \cos a_m x \frac{\sin ax}{x}\, dx = \frac{\pi}{2} \phi_1 \phi_2 \cdots \phi_n,$$

if $\phi_1, \phi_2, \ldots \phi_n, a_1, a_2, \ldots a_m$ be real and a be positive and
$$a > |\phi_1| + |\phi_2| + \cdots + |\phi_n| + |a_1| + \cdots + |a_m|.$$

(Störmer, *Acta Math.* XIX.)

7.   If a point z describes a circle C of centre a, and if $f(z)$ be analytic throughout C and its interior except at a number of poles inside C, then the point $u = f(z)$ will describe a closed curve γ in the u-plane.   Shew that if to each element of γ be attributed a mass proportional to the corresponding element of C, the centre of gravity of γ is the point r, where r is the sum of the residues of $\dfrac{f(z)}{z-a}$ at its poles in the interior of C.

(Amigues, *Nouv. Ann. de Math.* (3), XII. (1893), pp. 142–148.)

8.   Shew that

$$\int_{-\infty}^\infty \frac{dx}{(x^2 + b^2)(x^2 + a^2)^2} = \frac{\pi (2a + b)}{2a^3 b (a+b)^2}.$$

9.   Shew that

$$\int_0^\infty \frac{dx}{(a + bx^2)^n} = \frac{\pi}{2^n b^{\frac{1}{2}}} \frac{1 . 3 \ldots (2n-3)}{1 . 2 \ldots (n-1)} \frac{1}{a^{n-\frac{1}{2}}}.$$

10. If $F_n(z) = \prod_{m=1}^{n-1} \prod_{p=1}^{n-1} (1 - z^{mp})$, shew that the series

$$f(z) = -\sum_{n=2}^{\infty} \frac{F_n(zn^{-1})}{(z^n n^{-n} - 1) n^{n-1}}$$

is an analytic function when z is not a root of any of the equations $z^n = n^n$; and that the sum of the residues of $f(z)$ contained in the ring-shaped space included between two circles whose centres are at the origin, one having a small radius and the other having a radius between n and $n+1$, is equal to the number of prime numbers less than $n+1$.

(Laurent, *Nouv. Ann. de Math.* (3), XVIII. (1899), pp. 234–241.)

11. If A and B represent on the Argand diagram two given roots (real or imaginary) of the equation $f(z) = 0$ of degree n, with real or imaginary coefficients, shew that there is at least one root of the equation $f'(z) = 0$ within a circle whose centre is the middle point of AB and whose radius is $\frac{1}{2} AB \cot \frac{\pi}{n}$. (Grace, *Proc. Camb. Phil. Soc.* XI.)

12. Shew that, if $0 < \nu < 1$,

$$\frac{e_{2\pi i\nu x}}{1 - e^{2\pi ix}} = \frac{1}{2\pi i} \lim_{n \to \infty} \sum_{k=-n}^{n} \frac{e^{2k\nu\pi i}}{k - x}.$$

[Consider $\int \frac{e^{(2\nu-1) z\pi i}}{\sin \pi z} \frac{dz}{z - x}$ round a circle of radius $n + \frac{1}{2}$; and make $n \to \infty$.]

(Kronecker, *Journal für Math.* CV.)

13. Shew that, if $m > 0$, then

$$\int_0^{\infty} \frac{\sin^n mt}{t^n} dt$$

$$= \frac{\pi m^{n-1}}{2^n \cdot (n-1)!} \left\{ n^{n-1} - \frac{n}{1} (n-2)^{n-1} + \frac{n(n-1)}{2!} (n-4)^{n-1} - \frac{n(n-1)(n-2)}{3!} (n-6)^{n-1} + \ldots \right\}.$$

Discuss the discontinuity of the integral at $m = 0$.

14. If $A + B + C + \ldots = 0$ and $a, b, c, \ldots$ are positive, shew that

$$\int_0^{\infty} \frac{A \cos ax + B \cos bx + \ldots + K \cos kx}{x} dx = -A \log a - B \log b - \ldots - K \log k.$$

(Wolstenholme.)

15. By considering $\int \frac{e^{x(k+ti)}}{k + ti} dt$ taken round a rectangle indented at the origin, shew that, if $k > 0$,

$$i \lim_{\rho \to \infty} \int_{-\rho}^{\rho} \frac{e^{x(k+ti)}}{k + ti} dt = \pi i + \lim_{\rho \to \infty} P \int_{-\rho}^{\rho} \frac{e^{xti}}{t} dt,$$

and thence deduce, by using the contour of § 6·222 example 2, or its reflexion in the real axis (according as $x \geq 0$ or $x < 0$), that

$$\lim_{\rho \to \infty} \frac{1}{\pi} \int_{-\rho}^{\rho} \frac{e^{x(k+ti)}}{k + ti} dt = 2, 1 \text{ or } 0,$$

according as $x > 0$, $x = 0$ or $x < 0$.

[This integral is known as Cauchy's *discontinuous factor*.]

16. Shew that, if $0 < a < 2$, $b > 0$, $r > 0$, then

$$\int_0^{\infty} x^{a-1} \sin\left(\tfrac{1}{2} a\pi - bx\right) \frac{r\,dx}{x^2 + r^2} = \tfrac{1}{2} \pi r^{a-1} e^{-br}.$$

17.　Let $t > 0$ and let $\sum\limits_{n=-\infty}^{\infty} e^{-n^2\pi t} = \psi(t)$.

By considering $\int \dfrac{e^{-z^2\pi t}}{e^{2\pi i z} - 1}\, dz$ round a rectangle whose corners are $\pm(N + \tfrac{1}{2}) \pm i$, where N is an integer, and making $N \to \infty$, shew that

$$\psi(t) = \int_{-\infty-i}^{\infty-i} \frac{e^{-z^2\pi t}}{e^{2\pi i z} - 1}\, dz - \int_{-\infty+i}^{\infty+i} \frac{e^{-z^2\pi t}}{e^{2\pi i z} - 1}\, dz.$$

By expanding these integrands in powers of $e^{-2\pi i z}$, $e^{2\pi i z}$ respectively and integrating term-by-term, deduce from § 6·22 example 3 that

$$\psi(t) = \frac{1}{(\pi t)^{\frac{1}{2}}} \psi(1/t) \int_{-\infty}^{\infty} e^{-x^2}\, dx.$$

Hence, by putting $t = 1$ shew that

$$\psi(t) = t^{-\frac{1}{2}} \psi(1/t).$$

(This result is due to Poisson, *Journal de l'École polytechnique*, XII. (cahier XIX), (1823), p. 420; see also Jacobi, *Journal für Math.* XXXVI. (1848), p. 109 [*Ges. Werke*, II. (1882), p. 188].)

18.　Shew that, if $t > 0$,

$$\sum_{n=-\infty}^{\infty} e^{-n^2\pi t - 2n\pi a t} = t^{-\frac{1}{2}} e^{\pi a^2 t} \left\{ 1 + 2 \sum_{n=1}^{\infty} e^{-n^2\pi/t} \cos 2n\pi a \right\}.$$

(Poisson, *Mém. de l'Acad. des Sci.* VI. (1827), p. 592; Jacobi, *Journal für Math.* III. (1828), pp. 403–404 [*Ges. Werke*, I. (1881), pp. 264–265]; and Landsberg, *Journal für Math.* CXI. (1893), pp. 234–253; see also § 21·51.)

CHAPTER VII

THE EXPANSION OF FUNCTIONS IN INFINITE SERIES

7·1. *A formula due to Darboux*.*

Let $f(z)$ be analytic at all points of the straight line joining a to z, and let $\phi(t)$ be any polynomial of degree n in t.

Then if $0 \leqslant t \leqslant 1$, we have by differentiation

$$\frac{d}{dt} \sum_{m=1}^{n} (-)^m (z-a)^m \phi^{(n-m)}(t) f^{(m)}(a + t(z-a))$$

$$= -(z-a) \phi^{(n)}(t) f'(a + t(z-a)) + (-)^n (z-a)^{n+1} \phi(t) f^{(n+1)}(a + t(z-a)).$$

Noting that $\phi^{(n)}(t)$ is constant $= \phi^{(n)}(0)$, and integrating between the limits 0 and 1 of t, we get

$$\phi^{(n)}(0) \{f(z) - f(a)\}$$

$$= \sum_{m=1}^{n} (-)^{m-1} (z-a)^m \{\phi^{(n-m)}(1) f^{(m)}(z) - \phi^{(n-m)}(0) f^{(m)}(a)\}$$

$$+ (-)^n (z-a)^{n+1} \int_0^1 \phi(t) f^{(n+1)}(a + t(z-a)) \, dt,$$

which is the formula in question.

Taylor's series may be obtained as a special case of this by writing $\phi(t) = (t-1)^n$ and making $n \to \infty$.

Example. By substituting $2n$ for n in the formula of Darboux, and taking $\phi(t) = t^n(t-1)^n$, obtain the expansion (supposed convergent)

$$f(z) - f(a) = \sum_{n=1}^{\infty} \frac{(-)^{n-1} (z-a)^n}{2^n n!} \{f^{(n)}(z) + (-)^{n-1} f^{(n)}(a)\},$$

and find the expression for the remainder after n terms in this series.

7·2. *The Bernoullian numbers and the Bernoullian polynomials.*

The function $\frac{1}{2} z \cot \frac{1}{2} z$ is analytic when $|z| < 2\pi$, and, since it is an even function of z, it can be expanded into a Maclaurin series, thus

$$\frac{1}{2} z \cot \frac{1}{2} z = 1 - B_1 \frac{z^2}{2!} - B_2 \frac{z^4}{4!} - B_3 \frac{z^6}{6!} - \ldots;$$

then B_n is called the nth *Bernoullian number* †. It is found that ‡

$$B_1 = \frac{1}{6}, \quad B_2 = \frac{1}{30}, \quad B_3 = \frac{1}{42}, \quad B_4 = \frac{1}{30}, \quad B_5 = \frac{5}{66}, \quad \ldots.$$

---

* *Journal de Math.* (3), II. (1876), p. 271.

† These numbers were introduced by Jakob Bernoulli in his *Ars Conjectandi*, p. 97 (published posthumously, 1713).

‡ The first sixty-two Bernoullian numbers were computed by Adams, *Brit. Ass. Reports*, 1877; the first nine significant figures of the first 250 Bernoullian numbers were subsequently published by Glaisher, *Trans. Camb. Phil. Soc.* XII. (1879), pp. 384–391.

These numbers can be expressed as definite integrals as follows:

We have, by example 2 (p. 122) of Chapter VI,

$$\int_0^\infty \frac{\sin px\, dx}{e^{\pi x} - 1} = -\frac{1}{2p} + \frac{i}{2}\cot ip$$

$$= -\frac{1}{2p} + \frac{1}{2p}\left\{1 + B_1\frac{(2p)^2}{2!} - B_2\frac{(2p)^4}{4!} + \dots\right\}.$$

Since $$\int_0^\infty \frac{x^n \sin\left(px + \frac{1}{2}n\pi\right)}{e^{\pi x} - 1}\, dx$$

converges uniformly (by de la Vallée Poussin's test) near $p = 0$ we may, by § 4·44 corollary, differentiate both sides of this equation any number of times and then put $p = 0$; doing so and writing $2t$ for x, we obtain

$$B_n = 4n\int_0^\infty \frac{t^{2n-1}\, dt}{e^{2\pi t} - 1}.$$

A proof of this result, depending on contour integration, is given by Carda, *Monatshefte für Math. und Phys.* v. (1894), pp. 321–4.

Example. Shew that

$$B_n = \frac{2n}{\pi^{2n}(2^{2n}-1)}\int_0^\infty \frac{x^{2n-1}\, dx}{\sinh x} > 0.$$

Now consider the function $t\dfrac{e^{zt}-1}{e^t-1}$, which may be expanded into a Maclaurin series in powers of t valid when $|t| < 2\pi$.

The *Bernoullian polynomial*[*] of order n is defined to be the coefficient of $\dfrac{t^n}{n!}$ in this expansion. It is denoted by $\phi_n(z)$, so that

$$t\frac{e^{zt}-1}{e^t-1} = \sum_{n=1}^\infty \frac{\phi_n(z)\, t^n}{n!}.$$

This polynomial possesses several important properties. Writing $z + 1$ for z in the preceding equation and subtracting, we find that

$$te^{zt} = \sum_{n=1}^\infty \left\{\phi_n(z+1) - \phi_n(z)\right\}\frac{t^n}{n!}.$$

On equating coefficients of t^n on both sides of this equation we obtain

$$nz^{n-1} = \phi_n(z+1) - \phi_n(z),$$

which is a difference-equation satisfied by the function $\phi_n(z)$.

---

[*] The name was given by Raabe, *Journal für Math.* XLII. (1851), p. 348. For a full discussion of their properties, see Nörlund, *Acta Math.* XLIII. (1920), pp. 121–196.

An explicit expression for the Bernoullian polynomials can be obtained as follows.   We have

$$e^{zt} - 1 = zt + \frac{z^2 t^2}{2!} + \frac{z^3 t^3}{3!} + \dots,$$

and

$$\frac{t}{e^t - 1} = \frac{t}{2i} \cot \frac{t}{2i} - \frac{t}{2} = 1 - \frac{t}{2} + \frac{B_1 t^2}{2!} - \frac{B_2 t^4}{4!} + \dots.$$

Hence

$$\sum_{n=1}^{\infty} \frac{\phi_n(z) t^n}{n!} = \left\{ zt + \frac{z^2 t^2}{2!} + \frac{z^3 t^3}{3!} + \dots \right\} \left\{ 1 - \frac{t}{2} + \frac{B_1 t^2}{2!} - \frac{B_2 t^4}{4!} + \dots \right\}.$$

From this, by equating coefficients of t^n (§ 3·73), we have

$$\phi_n(z) = z^n - \frac{1}{2} n z^{n-1} + {}_n C_2 B_1 z^{n-2} - {}_n C_4 B_2 z^{n-4} + {}_n C_6 B_3 z^{n-6} - \dots,$$

the last term being that in z or z^2 and ${}_n C_2$, ${}_n C_4$, ... being the binomial coefficients; this is the Maclaurin series for the nth Bernoullian polynomial.

When z is an integer, it may be seen from the difference-equation that

$$\phi_n(z)/n = 1^{n-1} + 2^{n-1} + \dots + (z-1)^{n-1}.$$

The Maclaurin series for the expression on the right was given by Bernoulli.

Example.   Shew that, when $n > 1$,

$$\phi_n(z) = (-)^n \phi_n(1-z).$$

7·21.   *The Euler-Maclaurin expansion.*

In the formula of Darboux (§ 7·1) write $\phi_n(t)$ for $\phi(t)$, where $\phi_n(t)$ is the nth Bernoullian polynomial.

Differentiating the equation

$$\phi_n(t+1) - \phi_n(t) = n t^{n-1}$$

$n - k$ times, we have

$$\phi_n^{(n-k)}(t+1) - \phi_n^{(n-k)}(t) = n(n-1) \dots k t^{k-1}.$$

Putting $t = 0$ in this, we have $\phi_n^{(n-k)}(1) = \phi_n^{(n-k)}(0)$.

Now, from the Maclaurin series for $\phi_n(z)$, we have if $k > 0$

$$\phi_n^{(n-2k-1)}(0) = 0, \quad \phi_n^{(n-2k)}(0) = \frac{n!}{(2k)!} (-)^{k-1} B_k,$$

$$\phi_n^{(n-1)}(0) = -\frac{1}{2} \cdot n!, \quad \phi_n^{(n)}(0) = n!.$$

Substituting these values of $\phi_n^{(n-k)}(1)$ and $\phi_n^{(n-k)}(0)$ in Darboux's result, we obtain the *Euler-Maclaurin sum formula**,

<hr>

* A history of the formula is given by Barnes, *Proc. London Math. Soc.* (2), III. (1905), p. 253. It was discovered by Euler (1732), but was not published at the time.   Euler communicated it (June 9, 1736) to Stirling who replied (April 16, 1738) that it included his own theorem (see § 12·33) as a particular case, and also that the more general theorem had been discovered by Maclaurin; and Euler, in a lengthy reply, waived his claims to priority.   The theorem was published by Euler, *Comm. Acad. Imp. Petrop.* VI. (1732), [Published 1738], pp. 68–97, and by Maclaurin in 1742, *Treatise on Fluxions*, p. 672.   For information concerning the correspondence between Euler and Stirling, we are indebted to Mr C. Tweedie.

$$(z-a)f'(a) = f(z) - f(a) - \frac{z-a}{2}\{f'(z) - f'(a)\}$$

$$+ \sum_{m=1}^{n-1} \frac{(-)^{m-1}B_m(z-a)^{2m}}{(2m)!}\{f^{(2m)}(z) - f^{(2m)}(a)\}$$

$$- \frac{(z-a)^{2n+1}}{(2n)!}\int_0^1 \phi_{2n}(t)f^{(2n+1)}\{a+(z-a)t\}\,dt.$$

In certain cases the last term tends to zero as $n \to \infty$, and we can thus obtain an infinite series for $f(z) - f(a)$.

If we write ω for $z - a$ and $F(x)$ for $f'(x)$, the last formula becomes

$$\int_a^{a+\omega} F(x)\,dx = \tfrac{1}{2}\omega\{F(a) + F(a+\omega)\}$$

$$+ \sum_{m=1}^{n-1} \frac{(-)^m B_m \omega^{2m}}{(2m)!}\{F^{(2m-1)}(a+\omega) - F^{(2m-1)}(a)\}$$

$$+ \frac{\omega^{2n+1}}{(2n)!}\int_0^1 \phi_{2n}(t)F^{(2n)}(a+\omega t)\,dt.$$

Writing $a+\omega$, $a+2\omega$, ... $a+(r-1)\omega$ for a in this result and adding up, we get

$$\int_a^{a+r\omega} F(x)\,dx = \omega\left\{\tfrac{1}{2}F(a) + F(a+\omega) + F(a+2\omega) + \ldots + \tfrac{1}{2}F(a+r\omega)\right\}$$

$$+ \sum_{m=1}^{n-1}\frac{(-)^m B_m \omega^{2m}}{(2m)!}\{F^{(2m-1)}(a+r\omega) - F^{(2m-1)}(a)\} + R_n,$$

where

$$R_n = \frac{\omega^{2n+1}}{(2n)!}\int_0^1 \phi_{2n}(t)\left\{\sum_{m=0}^{r-1}F^{(2n)}(a+m\omega+\omega t)\right\}dt.$$

This last formula is of the utmost importance in connexion with the numerical evaluation of definite integrals. It is valid if $F(x)$ is analytic at all points of the straight line joining a to $a+r\omega$.

Example 1. If $f(z)$ be an odd function of z, shew that

$$zf'(z) = f(z) + \sum_{m=2}^n (-)^m \frac{B_{m-1}(2z)^{2m-2}}{(2m-2)!}f^{(2m-2)}(z) - \frac{2^{2n}z^{2n+1}}{(2n)!}\int_0^1 \phi_{2n}(t)f^{(2n+1)}(-z+2zt)\,dt.$$

Example 2. Shew, by integrating by parts, that the remainder after n terms of the expansion of $\frac{1}{2}z\cot\frac{1}{2}z$ may be written in the form

$$\frac{(-)^{n+1}z^{2n+1}}{(2n)!\sin z}\int_0^1 \phi_{2n}(t)\cos(zt)\,dt.$$

(Math. Trip. 1904.)

7·3. *Bürmann's theorem* *.

We shall next consider several theorems which have for their object *the expansion of one function in powers of another function*.

* *Mémoires de l'Institut*, II. (1799), p. 13. See also Dixon, *Proc. London Math. Soc.* xxxiv. (1902), pp. 151–153.

Let $\phi(z)$ be a function of z which is analytic in a closed region S of which a is an interior point; and let

$$\phi(a) = b.$$

Suppose also that $\phi'(a) \neq 0$. Then Taylor's theorem furnishes the expansion

$$\phi(z) - b = \phi'(a)(z - a) + \frac{\phi''(a)}{2!}(z - a)^2 + \ldots,$$

and if it is legitimate to revert this series we obtain

$$z - a = \frac{1}{\phi'(a)}\{\phi(z) - b\} - \frac{1}{2}\frac{\phi''(a)}{\{\phi'(a)\}^3}\{\phi(z) - b\}^2 + \ldots,$$

which expresses z as an analytic function of the variable $\{\phi(z) - b\}$, for sufficiently small values of $|z - a|$. If then $f(z)$ be analytic near $z = a$, it follows that $f(z)$ is an analytic function of $\{\phi(z) - b\}$ when $|z - a|$ is sufficiently small, and so there will be an expansion of the form

$$f(z) = f(a) + a_1\{\phi(z) - b\} + \frac{a_2}{2!}\{\phi(z) - b\}^2 + \frac{a_3}{3!}\{\phi(z) - b\}^3 + \ldots.$$

The actual coefficients in the expansion are given by the following theorem, which is generally known as *Bürmann's theorem.*

Let $\psi(z)$ be a function of z defined by the equation

$$\psi(z) = \frac{z - a}{\phi(z) - b};$$

then an analytic function $f(z)$ can, in a certain domain of values of z, be expanded in the form

$$f(z) = f(a) + \sum_{m=1}^{n-1} \frac{\{\phi(z) - b\}^m}{m!}\frac{d^{m-1}}{da^{m-1}}[f'(a)\{\psi(a)\}^m] + R_n,$$

where $$R_n = \frac{1}{2\pi i}\int_a^z \int_\gamma \left[\frac{\phi(z) - b}{\phi(t) - b}\right]^{n-1}\frac{f'(t)\,\phi'(z)\,dt\,dz}{\phi(t) - \phi(z)},$$

and γ is a contour in the t-plane, enclosing the points a and z and such that, if ζ be any point inside it, the equation $\phi(t) = \phi(\zeta)$ has no roots on or inside the contour except a simple root $t = \zeta$.*

To prove this, we have

$$f(z) - f(a) = \int_a^z f'(\zeta)\,d\zeta = \frac{1}{2\pi i}\int_a^z \int_\gamma \frac{f'(t)\,\phi'(\zeta)\,dt\,d\zeta}{\phi(t) - \phi(\zeta)}$$

$$= \frac{1}{2\pi i}\int_a^z \int_\gamma \frac{f'(t)\,\phi'(\zeta)\,dt\,d\zeta}{\phi(t) - b}\left[\sum_{m=0}^{n-2}\left\{\frac{\phi(\zeta) - b}{\phi(t) - b}\right\}^m\right.$$

$$\left. + \frac{\{\phi(\zeta) - b\}^{n-1}}{\{\phi(t) - b\}^{n-2}\{\phi(t) - \phi(\zeta)\}}\right].$$

---

* It is assumed that such a contour can be chosen if $|z - a|$ be sufficiently small; see § 7·31.

But, by § 4·3,

$$\frac{1}{2\pi i}\int_a^z\int_\gamma\left[\frac{\phi(\zeta)-b}{\phi(t)-b}\right]^m\frac{f'(t)\,\phi'(\zeta)\,dt\,d\zeta}{\phi(t)-b}=\frac{\{\phi(z)-b\}^{m+1}}{2\pi i\,(m+1)}\int_\gamma\frac{f'(t)\,dt}{\{\phi(t)-b\}^{m+1}}$$

$$=\frac{\{\phi(z)-b\}^{m+1}}{2\pi i\,(m+1)}\int_\gamma\frac{f'(t)\,\{\psi(t)\}^{m+1}\,dt}{(t-a)^{m+1}}=\frac{\{\phi(z)-b\}^{m+1}}{(m+1)!}\frac{d^m}{da^m}[f'(a)\,\{\psi(a)\}^{m+1}].$$

Therefore, writing $m-1$ for m,

$$f(z)=f(a)+\sum_{m=1}^{n-1}\frac{\{\phi(z)-b\}^m}{m!}\frac{d^{m-1}}{da^{m-1}}[f'(a)\,\{\psi(a)\}^m]$$

$$+\frac{1}{2\pi i}\int_a^z\int_\gamma\left[\frac{\phi(\zeta)-b}{\phi(t)-b}\right]^{n-1}\frac{f'(t)\,\phi'(\zeta)\,dt\,d\zeta}{\phi(t)-\phi(\zeta)}.$$

If the last integral tends to zero as $n\to\infty$, we may write the right-hand side of this equation as an infinite series.

Example 1. Prove that

$$z=a+\sum_{n=1}^\infty\frac{(-)^{n-1}C_n\,(z-a)^n\,e^{n(z^2-a^2)}}{n!},$$

where

$$C_n=(2na)^{n-1}-\frac{n(n-1)(n-2)}{1!}(2na)^{n-3}+\frac{n^2(n-1)(n-2)(n-3)(n-4)}{2!}(2na)^{n-5}-\dots.$$

To obtain this expansion, write

$$f(z)=z,\quad\phi(z)-b=(z-a)\,e^{z^2-a^2},\quad\psi(z)=e^{a^2-z^2},$$

in the above expression of Bürmann's theorem ; we thus have

$$z=a+\sum_{n=1}^\infty\frac{1}{n!}(z-a)^n\,e^{n(z^2-a^2)}\left\{\frac{d^{n-1}}{dz^{n-1}}e^{n(a^2-z^2)}\right\}_{z=a}.$$

But, putting $z=a+t$,

$$\left\{\frac{d^{n-1}}{dz^{n-1}}e^{n(a^2-z^2)}\right\}_{z=a}=\left\{\frac{d^{n-1}}{dt^{n-1}}e^{-n(2at+t^2)}\right\}_{t=0}$$

$$=(n-1)!\times\text{the coefficient of }t^{n-1}\text{ in the expansion of }e^{-nt(2a+t)}$$

$$=(n-1)!\times\text{the coefficient of }t^{n-1}\text{ in }\sum_{r=0}^\infty\frac{(-)^r\,n^r\,t^r\,(2a+t)^r}{r!}$$

$$=(n-1)!\times\sum_{r=0}^{n-1}\frac{(-)^r\,n^r\,(2a)^{2r-n+1}}{(n-1-r)!\,(2r-n+1)!}.$$

The highest value of r which gives a term in the summation is $r=n-1$. Arranging therefore the summation in descending indices r, beginning with $r=n-1$, we have

$$\left\{\frac{d^{n-1}}{dz^{n-1}}e^{n(a^2-z^2)}\right\}_{z=a}=(-)^{n-1}\left\{(2na)^{n-1}-\frac{n(n-1)(n-2)}{1!}(2na)^{n-3}+\dots\right\}$$

$$=(-)^{n-1}C_n,$$

which gives the required result.

Example 2. Obtain the expansion

$$z^2=\sin^2 z+\frac{2}{3}\cdot\frac{1}{2}\sin^4 z+\frac{2\cdot4}{3\cdot5}\cdot\frac{1}{3}\sin^6 z+\dots.$$

Example 3.   Let a line p be drawn through the origin in the z-plane, perpendicular to the line which joins the origin to any point a.   If z be any point on the z-plane which is on the same side of the line p as the point a is, shew that

$$\log z = \log a + 2 \sum_{m=1}^{\infty} \frac{1}{2m+1} \left(\frac{z-a}{z+a}\right)^{2m+1}.$$

7·31. *Teixeira's extended form of Bürmann's theorem.*

In the last section we have not investigated closely the conditions of convergence of Bürmann's series, for the reason that a much more general form of the theorem will next be stated; this generalisation bears the same relation to the theorem just given that Laurent's theorem bears to Taylor's theorem: viz., in the last paragraph we were concerned only with the expansion of a function in *positive* powers of another function, whereas we shall now discuss the expansion of a function in *positive and negative* powers of the second function.

The general statement of the theorem is due to Teixeira*, whose exposition we shall follow in this section.

Suppose (i) that $f(z)$ is a function of z analytic in a ring-shaped region A, bounded by an outer curve C and an inner curve c; (ii) that $\theta(z)$ is a function analytic on and inside C, and has only one zero a within this contour, the zero being a simple one; (iii) that x is a given point within A; (iv) that for all points z of C we have

$$|\theta(x)| < |\theta(z)|,$$

and for all points z of c we have

$$|\theta(x)| > |\theta(z)|.$$

The equation $$\theta(z) - \theta(x) = 0$$

has, in this case, a single root $z = x$ in the interior of C, as is seen from the equation†

$$\frac{1}{2\pi i} \int_C \frac{\theta'(z)\, dz}{\theta(z) - \theta(x)} = \frac{1}{2\pi i} \left[\int_C \frac{\theta'(z)}{\theta(z)}\, dz + \theta(x) \int_C \frac{\theta'(z)}{\{\theta(z)\}^2}\, dz + \dots\right]$$

$$= \frac{1}{2\pi i} \int_C \frac{\theta'(z)\, dz}{\theta(z)},$$

of which the left-hand and right-hand members represent respectively the number of roots of the equation considered (§ 6·31) and the number of the roots of the equation $\theta(z) = 0$ contained within C.

Cauchy's theorem therefore gives

$$f(x) = \frac{1}{2\pi i} \left[\int_C \frac{f(z)\, \theta'(z)\, dz}{\theta(z) - \theta(x)} - \int_c \frac{f(z)\, \theta'(z)\, dz}{\theta(z) - \theta(x)}\right].$$

---

* *Journal für Math.* cxxii. (1900), pp. 97–123. See also Bateman, *Trans. Amer. Math. Soc.* xxviii. (1926), pp. 346–356.

† The expansion is justified by § 4·7, since $\sum_{n=1}^{\infty} \left\{\frac{\theta(x)}{\theta(z)}\right\}^n$ converges uniformly when z is on C.

The integrals in this formula can be expanded, as in Laurent's theorem, in powers of $\theta(x)$, by the formulae

$$\int_C \frac{f(z)\,\theta'(z)\,dz}{\theta(z) - \theta(x)} = \sum_{n=0}^{\infty} \{\theta(x)\}^n \int_C \frac{f(z)\,\theta'(z)\,dz}{\{\theta(z)\}^{n+1}},$$

$$\int_c \frac{f(z)\,\theta'(z)\,dz}{\theta(z) - \theta(x)} = -\sum_{n=1}^{\infty} \frac{1}{\{\theta(x)\}^n} \int_c f(z)\,\{\theta(z)\}^{n-1}\,\theta'(z)\,dz.$$

We thus have the formula

$$f(x) = \sum_{n=0}^{\infty} A_n \{\theta(x)\}^n + \sum_{n=1}^{\infty} \frac{B_n}{\{\theta(x)\}^n},$$

where

$$A_n = \frac{1}{2\pi i} \int_C \frac{f(z)\,\theta'(z)\,dz}{\{\theta(z)\}^{n+1}}, \quad B_n = \frac{1}{2\pi i} \int_c f(z)\,\{\theta(z)\}^{n-1}\,\theta'(z)\,dz.$$

Integrating by parts, we get, if $n \neq 0$,

$$A_n = \frac{1}{2\pi i n} \int_C \frac{f'(z)}{\{\theta(z)\}^n}\,dz, \quad B_n = \frac{-1}{2\pi i n} \int_c \{\theta(z)\}^n f'(z)\,dz.$$

This gives a development of $f(x)$ in positive and negative powers of $\theta(x)$, valid for all points x within the ring-shaped space A.

If the zeros and poles of $f(z)$ and $\theta(z)$ inside C are known, A_n and B_n can be evaluated by § 5·22 or by § 6·1.

Example 1. Shew that, if $|x| < 1$, then

$$x = \frac{1}{2}\left(\frac{2x}{1+x^2}\right) + \frac{1}{2.4}\left(\frac{2x}{1+x^2}\right)^3 + \frac{1.3}{2.4.6}\left(\frac{2x}{1+x^2}\right)^5 + \dots.$$

Shew that, when $|x| > 1$, the second member represents x^{-1}.

Example 2. If $S_{2n}^{(m)}$ denote the sum of all combinations of the numbers

$$2^2, \ 4^2, \ 6^2, \dots (2n-2)^2,$$

taken m at a time, shew that

$$\frac{1}{z} = \frac{1}{\sin z} + \sum_{n=0}^{\infty} \frac{(-)^{n+1}}{(2n+2)!} \left\{ \frac{1}{2n+3} - \frac{S_{2(n+1)}^{(1)}}{2n+1} + \dots + \frac{(-)^n S_{2(n+1)}^{(n)}}{3} \right\} (\sin z)^{2n+1},$$

the expansion being valid for all values of z represented by points within the oval whose equation is $|\sin z| = 1$ and which contains the point $z = 0$.   (Teixeira.)

7·32. *Lagrange's theorem.*

Suppose now that the function $f(z)$ of § 7·31 is analytic at all points in the interior of C, and let $\theta(x) = (x - a)\,\theta_1(x)$. Then $\theta_1(x)$ is analytic and not zero on or inside C and the contour c can be dispensed with; therefore the formulae which give A_n and B_n now become, by § 5·22 and § 6·1,

$$A_n = \frac{1}{2\pi i n} \int_C \frac{f'(z)\,dz}{(z-a)^n\,\{\theta_1(z)\}^n} = \frac{1}{n!} \frac{d^{n-1}}{da^{n-1}} \left\{ \frac{f'(a)}{\theta_1{}^n(a)} \right\} \qquad (n \geqslant 1),$$

$$A_0 = \frac{1}{2\pi i} \int_C \frac{f(z)\,\theta'(z)}{\theta_1(z)} \frac{dz}{z-a} = f(a),$$

$$B_n = 0.$$

The theorem of the last section accordingly takes the following form, if we write $\theta_1(z) = 1/\phi(z)$:

Let $f(z)$ and $\phi(z)$ be functions of z analytic on and inside a contour C surrounding a point a, and let t be such that the inequality

$$|t\,\phi(z)| < |z-a|$$

is satisfied at all points z on the perimeter of C; then the equation

$$\zeta = a + t\,\phi(\zeta),$$

regarded as an equation in ζ, has one root in the interior of C; and further any function of ζ analytic on and inside C can be expanded as a power series in t by the formula

$$f(\zeta) = f(a) + \sum_{n=1}^{\infty} \frac{t^n}{n!} \frac{d^{n-1}}{da^{n-1}} [f'(a)\{\phi(a)\}^n].$$

This result was published by Lagrange* in 1770.

Example 1. Within the contour surrounding a defined by the inequality $|z(z-a)| > |a|$, where $|a| < \frac{1}{2}|a|$, the equation

$$z - a - \frac{a}{z} = 0$$

has one root ζ, the expansion of which is given by Lagrange's theorem in the form

$$\zeta = a + \sum_{n=1}^{\infty} \frac{(-)^{n-1}(2n-2)!}{n!\,(n-1)!\,a^{2n-1}}\, a^n.$$

Now, from the elementary theory of quadratic equations, we know that the equation

$$z - a - \frac{a}{z} = 0$$

has two roots, namely $\dfrac{a}{2}\left\{1 + \sqrt{\left(1 + \dfrac{4a}{a^2}\right)}\right\}$ and $\dfrac{a}{2}\left\{1 - \sqrt{\left(1 + \dfrac{4a}{a^2}\right)}\right\}$; and our expansion *represents the former*† *of these only*—an example of the need for care in the discussion of these series.

Example 2. If y be that one of the roots of the equation

$$y = 1 + zy^2$$

which tends to 1 when $z \to 0$, shew that

$$y^n = 1 + nz + \frac{n(n+3)}{2!}z^2 + \frac{n(n+4)(n+5)}{3!}z^3$$

$$+ \frac{n(n+5)(n+6)(n+7)}{4!}z^4 + \frac{n(n+6)(n+7)(n+8)(n+9)}{5!}z^5 + \ldots$$

so long as $|z| < \frac{1}{4}$.

Example 3. If x be that one of the roots of the equation

$$x = 1 + yx^a$$

which tends to 1 when $y \to 0$, shew that

$$\log x = y + \frac{2a-1}{2}y^2 + \frac{(3a-1)(3a-2)}{2.3}y^3 + \ldots,$$

the expansion being valid so long as

$$|y| < |(a-1)^{a-1}a^{-a}|. \qquad \text{(McClintock.)}$$

---

* *Mém. de l'Acad. de Berlin*, XXIV.; *Oeuvres*, II. p. 25.

† The latter is outside the given contour.

7·4. *The expansion of a class of functions in rational fractions*.*

Consider a function $f(z)$, whose only singularities in the finite part of the plane are simple poles $a_1, a_2, a_3, \ldots$, where $|a_1| \leqslant |a_2| \leqslant |a_3| \leqslant \ldots$: let $b_1, b_2, b_3, \ldots$ be the residues at these poles, and let it be possible to choose a sequence of circles C_m (the radius of C_m being R_m) with centre at O, not passing through any poles, such that $|f(z)|$ is bounded on C_m. (The function cosec z may be cited as an example of the class of functions considered, and we take $R_m = (m + \frac{1}{2}) \pi$.) Suppose further that $R_m \rightarrow \infty$ as $m \rightarrow \infty$ and that the upper bound† of $|f(z)|$ on C_m is itself bounded as‡ $m \rightarrow \infty$; so that, for all points on the circle C_m, $|f(z)| < M$, where M is independent of m.

Then, if x be not a pole of $f(z)$, since the only poles of the integrand are the poles of $f(z)$ and the point $z = x$, we have, by § 6·1,

$$\frac{1}{2\pi i} \int_{C_m} \frac{f(z)}{z - x} \, dz = f(x) + \sum_r \frac{b_r}{a_r - x},$$

where the summation extends over all poles in the interior of C_m.

But $\quad \dfrac{1}{2\pi i} \displaystyle\int_{C_m} \dfrac{f(z)}{z - x} \, dz = \dfrac{1}{2\pi i} \int_{C_m} \dfrac{f(z) \, dz}{z} + \dfrac{x}{2\pi i} \int_{C_m} \dfrac{f(z)}{z (z - x)} \, dz$

$$= f(0) + \sum_r \frac{b_r}{a_r} + \frac{x}{2\pi i} \int_{C_m} \frac{f(z) \, dz}{z (z - x)},$$

if we suppose the function $f(z)$ to be analytic at the origin.

Now as $m \rightarrow \infty$, $\displaystyle\int_{C_m} \dfrac{f(z) \, dz}{z (z - x)}$ is $O(R_m^{-1})$, and so tends to zero as m tends to infinity.

Therefore, making $m \rightarrow \infty$, we have

$$0 = f(x) - f(0) + \sum_{n=1}^{\infty} b_n \left(\frac{1}{a_n - x} - \frac{1}{a_n} \right) - \lim_{m \rightarrow \infty} \frac{x}{2\pi i} \int_{C_m} \frac{f(z) \, dz}{z (z - x)},$$

i.e. $\quad\quad\quad\quad f(x) = f(0) + \displaystyle\sum_{n=1}^{\infty} b_n \left\{ \frac{1}{x - a_n} + \frac{1}{a_n} \right\},$

which is an expansion of $f(x)$ in rational fractions of x; and the summation extends over *all* the poles of $f(x)$.

If $|a_n| < |a_{n+1}|$ this series converges uniformly throughout the region given by $|x| \leqslant a$, where a is any constant (except near the points a_n). For if R_m be the radius of the circle which encloses the points $|a_1|, \ldots |a_n|$, the modulus of the remainder of the terms of the series after the first n is

$$\left| \frac{x}{2\pi i} \int_{C_m} \frac{f(z) \, dz}{z (z - x)} \right| < \frac{Ma}{R_m - a},$$

by § 4·62; and, given ϵ, we can choose n *independent* of x such that $Ma/(R_m - a) < \epsilon$.

---

* Mittag-Leffler, *Acta Soc. Scient. Fennicae*, XI. (1880), pp. 273–293. See also *Acta Math.* IV. (1884), pp. 1–79.

† Which is a function of m.

‡ Of course R_m need not (and frequently must not) tend to infinity continuously; e.g. in the example taken $R_m = (m + \frac{1}{2}) \pi$, where m assumes only integer values.

The convergence is obviously still uniform even if $|a_n| \leqslant |a_{n+1}|$ provided the terms of the series are grouped so as to combine the terms corresponding to poles of equal moduli.

If, instead of the condition $|f(z)| < M$, we have the condition $|z^{-p} f(z)| < M$, where M is independent of m when z is on C_m, and p is a positive integer, then we should have to expand $\int_C \frac{f(z)\,dz}{z-x}$ by writing

$$\frac{1}{z-x} = \frac{1}{z} + \frac{x}{z^2} + \dots + \frac{x^{p+1}}{z^{p+1}(z-x)},$$

and should obtain a similar but somewhat more complicated expansion.

Example 1. Prove that

$$\operatorname{cosec} z = \frac{1}{z} + \Sigma\,(-)^n \left(\frac{1}{z-n\pi} + \frac{1}{n\pi}\right),$$

the summation extending to all positive and negative values of n.

To obtain this result, let $\operatorname{cosec} z - \frac{1}{z} = f(z)$. The singularities of this function are at the points $z = n\pi$, where n is any positive or negative integer.

The residue of $f(z)$ at the singularity $n\pi$ is therefore $(-)^n$, and the reader will easily see that $|f(z)|$ is bounded on the circle $|z| = (n+\frac{1}{2})\,\pi$ as $n \to \infty$.

Applying now the general theorem

$$f(z) = f(0) + \Sigma c_n \left[\frac{1}{z-a_n} + \frac{1}{a_n}\right],$$

where c_n is the residue at the singularity a_n, we have

$$f(z) = f(0) + \Sigma\,(-)^n \left\{\frac{1}{z-n\pi} + \frac{1}{n\pi}\right\}.$$

But

$$f(0) = \lim_{z \to 0} \frac{z - \sin z}{z \sin z} = 0.$$

Therefore

$$\operatorname{cosec} z = \frac{1}{z} + \Sigma\,(-)^n \left[\frac{1}{z-n\pi} + \frac{1}{n\pi}\right],$$

which is the required result.

Example 2. If $0 < a < 1$, shew that

$$\frac{e^{az}}{e^z - 1} = \frac{1}{z} + \sum_{n=1}^{\infty} \frac{2z \cos 2na\pi - 4n\pi \sin 2na\pi}{z^2 + 4n^2\pi^2}$$

Example 3. Prove that

$$\frac{1}{2\pi x^2(\cosh x - \cos x)} = \frac{1}{2\pi x^4} - \frac{1}{e^\pi - e^{-\pi}} \frac{1}{\pi^4 + \frac{1}{4}x^4} + \frac{2}{e^{2\pi} - e^{-2\pi}} \frac{1}{(2\pi)^4 + \frac{1}{4}x^4}$$
$$- \frac{3}{e^{3\pi} - e^{-3\pi}} \frac{1}{(3\pi)^4 + \frac{1}{4}x^4} + \dots.$$

The general term of the series on the right is

$$\frac{(-)^r\,r}{(e^{r\pi} - e^{-r\pi})\,\{(r\pi)^4 + \frac{1}{4}x^4\}},$$

which is the residue at each of the four singularities $r,\ -r,\ ri,\ -ri$ of the function

$$\frac{\pi z}{(\pi^4 z^4 + \frac{1}{4}x^4)\,(e^{\pi z} - e^{-\pi z}) \sin \pi z}.$$

The singularities of this latter function which are not of the type $r, -r, ri, -ri$ are at the five points

$$0, \frac{(\pm 1 \pm i) x}{2\pi}.$$

At $z = 0$ the residue is

$$\frac{2}{\pi x^4};$$

at each of the four points $z = \frac{(\pm 1 \pm i) x}{2\pi}$, the residue is

$$\{2\pi x^2 (\cos x - \cosh x)\}^{-1}.$$

Therefore

$$4 \sum_{r=1}^{\infty} \frac{(-1)^r r}{e^{r\pi} - e^{-r\pi}} \frac{1}{(r\pi)^4 + \frac{1}{4} x^4} + \frac{2}{\pi x^4} - \frac{2}{\pi x^2 (\cosh x - \cos x)}$$

$$= \frac{1}{2\pi i} \lim_{n \to \infty} \int_C \frac{\pi z \, dz}{(\pi^4 z^4 + \frac{1}{4} x^4)(e^{\pi z} - e^{-\pi z}) \sin \pi z},$$

where C is the circle whose radius is $n + \frac{1}{2}$, (n an integer), and whose centre is the origin. But, at points on C, this integrand is $O(|z|^{-3})$; the limit of the integral round C is therefore zero.

From the last equation the required result is now obvious.

Example 4.   Prove that $\sec x = 4\pi \left(\frac{1}{\pi^2 - 4x^2} - \frac{3}{9\pi^2 - 4x^2} + \frac{5}{25\pi^2 - 4x^2} - \ldots \right).$

Example 5.   Prove that $\operatorname{cosech} x = \frac{1}{x} - 2x \left(\frac{1}{\pi^2 + x^2} - \frac{1}{4\pi^2 + x^2} + \frac{1}{9\pi^2 + x^2} - \ldots \right).$

Example 6.   Prove that $\operatorname{sech} x = 4\pi \left(\frac{1}{\pi^2 + 4x^2} - \frac{3}{9\pi^2 + 4x^2} + \frac{5}{25\pi^2 + 4x^2} - \ldots \right).$

Example 7.   Prove that $\coth x = \frac{1}{x} + 2x \left(\frac{1}{\pi^2 + x^2} + \frac{1}{4\pi^2 + x^2} + \frac{1}{9\pi^2 + x^2} + \ldots \right).$

Example 8.   Prove that $\sum_{m=-\infty}^{\infty} \sum_{n=-\infty}^{\infty} \frac{1}{(m^2 + a^2)(n^2 + b^2)} = \frac{\pi^2}{ab} \coth \pi a \coth \pi b.$

(Math. Trip. 1899.)

7·5.   *The expansion of a class of functions as infinite products.*

The theorem of the last article can be applied to the expansion of a certain class of functions as infinite products.

For let $f(z)$ be a function which has simple zeros at the points[*] $a_1, a_2, a_3, \ldots$, where $\lim_{n \to \infty} |a_n|$ is infinite; and let $f(z)$ be analytic for all values of z.

Then $f'(z)$ is analytic for all values of z (§ 5·22), and so $\frac{f'(z)}{f(z)}$ can have singularities only at the points $a_1, a_2, a_3, \ldots$.

Consequently, by Taylor's theorem,

$$f(z) = (z - a_r) f'(a_r) + \frac{(z - a_r)^2}{2} f''(a_r) + \ldots$$

and

$$f'(z) = f'(a_r) + (z - a_r) f''(a_r) + \ldots.$$

* These being the only zeros of $f(z)$; and $a_n \neq 0$.

It follows immediately that at each of the points a_r, the function $\dfrac{f'(z)}{f(z)}$ has a simple pole, with residue $+1$.

If then we can find a sequence of circles C_m of the nature described in § 7·4, such that $\dfrac{f'(z)}{f(z)}$ is bounded on C_m as $m \to \infty$, it follows, from the expansion given in § 7·4, that

$$\frac{f'(z)}{f(z)} = \frac{f'(0)}{f(0)} + \sum_{n=1}^{\infty} \left\{ \frac{1}{z - a_n} + \frac{1}{a_n} \right\}.$$

Since this series converges uniformly when the terms are suitably grouped (§ 7·4), we may integrate term-by-term (§ 4·7). Doing so, and taking the exponential of each side, we get

$$f(z) = c e^{\frac{f'(0)}{f(0)} z} \prod_{n=1}^{\infty} \left\{ \left(1 - \frac{z}{a_n} \right) e^{\frac{z}{a_n}} \right\},$$

where c is independent of z.

Putting $z = 0$, we see that $f(0) = c$, and thus the general result becomes

$$f(z) = f(0) \, e^{\frac{f'(0)}{f(0)} z} \prod_{n=1}^{\infty} \left\{ \left(1 - \frac{z}{a_n} \right) e^{\frac{z}{a_n}} \right\}.$$

This furnishes the expansion, in the form of an infinite product, of any function $f(z)$ which fulfils the conditions stated.

Example 1. Consider the function $f(z) = \dfrac{\sin z}{z}$, which has simple zeros at the points $r\pi$, where r is any positive or negative integer.

In this case we have $\qquad f(0) = 1, \quad f'(0) = 0,$
and so the theorem gives immediately

$$\frac{\sin z}{z} = \prod_{n=1}^{\infty} \left\{ \left(1 - \frac{z}{n\pi} \right) e^{\frac{z}{n\pi}} \right\} \left\{ \left(1 + \frac{z}{n\pi} \right) e^{-\frac{z}{n\pi}} \right\};$$

for it is easily seen that the condition concerning the behaviour of $\dfrac{f'(z)}{f(z)}$ as $|z| \to \infty$ is fulfilled.

Example 2. Prove that

$$\left\{ 1 + \left(\frac{k}{x} \right)^2 \right\} \left\{ 1 + \left(\frac{k}{2\pi - x} \right)^2 \right\} \left\{ 1 + \left(\frac{k}{2\pi + x} \right)^2 \right\} \left\{ 1 + \left(\frac{k}{4\pi - x} \right)^2 \right\} \left\{ 1 + \left(\frac{k}{4\pi + x} \right)^2 \right\} \cdots$$
$$= \frac{\cosh k - \cos x}{1 - \cos x}.$$

(Trinity, 1899.)

7·6.   *The factor theorem of Weierstrass**.

The theorem of § 7·5 is very similar to a more general theorem in which the character of the function $f(z)$, as $|z| \to \infty$, is not so narrowly restricted.

---

* *Berliner Abh.* (1876), pp. 11–60 ; *Math. Werke*, II. (1895), pp. 77–124.

Let $f(z)$ be a function of z with no essential singularities (except at 'the point infinity'); and let the zeros and poles of $f(z)$ be at $a_1, a_2, a_3, \ldots$, where $0 < |a_1| \leqslant |a_2| \leqslant |a_3| \ldots$. Let the zero* at a_n be of (integer) order m_n.

If the number of zeros and poles is unlimited, it is necessary that $|a_n| \to \infty$, as $n \to \infty$; for, if not, the points a_n would have a limit point†, which would be an essential singularity of $f(z)$.

We proceed to shew first of all that it is possible to find polynomials $g_n(z)$ such that

$$\prod_{n=1}^{\infty} \left[\left\{ \left(1 - \frac{z}{a_n} \right) e^{g_n(z)} \right\}^{m_n} \right]$$

converges for all‡ finite values of z.

Let K be any constant, and let $|z| < K$; then, since $|a_n| \to \infty$, we can find N such that, when $n > N$, $|a_n| > 2K$.

The first N factors of the product do not affect its convergence‡; consider any value of n greater than N, and let

$$g_n(z) = \frac{z}{a_n} + \frac{1}{2} \left(\frac{z}{a_n} \right)^2 + \ldots + \frac{1}{k_n - 1} \left(\frac{z}{a_n} \right)^{k_n - 1}.$$

Then
$$\left| -\sum_{m=1}^{\infty} \frac{1}{m} \left(\frac{z}{a_n} \right)^m + g_n(z) \right| = \left| \sum_{m=k_n}^{\infty} \frac{1}{m} \left(\frac{z}{a_n} \right)^m \right|$$
$$< \left| \frac{z}{a_n} \right|^{k_n} \sum_{m=0}^{\infty} \left| \frac{z}{a_n} \right|^m$$
$$< 2 \left| (K a_n^{-1})^{k_n} \right|,$$

since $|z a_n^{-1}| < \frac{1}{2}$.

Hence
$$\left\{ \left(1 - \frac{z}{a_n} \right) e^{g_n(z)} \right\}^{m_n} = e^{u_n(z)},$$

where
$$|u_n(z)| \leqslant 2 \left| m_n (K a_n^{-1})^{k_n} \right|.$$

Now m_n and a_n are given, but k_n is at our disposal; since $K a_n^{-1} < \frac{1}{2}$, we choose k_n to be the smallest number such that $2 |m_n (K a_n^{-1})^{k_n}| < b_n$, where $\sum_{n=1}^{\infty} b_n$ is any convergent series§ of positive terms.

Hence
$$\prod_{n=N+1}^{\infty} \left[\left\{ \left(1 - \frac{z}{a_n} \right) e^{g_n(z)} \right\}^{m_n} \right] = \prod_{n=N+1}^{\infty} e^{u_n(z)},$$

where $|u_n(z)| < b_n$; and therefore, since b_n is independent of z, the product converges absolutely and uniformly when $|z| < K$, except near the points a_n.

* We here regard a pole as being a zero of negative order.
† From the two-dimensional analogue of § 2·21.
‡ Provided that z is not at one of the points a_n for which m_n is negative.
§ E.g. we might take $b_n = 2^{-n}$.

Now let
$$F(z) = \prod_{n=1}^{\infty} \left[\left\{ \left(1 - \frac{z}{a_n}\right) e^{g_n(z)} \right\}^{m_n} \right].$$

Then, if $f(z) \div F(z) = G_1(z)$, $G_1(z)$ is an integral function (§ 5·64) of z and has no zeros.

It follows that $\dfrac{1}{G_1(z)} \dfrac{d}{dz} G_1(z)$ is analytic for all finite values of z; and so, by Taylor's theorem, this function can be expressed as a series $\sum\limits_{n=1}^{\infty} n b_n z^{n-1}$ converging everywhere; integrating, it follows that
$$G_1(z) = c e^{G(z)},$$

where $G(z) = \sum\limits_{n=1}^{\infty} b_n z^n$ and c is a constant; this series converges everywhere, and so $G(z)$ is an integral function.

Therefore, finally,
$$f(z) = f(0) e^{G(z)} \prod_{n=1}^{\infty} \left[\left\{ \left(1 - \frac{z}{a_n}\right) e^{g_n(z)} \right\}^{m_n} \right],$$

where $G(z)$ is some integral function such that $G(0) = 0$.

[NOTE. The presence of the arbitrary element $G(z)$ which occurs in this formula for $f(z)$ is due to the lack of conditions as to the behaviour of $f(z)$ as $|z| \to \infty$.]

Corollary. If $m_n = 1$, it is sufficient to take $k_n = n$, by § 2·36.

7·7. *The expansion of a class of periodic functions in a series of cotangents.*

Let $f(z)$ be a periodic function of z, analytic except at a certain number of simple poles; for convenience, let π be the period of $f(z)$ so that $f(z) = f(z + \pi)$.

Let $z = x + iy$ and let $f(z) \to l$ uniformly with respect to x as $y \to +\infty$, when $0 \leqslant x \leqslant \pi$; similarly let $f(z) \to l'$ uniformly as $y \to -\infty$.

Let the poles of $f(z)$ in the strip $0 < x \leqslant \pi$ be at $a_1, a_2, \ldots a_n$; and let the residues at them be $c_1, c_2, \ldots c_n$.

Further, let $ABCD$ be a rectangle whose corners are* $-i\rho$, $\pi - i\rho$, $\pi + i\rho'$ and $i\rho'$ in order.

Consider
$$\frac{1}{2\pi i} \int f(t) \cot(t - z)\, dt$$

taken round this rectangle; the residue of the integrand at a_r is $c_r \cot(a_r - z)$, and the residue at z is $f(z)$.

Also the integrals along DA and CB cancel on account of the periodicity of the integrand; and as $\rho \to \infty$, the integrand on AB tends uniformly to $l'i$, while as $\rho' \to \infty$ the integrand on CD tends uniformly to $-li$; therefore
$$\tfrac{1}{2}(l' + l) = f(z) + \sum_{r=1}^{n} c_r \cot(a_r - z).$$

* If any of the poles are on $x = \pi$, shift the rectangle slightly to the right; ρ, ρ' are to be taken so large that $a_1, a_2, \ldots a_n$ are inside the rectangle.

That is to say, we have the expansion

$$f(z) = \frac{1}{2}(l' + l) + \sum_{r=1}^{n} c_r \cot(z - a_r).$$

Example 1.

$$\cot(x - a_1)\cot(x - a_2)\ldots\cot(x - a_n) = \sum_{r=1}^{n}\cot(a_r - a_1)\ldots*\ldots\cot(a_r - a_n)\cot(x - a_r) + (-)^{\frac{1}{2}n},$$

or

$$= \sum_{r=1}^{n}\cot(a_r - a_1)\ldots*\ldots\cot(a_r - a_n)\cot(x - a_r),$$

according as n is even or odd; the * means that the factor $\cot(a_r - a_r)$ is omitted.

Example 2.　Prove that

$$\frac{\sin(x - b_1)\sin(x - b_2)\ldots\sin(x - b_n)}{\sin(x - a_1)\sin(x - a_2)\ldots\sin(x - a_n)} = \frac{\sin(a_1 - b_1)\ldots\sin(a_1 - b_n)}{\sin(a_1 - a_2)\ldots\sin(a_1 - a_n)}\cot(x - a_1)$$

$$+ \frac{\sin(a_2 - b_1)\ldots\sin(a_2 - b_n)}{\sin(a_2 - a_1)\ldots\sin(a_2 - a_n)}\cot(x - a_2)$$

$$+ \ldots\ldots\ldots\ldots\ldots\ldots\ldots\ldots\ldots\ldots\ldots\ldots$$

$$+ \cos(a_1 + a_2 + \ldots + a_n - b_1 - b_2 - \ldots - b_n).$$

7·8.　*Borel's theorem* †.

Let $f(z) = \sum_{n=0}^{\infty} a_n z^n$ be analytic when $|z| \leqslant r$, so that, by § 5·23, $|a_n r^n| < M$, where M is independent of n.

Hence, if $\phi(z) = \sum_{n=0}^{\infty} \frac{a_n z^n}{n!}$, $\phi(z)$ is an integral function, and

$$|\phi(z)| < \sum_{n=0}^{\infty} \frac{M|z^n|}{r^n . n!} = Me^{|z|/r},$$

and similarly $|\phi^{(n)}(z)| < Me^{|z|/r}/r^n$.

Now consider $f_1(z) = \int_0^\infty e^{-t}\phi(zt)\,dt$; this integral is an analytic function of z when $|z| < r$, by § 5·32.

Also, if we integrate by parts,

$$f_1(z) = \left[-e^{-t}\phi(zt) \right]_0^\infty + z\int_0^\infty e^{-t}\phi'(zt)\,dt$$

$$= \sum_{m=0}^{n} z^m \left[-e^{-t}\phi^{(m)}(zt) \right]_0^\infty + z^{n+1}\int_0^\infty e^{-t}\phi^{(n+1)}(zt)\,dt.$$

But $\lim_{t\to 0} e^{-t}\phi^{(m)}(zt) = a_m$; and, when $|z| < r$, $\lim_{t\to\infty} e^{-t}\phi^{(m)}(zt) = 0$.

Therefore　　　　　　　　$f_1(z) = \sum_{m=0}^{n} a_m z^m + R_n,$

† *Leçons sur les séries divergentes* (1901), p. 94.　See also the memoirs there cited.

where
$$|R_n| < |z^{n+1}| \int_0^\infty e^{-t} . Me^{|zt|/r} r^{-n-1} dt$$

$$= |zr^{-1}|^{n+1} M \{1 - |z| r^{-1}\}^{-1} \to 0, \text{ as } n \to \infty .$$

Consequently, when $|z| < r$,
$$f_1(z) = \sum_{m=0}^\infty a_m z^m = f(z) ;$$

and so
$$f(z) = \int_0^\infty e^{-t} \phi(zt) dt,$$

where $\phi(z) = \sum_{n=0}^\infty \dfrac{a_n z^n}{n!}$; $\phi(z)$ is called *Borel's function* associated with $\sum_{n=0}^\infty a_n z^n$.

If $S = \sum_{n=0}^\infty a_n$ and $\phi(z) = \sum_{n=0}^\infty \dfrac{a_n z^n}{n!}$ and if we can establish the relation $S = \int_0^\infty e^{-t} \phi(t) dt$, the series S is said (§ 8·41) to be '*summable (B)*'; so that the theorem just proved shews that a Taylor's series representing an analytic function is summable (B).

7·81. *Borel's integral and analytic continuation.*

We next obtain Borel's result that his integral represents an analytic function in a more extended region than the interior of the circle $|z| = r$.

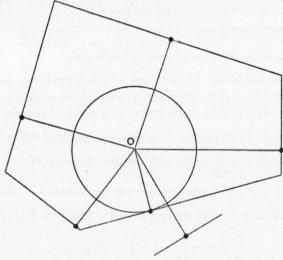

This extended region is obtained as follows: take the singularities a, b, c, ... of $f(z)$ and through each of them draw a line perpendicular to the line joining that singularity to the origin. The lines so drawn will divide the plane into regions of which one is a polygon with the origin inside it.

Then Borel's integral represents an analytic function (which, by § 5·5 and § 7·8, is obviously that defined by $f(z)$ and its continuations) *throughout the interior of this polygon.* The reader will observe that this is the first actual formula obtained for the analytic continuation of a function, except the trivial one of § 5·5, example.

For, take any point P with affix ζ inside the polygon; then the circle on OP as diameter has no singularity on or inside it*; and consequently we can draw a slightly

---

* The reader will see this from the figure; for if there were such a singularity the corresponding side of the polygon would pass between O and P; i.e. P would be outside the polygon.

larger concentric circle* C with no singularity on or inside it.   Then, by § 5·4,

$$a_n = \frac{1}{2\pi i} \int_C \frac{f(z)}{z^{n+1}} dz,$$

and so

$$\phi\,(\zeta t) = \frac{1}{2\pi i} . \sum_{n=0}^{\infty} \frac{\zeta^n t^n}{n\,!} \int_C \frac{f(z)}{z^{n+1}} dz\,;$$

but $\sum\limits_{n=0}^{\infty} \frac{\zeta^n t^n}{n\,!} \frac{f(z)}{z^{n+1}}$ converges uniformly (§ 3·34) on C since $f(z)$ is bounded and $|z| \geqslant \delta > 0$, where δ is independent of z; therefore, by § 4·7,

$$\phi\,(\zeta t) = \frac{1}{2\pi i} \int_C z^{-1} f(z) \exp\,(\zeta t z^{-1})\, dz,$$

and so, when t is real, $|\phi\,(\zeta t)| < F\,(\zeta)\,e^{\lambda t}$, where $F\,(\zeta)$ is bounded in any closed region lying wholly *inside* the polygon and is independent of t; and λ is the greatest value of the real part of ζ/z on C.

If we draw the circle traced out by the point z/ζ, we see that the real part of ζ/z is greatest when z is at the extremity of the diameter through ζ, and so the value of λ is $|\zeta| . \{|\zeta| + \delta\}^{-1} < 1$.

We can get a similar inequality for $\phi'\,(\zeta t)$ and hence, by § 5·32, $\int_0^{\infty} e^{-t} \phi\,(\zeta t)\, dt$ is analytic at ζ and is obviously a one-valued function of ζ.

This is the result stated above.

7·82.   *Expansions in series of inverse factorials.*

A mode of development of functions, which, after being used by Nicole† and Stirling‡ in the eighteenth century, was systematically investigated by Schlömilch§ in 1863, is that of expansion in a series of inverse factorials.

To obtain such an expansion of a function analytic when $|z| > r$, we let the function be $f(z) = \sum\limits_{n=0}^{\infty} a_n z^{-n}$, and use the formula $f(z) = \int_0^{\infty} z e^{-tz} \phi\,(t)\, dt$, where $\phi\,(t) = \sum\limits_{n=0}^{\infty} a_n t^n / (n\,!)$; this result may be obtained in the same way as that of § 7·8.   Modify this by writing $e^{-t} = 1 - \xi$, $\phi\,(t) = F\,(\xi)$; then

$$f(z) = \int_0^1 z\,(1 - \xi)^{z-1}\, F\,(\xi)\, d\xi.$$

Now if $t = u + iv$ and if t be confined to the strip $-\pi < v < \pi$, t is a one-valued function of ξ and $F\,(\xi)$ is an analytic function of ξ; and ξ is restricted so that $-\pi < \arg\,(1 - \xi) < \pi$.   Also the interior of the circle $|\xi| = 1$ corresponds

---

* The difference of the radii of the circles being, say, δ.

† *Mém de l'Acad. des Sci.* (Paris, 1717); see Tweedie, *Proc. Edin. Math. Soc.* xxxvi. (1918).

‡ *Methodus Differentialis* (London, 1730).

§ *Compendium der höheren Analysis.*   More recent investigations are due to Kluyver, Nielsen and Pincherle.   See *Comptes Rendus*, cxxxiii. (1901), cxxxiv. (1902), *Annales de l'École norm. sup.* (3), xix., xxii., xxiii., *Rendiconti dei Lincei*, (5), xi. (1902), and *Palermo Rendiconti*, xxxiv. (1912).   Properties of functions defined by series of inverse factorials have been studied in an important memoir by Nörlund, *Acta Math.* xxxvii. (1914), pp. 327–387.

to the interior of the curve traced out by the point $t = -\log\left(2\cos\frac{1}{2}\theta\right) + \frac{1}{2}i\theta$, (writing $\xi = \exp\{i(\theta+\pi)\}$); and inside this curve

$$|t| - R(t) \leqslant [\{R(t)\}^2 + \pi^2]^{\frac{1}{2}} - R(t) \to 0,$$

as $R(t) \to \infty$.

It follows that, when $|\xi| \leqslant 1$, $|F(\xi)| < Me^{r|t|} < M_1|e^{rt}|$, where M_1 is independent of t; and so $F(\xi) < M_1|(1-\xi)^{-r}|$.

Now suppose that $0 \leqslant \xi < 1$; then, by § 5·23, $|F^{(n)}(\xi)| < M_2 . n! \rho^{-n}$, where M_2 is the upper bound of $|F(z)|$ on a circle with centre ξ and radius $\rho < 1 - \xi$.

Taking $\rho = \dfrac{n}{n+1}(1-\xi)$ and observing that* $(1+n^{-1})^n < e$ we find that

$$|F^{(n)}(\xi)| < M_1\left[1 - \left\{\xi + \frac{n}{n+1}\xi\right\}\right]^{-r} . n! \left\{\frac{n(1-\xi)}{n+1}\right\}^{-n}$$

$$< M_1 e(n+1)^r . n! (1-\xi)^{-r-n}.$$

Remembering that, by § 4·5, $\displaystyle\int_0^1$ means $\displaystyle\lim_{\epsilon\to+0}\int_0^{1-\epsilon}$, we have, by repeated integrations by parts,

$$f(z) = \lim_{\epsilon\to+0}\left[-(1-\xi)^z F(\xi)\right]_0^{1-\epsilon} + \int_0^{1-\epsilon}(1-\xi)^z F'(\xi)\,d\xi$$

$$= \lim_{\epsilon\to+0}\left[-(1-\xi)^z F(\xi)\right]_0^{1-\epsilon} + \frac{1}{z+1}\left[-(1-\xi)^{z+1}F'(\xi)\right]_0^{1-\epsilon}$$

$$+ \frac{1}{z+1}\int_0^{1-\epsilon}(1-\xi)^{z+1}F''(\xi)\,d\xi$$

$$= \ldots\ldots\ldots$$

$$= b_0 + \frac{b_1}{z+1} + \frac{b_2}{(z+1)(z+2)} + \ldots + \frac{b_n}{(z+1)(z+2)\ldots(z+n)} + R_n,$$

where

$$b_n = \lim_{\epsilon\to0}\left[-(1-\xi)^{z+n}F^{(n)}(\xi)\right]_0^{1-\epsilon}$$

$$= F^{(n)}(0),$$

if the real part of $z + n - r - n > 0$, i.e. if $R(z) > r$; further

$$|R_n| \leqslant \frac{1}{|(z+1)(z+2)\ldots(z+n)|}\lim_{\epsilon\to0}\int_0^{1-\epsilon}|(1-\xi)^{z+n}F^{(n+1)}(\xi)|\,d\xi$$

$$< \frac{M_1 e(n+2)^r . n!}{|(z+1)(z+2)\ldots(z+n)| . R(z-r)}$$

$$< \frac{M_1 e(n+2)^r . n!}{(r+1+\delta)(r+2+\delta)\ldots(r+n+\delta) . \delta},$$

where $\delta = R(z-r)$.

---

* $(1+x^{-1})^x$ increases with x; for $\dfrac{1}{1-y} > e^y$, when $y < 1$, and so $\log\left(\dfrac{1}{1-y}\right) > y$. That is to say, putting $y^{-1} = 1+x$, $\dfrac{d}{dx}x\log(1+x^{-1}) = \log(1+x^{-1}) - \dfrac{1}{1+x} > 0$.

Now
$$\prod_{m=1}^{n} \left\{ \left(1 + \frac{r+\delta}{m}\right) e^{-\frac{r+\delta}{m}} \right\}$$

tends to a limit (§ 2·71) as $n \to \infty$, and so $|R_n| \to 0$ if $(n+2)^r e^{-(r+\delta)\sum_1^n 1/m}$ tends to zero; but

$$\sum_{m=1}^{n} 1/m > \int_1^{n+1} \frac{dx}{x} = \log(n+1),$$

by § 4·43 (II), and $(n+2)^r (n+1)^{-r-\delta} \to 0$ when $\delta > 0$; therefore $R_n \to 0$ as $n \to \infty$, and so, when $R(z) > r$, we have the convergent expansion

$$f(z) = b_0 + \frac{b_1}{z+1} + \frac{b_2}{(z+1)(z+2)} + \dots + \frac{b_n}{(z+1)(z+2)\dots(z+n)} + \dots.$$

Example 1. Obtain the same expansion by using the results

$$\frac{1}{(z+1)(z+2)\dots(z+n+1)} = \frac{1}{n!} \int_0^1 u^n (1-u)^z \, du,$$

$$\int_C \frac{f(t)\,dt}{z-t} = \int_C dt \int_0^1 f(t)(1-u)^{z-t-1}\,du.$$

Example 2. Obtain the expansion

$$\log\left(1 + \frac{1}{z}\right) = \frac{1}{z} - \frac{a_1}{z(z+1)} - \frac{a_2}{z(z+1)(z+2)} - \dots\dots,$$

where
$$a_n = \int_0^1 t(1-t)(2-t)\dots(n-1-t)\,dt,$$

and discuss the region in which it converges. (Schlömilch.)

REFERENCES.

E. GOURSAT, *Cours d'Analyse* (Paris, 1911), Chs. XV, XVI.

E. BOREL, *Leçons sur les séries divergentes* (Paris, 1901).

T. J. I'A. BROMWICH*, *Theory of Infinite Series* (1908), Chs. VIII, X, XI.

O. SCHLÖMILCH, *Compendium der höheren Analysis*, II. (Dresden, 1874).

MISCELLANEOUS EXAMPLES.

1. If $y - x - \phi(y) = 0$, where ϕ is a given function of its argument, obtain the expansion

$$f(y) = f(x) + \sum_{m=1}^{\infty} \frac{1}{m!} \{\phi(x)\}^m \left(\frac{1}{1-\phi'(x)} \frac{d}{dx}\right)^m f(x),$$

where f denotes any analytic function of its argument, and discuss the range of its validity. (Levi-Città, *Rend. dei Lincei*, (5), XVI. (1907), p. 3.)

2. Obtain (from the formula of Darboux or otherwise) the expansion

$$f(z) - f(a) = \sum_{n=1}^{\infty} \frac{(-)^{n-1}(z-a)^n}{n!(1-r)^n} \{f^{(n)}(z) - r^n f^{(n)}(a)\};$$

find the remainder after n terms, and discuss the convergence of the series.

* The expansions considered by Bromwich are obtained by elementary methods, i.e. without the use of Cauchy's theorem.

3. Shew that

$$f(x+h)-f(x)=\sum_{m=1}^{n} (-)^{m-1}\frac{1 \cdot 3 \cdot 5 \ldots (2m-1)}{(m!)^2}\frac{h^m}{2^m}\{f^{(m)}(x+h)-(-)^m f^{(m)}(x)\}$$

$$+(-)^n h^{n+1}\int_0^1 \gamma_n(t)f^{(n+1)}(x+ht)\,dt,$$

where

$$\gamma_n(x)=\frac{x^{n+\frac{1}{2}}(1-x)^{n+\frac{1}{2}}}{(n!)^2}\frac{d^n}{dx^n}\{x^{-\frac{1}{2}}(1-x)^{-\frac{1}{2}}\}=\frac{1}{\pi \cdot n!}\int_0^1 (x-z)^n z^{-\frac{1}{2}}(1-z)^{-\frac{1}{2}}\,dz,$$

and shew that $\gamma_n(x)$ is the coefficient of $n!\,t^n$ in the expansion of $\{(1-tx)(1+t-tx)\}^{-\frac{1}{2}}$ in ascending powers of t.

4. By taking

$$\phi(x+1)=\frac{1}{n!}\left[\frac{d^n}{du^n}\left\{\frac{(1-r)e^{xu}}{1-re^{-u}}\right\}\right]_{u=0}$$

in the formula of Darboux, shew that

$$f(x+h)-f(x)=-\sum_{m=1}^{n} a_m \frac{h^m}{m!}\left\{f^{(m)}(x+h)-\frac{1}{r}f^{(m)}(x)\right\}$$

$$+(-)^n h^{n+1}\int_0^1 \phi(t)f^{(n+1)}(x+ht)\,dt,$$

where

$$\frac{1-r}{1-re^{-u}}=1-a_1\frac{u}{1!}+a_2\frac{u^2}{2!}-a_3\frac{u^3}{3!}+\ldots.$$

5. Shew that

$$f(z)-f(a)=\sum_{m=1}^{n} (-)^{m-1}\frac{2B_m(2^{2n}-1)(z-a)^{2m-1}}{2m!}\{f^{(2m-1)}(a)+f^{(2m-1)}(z)\}$$

$$+\frac{(z-a)^{2n+1}}{2n!}\int_0^1 \psi_{2n}(t)f^{(2n+1)}\{a+t(z-a)\}\,dt,$$

where

$$\psi_n(t)=\frac{2}{n+1}\left[\frac{d^{n+1}}{du^{n+1}}\left(\frac{ue^{tu}}{e^u+1}\right)\right]_{u=0}.$$

6. Prove that.

$$f(z_2)-f(z_1)=C_1(z_2-z_1)f'(z_2)+C_2(z_2-z_1)^2 f''(z_1)-C_3(z_2-z_1)^3 f'''(z_2)$$

$$-C_4(z_2-z_1)^4 f^{\text{iv}}(z_1)+\ldots+(-)^n(z_2-z_1)^{n+1}\int_0^1 \left\{\frac{d^n}{du^n}(e^{tu}\operatorname{sech} u)\right\}_{u=0} f^{(n+1)}(z_1+tz_2-tz_1)\,dt\,;$$

in the series plus signs and minus signs occur in pairs, and the last term before the integral is that involving $(z_2-z_1)^n$; also C_n is the coefficient of z^n in the expansion of $\cot\left(\frac{\pi}{4}-\frac{z}{2}\right)$ in ascending powers of z.   (Trinity, 1899.)

7. If x_1 and x_2 are integers, and $\phi(z)$ is a function which is analytic and bounded for all values of z such that $x_1 \leqslant R(z) \leqslant x_2$, shew (by integrating

$$\int \frac{\phi(z)\,dz}{e^{\pm 2\pi i z}-1}$$

round indented rectangles whose corners are x_1, x_2, $x_2\pm\infty i$, $x_1\pm\infty i$) that

$$\tfrac{1}{2}\phi(x_1)+\phi(x_1+1)+\phi(x_1+2)+\ldots+\phi(x_2-1)+\tfrac{1}{2}\phi(x_2)$$

$$=\int_{x_1}^{x_2}\phi(z)\,dz+\frac{1}{i}\int_0^\infty \frac{\phi(x_2+iy)-\phi(x_1+iy)-\phi(x_2-iy)+\phi(x_1-iy)}{e^{2\pi y}-1}\,dy.$$

Hence, by applying the theorem

$$4n\int_0^\infty \frac{y^{2n-1}}{e^{2\pi y}-1}\,dy=B_n,$$

where B_1, B_2, ... are Bernoulli's numbers, shew that

$$\phi(1)+\phi(2)+...+\phi(n)=C+\tfrac{1}{2}\phi(n)+\int_0^n \phi(z)\,dz+\sum_{r=1}^{\infty}\frac{(-)^{r-1}B_r}{2r!}\phi^{(2r-1)}(n),$$

(where C is a constant not involving n), provided that the last series converges.

(This important formula is due to Plana, *Mem. della R. Accad. di Torino*, XXV. (1820), pp. 403–418; a proof by means of contour integration was published by Kronecker, *Journal für Math.* CV. (1889), pp. 345–348. For a detailed history, see Lindelöf, *Le Calcul des Résidus*. Some applications of the formula are given in Chapter XII.)

8. Obtain the expansion

$$u=\frac{x}{2}+\sum_{n=2}^{\infty}(-)^{n-1}\frac{1.3...(2n-3)}{n!}\frac{x^n}{2^n}$$

for one root of the equation $x=2u+u^2$, and shew that it converges so long as $|x|<1$.

9. If $S_{2n+1}^{(m)}$ denote the sum of all combinations of the numbers

$$1^2,\ 3^2,\ 5^2,\ ...\ (2n-1)^2,$$

taken m at a time, shew that

$$\frac{\cos z}{z}=\frac{1}{\sin z}+\sum_{n=0}^{\infty}\frac{(-)^{n+1}}{(2n+2)!}\left\{\frac{2^{2(n+1)}}{2n+3}-S_{2(n+1)}^{(1)}\frac{2^{2n}}{2n+1}+...+(-)^n S_{2(n+1)}^{(n)}\frac{2^2}{3}\right\}\sin^{2n+1}z.$$

(Teixeira.)

10. If the function $f(z)$ is analytic in the interior of that one of the ovals whose equation is $|\sin z|=C$ (where $C\leqslant 1$), which includes the origin, shew that $f(z)$ can, for all points z within this oval, be expanded in the form

$$f(z)=f(0)+\sum_{n=1}^{\infty}\frac{f^{(2n)}(0)+S_{2n}^{(1)}f^{(2n-2)}(0)+...+S_{2n}^{(n-1)}f''(0)}{2n!}\sin^{2n}z$$

$$+\sum_{n=0}^{\infty}\frac{f^{(2n+1)}(0)+S_{2n+1}^{(1)}f^{(2n-1)}(0)+...+S_{2n+1}^{(n)}f'(0)}{(2n+1)!}\sin^{2n+1}z,$$

where $S_{2n}^{(m)}$ is the sum of all combinations of the numbers

$$2^2,\ 4^2,\ 6^2,\ ...\ (2n-2)^2,$$

taken m at a time, and $S_{2n+1}^{(m)}$ denotes the sum of all combinations of the numbers

$$1^2,\ 3^2,\ 5^2,\ ...\ (2n-1)^2,$$

taken m at a time.

(Teixeira.)

11. Shew that the two series

$$2z+\frac{2z^3}{3^2}+\frac{2z^5}{5^2}+...,$$

and

$$\frac{2z}{1-z^2}-\frac{2}{1.3^2}\left(\frac{2z}{1-z^2}\right)^3+\frac{2.4}{3.5^2}\left(\frac{2z}{1-z^2}\right)^5-...,$$

represent the same function in a certain region of the z plane, and can be transformed into each other by Bürmann's theorem.

(Kapteyn, *Nieuw Archief*, (2), III. (1897), p. 225.)

12. If a function $f(z)$ is periodic, of period 2π, and is analytic at all points in the infinite strip of the plane, included between the two branches of the curve $|\sin z|=C$ (where $C>1$), shew that at all points in the strip it can be expanded in an infinite series of the form

$$f(z)=A_0+A_1\sin z+...+A_n\sin^n z+......$$

$$+\cos z\,(B_1+B_2\sin z+...+B_n\sin^{n-1}z+...);$$

and find the coefficients A_n and B_n.

13.   If ϕ and f are connected by the equation

$$\phi(x) + \lambda f(x) = 0,$$

of which one root is a, shew that

$$F(x) = F - \frac{\lambda}{1}\frac{1}{\phi'}, fF' + \frac{\lambda^2}{1!\,2!}\frac{1}{\phi'^3}\begin{vmatrix} \phi' & f^2F' \\ \phi'' & (f^2F')' \end{vmatrix} - \frac{\lambda^3}{1!\,2!\,3!}\frac{1}{\phi'^6}\begin{vmatrix} \phi' & (\phi^2)' & (f^3F') \\ \phi'' & (\phi^2)'' & (f^3F')' \\ \phi''' & (\phi^2)''' & (f^3F')'' \end{vmatrix} + \dots,$$

the general term being $(-)^m \dfrac{\lambda^m}{1!\,2!\,\dots\,m!\,(\phi')^{\frac{1}{2}m(m+1)}}$ multiplied by a determinant in which the elements of the first row are ϕ', $(\phi^2)'$, $(\phi^3)'$, $\dots$, $(\phi^{m-1})'$, (f^mF') and each row is the differential coefficient of the preceding one with respect to a; and F, f, F', $\dots$ denote $F(a)$, $f(a)$, $F'(a)$, $\dots$.

(Wronski, *Philosophie de la Technie*, Section II. p. 381.   For proofs of the theorem see Cayley, *Quarterly Journal*, XII. (1873), Transon, *Nouv. Ann. de Math.* XIII. (1874), and C. Lagrange, *Brux. Mém. Couronnés*, 4°, XLVII. (1886), no. 2.)

14.   If the function $W(a, b, x)$ be defined by the series

$$W(a, b, x) = x + \frac{a-b}{2!}x^2 + \frac{(a-b)(a-2b)}{3!}x^3 + \dots,$$

which converges so long as $\qquad |x| < \dfrac{1}{|b|}$,

shew that $\qquad \dfrac{d}{dx}W(a, b, x) = 1 + (a-b)\,W(a-b, b, x)$;

and shew that if $\qquad y = W(a, b, x)$,

then $\qquad x = W(b, a, y)$.

Examples of this function are

$$W(1, 0, x) = e^x - 1,$$
$$W(0, 1, x) = \log(1+x),$$
$$W(a, 1, x) = \frac{(1+x)^a - 1}{a}. \qquad\qquad \text{(Ježek.)}$$

15.   Prove that

$$\frac{1}{\sum\limits_{n=0}^{\infty} a_n x^n} = \frac{1}{a_0} + \sum_1^{\infty}\frac{(-)^n x^n}{n!\,a_0^{n+1}}G_n,$$

where $\quad G_n = \begin{vmatrix} 2a_1 & a_0 & 0 & 0 & \dots & 0 \\ 4a_2 & 3a_1 & 2a_0 & 0 & \dots & 0 \\ 6a_3 & 5a_2 & 4a_1 & 3a_0 & \dots & 0 \\ \hdotsfor{6} \\ (2n-2)a_{n-1} & \hdotsfor{4} & (n-1)a_0 \\ na_n & (n-1)a_{n-1} & \hdotsfor{3} & a_1 \end{vmatrix}$,

and obtain a similar expression for

$$\left\{\sum_{n=0}^{\infty} a_n x^n\right\}^{\frac{1}{2}}.$$

(Mangeot, *Ann. de l'École norm. sup.* (3), XIV.)

16.   Shew that

$$\frac{1}{\sum\limits_{r=0}^{n} a_r x^r} = -\sum_{r=0}^{\infty}\frac{1}{r+1}\frac{\partial S_{r+1}}{\partial a_1}x^r,$$

where S_r is the sum of the rth powers of the reciprocals of the roots of the equation

$$\sum_{r=0}^{n} a_r x^r = 0.$$

(Gambioli, *Bologna Memorie*, 1892.)

17.   If $f_n(z)$ denote the nth derivate of $f(z)$, and if $f_{-n}(z)$ denote that one of the nth integrals of $f(z)$ which has an n-ple zero at $z=0$, shew that if the series

$$\sum_{n=-\infty}^{\infty} f_n(z) g_{-n}(x)$$

is convergent it represents a function of $z+x$; and if the domain of convergence includes the origin in the x-plane, the series is equal to

$$\sum_{n=0}^{\infty} f_{-n}(z+x) g_n(0).$$

Obtain Taylor's series from this result, by putting $g(z)=1$.   (Guichard.)

18.   Shew that, if x be not an integer,

$$\sum_{m=-\nu}^{\nu} \sum_{n=-\nu}^{\nu} \frac{2x+m+n}{(x+m)^2(x+n)^2} \to 0$$

as $\nu \to \infty$, provided that all terms for which $m=n$ are omitted from the summation.

(Math. Trip. 1895.)

19.   Sum the series

$$\sum_{n=-q}^{p} \left(\frac{1}{(-)^n x - a - n} + \frac{1}{n} \right),$$

where the value $n=0$ is omitted, and p, q are positive integers to be increased without limit.

(Math. Trip. 1896.)

20.   If $F(x)=e^{\int_0^x x\pi \cot(x\pi)\,dx}$, shew that

$$F(x)=e^x \frac{\prod\limits_{n=1}^{\infty} \left\{ \left(1-\frac{x}{n}\right)^n e^{x+\frac{1}{2}\frac{x^2}{n}} \right\}}{\prod\limits_{n=1}^{\infty} \left\{ \left(1+\frac{x}{n}\right)^n e^{-x+\frac{1}{2}\frac{x^2}{n}} \right\}},$$

and that the function thus defined satisfies the relations

$$F(-x)=\frac{1}{F(x)}, \quad F(x)\,F(1-x)=2\sin x\pi.$$

Further, if $\psi(z)=z+\dfrac{z^2}{2^2}+\dfrac{z^3}{3^2}+\ldots = -\displaystyle\int_0^z \log(1-t)\,\frac{dt}{t},$

shew that $F(x)=e^{\frac{1}{2}\pi i x^2 - \frac{1}{2\pi i}\psi(1-e^{-2\pi i x})}$

when $|1-e^{-2\pi i x}| < 1.$ (Trinity, 1898.)

21.   Shew that

$$\left[1+\left(\frac{k}{x}\right)^n\right]\left[1+\left(\frac{k}{2\pi-x}\right)^n\right]\left[1+\left(\frac{k}{2\pi+x}\right)^n\right]\left[1+\left(\frac{k}{4\pi-x}\right)^n\right]\left[1+\left(\frac{k}{4\pi+x}\right)^n\right]\cdots$$

$$=\frac{\prod\limits_{g=1}^{\frac{1}{2}n} \{1-2e^{-a_g}\cos(x+\beta_g)+e^{-2a_g}\}^{\frac{1}{2}} \{1-2e^{-a_g}\cos(x-\beta_g)+e^{-2a_g}\}^{\frac{1}{2}}}{2^{\frac{1}{2}n}(1-\cos x)^{\frac{1}{2}n} e^{-k\cos \pi/n}},$$

where $a_g=k\sin\dfrac{2g-1}{n}\pi, \quad \beta_g=k\cos\dfrac{2g-1}{n}\pi,$

and $0<x<2\pi.$ (Mildner.)

22. If $|x| < 1$ and a is not a positive integer, shew that

$$\sum_{n=1}^{\infty} \frac{x^n}{n-a} = \frac{2\pi i x^a}{1-e^{2a\pi i}} + \frac{x}{1-e^{2a\pi i}} \int_C \frac{t^{a-1} - x^{a-1}}{t-x} \, dt,$$

where C is a contour in the t-plane enclosing the points 0, x.

(Lerch, *Casopis*, XXI. (1892), pp. 65–68.)

23. If $\phi_1(z)$, $\phi_2(z)$, ... are any polynomials in z, and if $F(z)$ be any integrable function, and if $\psi_1(z)$, $\psi_2(z)$, ... be polynomials defined by the equations

$$\int_a^b F(x) \frac{\phi_1(z) - \phi_1(x)}{z-x} \, dx = \psi_1(z),$$

$$\int_a^b F(x) \phi_1(x) \frac{\phi_2(z) - \phi_2(x)}{z-x} \, dx = \psi_2(z),$$

$$\int_a^b F(x) \phi_1(x) \phi_2(x) \dots \phi_{m-1}(x) \frac{\phi_m(z) - \phi_m(x)}{z-x} \, dx = \psi_m(z),$$

shew that $\displaystyle \int_a^b \frac{F(x)\,dx}{z-x} = \frac{\psi_1(z)}{\phi_1(z)} + \frac{\psi_2(z)}{\phi_1(z)\phi_2(z)} + \frac{\psi_3(z)}{\phi_1(z)\phi_2(z)\phi_3(z)} + \cdots\cdots$

$$+ \frac{\psi_m(z)}{\phi_1(z)\phi_2(z)\dots\phi_m(z)} + \frac{1}{\phi_1(z)\phi_2(z)\dots\phi_m(z)} \int_a^b F(x)\phi_1(x)\phi_2(x)\dots\phi_m(x) \frac{dx}{z-x}.$$

24. A system of functions $p_0(z)$, $p_1(z)$, $p_2(z)$, ... is defined by the equations

$$p_0(z) = 1, \quad p_{n+1}(z) = (z^2 + a_n z + b_n) p_n(z),$$

where a_n and b_n are given functions of n, which tend respectively to the limits 0 and -1 as $n \to \infty$.

Shew that the region of convergence of a series of the form $\Sigma e_n p_n(z)$, where e_1, e_2, ... are independent of z, is a Cassini's oval with the foci $+1$, -1.

Shew that every function $f(z)$, which is analytic on and inside the oval, can, for points inside the oval, be expanded in a series

$$f(z) = \Sigma(c_n + z c_n') p_n(z),$$

where

$$c_n = \frac{1}{2\pi i} \int (a_n + z) q_n(z) f(z) \, dz, \quad c_n' = \frac{1}{2\pi i} \int q_n(z) f(z) \, dz,$$

the integrals being taken round the boundary of the region, and the functions $q_n(z)$ being defined by the equations

$$q_0(z) = \frac{1}{z^2 + a_0 z + b_0}, \quad q_{n+1}(z) = \frac{1}{z^2 + a_{n+1} z + b_{n+1}} q_n(z).$$

(Pincherle, *Rend. dei Lincei*, (4), V. (1889), p. 8.)

25. Let C be a contour enclosing the point a, and let $\phi(z)$ and $f(z)$ be analytic when z is on or inside C. Let $|t|$ be so small that

$$|t\phi(z)| < |z-a|$$

when z is on the periphery of C.

By expanding

$$\frac{1}{2\pi i} \int_C f(z) \frac{1 - t\phi'(z)}{z - a - t\phi(z)} \, dz$$

in ascending powers of t, shew that it is equal to

$$f(a) + \sum_{n=1}^{\infty} \frac{t^n}{n!} \frac{d^{n-1}}{da^{n-1}} [f'(a) \{\phi(a)\}^n].$$

Hence, by using §§ 6·3, 6·31, obtain Lagrange's theorem.

CHAPTER VIII

ASYMPTOTIC EXPANSIONS AND SUMMABLE SERIES

8·1. *Simple example of an asymptotic expansion.*

Consider the function $f(x) = \int_x^\infty t^{-1} e^{x-t}\, dt$, where x is real and positive, and the path of integration is the real axis.

By repeated integrations by parts, we obtain

$$f(x) = \frac{1}{x} - \frac{1}{x^2} + \frac{2!}{x^3} - \dots + \frac{(-)^{n-1}(n-1)!}{x^n} + (-)^n n! \int_x^\infty \frac{e^{x-t}\, dt}{t^{n+1}}.$$

In connexion with the function $f(x)$, we therefore consider the expression

$$u_{n-1} = \frac{(-)^{n-1}(n-1)!}{x^n},$$

and we shall write

$$\sum_{m=0}^{n} u_m = \frac{1}{x} - \frac{1}{x^2} + \frac{2!}{x^3} - \dots + \frac{(-)^n n!}{x^{n+1}} = S_n(x).$$

Then we have $|u_m/u_{m-1}| = mx^{-1} \to \infty$ as $m \to \infty$. *The series Σu_m is therefore divergent for all values of x.* In spite of this, however, the series can be used for the calculation of $f(x)$; this can be seen in the following way.

Take any fixed value for the number n, and calculate the value of S_n. We have

$$f(x) - S_n(x) = (-)^{n+1}(n+1)! \int_x^\infty \frac{e^{x-t}\, dt}{t^{n+2}},$$

and therefore, since $e^{x-t} \leqslant 1$,

$$|f(x) - S_n(x)| = (n+1)! \int_x^\infty \frac{e^{x-t}\, dt}{t^{n+2}} < (n+1)! \int_x^\infty \frac{dt}{t^{n+2}} = \frac{n!}{x^{n+1}}.$$

For values of x which are sufficiently large, the right-hand member of this equation is very small. Thus, if we take $x \geqslant 2n$, we have

$$|f(x) - S_n(x)| < \frac{1}{2^{n+1}n^2},$$

which for large values of n is very small. It follows therefore that *the value of the function $f(x)$ can be calculated with great accuracy for large values of x, by taking the sum of a suitable number of terms of the series Σu_m.*

Taking even fairly small values of x and n

$$S_5(10) = 0\cdot09152, \quad \text{and} \quad 0 < f(10) - S_5(10) < 0\cdot00012.$$

The series is on this account said to be an *asymptotic expansion* of the function $f(x)$.   The precise definition of an asymptotic expansion will now be given.

8·2.   *Definition of an asymptotic expansion.*

A divergent series

$$A_0 + \frac{A_1}{z} + \frac{A_2}{z^2} + \dots + \frac{A_n}{z^n} + \dots,$$

in which the sum of the first $(n+1)$ terms is $S_n(z)$, is said to be an *asymptotic expansion* of a function $f(z)$ for a given range of values of $\arg z$, if the expression $R_n(z) = z^n \{f(z) - S_n(z)\}$ satisfies the condition

$$\lim_{|z| \to \infty} R_n(z) = 0 \quad (n \text{ fixed}),$$

even though
$$\lim_{n \to \infty} |R_n(z)| = \infty \quad (z \text{ fixed}).$$

When this is the case, we can make

$$| z^n \{f(z) - S_n(z)\} | < \epsilon,$$

where ϵ is arbitrarily small, by taking $|z|$ sufficiently large.

We denote the fact that the series is the asymptotic expansion of $f(z)$ by writing

$$f(z) \sim \sum_{n=0}^{\infty} A_n z^{-n}.$$

The definition which has just been given is due to Poincaré[*].   Special asymptotic expansions had, however, been discovered and used in the eighteenth century by Stirling, Maclaurin and Euler.   Asymptotic expansions are of great importance in the theory of Linear Differential Equations, and in Dynamical Astronomy; some applications will be given in subsequent chapters of the present work.

The example discussed in § 8·1 clearly satisfies the definition just given: for, when x is positive, $|x^n \{f(x) - S_n(x)\}| < n! \, x^{-1} \to 0$ as $x \to \infty$.

For the sake of simplicity, in this chapter we shall for the most part consider asymptotic expansions only in connexion with real positive values of the argument. The theory for complex values of the argument may be discussed by an extension of the analysis.

8·21.   *Another example of an asymptotic expansion.*

As a second example, consider the function $f(x)$, represented by the series

$$f(x) = \sum_{k=1}^{\infty} \frac{c^k}{x+k},$$

where $x > 0$ and $0 < c < 1$.

[*] *Acta Mathematica*, VIII. (1886), pp. 295–344.

The ratio of the kth term of this series to the $(k-1)$th is less than c, and consequently the series converges for all positive values of x. We shall confine our attention to positive values of x. We have, when $x > k$,

$$\frac{1}{x+k} = \frac{1}{x} - \frac{k}{x^2} + \frac{k^2}{x^3} - \frac{k^3}{x^4} + \frac{k^4}{x^5} - \dots.$$

If, therefore, it were allowable* to expand each fraction $\frac{1}{x+k}$ in this way, and to rearrange the series for $f(x)$ in descending powers of x, we should obtain the formal series

$$\frac{A_1}{x} + \frac{A_2}{x^2} + \dots + \frac{A_n}{x^n} + \dots,$$

where
$$A_n = (-)^{n-1} \sum_{k=1}^{\infty} k^{n-1} c^k.$$

But this procedure is not legitimate, and in fact $\sum_{n=1}^{\infty} A_n x^{-n}$ diverges. We can, however, shew that it is an asymptotic expansion of $f(x)$.

For let
$$S_n(x) = \frac{A_1}{x} + \frac{A_2}{x^2} + \dots + \frac{A_n}{x^{n+1}}.$$

Then
$$S_n(x) = \sum_{k=1}^{\infty} \left(\frac{c^k}{x} - \frac{kc^k}{x^2} + \frac{k^2 c^k}{x^3} + \dots + \frac{(-)^n k^n c^k}{x^{n+1}} \right)$$

$$= \sum_{k=1}^{\infty} \left\{ 1 - \left(-\frac{k}{x} \right)^{n+1} \right\} \frac{c^k}{x+k};$$

so that
$$| f(x) - S_n(x) | = \left| \sum_{k=1}^{\infty} \left(-\frac{k}{x} \right)^{n+1} \frac{c^k}{x+k} \right| < x^{-n-2} \sum_{k=1}^{\infty} k^n c^k.$$

Now $\sum_{k=1}^{\infty} k^n c^k$ converges for any given value of n and is equal to C_n, say; and hence $| f(x) - S_n(x) | < C_n x^{-n-2}$.

Consequently
$$f(x) \sim \sum_{n=1}^{\infty} A_n x^{-n}.$$

Example. If $f(x) = \int_{x}^{\infty} e^{x^2 - t^2} dt$, where x is positive and the path of integration is the real axis, prove that

$$f(x) \sim \frac{1}{2x} - \frac{1}{2^2 x^3} + \frac{1 \cdot 3}{2^3 x^5} - \frac{1 \cdot 3 \cdot 5}{2^4 x^7} + \dots.$$

[In fact, it was shewn by Stokes in 1857 that

$$\int_{0}^{x} e^{x^2 - t^2} dt \sim \pm \tfrac{1}{2} e^{x^2} \sqrt{\pi} - \left(\frac{1}{2x} - \frac{1}{2^2 x^3} + \frac{1 \cdot 3}{2^3 x^5} - \frac{1 \cdot 3 \cdot 5}{2^4 x^7} + \dots \right);$$

the upper or lower sign is to be taken according as $-\tfrac{1}{2}\pi < \arg x < \tfrac{1}{2}\pi$ or $\tfrac{1}{2}\pi < \arg x < \tfrac{3}{2}\pi$.]

8·3. *Multiplication of asymptotic expansions.*

We shall now shew that two asymptotic expansions, valid for a common range of values of $\arg z$, can be multiplied together in the same way as ordinary series, the result being a new asymptotic expansion.

For let
$$f(z) \sim \sum_{m=0}^{\infty} A_m z^{-m}, \qquad \phi(z) \sim \sum_{m=0}^{\infty} B_m z^{-m},$$

---

* It is not allowable, since $k > x$ for all terms of the series after some definite term.

and let $S_n(z)$ and $T_n(z)$ be the sums of their first $(n+1)$ terms; so that, n being fixed,

$$f(z) - S_n(z) = o(z^{-n}), \quad \phi(z) - T_n(z) = o(z^{-n}).$$

Then, if $C_m = A_0 B_m + A_1 B_{m-1} + \ldots + A_m B_0$, it is obvious that*

$$S_n(z) \, T_n(z) = \sum_{m=0}^{n} C_m z^{-m} + o(z^{-n}).$$

But
$$f(z)\,\phi(z) = \{S_n(z) + o(z^{-n})\} \{T_n(z) + o(z^{-n})\}$$

$$= S_n(z) \, T_n(z) + o(z^{-n})$$

$$= \sum_{m=0}^{n} C_m z^{-m} + o(z^{-n}).$$

This result being true for *any* fixed value of n, we see that

$$f(z)\,\phi(z) \sim \sum_{m=0}^{\infty} C_m z^{-m}.$$

8·31. *Integration of asymptotic expansions.*

We shall now shew that it is permissible to integrate an asymptotic expansion term by term, the resulting series being the asymptotic expansion of the integral of the function represented by the original series.

For let $\quad f(x) \sim \sum_{m=2}^{\infty} A_m x^{-m}$, and let $S_n(x) = \sum_{m=2}^{n} A_m x^{-m}$.

Then, given any positive number ϵ, we can find x_0 such that

$$|f(x) - S_n(x)| < \epsilon |x|^{-n} \text{ when } x > x_0,$$

and therefore

$$\left| \int_x^\infty f(x)\,dx - \int_x^\infty S_n(x)\,dx \right| \leqslant \int_x^\infty |f(x) - S_n(x)|\,dx$$

$$< \frac{\epsilon}{(n-1)\,x^{n-1}}.$$

But
$$\int_x^\infty S_n(x)\,dx = \frac{A_2}{x} + \frac{A_3}{2x^2} + \ldots + \frac{A_n}{(n-1)\,x^{n-1}},$$

and therefore
$$\int_x^\infty f(x)\,dx \sim \sum_{m=2}^{\infty} \frac{A_m}{(m-1)\,x^{m-1}}.$$

On the other hand, it is not in general permissible† to differentiate an asymptotic expansion; this may be seen by considering $e^{-x} \sin(e^x)$.

8·32. *Uniqueness of an asymptotic expansion.*

A question naturally suggests itself, as to whether a given series can be

---

* See § 2·11; we use $o(z^{-n})$ to denote *any* function $\psi(z)$ such that $z^n \psi(z) \to 0$ as $|z| \to \infty$.

† For a theorem concerning differentiation of asymptotic expansions representing analytic functions, see Ritt, *Bull. American Math. Soc.* xxiv. (1918), pp. 225–227.

the asymptotic expansion of several distinct functions. The answer to this is in the affirmative. To shew this, we first observe that there are functions $L(x)$ which are represented asymptotically by a series all of whose terms are zero, i.e. functions such that $\lim_{x \to \infty} x^n L(x) = 0$ for every fixed value of n. The function e^{-x} is such a function when x is positive. The asymptotic expansion[*] of a function $J(x)$ is therefore also the asymptotic expansion of

$$J(x) + L(x).$$

On the other hand, a function cannot be represented by more than one distinct asymptotic expansion over the whole of a given range of values of z; for, if

$$f(z) \sim \sum_{m=0}^{\infty} A_m z^{-m}, \quad f(z) \sim \sum_{m=0}^{\infty} B_m z^{-m},$$

then

$$\lim_{z \to \infty} z^n \left(A_0 + \frac{A_1}{z} + \ldots + \frac{A_n}{z^n} - B_0 - \frac{B_1}{z} - \ldots - \frac{B_n}{z^n} \right) = 0,$$

which can only be if

$$A_0 = B_0; \quad A_1 = B_1, \ldots.$$

Important examples of asymptotic expansions will be discussed later, in connexion with the Gamma-function (Chapter XII) and Bessel functions (Chapter XVII).

8·4. *Methods of 'summing' series.*

We have seen that it is possible to obtain a development of the form

$$f(x) = \sum_{m=0}^{n} A_m x^{-m} + R_n(x),$$

where $R_n(x) \to \infty$ as $n \to \infty$, and the series $\sum_{m=0}^{\infty} A_m x^{-m}$ does not converge.

We now consider what meaning, if any, can be attached to the 'sum' of a non-convergent series. That is to say, given the numbers $a_0, a_1, a_2, \ldots$, we wish to formulate definite rules by which we can obtain from them a number S such that $S = \sum_{n=0}^{\infty} a_n$ if $\sum_{n=0}^{\infty} a_n$ converges, and such that S exists when this series does not converge.

8·41. *Borel's[†] method of summation.*

We have seen (§ 7·81) that

$$\sum_{n=0}^{\infty} a_n z^n = \int_0^{\infty} e^{-t} \phi(tz) \, dt,$$

where $\phi(tz) = \sum_{n=0}^{\infty} \frac{a_n t^n z^n}{n!}$, the equation certainly being true inside the circle of convergence of $\sum_{n=0}^{\infty} a_n z^n$. If the integral exists at points z outside this circle, we define the 'Borel sum' of $\sum_{n=0}^{\infty} a_n z^n$ to mean the integral.

---

[*] It has been shewn that when the coefficients in the expansion satisfy certain inequalities, there is only one *analytic* function with that asymptotic expansion. See *Phil. Trans.* 213, A, (1911), pp. 279–313.

[†] Borel, *Leçons sur les Séries Divergentes* (1901), pp. 97–115.

Thus, whenever $R(z) < 1$, the 'Borel sum' of the series $\sum\limits_{n=0}^{\infty} z^n$ is

$$\int_0^{\infty} e^{-t} e^{tz} dt = (1 - z)^{-1}.$$

If the 'Borel sum' exists we say that the series is 'summable (B).'

8·42. *Euler's* method of summation.*

A method, practically due to Euler, is suggested by the theorem of § 3·71; the 'sum' of $\sum\limits_{n=0}^{\infty} a_n$ may be defined as $\lim\limits_{x \to 1-0} \sum\limits_{n=0}^{\infty} a_n x^n$, when this limit exists.

Thus the 'sum' of the series $1 - 1 + 1 - 1 + \ldots$ would be

$$\lim_{x \to 1-0} (1 - x + x^2 - \ldots) = \lim_{x \to 1-0} (1 + x)^{-1} = \tfrac{1}{2}.$$

8·43. *Cesàro's† method of summation.*

Let $s_n = a_1 + a_2 + \ldots + a_n$; then *if* $S = \lim\limits_{n \to \infty} \dfrac{1}{n}(s_1 + s_2 + \ldots + s_n)$ *exists, we* say that $\sum\limits_{n=1}^{\infty} a_n$ is '*summable* $(C\,1)$,' and that its sum $(C\,1)$ is S. It is necessary to establish the 'condition of consistency‡,' namely that $S = \sum\limits_{n=1}^{\infty} a_n$ when this series is convergent.

To obtain the required result, let $\sum\limits_{m=1}^{\infty} a_m = s$, $\sum\limits_{m=1}^{n} s_m = nS_n$; then we have to prove that $S_n \to s$.

Given ϵ, we can choose n such that $\left| \sum\limits_{m=n+1}^{n+p} a_m \right| < \epsilon$ for all values of p, and so $|s - s_n| \leqslant \epsilon$.

Then, if $\nu > n$, we have

$$S_\nu = a_1 + a_2 \left(1 - \frac{1}{\nu}\right) + \ldots + a_n \left(1 - \frac{n-1}{\nu}\right) + a_{n+1}\left(1 - \frac{n}{\nu}\right) + \ldots + a_\nu \left(1 - \frac{\nu-1}{\nu}\right).$$

Since $1, 1 - \nu^{-1}, 1 - 2\nu^{-1}, \ldots$ is a positive decreasing sequence, it follows from Abel's inequality (§ 2·301) that

$$\left| a_{n+1}\left(1 - \frac{n}{\nu}\right) + a_{n+2}\left(1 - \frac{n+1}{\nu}\right) + \ldots + a_\nu\left(1 - \frac{\nu-1}{\nu}\right) \right| < \left(1 - \frac{n}{\nu}\right)\epsilon.$$

Therefore

$$\left| S_\nu - \left\{ a_1 + a_2\left(1 - \frac{1}{\nu}\right) + \ldots + a_n\left(1 - \frac{n-1}{\nu}\right) \right\} \right| < \left(1 - \frac{n}{\nu}\right)\epsilon.$$

---

* *Instit. Calc. Diff.* (1755). See Borel, *loc. cit.* Introduction.

† *Bulletin des Sciences Math.* (2), xiv. (1890), p. 114.

‡ See the end of § 8·4.

Making $\nu \to \infty$, we see that, if S be any one of the limit points (§ 2·21) of S_ν, then

$$\left| S - \sum_{m=1}^{n} a_m \right| \leqslant \epsilon.$$

Therefore, since $|s - s_n| \leqslant \epsilon$, we have

$$|S - s| \leqslant 2\epsilon.$$

This inequality being true for *every* positive value of ϵ we infer, as in § 2·21, that $S = s$; that is to say S_ν has the unique limit s; this is the theorem which had to be proved.

Example 1. Frame a definition of 'uniform summability (C 1) of a series of variable terms.'

Example 2. If $b_{n, \nu} \geqslant b_{n+1, \nu} \geqslant 0$ when $n < \nu$, and if, when n is *fixed*, $\lim_{\nu \to \infty} b_{n, \nu} = 1$, and if $\sum_{m=1}^{\infty} a_m = s$, then $\lim_{\nu \to \infty} \left\{ \sum_{n=1}^{\nu} a_n b_{n, \nu} \right\} = S$.

8·431. *Cesàro's general method of summation.*

A series $\sum_{n=0}^{\infty} a_n$ is said to be 'summable (Cr)' if $\lim_{\nu \to \infty} \sum_{n=0}^{\nu} a_n b_{n, \nu}$ exists, where

$$b_{0, \nu} = 1, \quad b_{n, \nu} = \left\{ \left(1 + \frac{r}{\nu + 1 - n} \right) \left(1 + \frac{r}{\nu + 2 - n} \right) \cdots \left(1 + \frac{r}{\nu - 1} \right) \right\}^{-1}.$$

It follows from § 8·43 example 2 that the 'condition of consistency' is satisfied; in fact it can be proved[*] that if a series is summable (Cr') it is also summable (Cr) when $r > r'$; the condition of consistency is the particular case of this result when $r = 0$.

8·44. *The method of summation of Riesz[†].*

A more extended method of 'summing' a series than the preceding is by means of

$$\lim_{\nu \to \infty} \sum_{n=1}^{\nu} \left(1 - \frac{\lambda_n}{\lambda_\nu} \right)^r a_n,$$

in which λ_n is any real function of n which tends to infinity with n. A series for which this limit exists is said to be 'summable (Rr) with sum-function λ_n.'

8·5. HARDY'S[‡] CONVERGENCE THEOREM.

Let $\sum_{n=1}^{\infty} a_n$ be a series which is summable (C 1). Then if

$$a_n = O(1/n),$$

the series $\sum_{n=1}^{\infty} a_n$ converges.

---

[*] Bromwich, *Infinite Series*, § 122.

[†] *Comptes Rendus*, CXLIX. (1910), pp. 18–21.

[‡] *Proc. London Math. Soc.* (2), VIII. (1910), pp. 302–304. For the proof here given, we are indebted to Mr Littlewood.

Let $s_n = a_1 + a_2 + \ldots + a_n$; then since $\sum\limits_{n=1}^{\infty} a_n$ is summable $(C\,1)$, we have

$$s_1 + s_2 + \ldots + s_n = n\,\{s + o\,(1)\},$$

where s is the sum $(C\,1)$ of $\sum\limits_{n=1}^{\infty} a_n$.

Let $$s_m - s = t_m, \quad (m = 1, 2, \ldots n),$$

and let $$t_1 + t_2 + \ldots + t_n = \sigma_n.$$

With this notation, it is sufficient to shew that, if $|a_n| < Kn^{-1}$, where K is independent of n, and if $\sigma_n = n \,.\, o\,(1)$, then $t_n \to 0$ as $n \to \infty$.

Suppose first that $a_1, a_2, \ldots$ are real. Then, if t_n does not tend to zero, there is some positive number h such that there are an unlimited number of the numbers t_n which satisfy *either* (i) $t_n > h$ *or* (ii) $t_n < -h$. We shall shew that either of these hypotheses implies a contradiction. Take the former*, and choose n so that $t_n > h$.

Then, when $r = 0, 1, 2, \ldots,$

$$|a_{n+r}| < K/n.$$

Now plot the points P_r whose coordinates are $(r,\ t_{n+r})$ in a Cartesian diagram. Since $t_{n+r+1} - t_{n+r} = a_{n+r+1}$, the slope of the line $P_r P_{r+1}$ is less than $\theta = \arctan(K/n)$.

Therefore the points $P_0, P_1, P_2, \ldots$ lie above the line $y = h - x \tan \theta$. Let P_k be the last of the points $P_0, P_1, \ldots$ which lie on the left of $x = h \cot \theta$, so that $k \leqslant h \cot \theta$.

Draw rectangles as shewn in the figure. The area of these rectangles exceeds the area of the triangle bounded by $y = h - x \tan \theta$ and the axes; that is to say

$$\sigma_{n+k} - \sigma_{n-1} = t_n + t_{n+1} + \ldots + t_{n+k}$$
$$> \tfrac{1}{2} h^2 \cot \theta = \tfrac{1}{2} h^2 K^{-1} n.$$

---

* The reader will see that the latter hypothesis involves a contradiction by using arguments of a precisely similar character to those which will be employed in dealing with the former hypothesis.

But
$$|\sigma_{n+k} - \sigma_{n-1}| \leqslant |\sigma_{n+k}| + |\sigma_{n-1}|$$
$$= (n+k) . o(1) + (n-1) . o(1)$$
$$= n . o(1),$$

since $k \leqslant hnK^{-1}$, and h, K are independent of n.

Therefore, for a set of values of n tending to infinity,

$$\tfrac{1}{2} h^2 K^{-1} n < n . o(1),$$

which is impossible since $\tfrac{1}{2} h^2 K^{-1}$ is *not* $o(1)$ as $n \to \infty$.

This is the contradiction obtained on the hypothesis that $\overline{\lim} \, t_n \geqslant h > 0$; therefore $\overline{\lim} \, t_n \leqslant 0$. Similarly, by taking the corresponding case in which $t_n \leqslant -h$, we arrive at the result $\underline{\lim} \, t_n \geqslant 0$. Therefore since $\overline{\lim} \, t_n \geqslant \underline{\lim} \, t_n$, we have
$$\overline{\lim} \, t_n = \underline{\lim} \, t_n = 0,$$
and so
$$t_n \to 0.$$

That is to say $s_n \to s$, and so $\displaystyle\sum_{n=1}^{\infty} a_n$ is convergent and its sum is s.

If a_n be complex, we consider $R(a_n)$ and $I(a_n)$ separately, and find that $\displaystyle\sum_{n=1}^{\infty} R(a_n)$ and $\displaystyle\sum_{n=1}^{\infty} I(a_n)$ converge by the theorem just proved, and so $\displaystyle\sum_{n=1}^{\infty} a_n$ converges.

The reader will see in Chapter IX that this result is of great importance in the modern theory of Fourier series.

Corollary. *If $a_n(\xi)$ be a function of ξ such that $\displaystyle\sum_{n=1}^{\infty} a_n(\xi)$ is uniformly summable (C 1) throughout a domain of values of ξ, and if $|a_n(\xi)| < K^{n-1}$, where K is independent of ξ, $\displaystyle\sum_{n=1}^{\infty} a_n(\xi)$ converges uniformly throughout the domain.*

For, retaining the notation of the preceding section, if $t_n(\xi)$ does not tend to zero uniformly, we can find a positive number h independent of n and ξ such that an infinite sequence of values of n can be found for which $t_n(\xi_n) > h$ or $t_n(\xi_n) < -h$ for some point ξ_n of the domain*; the value of ξ_n depends on the value of n under consideration.

We then find, as in the original theorem,

$$\tfrac{1}{2} h^2 K^{-1} n < n . o(1)$$

for a set of values of n tending to infinity. The contradiction implied in the inequality shews† that h does not exist, and so $t_n(\xi) \to 0$ uniformly.

---

* It is assumed that $a_n(\xi)$ is real; the extension to complex variables can be made as in the former theorem. If no such number h existed, $t_n(\xi)$ would tend to zero uniformly.

† It is essential to observe that the constants involved in the inequality do not depend on ξ_n. For if, say, K depended on ξ_n, K^{-1} would really be a function of n and might be $o(1)$ *qua* function of n, and the inequality would not imply a contradiction.

REFERENCES.

H. POINCARÉ, *Acta Mathematica*, VIII. (1886), pp. 295–344.

E. BOREL, *Leçons sur les Séries Divergentes* (Paris, 1901).

T. J. I'A. BROMWICH, *Theory of Infinite Series* (1908), Ch. XI.

E. W. BARNES, *Phil. Trans. of the Royal Society*, 206, A (1906), pp. 249–297.

G. H. HARDY and J. E. LITTLEWOOD, *Proc. London Math. Soc.* (2), XI. (1913), pp. 1–16*.

G. N. WATSON, *Phil. Trans. of the Royal Society*, 213, A (1911), pp. 279–313.

S. CHAPMAN†, *Proc. London Math. Soc.* (2), IX. (1911), pp. 369–409.

HJ. MELLIN, *Congrès des math. à Helsingfors*, 1922, pp. 1–17.

MISCELLANEOUS EXAMPLES.

1. Shew that $\int_0^\infty \dfrac{e^{-xt}}{1+t^2}\,dt \sim \dfrac{1}{x} - \dfrac{2!}{x^3} + \dfrac{4!}{x^5} - \dots$ when x is real and positive.

2. Discuss the representation of the function

$$f(x) = \int_{-\infty}^0 \phi(t)\, e^{tx}\, dt$$

(where x is supposed real and positive, and ϕ is a function subject to certain general conditions) by means of the series

$$f(x) = \frac{\phi(0)}{x} - \frac{\phi'(0)}{x^2} + \frac{\phi''(0)}{x^3} - \dots.$$

Shew that in certain cases (e.g. $\phi(t) = e^{at}$) the series is absolutely convergent, and represents $f(x)$ for large positive values of x; but that in certain other cases the series is the asymptotic expansion of $f(x)$.

3. Shew that

$$e^z z^{-a} \int_z^\infty e^{-x} x^{a-1}\, dx \sim \frac{1}{z} + \frac{a-1}{z^2} + \frac{(a-1)(a-2)}{z^3} + \dots$$

for large positive values of z.

(Legendre, *Exercices de Calc. Int.* (1811), p. 340.)

4. Shew that if, when $x > 0$,

$$f(x) = \int_0^\infty \left\{ \log u + \log\left(\frac{1}{1-e^{-u}}\right) \right\} e^{-xu}\, \frac{du}{u},$$

then
$$f(x) \sim \frac{1}{2x} - \frac{B_1}{2^2 x^2} + \frac{B_2}{4^2 x^4} - \frac{B_3}{6^2 x^6} + \dots.$$

Shew also that $f(x)$ can be expanded into an absolutely convergent series of the form

$$f(x) = \sum_{k=1}^\infty \frac{c_k}{(x+1)(x+2)\dots(x+k)}.$$ (Schlömilch.)

5. Shew that if the series $1+0+0-1+0+1+0+0-1+\dots$, in which two zeros precede each -1 and one zero precedes each $+1$, be 'summed' by Cesàro's method, its sum is $\frac{3}{5}$.   (Euler, Borel.)

6. Shew that the series $1 - 2! + 4! - \dots$ cannot be summed by Borel's method, but the series $1 + 0 - 2! + 0 + 4! + \dots$ can be so summed.

---

* This paper contains many references to recent developments of the subject.

† A bibliography of the literature of summable series will be found on p. 372 of this memoir.

CHAPTER IX

FOURIER SERIES AND TRIGONOMETRICAL SERIES

9·1. *Definition of Fourier series*.*

Series of the type

$$\tfrac{1}{2}a_0 + (a_1 \cos x + b_1 \sin x) + (a_2 \cos 2x + b_2 \sin 2x) + \ldots$$
$$= \tfrac{1}{2}a_0 + \sum_{n=1}^{\infty} (a_n \cos nx + b_n \sin nx),$$

where a_n, b_n are independent of x, are of great importance in many investigations. They are called *trigonometrical series*.

If there is a function $f(t)$ such that $\displaystyle\int_{-\pi}^{\pi} f(t)\,dt$ exists as a Riemann integral or as an improper integral which converges absolutely, and such that

$$\pi a_n = \int_{-\pi}^{\pi} f(t) \cos nt\,dt, \quad \pi b_n = \int_{-\pi}^{\pi} f(t) \sin nt\,dt,$$

then the trigonometrical series is called a *Fourier series*.

Trigonometrical series first appeared in analysis in connexion with the investigations of Daniel Bernoulli on vibrating strings; d'Alembert had previously solved the equation of motion $\ddot{y} = a^2 \dfrac{d^2 y}{dx^2}$ in the form $y = \tfrac{1}{2}\{f(x+at) + f(x-at)\}$, where $y = f(x)$ is the initial shape of the string starting from rest; and Bernoulli shewed that a formal solution is

$$y = \sum_{n=1}^{\infty} b_n \sin \frac{n\pi x}{l} \cos \frac{n\pi at}{l},$$

the fixed ends of the string being $(0, 0)$ and $(l, 0)$; and he asserted that this was the most general solution of the problem. This appeared to d'Alembert and Euler to be impossible, since such a series, having period $2l$, could not possibly represent such a function as† $cx(l-x)$ when $t=0$. A controversy arose between these mathematicians, of which an account is given in Hobson's *Functions of a Real Variable*.

Fourier, in his *Théorie de la Chaleur*, investigated a number of trigonometrical series and shewed that, in a large number of particular cases, a Fourier series *actually converged to the sum $f(x)$*. Poisson attempted a general proof of this theorem, *Journal de l'École polytechnique*, XII. (1823), pp. 404–509. Two proofs were given by Cauchy, *Mém. de l'Acad. R. des Sci.* VI. (1823, published 1826), pp. 603–612 (*Oeuvres*, (1), II. pp. 12–19) and *Exercices de Math.* II. (1827), pp. 341–376 (*Oeuvres*, (2), VII. pp. 393–430); these proofs, which are based on the theory of contour integration, are concerned with rather particular classes of functions and one is invalid. The second proof has been investigated by Harnack, *Math. Ann.* XXXII. (1888), pp. 175–202.

---

* Throughout this chapter (except in § 9·11) it is supposed that all the numbers involved are *real*.

† This function gives a simple form to the initial shape of the string.

In 1829, Dirichlet gave the first rigorous proof* that, for a general class of functions, the Fourier series, defined as above, does converge to the sum $f(x)$. A modification of this proof was given later by Bonnet†.

The result of Dirichlet is that ‡ if $f(t)$ is defined and bounded in the range $(-\pi, \pi)$ and if $f(t)$ has only a finite number of maxima and minima and a finite number of discontinuities in this range and, further, if $f(t)$ is defined by the equation

$$f(t+2\pi)=f(t)$$

outside the range $(-\pi, \pi)$, then, provided that

$$\pi a_n=\int_{-\pi}^{\pi} f(t)\cos nt\,dt, \quad \pi b_n=\int_{-\pi}^{\pi} f(t)\sin nt\,dt,$$

the series $\frac{1}{2}a_0+\sum_{n=1}^{\infty}(a_n\cos nx+b_n\sin nx)$ converges to the sum $\frac{1}{2}\{f(x+0)+f(x-0)\}$.

Later, Riemann and Cantor developed the theory of trigonometrical series generally, while still more recently Hurwitz, Fejér and others have investigated properties of Fourier series when the series does not necessarily converge. Thus Fejér has proved the remarkable theorem that a Fourier series (even if not convergent) is 'summable $(C\,1)$' at all points at which $f(x\pm0)$ exist, and its sum $(C\,1)$ is $\frac{1}{2}\{f(x+0)+f(x-0)\}$, provided that $\int_{-\pi}^{\pi} f(t)\,dt$ is an absolutely convergent integral. One of the investigations of the convergence of Fourier series which we shall give later (§ 9·42) is based on this result.

For a fuller account of investigations subsequent to Riemann, the reader is referred to Hobson's *Functions of a Real Variable*, and to de la Vallée Poussin's *Cours d'Analyse Infinitésimale*.

9·11. *Nature of the region within which a trigonometrical series converges.*

Consider the series

$$\frac{1}{2}a_0+\sum_{n=1}^{\infty}(a_n\cos nz+b_n\sin nz),$$

where z may be complex. If we write $e^{iz}=\zeta$, the series becomes

$$\frac{1}{2}a_0+\sum_{n=1}^{\infty}\left\{\frac{1}{2}(a_n-ib_n)\zeta^n+\frac{1}{2}(a_n+ib_n)\zeta^{-n}\right\}.$$

This Laurent series will converge, if it converges at all, in a region in which $a\leqslant|\zeta|\leqslant b$, where a, b are positive constants.

But, if $z=x+iy$, $|\zeta|=e^{-y}$, and so we get, as the region of convergence of the trigonometrical series, the strip in the z plane defined by the inequality

$$\log a\leqslant-y\leqslant\log b.$$

The case which is of the greatest importance in practice is that in which $a=b=1$, and the strip consists of a single line, namely the real axis.

Example 1. Let

$$f(z)=\sin z-\frac{1}{2}\sin 2z+\frac{1}{3}\sin 3z-\frac{1}{4}\sin 4z+\ldots,$$

where $z=x+iy$:

---

* *Journal für Math.* iv. (1829), pp. 157–169.

† *Mémoires des Savants étrangers* of the Belgian Academy, xxiii. (1848–1850). Bonnet employs the second mean value theorem directly, while Dirichlet's original proof makes use of arguments precisely similar to those by which that theorem is proved. See § 9·43.

‡ The conditions postulated for $f(t)$ are known as *Dirichlet's conditions*; as will be seen in §§ 9·2, 9·42, they are unnecessarily stringent.

Writing this in the form

$$f(z) = -\frac{1}{2} i \left(e^{iz} - \frac{1}{2} e^{2iz} + \frac{1}{3} e^{3iz} - \ldots \right) + \frac{1}{2} i \left(e^{-iz} - \frac{1}{2} e^{-2iz} + \frac{1}{3} e^{-3iz} - \ldots \right)$$

we notice that the first series converges* only if $y \geqslant 0$, and the second only if $y \leqslant 0$.

Writing x in place of z (x being real), we see that by Abel's theorem (§ 3·71),

$$f(x) = \lim_{r \to 1} \left(r \sin x - \frac{1}{2} r^2 \sin 2x + \frac{1}{3} r^3 \sin 3x - \ldots \right)$$

$$= \lim_{r \to 1} \left\{ -\frac{1}{2} i \left(r e^{ix} - \frac{1}{2} r^2 e^{2ix} + \frac{1}{3} r^3 e^{3ix} - \ldots \right) \right.$$

$$\left. + \frac{1}{2} i \left(r e^{-ix} - \frac{1}{2} r^2 e^{-2ix} + \frac{1}{3} r^3 e^{-3ix} - \ldots \right) \right\}.$$

This is the limit of one of the values of

$$-\tfrac{1}{2} i \log (1 + r e^{ix}) + \tfrac{1}{2} i \log (1 + r e^{-ix}),$$

and as $r \to 1$ (if $-\pi < x < \pi$), this tends to $\frac{1}{2} x + k\pi$, where k is some integer.

Now $\sum_{n=1}^{\infty} \dfrac{(-)^{n-1} \sin nx}{n}$ converges uniformly (§ 3·35 example 1) and is therefore continuous in the range $-\pi + \delta \leqslant x \leqslant \pi - \delta$, where δ is any positive constant.

Since $\frac{1}{2} x$ is continuous, k has the same value wherever x lies in the range; and putting $x = 0$, we see that $k = 0$.

Therefore, when $-\pi < x < \pi$, $\qquad f(x) = \frac{1}{2} x$.

But, when $\pi < x < 3\pi$,

$$f(x) = f(x - 2\pi) = \tfrac{1}{2} (x - 2\pi) = \tfrac{1}{2} x - \pi,$$

and generally, if $(2n - 1)\pi < x < (2n + 1)\pi$,

$$f(x) = \tfrac{1}{2} x - n\pi.$$

We have thus arrived at an example in which $f(x)$ is not represented by a single analytical expression.

It must be observed that this phenomenon can only occur when the strip in which the Fourier series converges is a single line. For if the strip is not of zero breadth, the associated Laurent series converges in an annulus of non-zero breadth and represents an analytic function of ζ in that annulus; and, since ζ is an analytic function of z, the Fourier series represents an analytic function of z; such a series is given by

$$r \sin x - \tfrac{1}{2} r^2 \sin 2x + \tfrac{1}{3} r^3 \sin 3x - \ldots,$$

where $0 < r < 1$; its sum is arc $\tan \dfrac{r \sin x}{1 + r \cos x}$, the arc tan always representing an angle between $\pm \frac{1}{2}\pi$.

Example 2. When $-\pi \leqslant x \leqslant \pi$,

$$\sum_{n=1}^{\infty} \frac{(-)^{n-1} \cos nx}{n^2} = \frac{1}{12} \pi^2 - \frac{1}{4} x^2.$$

The series converges only when x is real; by § 3·34 the convergence is then absolute and uniform.

Since $\qquad \frac{1}{2} x = \sin x - \frac{1}{2} \sin 2x + \frac{1}{3} \sin 3x - \ldots \quad (-\pi + \delta \leqslant x \leqslant \pi - \delta, \ \delta > 0)$,

and this series converges uniformly, we may integrate term-by-term from 0 to x (§ 4·7), and consequently

$$\frac{1}{4} x^2 = \sum_{n=1}^{\infty} \frac{(-)^{n-1} (1 - \cos nx)}{n^2} \qquad (-\pi + \delta \leqslant x \leqslant \pi - \delta).$$

---

* The series *do converge* if $y = 0$, see § 2·31 example 2.

That is to say, when $-\pi + \delta \leqslant x \leqslant \pi - \delta$,

$$C - \frac{1}{4} x^2 = \sum_{n=1}^{\infty} \frac{(-)^{n-1} \cos nx}{n^2},$$

where C is a constant, at present undetermined.

But since the series on the right converges uniformly throughout the range $-\pi \leqslant x \leqslant \pi$, its sum is a continuous function of x in this extended range; and so, proceeding to the limit when $x \to \pm \pi$, we see that the last equation is still true when $x = \pm \pi$.

To determine C, integrate each side of the equation (§ 4·7) between the limits $-\pi, \pi$; and we get

$$2\pi C - \frac{1}{6} \pi^3 = 0.$$

Consequently $\dfrac{1}{12} \pi^2 - \dfrac{1}{4} x^2 = \sum\limits_{n=1}^{\infty} \dfrac{(-)^{n-1} \cos nx}{n^2}$ $(-\pi \leqslant x \leqslant \pi)$.

Example 3.   By writing $\pi - 2x$ for x in example 2, shew that

$$\sum_{n=1}^{\infty} \frac{\sin^2 nx}{n^2} \begin{cases} = \frac{1}{2} x (\pi - x) & (0 \leqslant x \leqslant \pi), \\ = \frac{1}{2} \{ \pi \, |x| - x^2 \} & (-\pi \leqslant x \leqslant \pi). \end{cases}$$

9·12.   *Values of the coefficients in terms of the sum of a trigonometrical series.*

Let the trigonometrical series $\frac{1}{2} c_0 + \sum\limits_{n=1}^{\infty} (c_n \cos nx + d_n \sin nx)$ be uniformly convergent in the range $(-\pi, \pi)$ and let its sum be $f(x)$. Using the obvious results

$$\int_{-\pi}^{\pi} \cos mx \cos nx \, dx \begin{cases} = 0 & (m \neq n), \\ = \pi & (m = n \neq 0), \end{cases}$$

$$\int_{-\pi}^{\pi} \sin mx \sin nx \, dx \begin{cases} = 0 & (m \neq n), \\ = \pi & (m = n \neq 0), \end{cases} \qquad \int_{-\pi}^{\pi} dx = 2\pi,$$

we find, on multiplying the equation $\frac{1}{2} c_0 + \sum\limits_{n=1}^{\infty} (c_n \cos nx + d_n \sin nx) = f(x)$ by* $\cos nx$ or by $\sin nx$ and integrating term-by-term† (§ 4·7),

$$\pi c_n = \int_{-\pi}^{\pi} f(x) \cos nx \, dx, \qquad \pi d_n = \int_{-\pi}^{\pi} f(x) \sin nx \, dx.$$

Corollary.   A trigonometrical series uniformly convergent in the range $(-\pi, \pi)$ is a Fourier series.

NOTE.   Lebesgue has given a proof (*Séries trigonométriques*, p. 124) of a theorem communicated to him by Fatou that the trigonometrical series $\sum\limits_{n=2}^{\infty} \sin nx / \log n$, which converges for all real values of x (§ 2·31 example 1), is *not* a Fourier series.

9·2.   *On Dirichlet's conditions and Fourier's theorem.*

A theorem, of the type described in § 9·1, concerning the expansibility of a function of a real variable into a trigonometrical series is usually described

---

* Multiplying by these factors does not destroy the uniformity of the convergence.

† These were given by Euler (with limits 0 and 2π), *Nova Acta Acad. Petrop.* XI. (1793).

as *Fourier's theorem*. On account of the length and difficulty of a formal proof of the theorem (even when the function to be expanded is subjected to unnecessarily stringent conditions), we defer the proof until §§ 9·42, 9·43. It is, however, convenient to state here certain *sufficient* conditions under which a function can be expanded into a trigonometrical series.

Let $f(t)$ be defined arbitrarily when $-\pi \leqslant t < \pi$ and defined* for all other real values of t by means of the equation

$$f(t + 2\pi) = f(t),$$

so that $f(t)$ is a periodic function with period 2π.

Let $f(t)$ be such that $\int_{-\pi}^{\pi} f(t)\, dt$ exists; and if this is an improper integral, let it be absolutely convergent.

Let a_n, b_n be defined by the equations†

$$\pi a_n = \int_{-\pi}^{\pi} f(t) \cos nt\, dt, \quad \pi b_n = \int_{-\pi}^{\pi} f(t) \sin nt\, dt \qquad (n = 0, 1, 2, \ldots).$$

Then, if x be an interior point of any interval (a, b) in which $f(t)$ has limited total fluctuation, the series

$$\tfrac{1}{2}a_0 + \sum_{n=1}^{\infty} (a_n \cos nx + b_n \sin nx)$$

is convergent, and its sum‡ is $\tfrac{1}{2}\{f(x + 0) + f(x - 0)\}$. If $f(t)$ is continuous at $t = x$, this sum reduces to $f(x)$.

This theorem will be assumed in §§ 9·21–9·32; these sections deal with theorems concerning Fourier series which are of some importance in practical applications. It should be stated here that every function which Applied Mathematicians need to expand into Fourier series satisfies the conditions just imposed on $f(t)$, so that the analysis given later in this chapter establishes the validity of all the expansions into Fourier series which are required in physical investigations.

The reader will observe that in the theorem just stated, $f(t)$ is subject to less stringent conditions than those contemplated by Dirichlet, and this decrease of stringency is of considerable practical importance. Thus, so simple a series as $\sum_{n=1}^{\infty} (-)^{n-1} (\cos nx)/n$ is the expansion of the function§ $\log | 2 \cos \tfrac{1}{2}x |$; and this function does not satisfy Dirichlet's condition of boundedness at $\pm\pi$.

It is convenient to describe the series $\tfrac{1}{2}a_0 + \sum_{n=1}^{\infty} (a_n \cos nx + b_n \sin nx)$ as *the Fourier series associated with $f(t)$*. This description must, however, be

---

* This definition frequently results in $f(t)$ not being expressible by a single analytical expression for all real values of t. Cf. § 9·11 example 1.

† The numbers a_n, b_n are called the *Fourier constants* of $f(t)$, and the symbols a_n, b_n will be used in this sense throughout §§ 9·2–9·5. It may be shewn that the convergence and absolute convergence of the integrals defining the Fourier constants are consequences of the convergence and absolute convergence of $\int_{-\pi}^{\pi} f(t)\, dt$. Cf. §§ 2·32, 4·5.

‡ The limits $f(x \pm 0)$ exist, by § 3·64 example 3.

§ Cf. example 6 at the end of the chapter (p. 190).

taken as implying nothing concerning the convergence of the series in question.

9·21. *The representation of a function by Fourier series for ranges other than* $(-\pi, \pi)$.

Consider a function $f(x)$ with an (absolutely) convergent integral, and with limited total fluctuation in the range $a \leqslant x \leqslant b$.

Write $\qquad x = \frac{1}{2}(a+b) - \frac{1}{2}(a-b)\pi^{-1}x', \quad f(x) = F(x').$

Then it is known (§ 9·2) that

$$\frac{1}{2}\{F(x'+0) + F(x'-0)\} = \frac{1}{2}a_0 + \sum_{n=1}^{\infty}(a_n \cos nx' + b_n \sin nx'),$$

and so

$$\frac{1}{2}\{f(x+0) + f(x-0)\}$$
$$= \frac{1}{2}a_0 + \sum_{n=1}^{\infty}\left\{a_n \cos \frac{n\pi(2x-a-b)}{b-a} + b_n \sin \frac{n\pi(2x-a-b)}{b-a}\right\},$$

where by an obvious transformation

$$\frac{1}{2}(b-a)a_n = \int_a^b f(x) \cos \frac{n\pi(2x-a-b)}{b-a}\,dx,$$

$$\frac{1}{2}(b-a)b_n = \int_a^b f(x) \sin \frac{n\pi(2x-a-b)}{b-a}\,dx.$$

9·22. *The cosine series and the sine series.*

Let $f(x)$ be defined in the range $(0, l)$ and let it have an (absolutely) convergent integral and also let it have limited total fluctuation in that range. *Define* $f(x)$ *in the range* $(0, -l)$ *by the equation*

$$f(-x) = f(x).$$

Then

$$\frac{1}{2}\{f(x+0) + f(x-0)\} = \frac{1}{2}a_0 + \sum_{n=1}^{\infty}\left\{a_n \cos \frac{n\pi x}{l} + b_n \sin \frac{n\pi x}{l}\right\},$$

where, by § 9·21,

$$la_n = \int_{-l}^{l} f(t) \cos \frac{n\pi t}{l}\,dt = 2\int_0^l f(t) \cos \frac{n\pi t}{l}\,dt,$$

$$lb_n = \int_{-l}^{l} f(t) \sin \frac{n\pi t}{l}\,dt = 0,$$

so that when $-l \leqslant x \leqslant l$,

$$\frac{1}{2}\{f(x+0) + f(x-0)\} = \frac{1}{2}a_0 + \sum_{n=1}^{\infty}a_n \cos \frac{n\pi x}{l}\,;$$

this is called the *cosine series.*

If, however, we define $f(x)$ in the range $(0, -l)$ by the equation

$$f(-x) = -f(-x),$$

we get, when $-l \leqslant x \leqslant l$,

$$\tfrac{1}{2}\{f(x+0)+f(x-0)\} = \sum_{n=1}^{\infty} b_n \sin\frac{n\pi x}{l},$$

where

$$lb_n = 2\int_0^l f(t)\sin\frac{n\pi t}{l}\,dt;$$

this is called the *sine series*.

Thus the series

$$\tfrac{1}{2}a_0 + \sum_{n=1}^{\infty} a_n\cos\frac{n\pi x}{l}, \qquad \sum_{n=1}^{\infty} b_n\sin\frac{n\pi x}{l},$$

where

$$\tfrac{1}{2}la_n = \int_0^l f(t)\cos\frac{n\pi t}{l}\,dt, \qquad \tfrac{1}{2}lb_n = \int_0^l f(t)\sin\frac{n\pi t}{l}\,dt,$$

have the same sum when $0 \leqslant x \leqslant l$; but their sums are numerically equal and opposite in sign when $0 \geqslant x \geqslant -l$.

The cosine series was given by Clairaut, *Hist. de l'Acad. R. des Sci.* 1754 [published, 1759], in a memoir dated July 9, 1757; the sine series was obtained between 1762 and 1765 by Lagrange, *Oeuvres*, I. p. 553.

Example 1. Expand $\tfrac{1}{2}(\pi - x)\sin x$ in a cosine series in the range $0 \leqslant x \leqslant \pi$.

[We have, by the formula just obtained,

$$\tfrac{1}{2}(\pi - x)\sin x = \tfrac{1}{2}a_0 + \sum_{n=1}^{\infty} a_n\cos nx,$$

where

$$\tfrac{1}{2}\pi a_n = \int_0^{\pi} \tfrac{1}{2}(\pi - x)\sin x\cos nx\,dx.$$

But, integrating by parts, if $n \neq 1$,

$$\int_0^{\pi} 2(\pi - x)\sin x\cos nx\,dx$$

$$= \int_0^{\pi} (\pi - x)\{\sin(n+1)x - \sin(n-1)x\}\,dx$$

$$= \left[(x-\pi)\left\{\frac{\cos(n+1)x}{n+1} - \frac{\cos(n-1)x}{n-1}\right\}\right]_0^{\pi} - \int_0^{\pi}\left\{\frac{\cos(n+1)x}{n+1} - \frac{\cos(n-1)x}{n-1}\right\}dx$$

$$= \pi\left(\frac{1}{n+1} - \frac{1}{n-1}\right) = \frac{-2\pi}{(n+1)(n-1)}.$$

Whereas if $n=1$, we get $\int_0^{\pi} 2(\pi - x)\sin x\cos x\,dx = \tfrac{1}{2}\pi$.

Therefore the required series is

$$\frac{1}{2} + \frac{1}{4}\cos x - \frac{1}{1.3}\cos 2x - \frac{1}{2.4}\cos 3x - \frac{1}{3.5}\cos 4x - \dots.$$

It will be observed that it is only for values of x between 0 and π that the sum of this series is proved to be $\tfrac{1}{2}(\pi - x)\sin x$; thus for instance when x has a value between 0 and $-\pi$, the sum of the series is not $\tfrac{1}{2}(\pi - x)\sin x$, but $-\tfrac{1}{2}(\pi + x)\sin x$; when x has a value between π and 2π, the sum of the series happens to be again $\tfrac{1}{2}(\pi - x)\sin x$, but this is a mere coincidence arising from the special function considered, and does not follow from the general theorem.]

Example 2. Expand $\tfrac{1}{8}\pi x(\pi - x)$ in a sine series, valid when $0 \leqslant x \leqslant \pi$.

[The series is $\sin x + \dfrac{\sin 3x}{3^3} + \dfrac{\sin 5x}{5^3} + \dots.$]

Example 3.   Shew that, when $0 \leqslant x \leqslant \pi$,

$$\frac{1}{96}\,\pi\,(\pi - 2x)\,(\pi^2 + 2\pi x - 2x^2) = \cos x + \frac{\cos 3x}{3^4} + \frac{\cos 5x}{5^4} + \dots.$$

[Denoting the left-hand side by $f(x)$, we have, on integrating by parts and observing that $f'(0) = f'(\pi) = 0$,

$$\int_0^\pi f(x) \cos nx\,dx = \frac{1}{n}\left[f(x) \sin nx\right]_0^\pi - \frac{1}{n}\int_0^\pi f'(x) \sin nx\,dx$$

$$= \frac{1}{n^2}\left[f'(x) \cos nx\right]_0^\pi - \frac{1}{n^2}\int_0^\pi f''(x) \cos nx\,dx$$

$$= -\frac{1}{n^3}\left[f''(x) \sin nx\right]_0^\pi + \frac{1}{n^3}\int_0^\pi f'''(x) \sin nx\,dx$$

$$= -\frac{1}{n^4}\left[f'''(x) \cos nx\right]_0^\pi = \frac{\pi}{4n^4}(1 - \cos n\pi).]$$

Example 4.   Shew that for values of x between 0 and π, e^{sx} can be expanded in the cosine series

$$\frac{2s}{\pi}\,(e^{s\pi} - 1)\left(\frac{1}{2s^2} + \frac{\cos 2x}{s^2 + 4} + \frac{\cos 4x}{s^2 + 16} + \dots\right) - \frac{2s}{\pi}\,(e^{s\pi} + 1)\left(\frac{\cos x}{s^2 + 1} + \frac{\cos 3x}{s^2 + 9} + \dots\right),$$

and draw graphs of the function e^{sx} and of the sum of the series.

Example 5.   Shew that for values of x between 0 and π, the function $\frac{1}{8}\pi\,(\pi - 2x)$ can be expanded in the cosine series

$$\cos x + \frac{\cos 3x}{3^2} + \frac{\cos 5x}{5^2} + \dots,$$

and draw graphs of the function $\frac{1}{8}\pi\,(\pi - 2x)$ and of the sum of the series.

9·3.   *The nature of the coefficients in a Fourier series**.

Suppose that (as in the numerical examples which have been discussed) ·the interval $(-\pi,\ \pi)$ can be divided into a finite number of ranges $(-\pi,\ k_1),\ (k_1,\ k_2) \dots (k_n,\ \pi)$ such that throughout each range $f(x)$ and all its differential coefficients are continuous with limited total fluctuation and that they have limits on the right and on the left (§ 3·2) at the end points of these ranges.

Then

$$\pi a_m = \int_{-\pi}^{k_1} f(t) \cos mt\,dt + \int_{k_1}^{k_2} f(t) \cos mt\,dt + \dots + \int_{k_n}^{\pi} f(t) \cos mt\,dt.$$

Integrating by parts we get

$$\pi a_m = \left[m^{-1} f(t) \sin mt\right]_{-\pi}^{k_1} + \left[m^{-1} f(t) \sin mt\right]_{k_1}^{k_2} + \dots + \left[m^{-1} f(t) \sin mt\right]_{k_n}^{\pi}$$

$$- m^{-1}\int_{-\pi}^{k_1} f'(t) \sin mt\,dt - m^{-1}\int_{k_1}^{k_2} f'(t) \sin mt\,dt - \dots - m^{-1}\int_{k_n}^{\pi} f'(t) \sin mt\,dt,$$

so that

$$a_m = \frac{A_m}{m} - \frac{b_m'}{m},$$

---

* The analysis of this section and of § 9·31 is contained in Stokes' great memoir, *Camb. Phil. Trans.* VIII. (1849), pp. 533–583 [*Math. Papers*, I. pp. 236–313].

where
$$\pi A_m = \sum_{r=1}^{n} \sin mk_r \{f(k_r - 0) - f(k_r + 0)\},$$

and $b_m{}'$ is a Fourier constant of $f'(x)$.

Similarly
$$b_m = \frac{B_m}{m} + \frac{a_m{}'}{m},$$

where
$$\pi B_m = - \sum_{r=1}^{n} \cos mk_r \{f(k_r - 0) - f(k_r + 0)\} - \cos m\pi \{f(\pi - 0) - f(-\pi + 0)\},$$

and $a_m{}'$ is a Fourier constant of $f'(x)$.

Similarly, we get
$$a_m{}' = \frac{A_m{}'}{m} - \frac{b_m{}''}{m}, \qquad b_m{}' = \frac{B_m{}'}{m} + \frac{a_m{}''}{m},$$

where $a_m{}''$, $b_m{}''$ are the Fourier constants of $f''(x)$ and

$$\pi A_m{}' = \sum_{r=1}^{n} \sin mk_r \{f'(k_r - 0) - f'(k_r + 0)\},$$

$$\pi B_m{}' = - \sum_{r=1}^{n} \cos mk_r \{f'(k_r - 0) - f'(k_r + 0)\}$$
$$- \cos m\pi \{f'(\pi - 0) - f'(-\pi + 0)\}.$$

Therefore
$$a_m = \frac{A_m}{m} - \frac{B_m{}'}{m^2} - \frac{a_m{}''}{m^2}, \qquad b_m = \frac{B_m}{m} + \frac{A_m{}'}{m^2} - \frac{b_m{}''}{m^2}.$$

Now as $m \to \infty$, we see that
$$A_m{}' = O(1), \qquad B_m{}' = O(1),$$

and, since the integrands involved in $a_m{}''$ and $b_m{}''$ are bounded, it is evident that
$$a_m{}'' = O(1), \qquad b_m{}'' = O(1).$$

Hence if $A_m = 0$, $B_m = 0$, the Fourier series for $f(x)$ converges absolutely and uniformly, by § 3·34.

The necessary and sufficient conditions that $A_m = B_m = 0$ for all values of m are that
$$f(k_r - 0) = f(k_r + 0), \quad f(\pi - 0) = f(-\pi + 0),$$

that is to say that* $f(x)$ should be continuous for all values of x.

9·31. *Differentiation of Fourier series.*

The result of differentiating
$$\tfrac{1}{2} a_0 + \sum_{m=1}^{\infty} (a_m \cos mx + b_m \sin mx)$$

term by term is
$$\sum_{m=1}^{\infty} \{mb_m \cos mx - ma_m \sin mx\}.$$

---

* Of course $f(x)$ is also subject to the conditions stated at the beginning of the section.

With the notation of § 9·3, this is the same as

$$\frac{1}{2}a_0' + \sum_{m=1}^{\infty} (a_m' \cos mx + b_m' \sin mx),$$

provided that $A_m = B_m = 0$ and $\displaystyle\int_{-\pi}^{\pi} f'(x)\,dx = 0$;

these conditions are satisfied if $f(x)$ is continuous for all values of x.

Consequently sufficient conditions for the legitimacy of differentiating a Fourier series term by term are that $f(x)$ should be continuous for *all* values of x and $f'(x)$ should have only a finite number of points of discontinuity in the range $(-\pi, \pi)$, both functions having limited total fluctuation throughout the range.

9·32. *Determination of points of discontinuity.*

The expressions for a_m and b_m which have been found in § 9·3 can frequently be applied in practical examples to determine the points at which the sum of a given Fourier series may be discontinuous. Thus, let it be required to determine the places at which the sum of the series

$$\sin x + \tfrac{1}{3} \sin 3x + \tfrac{1}{5} \sin 5x + \dots$$

is discontinuous.

Assuming that the series is a Fourier series and not *any* trigonometrical series and observing that $a_m = 0$, $b_m = (2m)^{-1}(1 - \cos m\pi)$, we get on considering the formula found in § 9·3,

$$A_m = 0, \quad B_m = \tfrac{1}{2} - \tfrac{1}{2} \cos m\pi, \quad a_m' = b_m' = 0.$$

Hence if $k_1, k_2, \dots$ are the places at which the analytic character of the sum is broken, we have

$$0 = \pi A_m = [\sin mk_1 \{f(k_1 - 0) - f(k_1 + 0)\} + \sin mk_2 \{f(k_2 - 0) - f(k_2 + 0)\} + \dots].$$

Since this is true for all values of m, the numbers $k_1, k_2, \dots$ must be multiples of π; but there is only one even multiple of π in the range $-\pi < x \leqslant \pi$, namely zero. So $k_1 = 0$, and $k_2, k_3, \dots$ do not exist. Substituting $k_1 = 0$ in the equation $B_m = \tfrac{1}{2} - \tfrac{1}{2}\cos m\pi$, we have

$$\pi \left(\tfrac{1}{2} - \tfrac{1}{2}\cos m\pi\right) = -[\cos m\pi \{f(\pi - 0) - f(-\pi + 0)\} + f(-0) - f(+0)].$$

Since this is true for all values of m, we have

$$\tfrac{1}{2}\pi = f(+0) - f(-0), \quad \tfrac{1}{2}\pi = f(\pi - 0) - f(-\pi + 0).$$

This shews that, if the series is a Fourier series, $f(x)$ has discontinuities at the points $n\pi$ (n any integer), and since $a_m' = b_m' = 0$, we should expect* $f(x)$ to be constant in the open range $(-\pi, 0)$ and to be another constant in the open range $(0, \pi)$.

9·4. Fejér's theorem.

We now begin the discussion of the theory of Fourier series by proving the following theorem, due to Fejér†, concerning the summability of the Fourier series associated with an arbitrary function, $f(t)$:

Let $f(t)$ be a function of the real variable t, defined arbitrarily when $-\pi \leqslant t < \pi$, and defined by the equation

$$f(t + 2\pi) = f(t)$$

---

* In point of fact $f(x) = -\tfrac{1}{4}\pi \quad (-\pi < x < 0)$;
$f(x) = \tfrac{1}{4}\pi \quad (0 < x < \pi)$.

† *Math. Ann.* LVIII. (1904), pp. 51–69.

for all other real values of t; and let $\int_{-\pi}^{\pi} f(t)\,dt$ *exist and (if it is an improper integral) let it be absolutely convergent.*

Then the Fourier series associated with the function $f(t)$ is summable* (C1) at all points x at which the two limits $f(x \pm 0)$ exist.

And its sum (C1) is

$$\tfrac{1}{2}\{f(x+0)+f(x-0)\}.$$

Let a_n, b_n, $(n = 0, 1, 2, \dots)$ denote the Fourier constants (§ 9·2) of $f(t)$ and let

$$\tfrac{1}{2}a_0 = A_0, \quad a_n \cos nx + b_n \sin nx = A_n(x), \quad \sum_{n=0}^{m} A_n(x) = S_m(x).$$

Then we have to prove that

$$\lim_{m \to \infty} \frac{1}{m} \{A_0 + S_1(x) + S_2(x) + \dots + S_{m-1}(x)\} = \tfrac{1}{2}\{f(x+0)+f(x-0)\},$$

provided that the limits on the right exist.

If we substitute for the Fourier constants their values in the form of integrals (§ 9·2), it is easy to verify that†

$$A_0 + \sum_{n=1}^{m-1} S_n(x) = mA_0 + (m-1)A_1(x) + (m-2)A_2(x) + \dots + A_{m-1}(x)$$

$$= \frac{1}{\pi} \int_{-\pi}^{\pi} \{\tfrac{1}{2}m + (m-1)\cos(x-t) + (m-2)\cos 2(x-t) + \dots$$
$$+ \cos(m-1)(x-t)\} f(t)\,dt$$

$$= \frac{1}{2\pi} \int_{-\pi}^{\pi} \frac{\sin^2 \tfrac{1}{2}m(x-t)}{\sin^2 \tfrac{1}{2}(x-t)} f(t)\,dt$$

$$= \frac{1}{2\pi} \int_{-\pi+x}^{\pi+x} \frac{\sin^2 \tfrac{1}{2}m(x-t)}{\sin^2 \tfrac{1}{2}(x-t)} f(t)\,dt,$$

the last step following from the periodicity of the integrand.

If now we bisect the path of integration and write $x \mp 2\theta$ in place of t in the two parts of the path, we get

$$A_0 + \sum_{n=1}^{m-1} S_n(x) = \frac{1}{\pi} \int_0^{\tfrac{1}{2}\pi} \frac{\sin^2 m\theta}{\sin^2 \theta} f(x+2\theta)\,d\theta + \frac{1}{\pi} \int_0^{\tfrac{1}{2}\pi} \frac{\sin^2 m\theta}{\sin^2 \theta} f(x-2\theta)\,d\theta.$$

Consequently it is sufficient to prove that, as $m \to \infty$, then

$$\frac{1}{m} \int_0^{\tfrac{1}{2}\pi} \frac{\sin^2 m\theta}{\sin^2 \theta} f(x+2\theta)\,d\theta \to \tfrac{1}{2}\pi f(x+0), \quad \frac{1}{m} \int_0^{\tfrac{1}{2}\pi} \frac{\sin^2 m\theta}{\sin^2 \theta} f(x-2\theta)\,d\theta \to \tfrac{1}{2}\pi f(x-0).$$

---

* See § 8·43.

† It is obvious that, if we write λ for $e^{i(x-t)}$ in the second line, then

$$m + (m-1)(\lambda + \lambda^{-1}) + (m-2)(\lambda^2 + \lambda^{-2}) + \dots + (\lambda^{m-1} + \lambda^{1-m})$$
$$= (1-\lambda)^{-1} \{\lambda^{1-m} + \lambda^{2-m} + \dots + \lambda^{-1} + 1 - \lambda - \lambda^2 - \dots - \lambda^m\}$$
$$= (1-\lambda)^{-2} \{\lambda^{1-m} - 2\lambda + \lambda^{m+1}\} = (\lambda^{\tfrac{1}{2}m} - \lambda^{-\tfrac{1}{2}m})^2 / (\lambda^{\tfrac{1}{2}} - \lambda^{-\tfrac{1}{2}})^2.$$

Now, if we integrate the equation

$$\frac{1}{2}\frac{\sin^2 m\theta}{\sin^2 \theta} = \tfrac{1}{2}m + (m-1)\cos 2\theta + \ldots + \cos 2(m-1)\theta,$$

we find that

$$\int_0^{\frac{1}{2}\pi} \frac{\sin^2 m\theta}{\sin^2 \theta}\, d\theta = \tfrac{1}{2}\pi m,$$

and so we have to prove that

$$\frac{1}{m}\int_0^{\frac{1}{2}\pi} \frac{\sin^2 m\theta}{\sin^2 \theta}\, \phi(\theta)\, d\theta \to 0 \text{ as } m \to \infty,$$

where $\phi(\theta)$ stands in turn for each of the two functions

$$f(x+2\theta) - f(x+0), \quad f(x-2\theta) - f(x-0).$$

Now, given an arbitrary positive number ϵ, we can choose δ so that*

$$|\phi(\theta)| < \epsilon$$

whenever $0 < \theta \leqslant \tfrac{1}{2}\delta$. This choice of δ is obviously independent of m.

Then

$$\left|\frac{1}{m}\int_0^{\frac{1}{2}\pi}\frac{\sin^2 m\theta}{\sin^2 \theta}\,\phi(\theta)\,d\theta\right| \leqslant \frac{1}{m}\int_0^{\frac{1}{2}\delta}\frac{\sin^2 m\theta}{\sin^2 \theta}\,|\phi(\theta)|\,d\theta + \frac{1}{m}\int_{\frac{1}{2}\delta}^{\frac{1}{2}\pi}\frac{\sin^2 m\theta}{\sin^2 \theta}\,|\phi(\theta)|\,d\theta$$

$$< \frac{\epsilon}{m}\int_0^{\frac{1}{2}\delta}\frac{\sin^2 m\theta}{\sin^2 \theta}\,d\theta + \frac{1}{m\sin^2 \frac{1}{2}\delta}\int_{\frac{1}{2}\delta}^{\frac{1}{2}\pi}|\phi(\theta)|\,d\theta$$

$$\leqslant \frac{\epsilon}{m}\int_0^{\frac{1}{2}\pi}\frac{\sin^2 m\theta}{\sin^2 \theta}\,d\theta + \frac{1}{m\sin^2 \frac{1}{2}\delta}\int_0^{\frac{1}{2}\pi}|\phi(\theta)|\,d\theta$$

$$= \tfrac{1}{2}\pi\epsilon + \frac{1}{m\sin^2 \frac{1}{2}\delta}\int_0^{\frac{1}{2}\pi}|\phi(\theta)|\,d\theta.$$

Now the convergence of $\displaystyle\int_{-\pi}^{\pi}|f(t)|\,dt$ entails the convergence of

$$\int_0^{\frac{1}{2}\pi}|\phi(\theta)|\,d\theta,$$

and so, given ϵ (and therefore δ), we can make

$$\tfrac{1}{2}\pi\epsilon m \sin^2 \tfrac{1}{2}\delta > \int_0^{\frac{1}{2}\pi}|\phi(\theta)|\,d\theta,$$

by taking m sufficiently large.

Hence, by taking m sufficiently large, we can make

$$\left|\frac{1}{m}\int_0^{\frac{1}{2}\pi}\frac{\sin^2 m\theta}{\sin^2 \theta}\,\phi(\theta)\,d\theta\right| < \pi\epsilon,$$

where ϵ is an arbitrary positive number; that is to say, from the definition of a limit,

$$\lim_{m \to \infty}\frac{1}{m}\int_0^{\frac{1}{2}\pi}\frac{\sin^2 m\theta}{\sin^2 \theta}\,\phi(\theta)\,d\theta = 0,$$

and so Fejér's theorem is established.

* On the assumption that $f(x \pm 0)$ exist.

Corollary 1. Let U and L be the upper and lower bounds of $f(t)$ in any interval (a, b) whose length does not exceed 2π, and let

$$\int_{-\pi}^{\pi} |f(t)| \, dt = \pi A.$$

Then, if $a + \eta \leqslant x \leqslant b - \eta$, where η is any positive number, we have

$$U - \frac{1}{m} \left\{ A_0 + \sum_{n=1}^{m-1} S_n(x) \right\} = \frac{1}{2m\pi} \left\{ \int_{-\pi+x}^{x-\eta} + \int_{x-\eta}^{x+\eta} + \int_{x+\eta}^{\pi+x} \right\} \frac{\sin^2 \frac{1}{2} m (x-t)}{\sin^2 \frac{1}{2}(x-t)} \{U - f(t)\} \, dt$$

$$\geqslant \frac{1}{2m\pi} \left\{ \int_{-\pi+x}^{x-\eta} + \int_{x+\eta}^{\pi+x} \right\} \frac{\sin^2 \frac{1}{2} m (x-t)}{\sin^2 \frac{1}{2}(x-t)} \{U - f(t)\} \, dt$$

$$\geqslant - \frac{1}{2m\pi} \left\{ \int_{-\pi+x}^{x-\eta} + \int_{x+\eta}^{\pi+x} \right\} \frac{|U| + |f(t)|}{\sin^2 \frac{1}{2}\eta} \, dt,$$

so that

$$\frac{1}{m} \left\{ A_0 + \sum_{n=1}^{m-1} S_n(x) \right\} \leqslant U + \{|U| + \tfrac{1}{2} A\} / \{m \sin^2 \tfrac{1}{2}\eta\}.$$

Similarly

$$\frac{1}{m} \left\{ A_0 + \sum_{n=1}^{m-1} S_n(x) \right\} \geqslant L - \{|L| + \tfrac{1}{2} A\} / \{m \sin^2 \tfrac{1}{2}\eta\}.$$

Corollary 2. Let $f(t)$ be continuous in the interval $a \leqslant t \leqslant b$. Since continuity implies uniformity of continuity (§ 3·61), the choice of δ corresponding to any value of x in (a, b) is independent of x, and the upper bound of $|f(x \pm 0)|$, i.e. of $|f(x)|$, is also independent of x, so that

$$\int_0^{\frac{1}{2}\pi} |\phi(\theta)| \, d\theta = \int_0^{\frac{1}{2}\pi} |f(x \pm 2\theta) - f(x \pm 0)| \, d\theta$$

$$\leqslant \tfrac{1}{2} \int_{-\pi}^{\pi} |f(t)| \, dt + \tfrac{1}{2}\pi |f(x \pm 0)|,$$

and the upper bound of the last expression is independent of x.

Hence the choice of m, which makes

$$\left| \frac{1}{m} \int_0^{\frac{1}{2}\pi} \frac{\sin^2 m\theta}{\sin^2 \theta} \, \phi(\theta) \, d\theta \right| < \pi \epsilon,$$

is independent of x, *and consequently* $\dfrac{1}{m} \left\{ A_0 + \sum\limits_{n=1}^{m-1} S_n(x) \right\}$ *tends to the limit* $f(x)$, *as* $m \to \infty$, *uniformly throughout the interval* $a \leqslant x \leqslant b$.

9·41. *The Riemann-Lebesgue lemmas.*

In order to be able to apply Hardy's theorem (§ 8·5) to deduce the convergence of Fourier series from Fejér's theorem, we need the two following lemmas:

(I) *Let* $\displaystyle\int_a^b \psi(\theta) \, d\theta$ *exist and (if it is an improper integral) let it be absolutely convergent. Then, as* $\lambda \to \infty$,

$$\int_a^b \psi(\theta) \sin(\lambda\theta) \, d\theta \text{ is } o(1).$$

(II) *If, further,* $\psi(\theta)$ *has limited total fluctuation in the range* (a, b) *then, as* $\lambda \to \infty$,

$$\int_a^b \psi(\theta) \sin(\lambda\theta) \, d\theta \text{ is } O(1/\lambda).$$

Of these results (I) was stated by W. R. Hamilton[*] and by Riemann[†] in the case of bounded functions. The truth of (II) seems to have been well known before its importance was realised; it is a generalisation of a result established by Dirksen[‡] and Stokes (see § 9·3) in the case of functions with a continuous differential coefficient.

The reader should observe that the analysis of this section remains valid when the sines are replaced throughout by cosines.

(I) It is convenient[§] to establish this lemma first in the case in which $\psi(\theta)$ is bounded in the range (a, b). In this case, let K be the upper bound of $|\psi(\theta)|$, and let ϵ be an arbitrary positive number. Divide the range (a, b) into n parts by the points $x_1, x_2, \dots x_{n-1}$, and form the sums S_n, s_n associated with the function $\psi(\theta)$ after the manner of § 4·1. Take n so large that $S_n - s_n < \epsilon$; this is possible since $\psi(\theta)$ is integrable.

In the interval (x_{r-1}, x_r) write

$$\psi(\theta) = \psi_r(x_{r-1}) + \omega_r(\theta),$$

so that
$$|\omega_r(\theta)| \leqslant U_r - L_r,$$

where U_r and L_r are the upper and lower bounds of $\psi(\theta)$ in the interval (x_{r-1}, x_r).

It is then clear that

$$\left| \int_a^b \psi(\theta) \sin(\lambda\theta) \, d\theta \right|$$

$$= \left| \sum_{r=1}^n \psi_r(x_{r-1}) \int_{x_{r-1}}^{x_r} \sin(\lambda\theta) \, d\theta + \sum_{r=1}^n \int_{x_{r-1}}^{x_r} \omega_r(\theta) \sin(\lambda\theta) \, d\theta \right|$$

$$\leqslant \sum_{r=1}^n |\psi_r(x_{r-1})| \cdot \left| \int_{x_{r-1}}^{x_r} \sin(\lambda\theta) \, d\theta \right| + \sum_{r=1}^n \int_{x_{r-1}}^{x_r} |\omega_r(\theta)| \, d\theta$$

$$\leqslant nK \cdot (2/\lambda) + (S_n - s_n)$$

$$< (2nK/\lambda) + \epsilon.$$

By taking λ sufficiently large (n remaining fixed after ϵ has been chosen), the last expression may be made less than 2ϵ, so that

$$\lim_{\lambda \to \infty} \int_a^b \psi(\theta) \sin(\lambda\theta) \, d\theta = 0,$$

and this is the result stated.

When $\psi(\theta)$ is unbounded, if it has an absolutely convergent integral, by § 4·5, we may enclose the points at which it is unbounded in a finite[||] number

[*] *Trans. Dublin Acad.* xix. (1843), p. 267.

[†] *Ges. Math. Werke*, p. 241. For Lebesgue's investigation see his *Séries trigonométriques* (1906), Ch. iii.

[‡] *Journal für Math.* iv. (1829), p. 172.

[§] For this proof we are indebted to Mr Hardy; it seems to be neater than the proofs given by other writers, e.g. de la Vallée Poussin, *Cours d'Analyse Infinitésimale*, ii. (1912), pp. 140–141.

[||] The *finiteness* of the number of intervals is assumed in the definition of an improper integral, § 4·5.

of intervals δ_1, δ_2, ... δ_p such that

$$\sum_{r=1}^{p} \int_{\delta_r} |\psi(\theta)| \, d\theta < \epsilon.$$

If K denote the upper bound of $|\psi(\theta)|$ for values of θ outside these intervals, and if γ_1, γ_2, ... γ_{p+1} denote the portions of the interval (a, b) which do not belong to δ_1, δ_2, ... δ_p we may prove as before that

$$\left| \int_a^b \psi(\theta) \sin(\lambda\theta) \, d\theta \right| = \left| \sum_{r=1}^{p+1} \int_{\gamma_r} \psi(\theta) \sin(\lambda\theta) \, d\theta + \sum_{r=1}^{p} \int_{\delta_r} \psi(\theta) \sin(\lambda\theta) \, d\theta \right|$$

$$\leqslant \left| \sum_{r=1}^{p+1} \int_{\gamma_r} \psi(\theta) \sin(\lambda\theta) \, d\theta \right| + \sum_{r=1}^{p} \int_{\delta_r} |\psi(\theta) \sin(\lambda\theta)| \, d\theta$$

$$< (2nK/\lambda) + 2\epsilon.$$

Now the choice of ϵ fixes n and K, so that the last expression may be made less than 3ϵ by taking λ sufficiently large. That is to say that, even if $\psi(\theta)$ be unbounded,

$$\lim_{\lambda \to \infty} \int_a^b \psi(\theta) \sin(\lambda\theta) \, d\theta = 0,$$

provided that $\psi(\theta)$ has an (improper) integral which is absolutely convergent.

The first lemma is therefore completely proved.

(II) When $\psi(\theta)$ has limited total fluctuation in the range (a, b), by § 3·64 example 2, we may write

$$\psi(\theta) = \chi_1(\theta) - \chi_2(\theta),$$

where $\chi_1(\theta)$, $\chi_2(\theta)$ are positive increasing bounded functions.

Then, by the second mean-value theorem (§ 4·14) à number ξ exists such that $a \leqslant \xi \leqslant b$ and

$$\left| \int_a^b \chi_1(\theta) \sin(\lambda\theta) \, d\theta \right| = \left| \chi_1(b) \int_\xi^b \sin(\lambda\theta) \, d\theta \right|$$

$$\leqslant 2\chi_1(b)/\lambda.$$

If we treat $\chi_2(\theta)$ in a similar manner, it follows that

$$\left| \int_a^b \psi(\theta) \sin(\lambda\theta) \, d\theta \right| \leqslant \left| \int_a^b \chi_1(\theta) \sin(\lambda\theta) \, d\theta \right| + \left| \int_a^b \chi_2(\theta) \sin(\lambda\theta) \, d\theta \right|$$

$$\leqslant 2 \{\chi_1(b) + \chi_2(b)\}/\lambda$$

$$= O(1/\lambda),$$

and the second lemma is established.

Corollary. If $f(t)$ be such that $\int_{-\pi}^{\pi} f(t)$ exists and is an absolutely convergent integral, the Fourier constants a_n, b_n of $f(t)$ are $o(1)$ as $n \to \infty$; and if, further, $f(t)$ has limited total fluctuation in the range $(-\pi, \pi)$, the Fourier constants are $O(1/n)$.

[Of course these results are not sufficient to ensure the convergence of the Fourier series associated with $f(t)$; for a series, in which the terms are of the order of magnitude of the terms in the harmonic series (§ 2·3), is not necessarily convergent.]

9·42. The proof of Fourier's theorem.

We shall now prove the theorem enunciated in § 9·2, namely:

Let $f(t)$ be a function defined arbitrarily when $-\pi \leqslant t < \pi$, and defined by the equation $f(t+2\pi) = f(t)$ for all other real values of t; and let $\int_{-\pi}^{\pi} f(t)\,dt$ exist and (if it is an improper integral) let it be absolutely convergent.

Let a_n, b_n be defined by the equations

$$\pi a_n = \int_{-\pi}^{\pi} f(t) \cos nt\,dt, \quad \pi b_n = \int_{-\pi}^{\pi} f(t) \sin nt\,dt.$$

Then, if x be an interior point of any interval (a, b) within which $f(t)$ has limited total fluctuation, the series

$$\tfrac{1}{2} a_0 + \sum_{n=1}^{\infty} (a_n \cos nx + b_n \sin nx)$$

is convergent and its sum is $\tfrac{1}{2}\{f(x+0) + f(x-0)\}$.

It is convenient to give two proofs, one applicable to functions for which it is permissible to take the interval (a, b) to be the interval $(-\pi+x, \pi+x)$, the other applicable to functions for which it is not permissible.

(I) When the interval (a, b) may be taken to be $(-\pi+x, \pi+x)$, it follows from § 9·41 (II) that $a_n \cos nx + b_n \sin nx$ is $O(1/n)$ as $n \to \infty$. Now by Fejér's theorem (§ 9·4) the series under consideration is summable $(C1)$ and its sum $(C1)$ is* $\tfrac{1}{2}\{f(x+0) + f(x-0)\}$. Therefore, by Hardy's convergence theorem (§ 8·5), the series under consideration is CONVERGENT and its sum (by § 8·43) is $\tfrac{1}{2}\{f(x+0) + f(x-0)\}$.

(II) Even if it is not permissible to take the interval (a, b) to be the whole interval $(-\pi+x, \pi+x)$, it is possible, by hypothesis, to choose a positive number δ, less than π, such that $f(t)$ has limited total fluctuation in the interval $(x-\delta, x+\delta)$. We now define an auxiliary function $g(t)$, which is equal to $f(t)$ when $x-\delta \leqslant t \leqslant x+\delta$, and which is equal to zero throughout the rest of the interval $(-\pi+x, \pi+x)$; and $g(t+2\pi)$ is to be equal to $g(t)$ for all real values of t.

Then $g(t)$ satisfies the conditions postulated for the functions under consideration in (I), namely that it has an integral which is absolutely convergent and it has limited total fluctuation in the interval $(-\pi+x, \pi+x)$; and so, if $a_n^{(1)}, b_n^{(1)}$ denote the Fourier constants of $g(t)$, the arguments used in (I) prove that the Fourier series associated with $g(t)$, namely

$$\tfrac{1}{2} a_0^{(1)} + \sum_{n=1}^{\infty} (a_n^{(1)} \cos nx + b_n^{(1)} \sin nx),$$

is convergent and has the sum $\tfrac{1}{2}\{g(x+0) + g(x-0)\}$, and this is equal to

$$\tfrac{1}{2}\{f(x+0) + f(x-0)\}.$$

---

* The limits $f(x \pm 0)$ exist, by § 3·64 example 3.

Now let $S_m(x)$ and $S_m^{(1)}(x)$ denote the sums of the first $m+1$ terms of the Fourier series associated with $f(t)$ and $g(t)$ respectively. Then it is easily seen that

$$S_m(x) = \frac{1}{\pi} \int_{-\pi}^{\pi} \left\{ \tfrac{1}{2} + \cos(x-t) + \cos 2(x-t) + \ldots + \cos m(x-t) \right\} f(t)\, dt$$

$$= \frac{1}{2\pi} \int_{-\pi}^{\pi} \frac{\sin(m+\tfrac{1}{2})(x-t)}{\sin \tfrac{1}{2}(x-t)} f(t)\, dt$$

$$= \frac{1}{2\pi} \int_{-\pi+x}^{\pi+x} \frac{\sin(m+\tfrac{1}{2})(x-t)}{\sin \tfrac{1}{2}(x-t)} f(t)\, dt$$

$$= \frac{1}{\pi} \int_{0}^{\tfrac{1}{2}\pi} \frac{\sin(2m+1)\theta}{\sin\theta} f(x+2\theta)\, d\theta + \frac{1}{\pi} \int_{0}^{\tfrac{1}{2}\pi} \frac{\sin(2m+1)\theta}{\sin\theta} f(x-2\theta)\, d\theta,$$

by steps analogous to those given in § 9·4.

In like manner

$$S_m^{(1)}(x) = \frac{1}{\pi} \int_{0}^{\tfrac{1}{2}\pi} \frac{\sin(2m+1)\theta}{\sin\theta} g(x+2\theta)\, d\theta + \frac{1}{\pi} \int_{0}^{\tfrac{1}{2}\pi} \frac{\sin(2m+1)\theta}{\sin\theta} g(x-2\theta)\, d\theta,$$

and so, using the definition of $g(t)$, we have

$$S_m(x) - S_m^{(1)}(x) = \frac{1}{\pi} \int_{\tfrac{1}{2}\delta}^{\tfrac{1}{2}\pi} \sin(2m+1)\theta \, \frac{f(x+2\theta)}{\sin\theta}\, d\theta$$

$$+ \frac{1}{\pi} \int_{\tfrac{1}{2}\delta}^{\tfrac{1}{2}\pi} \sin(2m+1)\theta \, \frac{f(x-2\theta)}{\sin\theta}\, d\theta.$$

Since $\operatorname{cosec}\theta$ is a continuous function in the range $(\tfrac{1}{2}\delta, \tfrac{1}{2}\pi)$, it follows that $f(x \pm 2\theta)\operatorname{cosec}\theta$ are integrable functions with absolutely convergent integrals; and so, by the Riemann-Lebesgue lemma of § 9·41 (I), *both the integrals on the right in the last equation tend to zero as $m \to \infty$*.

That is to say $\qquad \lim_{m\to\infty} \{S_m(x) - S_m^{(1)}(x)\} = 0.$

Hence, since $\qquad \lim_{m\to\infty} S_m^{(1)}(x) = \tfrac{1}{2}\{f(x+0) + f(x-0)\},$

it follows also that

$$\lim_{m\to\infty} S_m(x) = \tfrac{1}{2}\{f(x+0) + f(x-0)\}.$$

We have therefore proved that the Fourier series associated with $f(t)$, namely $\tfrac{1}{2}a_0 + \Sigma(a_n \cos nx + b_n \sin nx)$, is convergent and its sum is

$$\tfrac{1}{2}\{f(x+0) + f(x-0)\}.$$

9·43. *The Dirichlet-Bonnet proof of Fourier's theorem.*

It is of some interest to prove directly the theorem of § 9·42, without making use of the theory of summability; accordingly we now give a proof which is on the same general lines as the proofs due to Dirichlet and Bonnet.

As usual we denote the sum of the first $m + 1$ terms of the Fourier series by $S_m(x)$, and then, by the analysis of § 9·42, we have

$$S_m(x) = \frac{1}{\pi} \int_0^{\frac{1}{2}\pi} \frac{\sin(2m+1)\theta}{\sin\theta} f(x+2\theta)\, d\theta + \frac{1}{\pi} \int_0^{\frac{1}{2}\pi} \frac{\sin(2m+1)\theta}{\sin\theta} f(x-2\theta)\, d\theta.$$

Again, on integrating the equation

$$\frac{\sin(2m+1)\theta}{\sin\theta} = 1 + 2\cos 2\theta + 2\cos 4\theta + \dots + 2\cos 2m\,\theta,$$

we have

$$\int_0^{\frac{1}{2}\pi} \frac{\sin(2m+1)\theta}{\sin\theta}\, d\theta = \tfrac{1}{2}\pi,$$

so that

$$S_m(x) - \tfrac{1}{2}\{f(x+0) + f(x-0)\} = \frac{1}{\pi} \int_0^{\frac{1}{2}\pi} \frac{\sin(2m+1)\theta}{\sin\theta} \{f(x+2\theta) - f(x+0)\}\, d\theta$$

$$+ \frac{1}{\pi} \int_0^{\frac{1}{2}\pi} \frac{\sin(2m+1)\theta}{\sin\theta} \{f(x-2\theta) - f(x-0)\}\, d\theta.$$

In order to prove that

$$\lim_{m \to \infty} S_m(x) = \tfrac{1}{2}\{f(x+0) + f(x-0)\},$$

it is therefore sufficient to prove that

$$\lim_{m \to \infty} \int_0^{\frac{1}{2}\pi} \frac{\sin(2m+1)\theta}{\sin\theta}\, \phi(\theta)\, d\theta = 0,$$

where $\phi(\theta)$ stands in turn for each of the functions

$$f(x+2\theta) - f(x+0), \quad f(x-2\theta) - f(x-0).$$

Now, by § 3·64 example 4, $\theta\phi(\theta)\operatorname{cosec}\theta$ is a function with limited total fluctuation in an interval of which $\theta = 0$ is an end-point[*]; and so we may write

$$\theta\,\phi(\theta)\operatorname{cosec}\theta = \chi_1(\theta) - \chi_2(\theta),$$

where $\chi_1(\theta)$, $\chi_2(\theta)$ are bounded positive increasing functions of θ such that

$$\chi_1(+0) = \chi_2(+0) = 0.$$

Hence, given an arbitrary positive number ϵ, we can choose a positive number δ such that

$$0 \leqslant \chi_1(\theta) < \epsilon, \quad 0 \leqslant \chi_2(\theta) < \epsilon$$

whenever $0 \leqslant \theta \leqslant \tfrac{1}{2}\delta$.

We now obtain inequalities satisfied by the three integrals on the right of the obvious equation

$$\int_0^{\frac{1}{2}\pi} \frac{\sin(2m+1)\theta}{\sin\theta}\, \phi(\theta)\, d\theta = \int_{\frac{1}{2}\delta}^{\frac{1}{2}\pi} \sin(2m+1)\theta \cdot \frac{\phi(\theta)}{\sin\theta}\, d\theta$$

$$+ \int_0^{\frac{1}{2}\delta} \frac{\sin(2m+1)\theta}{\theta}\, \chi_1(\theta)\, d\theta - \int_0^{\frac{1}{2}\delta} \frac{\sin(2m+1)\theta}{\theta}\, \chi_2(\theta)\, d\theta.$$

[*] The other end-point is $\theta = \tfrac{1}{2}(b-x)$ or $\theta = \tfrac{1}{2}(x-a)$, according as $\phi(\theta)$ represents one or other of the two functions.

The modulus of the first integral can be made less than ϵ by taking m sufficiently large; this follows from § 9·41 (1) since $\phi(\theta)\operatorname{cosec}\theta$ has an integral which converges absolutely in the interval $(\tfrac{1}{2}\delta,\ \tfrac{1}{2}\pi)$.

Next, from the second mean-value theorem, it follows that there is a number ξ between 0 and δ such that

$$\left|\int_0^{\frac{1}{2}\delta}\frac{\sin(2m+1)\theta}{\theta}\chi_1(\theta)\,d\theta\right|=\left|\chi_1(\tfrac{1}{2}\delta)\cdot\int_{\frac{1}{2}\xi}^{\frac{1}{2}\delta}\frac{\sin(2m+1)\theta}{\theta}\,d\theta\right|$$

$$=\chi_1(\tfrac{1}{2}\delta)\cdot\left|\int_{(m+\frac{1}{2})\xi}^{(m+\frac{1}{2})\delta}\frac{\sin u}{u}\,du\right|.$$

Since $\int^\infty\frac{\sin t}{t}\,dt$ is convergent, it follows that $\left|\int_\beta^\infty\frac{\sin u}{u}\,du\right|$ has an upper bound* B which is independent of β, and it is then clear that

$$\left|\int_0^{\frac{1}{2}\delta}\frac{\sin(2m+1)\theta}{\theta}\chi_1(\theta)\,d\theta\right|\leqslant 2B\chi_1(\tfrac{1}{2}\delta)<2B\epsilon.$$

On treating the third integral in a similar manner, we see that we can make

$$\left|\int_0^{\frac{1}{2}\pi}\frac{\sin(2m+1)\theta}{\sin\theta}\phi(\theta)\,d\theta\right|<(4B+1)\epsilon$$

by taking m sufficiently large; *and so we have proved that*

$$\lim_{m\to\infty}\int_0^{\frac{1}{2}\pi}\frac{\sin(2m+1)\theta}{\sin\theta}\phi(\theta)\,d\theta=0.$$

But it has been seen that this is a sufficient condition for the limit of $S_m(x)$ to be $\tfrac{1}{2}\{f(x+0)+f(x-0)\}$; and we have therefore established the convergence of a Fourier series in the circumstances enunciated in § 9·42.

NOTE. The reader should observe that in either proof of the convergence of a Fourier series the *second* mean-value theorem is required; but to prove the summability of the series, the *first* mean-value theorem is adequate. It should also be observed that, while restrictions are laid upon $f(t)$ throughout the range $(-\pi,\pi)$ in establishing the *summability* at any point x, the only additional restriction necessary to ensure *convergence* is a restriction on the behaviour of the function in the *immediate neighbourhood* of the point x. The fact that the convergence depends only on the behaviour of the function in the immediate neighbourhood of x (provided that the function has an integral which is absolutely convergent) was noticed by Riemann and has been emphasised by Lebesgue, *Séries Trigonométriques*, p. 60.

It is obvious that the condition† that x should be an interior point of an interval in which $f(t)$ has limited total fluctuation is merely a *sufficient* condition for the convergence of the Fourier series; and it may be replaced by any condition which makes

$$\lim_{m\to\infty}\int_0^{\frac{1}{2}\pi}\frac{\sin(2m+1)\theta}{\sin\theta}\phi(\theta)\,d\theta=0.$$

* The reader will find it interesting to prove that $B=\int_0^\infty\frac{\sin u}{u}\,du=\tfrac{1}{2}\pi.$

† Due to Jordan, *Comptes Rendus*, XCII. (1881), p. 228.

Jordan's condition is, however, a natural modification of the Dirichlet condition that the function $f(t)$ should have only a finite number of maxima and minima, and it does not increase the difficulty of the proof.

Another condition with the same effect is due to Dini, *Sopra le Serie di Fourier* (Pisa, 1880), namely that, if

$$\Phi(\theta) = \{f(x+2\theta)+f(x-2\theta)-f(x+0)-f(x-0)\}/\theta,$$

then $\int_0^a \Phi(\theta)\,d\theta$ should converge absolutely for some positive value of a.

[If the condition is satisfied, given ϵ we can find δ so that

$$\int_0^{\frac{1}{2}\delta} |\Phi(\theta)|\,d\theta < \epsilon,$$

and then

$$\left| \int_0^{\frac{1}{2}\delta} \sin(2m+1)\theta\, \frac{\theta}{\sin\theta}\, \Phi(\theta)\,d\theta \right| < \tfrac{1}{2}\pi\epsilon;$$

the proof that $\left| \int_{\frac{1}{2}\delta}^{\frac{1}{2}\pi} \frac{\sin(2m+1)\theta}{\sin\theta}\, \phi(\theta)\,d\theta \right| < \epsilon$ for sufficiently large values of m follows from the Riemann-Lebesgue lemma.]

A more stringent condition than Dini's is due to Lipschitz, *Journal für Math.* LXIII. (1864), p. 296, namely $|\phi(\theta)| < C\theta^k$, where C and k are positive and independent of θ.

For other conditions due to Lebesgue and to de la Vallée Poussin, see the latter's *Cours d'Analyse Infinitésimale*, II. (1912), pp. 149–150. It should be noticed that Jordan's condition differs in character from Dini's condition; the latter is a condition that the series may converge *at a point*, the former that the series may converge *throughout an interval*.

9·44. *The uniformity of the convergence of Fourier series.*

Let $f(t)$ satisfy the conditions enunciated in § 9·42, and further let it be *continuous* (in addition to having limited total fluctuation) in an interval (a, b). *Then the Fourier series associated with $f(t)$ converges uniformly to the sum $f(x)$ at all points x for which $a+\delta \leqslant x \leqslant b-\delta$, where δ is any positive number.*

Let $h(t)$ be an auxiliary function defined to be equal to $f(t)$ when $a \leqslant t \leqslant b$ and equal to zero for other values of t in the range $(-\pi, \pi)$, and let a_n, β_n denote the Fourier constants of $h(t)$. Also let $S_m^{(2)}(x)$ denote the sum of the first $m+1$ terms of the Fourier series associated with $h(t)$.

Then, by § 9·4 corollary 2, it follows that $\frac{1}{2}a_0 + \sum_{n=1}^{\infty}(a_n \cos nx + \beta_n \sin nx)$ is *uniformly* summable throughout the interval $(a+\delta, b-\delta)$; and since

$$|a_n \cos nx + \beta_n \sin nx| \leqslant (a_n^2 + \beta_n^2)^{\frac{1}{2}},$$

which is independent of x and which, by § 9·41 (II), is $O(1/n)$, it follows from § 8·5 corollary that

$$\tfrac{1}{2}a_0 + \sum_{n=1}^{\infty}(a_n \cos nx + \beta_n \sin nx)$$

converges uniformly to the sum $h(x)$, which is equal to $f(x)$.

Now, as in § 9·42,

$$S_m(x) - S_m^{(2)}(x) = \frac{1}{\pi}\int_{\frac{1}{2}(b-x)}^{\frac{1}{2}\pi} \frac{\sin(2m+1)\theta}{\sin\theta} f(x+2\theta)\,d\theta + \frac{1}{\pi}\int_{\frac{1}{2}(x-a)}^{\frac{1}{2}\pi} \frac{\sin(2m+1)\theta}{\sin\theta} f(x-2\theta)\,d\theta.$$

As in § 9·41 we choose an arbitrary positive number ϵ and then enclose the points at which $f(t)$ is unbounded in a set of intervals $\delta_1, \delta_2, \ldots \delta_p$ such that $\sum\limits_{r=1}^{p} \int_{\delta_r} |f(t)| \, dt < \epsilon$.

If K be the upper bound of $|f(t)|$ outside these intervals, we then have, as in § 9·41,

$$|S_m(x) - S_m^{(2)}(x)| < \left(\frac{2nK}{2m+1} + 2\epsilon \right) \operatorname{cosec} \delta,$$

where the choice of n depends only on a and b and the form of the function $f(t)$. Hence, by a choice of m *independent* of x we can make

$$|S_m(x) - S_m^{(2)}(x)|$$

arbitrarily small; so that $S_m(x) - S_m^{(2)}(x)$ tends uniformly to zero. Since $S_m^{(2)}(x) \to f(x)$ uniformly, it is then obvious that $S_m(x) \to f(x)$ uniformly; and this is the result to be proved.

NOTE. It must be observed that no general statement can be made about uniformity or absoluteness of convergence of Fourier series. Thus the series of § 9·11 example 1 converges uniformly except near $x = (2n+1)\pi$ but converges absolutely only when $x = n\pi$, whereas the series of § 9·11 example 2 converges uniformly and absolutely for all real values of x.

Example 1. If $\phi(\theta)$ satisfies suitable conditions in the range $(0, \pi)$, shew that

$$\lim_{m \to \infty} \int_0^\pi \frac{\sin(2m+1)\theta}{\sin\theta} \phi(\theta) \, d\theta = \lim_{m \to \infty} \int_0^{\frac{1}{2}\pi} \frac{\sin(2m+1)\theta}{\sin\theta} \phi(\theta) \, d\theta$$

$$+ \lim_{m \to \infty} \int_0^{\frac{1}{2}\pi} \frac{\sin(2m+1)\theta}{\sin\theta} \phi(\pi - \theta) \, d\theta$$

$$= \tfrac{1}{2}\pi \{\phi(+0) + \phi(\pi - 0)\}.$$

Example 2. Prove that, if $a > 0$,

$$\lim_{n \to \infty} \int_0^\infty \frac{\sin(2n+1)\theta}{\sin\theta} e^{-a\theta} \, d\theta = \tfrac{1}{2}\pi \coth \tfrac{1}{2}a\pi.$$

(Math. Trip. 1894.)

[Shew that

$$\int_0^\infty \frac{\sin(2n+1)\theta}{\sin\theta} e^{-a\theta} \, d\theta = \lim_{m \to \infty} \int_0^{m\pi} \frac{\sin(2n+1)\theta}{\sin\theta} e^{-a\theta} \, d\theta$$

$$= \lim_{m \to \infty} \int_0^\pi \frac{\sin(2n+1)\theta}{\sin\theta} \{e^{-a\theta} + e^{-a(\theta+\pi)} + \ldots + e^{-a(\theta+m\pi)}\} \, d\theta$$

$$= \int_0^\pi \frac{\sin(2n+1)\theta}{\sin\theta} \frac{e^{-a\theta} \, d\theta}{1 - e^{-a\pi}},$$

and use example 1.]

Example 3. Discuss the uniformity of the convergence of Fourier series by means of the Dirichlet-Bonnet integrals, without making use of the theory of summability.

9·5. *The Hurwitz-Liapounoff* [*] *theorem concerning Fourier constants.*

Let $f(x)$ be bounded in the interval $(-\pi, \pi)$ and let $\int_{-\pi}^{\pi} f(x) \, dx$ exist, so

---

[*] *Math. Ann.* LVII. (1903), p. 429. Liapounoff discovered the theorem in 1896 and published it in the *Proceedings of the Math. Soc. of the Univ. of Kharkov.* See *Comptes Rendus*, CXXVI. (1898), p. 1024.

that the Fourier constants a_n, b_n of $f(x)$ exist.   Then the series

$$\tfrac{1}{2}a_0{}^2 + \sum_{n=1}^{\infty} (a_n{}^2 + b_n{}^2)$$

is convergent and its sum is * $\dfrac{1}{\pi}\displaystyle\int_{-\pi}^{\pi} \{f(x)\}^2\, dx.$

It will first be shewn that, with the notation of § 9·4,

$$\lim_{m\to\infty} \int_{-\pi}^{\pi} \left\{ f(x) - \frac{1}{m}\sum_{n=0}^{m-1} S_n(x) \right\}^2 dx = 0.$$

Divide the interval $(-\pi, \pi)$ into $4r$ parts, each of length δ; let the upper and lower bounds of $f(x)$ in the interval $\{(2p-1)\,\delta - \pi,\ (2p+3)\,\delta - \pi\}$ be U_p, L_p, and let the upper bound of $|f(x)|$ in the interval $(-\pi, \pi)$ be K. Then, by § 9·4 corollary 1,

$$\left| f(x) - \frac{1}{m}\sum_{n=0}^{m-1} S_n(x) \right| < U_p - L_p + 2K/\{m\sin^2\tfrac{1}{2}\delta\}$$
$$< 2K\,[1 + 1/\{m\sin^2\tfrac{1}{2}\delta\}],$$

when x lies between $2p\delta$ and $(2p+2)\,\delta$.

Consequently, by the first mean-value theorem,

$$\int_{-\pi}^{\pi} \left\{ f(x) - \frac{1}{m}\sum_{n=0}^{m-1} S_n(x) \right\}^2 dx < 2K \left\{ 1 + \frac{1}{m\sin^2\tfrac{1}{2}\delta} \right\} \left\{ 2\delta \sum_{p=0}^{2r-1} (U_p - L_p) + \frac{4Kr}{m\sin^2\tfrac{1}{2}\delta} \right\}.$$

Since $f(x)$ satisfies the Riemann condition of integrability (§ 4·12), it follows that both $4\delta \sum_{p=0}^{r-1} (U_{2p} - L_{2p})$ and $4\delta \sum_{p=0}^{r-1} (U_{2p+1} - L_{2p+1})$ can be made arbitrarily small by giving r a sufficiently large value. When r (and therefore also δ) has been given such a value, we may choose m_1 so large that $r/\{m_1\sin^2\tfrac{1}{2}\delta\}$ is arbitrarily small. That is to say, we can make the expression on the right of the last inequality arbitrarily small by giving m any value greater than a determinate value m_1. Hence the expression on the left of the inequality tends to zero as $m\to\infty$.

But evidently

$$\int_{-\pi}^{\pi} \left\{ f(x) - \frac{1}{m}\sum_{n=0}^{m-1} S_n(x) \right\}^2 dx$$

$$= \int_{-\pi}^{\pi} \left\{ f(x) - \sum_{n=0}^{m-1} \frac{m-n}{m} A_n(x) \right\}^2 dx$$

$$= \int_{-\pi}^{\pi} \left\{ f(x) - \sum_{n=0}^{m-1} A_n(x) + \sum_{n=0}^{m-1} \frac{n}{m} A_n(x) \right\}^2 dx$$

$$= \int_{-\pi}^{\pi} \left\{ f(x) - \sum_{n=0}^{m-1} A_n(x) \right\}^2 dx + \int_{-\pi}^{\pi} \left\{ \sum_{n=0}^{m-1} \frac{n}{m} A_n(x) \right\}^2 dx$$

$$\qquad + 2\int_{-\pi}^{\pi} \left\{ f(x) - \sum_{n=0}^{m-1} A_n(x) \right\} \cdot \left\{ \sum_{n=0}^{m-1} A_n(x) \right\} dx$$

$$= \int_{-\pi}^{\pi} \left\{ f(x) - \sum_{n=0}^{m-1} A_n(x) \right\}^2 dx + \frac{\pi}{m^2}\sum_{n=0}^{m-1} n^2\,(a_n{}^2 + b_n{}^2),$$

---

* This integral exists by § 4·12 example 1. A proof of the theorem has been given by de la Vallée Poussin, in which the sole restrictions on $f(x)$ are that the (improper) integrals of $f(x)$ and $\{f(x)\}^2$ exist in the interval $(-\pi, \pi)$. See his *Cours d'Analyse Infinitésimale*, II. (1912), pp. 165–166.

since
$$\int_{-\pi}^{\pi} f(x)\, A_r(x)\, dx = \int_{-\pi}^{\pi} \left\{ \sum_{n=0}^{m-1} A_n(x) \right\} A_r(x)\, dx$$

when $r = 0, 1, 2, \ldots m-1$.

Since the original integral tends to zero and since it has been proved equal to the sum of two positive expressions, it follows that each of these expressions tends to zero; that is to say

$$\int_{-\pi}^{\pi} \left\{ f(x) - \sum_{n=0}^{m-1} A_n(x) \right\}^2 dx \to 0.$$

Now the expression on the left is equal to

$$\int_{-\pi}^{\pi} \{ f(x) \}^2\, dx - 2 \int_{-\pi}^{\pi} \left\{ f(x) - \sum_{n=0}^{m-1} A_n(x) \right\} . \left\{ \sum_{n=0}^{m-1} A_n(x) \right\} dx$$

$$- \int_{-\pi}^{\pi} \left\{ \sum_{n=0}^{m-1} A_n(x) \right\}^2 dx$$

$$= \int_{-\pi}^{\pi} \{ f(x) \}^2\, dx - \int_{-\pi}^{\pi} \left\{ \sum_{n=0}^{m-1} A_n(x) \right\}^2 dx$$

$$= \int_{-\pi}^{\pi} \{ f(x) \}^2\, dx - \pi \left\{ \tfrac{1}{2} a_0{}^2 + \sum_{n=1}^{m-1} (a_n{}^2 + b_n{}^2) \right\},$$

so that, as $m \to \infty$,

$$\int_{-\pi}^{\pi} \{ f(x) \}^2\, dx - \pi \left\{ \tfrac{1}{2} a_0{}^2 + \sum_{n=1}^{m-1} (a_n{}^2 + b_n{}^2) \right\} \to 0.$$

This is the theorem stated.

Corollary. Parseval's theorem[*]. If $f(x)$, $F(x)$ both satisfy the conditions laid on $f(x)$ at the beginning of this section, and if A_n, B_n be the Fourier constants of $F(x)$, it follows by subtracting the pair of equations which may be combined in the one form

$$\int_{-\pi}^{\pi} \{ f(x) \pm F(x) \}^2\, dx = \pi \left[\tfrac{1}{2} (a_0 \pm A_0)^2 + \sum_{n=1}^{\infty} \{ (a_n \pm A_n)^2 + (b_n \pm B_n)^2 \} \right]$$

that
$$\int_{-\pi}^{\pi} f(x)\, F(x)\, dx = \pi \left\{ \tfrac{1}{2} a_0 A_0 + \sum_{n=1}^{\infty} (a_n A_n + b_n B_n) \right\}.$$

9·6. *Riemann's theory of trigonometrical series.*

The theory of Dirichlet concerning Fourier series is devoted to series which represent given functions. Important advances in the theory were made by Riemann, who considered properties of functions defined by a series of the type[†] $\tfrac{1}{2} a_0 + \sum_{n=1}^{\infty} (a_n \cos nx + b_n \sin nx)$, where it is assumed that $\lim_{n \to \infty} (a_n \cos nx + b_n \sin nx) = 0$. We shall give the propositions leading up to Riemann's theorem[‡] that if two trigonometrical series converge and are equal

---

[*] *Mém. par divers savans*, I. (1805), pp. 639–648. Parseval, of course, assumed the permissibility of integrating the trigonometrical series term-by-term.

[†] Throughout §§ 9·6–9·632 the letters a_n, b_n do not necessarily denote Fourier constants.

[‡] The proof given is due to G. Cantor, *Journal für Math.* LXXII. (1870), pp. 130–142.

at all points of the range $(-\pi, \pi)$ with the possible exception of a finite number of points, corresponding coefficients in the two series are equal.

9·61. *Riemann's associated function.*

Let the sum of the series $\frac{1}{2}a_0 + \sum\limits_{n=1}^{\infty} (a_n \cos nx + b_n \sin nx) = A_0 + \sum\limits_{n=1}^{\infty} A_n(x)$, at any point x where it converges, be denoted by $f(x)$.

Let $$F(x) = \frac{1}{2}A_0 x^2 - \sum_{n=1}^{\infty} n^{-2} A_n(x).$$

Then, if the series defining $f(x)$ converges at all points of any finite interval, the series defining $F(x)$ converges for all real values of x.

To obtain this result we need the following Lemma due to Cantor:

Cantor's lemma*. *If $\lim\limits_{n \to \infty} A_n(x) = 0$ for all values of x such that $a \leqslant x \leqslant b$, then $a_n \to 0$, $b_n \to 0$.*

For take two points x, $x + \delta$ of the interval. Then, given ϵ, we can find n_0 such that†, when $n > n_0$

$$| a_n \cos nx + b_n \sin nx | < \epsilon, \quad | a_n \cos n(x+\delta) + b_n \sin n(x+\delta) | < \epsilon.$$

Therefore

$$| \cos n\delta (a_n \cos nx + b_n \sin nx) + \sin n\delta (-a_n \sin nx + b_n \cos nx) | < \epsilon.$$

Since $\quad | \cos n\delta (a_n \cos nx + b_n \sin nx) | \quad < \epsilon,$

it follows that $\quad | \sin n\delta (-a_n \sin nx + b_n \cos nx) | < 2\epsilon,$

and it is obvious that $\quad | \sin n\delta (a_n \cos nx + b_n \sin nx) | \quad < 2\epsilon.$

Therefore, squaring and adding,

$$(a_n^2 + b_n^2)^{\frac{1}{2}} | \sin n\delta | < 2\epsilon \sqrt{2}.$$

Now suppose that a_n, b_n have not the unique limit 0; it will be shewn that this hypothesis involves a contradiction. For, by this hypothesis, *some* positive number ϵ_0 exists such that there is an unending increasing sequence $n_1, n_2, \dots$ of values of n, for which

$$(a_n^2 + b_n^2)^{\frac{1}{2}} > 4\epsilon_0.$$

Now let the range of values of δ be called the interval I_1 of length L_1 on the real axis.

Take n_1' the smallest of the integers n_r such that $n_1' L_1 > 2\pi$; then $\sin n_1' y$ goes through all its phases in the interval I_1; call I_2 that sub-interval‡ of I_1 in which $\sin n_1' y > 1/\sqrt{2}$; its length is $\pi/(2n_1') = L_2$. Next take n_2' the smallest of the integers n_r $(>n_1')$ such that $n_2' L_2 > 2\pi$, so that $\sin n_2' y$ goes through all its phases in the interval I_2; call I_3 that sub-interval‡ of I_2 in which $\sin n_2' y > 1/\sqrt{2}$; its length is $\pi/(2n_2') = L_3$. We thus get a sequence of decreasing intervals $I_1, I_2, \dots$ each contained in all the previous ones. It is obvious from the definition of an irrational number that there is a certain point a which is not outside any of these intervals, and $\sin na \geqslant 1/\sqrt{2}$ when $n = n_1', n_2', \dots (n'_{r+1} > n_r')$. For these values of n, $(a_n^2 + b_n^2)^{\frac{1}{2}} \sin na > 2\epsilon_0 \sqrt{2}$. But it has been shewn that corresponding

---

* Riemann appears to have regarded this result as obvious. The proof here given is a modification of Cantor's proof, *Math. Ann.* IV. (1871), pp. 139–143, and *Journal für Math.* LXXII. (1870), pp. 130–138.

† The value of n_0 depends on x and on δ.

‡ If there is more than one such sub-interval, take that which lies on the left.

to given numbers a and ϵ we can find n_0 such that when $n > n_0$, $(a_n^2 + b_n^2)^{\frac{1}{2}} (\sin na) < 2\epsilon \sqrt{2}$; since some values of n_r' are greater than n_0, the required contradiction has been obtained, because we may take $\epsilon < \epsilon_0$; therefore $a_n \to 0$, $b_n \to 0$.

Assuming that the series defining $f(x)$ converges at all points of a certain interval of the real axis, we have just seen that $a_n \to 0$, $b_n \to 0$. Then, for all real values of x, $|a_n \cos nx + b_n \sin nx| \leqslant (a_n^2 + b_n^2)^{\frac{1}{2}} \to 0$, and so, by § 3·34, the series $\frac{1}{2}A_0 x^2 - \sum\limits_{n=1}^{\infty} n^{-2} A_n(x) = F(x)$ converges absolutely and uniformly for all real values of x; therefore, (§ 3·32), $F(x)$ is continuous for all real values of x.

9·62. *Properties of Riemann's associated function; Riemann's first lemma.*

It is now possible to prove Riemann's first lemma *that if*

$$G(x, \alpha) = \frac{F(x + 2\alpha) + F(x - 2\alpha) - 2F(x)}{4\alpha^2},$$

then $\lim\limits_{\alpha \to 0} G(x, \alpha) = f(x)$, *provided that* $\sum\limits_{n=0}^{\infty} A_n(x)$ *converges for the value of* x *under consideration.*

Since the series defining $F(x)$, $F(x \pm 2\alpha)$ converge absolutely, we may rearrange them; and, observing that

$$\cos n(x + 2\alpha) + \cos n(x - 2\alpha) - 2\cos nx = -4\sin^2 n\alpha \cos nx,$$
$$\sin n(x + 2\alpha) + \sin n(x - 2\alpha) - 2\sin nx = -4\sin^2 n\alpha \sin nx,$$

it is evident that

$$G(x, \alpha) = A_0 + \sum\limits_{n=1}^{\infty} \left(\frac{\sin n\alpha}{n\alpha}\right)^2 A_n(x).$$

It will now be shewn that this series converges uniformly with regard to α for all values of α, provided that $\sum\limits_{n=1}^{\infty} A_n(x)$ converges. The result required is then an immediate consequence of § 3·32: for, if $f_n(\alpha) = \left(\dfrac{\sin n\alpha}{n\alpha}\right)^2$, $(\alpha \neq 0)$, and $f_n(0) = 1$, then $f_n(\alpha)$ is continuous for all values of α, and so $G(x, \alpha)$ is a continuous function of α, and therefore, by § 3·2, $G(x, 0) = \lim\limits_{\alpha \to 0} G(x, \alpha)$.

To prove that the series defining $G(x, \alpha)$ converges uniformly, we employ the test given in § 3·35 example 2. The expression corresponding to $\omega_n(x)$ is $f_n(\alpha)$, and it is obvious that $|f_n(\alpha)| \leqslant 1$; it is therefore sufficient to shew that $\sum\limits_{n=1}^{\infty} |f_{n+1}(\alpha) - f_n(\alpha)| < K$, where K is independent of α.

In fact[*], if s be the integer such that $s|a| \leqslant \pi < (s+1)|a|$, when $a \neq 0$ we have

$$\sum\limits_{n=1}^{s-1} |f_{n+1}(a) - f_n(a)| = \sum\limits_{n=1}^{s-1} (f_n(a) - f_{n+1}(a)) = \frac{\sin^2 a}{a^2} - \frac{\sin^2 sa}{s^2 a^2}.$$

[*] Since $x^{-1} \sin x$ decreases as x increases from 0 to π.

Also

$$\sum_{n=s+1}^{\infty} |f_{n+1}(a) - f_n(a)| = \sum_{n=s+1}^{\infty} \left| \left\{ \frac{\sin^2 na}{a^2} \left(\frac{1}{n^2} - \frac{1}{(n+1)^2} \right) \right\} + \frac{\sin^2 na - \sin^2 (n+1) a}{(n+1)^2 a^2} \right|$$

$$\leqslant \sum_{n=s+1}^{\infty} \frac{1}{a^2} \left(\frac{1}{n^2} - \frac{1}{(n+1)^2} \right) + \sum_{n=s+1}^{\infty} \frac{|\sin^2 na - \sin^2 (n+1) a|}{(n+1)^2 a^2}$$

$$\leqslant \frac{1}{(s+1)^2 a^2} + \sum_{n=s+1}^{\infty} \frac{|\sin a \sin (2n+1) a|}{(n^2+1)^2 a^2}$$

$$\leqslant \frac{1}{(s+1)^2 a^2} + \frac{|\sin a|}{a^2} \sum_{n=s+1}^{\infty} \frac{1}{(n+1)^2}$$

$$\leqslant \frac{1}{\pi^2} + \frac{|\sin a|}{a^2} \int_{s}^{\infty} \frac{dx}{(x+1)^2}$$

$$\leqslant \frac{1}{\pi^2} + \frac{1}{(s+1)|a|} .$$

Therefore

$$\sum_{n=1}^{\infty} |f_{n+1}(a) - f_n(a)| \leqslant \frac{\sin^2 a}{a^2} - \frac{\sin^2 sa}{s^2 a^2} + \left(\frac{\sin^2 sa}{s^2 a^2} + \frac{\sin^2 (s+1) a}{(s+1)^2 a^2} \right) + \frac{1}{\pi^2} + \frac{1}{\pi}$$

$$\leqslant 1 + \frac{1}{\pi} + \frac{2}{\pi^2} .$$

Since this expression is independent of a, the result required has been obtained*.

Hence, if $\sum_{n=0}^{\infty} A_n(x)$ converges, the series defining $G(x, a)$ converges uniformly with respect to a for all values of a, and, as stated above,

$$\lim_{a \to 0} G(x, a) = G(x, 0) = A_0 + \sum_{n=1}^{\infty} A_n(x) = f(x).$$

Example. If $H(x, a, \beta) = \dfrac{F(x+a+\beta) - F(x+a-\beta) - F(x-a+\beta) + F(x-a-\beta)}{4a\beta}$ shew that $H(x, a, \beta) \to f(x)$ when $f(x)$ converges if $a, \beta \to 0$ in such a way that a/β and β/a remain finite. (Riemann.)

9·621. *Riemann's second lemma.* With the notation of §§ 9·6–9·62, if $a_n, b_n \to 0$, then $\lim_{a \to 0} \dfrac{F(x+2a) + F(x-2a) - 2F(x)}{4a} = 0$ for all values of x.

For $\frac{1}{4} a^{-1} \{ F(x+2a) + F(x-2a) - 2F(x) \} = A_0 a + \sum_{n=1}^{\infty} \frac{\sin^2 na}{n^2 a} A_n(x)$; but by § 9·11 example 3, if $a > 0$, $\sum_{n=1}^{\infty} \dfrac{\sin^2 na}{n^2 a} = \frac{1}{2}(\pi - a)$; and so, since

$$A_0(x) a + \sum_{n=1}^{\infty} \frac{\sin^2 na}{n^2 a} A_n(x)$$

$$= A_0(x) a + \frac{1}{2}(\pi - a) A_1(x) + \sum_{n=1}^{\infty} \left\{ \frac{1}{2}(\pi - a) - \sum_{m=1}^{n} \frac{\sin^2 ma}{m^2 a} \right\} \{ A_{n+1}(x) - A_n(x) \},$$

it follows from § 3·35 example 2, that this series converges uniformly with regard to a for all values of a greater than, or equal to, zero†.

---

* This inequality is obviously true when $a = 0$.

† If we define $g_n(a)$ by the equations $g_n(a) = \frac{1}{2}(\pi - a) - \sum_{m=1}^{n} \dfrac{\sin^2 ma}{m^2 a}$, $(a \neq 0)$, and $g_n(0) = \frac{1}{2}\pi$, then $g_n(a)$ is continuous when $a \geqslant 0$, and $g_{n+1}(a) \leqslant g_n(a)$.

But $\qquad \lim_{a \to +0} \tfrac{1}{4}a^{-1}\{F(x+2a)+F(x-2a)-2F(x)\}$

$$= \lim_{a \to +0} \left[A_0(x)\,a + \tfrac{1}{2}(\pi-a)\,A_1(x) + \sum_{n=1}^{\infty} g_n(a)\{A_{n+1}(x)-A_n(x)\} \right],$$

and this limit is the value of the function when $a=0$, by § 3·32; and this value is zero since $\lim_{n \to \infty} A_n(x)=0$. By symmetry we see that $\lim_{a \to +0} = \lim_{a \to -0}$.

9·63.   *Riemann's theorem* * *on trigonometrical series.*

Two trigonometrical series which converge and are equal at all points of the range $(-\pi, \pi)$, *with the possible exception of a finite number of points, must have corresponding coefficients equal.*

An immediate deduction from this theorem is that a function of the type considered in § 9·42 cannot be represented by any trigonometrical series in the range $(-\pi, \pi)$ other than the Fourier series. This fact was first noticed by Du Bois Reymond.

We observe that it is certainly possible to have other expansions of (say) the form

$$a_0 + \sum_{m=1}^{\infty} (a_m \cos \tfrac{1}{2}mx + \beta_m \sin \tfrac{1}{2}mx),$$

which represent $f(x)$ between $-\pi$ and π; for write $x=2\xi$, and consider a function $\phi(\xi)$, which is such that $\phi(\xi)=f(2\xi)$ when $-\tfrac{1}{2}\pi < \xi < \tfrac{1}{2}\pi$, and $\phi(\xi)=g(\xi)$ when $-\pi < \xi < -\tfrac{1}{2}\pi$, and when $\tfrac{1}{2}\pi < \xi < \pi$, where $g(\xi)$ is any function satisfying the conditions of § 9·43. Then if we expand $\phi(\xi)$ in a Fourier series of the form

$$a_0 + \sum_{m=0}^{\infty} (a_m \cos m\xi + \beta_m \cos m\xi),$$

this expansion represents $f(x)$ when $-\pi < x < \pi$; and clearly by choosing the function $g(\xi)$ in different ways an unlimited number of such expansions can be obtained.

The question now at issue is, whether other series proceeding in sines and cosines of *integral* multiples of x exist, which differ from Fourier's expansion and yet represent $f(x)$ between $-\pi$ and π.

If possible, let there be two trigonometrical series satisfying the given conditions, and let their difference be the trigonometrical series

$$A_0 + \sum_{n=1}^{\infty} A_n(x) = f(x).$$

Then $f(x)=0$ at all points of the range $(-\pi, \pi)$ with a finite number of exceptions; let ξ_1, ξ_2 be a consecutive pair of these exceptional points, and let $F(x)$ be Riemann's associated function. We proceed to establish a lemma concerning the value of $F(x)$ when $\xi_1 < x < \xi_2$.

9·631.   *Schwartz' lemma* †. *In the range* $\xi_1 < x < \xi_2$, $F(x)$ *is a linear function of* x, *if* $f(x)=0$ *in this range.*

For if $\theta=1$ or if $\theta=-1$

$$\phi(x) = \theta\left[F(x) - F(\xi_1) - \frac{x-\xi_1}{\xi_2-\xi_1}\{F(\xi_2)-F(\xi_1)\} \right] - \tfrac{1}{2}h^2(x-\xi_1)(\xi_2-x)$$

is a continuous function of x in the range $\xi_1 \leqslant x \leqslant \xi_2$, and $\phi(\xi_1)=\phi(\xi_2)=0$.

---

* The proof we give is due to G. Cantor, *Journal für Math.* LXXII. (1870), pp. 139–142.
† Quoted by G. Cantor, *Journal für Math.* LXXII. (1870).

If the first term of $\phi(x)$ is not zero throughout the range* there will be some point $x = c$ at which it is not zero. Choose the sign of θ so that the first term is positive at c, and then choose h so small that $\phi(c)$ is still positive.

Since $\phi(x)$ is continuous it attains its upper bound (§ 3·62), and this upper bound is positive since $\phi(c) > 0$. Let $\phi(x)$ attain its upper bound at c_1, so that $c_1 \neq \xi_1$, $c_1 \neq \xi_2$.

Then, by Riemann's first lemma,

$$\lim_{a \to 0} \frac{\phi(c_1 + a) + \phi(c_1 - a) - 2\phi(c_1)}{a^2} = h^2.$$

But $\phi(c_1 + a) \leqslant \phi(c_1)$, $\phi(c_1 - a) \leqslant \phi(c_1)$, so this limit must be negative or zero.

Hence, by supposing that the first term of $\phi(x)$ is not everywhere zero in the range (ξ_1, ξ_2), we have arrived at a contradiction. Therefore it is zero; and consequently $F(x)$ is a linear function of x in the range $\xi_1 < x < \xi_2$. The lemma is therefore proved.

9·632. *Proof of Riemann's Theorem.*

We see that, in the circumstances under consideration, the curve $y = F(x)$ represents a series of segments of straight lines, the beginning and end of each line corresponding to an exceptional point; and as $F(x)$, being uniformly convergent, is a continuous function of x, these lines must be connected.

But, by Riemann's second lemma, even if ξ be an exceptional point,

$$\lim_{a \to 0} \frac{F(\xi + a) + F(\xi - a) - 2F(\xi)}{a} = 0.$$

Now the fraction involved in this limit is the difference of the slopes of the two segments which meet at that point whose abscissa is ξ; therefore the two segments are continuous in direction, so the equation $y = F(x)$ represents a single line. If then we write $F(x) = cx + c'$, it follows that c and c' have the same values for *all* values of x. Thus

$$\tfrac{1}{2} A_0 x^2 - cx - c' = \sum_{n=1}^{\infty} n^{-2} A_n(x),$$

the right-hand side of this equation being periodic, with period 2π.

The left-hand side of this equation must therefore be periodic, with period 2π. Hence

$$A_0 = 0, \quad c = 0,$$

and

$$-c' = \sum_{n=1}^{\infty} n^{-2} A_n(x).$$

Now the right-hand side of this equation converges uniformly, so we can multiply by $\cos nx$ or by $\sin nx$ and integrate.

This process gives

$$\pi n^{-2} a_n = -c' \int_{-\pi}^{\pi} \cos nx \, dx = 0,$$

$$\pi n^{-2} b_n = -c' \int_{-\pi}^{\pi} \sin nx \, dx = 0.$$

* If it is zero throughout the range, $F(x)$ is a linear function of x.

Therefore all the coefficients vanish, and therefore the two trigonometrical series whose difference is $A_0 + \overset{\infty}{\underset{n=1}{\Sigma}} A_n(x)$ have corresponding coefficients equal. This is the result stated in § 9·63.

9·7. *Fourier's representation of a function by an integral**.

It follows from § 9·43 that, if $f(x)$ be continuous except at a finite number of discontinuities and if it have limited total fluctuation in the range $(-\infty, \infty)$, then, if x be any *internal* point of the range $(-\alpha, \beta)$,

$$\lim_{m\to\infty} \int_{-\alpha}^{\beta} \frac{\sin(2m+1)(t-x)}{(t-x)} f(t)\,dt = \lim_{\theta\to0} \tfrac{1}{2}\pi\theta^{-1}\sin\theta\,\{f(x+2\theta)+f(x-2\theta)\}.$$

Now let λ be any real number, and choose the integer m so that $\lambda = 2m + 1 + 2\eta$ where $0 \leqslant \eta < 1$.

Then $\displaystyle\int_{-\alpha}^{\beta} \{\sin\lambda(t-x) - \sin(2m+1)(t-x)\}(t-x)^{-1}f(t)\,dt$

$$= \int_{-\alpha}^{\beta} 2\{\cos(2m+1+\eta)(t-x)\}.\{\sin\eta(t-x)\}(t-x)^{-1}f(t)\,dt$$

$$\to 0,$$

as $m\to\infty$ by § 9·41 (II), since $(t-x)^{-1}f(t)\sin\eta(t-x)$ has limited total fluctuation.

Consequently, from the proof of the Riemann-Lebesgue lemma of § 9·41, it is obvious that if $\int_{0}^{\infty} |f(t)|\,dt$ and $\int_{-\infty}^{0} |f(t)|\,dt$ converge, then†

$$\lim_{\lambda\to\infty} \int_{-\infty}^{\infty} \frac{\sin\lambda(t-x)}{(t-x)} f(t)\,dt = \tfrac{1}{2}\pi\,\{f(x+0)+f(x-0)\},$$

and so

$$\lim_{\lambda\to\infty} \int_{-\infty}^{\infty} \left\{\int_{0}^{\lambda} \cos u\,(t-x)\,du\right\} f(t)\,dt = \tfrac{1}{2}\pi\,\{f(x+0)+f(x-0)\}.$$

To obtain Fourier's result, we must reverse the order of integration in this repeated integral.

For any given value of λ and any arbitrary value of ϵ, there exists a number β such that

$$\int_{\beta}^{\infty} |f(t)|\,dt < \tfrac{1}{2}\epsilon/\lambda;$$

---

* *La Théorie Analytique de la Chaleur*, Ch. IX. For recent work on Fourier's integral and the modern theory of 'Fourier transforms,' see Titchmarsh, *Proc. Camb. Phil. Soc.* XXI. (1923), pp. 463–473 and *Proc. London Math. Soc.* (2) XXIII. (1924), pp. 279–289.

† $\displaystyle\int_{-\infty}^{\infty}$ means the double limit $\displaystyle\lim_{\rho\to\infty,\,\sigma\to\infty} \int_{-\rho}^{\sigma}$. If this limit exists, it is equal to $\displaystyle\lim_{\rho\to\infty} \int_{-\rho}^{\rho}$.

writing $\cos u\,(t-x)\,.\,f(t)=\phi\,(t,\,u)$, we have*

$$\left| \int_0^\infty \left\{ \int_0^\lambda \phi\,(t,\,u)\,du \right\} dt - \int_0^\lambda \left\{ \int_0^\infty \phi\,(t,\,u)\,dt \right\} du \right|$$

$$= \left| \int_0^\beta \left\{ \int_0^\lambda \phi\,(t,\,u)\,du \right\} dt + \int_\beta^\infty \left\{ \int_0^\lambda \phi\,(t,\,u)\,du \right\} dt \right.$$

$$\left. - \int_0^\lambda \left\{ \int_0^\beta \phi\,(t,\,u)\,dt \right\} du - \int_0^\lambda \left\{ \int_\beta^\infty \phi\,(t,\,u)\,dt \right\} du \right|$$

$$= \left| \int_\beta^\infty \left\{ \int_0^\lambda \phi\,(t,\,u)\,du \right\} dt - \int_0^\lambda \left\{ \int_\beta^\infty \phi\,(t,\,u)\,dt \right\} du \right|$$

$$< \int_\beta^\infty \left\{ \int_0^\lambda |\,\phi\,(t,\,u)\,|\,du \right\} dt + \int_0^\lambda \int_\beta^\infty |\,\phi\,(t,\,u)\,|\,dt\,du$$

$$< 2\lambda \int_\beta^\infty |\,f(t)\,|\,dt < \epsilon.$$

Since this is true for all values of ϵ, no matter how small, we infer that $\int_0^\infty \int_0^\lambda = \int_0^\lambda \int_0^\infty$; similarly $\int_0^{-\infty} \int_0^\lambda = \int_0^\lambda \int_0^{-\infty}$.

Hence $\quad \frac{1}{2}\pi\,\{f(x+0)+f(x-0)\} = \lim_{\lambda \to \infty} \int_0^\lambda \int_{-\infty}^\infty \cos u\,(t-x)\,f(t)\,dt\,du$

$$= \int_0^\infty \int_{-\infty}^\infty \cos u\,(t-x)\,f(t)\,dt\,du.$$

This result is known as *Fourier's integral theorem*†.

Example. Verify Fourier's integral theorem directly (i) for the function
$$f(x)=(a^2+x^2)^{-\frac{1}{2}},$$
(ii) for the function defined by the equations
$$f(x)=1,\quad (-1<x<1);\quad f(x)=0,\quad (|x|>1). \qquad \text{(Rayleigh.)}$$

REFERENCES.

G. F. B. RIEMANN, *Ges. Math. Werke*, pp. 213–250.

E. W. HOBSON, *Functions of a Real Variable* (1907), Ch. VII.

H. LEBESGUE, *Leçons sur les Séries Trigonométriques.* (Paris, 1906.)

C. J. DE LA VALLÉE POUSSIN, *Cours d'Analyse Infinitésimale*, II. (Louvain and Paris, 1912), Ch. IV.

H. BURKHARDT, *Encyclopädie der Math. Wiss.* II. 1 (7). (Leipzig, 1914.)

G. A. CARSE and G. SHEARER, *A course in Fourier's analysis and periodogram analysis* (Edinburgh Math. Tracts, No. 4, 1915).

---

* The equation $\int_0^\beta \int_0^\lambda = \int_0^\lambda \int_0^\beta$ is easily justified by § 4·3, by considering the ranges within which $f(x)$ is continuous.

† For a proof of the theorem when $f(x)$ is subject to less stringent restrictions, see Hobson, *Functions of a Real Variable*, §§ 492–493. The reader should observe that, although $\lim_{\lambda \to \infty} \int_{-\infty}^\infty \int_0^\lambda$ exists, the repeated integral $\int_{-\infty}^\infty \left\{ \int_0^\infty \sin u\,(t-x)\,du \right\} f(t)\,dt$ does not.

MISCELLANEOUS EXAMPLES.

1.   Obtain the expansions

(a) $\dfrac{1 - r\cos z}{1 - 2r\cos z + r^2} = 1 + r\cos z + r^2\cos 2z + \ldots,$

(b) $\dfrac{1}{2}\log(1 - 2r\cos z + r^2) = -r\cos z - \dfrac{1}{2}r^2\cos 2z - \dfrac{1}{3}r^3\cos 3z - \ldots,$

(c) $\arctan\dfrac{r\sin z}{1 - r\cos z} = r\sin z + \dfrac{1}{2}r^2\sin 2z + \dfrac{1}{3}r^3\sin 3z + \ldots,$

(d) $\dfrac{1}{2}\arctan\dfrac{2r\sin z}{1 - r^2} = r\sin z + \dfrac{1}{3}r^3\sin 3z + \dfrac{1}{5}r^5\sin 5z + \ldots,$

and shew that, when $|r| < 1$, they are convergent for all values of z in certain strips parallel to the real axis in the z-plane.

2.   Expand x^3 and x in Fourier sine series valid when $-\pi < x < \pi$; and hence find the value of the sum of the series

$$\sin x - \frac{1}{2^3}\sin 2x + \frac{1}{3^3}\sin 3x - \frac{1}{4^3}\sin 4x + \ldots,$$

for all values of x.   (Jesus, 1902.)

3.   Shew that the function of x represented by $\sum\limits_{n=1}^{\infty} n^{-1}\sin nx\sin^2 na$, is constant $(0 < x < 2a)$ and zero $(2a < x < \pi)$, and draw a graph of the function.

(Pembroke, 1907.)

4.   Find the cosine series representing $f(x)$ where

$$f(x) = \sin x + \cos x \qquad (0 < x \leqslant \tfrac{1}{2}\pi),$$
$$f(x) = \sin x - \cos x \qquad (\tfrac{1}{2}\pi \leqslant x < \pi). \qquad \text{(Peterhouse, 1906.)}$$

5.   Shew that

$$\sin \pi x + \frac{\sin 3\pi x}{3} + \frac{\sin 5\pi x}{5} + \frac{\sin 7\pi x}{7} + \ldots = \tfrac{1}{4}\pi\,[x],$$

where $[x]$ denotes $+1$ or -1 according as the integer next inferior to x is even or uneven, and is zero if x is an integer.   (Trinity, 1895.)

6.   Shew that the expansions

$$\log\left|\,2\cos\frac{1}{2}x\,\right| = \cos x - \frac{1}{2}\cos 2x + \frac{1}{3}\cos 3x \ldots$$

and

$$\log\left|\,2\sin\frac{1}{2}x\,\right| = -\cos x - \frac{1}{2}\cos 2x - \frac{1}{3}\cos 3x \ldots$$

are valid for all real values of x, except multiples of π.

7.   Obtain the expansion

$$\sum_{m=0}^{\infty}\frac{(-)^m\cos mx}{(m+1)(m+2)} = (\cos x + \cos 2x)\log\left(2\cos\frac{1}{2}x\right) + \frac{1}{2}x(\sin 2x + \sin x) - \cos x,$$

and find the range of values of x for which it is applicable.   (Trinity, 1898.)

8.   Prove that, if $0 < x < 2\pi$, then

$$\frac{\sin x}{a^2 + 1^2} + \frac{2\sin 2x}{a^2 + 2^2} + \frac{3\sin 3x}{a^2 + 3^2} + \ldots = \frac{\pi}{2}\frac{\sinh a(\pi - x)}{\sinh a\pi}\,.$$

(Trinity, 1895.)

9. Shew that between the values $-\pi$ and $+\pi$ of x the following expansions hold:

$$\sin mx = \frac{2}{\pi}\sin m\pi\left(\frac{\sin x}{1^2-m^2}-\frac{2\sin 2x}{2^2-m^2}+\frac{3\sin 3x}{3^2-m^2}-\cdots\right),$$

$$\cos mx = \frac{2}{\pi}\sin m\pi\left(\frac{1}{2m}+\frac{m\cos x}{1^2-m^2}-\frac{m\cos 2x}{2^2-m^2}+\frac{m\cos 3x}{3^2-m^2}-\cdots\right),$$

$$\frac{e^{mx}+e^{-mx}}{e^{m\pi}-e^{-m\pi}}=\frac{2}{\pi}\left(\frac{1}{2m}-\frac{m\cos x}{1^2+m^2}+\frac{m\cos 2x}{2^2+m^2}-\frac{m\cos 3x}{3^2+m^2}+\cdots\right).$$

10. Let x be a real variable between 0 and 1, and let n be an odd number $\geqslant 3$. Shew that

$$(-1)^s=\frac{1}{n}+\frac{2}{\pi}\sum_{m=1}^{\infty}\frac{1}{m}\tan\frac{m\pi}{n}\cos 2m\pi x,$$

if x is not a multiple of $\dfrac{1}{n}$, where s is the greatest integer contained in nx; but

$$0=\frac{1}{n}+\frac{2}{\pi}\sum_{m=1}^{\infty}\frac{1}{m}\tan\frac{m\pi}{n}\cos 2m\pi x,$$

if x is an integer multiple of $1/n$.   (Berger.)

11. Shew that the sum of the series

$$\tfrac{1}{3}+4\pi^{-1}\sum_{m=1}^{\infty}m^{-1}\sin\tfrac{2}{3}m\pi\cos 2m\pi x$$

is 1 when $0<x<\tfrac{1}{3}$, and when $\tfrac{2}{3}<x<1$, and is -1 when $\tfrac{1}{3}<x<\tfrac{2}{3}$.   (Trinity, 1901.)

12. If

$$\frac{ae^{ax}}{e^a-1}=\sum_{n=0}^{\infty}\frac{a^n V_n(x)}{n!},$$

shew that, when $-1<x<1$,

$$\cos 2\pi x+\frac{\cos 4\pi x}{2^{2n}}+\frac{\cos 6\pi x}{3^{2n}}+\cdots=(-)^{n-1}\frac{2^{2n-1}\pi^{2n}}{2n!}V_{2n}(x),$$

$$\sin 2\pi x+\frac{\sin 4\pi x}{2^{2n+1}}+\frac{\sin 6\pi x}{3^{2n+1}}+\cdots=(-)^{n+1}\frac{2^{2n}\pi^{2n+1}}{2n+1!}V_{2n+1}(x).$$

(Math. Trip. 1896.)

13. If m is an integer, shew that, for all real values of x,

$$\cos^{2m}x=2\,\frac{1.3.5\ldots(2m-1)}{2.4.6\ldots 2m}\left\{\frac{1}{2}+\frac{m}{m+1}\cos 2x+\frac{m(m-1)}{(m+1)(m+2)}\cos 4x\right.$$
$$\left.+\frac{m(m-1)(m-2)}{(m+1)(m+2)(m+3)}\cos 6x+\cdots\right\},$$

$$|\cos^{2m-1}x|=\frac{4}{\pi}\,\frac{2.4.6\ldots(2m-2)}{1.3.5\ldots(2m-1)}\left\{\frac{1}{2}+\frac{2m-1}{2m+1}\cos 2x+\frac{(2m-1)(2m-3)}{(2m+1)(2m+3)}\cos 4x+\cdots\right\}.$$

14. A point moves in a straight line with a velocity which is initially u, and which receives constant increments, each equal to u, at equal intervals τ. Prove that the velocity at any time t after the beginning of the motion is

$$\frac{u}{2}+\frac{ut}{\tau}+\frac{u}{\pi}\sum_{m=1}^{\infty}\frac{1}{m}\sin\frac{2m\pi t}{\tau},$$

and that the distance traversed is

$$\frac{ut}{2\tau}(t+\tau)+\frac{u\tau}{12}-\frac{u\tau}{2\pi^2}\sum_{m=1}^{\infty}\frac{1}{m^2}\cos\frac{2m\pi t}{\tau}.$$

(Trinity, 1894.)

15.   If

$$f(x) = \sum_{n=1}^{\infty} \frac{1}{2n-1} \sin(6n-3)x - 2\sum_{n=1}^{\infty} \frac{1}{2n-1} \sin(2n-1)x$$
$$+ \frac{3\sqrt{3}}{\pi}\left\{ \sin x - \frac{\sin 5x}{5^2} + \frac{\sin 7x}{7^2} - \frac{\sin 11x}{11^2} + \ldots \right\},$$

shew that $f(+0) = f(\pi - 0) = -\tfrac{1}{4}\pi,$

and $f(\tfrac{1}{3}\pi + 0) - f(\tfrac{1}{3}\pi - 0) = -\tfrac{1}{2}\pi, \quad f(\tfrac{2}{3}\pi + 0) - f(\tfrac{2}{3}\pi - 0) = \tfrac{1}{2}\pi.$

Observing that the last series is

$$\frac{6}{\pi}\sum_{n=1}^{\infty} \frac{\sin\tfrac{1}{3}(2n-1)\pi \sin(2n-1)x}{(2n-1)^2},$$

draw the graph of $f(x)$.   (Math. Trip. 1893.)

16.   Shew that, when $0 < x < \pi$,

$$f(x) = \frac{2\sqrt{3}}{3}\left(\cos x - \frac{1}{5}\cos 5x + \frac{1}{7}\cos 7x - \frac{1}{11}\cos 11x + \ldots \right)$$

$$= \sin 2x + \frac{1}{2}\sin 4x + \frac{1}{4}\sin 8x + \frac{1}{5}\sin 10x + \ldots$$

where $f(x) = \tfrac{1}{3}\pi$ $(0 < x < \tfrac{1}{3}\pi),$
                               $f(x) = 0$ $(\tfrac{1}{3}\pi < x < \tfrac{2}{3}\pi),$
                               $f(x) = -\tfrac{1}{3}\pi$ $(\tfrac{2}{3}\pi < x < \pi).$

Find the sum of each series when $x = 0, \tfrac{1}{3}\pi, \tfrac{2}{3}\pi, \pi$, and for all other values of x.

(Trinity, 1908.)

17.   Prove that the locus represented by

$$\sum_{n=1}^{\infty} \frac{(-)^{n-1}}{n^2} \sin nx \sin ny = 0$$

is two systems of lines at right angles, dividing the coordinate plane into squares of area π^2.   (Math. Trip. 1895.)

18.   Shew that the equation

$$\sum_{n=1}^{\infty} \frac{(-)^{n-1}\sin ny \cos nx}{n^3} = 0$$

represents the lines $y = \pm m\pi$, $(m = 0, 1, 2, \ldots)$ together with a set of arcs of ellipses whose semi-axes are π and $\pi/\sqrt{3}$, the arcs being placed in squares of area $2\pi^2$. Draw a diagram of the locus.   (Trinity, 1903.)

19.   Shew that, if the point (x, y, z) lies inside the octahedron bounded by the planes $\pm x \pm y \pm z = \pi$, then

$$\sum_{n=1}^{\infty} (-)^{n-1} \frac{\sin nx \sin ny \sin nz}{n^3} = \frac{1}{2}xyz.$$

(Math. Trip. 1904.)

20.   Circles of radius a are drawn having their centres at the alternate angular points of a regular hexagon of side a. Shew that the equation of the trefoil formed by the outer arcs of the circles can be put in the form

$$\frac{\pi r}{6\sqrt{3}a} = \frac{1}{2} + \frac{1}{2 \cdot 4}\cos 3\theta - \frac{1}{5 \cdot 7}\cos 6\theta + \frac{1}{8 \cdot 10}\cos 9\theta - \ldots,$$

the initial line being taken to pass through the centre of one of the circles.

(Pembroke, 1902.)

21.   Draw the graph represented by

$$\frac{r}{a} = 1 + \frac{2m}{\pi} \sin \frac{\pi}{m} \left\{ \frac{1}{2} + \sum_{n=1}^{\infty} \frac{(-)^n \cos nm\theta}{1 - (nm)^2} \right\},$$

where m is an integer.   (Jesus, 1908.)

22.   With each vertex of a regular hexagon of side $2a$ as centre the arc of a circle of radius $2a$ lying within the hexagon is drawn. Shew that the equation of the figure formed by the six arcs is

$$\frac{\pi r}{4a} = 6 - 3\sqrt{3} + 2 \sum_{n=1}^{\infty} \frac{\{(-)^{n-1} 6 + 3\sqrt{3}\}}{(6n-1)(6n+1)} \cos 6n\theta,$$

the prime vector bisecting a petal.   (Trinity, 1905.)

23.   Shew that, if $c > 0$,

$$\lim_{n \to \infty} \int_0^{\infty} e^{-cx} \cot x \sin (2n+1) x \,.\, dx = \frac{1}{2} \pi \tanh \frac{1}{2} c\pi.$$

(Trinity, 1894.)

24.   Shew that

$$\lim_{n \to \infty} \int_0^{\infty} \frac{\sin (2n+1) x}{\sin x} \frac{dx}{1+x^2} = \frac{1}{2} \pi \coth 1.$$

(King's, 1901.)

25.   Shew that, when $-1 < x < 1$ and a is real,

$$\lim_{n \to \infty} \int_0^{\infty} \frac{\sin (2n+1) \theta \sin (1+x) \theta}{\sin \theta} \frac{\theta}{a^2+\theta^2} d\theta = -\frac{1}{2} \pi \frac{\sinh ax}{\sinh a}.$$

(Math. Trip. 1905.)

26.   Assuming the possibility of expanding $f(x)$ in a uniformly convergent series of the form $\sum_k A_k \sin kx$, where k is a root of the equation $k \cos ak + b \sin ak = 0$ and the summation is extended to all positive roots of this equation, determine the constants A_k.

(Math. Trip. 1898.)

27.   If $$f(x) = \frac{1}{2} a_0 + \sum_{n=1}^{\infty} (a_n \cos nx + b_n \sin nx)$$

is a Fourier series, shew that, if $f(x)$ satisfies certain general conditions,

$$a_n = \frac{4}{\pi} P \int_0^{\infty} f(t) \cos nt \tan \frac{1}{2} t \frac{dt}{t}, \qquad b_n = \frac{4}{\pi} \int_0^{\infty} f(t) \sin nt \tan \frac{1}{2} t \frac{dt}{t}.$$

(Beau.)

28.   If $S_n(x) = 2 \sum_{r=1}^{n} (-)^{r-1} \frac{\sin rx}{r}$, prove that the highest maximum of $S_n(x)$ in the interval $(0, \pi)$ is at $x = \frac{n\pi}{n+1}$ and prove that, as $n \to \infty$,

$$S_n \left(\frac{n\pi}{n+1} \right) \to 2 \int_0^{\pi} \frac{\sin t}{t} dt.$$

Deduce that, as $n \to \infty$, the shape of the curve $y = S_n(x)$ in the interval $(0, \pi)$ tends to approximate to the shape of the curve formed by the line $y = x$, $(0 \leqslant x \leqslant \pi)$ together with the line $x = \pi$, $(0 \leqslant y \leqslant G)$, where

$$G = 2 \int_0^{\pi} \frac{\sin t}{t} dt.$$

[The fact that $G = 3.704... > \pi$ is known as *Gibbs' phenomenon*; see *Nature*, LXIX. (1899), p. 606. The phenomenon, is characteristic of a Fourier series in the neighbourhood of a point of ordinary discontinuity of the function which it represents. For a full discussion of the phenomenon, which was discovered by Wilbraham, *Camb. and Dublin Math. Journal*, III. (1848), pp. 198–201, see Carslaw, *Fourier's Series and Integrals* (1921), Ch. IX.]

CHAPTER X

LINEAR DIFFERENTIAL EQUATIONS

10·1. *Linear Differential Equations*. Ordinary points and singular points.*

In some of the later chapters of this work, we shall be concerned with the investigation of extensive and important classes of functions which satisfy linear differential equations of the second order. Accordingly, it is desirable that we should now establish some general results concerning solutions of such differential equations.

The standard form of the linear differential equation of the second order will be taken to be

$$\frac{d^2u}{dz^2} + p(z)\frac{du}{dz} + q(z)u = 0 \quad \dots\dots\dots\dots\dots\dots(A),$$

and it will be assumed that there is a domain S in which both $p(z)$, $q(z)$ are analytic except at a finite number of poles.

Any point of S at which $p(z)$, $q(z)$ are both analytic will be called an *ordinary point* of the equation; other points of S will be called *singular points*.

10·2. *Solution† of a differential equation valid in the vicinity of an ordinary point.*

Let b be an ordinary point of the differential equation, and let S_b be the domain formed by a circle of radius r_b, whose centre is b, and its interior, the radius of the circle being such that every point of S_b is a point of S, and is an ordinary point of the equation.

Let z be a variable point of S_b.

In the equation write $u = v \exp\left\{-\frac{1}{2}\int_b^z p(\zeta)d\zeta\right\}$, and it becomes

$$\frac{d^2v}{dz^2} + J(z)v = 0 \quad \dots\dots\dots\dots\dots\dots\dots(B),$$

where
$$J(z) = q(z) - \frac{1}{2}\frac{dp(z)}{dz} - \frac{1}{4}\{p(z)\}^2.$$

---

* The analysis contained in this chapter is mainly theoretical; it consists, for the most part, of existence theorems. It is assumed that the reader has some knowledge of practical methods of solving differential equations; these methods are given in works exclusively devoted to the subject, such as Forsyth, *A Treatise on Differential Equations* (1914).

† This method is applicable only to equations of the second order. For a method applicable to equations of any order, see Forsyth, *Theory of Differential Equations*, IV. (1902), Ch. I.

It is easily seen (§ 5·22) that an ordinary point of equation (A) is also an ordinary point of equation (B).

Now consider the sequence of functions $v_n(z)$, analytic in S_b, defined by the equations

$$v_0(z) = a_0 + a_1(z - b),$$

$$v_n(z) = \int_b^z (\zeta - z) J(\zeta) v_{n-1}(\zeta) \, d\zeta, \qquad (n = 1, 2, 3, \ldots)$$

where a_0, a_1 are arbitrary constants.

Let M, μ be the upper bounds of $|J(z)|$ and $|v_0(z)|$ in the domain S_b. *Then at all points of this domain*

$$|v_n(z)| \leqslant \mu M^n |z - b|^{2n}/(n!).$$

For this inequality is true when $n = 0$; if it is true when $n = 0, 1, \ldots m - 1$, we have, by taking the path of integration to be a straight line,

$$|v_m(z)| = \left| \int_b^z (\zeta - z) J(\zeta) v_{m-1}(\zeta) \, d\zeta \right|$$

$$\leqslant \frac{1}{(m-1)!} \int_b^z |\zeta - z| \cdot |J(\zeta)| \mu M^{m-1} |\zeta - b|^{2m-2} \cdot |d\zeta|$$

$$\leqslant \frac{1}{(m-1)!} \mu M^m |z - b| \int_0^{|z-b|} t^{2m-2} \, dt$$

$$< \frac{1}{m!} \mu M^m |z - b|^{2m}.$$

Therefore, by induction, the inequality holds for all values of n.

Also, since $|v_n(z)| \leqslant \dfrac{\mu M^n r_b^{2n}}{n!}$ when z is in S_b and $\sum\limits_{n=0}^{\infty} \mu M^n r_b^{2n}/(n!)$ converges, it follows (§ 3·34) that $v(z) = \sum\limits_{n=0}^{\infty} v_n(z)$ is a series of analytic functions uniformly convergent in S_b; while, from the definition of $v_n(z)$,

$$\frac{d}{dz} v_n(z) = -\int_b^z J(\zeta) v_{n-1}(\zeta) \, d\zeta, \qquad (n = 1, 2, 3, \ldots)$$

$$\frac{d^2}{dz^2} v_n(z) = -J(z) v_{n-1}(z);$$

hence it follows (§ 5·3) that

$$\frac{d^2 v(z)}{dz^2} = \frac{d^2 v_0(z)}{dz^2} + \sum_{n=1}^{\infty} \frac{d^2 v_n(z)}{dz^2}$$

$$= -J(z) v(z).$$

Therefore $v(z)$ is a function of z, analytic in S_b, which satisfies the differential equation

$$\frac{d^2 v(z)}{dz^2} + J(z) v(z) = 0,$$

and, from the value obtained for $\dfrac{d}{dz} v_n(z)$, *it is evident that*

$$v(b) = a_0, \quad v'(b) = \left\{\frac{d}{dz} v(z)\right\}_{z=b} = a_1,$$

where a_0, a_1 *are arbitrary.*

10·21.   *Uniqueness of the solution.*

If there were two analytic solutions of the equation for v, say $v_1(z)$ and $v_2(z)$ such that $v_1(b) = v_2(b) = a_0$, $v_1'(b) = v_2'(b) = a_1$, then, writing $w(z) = v_1(z) - v_2(z)$, we should have

$$\frac{d^2 w(z)}{dz^2} + J(z)\, w(z) = 0.$$

Differentiating this equation $n - 2$ times and putting $z = b$, we get

$$w^{(n)}(b) + J(b)\, w^{(n-2)}(b) + {}_{n-2}C_1 J'(b)\, w^{(n-3)}(b) + \ldots + J^{(n-2)}(b)\, w(b) = 0.$$

Putting $n = 2, 3, 4, \ldots$ in succession, we see that all the differential coefficients of $w(z)$ vanish at b; and so, by Taylor's theorem, $w(z) = 0$; that is to say the two solutions $v_1(z)$, $v_2(z)$ are identical.

Writing
$$u(z) = v(z) \exp\left\{-\tfrac{1}{2} \int_b^z p(\zeta)\, d\zeta\right\},$$

we infer without difficulty that $u(z)$ is the only analytic solution of (A) such that $u(b) = A_0$, $u'(b) = A_1$, where

$$A_0 = a_0, \quad A_1 = a_1 - \tfrac{1}{2} p(b)\, a_0.$$

Now that we know that a solution of (A) exists which is analytic in S_b and such that $u(b)$, $u'(b)$ have the arbitrary values A_0, A_1, the simplest method of obtaining the solution in the form of a Taylor's series is to assume $u(z) = \sum\limits_{n=0}^{\infty} A_n (z - b)^n$, substitute this series in the differential equation and equate coefficients of successive powers of $z - b$ to zero (§ 3·73) to determine in order the values of A_2, A_3, $\ldots$ in terms of A_0, A_1.

[NOTE. In practice, in carrying out this process of substitution, the reader will find it much more simple to have the equation 'cleared of fractions' rather than in the canonical form (A) of § 10·1. Thus the equations in examples 1 and 2 below should be treated in the form in which they stand; the factors $1 - z^2$, $(z - 2)(z - 3)$ should *not* be divided out. The same remark applies to the examples of §§ 10·3, 10·32.]

From the general theory of analytic continuation (§ 5·5) it follows that the solution obtained is analytic at all points of S except at singularities of the differential equation. The solution however is *not*, in general, 'analytic throughout S' (§ 5·2 cor. 2, footnote), except at these points, as it may not be one-valued; i.e. it may not return to the same value when z describes a circuit surrounding one or more singularities of the equation.

[The property that the solution of a linear differential equation is analytic except at singularities of the coefficients of the equation is common to linear equations of all orders.]

When two particular solutions of an equation of the second order are not constant multiples of each other, they are said to form a *fundamental system*.

Example 1.   Shew that the equation

$$(1 - z^2) \, u'' - 2zu' + \tfrac{3}{4}u = 0$$

has the fundamental system of solutions

$$u_1 = 1 - \tfrac{3}{8}z^2 - \tfrac{21}{128}z^4 - \ldots,$$
$$u_2 = z + \tfrac{5}{24}z^3 + \tfrac{15}{128}z^5 + \ldots.$$

Determine the general coefficient in each series, and shew that the radius of convergence of each series is 1.

Example 2.   Discuss the equation

$$(z - 2)(z - 3) \, u'' - (2z - 5) \, u' + 2u = 0$$

in a manner similar to that of example 1.

$10 \cdot 3$.   *Points which are regular for a differential equation.*

Suppose that a point c of S is such that, although $p(z)$ or $q(z)$ or both have poles at c, the poles are of such orders that $(z - c) \, p(z)$, $(z - c)^2 q(z)$ are analytic at c.   Such a point is called a *regular point*[*] for the differential equation.   Any poles of $p(z)$ or of $q(z)$ which are not of this nature are called *irregular points*.   The reason for making the distinction will become apparent in the course of this section.

If c be a regular point, the equation may be written[†]

$$(z - c)^2 \frac{d^2 u}{dz^2} + (z - c) \, . \, P(z - c) \frac{du}{dz} + Q(z - c) \, u = 0,$$

where $P(z - c)$, $Q(z - c)$ are analytic at c; hence, by Taylor's theorem,

$$P(z - c) = p_0 + p_1(z - c) + p_2(z - c)^2 + \ldots,$$
$$Q(z - c) = q_0 + q_1(z - c) + q_2(z - c)^2 + \ldots,$$

where p_0, p_1, $\ldots$, q_0, q_1, $\ldots$ are constants; and these series converge in the domain S_c formed by a circle of radius r (centre c) and its interior, where r is so small that c is the only singular point of the equation which is in S_c.

Let us assume as a *formal* solution of the equation

$$u = (z - c)^\alpha \left[1 + \sum_{n=1}^{\infty} a_n (z - c)^n \right],$$

where α, a_1, a_2, $\ldots$ are constants to be determined.

---

[*] The name 'regular point' is due to Thomé, *Journal für Math.* LXXV. (1873), p. 266. Fuchs had previously used the phrase 'point of determinateness.'

[†] Frobenius calls this the normal form of the equation.

Substituting in the differential equation (assuming that the term-by-term differentiations and multiplications of series are legitimate) we get

$$(z-c)^\alpha \left[\alpha(\alpha-1) + \sum_{n=1}^{\infty} a_n(\alpha+n)(\alpha+n-1)(z-c)^n \right]$$
$$+ (z-c)^\alpha P(z-c) . \left[\alpha + \sum_{n=1}^{\infty} a_n(\alpha+n)(z-c)^n \right]$$
$$+ (z-c)^\alpha Q(z-c) \left[1 + \sum_{n=1}^{\infty} a_n(z-c)^n \right] = 0.$$

Substituting the series for $P(z-c)$, $Q(z-c)$, multiplying out and equating to zero the coefficients of successive powers of $z-c$, we obtain the following sequence of equations :

$$\alpha^2 + (p_0-1)\alpha + q_0 = 0,$$
$$a_1\{(\alpha+1)^2 + (p_0-1)(\alpha+1) + q_0\} + \alpha p_1 + q_1 = 0,$$
$$a_2\{(\alpha+2)^2 + (p_0-1)(\alpha+2) + q_0\} + a_1\{(\alpha+1)p_1 + q_1\} + \alpha p_2 + q_2 = 0,$$
$$\cdots\cdots\cdots\cdots\cdots\cdots\cdots\cdots\cdots\cdots\cdots\cdots\cdots\cdots\cdots\cdots\cdots\cdots$$
$$a_n\{(\alpha+n)^2 + (p_0-1)(\alpha+n) + q_0\}$$
$$+ \sum_{m=1}^{n-1} a_{n-m}\{(\alpha+n-m)p_m + q_m\} + \alpha p_n + q_n = 0.$$

The first of these equations, called the *indicial equation**, determines two values (which may, however, be equal) for α. The reader will easily convince himself that if c had been an *irregular* point, the indicial equation would have been (at most) of the first degree; and he will now appreciate the distinction made between regular and irregular singular points.

Let $\alpha = \rho_1$, $\alpha = \rho_2$ be the roots† of the indicial equation

$$F(\alpha) \equiv \alpha^2 + (p_0-1)\alpha + q_0 = 0 ;$$

then the succeeding equations (when α has been chosen) determine $a_1, a_2, \ldots,$ in order, uniquely, provided that $F(\alpha+n)$ does not vanish when $n = 1, 2, 3, \ldots$; that is to say, if $\alpha = \rho_1$, that ρ_2 is not one of the numbers $\rho_1+1, \rho_1+2, \ldots$; and, if $\alpha = \rho_2$, that ρ_1 is not one of the numbers $\rho_2+1, \rho_2+2, \ldots$.

Hence, if the difference of the exponents is not zero, or an integer, it is always possible to obtain two distinct series which formally satisfy the equation.

Example. Shew that, if m is not zero or an integer, the equation

$$u'' + \left(\frac{\frac{1}{4} - m^2}{z^2} - \frac{1}{4} \right) u = 0$$

is formally satisfied by two series whose leading terms are

$$z^{\frac{1}{2}+m} \left\{ 1 + \frac{z^2}{16(1+m)} + \ldots \right\}, \quad z^{\frac{1}{2}-m} \left\{ 1 + \frac{z^2}{16(1-m)} + \ldots \right\} ;$$

determine the coefficient of the general term in each series, and shew that the series converge for all values of z.

* The name is due to Cayley, *Quarterly Journal*, xxi. (1886), p. 326.

† The roots ρ_1, ρ_2 of the indicial equation are called the *exponents* of the differential equation at the point c.

10·31.　*Convergence of the expansion of* § 10·3.

If the exponents ρ_1, ρ_2 are not equal, let ρ_1 be that one whose real part is not inferior to the real part of the other, and let $\rho_1 - \rho_2 = s$; then

$$F(\rho_1 + n) = n(s + n).$$

Now, by § 5·23, we can find a positive number M such that

$$|p_n| < Mr^{-n}, \quad |q_n| < Mr^{-n}, \quad |\rho_1 p_n + q_n| < Mr^{-n},$$

where M is independent of n; it is convenient to take $M \geqslant 1$.

Taking $\alpha = \rho_1$, we see that

$$|a_1| = \frac{|\rho_1 p_1 + q_1|}{|F(\rho_1 + 1)|} < \frac{M}{r|s+1|} < \frac{M}{r},$$

since $|s+1| \geqslant 1$.

If now we assume $|a_n| < M^n r^{-n}$ when $n = 1, 2, \ldots m-1$, we get

$$|a_m| = \left| \frac{\sum\limits_{t=1}^{m-1} a_{m-t}\{(\rho_1 + m - t)p_t + q_t\} + \rho_1 p_m + q_m}{F(\rho_1 + m)} \right|$$

$$\leqslant \frac{\sum\limits_{t=1}^{m-1} |a_{m-t}| \cdot |\rho_1 p_t + q_t| + |\rho_1 p_m + q_m| + \sum\limits_{t=1}^{m-1} (m-t)|a_{m-t}||p_t|}{m|s+m|}$$

$$< \frac{m M^m r^{-m} + \left\{ \sum\limits_{t=1}^{m-1} (m-t) \right\} M^m r^{-m}}{m^2 |1 + sm^{-1}|}.$$

Since $|1 + sm^{-1}| \geqslant 1$, because $R(s)$ is not negative, we get

$$|a_m| < \frac{m+1}{2m} M^m r^{-m} < M^m r^{-m},$$

and so, by induction, $|a_n| < M^n r^{-n}$ for all values of n.

If the values of the coefficients corresponding to the exponent ρ_2 be a_1', a_2', ... we should obtain, by a similar induction,

$$|a_n'| < M^n \kappa^n r^{-n},$$

where κ is the upper bound of $|1 - s|^{-1}$, $|1 - \frac{1}{2}s|^{-1}$, $|1 - \frac{1}{3}s|^{-1}$, ...; this bound exists when s is not a positive integer.

We have thus obtained two formal series

$$w_1(z) = (z - c)^{\rho_1} \left[1 + \sum_{n=1}^{\infty} a_n (z-c)^n \right],$$

$$w_2(z) = (z - c)^{\rho_2} \left[1 + \sum_{n=1}^{\infty} a_n'(z-c)^n \right].$$

The first, however, is a uniformly convergent series of analytic functions when $|z - c| < rM^{-1}$, as is also the second when $|z - c| < rM^{-1}\kappa^{-1}$, provided in each case that $\arg(z - c)$ is restricted in such a way that the series are one-valued; consequently, the formal substitution of these series into the left-hand side of the differential equation is justified, and each of the series is a solution of the equation; provided always that $\rho_1 - \rho_2$ is not a positive integer or zero*.

With this exception, we have therefore obtained a fundamental system of solutions valid in the vicinity of a regular singular point. And by the theory of analytic continuation, we see that if all the singularities in S of the equation are regular points, each member of a pair of fundamental solutions is analytic at all points of S except at the singularities of the equation, which are branch-points of the solution.

10·32. *Derivation of a second solution in the case when the difference of the exponents is an integer or zero.*

In the case when $\rho_1 - \rho_2 = s$ is a positive integer or zero, the solution $w_2(z)$ found in § 10·31 may break down† or coincide with $w_1(z)$.

If we write $u = w_1(z)\,\zeta$, the equation to determine ζ is

$$(z - c)^2 \frac{d^2\zeta}{dz^2} + \left\{ 2(z - c)^2 \frac{w_1'(z)}{w_1(z)} + (z - c) P(z - c) \right\} \frac{d\zeta}{dz} = 0,$$

of which the general solution is

$$\zeta = A + B \int^z \frac{1}{\{w_1(z)\}^2} \exp\left\{ -\int^z \frac{P(z - c)}{z - c}\, dz \right\}.\, dz$$

$$= A + B \int^z \frac{(z - c)^{-p_0}}{\{w_1(z)\}^2} \exp\left\{ -p_1(z - c) - \tfrac{1}{2} p_2 (z - c)^2 - \ldots \right\} dz$$

$$= A + B \int^z (z - c)^{-p_0 - 2\rho_1} g(z)\, dz,$$

where A, B are arbitrary constants and $g(z)$ is analytic throughout the interior of any circle whose centre is c, which does not contain any singularities of $P(z - c)$ or singularities or zeros of $(z - c)^{-\rho_1} w_1(z)$; also $g(c) = 1$.

Let $$g(z) = 1 + \sum_{n=1}^{\infty} g_n.(z - c)^n.$$

Then, if $s \neq 0$,

$$\zeta = A + B \int^z \left\{ 1 + \sum_{n=1}^{\infty} g_n (z - c)^n \right\} (z - c)^{-s-1}\, dz$$

$$= A + B \left[-\frac{1}{s}(z - c)^{-s} - \sum_{n=1}^{s-1} \frac{g_n}{s - n}(z - c)^{n-s} + g_s \log(z - c) \right.$$
$$\left. + \sum_{n=s+1}^{\infty} \frac{g_n}{n - s}(z - c)^{n-s} \right].$$

---

* If $\rho_1 - \rho_2$ is a positive integer, κ does not exist; if $\rho_1 = \rho_2$, the two solutions are the same.

† The coefficient a_s' may be indeterminate or it may be infinite; in the former case $w_2(z)$ will be a solution containing two arbitrary constants a_0' and a_s'; the series of which a_s' is a factor will be a constant multiple of $w_1(z)$.

Therefore the general solution of the differential equation, which is analytic at all points of C (c excepted), is

$$A\,w_1(z) + B\left[g_s w_1(z)\log(z-c) + \overline{w}(z)\right],$$

where, by § 2·53, $\quad \overline{w}(z) = (z-c)^{\rho_2}\left\{-\dfrac{1}{s} + \sum_{n=1}^{\infty} h_n(z-c)^n\right\},$

the coefficients h_n being constants.

When $s = 0$, the corresponding form of the solution is

$$A\,w_1(z) + B\left[w_1(z)\log(z-c) + (z-c)^{\rho_2}\sum_{n=1}^{\infty} h_n(z-c)^n\right].$$

The statement made at the end of § 10·31 is now seen to hold in the exceptional case when s is zero or a positive integer.

In the special case when $g_s = 0$, the second solution does not involve a logarithm.

The solutions obtained, which are valid in the vicinity of a regular point of the equation, are called *regular integrals*.

Integrals of an equation valid near a regular point c may be obtained practically by first obtaining $w_1(z)$, and then determining the coefficients in a function $\overline{w}_1(z) = \sum_{n=0}^{\infty} b_n(z-c)^{\rho_2+n}$, by substituting $w_1(z)\log(z-c) + \overline{w}_1(z)$ in the left-hand side of the equation and equating to zero the coefficients of the various powers of $z - c$ in the resulting expression. An alternative method due to Frobenius[*] is given by Forsyth, *Treatise on Differential Equations*, pp. 243–258.

Example 1.　Shew that integrals of the equation

$$\frac{d^2u}{dz^2} + \frac{1}{z}\frac{du}{dz} - m^2 u = 0$$

regular near $z = 0$ are

$$w_1(z) = 1 + \sum_{n=1}^{\infty} \frac{m^{2n}z^{2n}}{2^{2n}\cdot(n!)^2}$$

and

$$w_1(z)\log z - \sum_{n=1}^{\infty} \frac{m^{2n}z^{2n}}{2^{2n}(n!)^2}\left(\frac{1}{1} + \frac{1}{2} + \dots + \frac{1}{n}\right).$$

Verify that these series converge for all values of z.

Example 2.　Shew that integrals of the equation

$$z(z-1)\frac{d^2u}{dz^2} + (2z-1)\frac{du}{dz} + \frac{1}{4}u = 0$$

regular near $z = 0$ are

$$w_1(z) = 1 + \sum_{n=1}^{\infty}\left(\frac{1.3\dots 2n-1}{2.4\dots 2n}\right)^2 z^n$$

and

$$w_1(z)\log z + 4\sum_{n=1}^{\infty}\left(\frac{1.3\dots 2n-1}{2.4\dots 2n}\right)^2\left(\frac{1}{1} - \frac{1}{2} + \frac{1}{3} - \dots - \frac{1}{2n}\right)z^n.$$

Verify that these series converge when $|z| < 1$ and obtain integrals regular near $z = 1$.

[*] *Journal für Math.* LXXVI. (1874), pp. 214–224.

Example 3.   Shew that the hypergeometric equation

$$z(1-z)\frac{d^2u}{dz^2}+\{c-(a+b+1)z\}\frac{du}{dz}-abu=0$$

is satisfied by the hypergeometric series of § 2·38.

Obtain the complete solution of the equation when $c=1$.

10·4.   *Solutions valid for large values of* $|z|$.

Let $z=1/z_1$; then a solution of the differential equation is said to be valid for 'large values of $|z|$' if it is valid for sufficiently small values of $|z_1|$; and it is said that 'the point at infinity is an ordinary (or regular or irregular) point of the equation' when the point $z_1=0$ is an ordinary (or regular or irregular) point of the equation when it has been transformed so that z_1 is the independent variable.

Since

$$\frac{d^2u}{dz^2}+p(z)\frac{du}{dz}+q(z)u\equiv z_1^4\frac{d^2u}{dz_1^2}+\left\{2z_1^3-z_1^2 p\left(\frac{1}{z_1}\right)\right\}\frac{du}{dz_1}+q\left(\frac{1}{z_1}\right)u,$$

we see that the conditions that the point $z=\infty$ should be (i) an ordinary point, (ii) a regular point, are (i) that $2z-z^2 p(z)$, $z^4 q(z)$ should be analytic at infinity (§ 5·62) and (ii) that $zp(z)$, $z^2 q(z)$ should be analytic at infinity.

Example 1.   Shew that every point (including infinity) is either an ordinary point or a regular point for each of the equations

$$z(1-z)\frac{d^2u}{dz^2}+\{c-(a+b+1)z\}\frac{du}{dz}-abu=0,$$

$$(1-z^2)\frac{d^2u}{dz^2}-2z\frac{du}{dz}+n(n+1)u=0,$$

where a, b, c, n are constants.

Example 2.   Shew that every point except infinity is either an ordinary point or a regular point for the equation

$$z^2\frac{d^2u}{dz^2}+z\frac{du}{dz}+(z^2-n^2)u=0,$$

where n is a constant.

Example 3.   Shew that the equation

$$(1-z^2)\frac{d^2u}{dz^2}-2z\frac{du}{dz}+6u=0$$

has the two solutions

$$z^2-\frac{1}{3},\quad \frac{1}{z^3}+\frac{3.4}{2.7}\frac{1}{z^5}+\frac{3.4.5.6}{2.4.7.9}\frac{1}{z^7}+\dots,$$

the latter converging when $|z|>1$.

10·5.   *Irregular singularities and confluence.*

Near a point which is not a regular point, an equation of the second order cannot have two regular integrals, for the indicial equation is at most of the first degree; there may be one regular integral or there may be none. We shall see later (e.g. § 16·3) what is the nature of the solution near

such points in some simple cases. A general investigation of such solutions*
is beyond the scope of this book.

It frequently happens that a differential equation may be derived from
another differential equation by making two or more singularities of the
latter tend to coincidence. Such a limiting process is called *confluence*;
and the former equation is called a *confluent form* of the latter. It will be
seen in § 10·6 that the singularities of the former equation may be of a more
complicated nature than those of the latter.

10·6. *The differential equations of mathematical physics.*

The most general differential equation of the second order which has
every point except a_1, a_2, a_3, a_4 and ∞ as an ordinary point, these five points
being regular points with exponents α_r, β_r at a_r ($r = 1, 2, 3, 4$) and exponents
μ_1, μ_2 at ∞, may be verified† to be

$$\frac{d^2u}{dz^2} + \left\{ \sum_{r=1}^{4} \frac{1 - \alpha_r - \beta_r}{z - a_r} \right\} \frac{du}{dz} + \left\{ \sum_{r=1}^{4} \frac{\alpha_r \beta_r}{(z - a_r)^2} + \frac{Az^2 + 2Bz + C}{\prod\limits_{r=1}^{4} (z - a_r)} \right\} u = 0,$$

where A is such that‡ μ_1 and μ_2 are the roots of

$$\mu^2 + \mu \left\{ \sum_{r=1}^{4} (\alpha_r + \beta_r) - 3 \right\} + \sum_{r=1}^{4} \alpha_r \beta_r + A = 0,$$

and B, C are constants.

The remarkable theorem has been proved by Klein§ and Bôcher‖ that
all the linear differential equations which occur in certain branches of
Mathematical Physics are confluent forms of the special equation of this
type in which *the difference of the two exponents at each singularity is* $\frac{1}{2}$;
a brief investigation of these forms will now be given.

If we put $\beta_r = \alpha_r + \frac{1}{2}$, ($r = 1, 2, 3, 4$) and write ζ in place of z, the last
written equation becomes

$$\frac{d^2u}{d\zeta^2} + \left\{ \sum_{r=1}^{4} \frac{\frac{1}{2} - 2\alpha_r}{\zeta - a_r} \right\} \frac{du}{d\zeta} + \left\{ \sum_{r=1}^{4} \frac{\alpha_r (\alpha_r + \frac{1}{2})}{(\zeta - a_r)^2} + \frac{A\zeta^2 + 2B\zeta + C}{\prod\limits_{r=1}^{4} (\zeta - a_r)} \right\} u = 0,$$

---

* Some elementary investigations are given in Forsyth's *Differential Equations* (1914).
Complete investigations are given in his *Theory of Differential Equations*, IV. (1902).

† The coefficients of $\frac{du}{dz}$ and u must be rational or they would have an essential singularity
at some point; the denominators of $p(z)$, $q(z)$ must be $\prod\limits_{r=1}^{4} (z - a_r)$, $\prod\limits_{r=1}^{4} (z - a_r)^2$ respectively;
putting $p(z)$ and $q(z)$ into partial fractions and remembering that $p(z) = O(z^{-1})$, $q(z) = O(z^{-2})$
as $|z| \to \infty$, we obtain the required result without difficulty.

‡ It will be observed that μ_1, μ_2 are connected by the relation $\mu_1 + \mu_2 + \sum\limits_{r=1}^{4} (\alpha_r + \beta_r) = 3$.

§ *Ueber lineare Differentialgleichungen der zweiter Ordnung* (1894), p. 40; see also *Vorlesung
über Lamé'schen Funktionen.*

‖ *Ueber die Reihenentwickelungen der Potentialtheorie* (1894), p. 193.

where (on account of the condition $\mu_2 - \mu_1 = \frac{1}{2}$)

$$A = \left(\sum_{r=1}^{4} \alpha_r \right)^2 - \sum_{r=1}^{4} \alpha_r^2 - \frac{3}{2} \sum_{r=1}^{4} \alpha_r + \frac{3}{16}.$$

This differential equation is called the *generalised Lamé equation*.

It is evident, on writing $a_1 = a_2$ throughout the equation, that the confluence of the two singularities a_1, a_2 yields a singularity at which the exponents α, β are given by the equations

$$\alpha + \beta = 2(\alpha_1 + \alpha_2), \quad \alpha\beta = \alpha_1(\alpha_1 + \tfrac{1}{2}) + \alpha_2(\alpha_2 + \tfrac{1}{2}) + D,$$

where

$$D = (Aa_1^2 + 2Ba_1 + C)/\{(a_1 - a_3)(a_1 - a_4)\}.$$

Therefore the exponent-difference at the confluent singularity *is not* $\frac{1}{2}$, *but it may have any assigned value by suitable choice of B and C.* In like manner, by the confluence of three or more singularities, we can obtain one irregular singularity.

By suitable confluences of the five singularities at our disposal, we can obtain six types of equations, which may be classified according to (a) the number of their singularities with exponent-difference $\frac{1}{2}$, (b) the number of their other regular singularities, (c) the number of their irregular singularities, by means of the following scheme, which is easily seen to be exhaustive*:

	(a)	(b)	(c)	
(I)	3	1	0	Lamé
(II)	2	0	1	Mathieu
(III)	1	2	0	Legendre
(IV)	0	1	1	Bessel
(V)	1	0	1	Weber, Hermite
(VI)	0	0	1	Stokes †

These equations are usually known by the names of the mathematicians in the last column. Speaking generally, the later an equation comes in this scheme, the more simple are the properties of its solution. The solutions of (II)–(VI) are discussed in Chapters XV–XIX of this work, and‡ of (I) in Chapter XXIII. The derivation of the standard forms of the equations from the generalised Lamé equation is indicated by the following examples:

---

* For instance the arrangement (a) 3, (b) 0, (c) 1 is inadmissible as it would necessitate *six* initial singularities.

† The equation of this type was considered by Stokes in his researches on Diffraction, *Camb. Phil. Trans.* IX. (1856), pp. 168–182; it is, however, easily transformed into a particular case of Bessel's equation (example 6, below).

‡ For properties of equations of type (I), see the works of Klein and Forsyth cited at the end of this chapter; also Todhunter, *The Functions of Laplace, Lamé and Bessel* (1875).

Example 1.   Obtain Lamé's equation

$$\frac{d^2 u}{d\zeta^2} + \left\{ \sum_{r=1}^{3} \frac{\frac{1}{2}}{(\zeta - a_r)} \right\} \frac{du}{d\zeta} - \frac{\{n(n+1)\zeta + h\}\, u}{4 \prod_{r=1}^{3} (\zeta - a_r)} = 0,$$

(where h and n are constants) by taking

$$a_1 = a_2 = a_3 = a_4 = 0, \quad 8B = n(n+1)\, a_4, \quad 4C = ha_4,$$

and making $a_4 \to \infty$.

Example 2.   Obtain the equation

$$\frac{d^2 u}{d\zeta^2} + \left(\frac{\frac{1}{2}}{\zeta} + \frac{\frac{1}{2}}{\zeta - 1} \right) \frac{du}{d\zeta} - \frac{(a - 16q + 32q\zeta)\, u}{4\zeta(\zeta - 1)} = 0,$$

(where a and q are constants) by taking $a_1 = 0$, $a_2 = 1$, and making $a_3 = a_4 \to \infty$.   Derive Mathieu's equation (§ 19·1)

$$\frac{d^2 u}{dz^2} + (a + 16q \cos 2z)\, u = 0$$

by the substitution $\zeta = \cos^2 z$.

Example 3.   Obtain the equation

$$\frac{d^2 u}{d\zeta^2} + \left\{ \frac{\frac{1}{2}}{\zeta} + \frac{1}{\zeta - 1} \right\} \frac{du}{d\zeta} + \frac{1}{4} \left\{ \frac{n(n+1)}{\zeta} - \frac{m^2}{\zeta - 1} \right\} \frac{u}{\zeta(\zeta - 1)} = 0,$$

by taking

$$a_1 = a_2 = 1, \quad a_3 = a_4 = 0, \quad a_1 = a_2 = a_3 = 0, \quad a_4 = \tfrac{1}{4}.$$

Derive Legendre's equation (§§ 15·13, 15·5)

$$(1 - z^2) \frac{d^2 u}{dz^2} - 2z \frac{du}{dz} + \left\{ n(n+1) - \frac{m^2}{1 - z^2} \right\} u = 0$$

by the substitution $\zeta = z^{-2}$.

Example 4.   By taking $a_1 = a_2 = 0$, $a_1 = a_2 = a_3 = a_4 = 0$, and making $a_3 = a_4 \to \infty$, obtain the equation

$$\zeta^2 \frac{d^2 u}{d\zeta^2} + \zeta \frac{du}{d\zeta} + \tfrac{1}{4} (\zeta - n^2)\, u = 0.$$

Derive Bessel's equation (§ 17·11)

$$z^2 \frac{d^2 u}{dz^2} + z \frac{du}{dz} + (z^2 - n^2)\, u = 0$$

by the substitution $\zeta = z^2$.

Example 5.   By taking $a_1 = 0$, $a_1 = a_2 = a_3 = a_4 = 0$, and making $a_2 = a_3 = a_4 \to \infty$, obtain the equation

$$\zeta \frac{d^2 u}{d\zeta^2} + \tfrac{1}{2} \frac{du}{d\zeta} + \tfrac{1}{4} (n + \tfrac{1}{2} - \tfrac{1}{4}\zeta)\, u = 0.$$

Derive Weber's equation (§ 16·5)

$$\frac{d^2 u}{dz^2} + (n + \tfrac{1}{2} - \tfrac{1}{4}z^2)\, u = 0$$

by the substitution $\zeta = z^2$.

Example 6.   By taking $a_r = 0$, and making $a_r \to \infty$ $(r = 1, 2, 3, 4)$, obtain the equation

$$\frac{d^2 u}{d\zeta^2} + (B_1 \zeta + C_1)\, u = 0.$$

By taking

$$u = (B_1 \zeta + C_1)^{\frac{1}{2}}\, v, \quad B_1 \zeta + C_1 = (\tfrac{3}{2} B_1 z)^{\frac{2}{3}},$$

shew that

$$z^2 \frac{d^2 v}{dz^2} + z \frac{dv}{dz} + (z^2 - \tfrac{1}{9})\, v = 0.$$

Example 7. Shew that the general form of the generalised Lamé equation is un-altered (i) by any homographic change of independent variable such that ∞ is a singular point of the transformed equation, (ii) by any change of dependent variable of the type $u = (z - a_r)^\lambda v$.

Example 8. Deduce from example 7 that the various confluent forms of the generalised Lamé equation may always be reduced to the forms given in examples 1–6.

[Note that a suitable homographic change of variable will transform any three distinct points into the points 0, 1, ∞.]

10·7. *Linear differential equations with three singularities.*

Let
$$\frac{d^2 u}{dz^2} + p(z)\frac{du}{dz} + q(z)u = 0$$

have three, and only three singularities*, a, b, c; let these points be regular points, the exponents thereat being α, α'; β, β'; γ, γ'.

Then $p(z)$ is a rational function with simple poles at a, b, c, its residues at these poles being $1 - \alpha - \alpha'$, $1 - \beta - \beta'$, $1 - \gamma - \gamma'$; and as $z \to \infty$, $p(z) - 2z^{-1}$ is $O(z^{-2})$. Therefore

$$p(z) = \frac{1 - \alpha - \alpha'}{z - a} + \frac{1 - \beta - \beta'}{z - b} + \frac{1 - \gamma - \gamma'}{z - c}$$

and†
$$\alpha + \alpha' + \beta + \beta' + \gamma + \gamma' = 1.$$

In a similar manner

$$q(z) = \left\{ \frac{\alpha\alpha'(a-b)(a-c)}{z-a} + \frac{\beta\beta'(b-c)(b-a)}{z-b} + \frac{\gamma\gamma'(c-a)(c-b)}{z-c} \right\} \\ \times \frac{1}{(z-a)(z-b)(z-c)},$$

and hence the differential equation is

$$\frac{d^2 u}{dz^2} + \left\{ \frac{1 - \alpha - \alpha'}{z-a} + \frac{1 - \beta - \beta'}{z-b} + \frac{1 - \gamma - \gamma'}{z-c} \right\} \frac{du}{dz}$$
$$+ \left\{ \frac{\alpha\alpha'(a-b)(a-c)}{z-a} + \frac{\beta\beta'(b-c)(b-a)}{z-b} + \frac{\gamma\gamma'(c-a)(c-b)}{z-c} \right\}$$
$$\times \frac{u}{(z-a)(z-b)(z-c)} = 0.$$

This equation was first given by Papperitz‡.

To express the fact that u satisfies an equation of this type (which will be called Riemann's P-equation), Riemann§ wrote

$$u = P \left\{ \begin{matrix} a & b & c \\ \alpha & \beta & \gamma & z \\ \alpha' & \beta' & \gamma' \end{matrix} \right\}.$$

---

* The point at infinity is to be an ordinary point.

† This relation must be satisfied by the exponents.

‡ *Math. Ann.* xxv. (1885), p. 213.

§ *Abh. d. k. Ges. d. Wiss. zu Göttingen*, vii. (1857). It will be seen from this memoir that, although Riemann did not apparently construct the equation, he must have inferred its existence from the hypergeometric equation.

The singular points of the equation are placed in the first row with the corresponding exponents directly beneath them, and the independent variable is placed in the fourth column.

Example. Shew that the hypergeometric equation

$$z(1-z)\frac{d^2u}{dz^2}+\{c-(a+b+1)z\}\frac{du}{dz}-abu=0$$

is defined by the scheme

$$P\left\{\begin{matrix}0 & \infty & 1 \\ 0 & a & 0 \\ 1-c & b & c-a-b\end{matrix}\; z\right\}.$$

10·71. *Transformations of Riemann's P-equation.*

The two transformations which are typified by the equations

$$\text{(I)}\quad \left(\frac{z-a}{z-b}\right)^k\left(\frac{z-c}{z-b}\right)^l P\left\{\begin{matrix}a & b & c \\ \alpha & \beta & \gamma \\ \alpha' & \beta' & \gamma'\end{matrix}\; z\right\} = P\left\{\begin{matrix}a & b & c \\ \alpha+k & \beta-k-l & \gamma+l \\ \alpha'+k & \beta'-k-l & \gamma'+l\end{matrix}\; z\right\},$$

$$\text{(II)}\quad P\left\{\begin{matrix}a & b & c \\ \alpha & \beta & \gamma \\ \alpha' & \beta' & \gamma'\end{matrix}\; z\right\} = P\left\{\begin{matrix}a_1 & b_1 & c_1 \\ \alpha & \beta & \gamma \\ \alpha' & \beta' & \gamma'\end{matrix}\; z_1\right\}$$

(where z_1, a_1, b_1, c_1 are derived from z, a, b, c by the same homographic transformation) are of great importance. They may be derived by direct transformation of the differential equation of Papperitz and Riemann by suitable changes in the dependent and independent variables respectively; but the truth of the results of the transformations may be seen intuitively when we consider that Riemann's P-equation is determined *uniquely* by a knowledge of the three singularities and their exponents, and (I) that if

$$u = P\left\{\begin{matrix}a & b & c \\ \alpha & \beta & \gamma \\ \alpha' & \beta' & \gamma'\end{matrix}\; z\right\},$$

then $u_1 = \left(\frac{z-a}{z-b}\right)^k\left(\frac{z-c}{z-b}\right)^l u$ satisfies a differential equation of the second order with the same three singular points and exponents $\alpha+k$, $\alpha'+k$; $\beta-k-l$, $\beta'-k-l$; $\gamma+l$, $\gamma'+l$; and that the sum of the exponents is 1.

Also (II) if we write $z=\frac{Az_1+B}{Cz_1+D}$, the equation in z_1 is a linear equation of the second order with singularities at the points derived from a, b, c by this homographic transformation, and exponents α, α'; β, β'; γ, γ' thereat.

10·72. *The connexion of Riemann's P-equation with the hypergeometric equation.*

By means of the results of § 10·71 it follows that

$$
P \begin{Bmatrix} a & b & c & \\ \alpha & \beta & \gamma & z \\ \alpha' & \beta' & \gamma' & \end{Bmatrix} = \left(\frac{z-a}{z-b}\right)^{\alpha} \left(\frac{z-c}{z-b}\right)^{\gamma} P \begin{Bmatrix} a & b & c & \\ 0 & \beta+\alpha+\gamma & 0 & z \\ \alpha'-\alpha & \beta'+\alpha+\gamma & \gamma'-\gamma & \end{Bmatrix}
$$

$$
= \left(\frac{z-a}{z-b}\right)^{\alpha} \left(\frac{z-c}{z-b}\right)^{\gamma} P \begin{Bmatrix} 0 & \infty & 1 & \\ 0 & \beta+\alpha+\gamma & 0 & x \\ \alpha'-\alpha & \beta'+\alpha+\gamma & \gamma'-\gamma & \end{Bmatrix},
$$

where
$$ x = \frac{(z-a)(c-b)}{(z-b)(c-a)}. $$

Hence, by § 10·7 example, the solution of Riemann's P-equation can always be obtained in terms of the solution of the hypergeometric equation whose elements a, b, c, x are $\alpha+\beta+\gamma$, $\alpha+\beta'+\gamma$, $1+\alpha-\alpha'$, $\dfrac{(z-a)(c-b)}{(z-b)(c-a)}$ respectively.

10·8. *Linear differential equations with two singularities.*

If, in § 10·7, we make the point c an ordinary point, we must have $1-\gamma-\gamma'=0$, $\gamma\gamma'=0$ and $\dfrac{\alpha\alpha'(a-b)(a-c)}{z-a} + \dfrac{\beta\beta'(b-c)(b-a)}{z-b}$ must be divisible by $z-c$, in order that $p(z)$ and $q(z)$ may be analytic at c.

Hence $\alpha+\alpha'+\beta+\beta'=0$, $\alpha\alpha'=\beta\beta'$, and the equation is

$$
\frac{d^2u}{dz^2} + \left\{\frac{1-\alpha-\alpha'}{z-a} + \frac{1+\alpha+\alpha'}{z-b}\right\} \frac{du}{dz} + \frac{\alpha\alpha'(a-b)^2 u}{(z-a)^2(z-b)^2} = 0,
$$

of which the solution is

$$
u = A \left(\frac{z-a}{z-b}\right)^{\alpha} + B \left(\frac{z-a}{z-b}\right)^{\alpha'};
$$

that is to say, the solution involves elementary functions only.

When $\alpha = \alpha'$, the solution is

$$
u = A \left(\frac{z-a}{z-b}\right)^{\alpha} + B_1 \left(\frac{z-a}{z-b}\right)^{\alpha} \log\left(\frac{z-a}{z-b}\right).
$$

REFERENCES.

L. Fuchs, *Journal für Math.* LXVI. (1866), pp. 121–160.

L. W. Thomé, *Journal für Math.* LXXV. (1873), pp. 265–291, LXXXVII. (1879), pp. 222–349.

L. Schlesinger, *Handbuch der linearen Differentialgleichungen.* (Leipzig, 1895–1898.)

G. Frobenius, *Journal für Math.* LXXVI. (1874), pp. 214–235.

G. F. B. Riemann, *Ges. Math. Werke*, pp. 67–87.

F. C. Klein, *Ueber lineare Differentialgleichungen der zweiter Ordnung.* (Göttingen, 1894.)

A. R. Forsyth, *Theory of Differential Equations*, IV. (1902).

T. Craig, *Differential Equations.* (New York, 1889.)

E. Goursat, *Cours d'Analyse*, II. (Paris, 1911.)

MISCELLANEOUS EXAMPLES.

1. Shew that two solutions of the equation

$$\frac{d^2 u}{dz^2} + zu = 0$$

are $z - \frac{1}{12} z^4 + \dots$, $1 - \frac{1}{6} z^3 + \dots$, and investigate the region of convergence of these series.

2. Obtain integrals of the equation

$$\frac{d^2 u}{dz^2} + \frac{1}{4z^2}(1 - z^2) u = 0,$$

regular near $z = 0$, in the form

$$u_1 = z^{\frac{1}{2}} \left\{ 1 + \frac{z^2}{16} + \frac{z^4}{1024} + \dots \right\},$$

$$u_2 = u_1 \log z - \frac{z^{\frac{3}{2}}}{16} + \dots.$$

3. Shew that the equation

$$\frac{d^2 u}{dz^2} + \left(n + \frac{1}{2} - \frac{1}{4} z^2 \right) u = 0$$

has the solutions

$$1 - \frac{2n+1}{4} z^2 + \frac{4n^2 + 4n + 3}{96} z^4 - \dots,$$

$$z - \frac{2n+1}{12} z^3 + \frac{4n^2 + 4n + 7}{480} z^5 - \dots,$$

and that these series converge for all values of z.

4. Shew that the equation

$$\frac{d^2 u}{dz^2} + \left\{ \sum_{r=1}^{n} \frac{1 - a_r - \beta_r}{z - a_r} \right\} \frac{du}{dz} + \left\{ \sum_{r=1}^{n} \frac{a_r \beta_r}{(z - a_r)^2} + \sum_{r=1}^{n} \frac{D_r}{z - a_r} \right\} u = 0,$$

where

$$\sum_{r=1}^{n} (a_r + \beta_r) = n - 2, \quad \sum_{r=1}^{n} D_r = 0, \quad \sum_{r=1}^{n} (a_r D_r + a_r \beta_r) = 0, \quad \sum_{r=1}^{n} (a_r^2 D_r + 2a_r a_r \beta_r) = 0,$$

is the most general equation for which all points (including ∞), except $a_1, a_2, \dots a_n$, are ordinary points, and the points a_r are regular points with exponents a_r, β_r respectively.

(Klein.)

5. Shew that, if $\beta + \gamma + \beta' + \gamma' = \frac{1}{2}$, then

$$P \left\{ \begin{matrix} 0 & \infty & 1 \\ 0 & \beta & \gamma \\ \frac{1}{2} & \beta' & \gamma' \end{matrix} \ z^2 \right\} = P \left\{ \begin{matrix} -1 & \infty & 1 \\ \gamma & 2\beta & \gamma \\ \gamma' & 2\beta' & \gamma' \end{matrix} \ z \right\}.$$

(Riemann.)

[The differential equation in each case is

$$\frac{d^2 u}{dz^2} + \frac{2z(1 - \gamma - \gamma')}{z^2 - 1} \frac{du}{dz} + \left\{ \beta\beta' + \frac{\gamma\gamma'}{z^2 - 1} \right\} \frac{4u}{z^2 - 1} = 0.]$$

6. Shew that, if $\gamma + \gamma' = \frac{1}{3}$ and if ω, ω^2 are the complex cube roots of unity, then

$$P \left\{ \begin{matrix} 0 & \infty & 1 \\ 0 & 0 & \gamma \\ \frac{1}{3} & \frac{1}{3} & \gamma' \end{matrix} \ z^3 \right\} = P \left\{ \begin{matrix} 1 & \omega & \omega^2 \\ \gamma & \gamma & \gamma \\ \gamma' & \gamma' & \gamma' \end{matrix} \ z \right\}.$$

(Riemann.)

[The differential equation in each case is

$$\frac{d^2 u}{dz^2} + \frac{2z^2}{z^3 - 1} \frac{du}{dz} + \frac{9\gamma\gamma' zu}{(z^3 - 1)^2} = 0.]$$

7. Shew that the equation

$$(1-z^2)\frac{d^2u}{dz^2} - (2a+1)z\frac{du}{dz} + n(n+2a)u = 0$$

is defined by the scheme

$$P\left\{\begin{array}{ccc} 1 & \infty & -1 \\ 0 & -n & 0 \\ \frac{1}{2}-a & n+2a & \frac{1}{2}-a \end{array} z\right\},$$

and that the equation

$$(1+\zeta^2)^2\frac{d^2u}{d\zeta^2} + n(n+2)u = 0$$

may be obtained from it by taking $a=1$ and changing the independent variable.

(Halm.)

8. Discuss the solutions of the equation

$$z\frac{d^2u}{dz^2} + (z+1+m)\frac{du}{dz} + \left(n+1+\frac{1}{2}m\right)u = 0$$

valid near $z=0$ and those valid near $z=\infty$. (Cunningham.)

9. Discuss the solutions of the equation

$$\frac{d^2u}{dz^2} + \frac{2\mu}{z}\frac{du}{dz} - 2z\frac{du}{dz} + 2(\nu-\mu)u = 0$$

valid near $z=0$ and those valid near $z=\infty$.

Consider the following special cases :

(i) $\mu=-\frac{3}{2}$, (ii) $\mu=\frac{1}{2}$, (iii) $\mu+\nu=3$. (Curzon.)

10. Prove that the equation

$$z(1-z)\frac{d^2u}{dz^2} + \frac{1}{2}(1-2z)\frac{du}{dz} + (az+b)u = 0$$

has two particular integrals the product of which is a single-valued transcendental function. Under what circumstances are these two particular integrals coincident? If their product be $F(z)$, prove that the particular integrals are

$$u_1,\ u_2 = \{F(z)\}^{\frac{1}{2}} \cdot \exp\left\{\pm C\int^z \frac{dz}{F(z)\sqrt{\{z(1-z)\}}}\right\},$$

where C is a determinate constant. (Lindemann; see § 19·5.)

11. Prove that the general linear differential equation of the third order, whose singularities are $0, 1, \infty$, which has all its integrals regular near each singularity (the exponents at each singularity being $1, 1, -1$), is

$$\frac{d^3u}{dz^3} + \left\{\frac{2}{z} + \frac{2}{z-1}\right\}\frac{d^2u}{dz^2} - \left\{\frac{1}{z^2} - \frac{3}{z(z-1)} + \frac{1}{(z-1)^2}\right\}\frac{du}{dz}$$

$$+ \left\{\frac{1}{z^3} - \frac{3\cos^2 a}{z^2(z-1)} - \frac{3\sin^2 a}{z(z-1)^2} + \frac{1}{(z-1)^3}\right\}u = 0,$$

where a may have any constant value. (Math. Trip. 1912.)

CHAPTER XI

INTEGRAL EQUATIONS

11·1. *Definition of an integral equation.*

An integral equation is one which involves an unknown function under the sign of integration; and the process of determining the unknown function is called solving the equation*.

The introduction of integral equations into analysis is due to Laplace (1782) who considered the equations

$$f(x) = \int e^{xt}\,\phi(t)\,dt, \quad g(x) = \int t^{x-1}\,\phi(t)\,dt$$

(where in each case ϕ represents the unknown function), in connexion with the solution of differential equations. The first integral equation of which a solution was obtained, was Fourier's equation

$$f(x) = \int_{-\infty}^{\infty} \cos(xt)\,\phi(t)\,dt,$$

of which, in certain circumstances, a solution is†

$$\phi(x) = \frac{2}{\pi}\int_{0}^{\infty} \cos(ux)f(u)\,du,$$

$f(x)$ being an even function of x, since $\cos(xt)$ is an even function.

Later, Abel‡ was led to an integral equation in connexion with a mechanical problem and obtained two solutions of it; after this, Liouville investigated an integral equation which arose in the course of his researches on differential equations and discovered an important method for solving integral equations §, which will be discussed in § 11·4.

In recent years, the subject of integral equations has become of some importance in various branches of Mathematics; such equations (in physical problems) frequently involve repeated integrals and the investigation of them naturally presents greater difficulties than do those elementary equations which will be treated in this chapter.

To render the analysis as easy as possible, we shall suppose throughout that the constants a, b and the variables x, y, ξ are real and further that

---

* Except in the case of Fourier's integral (§ 9·7) we practically *always* need *continuous* solutions of integral equations.

† If this value of ϕ be substituted in the equation we obtain a result which is, effectively, that of § 9·7.

‡ *Solution de quelques problèmes à l'aide d'intégrales définies* (1823). See *Oeuvres*, I. pp. 11, 97.

§ The numerical computation of solutions of integral equations has been investigated by Whittaker, *Proc. Roy. Soc.* xciv. (A), (1918), pp. 367–383.

$a \leqslant x, y, \xi \leqslant b$; also that the given function* $K(x, y)$, which occurs under the integral sign in the majority of equations considered, is a real function of x and y and either (i) it is a continuous function of both variables in the range $(a \leqslant x \leqslant b, a \leqslant y \leqslant b)$, or (ii) it is a continuous function of both variables in the range $a \leqslant y \leqslant x \leqslant b$ and $K(x, y) = 0$ when $y > x$; in the latter case $K(x, y)$ has its discontinuities regularly distributed, and in either case it is easily proved that, if $f(y)$ is continuous when $a \leqslant y \leqslant b$, $\int_a^b f(y) K(x, y) \, dy$ is a continuous function of x when $a \leqslant x \leqslant b$.

11·11.   *An algebraical lemma.*

The algebraical result which will now be obtained is of great importance in Fredholm's theory of integral equations.

Let (x_1, y_1, z_1), (x_2, y_2, z_2), (x_3, y_3, z_3) be three points at unit distance from the origin. The greatest (numerical) value of the volume of the parallelepiped, of which the lines joining the origin to these points are conterminous edges, is $+1$, the edges then being perpendicular. Therefore, if $x_r^2 + y_r^2 + z_r^2 = 1$ $(r = 1, 2, 3)$, the upper and lower bounds of the determinant

$$
\begin{vmatrix}
x_1 & y_1 & z_1 \\
x_2 & y_2 & z_2 \\
x_3 & y_3 & z_3
\end{vmatrix}
$$

are ± 1.

A lemma due to Hadamard† generalises this result.

Let

$$
\begin{vmatrix}
a_{11}, & a_{12}, & \dots a_{1n} \\
a_{21}, & a_{22}, & \dots a_{2n} \\
\multicolumn{3}{c}{\dotfill} \\
a_{n1}, & a_{n2}, & \dots a_{nn}
\end{vmatrix} = D,
$$

where a_{mr} is real and $\sum\limits_{r=1}^{n} a^2_{mr} = 1$ $(m = 1, 2, \dots n)$; let A_{mr} be the cofactor of a_{mr} in D and let Δ be the determinant whose elements are A_{mr}, so that, by a well-known theorem‡,

$$\Delta = D^{n-1}.$$

Since D is a continuous function of its elements, and is obviously bounded, the ordinary theory of maxima and minima is applicable, and if we consider variations in a_{1r} $(r = 1, 2, \dots n)$ only, D is stationary for such variations if $\sum\limits_{r=1}^{n} \dfrac{\partial D}{\partial a_{1r}} \delta a_{1r} = 0$, where $\delta a_{1r}, \dots$ are variations subject to the sole condition $\sum\limits_{r=1}^{n} a_{1r} \delta a_{1r} = 0$; therefore §

$$A_{1r} = \frac{\partial D}{\partial a_{1r}} = \lambda a_{1r},$$

but $\sum\limits_{r=1}^{n} a_{1r} A_{1r} = D$, and so $\lambda \Sigma a^2_{1r} = D$; therefore $A_{1r} = D a_{1r}$.

---

* Bôcher in his important work on integral equations (*Camb. Math. Tracts*, No. 10), always considers the more general case in which $K(x, y)$ has discontinuities *regularly distributed*, i.e. the discontinuities are of the nature described in Chapter IV, example 11. The reader will see from that example that the results of this chapter can almost all be generalised in this way. To make this chapter more simple we shall not consider such generalisations.

† *Bulletin des Sci. Math.* (2), XVII. (1893), p. 240.

‡ Burnside and Panton, *Theory of Equations*, II. p. 40.

§ By the ordinary theory of undetermined multipliers.

Considering variations in the other elements of D, we see that D is stationary for variations in all elements when $A_{mr} = Da_{mr}$ $(m = 1, 2, \dots n \; ; \; r = 1, 2, \dots n)$. Consequently $\Delta = D^n . D$, and so $D^{n+1} = D^{n-1}$. Hence the maximum and minimum values of D are ± 1.

Corollary. If a_{mr} be real and subject only to the condition $|a_{mr}| < M$, since

$$\sum_{r=1}^{n} \{a_{mr}/(n^{\frac{1}{2}} M)\}^2 \leqslant 1,$$

we easily see that the maximum value of $|D|$ is $(n^{\frac{1}{2}} M)^n = n^{\frac{1}{2}n} M^n$.

11·2. *Fredholm's* equation and its tentative solution.*

An important integral equation of a general type is

$$\phi(x) = f(x) + \lambda \int_a^b K(x, \xi) \phi(\xi) \, d\xi,$$

where $f(x)$ is a given continuous function, λ is a parameter (in general complex) and $K(x, \xi)$ is subject to the conditions† laid down in § 11·1. $K(x, \xi)$ is called the *nucleus*‡ of the equation.

This integral equation is known as *Fredholm's equation* or *the integral equation of the second kind* (see § 11·3). It was observed by Volterra that an equation of this type could be regarded as a limiting form of a system of linear equations. Fredholm's investigation involved the tentative carrying out of a similar limiting process, and justifying it by the reasoning given below in § 11·21. Hilbert (*Göttinger Nach.* 1904, pp. 49–91) justified the limiting process directly.

We now proceed to write down the system of linear equations in question, and shall then investigate Fredholm's method of justifying the passage to the limit.

The integral equation is the limiting form (when $\delta \to 0$) of the equation

$$\phi(x) = f(x) + \lambda \sum_{q=1}^{n} K(x, x_q) \phi(x_q) \delta,$$

where $x_q - x_{q-1} = \delta$, $x_0 = a$, $x_n = b$.

Since this equation is to be true when $a \leqslant x \leqslant b$, it is true when x takes the values $x_1, x_2, \dots x_n$; and so

$$-\lambda\delta \sum_{q=1}^{n} K(x_p, x_q) \phi(x_q) + \phi(x_p) = f(x_p) \qquad (p = 1, 2, \dots n).$$

---

* Fredholm's first paper on the subject appeared in the *Öfversigt af K. Vetenskaps-Akad. Förhandlingar* (Stockholm), LVII. (1900), pp. 39–46. His researches are also given in *Acta Math.* XXVII. (1903), pp. 365–390.

† The reader will observe that if $K(x, \xi) = 0 \; (\xi > x)$, the equation may be written

$$\phi(x) = f(x) + \lambda \int_a^x K(x, \xi) \phi(\xi) \, d\xi.$$

This is called an equation with *variable upper limit.*

‡ Another term is *kernel* ; French *noyau*, German *Kern*.

This system of equations for $\phi(x_p)$, $(p=1, 2, \ldots n)$ has a unique solution if the determinant formed by the coefficients of $\phi(x_p)$ does not vanish. This determinant is

$$D_n(\lambda) = \begin{vmatrix} 1-\lambda\delta K(x_1, x_1) & -\lambda\delta K(x_1, x_2) \ldots & -\lambda\delta K(x_1, x_n) \\ -\lambda\delta K(x_2, x_1) & 1-\lambda\delta K(x_2, x_2) \ldots & -\lambda\delta K(x_2, x_n) \\ \cdots\cdots\cdots\cdots\cdots\cdots\cdots\cdots\cdots\cdots\cdots\cdots\cdots\cdots\cdots \\ -\lambda\delta K(x_n, x_1) & -\lambda\delta K(x_n, x_2) \ldots & 1-\lambda\delta K(x_n, x_n) \end{vmatrix}$$

$$= 1 - \lambda \sum_{p=1}^{n} \delta K(x_p, x_p) + \frac{\lambda^2}{2!} \sum_{p,q=1}^{n} \delta^2 \begin{vmatrix} K(x_p, x_p) & K(x_p, x_q) \\ K(x_q, x_p) & K(x_q, x_q) \end{vmatrix}$$

$$- \frac{\lambda^3}{3!} \sum_{p,q,r=1}^{n} \delta^3 \begin{vmatrix} K(x_p, x_p) & K(x_p, x_q) & K(x_p, x_r) \\ K(x_q, x_p) & K(x_q, x_q) & K(x_q, x_r) \\ K(x_r, x_p) & K(x_r, x_q) & K(x_r, x_r) \end{vmatrix} + \ldots$$

on expanding* in powers of λ.

Making $\delta \to 0$, $n \to \infty$, and writing the summations as integrations, we are thus led to consider the series

$$D(\lambda) = 1 - \lambda \int_a^b K(\xi_1, \xi_1)\, d\xi_1 + \frac{\lambda^2}{2!} \int_a^b \int_a^b \begin{vmatrix} K(\xi_1, \xi_1) & K(\xi_1, \xi_2) \\ K(\xi_2, \xi_1) & K(\xi_2, \xi_2) \end{vmatrix} d\xi_1 d\xi_2 - \ldots.$$

Further, if $D_n(x_\mu, x_\nu)$ is the cofactor of the term in $D_n(\lambda)$ which involves $K(x_\nu, x_\mu)$, the solution of the system of linear equations is

$$\phi(x_\mu) = \frac{f(x_1) D_n(x_\mu, x_1) + f(x_2) D_n(x_\mu, x_2) + \ldots + f(x_n) D_n(x_\mu, x_n)}{D_n(\lambda)}.$$

Now it is easily seen that the appropriate limiting form to be considered in association with $D_n(x_\mu, x_\mu)$ is $D(\lambda)$; also that, if $\mu \neq \nu$,

$$D_n(x_\mu, x_\nu) = \lambda\delta \left\{ K(x_\mu, x_\nu) - \lambda\delta \sum_{p=1}^{n} \begin{vmatrix} K(x_\mu, x_\nu) & K(x_\mu, x_p) \\ K(x_p, x_\nu) & K(x_p, x_p) \end{vmatrix} \right.$$

$$\left. + \frac{1}{2!} \lambda^2 \delta^2 \sum_{p,q=1}^{n} \begin{vmatrix} K(x_\mu, x_\nu) & K(x_\mu, x_p) & K(x_\mu, x_q) \\ K(x_p, x_\nu) & K(x_p, x_p) & K(x_p, x_q) \\ K(x_q, x_\nu) & K(x_q, x_p) & K(x_q, x_q) \end{vmatrix} - \ldots \right\}.$$

So that the limiting form for $\delta^{-1} D(x_\mu, x_\nu)$ to be considered† is

$$D(x_\mu, x_\nu; \lambda) = \lambda K(x_\mu, x_\nu) - \lambda^2 \int_a^b \begin{vmatrix} K(x_\mu, x_\nu) & K(x_\mu, \xi_1) \\ K(\xi_1, x_\nu) & K(\xi_1, \xi_1) \end{vmatrix} d\xi_1$$

$$+ \frac{1}{2!} \lambda^3 \int_a^b \int_a^b \begin{vmatrix} K(x_\mu, x_\nu) & K(x_\mu, \xi_1) & K(x_\mu, \xi_2) \\ K(\xi_1, x_\nu) & K(\xi_1, \xi_1) & K(\xi_1, \xi_2) \\ K(\xi_2, x_\nu) & K(\xi_2, \xi_1) & K(\xi_2, \xi_2) \end{vmatrix} d\xi_1 d\xi_2 - \ldots.$$

Consequently we are led to consider the possibility of the equation

$$\phi(x) = f(x) + \frac{1}{D(\lambda)} \int_a^b D(x, \xi; \lambda) f(\xi)\, d\xi$$

giving the solution of the integral equation.

---

* The factorials appear because each determinant of s rows and columns occurs $s!$ times as $p, q, \ldots$ take *all* the values $1, 2, \ldots n$, whereas it appears only once in the original determinant for $D_n(\lambda)$.

† The law of formation of successive terms is obvious from those written down.

Example 1. Shew that, in the case of the equation

$$\phi(x) = x + \lambda \int_0^1 xy\,\phi(y)\,dy,$$

we have

$$D(\lambda) = 1 - \tfrac{1}{3}\lambda, \quad D(x, y; \lambda) = \lambda xy$$

and a solution is

$$\phi(x) = \frac{3x}{3 - \lambda}.$$

Example 2. Shew that, in the case of the equation

$$\phi(x) = x + \lambda \int_0^1 (xy + y^2)\,\phi(y)\,dy,$$

we have

$$D(\lambda) = 1 - \tfrac{2}{3}\lambda - \tfrac{1}{72}\lambda^2,$$

$$D(x, y; \lambda) = \lambda(xy + y^2) + \lambda^2(\tfrac{1}{3}xy^2 - \tfrac{1}{3}xy - \tfrac{1}{3}y^2 + \tfrac{1}{4}y),$$

and obtain a solution of the equation.

11·21. *Investigation of Fredholm's solution.*

So far the construction of the solution has been purely tentative; we now start *ab initio* and verify that we actually do get a solution of the equation; to do this we consider the two functions $D(\lambda)$, $D(x, y; \lambda)$ arrived at in § 11·2.

We write the series, by which $D(\lambda)$ was defined in § 11·2, in the form $1 + \sum_{n=1}^{\infty} \frac{a_n \lambda^n}{n!}$ so that

$$a_n = (-)^n \int_a^b \int_a^b \dots \int_a^b \begin{vmatrix} K(\xi_1, \xi_1) & K(\xi_1, \xi_2) \dots K(\xi_1, \xi_n) \\ K(\xi_2, \xi_1) & K(\xi_2, \xi_2) \dots K(\xi_2, \xi_n) \\ \dots\dots\dots\dots\dots\dots\dots\dots\dots\dots\dots\dots \\ K(\xi_n, \xi_1) & K(\xi_n, \xi_2) \dots K(\xi_n, \xi_n) \end{vmatrix} d\xi_1 d\xi_2 \dots d\xi_n;$$

since $K(x, y)$ is continuous and therefore bounded, we have $|K(x, y)| < M$, where M is independent of x and y; since $K(x, y)$ is real, we may employ Hadamard's lemma (§ 11·11) and we see at once that

$$|a_n| < n^{\frac{1}{2}n} M^n \cdot (b - a)^n.$$

Write $n^{\frac{1}{2}n} M^n (b - a)^n = n! b_n$; then

$$\lim_{n \to \infty} (b_{n+1}/b_n) = \lim_{n \to \infty} \frac{(b - a) M}{(n + 1)^{\frac{1}{2}}} \left\{ \left(1 + \frac{1}{n}\right)^n \right\}^{\frac{1}{2}} = 0,$$

since $\left(1 + \frac{1}{n}\right)^n \to e$.

The series $\sum_{n=1}^{\infty} b_n \lambda^n$ is therefore absolutely convergent for all values of λ; and so (§ 2·34) the series $1 + \sum_{n=1}^{\infty} \frac{a_n \lambda^n}{n!}$ converges for all values of λ and therefore (§ 5·64) represents an integral function of λ.

Now write the series for $D(x, y; \lambda)$ in the form $\sum_{n=0}^{\infty} \frac{v_n(x, y) \lambda^{n+1}}{n!}$.

Then, by Hadamard's lemma (§ 11·11),

$$| v_{n-1}(x, y) | < n^{\frac{1}{2}n} M^n (b-a)^{n-1},$$

and hence $\left| \dfrac{v_n(x, y)}{n!} \right| < c_n$, where c_n is independent of x and y and $\sum\limits_{n=0}^{\infty} c_n \lambda^{n+1}$ is absolutely convergent.

Therefore $D(x, y; \lambda)$ is an integral function of λ and the series for $D(x, y; \lambda) - \lambda K(x, y)$ is a uniformly convergent (§ 3·34) series of continuous* functions of x and y when $a \leqslant x \leqslant b$, $a \leqslant y \leqslant b$.

Now pick out the coefficient of $K(x, y)$ in $D(x, y; \lambda)$; and we get

$$D(x, y; \lambda) = \lambda D(\lambda) K(x, y) + \sum_{n=1}^{\infty} (-)^n \lambda^{n+1} \frac{Q_n(x, y)}{n!},$$

where

$$Q_n(x, y) = \int_a^b \int_a^b \cdots \int_a^b \begin{vmatrix} 0, & K(x, \xi_1), & K(x, \xi_2), \ldots K(x, \xi_n) \\ K(\xi_1, y), & K(\xi_1, \xi_1), & K(\xi_1, \xi_2), \ldots K(\xi_1, \xi_n) \\ \hdotsfor{4} \\ K(\xi_n, y), & K(\xi_n, \xi_1), & K(\xi_n, \xi_2), \ldots K(\xi_n, \xi_n) \end{vmatrix} d\xi_1 \ldots d\xi_n.$$

Expanding in minors of the first column, we get $Q_n(x, y)$ equal to the integral of the sum of n determinants; writing $\xi_1, \xi_2, \ldots \xi_{m-1}, \xi, \xi_m, \ldots \xi_{n-1}$ in place of $\xi_1, \xi_2, \ldots \xi_n$ in the mth of them, we see that the integrals of all the determinants† are equal and so

$$Q_n(x, y) = -n \int_a^b \int_a^b \cdots \int_a^b K(\xi, y) P_n d\xi d\xi_1 \ldots d\xi_{n-1},$$

where

$$P_n = \begin{vmatrix} K(x, \xi), & K(x, \xi_1), & \ldots K(x, \xi_{n-1}) \\ K(\xi_1, \xi), & K(\xi_1, \xi_1), & \ldots K(\xi_1, \xi_{n-1}) \\ \hdotsfor{3} \\ K(\xi_{n-1}, \xi), & K(\xi_{n-1}, \xi_1), & \ldots K(\xi_{n-1}, \xi_{n-1}) \end{vmatrix}.$$

It follows at once that

$$D(x, y; \lambda) = \lambda D(\lambda) K(x, y) + \lambda \int_a^b D(x, \xi; \lambda) K(\xi, y) d\xi.$$

Now take the equation

$$\phi(\xi) = f(\xi) + \lambda \int_a^b K(\xi, y) \phi(y) dy,$$

multiply by $D(x, \xi; \lambda)$ and integrate, and we get

$$\int_a^b f(\xi) D(x, \xi; \lambda) d\xi$$

$$= \int_a^b \phi(\xi) D(x, \xi; \lambda) d\xi - \lambda \int_a^b \int_a^b D(x, \xi; \lambda) K(\xi, y) \phi(y) dy d\xi,$$

the integrations in the repeated integral being in either order.

---

* It is easy to verify that every term (except possibly the first) of the series for $D(x, y; \lambda)$ is a continuous function under either hypothesis (i) or hypothesis (ii) of § 11·1.

† The order of integration is immaterial (§ 4·3).

That is to say

$$\int_a^b f(\xi)\, D\,(x,\,\xi\,;\lambda)\, d\xi$$

$$= \int_a^b \phi\,(\xi)\, D\,(x,\,\xi\,;\lambda)\, d\xi - \int_a^b \{D\,(x,\,y\,;\lambda) - \lambda D\,(\lambda)\, K\,(x,\,y)\}\,\phi\,(y)\, dy$$

$$= \lambda D\,(\lambda) \int_a^b K\,(x,\,y)\,\phi\,(y)\, dy$$

$$= D\,(\lambda)\,\{\phi\,(x) - f\,(x)\},$$

in virtue of the given equation.

Therefore if $D\,(\lambda) \neq 0$ and if Fredholm's equation has a solution it can be none other than

$$\phi\,(x) = f\,(x) + \int_a^b f\,(\xi)\, \frac{D\,(x,\,\xi\,;\lambda)}{D\,(\lambda)}\, d\xi;$$

and, by actual substitution of this value of $\phi\,(x)$ in the integral equation, we see that it actually is a solution.

This is, therefore, the unique continuous solution of the equation if $D\,(\lambda) \neq 0$.

Corollary. If we put $f\,(x) \equiv 0$, the 'homogeneous' equation

$$\phi\,(x) = \lambda \int_a^b K\,(x,\,\xi)\,\phi\,(\xi)\, d\xi$$

has no continuous solution except $\phi\,(x) = 0$ unless $D\,(\lambda) = 0$.

Example 1. By expanding the determinant involved in $Q_n\,(x,\,y)$ in minors of its first row, shew that

$$D\,(x,\,y\,;\,\lambda) = \lambda D\,(\lambda)\, K\,(x,\,y) + \lambda \int_a^b K\,(x,\,\xi)\, D\,(\xi,\,y\,;\,\lambda)\, d\xi.$$

Example 2. By using the formulae

$$D\,(\lambda) = 1 + \sum_{n=1}^{\infty} \frac{a_n \lambda^n}{n\,!}, \quad D\,(x,\,y\,;\,\lambda) = \lambda D\,(\lambda)\, K\,(x,\,y) + \sum_{n=1}^{\infty} (-)^n \frac{\lambda^{n+1}\, Q_n\,(x,\,y)}{n\,!},$$

shew that

$$\int_a^b D\,(\xi,\,\xi\,;\,\lambda)\, d\xi = -\lambda\, \frac{dD\,(\lambda)}{d\lambda}.$$

Example 3. If $K\,(x,\,y) = 1$ $(y \leqslant x)$, $K\,(x,\,y) = 0$ $(y > x)$,

shew that $D\,(\lambda) = \exp\{-(b-a)\,\lambda\}$.

Example 4. Shew that, if $K\,(x,\,y) = f_1\,(x)\,.\,f_2\,(y)$, and if

$$\int_a^b f_1\,(x)\, f_2\,(x)\, dx = A,$$

then

$$D\,(\lambda) = 1 - A\lambda, \quad D\,(x,\,y\,;\,\lambda) = \lambda f_1\,(x)\, f_2\,(y),$$

and the solution of the corresponding integral equation is

$$\phi\,(x) = f\,(x) + \frac{\lambda f_1\,(x)}{1 - A\lambda} \int_a^b f\,(\xi)\, f_2\,(\xi)\, d\xi,$$

Example 5.   Shew that, if

$$K(x, y) = f_1(x) g_1(y) + f_2(x) g_2(y),$$

then $D(\lambda)$ and $D(x, y; \lambda)$ are quadratic in λ; and, more generally, if

$$K(x, y) = \sum_{m=1}^{n} f_m(x) g_m(y),$$

then $D(\lambda)$ and $D(x, y, \lambda)$ are polynomials of degree n in λ.

11·22.   *Volterra's reciprocal functions.*

Two functions $K(x, y)$, $k(x, y; \lambda)$ are said to be *reciprocal* if they are bounded in the ranges $a \leqslant x, y \leqslant b$, if any discontinuities they may have are regularly distributed (§ 11·1, footnote), and if

$$K(x, y) + k(x, y; \lambda) = \lambda \int_a^b k(x, \xi; \lambda) K(\xi, y) d\xi.$$

We observe that, since the right-hand side is continuous*, the sum of two reciprocal functions is continuous.

Also, a function $K(x, y)$ can only have one reciprocal if $D(\lambda) \neq 0$; for if there were two, their difference $k_1(x, y)$ would be a continuous solution of the homogeneous equation

$$k_1(x, y; \lambda) = \lambda \int_a^b k_1(x, \xi; \lambda) K(\xi, y) d\xi,$$

(where x is to be regarded as a parameter), and by § 11·21 corollary, the only continuous solution of this equation is zero.

By the use of reciprocal functions, Volterra has obtained an elegant reciprocal relation between pairs of equations of Fredholm's type.

We first observe, from the relation

$$D(x, y; \lambda) = \lambda D(\lambda) K(x, y) + \lambda \int_a^b D(x, \xi; \lambda) K(\xi, y) d\xi,$$

proved in § 11·21, that the value of $k(x, y; \lambda)$ is

$$- D(x, y; \lambda)/\{\lambda D(\lambda)\},$$

and from § 11·21 example 1, the equation

$$k(x, y; \lambda) + K(x, y) = \lambda \int_a^b K(x, \xi) k(\xi, y; \lambda) d\xi$$

is evidently true.

Then, if we take the integral equation

$$\phi(x) = f(x) + \lambda \int_a^b K(x, \xi) \phi(\xi) d\xi,$$

when $a \leqslant x \leqslant b$, we have, on multiplying the equation

$$\phi(\xi) = f(\xi) + \lambda \int_a^b K(\xi, \xi_1) \phi(\xi_1) d\xi_1$$

---

* By example 11 at the end of Chapter IV.

by $k(x, \xi; \lambda)$ and integrating,

$$\int_a^b k(x, \xi; \lambda)\,\phi(\xi)\,d\xi$$

$$= \int_a^b k(x, \xi; \lambda) f(\xi)\,d\xi + \lambda \int_a^b \int_a^b k(x, \xi; \lambda)\,K(\xi, \xi_1)\,\phi(\xi_1)\,d\xi_1 d\xi.$$

Reversing the order of integration* in the repeated integral and making use of the relation defining reciprocal functions, we get

$$\int_a^b k(x, \xi; \lambda)\,\phi(\xi)\,d\xi$$

$$= \int_a^b k(x, \xi; \lambda) f(\xi)\,d\xi + \int_a^b \{K(x, \xi_1) + k(x, \xi_1; \lambda)\}\,\phi(\xi_1)\,d\xi_1,$$

and so $\lambda \displaystyle\int_a^b k(x, \xi; \lambda) f(\xi)\,d\xi = -\lambda \int_a^b K(x, \xi_1)\,\phi(\xi_1)\,d\xi_1$

$$= -\phi(x) + f(x).$$

Hence $f(x) = \phi(x) + \lambda \displaystyle\int_a^b k(x, \xi; \lambda) f(\xi)\,d\xi$;

similarly, from this equation we can derive the equation

$$\phi(x) = f(x) + \lambda \int_a^b K(x, \xi)\,\phi(\xi)\,d\xi,$$

so that either of these equations with reciprocal nuclei may be regarded as the solution of the other.

11·23. *Homogeneous integral equations.*

The equation $\phi(x) = \lambda \displaystyle\int_a^b K(x, \xi)\,\phi(\xi)\,d\xi$ is called a homogeneous integral equation. We have seen (§ 11·21 corollary) that the only continuous solution of the homogeneous equation, when $D(\lambda) \neq 0$, is $\phi(x) = 0$.

The roots of the equation $D(\lambda) = 0$ are therefore of considerable importance in the theory of the integral equation. They are called the *characteristic numbers*† *of the nucleus.*

It will now be shewn that, when $D(\lambda) = 0$, a solution which is not identically zero can be obtained.

Let‡ $\lambda = \lambda_0$ be a root m times repeated of the equation $D(\lambda) = 0$.

Since $D(\lambda)$ is an integral function, we may expand it into the convergent series

$$D(\lambda) = c_m (\lambda - \lambda_0)^m + c_{m+1} (\lambda - \lambda_0)^{m+1} + \ldots \qquad (m > 0,\ c_m \neq 0).$$

* The reader will have no difficulty in extending the result of § 4·3 to the integral under consideration.

† French *valeurs caractéristiques*, German *Eigenwerthe*.

‡ It will be proved in § 11·51 that, if $K(x, y) \equiv K(y, x)$, the equation $D(\lambda) = 0$ has at least one root.

Similarly, since $D(x, y; \lambda)$ is an integral function of λ, there exists a Taylor series of the form

$$D(x, y; \lambda) = \frac{g_l(x, y)}{l!}(\lambda - \lambda_0)^l + \frac{g_{l+1}(x, y)}{(l+1)!}(\lambda - \lambda_0)^{l+1} + \dots \qquad (l \geqslant 0, g_l \not\equiv 0);$$

by § 3·34 it is easily verified that the series defining $g_n(x, y)$, $(n = l, l+1, \dots)$ converges absolutely and uniformly when $a \leqslant x \leqslant b$, $a \leqslant y \leqslant b$, and thence that the series for $D(x, y; \lambda)$ converges absolutely and uniformly in the same domain of values of x and y.

But, by § 11·21 example 2,

$$\int_a^b D(\xi, \xi; \lambda)\, d\xi = -\lambda \frac{dD(\lambda)}{d\lambda};$$

now the right-hand side has a zero of order $m-1$ at λ_0, while the left-hand side has a zero of order at least l, *and so we have* $m - 1 \geqslant l$.

Substituting the series just given for $D(\lambda)$ and $D(x, y; \lambda)$ in the result of § 11·21 example 1, viz.

$$D(x, y; \lambda) = \lambda D(\lambda) K(x, y) + \lambda \int_a^b K(x, \xi) D(\xi, y; \lambda)\, d\xi,$$

dividing by $(\lambda - \lambda_0)^l$ and making $\lambda \to \lambda_0$, we get

$$g_l(x, y) = \lambda_0 \int_a^b K(x, \xi) g_l(\xi, y)\, d\xi.$$

Hence if y have any constant value, $g_l(x, y)$ satisfies the homogeneous integral equation, and any linear combination of such solutions, obtained by giving y various values, is a solution.

Corollary.   The equation

$$\phi(x) = f(x) + \lambda_0 \int_a^b K(x, \xi) \phi(\xi)\, d\xi$$

has no solution or an infinite number.   For, if $\phi(x)$ is a solution, so is $\phi(x) + \sum_y c_y g_l(x, y)$, where c_y may be any function of y.

Example 1.   Shew that solutions of

$$\phi(x) = \lambda \int_{-\pi}^{\pi} \cos^n(x - \xi) \phi(\xi)\, d\xi$$

are $\phi(x) = \cos(n - 2r)x$, and $\phi(x) = \sin(n - 2r)x$; where r assumes all positive integral values (zero included) not exceeding $\frac{1}{2}n$.

Example 2.   Shew that

$$\phi(x) = \lambda \int_{-\pi}^{\pi} \cos^n(x + \xi) \phi(\xi)\, d\xi$$

has the same solutions as those given in example 1, and shew that the corresponding values of λ give all the roots of $D(\lambda) = 0$.

11·3.　*Integral equations of the first and second kinds.*

Fredholm's equation is sometimes called an *integral equation of the second kind*; while the equation

$$f(x) = \lambda \int_a^b K(x, \xi)\, \phi(\xi)\, d\xi$$

is called the *integral equation of the first kind*.

In the case when $K(x, \xi) = 0$ if $\xi > x$, we may write the equations of the first and second kinds in the respective forms

$$f(x) = \lambda \int_a^x K(x, \xi)\, \phi(\xi)\, d\xi,$$

$$\phi(x) = f(x) + \lambda \int_a^x K(x, \xi)\, \phi(\xi)\, d\xi.$$

These are described as equations with *variable upper limits*.

11·31.　*Volterra's equation.*

The equation of the first kind with variable upper limit is frequently known as Volterra's equation. The problem of solving it has been reduced by that writer to the solution of Fredholm's equation.

Assuming that $K(x, \xi)$ is a continuous function of both variables when $\xi \leqslant x$, we have

$$f(x) = \lambda \int_a^x K(x, \xi)\, \phi(\xi)\, d\xi.$$

The right-hand side has a differential coefficient (§ 4·2 example 1) if $\dfrac{\partial K}{\partial x}$ exists and is continuous, and so

$$f'(x) = \lambda K(x, x)\, \phi(x) + \lambda \int_a^x \frac{\partial K}{\partial x}\, \phi(\xi)\, d\xi.$$

This is an equation of Fredholm's type. If we denote its solution by $\phi(x)$, we get on integrating from a to x,

$$f(x) - f(a) = \lambda \int_a^x K(x, \xi)\, \phi(\xi)\, d\xi,$$

and so the solution of the Fredholm equation gives a solution of Volterra's equation if $f(a) = 0$.

The solution of the equation of the first kind with constant upper limit can frequently be obtained in the form of a series*.

11·4.　*The Liouville-Neumann method of successive substitutions†.*

A method of solving the equation

$$\phi(x) = f(x) + \lambda \int_a^b K(x, \xi)\, \phi(\xi)\, d\xi,$$

which is of historical importance, is due to Liouville.

---

* See example 7, p. 231; a solution valid under fewer restrictions is given by Bôcher.

† *Journal de Math.* ii. (1837), iii. (1838). K. Neumann's investigations were later (1870); see his *Untersuchungen über das logarithmische und Newton'sche Potential.*

It consists in continually substituting the value of $\phi(x)$ given by the right-hand side in the expression $\phi(\xi)$ which occurs on the right-hand side.

This procedure gives the series

$$S(x) = f(x) + \lambda \int_a^b K(x, \xi) f(\xi)\, d\xi + \sum_{m=2}^\infty \lambda^m \int_a^b K(x, \xi_1) \int_a^b K(\xi_1, \xi_2)$$

$$\cdots \int_a^b K(\xi_{m-1}, \xi_m) f(\xi_m)\, d\xi_m \cdots d\xi_1.$$

Since $|K(x, y)|$ and $|f(x)|$ are bounded, let their upper bounds be M, M'.

Then the modulus of the general term of the series does not exceed

$$|\lambda|^m M^m M'(b-a)^m.$$

The series for $S(x)$ therefore converges uniformly when

$$|\lambda| < M^{-1}(b-a)^{-1};$$

and, by actual substitution, it satisfies the integral equation.

If $K(x, y) = 0$ when $y > x$, we find by induction that the modulus of the general term in the series for $S(x)$ does not exceed

$$|\lambda|^m M^m M'(x-a)^m/(m!) \leqslant |\lambda|^m M^m M'(b-a)^m/m!,$$

and so the series converges uniformly for *all* values of λ; and we infer that in this case Fredholm's solution is an integral function of λ.

It is obvious from the form of the solution that when $|\lambda| < M^{-1}(b-a)^{-1}$, the reciprocal function $k(x, \xi; \lambda)$ may be written in the form

$$k(x, \xi; \lambda) = -K(x, \xi) - \sum_{m=2}^\infty \lambda^{m-1} \int_a^b K(x, \xi_1) \int_a^b K(\xi_1, \xi_2)$$

$$\cdots \int_a^b K(\xi_{m-1}, \xi)\, d\xi_{m-1} d\xi_{m-2} \cdots d\xi_1,$$

for with this definition of $k(x, \xi; \lambda)$, we see that

$$S(x) = f(x) - \lambda \int_a^b k(x, \xi; \lambda) f(\xi)\, d\xi,$$

so that $k(x, \xi; \lambda)$ is a reciprocal function, and by § 11·22 there is *only one* reciprocal function if $D(\lambda) \neq 0$.

Write

$$K(x, \xi) = K_1(x, \xi), \quad \int_a^b K(x, \xi') K_n(\xi', \xi)\, d\xi' = K_{n+1}(x, \xi),$$

and then we have

$$-k(x, \xi; \lambda) = \sum_{m=0}^\infty \lambda^m K_{m+1}(x, \xi),$$

while

$$\int_a^b K_m(x, \xi') K_n(\xi', \xi)\, d\xi' = K_{m+n}(x, \xi),$$

as may be seen at once on writing each side as an $(m+n-1)$-tuple integral.

The functions $K_m(x, \xi)$ are called *iterated* functions.

11·5. *Symmetric nuclei.*

Let $K_1(x, y) \equiv K_1(y, x)$; then the nucleus $K(x, y)$ is said to be *symmetric*.

The iterated functions of such a nucleus are also symmetric, i.e. $K_n(x, y) = K_n(y, x)$ for all values of n; for, if $K_n(x, y)$ is symmetric, then

$$K_{n+1}(x, y) = \int_a^b K_1(x, \xi) K_n(\xi, y)\, d\xi = \int_a^b K_1(\xi, x) K_n(y, \xi)\, d\xi$$

$$= \int_a^b K_n(y, \xi) K_1(\xi, x)\, d\xi = K_{n+1}(y, x),$$

and the required result follows by induction.

Also, none of the iterated functions are identically zero; for, if possible, let $K_p(x, y) \equiv 0$; let n be chosen so that $2^{n-1} < p \leqslant 2^n$, and, since $K_p(x, y) \equiv 0$, it follows that $K_{2^n}(x, y) \equiv 0$, from the recurrence formula.

But then

$$0 = K_{2^n}(x, x) = \int_a^b K_{2^{n-1}}(x, \xi) K_{2^{n-1}}(\xi, x)\, d\xi$$

$$= \int_a^b \{K_{2^{n-1}}(x, \xi)\}^2\, d\xi,$$

and so $K_{2^{n-1}}(x, \xi) \equiv 0$; continuing this argument, we find ultimately that $K_1(x, y) \equiv 0$, and the integral equation is trivial.

11·51. *Schmidt's* theorem that, if the nucleus is symmetric, the equation $D(\lambda) = 0$ has at least one root.*

To prove this theorem, let

$$U_n = \int_a^b K_n(x, x)\, dx,$$

so that, when $|\lambda| < M^{-1}(b-a)^{-1}$, we have, by § 11·21 example 2 and § 11·4,

$$-\frac{1}{D(\lambda)} \frac{dD(\lambda)}{d\lambda} = \sum_{n=1}^{\infty} U_n \lambda^{n-1}.$$

Now since $\displaystyle\int_a^b \int_a^b \{\mu K_{n+1}(x, \xi) + K_{n-1}(x, \xi)\}^2\, d\xi\, dx \geqslant 0$

for all real values of μ, we have

$$\mu^2 U_{2n+2} + 2\mu U_{2n} + U_{2n-2} \geqslant 0,$$

and so $U_{2n+2} U_{2n-2} \geqslant U_{2n}{}^2, \quad U_{2n-2} > 0.$

Therefore $U_2, U_4, \ldots$ are all positive, and if $U_4/U_2 = \nu$, it follows, by induction from the inequality $U_{2n+2} U_{2n-2} \geqslant U_{2n}{}^2$, that $U_{2n+2}/U_{2n} \geqslant \nu^n$.

Therefore when $|\lambda^2| \geqslant \nu^{-1}$, the terms of $\sum\limits_{n=1}^{\infty} U_n \lambda^{n-1}$ do not tend to zero; and so, by § 5·4, the function $\dfrac{1}{D(\lambda)} \dfrac{dD(\lambda)}{d\lambda}$ has a singularity inside or on the

---

* The proof given is due to Kneser, *Palermo Rendiconti*, XXII. (1906), p. 236.

circle $|\lambda| = \nu^{-\frac{1}{2}}$; but since $D(\lambda)$ is an integral function, the only possible singularities of $\dfrac{1}{D(\lambda)} \dfrac{dD(\lambda)}{d\lambda}$ are at zeros of $D(\lambda)$; therefore $D(\lambda)$ has a zero inside or on the circle $|\lambda| = \nu^{-\frac{1}{2}}$.

[NOTE. By § 11·21, $D(\lambda)$ is either an integral function or else a mere polynomial; in the latter case, it has a zero by § 6·31 example 1; the point of the theorem is that in the former case $D(\lambda)$ cannot be such a function as e^{λ^2}, which has no zeros.]

11·6. *Orthogonal functions.*

The real continuous functions $\phi_1(x)$, $\phi_2(x)$, ... are said to be orthogonal and normal* for the range (a, b) if

$$\int_a^b \phi_m(x)\, \phi_n(x)\, dx \begin{cases} = 0 & (m \neq n), \\ = 1 & (m = n). \end{cases}$$

If we are given n real continuous linearly independent functions $u_1(x)$, $u_2(x)$, ... $u_n(x)$, we can form n linear combinations of them which are orthogonal.

For suppose we can construct $m-1$ orthogonal functions ϕ_1, ... ϕ_{m-1} such that ϕ_p is a linear combination of $u_1, u_2, ... u_p$ (where $p = 1, 2, ... m-1$); we shall now shew how to construct the function ϕ_m such that $\phi_1, \phi_2, ... \phi_m$ are all normal and orthogonal.

Let $\quad {}_1\phi_m(x) = c_{1,m}\, \phi_1(x) + c_{2,m}\, \phi_2(x) + ... + c_{m-1}\, \phi_{m-1}(x) + u_m(x),$

so that ${}_1\phi_m$ is a function of $u_1, u_2, ... u_m$.

Then, multiplying by ϕ_p and integrating,

$$\int_a^b {}_1\phi_m(x)\, \phi_p(x)\, dx = c_{p,m} + \int_a^b u_m(x)\, \phi_p(x)\, dx \qquad (p < m).$$

Hence $\qquad \displaystyle\int_a^b {}_1\phi_m(x)\, \phi_p(x)\, dx = 0$

if $\qquad\qquad c_{p,m} = -\displaystyle\int_a^b u_m(x)\, \phi_p(x)\, dx;$

a function ${}_1\phi_m(x)$, orthogonal to $\phi_1(x)$, $\phi_2(x)$, ... $\phi_{m-1}(x)$, is therefore constructed.

Now choose α so that $\qquad \alpha^2 \displaystyle\int_a^b \{{}_1\phi_m(x)\}^2\, dx = 1;$

and take $\qquad\qquad\qquad \phi_m(x) = \alpha \cdot {}_1\phi_m(x).$

Then $\qquad\qquad \displaystyle\int_a^b \phi_m(x)\, \phi_p(x)\, dx \begin{cases} = 0 & (p < m), \\ = 1 & (p = m). \end{cases}$

We can thus obtain the functions $\phi_1, \phi_2, ...$ in order.

---

* They are said to be orthogonal if the first equation only is satisfied; the systematic study of such functions is due to Murphy, *Camb. Phil. Trans.* IV. (1833), pp. 353–408, and V. (1835), pp. 113–148, 315–394.

The members of a finite set of orthogonal functions are linearly independent. For, if

$$\alpha_1 \phi_1(x) + \alpha_2 \phi_2(x) + \ldots + \alpha_n \phi_n(x) \equiv 0,$$

we should get, on multiplying by $\phi_p(x)$ and integrating, $\alpha_p = 0$; therefore all the coefficients α_p vanish and the relation is nugatory.

It is obvious that $\pi^{-\frac{1}{2}} \cos mx$, $\pi^{-\frac{1}{2}} \sin mx$ form a set of normal orthogonal functions for the range $(-\pi, \pi)$.

Example 1. From the functions $1, x, x^2, \ldots$ construct the following set of functions which are orthogonal (but not normal) for the range $(-1, 1)$:

$$1, \; x, \; x^2 - \tfrac{1}{3}, \; x^3 - \tfrac{3}{5}x, \; x^4 - \tfrac{6}{7}x^2 + \tfrac{3}{35}, \; \ldots.$$

Example 2. From the functions $1, x, x^2, \ldots$ construct a set of functions

$$f_0(x), \, f_1(x), \, f_2(x), \, \ldots$$

which are orthogonal (but not normal) for the range (a, b); where

$$f_n(x) = \frac{d^n}{dx^n} \{(x-a)^n (x-b)^n\}.$$

[A similar investigation is given in § 15·14.]

11·61. *The connexion of orthogonal functions with homogeneous integral equations.*

Consider the homogeneous equation

$$\phi(x) = \lambda_0 \int_a^b \phi(\xi) K(x, \xi) \, d\xi,$$

where λ_0 is a *real** characteristic number for $K(x, \xi)$; we have already seen how solutions of it may be constructed; let n linearly independent solutions be taken and construct from them n orthogonal and normal functions $\phi_1, \phi_2, \ldots \phi_n$.

Then, since the functions ϕ_m are orthogonal and normal,

$$\int_a^b \left[\sum_{m=1}^n \phi_m(y) \int_a^b K(x, \xi) \phi_m(\xi) \, d\xi \right]^2 dy = \sum_{m=1}^n \int_a^b \left[\phi_m(y) \int_a^b K(x, \xi) \phi_m(\xi) \, d\xi \right]^2 dy,$$

and it is easily seen that the expression on the right may be written in the form

$$\sum_{m=1}^n \left\{ \int_a^b K(x, \xi) \phi_m(\xi) \, d\xi \right\}^2$$

on performing the integration with regard to y; and this is the same as

$$\sum_{m=1}^n \int_a^b K(x, y) \phi_m(y) \, dy \int_a^b K(x, \xi) \phi_m(\xi) \, d\xi.$$

Therefore, if we write K for $K(x, y)$ and Λ for

$$\sum_{m=1}^n \phi_m(y) \int_a^b K(x, \xi) \phi_m(\xi) \, d\xi,$$

---

* It will be seen immediately that the characteristic numbers of a symmetric nucleus are all real.

we have
$$\int_a^b \Lambda^2 dy = \int_a^b K\Lambda \, dy,$$

and so
$$\int_a^b \Lambda^2 dy = \int_a^b K^2 dy - \int_a^b (K - \Lambda)^2 \, dy.$$

Therefore
$$\int_a^b \left\{ \sum_{m=1}^n \frac{\phi_m(y)\,\phi_m(x)}{\lambda_0} \right\}^2 dy \leqslant \int_a^b \{K(x, y)\}^2 \, dy,$$

and so
$$\lambda_0^{-2} \sum_{m=1}^n \{\phi_m(x)\}^2 \leqslant \int_a^b \{K(x, y)\}^2 \, dy.$$

Integrating, we get
$$n \leqslant \lambda_0^2 \int_a^b \int_a^b \{K(x, y)\}^2 dy \, dx.$$

This formula gives an upper limit to the number, n, of orthogonal functions corresponding to any characteristic number λ_0.

These n orthogonal functions are called *characteristic functions* (or *auto-functions*) corresponding to λ_0.

Now let $\phi^{(0)}(x)$, $\phi^{(1)}(x)$ be characteristic functions corresponding to *different* characteristic numbers λ_0, λ_1.

Then
$$\phi^{(0)}(x)\,\phi^{(1)}(x) = \lambda_1 \int_a^b K(x, \xi)\,\phi^{(0)}(x)\,\phi^{(1)}(\xi)\,d\xi,$$
and so
$$\int_a^b \phi^{(0)}(x)\,\phi^{(1)}(x)\,dx = \lambda_1 \int_a^b \int_a^b K(x, \xi)\,\phi^{(0)}(x)\,\phi^{(1)}(\xi)\,d\xi dx \quad \ldots(1),$$
and similarly
$$\int_a^b \phi^{(0)}(x)\,\phi^{(1)}(x)\,dx = \lambda_0 \int_a^b \int_a^b K(x, \xi)\,\phi^{(0)}(\xi)\,\phi^{(1)}(x)\,d\xi dx$$
$$= \lambda_0 \int_a^b \int_a^b K(\xi, x)\,\phi^{(0)}(x)\,\phi^{(1)}(\xi)\,dx d\xi \quad \ldots(2),$$
on interchanging x and ξ.

We infer from (1) and (2) that if $\lambda_1 \neq \lambda_0$ *and if* $K(x, \xi) = K(\xi, x)$,
$$\int_a^b \phi^{(0)}(x)\,\phi^{(1)}(x)\,dx = 0,$$
and so the functions $\phi^{(0)}(x)$, $\phi^{(1)}(x)$ are *mutually* orthogonal.

If therefore the *nucleus be symmetric* and if, corresponding to each characteristic number, we construct the complete system of orthogonal functions, *all* the functions so obtained will be orthogonal.

Further, if the nucleus be symmetric *all the characteristic numbers are real*; for if λ_0, λ_1 be conjugate complex roots and if* $u_0(x) = v(x) + iw(x)$ be

* $v(x)$ and $w(x)$ being real.

a solution for the characteristic number λ_0, then $u_1(x) = v(x) - iw(x)$ is a solution for the characteristic number λ_1; replacing $\phi^{(0)}(x)$, $\phi^{(1)}(x)$ in the equation

$$\int_a^b \phi^{(0)}(x) \, \phi^{(1)}(x) \, dx = 0$$

by $v(x) + iw(x)$, $v(x) - iw(x)$, (which is obviously permissible), we get

$$\int_a^b [\{v(x)\}^2 + \{w(x)\}^2] \, dx = 0,$$

which implies $v(x) \equiv w(x) \equiv 0$, so that the integral equation has no solution except zero corresponding to the characteristic numbers λ_0, λ_1; this is contrary to § 11·23; hence, if the nucleus be symmetric, the characteristic numbers are real.

11·7. *The development* of a symmetric nucleus.*

Let $\phi_1(x)$, $\phi_2(x)$, $\phi_3(x)$, ... be a complete set of orthogonal functions satisfying the homogeneous integral equation with symmetric nucleus

$$\phi(x) = \lambda \int_a^b K(x, \xi) \, \phi(\xi) \, d\xi,$$

the corresponding characteristic numbers being† λ_1, λ_2, λ_3, ...

Now *suppose‡* that the series $\sum\limits_{n=1}^{\infty} \dfrac{\phi_n(x) \, \phi_n(y)}{\lambda_n}$ is uniformly convergent when $a \leqslant x \leqslant b$, $a \leqslant y \leqslant b$. *Then it will be shewn that*

$$K(x, y) = \sum_{n=1}^{\infty} \frac{\phi_n(x) \, \phi_n(y)}{\lambda_n}.$$

For consider the symmetric nucleus

$$H(x, y) = K(x, y) - \sum_{n=1}^{\infty} \frac{\phi_n(x) \, \phi_n(y)}{\lambda_n}.$$

If this nucleus is not identically zero, it will possess (§ 11·51) at least one characteristic number μ.

Let $\psi(x)$ be any solution of the equation

$$\psi(x) = \mu \int_a^b H(x, \xi) \, \psi(\xi) \, d\xi,$$

which does not vanish identically.

Multiply by $\phi_n(x)$ and integrate and we get

$$\int_a^b \psi(x) \, \phi_n(x) \, dx = \mu \int_a^b \int_a^b \left\{ K(x, \xi) - \sum_{m=1}^{\infty} \frac{\phi_m(x) \, \phi_m(\xi)}{\lambda_m} \right\} \psi(\xi) \, \phi_n(x) \, dx \, d\xi;$$

---

* This investigation is due to Schmidt, the result to Hilbert.

† These numbers are not all different if there is more than one orthogonal function to each characteristic number.

‡ The supposition is, of course, a matter for verification with any particular equation.

since the series converges uniformly, we may integrate term by term and get

$$\int_a^b \psi(x)\,\phi_n(x)\,dx = \frac{\mu}{\lambda_n}\int_a^b \psi(\xi)\,\phi_n(\xi)\,d\xi - \frac{\mu}{\lambda_n}\int_a^b \phi_n(\xi)\,\psi(\xi)\,d\xi$$
$$= 0.$$

Therefore $\psi(x)$ is orthogonal to $\phi_1(x)$, $\phi_2(x)$, ...; and so taking the equation

$$\psi(x) = \mu \int_a^b \left\{ K(x,\xi) - \sum_{n=1}^{\infty} \frac{\phi_n(x)\,\phi_n(\xi)}{\lambda_n} \right\} \psi(\xi)\,d\xi,$$

we have
$$\psi(x) = \mu \int_a^b K(x,\xi)\,\psi(\xi)\,d\xi.$$

Therefore μ is a characteristic number of $K(x,y)$, and so $\psi(x)$ must be a linear combination of the (finite number of) functions $\phi_n(x)$ corresponding to this number; let

$$\psi(x) = \sum_m a_m \phi_m(x).$$

Multiply by $\phi_m(x)$ and integrate; then since $\psi(x)$ is orthogonal to all the functions $\phi_n(x)$, we see that $a_m = 0$, so, contrary to hypothesis, $\psi(x) \equiv 0$.

The contradiction implies that the nucleus $H(x,y)$ must be identically zero; that is to say, $K(x,y)$ can be expanded in the given series, if it is uniformly convergent.

Example. Shew that, if λ_0 be a characteristic number, the equation

$$\phi(x) = f(x) + \lambda_0 \int_a^b K(x,\xi)\,\phi(\xi)\,d\xi$$

certainly has no solution when the nucleus is symmetric, unless $f(x)$ is orthogonal to all the characteristic functions corresponding to λ_0.

11·71. *The solution of Fredholm's equation by a series.*

Retaining the notation of § 11·7, consider the integral equation

$$\Phi(x) = f(x) + \lambda \int_a^b K(x,\xi)\,\Phi(\xi)\,d\xi,$$

where $K(x,\xi)$ is symmetric.

If we *assume* that $\Phi(\xi)$ can be expanded into a uniformly convergent series $\sum\limits_{n=1}^{\infty} a_n \phi_n(\xi)$, we have

$$\sum_{n=1}^{\infty} a_n \phi_n(x) = f(x) + \sum_{n=1}^{\infty} \frac{\lambda}{\lambda_n} a_n \phi_n(x),$$

so that $f(x)$ can be expanded in the series

$$\sum_{n=1}^{\infty} a_n \frac{\lambda_n - \lambda}{\lambda_n} \phi_n(x).$$

Hence *if the function $f(x)$ can be expanded into the convergent series $\sum\limits_{n=1}^{\infty} b_n \phi_n(x)$, then the series $\sum\limits_{n=1}^{\infty} \dfrac{b_n \lambda_n}{\lambda_n - \lambda} \phi_n(x)$, if it converges uniformly in the range (a, b), is the solution of Fredholm's equation.*

To determine the coefficients b_n we observe that $\sum\limits_{n=1}^{\infty} b_n \phi_n(x)$ converges uniformly by § 3·35 *; then, multiplying by $\phi_n(x)$ and integrating, we get

$$b_n = \int_a^b \phi_n(x) f(x)\, dx.$$

11·8. *Solution of Abel's integral equation.*

This equation is of the form

$$f(x) = \int_a^x \frac{u(\xi)}{(x-\xi)^\mu}\, d\xi \qquad (0 < \mu < 1, \quad a \leqslant x \leqslant b),$$

where $f'(x)$ is continuous and $f(a) = 0$; we proceed to find a continuous solution $u(x)$.

Let $\phi(x) = \int_a^x u(\xi)\, d\xi$, and take the formula †

$$\frac{\pi}{\sin \mu \pi} = \int_\xi^z \frac{dx}{(z-x)^{1-\mu}(x-\xi)^\mu},$$

multiply by $u(\xi)$ and integrate, and we get, on using Dirichlet's formula (§ 4·51 corollary),

$$\frac{\pi}{\sin \mu \pi}\{\phi(z) - \phi(a)\} = \int_a^z d\xi \int_\xi^z \frac{u(\xi)\, dx}{(z-x)^{1-\mu}(x-\xi)^\mu}$$
$$= \int_a^z dx \int_a^x \frac{u(\xi)\, d\xi}{(z-x)^{1-\mu}(x-\xi)^\mu}$$
$$= \int_a^z \frac{f(x)\, dx}{(z-x)^{1-\mu}}.$$

Since the original expression has a continuous derivate, so has the final one; therefore the continuous solution, *if it exist*, can be none other than

$$u(z) = \frac{\sin \mu \pi}{\pi} \frac{d}{dz} \int_a^z \frac{f(x)\, dx}{(z-x)^{1-\mu}};$$

and it can be verified by substitution ‡ that this function actually *is* a solution.

11·81. *Schlömilch's§ integral equation.*

Let $f(x)$ have a continuous differential coefficient when $-\pi \leqslant x \leqslant \pi$. Then the equation

$$f(x) = \frac{2}{\pi} \int_0^{\frac{1}{2}\pi} \phi(x \sin \theta)\, d\theta$$

has one solution with a continuous differential coefficient when $-\pi \leqslant x \leqslant \pi$, namely

$$\phi(x) = f(0) + x \int_0^{\frac{1}{2}\pi} f'(x \sin \theta)\, d\theta.$$

From § 4·2 it follows that

$$f'(x) = \frac{2}{\pi} \int_0^{\frac{1}{2}\pi} \sin \theta \phi'(x \sin \theta)\, d\theta$$

(so that we have $\phi(0) = f(0)$, $\phi'(0) = \frac{1}{2}\pi f'(0)$).

---

* Since the numbers λ_n are all real we may arrange them in two sets, one negative the other positive, the members in each set being in order of magnitude; then, when $|\lambda_n| > \lambda$, it is evident that $\lambda_n/(\lambda_n - \lambda)$ is a monotonic sequence in the case of either set.

† This follows from § 6·24 example 1, by writing $(z-x)/(x-\xi)$ in place of x.

‡ For the details we refer to Bôcher's tract.

§ *Zeitschrift für Math. und Phys.* II. (1857). The reader will easily see that this is reducible to a case of Volterra's equation with a discontinuous nucleus.

Write $x \sin \psi$ for x, and we have on multiplying by x and integrating

$$x \int_0^{\frac{1}{2}\pi} f'(x \sin \psi) \, d\psi = \frac{2x}{\pi} \int_0^{\frac{1}{2}\pi} \left\{ \int_0^{\frac{1}{2}\pi} \sin \theta \phi'(x \sin \theta \sin \psi) \, d\theta \right\} d\psi.$$

Change the order of integration in the repeated integral (§ 4·3) and take a new variable χ in place of ψ, defined by the equation $\sin \chi = \sin \theta \sin \psi$.

Then

$$x \int_0^{\frac{1}{2}\pi} f'(x \sin \psi) \, d\psi = \frac{2x}{\pi} \int_0^{\frac{1}{2}\pi} \left\{ \int_0^{\theta} \frac{\phi'(x \sin \chi) \cos \chi \, d\chi}{\cos \psi} \right\} d\theta.$$

Changing the order of integration again (§ 4·51),

$$x \int_0^{\frac{1}{2}\pi} f'(x \sin \psi) \, d\psi = \frac{2x}{\pi} \int_0^{\frac{1}{2}\pi} \left\{ \int_\chi^{\frac{1}{2}\pi} \frac{\phi'(x \sin \chi) \cos \chi \sin \theta}{\sqrt{(\sin^2 \theta - \sin^2 \chi)}} \, d\theta \right\} d\chi.$$

But

$$\int_\chi^{\frac{1}{2}\pi} \frac{\sin \theta \, d\theta}{\sqrt{(\cos^2 \chi - \cos^2 \theta)}} = \left[-\arcsin \left(\frac{\cos \theta}{\cos \chi} \right) \right]_\chi^{\frac{1}{2}\pi} = \tfrac{1}{2}\pi,$$

and so

$$x \int_0^{\frac{1}{2}\pi} f'(x \sin \psi) \, d\psi = x \int_0^{\frac{1}{2}\pi} \phi'(x \sin \chi) \cos \chi \, d\chi$$
$$= \phi(x) - \phi(0).$$

Since $\phi(0) = f(0)$, we must have

$$\phi(x) = f(0) + x \int_0^{\frac{1}{2}\pi} f'(x \sin \psi) \, d\psi \, ;$$

and it can be verified by substitution that this function actually is a solution.

REFERENCES.

H. BATEMAN, *Report to the British Association**, 1910.

M. BÔCHER, *Introduction to Integral Equations* (Cambridge Math. Tracts, No. 10, 1909).

H. B. HEYWOOD et M. FRÉCHET, *L'Équation de Fredholm* (Paris, 1912).

V. VOLTERRA, *Leçons sur les équations intégrales et les équations intégro-différentielles* (Paris, 1913).

T. LALESCO, *Introduction à la théorie des equations intégrales* (Paris, 1912).

I. FREDHOLM, *Acta Mathematica*, XXVII. (1903), pp. 365–390.

D. HILBERT, *Grundzüge einer allgemeinen Theorie der linearen Integralgleichungen* (Leipzig, 1912).

E. SCHMIDT, *Math. Ann.* LXIII. (1907), pp. 433–476.

E. GOURSAT, *Cours d'Analyse*, III. (Paris, 1915), Chs. XXX–XXXIII.

R. COURANT u. D. HILBERT, *Methoden der Mathematischen Physik* (Berlin, 1924).

MISCELLANEOUS EXAMPLES.

1. Shew that if the time of descent of a particle down a smooth curve to its lowest point is independent of the starting-point (the particle starting from rest) the curve is a cycloid. (Abel.)

* The reader will find a more complete bibliography in this Report than it is possible to give here.

2. Shew that, if $f(x)$ is continuous, the solution of

$$\phi(x) = f(x) + \lambda \int_0^\infty \cos(2xs)\, \phi(s)\, ds$$

is
$$\phi(x) = \frac{f(x) + \lambda \int_0^\infty f(s)\cos(2xs)\, ds}{1 - \frac{1}{4}\lambda^2 \pi},$$

assuming the legitimacy of a certain change of order of integration.

3. Shew that the Weber-Hermite functions

$$D_n(x) = (-)^n e^{\frac{1}{4}x^2} \frac{d^n}{dx^n}\left(e^{-\frac{1}{2}x^2}\right)$$

satisfy
$$\phi(x) = \lambda \int_{-\infty}^\infty e^{\frac{1}{2}isx}\, \phi(s)\, ds$$

for the characteristic values of λ.   (A. Milne.)

4. Shew that even periodic solutions (with period 2π) of the differential equation

$$\frac{d^2\phi(x)}{dx^2} + (a^2 + k^2 \cos^2 x)\, \phi(x) = 0$$

satisfy the integral equation

$$\phi(x) = \lambda \int_{-\pi}^\pi e^{k\cos x \cos s}\, \phi(s)\, ds. \qquad \text{(Whittaker; see § 19·21.)}$$

5. Shew that the characteristic functions of the equation

$$\phi(x) = \lambda \int_{-\pi}^\pi \left\{ \frac{1}{4}\pi^{-1}(x-y)^2 - \frac{1}{2}\,|\,x-y\,| \right\} \phi(y)\, dy$$

are
$$\phi(x) = \cos mx, \quad \sin mx,$$

where $\lambda = m^2$ and m is any integer.

6. Shew that
$$\phi(x) = \int_0^x \xi^{x-\xi}\, \phi(\xi)\, d\xi$$

has the discontinuous solution $\qquad \phi(x) = kx^{x-1}$.   (Bôcher.)

7. Shew that a solution of the integral equation with a symmetric nucleus

$$f(x) = \int_a^b K(x, \xi)\, \phi(\xi)\, d\xi$$

is
$$\phi(x) = \sum_{n=1}^\infty a_n \lambda_n \phi_n(x),$$

provided that this series converges uniformly, where λ_n, $\phi_n(x)$ are the characteristic numbers and functions of $K(x, \xi)$ and $\sum_{n=1}^\infty a_n \phi_n(x)$ is the expansion of $f(x)$.

8. Shew that, if $|\,h\,| < 1$, the characteristic functions of the equation

$$\phi(x) = \frac{\lambda}{2\pi} \int_{-\pi}^\pi \frac{1-h^2}{1 - 2h\cos(\xi-x) + h^2}\, \phi(\xi)\, d\xi$$

are 1, $\cos mx$, $\sin mx$, the corresponding characteristic numbers being 1, $1/h^m$, $1/h^m$, where m takes all positive integral values.

PART II

THE TRANSCENDENTAL FUNCTIONS

CHAPTER XII

THE GAMMA FUNCTION

12·1. *Definitions of the Gamma-function. The Weierstrassian product.*

Historically, the Gamma-function* $\Gamma(z)$ was first defined by Euler as the limit of a product (§ 12·11) from which can be derived the infinite integral $\int_0^\infty t^{z-1}e^{-t}dt$; but in developing the theory of the function, it is more convenient to define it by means of an infinite product of Weierstrass' canonical form.

Consider the product $\quad ze^{\gamma z} \prod_{n=1}^{\infty} \left\{ \left(1+\frac{z}{n}\right)e^{-\frac{z}{n}} \right\}$,

where $\qquad \gamma = \lim_{m \to \infty} \left\{ \frac{1}{1}+\frac{1}{2}+ \ldots +\frac{1}{m} - \log m \right\} = 0\cdot 5772157\ldots$

[The constant γ is known as Euler's or Mascheroni's constant; to prove that it exists we observe that, if

$$u_n = \int_0^1 \frac{t}{n(n+t)}\,dt = \frac{1}{n} - \log\frac{n+1}{n},$$

u_n is positive and less than $\int_0^1 \frac{dt}{n^2} = \frac{1}{n^2}$; therefore $\sum_{n=1}^{\infty} u_n$ converges, and

$$\lim_{m \to \infty} \left\{ \frac{1}{1}+\frac{1}{2}+\ldots+\frac{1}{m}-\log m \right\} = \lim_{m \to \infty} \left\{ \sum_{n=1}^{m} u_n + \log\frac{m+1}{m} \right\} = \sum_{n=1}^{\infty} u_n.$$

The value of γ has been calculated by J. C. Adams to 260 places of decimals.]

The product under consideration represents an analytic function of z, for all values of z; for, if N be an integer such that $|z| \leqslant \frac{1}{2}N$, we have†, if $n > N$,

$$\left| \log\left(1+\frac{z}{n}\right) - \frac{z}{n} \right| = \left| -\frac{1}{2}\frac{z^2}{n^2}+\frac{1}{3}\frac{z^3}{n^3}-\ldots \right|$$

$$\leqslant \frac{|z|^2}{n^2}\left\{ 1+\left|\frac{z}{n}\right|+\left|\frac{z^2}{n^2}\right|+\ldots \right\}$$

$$\leqslant \frac{1}{4}\frac{N^2}{n^2}\left\{ 1+\frac{1}{2}+\frac{1}{2^2}+\ldots \right\} \leqslant \frac{1}{2}\frac{N^2}{n^2}.$$

Since the series $\sum_{n=N+1}^{\infty} \{N^2/(2n^2)\}$ converges, it follows that, when $|z| \leqslant \frac{1}{2}N$,

---

* The notation $\Gamma(z)$ was introduced by Legendre in 1814.

† Taking the principal value of $\log(1+z/n)$.

$\sum\limits_{n=N+1}^{\infty} \left\{ \log\left(1 + \dfrac{z}{n}\right) - \dfrac{z}{n} \right\}$ is an absolutely and uniformly convergent series of analytic functions, and so it is an analytic function (§ 5·3); consequently its exponential $\prod\limits_{n=N+1}^{\infty} \left\{ \left(1 + \dfrac{z}{n}\right) e^{-\frac{z}{n}} \right\}$ is an analytic function, and so $z e^{\gamma z} \prod\limits_{n=1}^{\infty} \left\{ \left(1 + \dfrac{z}{n}\right) e^{-\frac{z}{n}} \right\}$ is an analytic function when $|z| \leqslant \frac{1}{2}N$, where N is any integer; that is to say, the product is analytic for all finite values of z.

The Gamma-function was defined by Weierstrass* by the equation

$$\frac{1}{\Gamma(z)} = z e^{\gamma z} \prod_{n=1}^{\infty} \left\{ \left(1 + \frac{z}{n}\right) e^{-\frac{z}{n}} \right\};$$

from this equation *it is apparent that* $\Gamma(z)$ *is analytic except at the points* $z = 0, -1, -2, \ldots$, *where it has simple poles.*

Proofs have been published by Hölder†, Moore‡, and Barnes§ of a theorem known to Weierstrass that the Gamma-function does not satisfy any differential equation with rational coefficients.

Example 1.   Prove that
$$\Gamma(1) = 1, \quad \Gamma'(1) = -\gamma,$$
where γ is Euler's constant.

[Justify differentiating logarithmically the equation
$$\frac{1}{\Gamma(z)} = z e^{\gamma z} \prod_{1}^{\infty} \left\{ \left(1 + \frac{z}{n}\right) e^{-\frac{z}{n}} \right\}$$
by § 4·7, and put $z = 1$ after the differentiations have been performed.]

Example 2.   Shew that
$$1 + \frac{1}{2} + \frac{1}{3} + \ldots + \frac{1}{n} = \int_0^1 \frac{1 - (1-t)^n}{t}\, dt,$$
and hence that Euler's constant γ is given by‖
$$\lim_{n \to \infty} \left[\int_0^1 \left\{ 1 - \left(1 - \frac{t}{n}\right)^n \right\} \frac{dt}{t} - \int_1^n \left(1 - \frac{t}{n}\right)^n \frac{dt}{t} \right].$$

Example 3.   Shew that
$$\prod_{n=1}^{\infty} \left\{ \left(1 - \frac{x}{z+n}\right) e^{\frac{x}{n}} \right\} = \frac{e^{\gamma x}\, \Gamma(z+1)}{\Gamma(z - x + 1)}.$$

---

* *Journal für Math.* LI. (1856).   This formula for $\Gamma(z)$ had been obtained from Euler's formula (§ 12·11) in 1848 by F. W. Newman, *Cambridge and Dublin Math. Journal*, III. (1848), p. 60.

† *Math. Ann.* XXVIII. (1887), pp. 1–13.

‡ *Math. Ann.* XLVIII. (1897), pp. 70–74.

§ *Messenger of Math.* XXIX. (1900), pp. 122–128.

‖ The reader will see later (§ 12·2 example 4) that this limit may be written
$$\int_0^1 (1 - e^{-t})\, \frac{dt}{t} - \int_1^\infty \frac{e^{-t}\, dt}{t}.$$

12·11. *Euler's formula for the Gamma-function.*

By the definition of an infinite product we have

$$\frac{1}{\Gamma(z)} = z \left[\lim_{m \to \infty} e^{\left(1 + \frac{1}{2} + \dots + \frac{1}{m} - \log m\right)z} \right] \left[\lim_{m \to \infty} \prod_{n=1}^{m} \left\{ \left(1 + \frac{z}{n}\right) e^{-\frac{z}{n}} \right\} \right]$$

$$= z \lim_{m \to \infty} \left[e^{\left(1 + \frac{1}{2} + \dots + \frac{1}{m} - \log m\right)z} \prod_{n=1}^{m} \left\{ \left(1 + \frac{z}{n}\right) e^{-\frac{z}{n}} \right\} \right]$$

$$= z \lim_{m \to \infty} \left[m^{-z} \prod_{n=1}^{m} \left(1 + \frac{z}{n}\right) \right]$$

$$= z \lim_{m \to \infty} \left[\prod_{n=1}^{m-1} \left(1 + \frac{1}{n}\right)^{-z} \prod_{n=1}^{m} \left(1 + \frac{z}{n}\right) \right]$$

$$= z \lim_{m \to \infty} \left[\prod_{n=1}^{m} \left\{ \left(1 + \frac{z}{n}\right) \left(1 + \frac{1}{n}\right)^{-z} \right\} \left(1 + \frac{1}{m}\right)^{z} \right].$$

Hence
$$\Gamma(z) = \frac{1}{z} \prod_{n=1}^{\infty} \left\{ \left(1 + \frac{1}{n}\right)^{z} \left(1 + \frac{z}{n}\right)^{-1} \right\}.$$

This formula is due to Euler*; it is valid except when $z = 0, -1, -2, \dots$.

Example. Prove that

$$\Gamma(z) = \lim_{n \to \infty} \frac{1 \cdot 2 \dots (n-1)}{z(z+1) \dots (z+n-1)} n^z. \qquad \text{(Euler.)}$$

12·12. *The difference equation satisfied by the Gamma-function.*

We shall now shew that the function $\Gamma(z)$ satisfies the difference equation

$$\Gamma(z+1) = z\Gamma(z).$$

For, by Euler's formula, if z is not a negative integer,

$$\Gamma(z+1)/\Gamma(z) = \frac{1}{z+1} \left[\lim_{m \to \infty} \prod_{n=1}^{m} \frac{\left(1 + \frac{1}{n}\right)^{z+1}}{1 + \frac{z+1}{n}} \right] \div \left[\frac{1}{z} \lim_{m \to \infty} \prod_{n=1}^{m} \frac{\left(1 + \frac{1}{n}\right)^{z}}{1 + \frac{z}{n}} \right]$$

$$= \frac{z}{z+1} \lim_{m \to \infty} \prod_{n=1}^{m} \left\{ \frac{\left(1 + \frac{1}{n}\right)(z+n)}{z+n+1} \right\}$$

$$= z \lim_{m \to \infty} \frac{m+1}{z+m+1} = z.$$

This is one of the most important properties of the Gamma-function.

Since $\Gamma(1) = 1$, it follows that, if z is a positive integer, $\Gamma(z) = (z-1)!$.

---

* It was given in 1729 in a letter to Goldbach, printed in Fuss' *Corresp. Math.*

Example. Prove that

$$\frac{1}{\Gamma(z+1)} + \frac{1}{\Gamma(z+2)} + \frac{1}{\Gamma(z+3)} + \dots = \frac{e}{\Gamma(z)}\left\{\frac{1}{z} - \frac{1}{1!}\frac{1}{z+1} + \frac{1}{2!}\frac{1}{z+2} - \dots\right\}.$$

[Consider the expression

$$\frac{1}{z} + \frac{1}{z(z+1)} + \frac{1}{z(z+1)(z+2)} + \dots + \frac{1}{z(z+1)\dots(z+m)}.$$

It can be expressed in partial fractions in the form $\sum\limits_{n=0}^{m}\frac{a_n}{z+n}$, where

$$a_n = \frac{(-)^n}{n!}\left\{1 + \frac{1}{1!} + \frac{1}{2!} + \dots + \frac{1}{(m-n)!}\right\} = \frac{(-)^n}{n!}\left\{e - \sum\limits_{r=m-n+1}^{\infty}\frac{1}{r!}\right\}.$$

Noting that $\sum\limits_{r=m-n+1}^{\infty}\frac{1}{r!} < \frac{e}{(m-n+1)!}$, prove that $\sum\limits_{n=0}^{m}\frac{(-)^n}{n!}\frac{1}{z+n}\left\{\sum\limits_{r=m-n+1}^{\infty}\frac{1}{r!}\right\} \to 0$ as $m \to \infty$ when z is not a negative integer.]

12·13.   *The evaluation of a general class of infinite products.*

By means of the Gamma-function, it is possible to evaluate the general class of infinite products of the form

$$\prod_{n=1}^{\infty} u_n,$$

where u_n is any rational function of the index n.

For, resolving u_n into its factors, we can write the product in the form

$$\prod_{n=1}^{\infty}\left\{\frac{A(n-a_1)(n-a_2)\dots(n-a_k)}{(n-b_1)\dots(n-b_l)}\right\};$$

and it is supposed that no factor in the denominator vanishes.

In order that this product may converge, the number of factors in the numerator must clearly be the same as the number of factors in the denominator, and also $A = 1$; for, otherwise, the general factor of the product would not tend to the value unity as n tends to infinity.

We have therefore $k = l$, and, denoting the product by P, we may write

$$P = \prod_{n=1}^{\infty}\left\{\frac{(n-a_1)\dots(n-a_k)}{(n-b_1)\dots(n-b_k)}\right\}.$$

The general term in this product can be written

$$\left(1 - \frac{a_1}{n}\right)\dots\left(1 - \frac{a_k}{n}\right)\left(1 - \frac{b_1}{n}\right)^{-1}\dots\left(1 - \frac{b_k}{n}\right)^{-1}$$

$$= 1 - \frac{a_1 + a_2 + \dots + a_k - b_1 - \dots - b_k}{n} + A_n,$$

where A_n is $O(n^{-2})$ when n is large.

In order that the infinite product may be absolutely convergent, it is therefore necessary further (§ 2·7) that

$$a_1 + \dots + a_k - b_1 - \dots - b_k = 0.$$

We can therefore introduce the factor

$$\exp\{n^{-1}(a_1 + \dots + a_k - b_1 - \dots - b_k)\}$$

into the general factor of the product, without altering its value; and thus we have

$$P = \prod_{n=1}^{\infty} \left\{ \frac{\left(1 - \frac{a_1}{n}\right) e^{\frac{a_1}{n}} \left(1 - \frac{a_2}{n}\right) e^{\frac{a_2}{n}} \dots \left(1 - \frac{a_k}{n}\right) e^{\frac{a_k}{n}}}{\left(1 - \frac{b_1}{n}\right) e^{\frac{b_1}{n}} \dots \left(1 - \frac{b_k}{n}\right) e^{\frac{b_k}{n}}} \right\}$$

But it is obvious from the Weierstrassian definition of the Gamma-function that

$$\prod_{n=1}^{\infty} \left\{ \left(1 - \frac{z}{n}\right) e^{\frac{z}{n}} \right\} = \frac{1}{-z \Gamma(-z) e^{-\gamma z}},$$

and so
$$P = \frac{b_1 \Gamma(-b_1) b_2 \Gamma(-b_2) \dots b_k \Gamma(-b_k)}{a_1 \Gamma(-a_1) \dots a_k \Gamma(-a_k)} = \prod_{m=1}^{k} \frac{\Gamma(1 - b_m)}{\Gamma(1 - a_m)};$$

a formula which expresses the general infinite product P in terms of the Gamma-function.

Example 1.　Prove that

$$\prod_{s=1}^{\infty} \frac{s(a+b+s)}{(a+s)(b+s)} = \frac{\Gamma(a+1)\Gamma(b+1)}{\Gamma(a+b+1)}.$$

Example 2.　Shew that, if $a = \cos(2\pi/n) + i \sin(2\pi/n)$, then

$$x\left(1 - \frac{x}{1^n}\right)\left(1 - \frac{x}{2^n}\right)\dots = \{-\Gamma(-x^{\frac{1}{n}})\Gamma(-ax^{\frac{1}{n}})\dots\Gamma(-a^{n-1}x^{\frac{1}{n}})\}^{-1}.$$

12·14.　*Connexion between the Gamma-function and the circular functions.*

We now proceed to establish another most important property of the Gamma-function, expressed by the equation

$$\Gamma(z)\Gamma(1-z) = \frac{\pi}{\sin \pi z}.$$

We have, by the definition of Weierstrass (§ 12·1),

$$\Gamma(z)\Gamma(-z) = -\frac{1}{z^2} \prod_{n=1}^{\infty} \left\{ \left(1 + \frac{z}{n}\right) e^{-\frac{z}{n}} \right\}^{-1} \prod_{n=1}^{\infty} \left\{ \left(1 - \frac{z}{n}\right) e^{\frac{z}{n}} \right\}^{-1}$$

$$= \frac{-\pi}{z \sin \pi z},$$

by § 7·5 example 1.　Since, by § 12·12,

$$\Gamma(1 - z) = -z\Gamma(-z)$$

we have the result stated.

Corollary 1. If we assign to z the value $\frac{1}{2}$, this formula gives $\{\Gamma(\frac{1}{2})\}^2 = \pi$; since, by the formula of Weierstrass, $\Gamma(\frac{1}{2})$ is positive, we have

$$\Gamma(\tfrac{1}{2}) = \pi^{\frac{1}{2}}.$$

Corollary 2. If $\psi(z) = \Gamma'(z)/\Gamma(z)$, then $\psi(1-z) - \psi(z) = \pi \cot \pi z$.

12·15. *The multiplication-theorem of Gauss* and Legendre.*

We shall next obtain the result

$$\Gamma(z)\,\Gamma\left(z+\frac{1}{n}\right)\Gamma\left(z+\frac{2}{n}\right)\dots\Gamma\left(z+\frac{n-1}{n}\right) = (2\pi)^{\frac{1}{2}(n-1)}\,n^{\frac{1}{2}-nz}\,\Gamma(nz).$$

For let
$$\phi(z) = \frac{n^{nz}\,\Gamma(z)\,\Gamma\left(z+\dfrac{1}{n}\right)\dots\Gamma\left(z+\dfrac{n-1}{n}\right)}{n\,\Gamma(nz)}.$$

Then we have, by Euler's formula (§ 12·11 example),

$$\phi(z) = \frac{n^{nz}\displaystyle\prod_{r=0}^{n-1}\lim_{m\to\infty}\frac{1\,.\,2\dots(m-1)\,.\,m^{z+r/n}}{\left(z+\dfrac{r}{n}\right)\left(z+\dfrac{r}{n}+1\right)\dots\left(z+\dfrac{r}{n}+m-1\right)}}{n\displaystyle\lim_{m\to\infty}\frac{1\,.\,2\dots(nm-1)\,.\,(nm)^{nz}}{nz(nz+1)\dots(nz+nm-1)}}$$

$$= n^{nz-1}\lim_{m\to\infty}\frac{\{(m-1)!\}^n\,m^{nz+\frac{1}{2}(n-1)}\,n^{mn}}{(nm-1)!\,(nm)^{nz}}$$

$$= \lim_{m\to\infty}\frac{\{(m-1)!\}^n\,m^{\frac{1}{2}(n-1)}\,n^{mn-1}}{(nm-1)!}.$$

It is evident from this last equation that $\phi(z)$ is independent of z.

Thus $\phi(z)$ is equal to the value which it has when $z = \dfrac{1}{n}$; and so

$$\phi(z) = \Gamma\left(\frac{1}{n}\right)\Gamma\left(\frac{2}{n}\right)\dots\Gamma\left(\frac{n-1}{n}\right).$$

Therefore
$$\{\phi(z)\}^2 = \prod_{r=1}^{n-1}\left\{\Gamma\left(\frac{r}{n}\right)\Gamma\left(1-\frac{r}{n}\right)\right\}$$

$$= \frac{\pi^{n-1}}{\sin\dfrac{\pi}{n}\sin\dfrac{2\pi}{n}\dots\sin\dfrac{(n-1)\pi}{n}} = \frac{(2\pi)^{n-1}}{n}.$$

Thus, since $\phi(n^{-1})$ is positive,

$$\phi(z) = (2\pi)^{\frac{1}{2}(n-1)}\,n^{-\frac{1}{2}},$$

i.e.
$$\Gamma(z)\,\Gamma\left(z+\frac{1}{n}\right)\dots\Gamma\left(z+\frac{n-1}{n}\right) = n^{\frac{1}{2}-nz}\,(2\pi)^{\frac{1}{2}(n-1)}\,\Gamma(nz).$$

Corollary. Taking $n=2$, we have
$$2^{2z-1}\,\Gamma(z)\,\Gamma(z+\tfrac{1}{2}) = \pi^{\frac{1}{2}}\,\Gamma(2z).$$

This is called the *duplication formula*.

* *Werke*, III. p. 149. The case in which $n=2$ was given by Legendre.

Example. If
$$B(p, q) = \frac{\Gamma(p)\,\Gamma(q)}{\Gamma(p+q)},$$
shew that
$$B(np, nq) = n^{-nq} \frac{B(p, q)\, B\left(p+\dfrac{1}{n}, q\right) \dots B\left(p+\dfrac{n-1}{n}, q\right)}{B(q, q)\, B(2q, q) \dots B\{(n-1)q, q\}}.$$

12·16. *Expansions for the logarithmic derivates of the Gamma-function.*

We have
$$\{\Gamma(z+1)\}^{-1} = e^{\gamma z} \prod_{n=1}^{\infty} \left\{\left(1+\frac{z}{n}\right) e^{-\frac{z}{n}}\right\}.$$

Differentiating logarithmically (§ 4·7), this gives
$$\frac{d \log \Gamma(z+1)}{dz} = -\gamma + \frac{z}{1\,(z+1)} + \frac{z}{2\,(z+2)} + \frac{z}{3\,(z+3)} + \dots.$$

Therefore, since $\log \Gamma(z+1) = \log z + \log \Gamma(z)$, we have
$$\frac{d}{dz} \log \Gamma(z) = -\gamma - \frac{1}{z} + z \sum_{n=1}^{\infty} \frac{1}{n\,(z+n)}.$$

Differentiating again, $\dfrac{d^2}{dz^2} \log \Gamma(z+1) = \dfrac{d}{dz} \left\{\dfrac{z}{1\,(z+1)} + \dfrac{z}{2\,(z+2)} + \dots\right\}$
$$= \frac{1}{(z+1)^2} + \frac{1}{(z+2)^2} + \dots.$$

These expansions are occasionally used in applications of the theory.

12·2. *Euler's expression of $\Gamma(z)$ as an infinite integral.*

The infinite integral $\displaystyle\int_0^{\infty} e^{-t}\, t^{z-1}\, dt$ represents an analytic function of z when* the real part of z is positive (§ 5·32); it is called the *Eulerian Integral of the Second Kind*†. It will now be shewn that, when $R(z) > 0$, the integral is equal to $\Gamma(z)$. Denoting the real part of z by x, we have $x > 0$. Now, if ‡
$$\Pi(z, n) = \int_0^n \left(1 - \frac{t}{n}\right)^n t^{z-1}\, dt,$$
we have
$$\Pi(z, n) = n^z \int_0^1 (1-\tau)^n\, \tau^{z-1}\, d\tau,$$

if we write $t = n\tau$; it is easily shewn by repeated integrations by parts that, when $x > 0$ and n is a positive integer,
$$\int_0^1 (1-\tau)^n \tau^{z-1}\, d\tau = \left[\frac{1}{z}\, \tau^z (1-\tau)^n\right]_0^1 + \frac{n}{z} \int_0^1 (1-\tau)^{n-1} \tau^z\, d\tau$$
$$= \dots\dots\dots$$
$$= \frac{n\,(n-1)\dots 1}{z\,(z+1)\dots(z+n-1)} \int_0^1 \tau^{z+n-1}\, d\tau,$$

and so
$$\Pi(z, n) = \frac{1 \cdot 2 \dots n}{z\,(z+1)\dots(z+n)}\, n^z.$$

Hence, by the example of § 12·11, $\Pi(z, n) \to \Gamma(z)$ as $n \to \infty$.

---

* If the real part of z is not positive the integral does not converge on account of the singularity of the integrand at $t = 0$.

† The name was given by Legendre; see § 12·4 for the Eulerian Integral of the First Kind.

‡ The many-valued function t^{z-1} is made precise by the equation $t^{z-1} = e^{(z-1)\log t}$, $\log t$ being purely real.

Consequently $\qquad \Gamma(z) = \lim_{n \to \infty} \int_0^n \left(1 - \frac{t}{n}\right)^n t^{z-1} dt.$

And so, if $\qquad \Gamma_1(z) = \int_0^\infty e^{-t} t^{z-1} dt,$

we have

$$\Gamma_1(z) - \Gamma(z) = \lim_{n \to \infty} \left[\int_0^n \left\{ e^{-t} - \left(1 - \frac{t}{n}\right)^n \right\} t^{z-1} dt + \int_n^\infty e^{-t} t^{z-1} dt \right].$$

Now $\qquad\qquad\qquad\qquad \lim_{n \to \infty} \int_n^\infty e^{-t} t^{z-1} dt = 0,$

since $\int_0^\infty e^{-t} t^{z-1} dt$ converges.

To shew that zero is the limit of the first of the two integrals in the formula for $\Gamma_1(z) - \Gamma(z)$ we observe that

$$0 \leqslant e^{-t} - \left(1 - \frac{t}{n}\right)^n \leqslant n^{-1} t^2 e^{-t}.$$

[To establish these inequalities, we proceed as follows: when $0 \leqslant y < 1$,

$$1 + y \leqslant e^y \leqslant (1-y)^{-1},$$

from the series for e^y and $(1-y)^{-1}$. Writing t/n for y, we have

$$\left(1 + \frac{t}{n}\right)^{-n} \geqslant e^{-t} \geqslant \left(1 - \frac{t}{n}\right)^n,$$

and so $\qquad\qquad 0 \leqslant e^{-t} - \left(1 - \frac{t}{n}\right)^n$

$$= e^{-t} \left\{ 1 - e^t \left(1 - \frac{t}{n}\right)^n \right\}$$

$$\leqslant e^{-t} \left\{ 1 - \left(1 - \frac{t^2}{n^2}\right)^n \right\}.$$

Now, if $0 \leqslant a \leqslant 1$, $(1-a)^n \geqslant 1 - na$ by induction when $na < 1$ and obviously when $na \geqslant 1$; and, writing t^2/n^2 for a, we get

$$1 - \left(1 - \frac{t^2}{n^2}\right)^n \leqslant \frac{t^2}{n}$$

and so* $\qquad\qquad 0 \leqslant e^{-t} - \left(1 - \frac{t}{n}\right)^n \leqslant e^{-t} t^2/n,$

which is the required result.]

From the inequalities, it follows at once that

$$\left| \int_0^n \left\{ e^{-t} - \left(1 - \frac{t}{n}\right)^n \right\} t^{z-1} dt \right| \leqslant \int_0^n n^{-1} e^{-t} t^{x+1} dt$$

$$< n^{-1} \int_0^\infty e^{-t} t^{x+1} dt \to 0,$$

as $n \to \infty$, since the last integral converges.

* This analysis is a modification of that given by Schlömilch, *Compendium der höheren Analysis*, II. p. 243. A simple method of obtaining a less precise inequality (which is sufficient for the object required) is given by Bromwich, *Infinite Series*, p. 459.

Consequently $\Gamma_1(z) = \Gamma(z)$ when the integral, by which $\Gamma_1(z)$ is defined, converges; that is to say that, when the real part of z is positive,

$$\Gamma(z) = \int_0^\infty e^{-t} t^{z-1} dt.$$

And so, when the real part of z is positive, $\Gamma(z)$ may be defined either by this integral or by the Weierstrassian product.

Example 1.   Prove that, when $R(z)$ is positive,

$$\Gamma(z) = \int_0^1 \left(\log \frac{1}{x} \right)^{z-1} dx.$$

Example 2.   Prove that, if $R(z) > 0$ and $R(s) > 0$,

$$\int_0^\infty e^{-zx} x^{s-1} dx = \frac{\Gamma(s)}{z^s}.$$

Example 3.   Prove that, if $R(z) > 0$ and $R(s) > 1$,

$$\frac{1}{(z+1)^s} + \frac{1}{(z+2)^s} + \frac{1}{(z+3)^s} + \ldots = \frac{1}{\Gamma(s)} \int_0^\infty \frac{e^{-zx} x^{s-1} dx}{e^x - 1}$$

Example 4.   From § 12·1 example 2, by using the inequality

$$0 \leqslant e^{-t} - \left(1 - \frac{t}{n} \right)^n \leqslant t^2 e^{-t}/n,$$

deduce that

$$\gamma = \int_0^1 \frac{1 - e^{-t} - e^{-1/t}}{t} dt.$$

12·21.   *Extension of the infinite integral to the case in which the argument of the Gamma-function is negative.*

The formula of the last article is no longer applicable when the real part of z is negative.   Cauchy[*] and Saalschütz[†] have shewn, however, that, for negative arguments, an analogous theorem exists.   This can be obtained in the following way.

Consider the function

$$\Gamma_2(z) = \int_0^\infty t^{z-1} \left(e^{-t} - 1 + t - \frac{t^2}{2!} + \ldots + (-)^{k+1} \frac{t^k}{k!} \right) dt,$$

where k is the integer so chosen that $-k > x > -k-1$, x being the real part of z.

By partial integration we have, when $z < -1$,

$$\Gamma_2(z) = \left[\frac{t^z}{z} \left(e^{-t} - 1 + t - \frac{t^2}{2!} + \ldots + (-)^{k+1} \frac{t^k}{k!} \right) \right]_0^\infty$$
$$+ \frac{1}{z} \int_0^\infty t^z \left(e^{-t} - 1 + t - \ldots + (-)^k \frac{t^{k-1}}{(k-1)!} \right) dt.$$

The integrated part tends to zero at each limit, since $x + k$ is negative and $x + k + 1$ is positive: so we have

$$\Gamma_2(z) = \frac{1}{z} \Gamma_2(z+1).$$

The same proof applies when x lies between 0 and -1, and leads to the result

$$\Gamma(z+1) = z \Gamma_2(z) \qquad\qquad (0 > x > -1).$$

The last equation shews that, between the values 0 and -1 of x,

$$\Gamma_2(z) = \Gamma(z).$$

[*] *Exercices de Math.* II. (1827), pp. 91–92.
[†] *Zeitschrift für Math. und Phys.* XXXII. (1887), XXXIII. (1888).

The preceding equation then shews that $\Gamma_2(z)$ is the same as $\Gamma(z)$ for all negative values of $R(z)$ less than -1. Thus, for all negative values of $R(z)$, we have the result of Cauchy and Saalschütz

$$\Gamma(z) = \int_0^\infty t^{z-1}\left(e^{-t} - 1 + t - \frac{t^2}{2!} + \ldots + (-)^{k+1}\frac{t^k}{k!}\right)dt,$$

where k is the integer next less than $-R(z)$.

Example. If a function $P(\mu)$ be such that for positive values of μ we have

$$P(\mu) = \int_0^1 x^{\mu-1}e^{-x}dx,$$

and if for negative values of μ we define $P_1(\mu)$ by the equation

$$P_1(\mu) = \int_0^1 x^{\mu-1}\left(e^{-x} - 1 + x - \ldots + (-)^{k+1}\frac{x^k}{k!}\right)dx,$$

where k is the integer next less than $-\mu$, shew that

$$P_1(\mu) = P(\mu) - \frac{1}{\mu} + \frac{1}{1!(\mu+1)} - \ldots + (-)^{k-1}\frac{1}{k!(\mu+k)}. \qquad \text{(Saalschütz.)}$$

12·22. *Hankel's expression of $\Gamma(z)$ as a contour integral.*

The integrals obtained for $\Gamma(z)$ in §§ 12·2, 12·21 are members of a large class of definite integrals by which the Gamma-function can be defined. The most general integral of the class in question is due to Hankel[*]; this integral will now be investigated.

Let D be a contour which starts from a point ρ on the real axis, encircles the origin once counter-clockwise and returns to ρ.

Consider $\int_D (-t)^{z-1}e^{-t}dt$, when the real part of z is positive and z is not an integer.

The many-valued function $(-t)^{z-1}$ is to be made definite by the convention that $(-t)^{z-1} = e^{(z-1)\log(-t)}$ and $\log(-t)$ is purely real when t is on the negative part of the real axis, so that, on D, $-\pi \leqslant \arg(-t) \leqslant \pi$.

The integrand is not analytic inside D, but, by § 5·2 corollary 1, the path of integration may be deformed (without affecting the value of the integral) into the path of integration which starts from ρ, proceeds along the real axis to δ, describes a circle of radius δ counter-clockwise round the origin and returns to ρ along the real axis.

On the real axis in the first part of this new path we have $\arg(-t) = -\pi$, so that $(-t)^{z-1} = e^{-i\pi(z-1)}t^{z-1}$ (where $\log t$ is purely real); and on the last part of the new path $(-t)^{z-1} = e^{i\pi(z-1)}t^{z-1}$.

On the circle we write $-t = \delta e^{i\theta}$; then we get

$$\int_D (-t)^{z-1}e^{-t}dt = \int_\rho^\delta e^{-i\pi(z-1)}t^{z-1}e^{-t}dt + \int_{-\pi}^\pi (\delta e^{i\theta})^{z-1}e^{\delta(\cos\theta + i\sin\theta)}\delta e^{i\theta}i\,d\theta$$

$$+ \int_\delta^\rho e^{i\pi(z-1)}t^{z-1}e^{-t}dt$$

$$= -2i\sin(\pi z)\int_\delta^\rho t^{z-1}e^{-t}dt + i\delta^z\int_{-\pi}^\pi e^{iz\theta + \delta(\cos\theta + i\sin\theta)}d\theta.$$

[*] *Zeitschrift für Math. und Phys.* IX. (1864), p. 7.

This is true for all positive values of $\delta \leqslant \rho$; now make $\delta \to 0$; then $\delta^z \to 0$ and $\int_{-\pi}^{\pi} e^{iz\theta + \delta(\cos\theta + i\sin\theta)} \, d\theta \to \int_{-\pi}^{\pi} e^{iz\theta} \, d\theta$ since the integrand tends to its limit uniformly.

We consequently infer that

$$\int_D (-t)^{z-1} e^{-t} \, dt = -2i \sin(\pi z) \int_0^\rho t^{z-1} e^{-t} \, dt.$$

This is true for all positive values of ρ; make $\rho \to \infty$, and let C be the limit of the contour D.

Then

$$\int_C (-t)^{z-1} e^{-t} \, dt = -2i \sin(\pi z) \int_0^\infty t^{z-1} e^{-t} \, dt.$$

Therefore

$$\Gamma(z) = -\frac{1}{2i \sin \pi z} \int_C (-t)^{z-1} e^{-t} \, dt.$$

Now, since the contour C does not pass through the point $t = 0$, there is no need longer to stipulate that the real part of z is positive; and $\int_C (-t)^{z-1} e^{-t} \, dt$ is a one-valued analytic function of z for all values of z. *Hence, by § 5·5, the equation, just proved when the real part of z is positive, persists for all values of z with the exception of the values $0, \pm 1, \pm 2, \ldots$.*

Consequently, for all except integer values of z,

$$\Gamma(z) = -\frac{1}{2i \sin \pi z} \int_C (-t)^{z-1} e^{-t} \, dt.$$

This is Hankel's formula; if we write $1 - z$ for z and make use of § 12·14, we get the further result that

$$\frac{1}{\Gamma(z)} = \frac{i}{2\pi} \int_C (-t)^{-z} e^{-t} \, dt.$$

We shall write $\int_\infty^{(0+)}$ for $\int_C$, meaning thereby that the path of integration starts at 'infinity' on the real axis, encircles the origin in the positive direction and returns to the starting point.

Example 1. Shew that, if the real part of z be positive and if a be any positive constant, $\int (-t)^{-z} e^{-t} \, dt$ tends to zero as $\rho \to \infty$, when the path of integration is either of the quadrants of circles of radius $\rho + a$ with centres at $-a$, the end points of one quadrant being ρ and $-a + i(\rho + a)$, and of the other ρ and $-a - i(\rho + a)$.

Deduce that
$$\lim_{\rho \to \infty} \int_{-a+i\rho}^{-a-i\rho} (-t)^{-z} e^{-t} dt = \lim_{\rho \to \infty} \int_C (-t)^{-z} e^{-t} dt,$$
and hence, by writing $t = -a - iu$, shew that
$$\frac{1}{\Gamma(z)} = \frac{1}{2\pi} \int_{-\infty}^{\infty} e^{a+iu} (a+iu)^{-z} du.$$

[This formula was given by Laplace, *Théorie Analytique des Probabilités* (1812), p. 134, and it is substantially equivalent to Hankel's formula involving a contour integral.]

Example 2. By taking $a = 1$, and putting $t = -1 + i \tan \theta$ in example 1, shew that
$$\frac{1}{\Gamma(z)} = \frac{e}{\pi} \int_0^{\frac{1}{2}\pi} \cos(\tan\theta - z\theta) \cos^{z-2} \theta \, d\theta.$$

Example 3. By taking as contour of integration a parabola whose focus is the origin, shew that, if $a > 0$, then
$$\Gamma(z) = \frac{2a^z e^a}{\sin \pi z} \int_0^{\infty} e^{-at^2} (1+t^2)^{z-\frac{1}{2}} \cos\{2at + (2z-1) \arctan t\} dt.$$
(Bourguet, Acta Math. I.)

Example 4. Investigate the values of x for which the integral
$$\frac{2}{\pi} \int_0^{\infty} t^{x-1} \sin t \, dt$$
converges; for such values of x express it in terms of Gamma-functions, and thence shew that it is equal to
$$e^{-\gamma x} \prod_{n=1}^{\infty} \left\{ \left(1 - \frac{x}{2n}\right) e^{x/(2n)} \right\} \Big/ \prod_{n=1}^{\infty} \left\{ \left(1 + \frac{x}{2n-1}\right) e^{-x/(2n-1)} \right\}.$$
(St John's, 1902.)

Example 5. Prove that $\int_0^{\infty} (\log t)^m \frac{\sin t}{t} dt$ converges when $m > 0$, and, by means of example 4, evaluate it when $m = 1$ and when $m = 2$. (St John's, 1902.)

12·3. *Gauss' expression for the logarithmic derivate of the Gamma-function as an infinite integral* *.

We shall now express the function $\dfrac{d}{dz} \log \Gamma(z) = \dfrac{\Gamma'(z)}{\Gamma(z)}$ as an infinite integral when the real part of z is positive; the function in question is frequently written $\psi(z)$. We first need a new formula for γ.

Take the formula (§ 12·2 example 4)
$$\gamma = \int_0^1 \frac{1-e^{-t}}{t} dt - \int_1^{\infty} \frac{e^{-t}}{t} dt = \lim_{\delta \to 0} \left\{ \int_\delta^1 \frac{dt}{t} - \int_\delta^{\infty} \frac{e^{-t}}{t} dt \right\} = \lim_{\delta \to 0} \left\{ \int_\Delta^1 \frac{dt}{t} - \int_\delta^{\infty} \frac{e^{-t}}{t} dt \right\},$$
where $\Delta = 1 - e^{-\delta}$, since
$$\int_\Delta^\delta \frac{dt}{t} = \log \frac{\delta}{1 - e^{-\delta}} \to 0 \text{ as } \delta \to 0.$$

Writing $t = 1 - e^{-u}$ in the first of these integrals and then replacing u by t we have
$$\gamma = \lim_{\delta \to 0} \left\{ \int_\delta^{\infty} \frac{e^{-t}}{1-e^{-t}} dt - \int_\delta^{\infty} \frac{e^{-t}}{t} dt \right\} = \int_0^{\infty} \left\{ \frac{1}{1-e^{-t}} - \frac{1}{t} \right\} e^{-t} dt.$$

This is the formula for γ which was required.

* Werke, III. p. 159.

To get Gauss' formula, take the equation (§ 12·16)

$$\frac{\Gamma'(z)}{\Gamma(z)} = -\gamma - \frac{1}{z} + \lim_{n \to \infty} \sum_{m=1}^{n} \left(\frac{1}{m} - \frac{1}{z+m} \right),$$

and write

$$\frac{1}{z+m} = \int_0^\infty e^{-t(z+m)} dt;$$

this is permissible when $m = 0, 1, 2, \ldots$ if the real part of z is positive.

It follows that

$$\frac{\Gamma'(z)}{\Gamma(z)} = -\gamma - \int_0^\infty e^{-zt} dt + \lim_{n \to \infty} \int_0^\infty \sum_{m=1}^{n} (e^{-mt} - e^{-(m+z)t}) dt$$

$$= -\gamma + \lim_{n \to \infty} \int_0^\infty \frac{e^{-t} - e^{-zt} - e^{-(n+1)t} + e^{-(z+n+1)t}}{1 - e^{-t}} dt$$

$$= \int_0^\infty \left(\frac{e^{-t}}{t} - \frac{e^{-zt}}{1-e^{-t}} \right) dt - \lim_{n \to \infty} \int_0^\infty \frac{1-e^{-zt}}{1-e^{-t}} e^{-(n+1)t} dt.$$

Now, when $0 < t \leqslant 1$, $\left| \dfrac{1-e^{-zt}}{1-e^{-t}} \right|$ is a bounded function of t whose limit as $t \to 0$ is finite; and when $t \geqslant 1$,

$$\left| \frac{1-e^{-zt}}{1-e^{-t}} \right| < \frac{1 + |e^{-zt}|}{1-e^{-1}} < \frac{2}{1-e^{-1}}.$$

Therefore we can find a number K independent of t such that, on the path of integration,

$$\left| \frac{1-e^{-zt}}{1-e^{-t}} \right| < K;$$

and so

$$\left| \int_0^\infty \frac{1-e^{-zt}}{1-e^{-t}} e^{(n+1)t} dt \right| < K \int_0^\infty e^{-(n+1)t} dt = K(n+1)^{-1} \to 0 \text{ as } n \to \infty.$$

We have thus proved the formula

$$\psi(z) = \frac{d}{dz} \log \Gamma(z) = \int_0^\infty \left(\frac{e^{-t}}{t} - \frac{e^{-zt}}{1-e^{-t}} \right) dt,$$

which is Gauss' expression of $\psi(z)$ as an infinite integral. It may be remarked that this is the first integral which we have encountered connected with the Gamma-function in which the integrand is a single-valued function.

Writing $t = \log(1+x)$ in Gauss' result, we get, if $\Delta = e^\delta - 1$,

$$\frac{\Gamma'(z)}{\Gamma(z)} = \lim_{\delta \to 0} \int_\delta^\infty \left\{ \frac{e^{-t}}{t} - \frac{e^{-zt}}{1-e^{-t}} \right\} dt$$

$$= \lim_{\delta \to 0} \left\{ \int_\delta^\infty \frac{e^{-t}}{t} dt - \int_\Delta^\infty \frac{dx}{x(1+x)^z} \right\}$$

$$= \lim_{\delta \to 0} \left\{ \int_\Delta^\infty \frac{e^{-t}}{t} dt - \int_\Delta^\infty \frac{dx}{x(1+x)^z} \right\},$$

since

$$0 < \int_\delta^\Delta \frac{e^{-t}}{t} dt < \int_\delta^\Delta \frac{dt}{t} = \log \frac{e^\delta - 1}{\delta} \to 0 \text{ as } \delta \to 0.$$

Hence

$$\frac{\Gamma'(z)}{\Gamma(z)} = \lim_{\Delta \to 0} \int_\Delta^\infty \left\{ e^{-x} - \frac{1}{(1+x)^z} \right\} \frac{dx}{x},$$

so that

$$\Gamma'(z) = \Gamma(z) \int_0^\infty \left\{ e^{-x} - \frac{1}{(1+x)^z} \right\} \frac{dx}{x},$$

an equation due to Dirichlet*.

* *Werke*, I. p. 275.

Example 1. Prove that, if the real part of z is positive,

$$\psi(z) = \int_0^1 \left\{ \frac{1}{-\log t} - \frac{t^{s-1}}{1-t} \right\} dt. \tag{Gauss.}$$

Example 2. Shew that $\qquad \gamma = \int_0^\infty \{(1+t)^{-1} - e^{-t}\} t^{-1} dt.$ $\qquad$ (Dirichlet.)

12·31. *Binet's first expression for* $\log \Gamma(z)$ *in terms of an infinite integral.*

Binet* has given two expressions for $\log \Gamma(z)$ which are of great importance as shewing the way in which $\log \Gamma(z)$ behaves as $|z| \to \infty$. To obtain the first of these expressions, we observe that, when the real part of z is positive,

$$\frac{\Gamma'(z+1)}{\Gamma(z+1)} = \int_0^\infty \left\{ \frac{e^{-t}}{t} - \frac{e^{-tz}}{e^t - 1} \right\} dt,$$

writing $z+1$ for z in § 12·3.

Now, by § 6·222 example 6, we have

$$\log z = \int_0^\infty \frac{e^{-t} - e^{-tz}}{t} dt,$$

and so, since $\qquad (2z)^{-1} = \int_0^\infty \frac{1}{2} e^{-tz} dt,$

we have

$$\frac{d}{dz} \log \Gamma(z+1) = \frac{1}{2z} + \log z - \int_0^\infty \left\{ \frac{1}{2} - \frac{1}{t} + \frac{1}{e^t - 1} \right\} e^{-tz} dt.$$

The integrand in the last integral is continuous as $t \to 0$; and since $\frac{1}{2} - \frac{1}{t} + \frac{1}{e^t - 1}$ is bounded as $t \to \infty$, it follows without difficulty that the integral converges uniformly when the real part of z is positive; we may consequently integrate from 1 to z under the sign of integration (§ 4·44) and we get†

$$\log \Gamma(z+1) = \left(z + \frac{1}{2} \right) \log z - z + 1 + \int_0^\infty \left\{ \frac{1}{2} - \frac{1}{t} + \frac{1}{e^t - 1} \right\} \frac{e^{-tz} - e^{-t}}{t} dt.$$

Since $\left\{ \frac{1}{2} - \frac{1}{t} + \frac{1}{e^t - 1} \right\} \frac{1}{t}$ is continuous as $t \to 0$ by § 7·2, and since

$$\log \Gamma(z+1) = \log z + \log \Gamma(z),$$

we have

$$\log \Gamma(z) = \left(z - \frac{1}{2} \right) \log z - z + 1 + \int_0^\infty \left\{ \frac{1}{2} - \frac{1}{t} + \frac{1}{e^t - 1} \right\} \frac{e^{-tz}}{t} dt$$

$$- \int_0^\infty \left\{ \frac{1}{2} - \frac{1}{t} + \frac{1}{e^t - 1} \right\} \frac{e^{-t}}{t} dt.$$

---

* *Journal de l'École Polytechnique*, XVI. (1839), pp. 123–143.

† $\operatorname{Log} \Gamma(z+1)$ means the sum of the principal values of the logarithms in the factors of the Weierstrassian product.

To evaluate the second of these integrals, let*

$$\int_0^\infty \left(\frac{1}{2} - \frac{1}{t} + \frac{1}{e^t-1}\right)\frac{e^{-t}}{t}\,dt = I, \qquad \int_0^\infty \left(\frac{1}{2} - \frac{1}{t} + \frac{1}{e^t-1}\right)\frac{e^{-\frac{1}{2}t}}{t}\,dt = J\,;$$

so that, taking $z = \frac{1}{2}$ in the last expression for $\log\Gamma(z)$, we get

$$\tfrac{1}{2}\log\pi = \tfrac{1}{2} + J - I.$$

Also, since $I = \int_0^\infty \left(\frac{1}{2} - \frac{2}{t} + \frac{1}{e^{\frac{1}{2}t}-1}\right)\frac{e^{-\frac{1}{2}t}}{t}\,dt$, we have

$$J - I = \int_0^\infty \left(\frac{1}{t} - \frac{e^{\frac{1}{2}t}}{e^t-1}\right)\frac{e^{-\frac{1}{2}t}\,dt}{t}$$

$$= \int_0^\infty \left(\frac{e^{-\frac{1}{2}t}}{t} - \frac{1}{e^t-1}\right)\frac{dt}{t}.$$

And so

$$J = \int_0^\infty \left\{\frac{e^{-\frac{1}{2}t}}{t} - \frac{1}{e^t-1} + \tfrac{1}{2}e^{-t} - \frac{e^{-t}}{t} + \frac{e^{-t}}{e^t-1}\right\}\frac{dt}{t}$$

$$= \int_0^\infty \left\{\frac{e^{-\frac{1}{2}t} - e^{-t}}{t} - \tfrac{1}{2}e^{-t}\right\}\frac{dt}{t}$$

$$= \int_0^\infty \left\{-\frac{d}{dt}\left(\frac{e^{-\frac{1}{2}t}-e^{-t}}{t}\right) - \frac{\tfrac{1}{2}e^{-\frac{1}{2}t}-e^{-t}}{t} - \frac{e^{-t}}{2t}\right\}dt$$

$$= \left[-\frac{e^{-\frac{1}{2}t}-e^{-t}}{t}\right]_0^\infty + \tfrac{1}{2}\int_0^\infty \frac{e^{-t}-e^{-\frac{1}{2}t}}{t}\,dt$$

$$= \tfrac{1}{2} + \tfrac{1}{2}\log\tfrac{1}{2}.$$

Consequently $I = 1 - \tfrac{1}{2}\log(2\pi)$.

We therefore have Binet's result that, when the real part of z is positive,

$$\log\Gamma(z) = \left(z - \frac{1}{2}\right)\log z - z + \frac{1}{2}\log(2\pi) + \int_0^\infty \left(\frac{1}{2} - \frac{1}{t} + \frac{1}{e^t-1}\right)\frac{e^{-tz}}{t}\,dt.$$

If $z = x + iy$, we see that, if the upper bound of $\left|\left(\dfrac{1}{2} - \dfrac{1}{t} + \dfrac{1}{e^t-1}\right)\dfrac{1}{t}\right|$ for real values of t is K, then

$$\left|\log\Gamma(z) - \left(z - \frac{1}{2}\right)\log z + z - \frac{1}{2}\log(2\pi)\right| < K\int_0^\infty e^{-tx}\,dt$$

$$= Kx^{-1},$$

so that, when x is large, the terms $\left(z - \dfrac{1}{2}\right)\log z - z + \dfrac{1}{2}\log(2\pi)$ furnish an approximate expression for $\log\Gamma(z)$.

Example 1. Prove that, when $R(z) > 0$,

$$\log\Gamma(z) = \int_0^\infty \left\{\frac{e^{-zt}-e^{-t}}{1-e^{-t}} + (z-1)e^{-t}\right\}\frac{dt}{t}. \qquad \text{(Malmstén.)}$$

Example 2. Prove that, when $R(z) > 0$,

$$\log\Gamma(z) = \int_0^\infty \left\{(z-1)e^{-t} + \frac{(1+t)^{-z}-(1+t)^{-1}}{\log(1+t)}\right\}\frac{dt}{t}. \qquad \text{(Féaux.)}$$

---

* This artifice is due to Pringsheim, *Math. Ann.* xxxi. (1888), p. 473.

Example 3.   From the formula of § 12·14, shew that, if $0 < x < 1$,

$$2 \log \Gamma(x) - \log \pi + \log \sin \pi x = \int_0^\infty \left\{ \frac{\sinh (\frac{1}{2} - x) t}{\sinh \frac{1}{2} t} - (1 - 2x) e^{-t} \right\} \frac{dt}{t}.$$

(Kummer.)

Example 4.   By expanding $\sinh (\frac{1}{2} - x) t$ and $1 - 2x$ in Fourier sine series, shew from example 3 that, if $0 < x < 1$,

$$\log \Gamma(x) = \tfrac{1}{2} \log \pi - \tfrac{1}{2} \log \sin \pi x + 2 \sum_{n=1}^\infty a_n \sin 2n\pi x,$$

where

$$a_n = \int_0^\infty \left\{ \frac{2n\pi}{t^2 + 4n^2\pi^2} - \frac{e^{-t}}{2n\pi} \right\} \frac{dt}{t}.$$

Deduce from example 2 of § 12·3 that

$$a_n = \frac{1}{2n\pi} (\gamma + \log 2\pi + \log n).$$

(Kummer, *Journal für Math.* xxxv. (1847), p. 1.)

12·32.   *Binet's second expression for* $\log \Gamma(z)$ *in terms of an infinite integral.*

Consider the application of example 7 of Chapter VII (p. 145) to the equation (§ 12·16)

$$\frac{d^2}{dz^2} \log \Gamma(z) = \sum_{n=0}^\infty \frac{1}{(z + n)^2}.$$

The conditions there stated as sufficient for the transformation of a series into integrals are obviously satisfied by the function $\phi(\zeta) = \dfrac{1}{(z + \zeta)^2}$, if the real part of z be positive; and we have

$$\frac{d^2}{dz^2} \log \Gamma(z) = \frac{1}{2z^2} + \int_0^\infty \frac{d\xi}{(z + \xi)^2} - 2 \int_0^\infty \frac{q(t, z)}{e^{2\pi t} - 1} dt + 2 \lim_{n \to \infty} \int_0^\infty \frac{q(t, z + n)}{e^{2\pi t} - 1} dt,$$

where

$$2iq(t) = \frac{1}{(z + it)^2} - \frac{1}{(z - it)^2}.$$

Since $|q(t, z + n)|$ is easily seen to be less than $K_1 t/n$, where K_1 is independent of t and n, it follows that the limit of the last integral is zero.

Hence

$$\frac{d^2}{dz^2} \log \Gamma(z) = \frac{1}{2z^2} + \frac{1}{z} + \int_0^\infty \frac{4tz}{(z^2 + t^2)^2} \frac{dt}{e^{2\pi t} - 1}.$$

Since $\left| \dfrac{2z}{z^2 + t^2} \right|$ does not exceed K (where K depends only on δ) when the real part of z exceeds δ, the integral converges uniformly and we may integrate under the integral sign (§ 4·44) from 1 to z.

We get

$$\frac{d}{dz} \log \Gamma(z) = -\frac{1}{2z} + \log z + C - 2 \int_0^\infty \frac{t\,dt}{(z^2 + t^2)(e^{2\pi t} - 1)},$$

where C is a constant.   Integrating again,

$$\log \Gamma(z) = \left(z - \frac{1}{2} \right) \log z + (C - 1) z + C' + 2 \int_0^\infty \frac{\arctan (t/z)}{e^{2\pi t} - 1} dt,$$

where C' is a constant.

Now, if z is real, $\qquad 0 \leqslant \arctan t/z \leqslant t/z,$

and so

$$\left| \log \Gamma (z) - \left(z - \frac{1}{2} \right) \log z - (C - 1) z - C' \right| < \frac{2}{z} \int_0^\infty \frac{t}{e^{2\pi t} - 1} \, dt.$$

But it has been shewn in § 12·31 that

$$\left| \log \Gamma (z) - \left(z - \frac{1}{2} \right) \log z + z - \frac{1}{2} \log (2\pi) \right| \to 0,$$

as $z \to \infty$ through real values. Comparing these results we see that $C = 0$, $C' = \frac{1}{2} \log (2\pi)$.

Hence for all values of z whose real part is positive,

$$\log \Gamma (z) = \left(z - \frac{1}{2} \right) \log z - z + \frac{1}{2} \log (2\pi) + 2 \int_0^\infty \frac{\arctan (t/z)}{e^{2\pi t} - 1} \, dt,$$

where $\arctan u$ is defined by the equation

$$\arctan u = \int_0^u \frac{dt}{1 + t^2},$$

in which the path of integration is a straight line.

This is Binet's second expression for $\log \Gamma (z)$.

Example. Justify differentiating with regard to z under the sign of integration, so as to get the equation

$$\frac{\Gamma' (z)}{\Gamma (z)} = \log z - \frac{1}{2z} - 2 \int_0^\infty \frac{t \, dt}{(t^2 + z^2)(e^{2\pi t} - 1)}.$$

12·33. THE ASYMPTOTIC EXPANSION OF THE LOGARITHM OF THE GAMMA-FUNCTION (STIRLING'S SERIES).

We can now obtain an expansion which represents the function $\log \Gamma (z)$ asymptotically (§ 8·2) for large values of $|z|$, and which is used in the calculation of the Gamma-function.

Let us assume that, if $z = x + iy$, then $x \geqslant \delta > 0$; and we have, by Binet's second formula,

$$\log \Gamma (z) = \left(z - \frac{1}{2} \right) \log z - z + \frac{1}{2} \log (2\pi) + \phi (z),$$

where $\qquad\qquad \phi (z) = 2 \int_0^\infty \frac{\arctan (t/z)}{e^{2\pi t} - 1} \, dt.$

Now

$$\arctan (t/z) = \frac{t}{z} - \frac{1}{3} \frac{t^3}{z^3} + \frac{1}{5} \frac{t^5}{z^5} - \cdots + \frac{(-)^{n-1}}{2n-1} \frac{t^{2n-1}}{z^{2n-1}} + \frac{(-)^n}{z^{n-1}} \int_0^t \frac{u^{2n} \, du}{u^2 + z^2}.$$

Substituting and remembering (§ 7·2) that

$$\int_0^\infty \frac{t^{2n-1} dt}{e^{2\pi t} - 1} = \frac{B_n}{4n},$$

where B_1, B_2, ... are Bernoulli's numbers, we have

$$\phi(z) = \sum_{r=1}^{n} \frac{(-)^{r-1} B_r}{2r(2r-1) z^{2r-1}} + \frac{2(-)^n}{z^{2n-1}} \int_0^\infty \left\{ \int_0^t \frac{u^{2n}\, du}{u^2 + z^2} \right\} \frac{dt}{e^{2\pi t} - 1}.$$

Let the upper bound* of $\left| \dfrac{z^2}{u^2 + z^2} \right|$ for positive values of u be K_z.

Then

$$\left| \int_0^\infty \left\{ \int_0^t \frac{u^{2n}\, du}{u^2 + z^2} \right\} \frac{dt}{e^{2\pi t} - 1} \right| \leqslant K_z |z|^{-2} \int_0^\infty \left\{ \int_0^t u^{2n}\, du \right\} \frac{dt}{e^{2\pi t} - 1}$$

$$\leqslant \frac{K_z B_{n+1}}{4(n+1)(2n+1)|z|^2}.$$

Hence

$$\left| \frac{2(-)^n}{z^{2n-1}} \int_0^\infty \left\{ \int_0^t \frac{u^{2n}\, du}{u^2 + z^2} \right\} \frac{dt}{e^{2\pi t} - 1} \right| < \frac{K_z B_{n+1}}{2(n+1)(2n+1)|z|^{2n+1}},$$

and it is obvious that this tends to zero uniformly as $|z| \to \infty$ if $|\arg z| \leqslant \frac{1}{2}\pi - \Delta$, where $\frac{1}{4}\pi > \Delta > 0$, so that $K_z \leqslant \operatorname{cosec} 2\Delta$.

Also it is clear that if $|\arg z| \leqslant \frac{1}{4}\pi$ (so that $K_z = 1$) the error in taking the first n terms of the series

$$\sum_{r=1}^{\infty} \frac{(-)^{r-1} B_r}{2r(2r-1)} \frac{1}{z^{2r-1}}$$

as an approximation to $\phi(z)$ is numerically less than the $(n+1)$th term.

Since, if $|\arg z| \leqslant \frac{1}{2}\pi - \Delta$,

$$\left| z^{2n-1} \left\{ \phi(z) - \sum_{r=1}^{n} \frac{(-)^{r-1} B_r}{2r(2r-1)} \right\} \right| < \operatorname{cosec}^2 2\Delta \cdot \frac{B_{n+1}}{2(n+1)(2n+1)} |z|^{-2}$$

$$\to 0,$$

as $z \to \infty$, it is clear that

$$\frac{B_1}{1.2.z} - \frac{B_2}{3.4.z^3} + \frac{B_3}{5.6.z^5} - \cdots$$

is the asymptotic expansion† (§ 8·2) of $\phi(z)$.

We see therefore that the series

$$\left(z - \frac{1}{2} \right) \log z - z + \frac{1}{2} \log(2\pi) + \sum_{r=1}^{\infty} \frac{(-)^{r-1} B_r}{2r(2r-1) z^{2r-1}}$$

is the asymptotic expansion of $\log \Gamma(z)$ when $|\arg z| \leqslant \frac{1}{2}\pi - \Delta$.

---

* K_z^{-2} is the lower bound of $\dfrac{\{u^2 + (x^2 - y^2)\}^2 + 4x^2 y^2}{(x^2 + y^2)^2}$ and is consequently equal to

$$\frac{4x^2 y^2}{(x^2 + y^2)^2} \text{ or } 1 \text{ as } x^2 < y^2 \text{ or } x^2 \geqslant y^2.$$

† The development is asymptotic; for if it converged when $|z| \geqslant \rho$, by § 2·6 we could find K, such that $B_n < (2n-1) 2nK\rho^{2n}$; and then the series $\sum_{n=1}^{\infty} \dfrac{(-)^{n-1} B_n t^{2n}}{(2n)!}$ would define an integral function; this is contrary to § 7·2.

This is generally known as *Stirling's series*. In § 13·6 it will be established over the extended range $|\arg z| \leqslant \pi - \Delta$.

In particular when z is positive $(=x)$, we have

$$0 < 2\int_0^\infty \left\{\int_0^t \frac{u^{2n}\,du}{u^2 + x^2}\right\} \frac{dt}{e^{2\pi t} - 1} < \frac{B_{n+1}}{2(n+1)(2n+1)x^2}.$$

Hence, when $x > 0$, the value of $\phi(x)$ always lies between the sum of n terms and the sum of $n+1$ terms of the series for all values of n.

In particular $0 < \phi(x) < \dfrac{B_1}{1 \cdot 2x}$, so that $\phi(x) = \dfrac{\theta}{12x}$ where $0 < \theta < 1$.

Hence $\qquad\qquad \Gamma(x) = x^{x-\frac{1}{2}} e^{-x} (2\pi)^{\frac{1}{2}} e^{\theta/(12x)}.$

Also, taking the exponential of Stirling's series, we get

$$\Gamma(x) = e^{-x} x^{x-\frac{1}{2}} (2\pi)^{\frac{1}{2}} \left\{1 + \frac{1}{12x} + \frac{1}{288x^2} - \frac{139}{51840x^3} - \frac{571}{2488320x^4} + O\left(\frac{1}{x^5}\right)\right\}.$$

This is an *asymptotic formula for the Gamma-function*. In conjunction with the formula $\Gamma(x+1) = x\Gamma(x)$, it is very useful for the purpose of computing the numerical value of the function for real values of x.

Tables of the function $\log_{10} \Gamma(x)$, correct to 12 decimal places, for values of x between 1 and 2, were constructed in this way by Legendre, and published in his *Exercices de Calcul Intégral*, II. p. 85, in 1817, and his *Traité des fonctions elliptiques* (1826), p. 489.

It may be observed that $\Gamma(x)$ has one minimum for positive values of x, when $x = 1\cdot4616321\ldots$, the value of $\log_{10} \Gamma(x)$ then being $\overline{1}\cdot9472391\ldots$.

Example. Obtain the expansion, convergent when $R(z) > 0$,

$$\log_e \Gamma(z) = (z - \tfrac{1}{2})\log_e z - z + \tfrac{1}{2}\log_e(2\pi) + J(z),$$

where

$$J(z) = \tfrac{1}{2}\left\{\frac{c_1}{z+1} + \frac{c_2}{2(z+1)(z+2)} + \frac{c_3}{3(z+1)(z+2)(z+3)} + \ldots\right\},$$

in which

$$c_1 = \tfrac{1}{6}, \quad c_2 = \tfrac{1}{3}, \quad c_3 = \tfrac{59}{60}, \quad c_4 = \tfrac{227}{60},$$

and generally

$$c_n = \int_0^1 (x+1)(x+2)\ldots(x+n-1)(2x-1)\,x\,dx. \qquad\qquad \text{(Binet.)}$$

$12\cdot4$. *The Eulerian Integral of the First Kind.*

The name *Eulerian Integral of the First Kind* was given by Legendre to the integral

$$B(p, q) = \int_0^1 x^{p-1}(1-x)^{q-1}\,dx,$$

which was first studied by Euler and Legendre*. In this integral, the real parts of p and q are supposed to be positive; and x^{p-1}, $(1-x)^{q-1}$ are to be understood to mean those values of $e^{(p-1)\log x}$ and $e^{(q-1)\log(1-x)}$ which correspond to the real determinations of the logarithms.

---

* Euler, *Nov. Comm. Petrop.* XVI. (1772); Legendre, *Exercices*, I. p. 221.

With these stipulations, it is easily seen that $B(p, q)$ exists, as a (possibly improper) integral (§ 4·5 example 2).

We have, on writing $(1 - x)$ for x,

$$B(p, q) = B(q, p).$$

Also, integrating by parts,

$$\int_0^1 x^{p-1}(1-x)^q\, dx = \left[\frac{x^p(1-x)^q}{p}\right]_0^1 + \frac{q}{p}\int_0^1 x^p(1-x)^{q-1}\, dx,$$

so that

$$B(p, q+1) = \frac{q}{p} B(p+1, q).$$

Example 1. Shew that

$$B(p, q) = B(p+1, q) + B(p, q+1).$$

Example 2. Deduce from example 1 that

$$B(p, q+1) = \frac{q}{p+q} B(p, q).$$

Example 3. Prove that if n is a positive integer,

$$B(p, n+1) = \frac{1 . 2 \dots n}{p(p+1)\dots(p+n)}.$$

Example 4. Prove that

$$B(x, y) = \int_0^\infty \frac{a^{x-1}}{(1+a)^{x+y}}\, da.$$

Example 5. Prove that

$$\Gamma(z) = \lim_{n \to \infty} n^z B(z, n).$$

12·41. *Expression of the Eulerian Integral of the First Kind in terms of the Gamma-function.*

We shall now establish the important theorem that

$$B(m, n) = \frac{\Gamma(m)\,\Gamma(n)}{\Gamma(m+n)}.$$

First let the real parts of m and n exceed $\frac{1}{2}$; then

$$\Gamma(m)\,\Gamma(n) = \int_0^\infty e^{-x} x^{m-1}\, dx \times \int_0^\infty e^{-y} y^{n-1}\, dy.$$

On writing x^2 for x, and y^2 for y, this gives

$$\Gamma(m)\,\Gamma(n) = 4 \lim_{R \to \infty} \int_0^R e^{-x^2} x^{2m-1}\, dx \times \int_0^R e^{-y^2} y^{2n-1}\, dy$$

$$= 4 \lim_{R \to \infty} \int_0^R \int_0^R e^{-(x^2+y^2)} x^{2m-1} y^{2n-1}\, dx\, dy.$$

Now, for the values of m and n under consideration, the integrand is continuous over the range of integration, and so the integral may be considered as a double integral taken over a square S_R. Calling the integrand

$f(x, y)$, and calling Q_R the quadrant with centre at the origin and radius R, we have, if T_R be the part of S_R outside Q_R,

$$\left| \iint_{S_R} f(x, y)\, dx dy - \iint_{Q_R} f(x, y)\, dx dy \right|$$

$$= \left| \iint_{T_R} f(x, y)\, dx dy \right|$$

$$\leqslant \iint_{T_R} |f(x, y)|\, dx dy$$

$$\leqslant \iint_{S_R} |f(x, y)|\, dx dy - \iint_{S_{\frac{1}{2}R}} |f(x, y)|\, dx dy|$$

$$\to 0 \text{ as } R \to \infty,$$

since $\iint_{S_R} |f(x, y)|\, dx dy$ converges to a limit, namely

$$2 \int_0^\infty e^{-x^2} |x^{2m-1}|\, dx \times 2 \int_0^\infty e^{-y} |y^{2n-1}|\, dy.$$

Therefore

$$\lim_{R \to \infty} \iint_{S_R} f(x, y)\, dx dy = \lim_{R \to \infty} \iint_{Q_R} f(x, y)\, dx dy.$$

Changing to polar* coordinates ($x = r \cos\theta$, $y = r \sin\theta$), we have

$$\iint_{Q_R} f(x, y)\, dx dy = \int_0^R \int_0^{\frac{1}{2}\pi} e^{-r^2} (r\cos\theta)^{2m-1} (r\sin\theta)^{2n-1} r\, dr d\theta.$$

Hence

$$\Gamma(m)\, \Gamma(n) = 4 \int_0^\infty e^{-r^2} r^{2(m+n)-1}\, dr \int_0^{\frac{1}{2}\pi} \cos^{2m-1}\theta \sin^{2n-1}\theta\, d\theta$$

$$= 2\Gamma(m+n) \int_0^{\frac{1}{2}\pi} \cos^{2m-1}\theta \sin^{2n-1}\theta\, d\theta.$$

Writing $\cos^2\theta = u$ we at once get

$$\Gamma(m)\, \Gamma(n) = \Gamma(m+n) . B(m, n).$$

This has only been proved when the real parts of m and n exceed $\frac{1}{2}$; but it can obviously be deduced when these are less than $\frac{1}{2}$ by § 12·4 example 2.

This result, discovered by Euler, connects the Eulerian Integral of the First Kind with the Gamma-function.

Example 1. Shew that

$$\int_{-1}^1 (1+x)^{p-1} (1-x)^{q-1}\, dx = 2^{p+q-1} \frac{\Gamma(p)\Gamma(q)}{\Gamma(p+q)}.$$

* It is easily proved by the methods of § 4·11 that the areas $A_{m,\mu}$ of § 4·3 need not be rectangles provided only that their greatest diameters can be made arbitrarily small by taking the number of areas sufficiently large; so the areas may be taken to be the regions bounded by radii vectores and circular arcs.

Example 2. Shew that, if

$$f(x, y) = \frac{1}{x} - y\,\frac{1}{x+1} + \frac{y\,(y-1)}{2\,!}\,\frac{1}{x+2} - \frac{y\,(y-1)\,(y-2)}{3\,!}\,\frac{1}{x+3} + \cdots,$$

then

$$f(x, y) = f(y+1,\ x-1),$$

where x and y have such values that the series are convergent.　　　　　(Jesus, 1901.)

Example 3. Prove that

$$\int_0^1 \int_0^1 f(xy)\,(1-x)^{\mu-1}\,y^\mu\,(1-y)^{\nu-1}\,dx\,dy = \frac{\Gamma\,(\mu)\,\Gamma\,(\nu)}{\Gamma\,(\mu+\nu)} \int_0^1 f(z)\,(1-z)^{\mu+\nu-1}\,dz.$$

(Math. Trip. 1894.)

12·42. *Evaluation of trigonometrical integrals in terms of the Gamma-function.*

We can now evaluate the integral $\int_0^{\frac{1}{2}\pi} \cos^{m-1} x \sin^{n-1} x\,dx$, where m and n are not restricted to be integers, but have their real parts positive.

For, writing $\cos^2 x = t$, we have, as in § 12·41,

$$\int_0^{\frac{1}{2}\pi} \cos^{m-1} x \sin^{n-1} x\,dx = \frac{1}{2}\,\frac{\Gamma\,(\frac{1}{2}m)\,\Gamma\,(\frac{1}{2}n)}{\Gamma\,(\frac{1}{2}m + \frac{1}{2}n)}.$$

The well-known elementary formulae for the cases in which m and n are integers can be at once derived from this result.

Example. Prove that, when $|k| < 1$,

$$\int_0^{\frac{1}{2}\pi} \frac{\cos^m \theta \sin^n \theta\,d\theta}{(1 - k \sin^2 \theta)^{\frac{1}{2}}} = \frac{\Gamma\,(\frac{1}{2}m + \frac{1}{2})\,\Gamma\,(\frac{1}{2}n + \frac{1}{2})}{\Gamma\,(\frac{1}{2}m + \frac{1}{2}n + \frac{1}{2})\,\sqrt{\pi}} \int_0^{\frac{1}{2}\pi} \frac{\cos^{m+n} \theta\,d\theta}{(1 - k \sin^2 \theta)^{\frac{1}{2}n + \frac{1}{2}}}.$$

(Trinity, 1898.)

12·43. *Pochhammer's* extension of the Eulerian Integral of the First Kind.*

We have seen in § 12·22 that it is possible to replace the second Eulerian integral for $\Gamma\,(z)$ by a contour integral which converges for all values of z. A similar process has been carried out by Pochhammer for Eulerian integrals of the first kind.

Let P be any point on the real axis between 0 and 1; consider the integral

$$e^{-\pi i (\alpha+\beta)} \int_P^{(1+,\,0+,\,1-,\,0-)} t^{\alpha-1}\,(1-t)^{\beta-1}\,dt = \epsilon\,(\alpha,\,\beta).$$

The notation employed is that introduced at the end of § 12·22 and means that the path of integration starts from P, encircles the point 1 in the positive (counter-clockwise) direction and returns to P, then encircles the origin in the positive direction and returns to P, and so on.

---

* *Math. Ann.* xxxv. (1890), p. 495. The use of the double circuit integrals of this section seems to be due to Jordan, *Cours d'Analyse*, iii. (1887).

At the starting-point the arguments of t and $1-t$ are both zero; after the circuit $(1+)$ they are 0 and 2π; after the circuit $(0+)$ they are 2π and 2π; after the circuit $(1-)$ they are 2π and 0 and after the circuit $(0-)$ they are both zero, so that the final value of the integrand is the same as the initial value.

It is easily seen that, since the path of integration may be deformed in any way so long as it does not pass over the branch points 0, 1 of the integrand, the path may be taken to be that shewn in the figure, wherein the four parallel lines are supposed to coincide with the real axis.

If the real parts of α and β are positive the integrals round the circles tend to zero as the radii of the circles tend to zero*; the integrands on the paths marked a, b, c, d are

$$t^{\alpha-1}(1-t)^{\beta-1}, \quad t^{\alpha-1}(1-t)^{\beta-1}e^{2\pi i(\beta-1)},$$
$$t^{\alpha-1}e^{2\pi i(\alpha-1)}(1-t)^{\beta-1}e^{2\pi i(\beta-1)}, \quad t^{\alpha-1}e^{2\pi i(\alpha-1)}(1-t)^{\beta-1}$$

respectively, the arguments of t and $1-t$ now being zero in each case.

Hence we may write $\epsilon(\alpha, \beta)$ as the sum of four (possibly improper) integrals, thus:

$$\epsilon(\alpha, \beta) = e^{-\pi i(\alpha+\beta)}\left[\int_0^1 t^{\alpha-1}(1-t)^{\beta-1}dt + \int_1^0 t^{\alpha-1}(1-t)^{\beta-1}e^{2\pi i\beta}\,dt\right.$$
$$\left. + \int_0^1 t^{\alpha-1}(1-t)^{\beta-1}e^{2\pi i(\alpha+\beta)}\,dt + \int_1^0 t^{\alpha-1}(1-t)^{\beta-1}e^{2\pi i\alpha}\,dt\right].$$

Hence

$$\epsilon(\alpha, \beta) = e^{-\pi i(\alpha+\beta)}(1-e^{2\pi i\alpha})(1-e^{2\pi i\beta})\int_0^1 t^{\alpha-1}(1-t)^{\beta-1}\,dt$$

$$= -4\sin(\alpha\pi)\sin(\beta\pi)\frac{\Gamma(\alpha)\Gamma(\beta)}{\Gamma(\alpha+\beta)}$$

$$= \frac{-4\pi^2}{\Gamma(1-\alpha)\Gamma(1-\beta)\Gamma(\alpha+\beta)}.$$

Now $\epsilon(\alpha, \beta)$ and this last expression are analytic functions of α and of β for all values of α and β. So, by the theory of analytic continuation, this equality, proved when the real parts of α and β are positive, holds for all values of α and β. *Hence for all values of α and β we have proved that*

$$\epsilon(\alpha, \beta) = \frac{-4\pi^2}{\Gamma(1-\alpha)\Gamma(1-\beta)\Gamma(\alpha+\beta)}.$$

* The reader ought to have no difficulty in proving this.

12·5. *Dirichlet's integral**.

We shall now shew how the repeated integral

$$I = \iint \dots \int f(t_1 + t_2 + \dots + t_n) \, t_1^{a_1-1} t_2^{a_2-1} \dots t_n^{a_n-1} dt_1 dt_2 \dots dt_n$$

may be reduced to a simple integral, where f is continuous, $\alpha_r > 0 \,(r = 1, 2, \dots n)$ and the integration is extended over all positive values of the variables such that $t_1 + t_2 + \dots + t_n \leqslant 1$.

To simplify $\qquad \displaystyle\int_0^{1-\lambda} \int_0^{1-\lambda-T} f(t + T + \lambda) \, t^{a-1} T^{\beta-1} dt dT$

(where we have written t, T, α, β for $t_1, t_2, \alpha_1, \alpha_2$ and λ for $t_3 + t_4 + \dots + t_n$), put $t = T(1 - v)/v$; the integral becomes (if $\lambda \neq 0$)

$$\int_0^{1-\lambda} \int_{T/(1-\lambda)}^1 f(\lambda + T/v)(1 - v)^{a-1} v^{-a-1} T^{a+\beta-1} \, dv \, dT.$$

Changing the order of integration (§ 4·51), the integral becomes

$$\int_0^1 \int_0^{(1-\lambda)v} f(\lambda + T/v)(1 - v)^{a-1} v^{-a-1} T^{a+\beta-1} dT \, dv.$$

Putting $T = v\tau_2$, the integral becomes

$$\int_0^1 \int_0^{1-\lambda} f(\lambda + \tau_2)(1 - v)^{a-1} v^{\beta-1} \tau_2^{a+\beta-1} \, d\tau_2 \, dv$$
$$= \frac{\Gamma(\alpha)\,\Gamma(\beta)}{\Gamma(\alpha + \beta)} \int_0^{1-\lambda} f(\lambda + \tau_2) \, \tau_2^{a+\beta-1} \, d\tau_2.$$

Hence

$$I = \frac{\Gamma(\alpha_1)\,\Gamma(\alpha_2)}{\Gamma(\alpha_1 + \alpha_2)} \iint \dots \int f(\tau_2 + t_3 + \dots + t_n) \, \tau_2^{a_1+a_2-1} t_3^{a_3-1} \dots t_n^{a_n-1} d\tau_2 dt_3 \dots dt_n,$$

the integration being extended over all positive values of the variables such that $\tau_2 + t_3 + \dots + t_n \leqslant 1$.

Continually reducing in this way we get

$$I = \frac{\Gamma(\alpha_1)\,\Gamma(\alpha_2) \dots \Gamma(\alpha_n)}{\Gamma(\alpha_1 + \alpha_2 + \dots + \alpha_n)} \int_0^1 f(\tau) \, \tau^{\Sigma a - 1} \, d\tau,$$

which is Dirichlet's result.

Example 1.   Reduce

$$\iiint f\left\{ \left(\frac{x}{a}\right)^a + \left(\frac{y}{b}\right)^\beta + \left(\frac{z}{c}\right)^\gamma \right\} x^{p-1} y^{q-1} z^{r-1} \, dx \, dy \, dz$$

to a simple integral; the range of integration being extended over all positive values of the variables such that

$$\left(\frac{x}{a}\right)^a + \left(\frac{y}{b}\right)^\beta + \left(\frac{z}{c}\right)^\gamma \leqslant 1,$$

it being assumed that $a, b, c, a, \beta, \gamma, p, q, r$ are positive.   (Dirichlet.)

* *Werke*, I. pp. 375, 391.

Example 2.   Evaluate $\iint x^p y^q \, dx \, dy,$

m and n being positive and

$$x \geqslant 0, \quad y \geqslant 0, \quad x^m + y^n \leqslant 1. \qquad \text{(Pembroke, 1907.)}$$

Example 3.   Shew that the moment of inertia of a homogeneous ellipsoid of unit density, taken about the axis of z, is

$$\tfrac{4}{15} (a^2 + b^2) \, \pi abc,$$

where a, b, c are the semi-axes.

Example 4.   Shew that the area of the hypocycloid $x^{\frac{2}{3}} + y^{\frac{2}{3}} = l^{\frac{2}{3}}$ is $\tfrac{3}{8} \pi l^2$.

REFERENCES.

N. NIELSEN, *Handbuch der Theorie der Gamma-funktion**.   (Leipzig, 1906.)

O. SCHLÖMILCH, *Compendium der höheren Analysis*, II.   (Brunswick, 1874.)

E. L. LINDELÖF, *Le Calcul des Résidus*, Ch. IV.   (Paris, 1905.)

A. PRINGSHEIM, *Math. Ann.* XXXI. (1888), pp. 455–481.

HJ. MELLIN, *Math. Ann.* LXVIII. (1910), pp. 305–337.

MISCELLANEOUS EXAMPLES.

1. Shew that

$$(1-z) \left(1+\frac{z}{2}\right) \left(1-\frac{z}{3}\right) \left(1+\frac{z}{4}\right) \cdots = \frac{\pi^{\frac{1}{2}}}{\Gamma\left(1+\tfrac{1}{2}z\right) \Gamma\left(\tfrac{1}{2}-\tfrac{1}{2}z\right)}.$$

(Trinity, 1897.)

2. Shew that

$$\lim_{n \to \infty} \frac{1}{1+x} \frac{1}{1+\tfrac{1}{2}x} \frac{1}{1+\tfrac{1}{3}x} \cdots \frac{1}{1+\tfrac{1}{n}x} \, n^x = \Gamma(x+1). \qquad \text{(Trinity, 1885.)}$$

3. Prove that

$$\frac{\Gamma'(1)}{\Gamma(1)} - \frac{\Gamma'\left(\tfrac{1}{2}\right)}{\Gamma\left(\tfrac{1}{2}\right)} = 2 \log 2. \qquad \text{(Jesus, 1903.)}$$

4. Shew that

$$\frac{\{\Gamma\left(\tfrac{1}{4}\right)\}^4}{16 \pi^2} = \frac{3^2}{3^2-1} \cdot \frac{5^2-1}{5^2} \cdot \frac{7^2}{7^2-1} \cdot \frac{9^2-1}{9^2} \cdot \frac{11^2}{11^2-1} \cdots. \qquad \text{(Trinity, 1891.)}$$

5. Shew that

$$\prod_{n=0}^{\infty} \left\{ \frac{(n-a)(n+\beta+\gamma)}{(n+\beta)(n+\gamma)} \left(1+\frac{a}{n+1}\right) \right\} = -\frac{1}{\pi} \sin(a\pi) \, B(\beta, \gamma).$$

(Trinity, 1905.)

6. Shew that $$\prod_{r=1}^{8} \Gamma\left(\frac{r}{3}\right) = \frac{640}{3^6} \left(\frac{\pi}{\sqrt{3}}\right)^3. \qquad \text{(Peterhouse, 1906.)}$$

7. Shew that, if $z = i\zeta$ where ζ is real, then

$$|\Gamma(z)| = \sqrt{\left(\frac{\pi}{\zeta \sinh \pi \zeta}\right)}. \qquad \text{(Trinity, 1904.)}$$

8. When x is positive, shew that†

$$\frac{\Gamma(x) \Gamma\left(\tfrac{1}{2}\right)}{\Gamma\left(x+\tfrac{1}{2}\right)} = \sum_{n=0}^{\infty} \frac{2n!}{2^{2n} . \, n! \, n!} \frac{1}{x+n}. \qquad \text{(Math. Trip. 1897.)}$$

---

* This work contains a complete bibliography.

† This and some other examples are most easily proved by the result of § 14·11.

9. If a is positive, shew that

$$\frac{\Gamma(z)\,\Gamma(a+1)}{\Gamma(z+a)} = \sum_{n=0}^{\infty} \frac{(-)^n\,a\,(a-1)\,(a-2)\dots(a-n)}{n!}\,\frac{1}{z+n}\,.$$

10. If $x > 0$ and

$$P(x) = \int_0^1 e^{-t}\,t^{x-1}\,dt,$$

shew that

$$P(x) = \frac{1}{x} - \frac{1}{1!}\frac{1}{x+1} + \frac{1}{2!}\frac{1}{x+2} - \frac{1}{3!}\frac{1}{x+3} + \dots,$$

and

$$P(x+1) = xP(x) - e^{-1}.$$

11. Shew that if $\lambda > 0$, $x > 0$, $-\tfrac{1}{2}\pi < a < \tfrac{1}{2}\pi$, then

$$\int_0^\infty t^{x-1}\,e^{-\lambda t \cos a}\cos(\lambda t \sin a)\,dt = \lambda^{-x}\,\Gamma(x)\cos ax,$$

$$\int_0^\infty t^{x-1}\,e^{-\lambda t \cos a}\sin(\lambda t \sin a)\,dt = \lambda^{-x}\,\Gamma(x)\sin ax. \qquad \text{(Euler.)}$$

12. Prove that, if $b > 0$, then, when $0 < z < 2$,

$$\int_0^\infty \frac{\sin bx}{x^z}\,dx = \tfrac{1}{2}\pi b^{z-1}\operatorname{cosec}(\tfrac{1}{2}\pi z)/\Gamma(z),$$

and, when $0 < z < 1$,

$$\int_0^\infty \frac{\cos bx}{x^z}\,dx = \tfrac{1}{2}\pi b^{z-1}\sec(\tfrac{1}{2}\pi z)/\Gamma(z). \qquad \text{(Euler.)}$$

13. If $0 < n < 1$, prove that

$$\int_0^\infty (1+x)^{n-1}\cos x\,dx = \Gamma(n)\left\{\cos\left(\frac{n\pi}{2}-1\right) - \frac{1}{\Gamma(n+1)} + \frac{1}{\Gamma(n+3)} - \dots\right\}.$$

(Peterhouse, 1895.)

14. By taking as contour of integration a parabola with its vertex at the origin, derive from the formula

$$\Gamma(a) = -\frac{1}{2i\sin a\pi}\int_\infty^{(0+)} (-z)^{a-1}\,e^{-z}\,dz$$

the result

$$\Gamma(a) = \frac{1}{2\sin a\pi}\int_0^\infty e^{-x^2}\,x^{a-1}\,(1+x^2)^{\frac{1}{2}a}\,[3\sin\{x + a \operatorname{arc\,cot}(-x)\}$$
$$+ \sin\{x + (a-2)\operatorname{arc\,cot}(-x)\}]\,dx,$$

the arc cot denoting an obtuse angle.

(Bourguet, Acta Math. i. p. 367.)

15. Shew that, if the real part of a_n is positive and $\sum_{n=1}^{\infty} 1/a_n{}^2$ is convergent, then

$$\prod_{n=1}^{\infty}\left[\frac{\Gamma(a_n)}{\Gamma(z+a_n)}\exp\left\{\sum_{s=1}^{m}\frac{z^s}{s!}\psi^{(s)}(a_n)\right\}\right]$$

is convergent when $m > 2$, where $\psi^{(s)}(z) = \dfrac{d^s}{dz^s}\log\Gamma(z)$.   (Math. Trip. 1907.)

16. Prove that

$$\frac{d\log\Gamma(z)}{dz} = \int_0^\infty \frac{e^{-a} - e^{-za}}{1 - e^{-a}}\,da - \gamma$$

$$= \int_0^\infty \{(1+a)^{-1} - (1+a)^{-z}\}\,\frac{da}{a} - \gamma$$

$$= \int_0^1 \frac{x^{z-1} - 1}{x-1}\,dx - \gamma. \qquad \text{(Legendre.)}$$

17. Prove that, when $R(z) > 0$,

$$\log \Gamma(z) = \int_0^1 \left\{ \frac{x^z - x}{x - 1} - x(z - 1) \right\} \frac{dx}{x \log x}.$$ (Binet.)

18. Prove that, for all values of z except negative real values,

$$\log \Gamma(z) = (z - \tfrac{1}{2}) \log z - z + \tfrac{1}{2} \log (2\pi)$$

$$+ \tfrac{1}{2} \left\{ \frac{1}{2 \cdot 3} \sum_{r=1}^{\infty} \frac{1}{(z+r)^2} + \frac{2}{3 \cdot 4} \sum_{r=1}^{\infty} \frac{1}{(z+r)^3} + \frac{3}{4 \cdot 5} \sum_{r=1}^{\infty} \frac{1}{(z+r)^4} + \dots \right\}.$$

19. Prove that, when $R(z) > 0$,

$$\frac{d}{dz} \log \Gamma(z) = \log z - \int_0^1 \frac{x^{z-1} \, dx}{(1 - x) \log x} \{1 - x + \log x\}.$$

20. Prove that, when $R(z) > 0$,

$$\frac{d^2}{dz^2} \log \Gamma(z) = \int_0^{\infty} \frac{x e^{-xz} \, dx}{1 - e^{-x}}.$$

21. If

$$\int_z^{z+1} \log \Gamma(t) \, dt = u,$$

shew that

$$\frac{du}{dz} = \log z,$$

and deduce from § 12·33 that, for all values of z except negative real values,

$$u = z \log z - z + \tfrac{1}{2} \log (2\pi).$$

(Raabe, *Journal für Math.* xxv.)

22. Prove that, for all values of z except negative real values,

$$\log \Gamma(z) = (z - \tfrac{1}{2}) \log z - z + \tfrac{1}{2} \log (2\pi) + \sum_{n=1}^{\infty} \int_0^{\infty} \frac{dx}{x + z} \frac{\sin 2n\pi x}{n\pi}.$$

(Bourguet*.)

23. Prove that

$$B(p, p) \, B(p + \tfrac{1}{2}, \, p + \tfrac{1}{2}) = \frac{\pi}{2^{4p-1} p}.$$ (Binet.)

24. Prove that, when $-t < r < t$,

$$B(t + r, \, t - r) = \frac{1}{4^{t-1}} \int_0^{\infty} \frac{\cosh (2ru) \, du}{\cosh^{2t} u}.$$

25. Prove that, when $q > 1$,

$$B(p, q) + B(p + 1, q) + B(p + 2, q) + \dots = B(p, q - 1).$$

26. Prove that, when $p - a > 0$,

$$\frac{B(p - a, q)}{B(p, q)} = 1 + \frac{aq}{p + q} + \frac{a(a + 1) \, q \, (q + 1)}{1 \cdot 2 \cdot (p + q) \, (p + q + 1)} + \dots.$$

27. Prove that

$$B(p, q) \, B(p + q, r) = B(q, r) \, B(q + r, p).$$ (Euler.)

28. Shew that

$$\int_0^1 x^{a-1} (1 - x)^{b-1} \frac{dx}{(x + p)^{a+b}} = \frac{\Gamma(a) \Gamma(b)}{\Gamma(a + b)} \frac{1}{(1 + p)^a \, p^b},$$

if $a > 0$, $b > 0$, $p > 0$. (Trinity, 1908.)

---

* This result is attributed to Bourguet by Stieltjes, *Journal de Math.* (4), v. p. 432.

29.   Shew that, if $m > 0$, $n > 0$, then

$$\int_{-1}^{1} \frac{(1+x)^{2m-1}(1-x)^{2n-1}}{(1+x^2)^{m+n}}\, dx = 2^{m+n-2} \frac{\Gamma(m)\,\Gamma(n)}{\Gamma(m+n)};$$

and deduce that, when a is real and not an integer multiple of $\frac{1}{2}\pi$,

$$\int_{-\frac{1}{4}\pi}^{\frac{1}{4}\pi} \left(\frac{\cos\theta + \sin\theta}{\cos\theta - \sin\theta}\right)^{\cos 2a} d\theta = \frac{\pi}{2\sin(\pi\cos^2 a)}.$$

(St John's, 1904.)

30.   Shew that, if $a > 0$, $\beta > 0$,

$$\int_0^1 \frac{t^{a-1}}{1+t}\, dt = \tfrac{1}{2}\psi\left(\tfrac{1}{2} + \tfrac{1}{2}a\right) - \tfrac{1}{2}\psi\left(\tfrac{1}{2}a\right),$$

and

$$\int_0^1 \frac{t^{a-1} - t^{\beta-1}}{(1+t)\log t}\, dt = \log \frac{\Gamma\left(\tfrac{1}{2} + \tfrac{1}{2}a\right)\Gamma\left(\tfrac{1}{2}\beta\right)}{\Gamma\left(\tfrac{1}{2}a\right)\Gamma\left(\tfrac{1}{2} + \tfrac{1}{2}\beta\right)}.$$

(Kummer.)

31.   Shew that, if $a > 0$, $a + b > 0$,

$$\int_0^1 \frac{x^{a-1}(1-x^b)}{1-x}\, dx = \lim_{\delta \to 0}\left\{\frac{\Gamma(a)\,\Gamma(\delta)}{\Gamma(a+\delta)} - \frac{\Gamma(a+b)\,\Gamma(\delta)}{\Gamma(a+b+\delta)}\right\} = \psi(a+b) - \psi(a).$$

Deduce that, if in addition $a + c > 0$, $a + b + c > 0$,

$$\int_0^1 \frac{x^{a-1}(1-x^b)(1-x^c)}{(1-x)(-\log x)}\, dx = \log \frac{\Gamma(a)\,\Gamma(a+b+c)}{\Gamma(a+b)\,\Gamma(a+c)}.$$

32.   Shew that, if a, b, c be such that the integral converges,

$$\int_0^1 \frac{(1-x^a)(1-x^b)(1-x^c)}{(1-x)(-\log x)}\, dx = \log \frac{\Gamma(b+c+1)\,\Gamma(c+a+1)\,\Gamma(a+b+1)}{\Gamma(a+1)\,\Gamma(b+1)\,\Gamma(c+1)\,\Gamma(a+b+c+1)}.$$

33.   By the substitution $\cos\theta = 1 - 2\tan\tfrac{1}{2}\phi$, shew that

$$\int_0^\pi \frac{d\theta}{(3-\cos\theta)^{\frac{1}{2}}} = \frac{\{\Gamma(\tfrac{1}{4})\}^2}{4\sqrt{\pi}}.$$

(St John's, 1896.)

34.   Evaluate in terms of Gamma-functions the integral $\displaystyle\int_0^\infty \frac{\sin^p x}{x}\, dx$, when p is a fraction greater than unity whose numerator and denominator are both odd integers.

[Shew that the integral is $\displaystyle\frac{1}{2}\int_0^\pi \sin^p x \left\{\frac{1}{x} + \sum_{n=1}^\infty (-)^n \left(\frac{1}{x+n\pi} + \frac{1}{x-n\pi}\right)\right\} dx$.]

(Clare, 1898.)

35.   Shew that

$$\int_0^{\frac{1}{2}\pi} (1 - \tfrac{1}{2}\sin^2 x)^{n-\frac{1}{2}}\, dx = \frac{n!}{2^{n+2}\,\pi^{\frac{1}{2}}} \sum_{r=0}^n \frac{2^{3r}}{2r!\,(n-r)!} \left\{\Gamma\left(\frac{2r+1}{4}\right)\right\}^2.$$

36.   Prove that

$$\log B(p, q) = \log\left(\frac{p+q}{pq}\right) + \int_0^1 \frac{(1-v^p)(1-v^q)}{(1-v)\log v}\, dv.$$

(Euler.)

37.   Prove that, if $p > 0$, $p + s > 0$, then

$$B(p, p+s) = \frac{B(p, p)}{2^s}\left\{1 + \frac{s(s-1)}{2(2p+1)} + \frac{s(s-1)(s-2)(s-3)}{2\cdot 4 \cdot (2p+1)(2p+3)} + \ldots\right\}.$$

(Binet.)

38.   The curve $r^m = 2^{m-1}\,a^m \cos m\theta$ is composed of m equal closed loops. Shew that the length of the arc of half of one of the loops is

$$m^{-1}\,a \int_0^{\frac{1}{2}\pi} (\tfrac{1}{2}\cos x)^{\frac{1}{m}-1}\, dx,$$

and hence that the total perimeter of the curve is

$$a\left\{\Gamma\left(\frac{1}{2m}\right)\right\}^2 \Big/ \Gamma\left(\frac{1}{m}\right).$$

39. Draw the straight line joining the points $\pm i$, and the semicircle of $|z|=1$ which lies on the right of this line. Let C be the contour formed by indenting this figure at $-i, 0, i$. By considering $\int_C z^{p-q-1}(z+z^{-1})^{p+q-2}\,dz$, shew that, if $p+q>1,\ q<1$,

$$\int_0^{\frac{1}{2}\pi}\cos^{p+q-2}\theta\,\cos{(p-q)}\,\theta\,d\theta = \frac{\pi}{(p+q-1)\,2^{p+q-1}\,B\,(p,\,q)}.$$

Prove that the result is true for all values of p and q such that $p+q>1$.

(Cauchy.)

40. If s is positive (not necessarily integral), and $-\frac{1}{2}\pi \leqslant x \leqslant \frac{1}{2}\pi$, shew that

$$\cos^s x = \frac{1}{2^{s-1}}\frac{\Gamma\,(s+1)}{\{\Gamma\,(\frac{1}{2}s+1)\}^2}\left\{\frac{1}{2}+\frac{s}{s+2}\cos 2x+\frac{s\,(s-2)}{(s+2)\,(s+4)}\cos 4x+\ldots\right\},$$

and draw graphs of the series and of the function $\cos^s x$.

41. Obtain the expansion

$$\cos^s x = \frac{a}{2^{s-1}}\Gamma\,(s+1)\left[\frac{\cos ax}{\Gamma\,(\frac{1}{2}s+\frac{1}{2}a+1)\,\Gamma\,(\frac{1}{2}s-\frac{1}{2}a+1)}+\frac{\cos 3ax}{\Gamma\,(\frac{1}{2}s+\frac{3}{2}a+1)\,\Gamma\,(\frac{1}{2}s-\frac{3}{2}a+1)}+\ldots\right],$$

and find the values of x for which it is applicable.

(Cauchy.)

42. Prove that, if $p>\frac{1}{2}$,

$$\Gamma\,(2p)=\frac{2^{2p-1}}{\sqrt{\pi}}\{\Gamma\,(p)\}^2\left[\frac{2p^2}{2p+1}\left\{1+\frac{1^2}{2\,(2p+3)}+\frac{1^2\cdot3^2}{2\cdot4\cdot(2p+3)\,(2p+5)}+\ldots\right\}\right]^{\frac{1}{2}}.$$

(Binet.)

43. Shew that, if $x<0,\ x+z>0$, then

$$\frac{\Gamma\,(-x)}{\Gamma\,(z)}\left\{\frac{-x}{z}+\frac{1}{2}\frac{(-x)\,(1-x)}{z\,(1+z)}+\frac{1}{3}\frac{(-x)\,(1-x)\,(2-x)}{z\,(1+z)\,(2+z)}+\ldots\right\}$$

$$=\frac{1}{\Gamma\,(x+z)}\int_0^1 t^{-x-1}\,\{-\log{(1-t)}\}\,(1-t)^{x+z-1}\,dt,$$

and deduce that, when $x+z>0$,

$$\frac{d}{dz}\log\frac{\Gamma\,(z+x)}{\Gamma\,(z)}=\frac{x}{z}-\frac{1}{2}\frac{x\,(x-1)}{z\,(z+1)}+\frac{1}{3}\frac{x\,(x-1)\,(x-2)}{z\,(z+1)\,(z+2)}-\ldots.$$

44. Using the result of example 43, prove that

$$\log\Gamma\,(z+a)=\log\Gamma\,(z)+a\log z-\frac{a-a^2}{2z}$$

$$-\sum_{n=1}^{\infty}\frac{a\int_0^1 t\,(1-t)\,(2-t)\ldots(n-t)\,dt-\int_0^a t\,(1-t)\,(2-t)\ldots(n-t)\,dt}{(n+1)\,z\,(z+1)\,(z+2)\ldots(z+n)},$$

investigating the region of convergence of the series.

(Binet, *Journal de l'École polytechnique*, XVI. (1839), p. 256.)

45. Prove that, if $p>0,\ q>0$, then

$$B\,(p,\,q)=\frac{p^{p-\frac{1}{2}}\,q^{q-\frac{1}{2}}}{(p+q)^{p+q-\frac{1}{2}}}\,(2\pi)^{\frac{1}{2}}\,e^{M\,(p,\,q)},$$

where

$$M(p, q) = 2\rho \int_0^\infty \frac{dt}{e^{2\pi t \rho} - 1} \text{ arc tan} \left\{ \frac{(t^3 + t) \rho^3}{pq(p+q)} \right\},$$

and

$$\rho^2 = p^2 + q^2 + pq.$$

46. If

$$U = 2^{\frac{1}{2}x} / \Gamma(1 - \tfrac{1}{2}x), \quad V = 2^{\frac{1}{2}x} / \Gamma(\tfrac{1}{2} - \tfrac{1}{2}x),$$

and if the function $F(x)$ be defined by the equation

$$F(x) = \pi^{\frac{1}{2}} \left(V \frac{dU}{dx} - U \frac{dV}{dx} \right),$$

shew (1) that $F(x)$ satisfies the equation

$$F(x+1) = xF(x) + \frac{1}{\Gamma(1-x)},$$

(2) that, for all positive integral values of x,

$$F(x) = \Gamma(x),$$

(3) that $F(x)$ is analytic for all finite values of x,

(4) that

$$F(x) = \frac{1}{\Gamma(1-x)} \frac{d}{dx} \log \frac{\Gamma\left(\dfrac{1-x}{2}\right)}{\Gamma\left(1 - \dfrac{x}{2}\right)}.$$

47. Expand

$$\{\Gamma(a)\}^{-1}$$

as a series of ascending powers of a.

(Various evaluations of the coefficients in this expansion have been given by Bourguet, *Bull. des Sci. Math.* v. (1881), p. 43; Bourguet, *Acta Math.* II. (1883), p. 261 ; Schlömilch, *Zeitschrift für Math. und Phys.* xxv. (1880), pp. 35, 351.)

48. Prove that the G-function, defined by the equation

$$G(z+1) = (2\pi)^{\frac{1}{2}z} e^{-\frac{1}{2}z(z+1) - \frac{1}{2}\gamma z^2} \prod_{n=1}^{\infty} \left\{ \left(1 + \frac{z}{n}\right)^n e^{-z + z^2/(2n)} \right\},$$

is an integral function which satisfies the relations

$$G(z+1) = \Gamma(z) G(z), \quad G(1) = 1,$$

$$(n!)^n / G(n+1) = 1^1 \cdot 2^2 \cdot 3^3 \ldots n^n. \qquad \text{(Alexeiewsky.)}$$

(The most important properties of the G-function are discussed in Barnes' memoir, *Quarterly Journal*, XXXI.)

49. Shew that

$$\frac{G'(z+1)}{G(z+1)} = \tfrac{1}{2} \log(2\pi) + \tfrac{1}{2} - z + z \frac{\Gamma'(z)}{\Gamma(z)},$$

and deduce that

$$\log \frac{G(1-z)}{G(1+z)} = \int_0^z \pi z \cot \pi z \, dz - z \log(2\pi).$$

50. Shew that

$$\int_0^z \log \Gamma(t+1) \, dt = \tfrac{1}{2} z \log(2\pi) - \tfrac{1}{2} z(z+1) + z \log \Gamma(z+1) - \log G(z+1).$$

CHAPTER XIII

THE ZETA FUNCTION OF RIEMANN

13·1. *Definition of the Zeta-function.*

Let $s = \sigma + it$ where σ and t are real[*]; then, if $\delta > 0$, the series

$$\zeta(s) = \sum_{n=1}^{\infty} \frac{1}{n^s}$$

is a uniformly convergent series of analytic functions (§§ 2·33, 3·34) in any domain in which $\sigma \geqslant 1 + \delta$; and consequently the series is an analytic function of s in such a domain. The function is called the *Zeta-function*; although it was known to Euler[†], its most remarkable properties were not discovered before Riemann[‡] who discussed it in his memoir on prime numbers; it has since proved to be of fundamental importance, not only in the Theory of Prime Numbers, but also in the higher theory of the Gamma-function and allied functions.

13·11. *The generalised Zeta-function*[§].

Many of the properties possessed by the Zeta-function are particular cases of properties possessed by a more general function defined, when $\sigma \geqslant 1 + \delta$, by the equation

$$\zeta(s, a) = \sum_{n=0}^{\infty} \frac{1}{(a+n)^s},$$

where a is a constant. For simplicity, we shall suppose[‖] that $0 < a \leqslant 1$, and then we take $\arg(a+n) = 0$. It is evident that $\zeta(s, 1) = \zeta(s)$.

13·12. *The expression of $\zeta(s, a)$ as an infinite integral.*

Since $(a + n)^{-s}\,\Gamma(s) = \displaystyle\int_0^{\infty} x^{s-1} e^{-(n+a)x}\,dx$, when $\arg x = 0$ and $\sigma > 0$ (and *a fortiori* when $\sigma \geqslant 1 + \delta$), we have, when $\sigma \geqslant 1 + \delta$,

$$\Gamma(s)\,\zeta(s, a) = \lim_{N \to \infty} \sum_{n=0}^{N} \int_0^{\infty} x^{s-1} e^{-(n+a)x}\,dx$$

$$= \lim_{N \to \infty} \left\{ \int_0^{\infty} \frac{x^{s-1} e^{-ax}}{1 - e^{-x}}\,dx - \int_0^{\infty} \frac{x^{s-1}}{1 - e^{-x}} e^{-(N+1+a)x}\,dx \right\}.$$

---

[*] The letters σ, t will be used in this sense throughout the chapter.

[†] *Commentationes Acad. Sci. Imp. Petropolitanae*, IX. (1737), pp. 160–188.

[‡] *Berliner Monatsberichte*, 1859, pp. 671–680. *Ges. Werke* (1876), pp. 136–144.

[§] The definition of this function appears to be due to Hurwitz, *Zeitschrift für Math. und Phys.* XXVII. (1882), pp. 86–101.

[‖] When a has this range of values, the properties of the function are, in general, much simpler than the corresponding properties for other values of a. The results of § 13·14 are true for all values of a (negative integer values excepted); and the results of §§ 13·12, 13·13, 13·2 are true when $R(a) > 0$.

Now, when $x \geqslant 0$, $e^x \geqslant 1 + x$, and so the modulus of the second of these integrals does not exceed

$$\int_0^\infty x^{\sigma-2} e^{-(N+a)x} dx = (N+a)^{1-\sigma} \Gamma(\sigma-1),$$

which (when $\sigma \geqslant 1 + \delta$) tends to 0 as $N \to \infty$.

Hence, when $\sigma \geqslant 1 + \delta$ and $\arg x = 0$,

$$\zeta(s, a) = \frac{1}{\Gamma(s)} \int_0^\infty \frac{x^{s-1} e^{-ax}}{1 - e^{-x}} dx;$$

this formula corresponds in some respects to Euler's integral for the Gamma-function.

13·13. *The expression* of $\zeta(s, a)$ as a contour integral.*

When $\sigma \geqslant 1 + \delta$, consider

$$\int_\infty^{(0+)} \frac{(-z)^{s-1} e^{-az}}{1 - e^{-z}} dz,$$

the contour of integration being of Hankel's type (§ 12·22) and not containing the points $\pm 2n\pi i$ ($n = 1, 2, 3, \ldots$) which are poles of the integrand; it is supposed (as in § 12·22) that $|\arg(-z)| \leqslant \pi$.

It is legitimate to modify the contour, precisely as in § 12·22, when† $\sigma \geqslant 1 + \delta$; and we get

$$\int_\infty^{(0+)} \frac{(-z)^{s-1} e^{-az}}{1 - e^{-z}} dz = \{e^{\pi i(s-1)} - e^{-\pi i(s-1)}\} \int_0^\infty \frac{x^{s-1} e^{-ax}}{1 - e^{-x}} dx.$$

Therefore

$$\zeta(s, a) = -\frac{\Gamma(1-s)}{2\pi i} \int_\infty^{(0+)} \frac{(-z)^{s-1} e^{-az}}{1 - e^{-z}} dz.$$

Now this last integral is a one-valued analytic function of s for *all* values of s. Hence the only possible singularities of $\zeta(s, a)$ are at the singularities of $\Gamma(1-s)$, i.e. at the points $1, 2, 3, \ldots$, and, with the exception of these points, the integral affords a representation of $\zeta(s, a)$ valid over the whole plane. The result obtained corresponds to Hankel's integral for the Gamma-function. Also, we have seen that $\zeta(s, a)$ is analytic when $\sigma \geqslant 1 + \delta$, and so the only singularity of $\zeta(s, a)$ is at the point $s = 1$. Writing $s = 1$ in the integral, we get

$$\frac{1}{2\pi i} \int_\infty^{(0+)} \frac{e^{-az}}{1 - e^{-z}} dz,$$

which is the residue at $z = 0$ of the integrand, and this residue is 1.

Hence $$\lim_{s \to 1} \frac{\zeta(s, a)}{\Gamma(1-s)} = -1.$$

---

* Given by Riemann for the ordinary Zeta-function.

† If $\sigma \leqslant 1$, the integral taken along any straight line up to the origin does not converge.

Since $\Gamma(1-s)$ has a single pole at $s=1$ with residue -1, it follows that the only singularity of $\zeta(s, a)$ is a simple pole with residue $+1$ at $s=1$.

Example 1. Shew that, when $R(s) > 0$,

$$(1 - 2^{1-s})\,\zeta(s) = \frac{1}{1^s} - \frac{1}{2^s} + \frac{1}{3^s} - \frac{1}{4^s} + \dots$$

$$= \frac{1}{\Gamma(s)} \int_0^\infty \frac{x^{s-1}}{e^x + 1}\,dx.$$

Example 2. Shew that, when $R(s) > 1$,

$$(2^s - 1)\,\zeta(s) = \zeta(s, \tfrac{1}{2})$$

$$= \frac{2^s}{\Gamma(s)} \int_0^\infty \frac{x^{s-1}\,e^x}{e^{2x} - 1}\,dx.$$

Example 3. Shew that

$$\zeta(s) = -\frac{2^{1-s}\,\Gamma(1-s)}{2\pi i\,(2^{1-s} - 1)} \int_\infty^{(0+)} \frac{(-z)^{s-1}}{e^z + 1}\,dz,$$

where the contour does not include any of the points $\pm\pi i,\ \pm 3\pi i,\ \pm 5\pi i,\ \dots$.

13·14. *Values of $\zeta(s, a)$ for special values of s.*

In the special case when s is an integer (positive or negative), $\dfrac{(-z)^{s-1}\,e^{-az}}{1 - e^{-z}}$ is a one-valued function of z. We may consequently apply Cauchy's theorem, so that $\dfrac{1}{2\pi i} \displaystyle\int_\infty^{(0+)} \frac{(-z)^{s-1}\,e^{-az}}{1 - e^{-z}}\,dz$ is the residue of the integrand at $z = 0$, that is to say, it is the coefficient of z^{-s} in $\dfrac{(-)^{s-1}\,e^{-az}}{1 - e^{-z}}$.

To obtain this coefficient we differentiate the expansion (§ 7·2)

$$-z\,\frac{e^{-az} - 1}{e^{-z} - 1} = \sum_{n=1}^\infty \frac{(-)^n \phi_n(a)\,z^n}{n!}$$

term-by-term with regard to a, where $\phi_n(a)$ denotes the Bernoullian polynomial.

(This is obviously legitimate, by § 4·7, when $|z| < 2\pi$, since $\dfrac{z^2\,e^{-az}}{e^{-z} - 1}$ can be expanded into a power series in z uniformly convergent with respect to a.)

Then
$$\frac{z^2 e^{-az}}{e^{-z} - 1} = \sum_{n=1}^\infty \frac{(-)^n \phi_n'(a)\,z^n}{n!}.$$

Therefore if s is zero or a negative integer $(= -m)$, we have

$$\zeta(-m, a) = -\phi'_{m+2}(a)/\{(m+1)(m+2)\}.$$

In the special case when $a = 1$, if $s = -m$, then $\zeta(s)$ is the coefficient of z^{1-s} in the expansion of $\dfrac{(-)^s.\,m!\,z}{e^z - 1}$.

Hence, by § 7·2,

$$\zeta(-2m) = 0, \quad \zeta(1 - 2m) = (-)^m B_m/(2m) \quad (m = 1, 2, 3, \ldots),$$

$$\zeta(0) = -\tfrac{1}{2}.$$

These equations give the value of $\zeta(s)$ when s is a negative integer or zero.

13·15.   *The formula* of Hurwitz for $\zeta(s, a)$ when $\sigma < 0$.*

Consider $-\dfrac{1}{2\pi i} \displaystyle\int_C \dfrac{(-z)^{s-1} e^{-az}}{1 - e^{-z}} \, dz$ taken round a contour C consisting of a (large) circle of radius $(2N + 1)\pi$, (N an integer), starting at the point $(2N + 1)\pi$ and encircling the origin in the positive direction, $\arg(-z)$ being zero at $z = -(2N + 1)\pi$.

In the region between C and the contour $(2N\pi + \pi; 0+)$, of which the contour of § 13·13 is the limiting form, $(-z)^{s-1} e^{-az} (1 - e^{-z})^{-1}$ is analytic and one-valued except at the simple poles $\pm 2\pi i, \pm 4\pi i, \ldots, \pm 2N\pi i$.

Hence

$$\frac{1}{2\pi i} \int_C \frac{(-z)^{s-1} e^{-az}}{1 - e^{-z}} \, dz - \frac{1}{2\pi i} \int_{(2N+1)\pi}^{(0+)} \frac{(-z)^{s-1} e^{-az}}{1 - e^{-z}} \, dz = \sum_{n=1}^{N} (R_n + R_n'),$$

where R_n, R_n' are the residues of the integrand at $2n\pi i$, $-2n\pi i$ respectively. At the point at which $-z = 2n\pi e^{-\frac{1}{2}\pi i}$, the residue is

$$(2n\pi)^{s-1} e^{-\frac{1}{2}\pi i (s-1)} e^{-2an\pi i},$$

and hence

$$R_n + R_n' = (2n\pi)^{s-1} 2 \sin\left(\tfrac{1}{2} s\pi + 2\pi a n\right).$$

Hence

$$-\frac{1}{2\pi i} \int_{(2N+1)\pi}^{(0+)} \frac{(-z)^{s-1} e^{-az}}{1 - e^{-z}} \, dz$$

$$= \frac{2 \sin \frac{1}{2} s\pi}{(2\pi)^{1-s}} \sum_{n=1}^{N} \frac{\cos(2\pi a n)}{n^{1-s}} + \frac{2 \cos \frac{1}{2} s\pi}{(2\pi)^{1-s}} \sum_{n=1}^{N} \frac{\sin(2\pi a n)}{n^{1-s}}$$

$$- \frac{1}{2\pi i} \int_C \frac{(-z)^{s-1} e^{-az}}{1 - e^{-z}} \, dz.$$

Now, since $0 < a \leqslant 1$, it is easy to see that we can find a number K independent of N such that $|e^{-az} (1 - e^{-z})^{-1}| < K$ when z is on C.

Hence

$$\left| \frac{1}{2\pi i} \int_C \frac{(-z)^{s-1} e^{-az}}{1 - e^{-z}} \, dz \right| < \frac{1}{2\pi} K \int_{-\pi}^{\pi} |\{(2N + 1)\pi\}^s e^{si\theta}| \, d\theta$$

$$< K \{(2N + 1)\pi\}^\sigma e^{\pi|s|}$$

$$\to 0 \text{ as } N \to \infty \text{ if } \sigma < 0.$$

---

* *Zeitschrift für Math. und Phys.* XXVII. (1882), p. 95.

Making $N \to \infty$, we obtain the result of Hurwitz that, if $\sigma < 0$,

$$\zeta(s, a) = \frac{2\Gamma(1-s)}{(2\pi)^{1-s}} \left\{ \sin\left(\frac{1}{2}s\pi\right) \sum_{n=1}^{\infty} \frac{\cos(2\pi an)}{n^{1-s}} + \cos\left(\frac{1}{2}s\pi\right) \sum_{n=1}^{\infty} \frac{\sin(2\pi an)}{n^{1-s}} \right\},$$

each of these series being convergent.

13·151.   *Riemann's relation between $\zeta(s)$ and $\zeta(1-s)$.*

If we write $a = 1$ in the formula of Hurwitz given in § 13·15, and employ § 12·14, we get the remarkable result, due to Riemann, that

$$2^{1-s} \Gamma(s) \zeta(s) \cos\left(\frac{1}{2}s\pi\right) = \pi^s \zeta(1-s).$$

Since both sides of this equation are analytic functions of s, save for isolated values of s at which they have poles, this equation, proved when $\sigma < 0$, persists (by § 5·5) for all values of s save those isolated values.

Example 1.   If m be a positive integer, shew that

$$\zeta(2m) = 2^{2m-1} \pi^{2m} B_m/(2m)!.$$

Example 2.   Shew that $\Gamma\left(\frac{1}{2}s\right) \pi^{-\frac{1}{2}s} \zeta(s)$ is unaltered by replacing s by $1-s$.

(Riemann.)

Example 3.   Deduce from Riemann's relation that the zeros of $\zeta(s)$ at $-2, -4, -6, \ldots$ are zeros of the first order.

13·2.   *Hermite's* formula for $\zeta(s, a)$.*

Let us apply Plana's theorem (example 7, p. 145) to the function $\phi(z) = (a+z)^{-s}$, where $\arg(a+z)$ has its principal value.

Define the function $q(x, y)$ by the equation

$$q(x, y) = \frac{1}{2i} \{(a+x+iy)^{-s} - (a+x-iy)^{-s}\}$$

$$= -\{(a+x)^2 + y^2\}^{-\frac{1}{2}s} \sin\left\{s \arctan\frac{y}{x+a}\right\}.$$

Since† $\left|\arctan\dfrac{y}{x+a}\right|$ does not exceed the smaller of $\frac{1}{2}\pi$ and $\dfrac{|y|}{x+a}$, we have

$$|q(x, y)| \leqslant \{(a+x)^2 + y^2\}^{\frac{1}{2} - \frac{1}{2}\sigma} |y^{-1}| \sinh\left\{\frac{1}{2}\pi|s|\right\},$$

$$|q(x, y)| \leqslant \{(a+x)^2 + y^2\}^{-\frac{1}{2}\sigma} \left|\left\{\sinh\frac{y|s|}{x+a}\right\}\right|.$$

Using the first result when $|y| > a$ and the second when $|y| < a$ it is

---

* *Annali di Matematica*, (3), v. (1901), pp. 57–72.

† If $\xi > 0$, $\arctan \xi = \displaystyle\int_0^\xi \frac{dt}{1+t^2} < \int_0^\infty \frac{dt}{1+t^2}$; and $\arctan \xi < \displaystyle\int_0^\xi dt.$

evident that, if $\sigma > 0$, $\int_0^\infty q(x, y)(e^{2\pi y} - 1)^{-1} dy$ is convergent when $x \geqslant 0$ and tends to 0 as $x \to \infty$; also $\int_0^\infty (a + x)^{-s} dx$ converges if $\sigma > 1$.

Hence, if $\sigma > 1$, it is legitimate to make $x_2 \to \infty$ in the result contained in the example cited; and we have

$$\zeta(s, a) = \frac{1}{2} a^{-s} + \int_0^\infty (a + x)^{-s} dx + 2 \int_0^\infty (a^2 + y^2)^{-\frac{1}{2}s} \left\{ \sin\left(s \arctan \frac{y}{a}\right) \right\} \frac{dy}{e^{2\pi y} - 1}.$$

So

$$\zeta(s, a) = \frac{1}{2} a^{-s} + \frac{a^{1-s}}{s - 1} + 2 \int_0^\infty (a^2 + y^2)^{-\frac{1}{2}s} \left\{ \sin\left(s \arctan \frac{y}{a}\right) \right\} \frac{dy}{e^{2\pi y} - 1}.$$

This is Hermite's formula[*]; using the results that, if $y \geqslant 0$,

$$\arctan y/a \leqslant y/a \quad \left(y < \frac{1}{2} a\pi \right), \qquad \arctan y/a < \frac{1}{2} \pi \quad \left(y > \frac{1}{2} a\pi \right),$$

we see that the integral involved in the formula converges for all values of s. Further, the integral defines an analytic function of s for all values of s.

To prove this, it is sufficient (§ 5·31) to shew that the integral obtained by differentiating under the sign of integration converges uniformly; that is to say we have to prove that

$$\int_0^\infty \left[-\frac{1}{2} \log (a^2 + y^2)(a^2 + y^2)^{-\frac{1}{2}s} \sin \left(s \arctan \frac{y}{a}\right) \right] \frac{dy}{e^{2\pi y} - 1}$$

$$+ \int_0^\infty \left[(a^2 + y^2)^{-\frac{1}{2}s} \arctan \frac{y}{a} \cos \left(s \arctan \frac{y}{a}\right) \right] \frac{dy}{e^{2\pi y} - 1}$$

converges uniformly with respect to s in any domain of values of s. Now when $|s| \leqslant \Delta$, where Δ is any positive number, we have

$$\left| (a^2 + y^2)^{-\frac{1}{2}s} \arctan \frac{y}{a} \cos \left(s \arctan \frac{y}{a} \right) \right| < (a^2 + y^2)^{\frac{1}{2}\Delta} \frac{y}{a} \cosh \left(\frac{1}{2} \pi \Delta \right);$$

since

$$\frac{\Delta}{a} \int_0^\infty (a^2 + y^2)^{\frac{1}{2}\Delta} \frac{y \, dy}{e^{2\pi y} - 1}$$

converges, the second integral converges uniformly by § 4·431 (I).

By dividing the path of integration of the first integral into two parts $(0, \frac{1}{2}\pi a)$, $(\frac{1}{2}\pi a, \infty)$ and using the results

$$\left| \sin \left(s \arctan \frac{y}{a} \right) \right| < \sinh \frac{\Delta y}{a}, \qquad \left| \sin \left(s \arctan \frac{y}{a} \right) \right| < \sinh \frac{1}{2} \pi \Delta$$

in the respective parts, we can similarly shew that the first integral converges uniformly.

Consequently Hermite's formula is valid (§ 5·5) for all values of s, and it is legitimate to differentiate under the sign of integration, and the differentiated integral is a continuous function of s.

[*] The corresponding formula when $a = 1$ had been previously given by Jensen.

13·21. *Deductions from Hermite's formula.*

Writing $s = 0$ in Hermite's formula, we see that

$$\zeta(0, a) = \tfrac{1}{2} - a.$$

Making $s \to 1$, from the uniformity of convergence of the integral involved in Hermite's formula we see that

$$\lim_{s \to 1} \left\{ \zeta(s, a) - \frac{1}{s-1} \right\} = \lim_{s \to 1} \frac{a^{1-s} - 1}{s-1} + \frac{1}{2a} + 2 \int_0^\infty \frac{y \, dy}{(a^2 + y^2)(e^{2\pi y} - 1)}.$$

Hence, by the example of § 12·32, we have

$$\lim_{s \to 1} \left\{ \zeta(s, a) - \frac{1}{s-1} \right\} = - \frac{\Gamma'(a)}{\Gamma(a)}.$$

Further, differentiating* the formula for $\zeta(s, a)$ and then making $s \to 0$, we get

$$\left\{ \frac{d}{ds} \zeta(s, a) \right\}_{s=0} = \lim_{s \to 0} \left[- \frac{1}{2} a^{-s} \log a - \frac{a^{1-s} \log a}{s-1} - \frac{a^{1-s}}{(s-1)^2} \right.$$

$$+ 2 \int_0^\infty \left\{ - \frac{1}{2} \log(a^2 + y^2) \cdot (a^2 + y^2)^{-\frac{1}{2}s} \sin\left(s \arctan \frac{y}{a} \right) \right.$$

$$\left. \left. + (a^2 + y^2)^{-\frac{1}{2}s} \arctan \frac{y}{a} \cos\left(s \arctan \frac{y}{a} \right) \right\} \frac{dy}{e^{2\pi y} - 1} \right]$$

$$= \left(a - \frac{1}{2} \right) \log a - a + 2 \int_0^\infty \frac{\arctan(y/a)}{e^{2\pi y} - 1} \, dy.$$

Hence, by § 12·32,

$$\left\{ \frac{d}{ds} \zeta(s, a) \right\}_{s=0} = \log \Gamma(a) - \frac{1}{2} \log(2\pi).$$

These results had previously been obtained in a different manner by Lerch†.

Corollary. $\displaystyle \lim_{s \to 1} \left\{ \zeta(s) - \frac{1}{s-1} \right\} = \gamma, \quad \zeta'(0) = - \frac{1}{2} \log(2\pi).$

13·3. *Euler's product for $\zeta(s)$.*

Let $\sigma \geqslant 1 + \delta$; and let $2, 3, 5, \ldots p, \ldots$ be the prime numbers in order. Then, subtracting the series for $2^{-s} \zeta(s)$ from the series for $\zeta(s)$, we get

$$\zeta(s) \cdot (1 - 2^{-s}) = \frac{1}{1^s} + \frac{1}{3^s} + \frac{1}{5^s} + \frac{1}{7^s} + \ldots,$$

---

* This was justified in § 13·2.

† The formula for $\zeta(s, a)$ from which Lerch derived these results is given in a memoir published by the Academy of Sciences of Prague. A summary of his memoir is contained in the *Jahrbuch über die Fortschritte der Math.* 1893–1894, p. 484.

all the terms of Σn^{-s} for which n is a multiple of 2 being omitted; then in like manner

$$\zeta(s).(1-2^{-s})(1-3^{-s}) = \frac{1}{1^s} + \frac{1}{5^s} + \frac{1}{7^s} + \dots,$$

all the terms for which n is a multiple of 2 or 3 being omitted; and so on; so that

$$\zeta(s).(1-2^{-s})(1-3^{-s})\dots(1-p^{-s}) = 1 + \Sigma' n^{-s},$$

the ′ denoting that only those values of n (greater than p) which are prime to 2, 3, ... p occur in the summation.

Now* $\qquad |\Sigma' n^{-s}| \leqslant \Sigma' n^{-1-\delta} \leqslant \sum\limits_{n=p+1}^{\infty} n^{-1-\delta} \to 0$ as $p \to \infty$.

Therefore if $\sigma \geqslant 1 + \delta$, the product $\zeta(s) \prod\limits_{p} (1 - p^{-s})$ converges to 1, where the number p assumes the prime values 2, 3, 5, ... only.

But the product $\prod\limits_{p} (1 - p^{-s})$ converges when $\sigma \geqslant 1 + \delta$, for it consists of some of the factors of the absolutely convergent product $\prod\limits_{n=2}^{\infty} (1 - n^{-s})$.

Consequently we infer that $\zeta(s)$ *has no zeros at which* $\sigma \geqslant 1 + \delta$; for if it had any such zeros, $\prod\limits_{p} (1 - p^{-s})$ would not converge at them.

Therefore, if $\sigma \geqslant 1 + \delta$,

$$\prod\limits_{p} \left(1 - \frac{1}{p^s}\right) = \frac{1}{\zeta(s)}.$$

This is Euler's result.

13·31. *Riemann's hypothesis concerning the zeros of $\zeta(s)$.*

It has just been proved that $\zeta(s)$ has no zeros at which $\sigma > 1$.

From the formula (§ 13·151)

$$\zeta(s) = 2^{s-1} \pi^s \{\Gamma(s)\}^{-1} \sec\left(\tfrac{1}{2} s\pi\right) \zeta(1-s)$$

it is now apparent that the only zeros of $\zeta(s)$ for which $\sigma < 0$ are the zeros of $\{\Gamma(s)\}^{-1} \sec\left(\tfrac{1}{2} s\pi\right)$, i.e. the points $s = -2, -4, \dots$.

Hence all the zeros of $\zeta(s)$ except those at $-2, -4, \dots$ lie in that strip of the domain of the complex variable s which is defined by $0 \leqslant \sigma \leqslant 1$.

It was conjectured by Riemann, but it has not yet been proved, that all the zeros of $\zeta(s)$ in this strip lie on the line $\sigma = \frac{1}{2}$; while it has quite recently been proved by Hardy† that an infinity of zeros of $\zeta(s)$ actually lie on $\sigma = \frac{1}{2}$. It is highly probable that Riemann's conjecture is correct, and the proof of it would have far-reaching consequences in the theory of Prime Numbers.

---

* The first term of Σ' starts with the prime next greater than p.

† *Comptes Rendus*, CLVIII. (1914), p. 1012; see p. 280.

13·4. *Riemann's integral for $\zeta(s)$.*

It is easy to see that, if $\sigma > 0$,

$$n^{-s} \Gamma\left(\tfrac{1}{2}s\right) \pi^{-\frac{1}{2}s} = \int_0^\infty e^{-n^2\pi x} x^{\frac{1}{2}s-1} dx.$$

Hence, when $\sigma > 0$,

$$\zeta(s) \Gamma\left(\tfrac{1}{2}s\right) \pi^{-\frac{1}{2}s} = \lim_{N\to\infty} \int_0^\infty \sum_{n=1}^N e^{-n^2\pi x} x^{\frac{1}{2}s-1} dx.$$

Now, if $\varpi(x) = \sum_{n=1}^\infty e^{-n^2\pi x}$, since, by example 17 of Chapter VI (p. 124), $1 + 2\varpi(x) = x^{-\frac{1}{2}}\{1 + 2\varpi(1/x)\}$, we have $\lim_{x\to 0} x^{\frac{1}{2}} \varpi(x) = 1$; and hence $\int_0^\infty \varpi(x) x^{\frac{1}{2}s-1} dx$ converges when $\sigma > 1$.

Consequently, if $\sigma > 2$,

$$\zeta(s) \Gamma\left(\tfrac{1}{2}s\right) \pi^{-\frac{1}{2}s} = \lim_{N\to\infty} \left[\int_0^\infty \varpi(x) x^{\frac{1}{2}s-1} dx - \int_0^\infty \sum_{n=N+1}^\infty e^{-n^2\pi x} x^{\frac{1}{2}s-1} dx \right].$$

Now, as in § 13·12, the modulus of the last integral does not exceed

$$\int_0^\infty \left\{ \sum_{n=N+1}^\infty e^{-n(N+1)\pi x} \right\} x^{\frac{1}{2}\sigma-1} dx = \int_0^\infty \frac{e^{-(N+1)^2\pi x} x^{\frac{1}{2}\sigma-1}}{1 - e^{-(N+1)\pi x}} dx$$

$$< \{\pi(N+1)\}^{-1} \int_0^\infty e^{-(N^2+2N)\pi x} x^{\frac{1}{2}\sigma-2} dx$$

$$= \{\pi(N+1)\}^{-1} \{(N^2+2N)\pi\}^{1-\frac{1}{2}\sigma} \Gamma\left(\tfrac{1}{2}\sigma-1\right)$$

$$\to 0 \text{ as } N \to \infty, \text{ since } \sigma > 2.$$

Hence, when $\sigma > 2$,

$$\zeta(s) \Gamma\left(\tfrac{1}{2}s\right) \pi^{-\frac{1}{2}s} = \int_0^\infty \varpi(x) x^{\frac{1}{2}s-1} dx$$

$$= \int_0^1 \left\{ -\tfrac{1}{2} + \tfrac{1}{2}x^{-\frac{1}{2}} + x^{-\frac{1}{2}} \varpi(1/x) \right\} x^{\frac{1}{2}s-1} dx + \int_1^\infty \varpi(x) x^{\frac{1}{2}s-1} dx$$

$$= -\frac{1}{s} + \frac{1}{s-1} + \int_\infty^1 x^{\frac{1}{2}} \varpi(x) x^{-\frac{1}{2}s+1} \left(-\frac{1}{x^2}\right) dx + \int_1^\infty \varpi(x) x^{\frac{1}{2}s-1} dx.$$

Consequently

$$\zeta(s) \Gamma\left(\tfrac{1}{2}s\right) \pi^{-\frac{1}{2}s} - \frac{1}{s(s-1)} = \int_1^\infty \left(x^{\frac{1}{2}(1-s)} + x^{\frac{1}{2}s} \right) x^{-1} \varpi(x) dx.$$

Now the integral on the right represents an analytic function of s for *all* values of s, by § 5·32, since on the path of integration

$$\varpi(x) < e^{-\pi x} \sum_{n=0}^\infty e^{-m\pi x} \leqslant e^{-\pi x} (1 - e^{-\pi})^{-1}.$$

Consequently, by § 5·5, the above equation, proved when $\sigma > 2$, persists for all values of s.

If now we put

$$s = \frac{1}{2} + it, \quad \frac{1}{2} s (s - 1) \zeta(s) \Gamma\left(\frac{1}{2}s\right) \pi^{-\frac{1}{2}s} = \xi(t),$$

we have

$$\xi(t) = \frac{1}{2} - \left(t^2 + \frac{1}{4}\right) \int_1^\infty x^{-\frac{3}{4}} \varpi(x) \cos\left(\frac{1}{2} t \log x\right) dx.$$

Since

$$\int_1^\infty x^{-\frac{3}{4}} \varpi(x) \left\{\frac{1}{2} \log x\right\}^n \cos\left(\frac{1}{2} t \log x + \frac{1}{2} n\pi\right) dx$$

satisfies the test of § 4·44 corollary, we may differentiate any number of times under the sign of integration, and then put $t = 0$. Hence, by Taylor's theorem, we have for all values* of t

$$\xi(t) = \sum_{n=0}^\infty a_{2n} t^{2n};$$

by considering the last integral a_{2n} is obviously real.

This result is fundamental in Riemann's researches.

13·5. *Inequalities satisfied by $\zeta(s, a)$ when $\sigma > 0$.*

We shall now investigate the behaviour of $\zeta(s, a)$ as $t \to \pm \infty$, for given values of σ.

When $\sigma > 1$, it is easy to see that, if N be any integer,

$$\zeta(s, a) = \sum_{n=0}^N (a+n)^{-s} - \frac{1}{(1-s)(N+a)^{s-1}} - \sum_{n=N}^\infty f_n(s),$$

where

$$f_n(s) = \frac{1}{1-s}\left\{\frac{1}{(n+1+a)^{s-1}} - \frac{1}{(n+a)^{s-1}}\right\} - \frac{1}{(n+1+a)^s}$$

$$= s \int_n^{n+1} \frac{u-n}{(u+a)^{s+1}} du.$$

Now, when $\sigma > 0$,

$$|f_n(s)| \leqslant |s| \int_n^{n+1} \frac{u-n}{(u+a)^{\sigma+1}} du$$

$$< |s| \int_n^{n+1} \frac{du}{(n+a)^{\sigma+1}}$$

$$= |s|(n+a)^{-\sigma-1}.$$

Therefore the series $\sum\limits_{n=N}^\infty f_n(s)$ is a uniformly convergent series of analytic functions when $\sigma > 0$; so that $\sum\limits_{n=N}^\infty f_n(s)$ is an analytic function when $\sigma > 0$; and consequently, by § 5·5, the function $\zeta(s, a)$ may be defined when $\sigma > 0$ by the series

$$\zeta(s, a) = \sum_{n=0}^N (a+n)^{-s} - \frac{1}{(1-s)(N+a)^{s-1}} - \sum_{n=N}^\infty f_n(s).$$

Now let $[t]$ be the greatest integer in $|t|$; and take $N = [t]$. Then

$$|\zeta(s, a)| \leqslant \sum_{n=0}^{[t]} |(a+n)^{-s}| + |\{(1-s)^{-1}([t]+a)^{1-s}\}| + \sum_{n=[t]}^\infty |s|(n+a)^{-\sigma-1}$$

$$< \sum_{n=0}^{[t]} (a+n)^{-\sigma} + |t|^{-1}([t]+a)^{1-\sigma} + |s| \sum_{n=[t]}^\infty (n+a)^{-\sigma-1}.$$

---

* In this particular piece of analysis it is convenient to regard t as a complex variable, defined by the equation $s = \frac{1}{2} + it$; and then $\xi(t)$ is an integral function of t.

Using the Maclaurin-Cauchy sum formula (§ 4·43), we get

$$| \zeta(s, a) | < a^{-\sigma} + \int_0^{[t]} (a+x)^{-\sigma} dx + | t |^{-1} ([t]+a)^{1-\sigma} + | s | \int_{[t]-1}^{\infty} (x+a)^{-\sigma-1} dx.$$

Now when $\delta \leqslant \sigma \leqslant 1 - \delta$ where $\delta > 0$, we have

$$| \zeta(s, a) | < a^{-\sigma} + (1-\sigma)^{-1} \{ (a+[t])^{1-\sigma} - a^{1-\sigma} \} + | t |^{-1} ([t]+a)^{1-\sigma} + | s | \sigma^{-1} ([t]-1+a)^{-\sigma}.$$

Hence $\zeta(s, a) = O(| t |^{1-\sigma})$, *the constant implied in the symbol* O *being independent of* s.

But, when $1 - \delta \leqslant \sigma \leqslant 1 + \delta$, *we have*

$$| \zeta(s, a) | = O(| t |^{1-\sigma}) + \int_0^{[t]} (a+x)^{-\sigma} dx$$

$$< O(| t |^{1-\sigma}) + \{ a^{1-\sigma} + (a+t)^{1-\sigma} \} \int_0^{[t]} (a+x)^{-1} dx,$$

since $(a+x)^{-\sigma} \leqslant a^{1-\sigma} (a+x)^{-1}$ when $\sigma \geqslant 1$, and $(a+x)^{-\sigma} \leqslant (a+[t])^{1-\sigma} (a+x)^{-1}$ when $\sigma \leqslant 1$, *and so*

$$\zeta(s, a) = O \{ | t |^{1-\sigma} \log | t | \}.$$

When $\sigma \geqslant 1 + \delta$,

$$| \zeta(s, a) | \leqslant a^{-\sigma} + \sum_{n=1}^{\infty} (a+n)^{-1-\delta} = O(1).$$

13·51. *Inequalities satisfied by* $\zeta(s, a)$ *when* $\sigma \leqslant 0$.

We next obtain inequalities of a similar nature when $\sigma \leqslant \delta$. In the case of the function $\zeta(s)$ we use Riemann's relation

$$\zeta(s) = 2^s \pi^{s-1} \Gamma(1-s) \zeta(1-s) \sin(\tfrac{1}{2} s \pi).$$

Now, when $\sigma < 1 - \delta$, we have, by § 12·33,

$$\Gamma(1-s) = O \{ e^{(\frac{1}{2}-s) \log (1-s) - (1-s)} \}$$

and so

$$\zeta(s) = O [\exp \{ \tfrac{1}{2} \pi | t | + (\tfrac{1}{2} - \sigma - it) \log | 1 - s | + i \arctan t/(1-\sigma) \}] \zeta(1-s).$$

Since $\arctan t/(1-\sigma) = \pm \tfrac{1}{2} \pi + O(t^{-1})$, according as t is positive or negative, we see, from the results already obtained for $\zeta(s, a)$, that

$$\zeta(s) = O \{ | t |^{\frac{1}{2}-\sigma} \} \zeta(1-s).$$

In the case of the function $\zeta(s, a)$, we have to use the formula of Hurwitz (§ 13·15) to obtain the generalisation of this result; we have, when $\sigma < 0$,

$$\zeta(s, a) = -i (2\pi)^{s-1} \Gamma(1-s) [e^{\frac{1}{2} s \pi i} \zeta_a(1-s) - e^{-\frac{1}{2} s \pi i} \zeta_{-a}(1-s)],$$

where

$$\zeta_a(1-s) = \sum_{n=1}^{\infty} \frac{e^{2n\pi i a}}{n^{1-s}}.$$

Hence

$$(1 - e^{2\pi i a}) \zeta_a(1-s) = e^{2\pi i a} + \sum_{n=2}^{N} e^{2n\pi i a} [n^{s-1} - (n-1)^{s-1}]$$

$$+ (s-1) \sum_{n=N+1}^{\infty} e^{2n\pi i a} \int_{n-1}^{n} u^{s-2} du;$$

since the series on the right is a uniformly convergent series of analytic functions whenever $\sigma \leqslant 1 - \delta$, this equation gives the continuation of $\zeta_a(1-s)$ over the range $0 \leqslant \sigma \leqslant 1 - \delta$; so that, whenever $\sigma \leqslant 1 - \delta$, we have

$$\sin \pi a \zeta_a(1-s) | \leqslant 1 + \sum_{n=2}^{N} \{ n^{\sigma-1} + (n-1)^{\sigma-1} \} + | s - 1 | \sum_{n=N+1}^{\infty} \int_{n-1}^{n} u^{\sigma-2} du.$$

18—2

Taking $N = [t]$, we obtain, as in § 13·5,

$$\zeta_a(1-s) = O(|t|^\sigma) \qquad\qquad (\delta \leqslant \sigma \leqslant 1-\delta)$$
$$= O(|t|^\sigma \log|t|) \quad (-\delta \leqslant \sigma < \delta).$$

And obviously

$$\zeta_a(1-s) = O(1) \qquad\qquad (\sigma < -\delta).$$

Consequently, whether a is unity or not, we have the results

$$\zeta(s, a) = O(|t|^{\frac{1}{2}-\sigma}) \qquad\qquad (\sigma \leqslant \delta)$$
$$= O(|t|^{\frac{1}{2}}) \qquad\qquad (\delta \leqslant \sigma \leqslant 1-\delta)$$
$$= O(|t|^{\frac{1}{2}} \log|t|) \quad (-\delta \leqslant \sigma \leqslant \delta).$$

We may combine these results and those of § 13·5, into the single formula

$$\zeta(s, a) = O(|t|^{\tau(\sigma)} \log|t|),$$

where*

$$\tau(\sigma) = \tfrac{1}{2} - \sigma, \ (\sigma \leqslant 0); \ \tau(\sigma) = \tfrac{1}{2}, \ (0 \leqslant \sigma \leqslant \tfrac{1}{2}); \ \tau(\sigma) = 1 - \sigma, \ (\tfrac{1}{2} \leqslant \sigma \leqslant 1); \ \tau(\sigma) = 0, \ (\sigma \geqslant 1);$$

and the $\log|t|$ may be suppressed except when $-\delta \leqslant \sigma \leqslant \delta$ or when $1-\delta \leqslant \sigma \leqslant 1+\delta$.

13·6. *The asymptotic expansion of* $\log \Gamma(z+a)$.

From § 12·1 example 3, it follows that

$$\left(1 + \frac{z}{a}\right) \prod_{n=1}^\infty \left\{\left(1 + \frac{z}{a+n}\right) e^{-z/n}\right\} = \frac{e^{-\gamma z} \Gamma(a)}{\Gamma(z+a)}.$$

Now, the principal values of the logarithms being taken,

$$\log\left(1 + \frac{z}{a}\right) + \log \prod_{n=1}^\infty \left\{\left(1 + \frac{z}{a+n}\right) e^{-z/n}\right\}$$
$$= \sum_{n=1}^\infty \left[\left(\frac{-az}{n(a+n)}\right) + \sum_{m=2}^\infty \frac{(-)^{m-1}}{m} \frac{z^m}{(a+n)^m}\right] + \sum_{m=1}^\infty \frac{(-)^{m-1}}{m} \frac{z^m}{a^m}.$$

If $|z| < a$, the double series is absolutely convergent since

$$\sum_{n=1}^\infty \left[\frac{a|z|}{n(a+n)} - \log\left(1 - \frac{|z|}{a+n}\right) + \frac{|z|}{a+n}\right]$$

converges.

Consequently

$$\log \frac{e^{-\gamma z} \Gamma(a)}{\Gamma(z+a)} = \frac{z}{a} - \sum_{n=1}^\infty \frac{az}{n(a+n)} + \sum_{m=2}^\infty \frac{(-)^{m-1}}{m} z^m \zeta(m, a).$$

Now consider $\dfrac{-1}{2\pi i} \displaystyle\int_C \frac{\pi z^s}{s \sin \pi s} \zeta(s, a)\, ds$, the contour of integration being similar to that of § 12·22 enclosing the points $s = 2, 3, 4, \ldots$ but not the points $1, 0, -1, -2, \ldots$; the residue of the integrand at $s = m \ (m \geqslant 2)$ is $\dfrac{(-)^m}{m} z^m \zeta(m, a)$; and since, as $\sigma \to \infty$ (where $s = \sigma + it$), $\zeta(s, a) = O(1)$, the integral converges if $|z| < 1$.

---

* It can be proved that $\tau(\sigma)$ may be taken to be $\tfrac{1}{2}(1 - \sigma)$ when $0 \leqslant \sigma \leqslant 1$. See Landau, *Primzahlen*, § 237.

Consequently

$$\log \frac{e^{-\gamma z}\,\Gamma(a)}{\Gamma(z+a)} = \frac{z}{a} - \sum_{n=1}^{\infty} \frac{az}{n(a+n)} - \frac{1}{2\pi i} \int_C \frac{\pi z^s}{s \sin \pi s} \zeta(s,a)\,ds.$$

Hence

$$\log \frac{\Gamma(a)}{\Gamma(z+a)} = -z\,\frac{\Gamma'(a)}{\Gamma(a)} - \frac{1}{2\pi i} \int_C \frac{\pi z^s}{s \sin \pi s} \zeta(s,a)\,ds.$$

Now let D be a semicircle of (large) radius N with centre at $s = \frac{3}{2}$, the semicircle lying on the right of the line $\sigma = \frac{3}{2}$. On this semicircle $\zeta(s,a) = O(1)$, $|z^s| \doteq |z|^\sigma e^{-t \arg z}$, and so the integrand is* $O\{|z|^\sigma e^{-\pi|t| - t \arg z}\}$. Hence if $|z| < 1$ and $-\pi + \delta \leqslant \arg z \leqslant \pi - \delta$, where δ is positive, the integrand is $O(|z|^\sigma e^{-\delta|t|})$, and hence

$$\int_D \frac{\pi z^s}{s \sin \pi s} \zeta(s,a)\,ds \to 0$$

as $N \to \infty$. It follows at once that, if $|\arg z| \leqslant \pi - \delta$ and $|z| < 1$,

$$\log \frac{\Gamma(a)}{\Gamma(z+a)} = -z\,\frac{\Gamma'(a)}{\Gamma(a)} + \frac{1}{2\pi i} \int_{\frac{3}{2}-\infty i}^{\frac{3}{2}+\infty i} \frac{\pi z^s}{s \sin \pi s} \zeta(s,a)\,ds.$$

But this integral defines an analytic function of z for all values of $|z|$ if

$$|\arg z| \leqslant \pi - \delta.$$

Hence, by § 5·5, the above equation, proved when $|z| < 1$, persists for all values of $|z|$ when $|\arg z| \leqslant \pi - \delta$.

Now consider $\displaystyle \int_{-n-\frac{1}{2}\pm Ri}^{\frac{3}{2}\pm Ri} \frac{\pi z^s}{s \sin \pi s} \zeta(s,a)\,ds$, where n is a fixed integer and R is going to tend to infinity. By § 13·51, the integrand is $O\{z^\sigma e^{-\delta R} R^{\tau(\sigma)}\}$, where $-n-\frac{1}{2} \leqslant \sigma \leqslant \frac{3}{2}$; and hence if the upper signs be taken, or if the lower signs be taken, the integral tends to zero as $R \to \infty$.

Therefore, by Cauchy's theorem,

$$\log \frac{\Gamma(a)}{\Gamma(z+a)} = -z\,\frac{\Gamma'(a)}{\Gamma(a)} + \frac{1}{2\pi i} \int_{-n-\frac{1}{2}-\infty i}^{-n-\frac{1}{2}+\infty i} \frac{\pi z^s}{s \sin \pi s} \zeta(s,a)\,ds + \sum_{m=-1}^{n} R_m,$$

where R_m is the residue of the integrand at $s = -m$.

Now, on the new path of integration

$$\left| \frac{\pi z^s}{s \sin \pi s} \zeta(s,a) \right| < K z^{-n-\frac{1}{2}} e^{-\delta|t|} |\tau(-n-\tfrac{1}{2})| \,|t|,$$

where K is independent of z and t, and $\tau(\sigma)$ is the function defined in § 13·51.

---

* The constants implied in the symbol O are independent of s and z throughout.

Consequently, since $\int_{-\infty}^{\infty} e^{-\delta|t|} |t|^{\tau(-n-\frac{1}{2})} dt$ converges, we have

$$\log \frac{\Gamma(a)}{\Gamma(z+a)} = -z \frac{\Gamma'(a)}{\Gamma(a)} + \sum_{m=-1}^{n} R_m + O(z^{-n-\frac{1}{2}}),$$

when $|z|$ is large.

Now, when m is a positive integer, $R_m = \dfrac{(-)^m z^{-m} \zeta(-m, a)}{-m}$, and so by § 13·14, $R_m = \dfrac{(-)^m z^{-m} \phi'_{m+2}(a)}{m(m+1)(m+2)}$, where $\phi_m'(a)$ denotes the derivate of Bernoulli's polynomial.

Also R_0 is the residue at $s = 0$ of

$$\frac{1}{s} \left(1 + \frac{\pi^2 s^2}{6} + \dots \right) (1 + s \log z + \dots) \left\{ \frac{1}{2} - a + s\zeta'(0, a) + \dots \right\},$$

and so
$$R_0 = \left(\frac{1}{2} - a \right) \log z + \zeta'(0, a)$$

$$= \left(\frac{1}{2} - a \right) \log z + \log \Gamma(a) - \frac{1}{2} \log(2\pi),$$

by § 13·21.

And, using § 13·21, R_{-1} is the residue* at $S = 0$ of

$$-\frac{1}{S}(1 - S + S^2 - \dots) \left(1 + \frac{\pi^2 S^2}{6} + \dots \right) z(1 + S \log z + \dots) \left(\frac{1}{S} - \frac{\Gamma'(a)}{\Gamma(a)} + \dots \right).$$

Hence
$$R_{-1} = -z \log z + z \frac{\Gamma'(a)}{\Gamma(a)} + z.$$

Consequently, finally, if $|\arg z| \leqslant \pi - \delta$ and $|z|$ is large,

$$\log \Gamma(z+a) = \left(z + a - \frac{1}{2} \right) \log z - z + \frac{1}{2} \log(2\pi)$$

$$+ \sum_{m=1}^{n} \frac{(-)^{m-1} \phi'_{m+2}(a)}{m(m+1)(m+2) z^m} + O(z^{-n-\frac{1}{2}}).$$

In the special case when $a = 1$, this reduces to the formula found previously in § 12·33 for a more restricted range of values of $\arg z$.

The asymptotic expansion just obtained is valid when a is not restricted by the inequality $0 < a \leqslant 1$; but the investigation of it involves the rather more elaborate methods which are necessary for obtaining inequalities satisfied by $\zeta(s, a)$ when a does not satisfy the inequality $0 < a \leqslant 1$. But if, in the formula just obtained, we write $a = 1$ and then put $z + a$ for z, it is easily seen that, when $|\arg(z+a)| \leqslant \pi - \delta$, we have

$$\log \Gamma(z+a+1) = \left(z + a + \frac{1}{2} \right) \log(z+a) - z - a + \frac{1}{2} \log(2\pi) + o(1);$$

* Writing $s = S + 1$.

subtracting $\log(z+a)$ from each side, we easily see that when both

$$|\arg(z+a)| \leqslant \pi - \delta \ \ \text{and} \ \ |\arg z| \leqslant \pi - \delta,$$

we have the asymptotic formula

$$\log \Gamma(z+a) = \left(z+a-\tfrac{1}{2}\right)\log z - z + \tfrac{1}{2}\log(2\pi) + o(1),$$

where the expression which is $o(1)$ tends to zero as $|z| \to \infty$.

REFERENCES.

G. F. B. RIEMANN, *Ges. Werke*, pp. 145–155.

E. G. H. LANDAU, *Handbuch der Primzahlen.* (Leipzig, 1909.)

E. L. LINDELÖF, *Le Calcul des Résidus*, Ch. IV. (Paris, 1905.)

E. W. BARNES, *Messenger of Mathematics*, XXIX. (1899), pp. 64–128.

G. H. HARDY and J. E. LITTLEWOOD, *Acta Mathematica*, XLI. (1917), pp. 119–196.

MISCELLANEOUS EXAMPLES.

1. Shew that

$$(2^s - 1)\,\zeta(s) = \frac{2^{s-1}s}{s-1} + 2\int_0^\infty (\tfrac{1}{4}+y^2)^{-\frac{1}{2}s}\sin(s \arctan 2y)\,\frac{dy}{e^{2\pi y}-1}.$$

(Jensen, *L'Intermédiaire des Math.* (1895), p. 346.)

2. Shew that

$$\zeta(s) = \frac{2^{s-1}}{s-1} - 2^s \int_0^\infty (1+y^2)^{-\frac{1}{2}s}\sin(s \arctan y)\,\frac{dy}{e^{\pi y}+1}.$$

(Jensen.)

3. Discuss the asymptotic expansion of $\log G(z+a)$, (Chapter XII example 48) by aid of the generalised Zeta-function.   (Barnes.)

4. Shew that, if $\sigma > 1$,

$$\log \zeta(s) = \sum_p \sum_{m=1}^\infty \frac{1}{mp^{ms}},$$

the summation extending over the prime numbers $p = 2, 3, 5, \ldots$.

(Dirichlet, *Journal de Math.* IV. (1839), p. 407.)

5. Shew that, if $\sigma > 1$,

$$-\frac{\zeta'(s)}{\zeta(s)} = \sum_{n=1}^\infty \frac{\Lambda(n)}{n^s},$$

where $\Lambda(n) = 0$ when n is not a power of a prime, and $\Lambda(n) = \log p$ when n is a power of a prime p.

6. Prove that

$$\int_0^\infty \frac{e^{-x^2}\,dx}{\left(1+\dfrac{w^2}{4x^2}\right)^{\frac{1}{2}s}} = \frac{\pi^{\frac{1}{2}}}{\Gamma(\tfrac{1}{2}s)}\int_0^\infty e^{-x^2 - wx}\,x^{s-1}\,dx.$$

(Lerch, *Kraków Rozprawy**, II.)

* See the *Jahrbuch über die Fortschritte der Math.* 1893–1894, p. 482.

7. If

$$\phi(s, x) = \sum_{n=1}^{\infty} \frac{x^n}{n^s},$$

where $|x| < 1$, and the real part of s is positive, shew that

$$\phi(s, x) = \frac{1}{\Gamma(s)} \int_0^\infty \frac{xz^{s-1} dz}{e^z - x}$$

and, if $s < 1$,

$$\lim_{x \to 1} (1-x)^{1-s} \phi(s, x) = \Gamma(1-s).$$

(Appell, *Comptes Rendus*, LXXXVII.)

8. If x, a, and s be real, and $0 < a < 1$, and $s > 1$, and if

$$\phi(x, a, s) = \sum_{n=0}^{\infty} \frac{e^{2n\pi ix}}{(a+n)^s},$$

shew that

$$\phi(x, a, s) = \frac{1}{\Gamma(s)} \int_0^\infty \frac{e^{-az} z^{s-1} dz}{1 - e^{2\pi ix - z}}$$

and

$$\phi(x, a, 1-s) = \frac{\Gamma(s)}{(2\pi)^s} \left\{ \begin{array}{l} e^{\pi i(\frac{1}{2}s - 2ax)} \phi(-a, x, s) \\ + e^{\pi i\{-\frac{1}{2}s + 2a(1-x)\}} \phi(a, 1-x, s) \end{array} \right\}.$$

(Lerch, *Acta Math.* XI.)

9. By evaluating the residues at the poles on the left of the straight line taken as contour, shew that, if $k > 0$, and $|\arg y| < \frac{1}{2}\pi$,

$$e^{-y} = \frac{1}{2\pi i} \int_{k-\infty i}^{k+\infty i} \Gamma(u) y^{-u} du,$$

and deduce that, if $k > \frac{1}{2}$,

$$\frac{1}{2\pi i} \int_{k-\infty i}^{k+\infty i} \Gamma(u) \cdot (\pi x)^{-u} \zeta(2u) du = \varpi(x),$$

and thence that, if a is an acute angle,

$$\int_0^\infty \frac{\cosh \frac{1}{2}at}{t^2 + \frac{1}{4}} \xi(t) dt = \pi \cos \frac{1}{4}a - \frac{1}{2}\pi e^{\frac{1}{2}ia} \{1 + 2\varpi(e^{ia})\}.$$

(Hardy.)

10. By differentiating $2n$ times under the integral sign in the last result of example 9, and then making $a \to \frac{1}{2}\pi$, deduce from example 17 on p. 124 that

$$\int_0^\infty \frac{\cosh \frac{1}{4}\pi t}{t^2 + \frac{1}{4}} t^{2n} \xi(t) dt = \frac{(-)^n \pi}{2^{2n}} \cos \frac{\pi}{8}.$$

By taking n large, deduce that there is no number t_0 such that $\xi(t)$ is of fixed sign when $t > t_0$, and thence that $\zeta(s)$ has an infinity of zeros on the line $\sigma = \frac{1}{2}$.

(Hardy.)

[Hardy and Littlewood, *Proc. London Math. Soc.* XIX. (1920), have shewn that the number of zeros on the line $\sigma = \frac{1}{2}$ for which $0 < t < T$ is at least $O(T)$ as $T \to \infty$; if the Riemann hypothesis is true, the number is $\frac{1}{2\pi} T \log T - \frac{1 + \log 2\pi}{2\pi} T + O(\log T)$; see Landau, *Primzahlen*, I. p. 370.]

CHAPTER XIV

THE HYPERGEOMETRIC FUNCTION

14·1. *The hypergeometric series.*

We have already (§ 2·38) considered the *hypergeometric series*[*]

$$1 + \frac{a \cdot b}{1 \cdot c} z + \frac{a(a+1) b(b+1)}{1 \cdot 2 \cdot c(c+1)} z^2 + \frac{a(a+1)(a+2) b(b+1)(b+2)}{1 \cdot 2 \cdot 3 \cdot c(c+1)(c+2)} z^3 + \cdots$$

from the point of view of its convergence. It follows from § 2·38 and § 5·3 that the series defines a function which is analytic when $|z| < 1$.

It will appear later (§ 14·53) that this function has a branch point at $z = 1$ and that if a cut[†] (i.e. an impassable barrier) is made from $+1$ to $+\infty$ along the real axis, the function is analytic and one-valued throughout the cut plane. The function will be denoted by $F(a, b; c; z)$.

Many important functions employed in Analysis can be expressed by means of hypergeometric functions. Thus[‡]

$$(1 + z)^n = F(-n, \beta; \beta; -z),$$

$$\log(1 + z) = zF(1, 1; 2; -z),$$

$$e^z = \lim_{\beta \to \infty} F(1, \beta; 1; z/\beta).$$

Example. Shew that

$$\frac{d}{dz} F(a, b; c; z) = \frac{ab}{c} F(a+1, b+1; c+1; z).$$

14·11. *The value[§] of $F(a, b; c; 1)$ when $R(c - a - b) > 0$.*

The reader will easily verify, by considering the coefficients of x^n in the

---

[*] The name was given by Wallis in 1655 to the series whose nth term is

$$a \{a + b\} \{a + 2b\} \dots \{a + (n-1) b\}.$$

Euler used the term hypergeometric in this sense, the modern use of the term being apparently due to Kummer, *Journal für Math.* xv. (1836).

[†] The plane of the variable z is said to be *cut* along a curve when it is convenient to consider only such variations in z which do not involve a passage across the curve in question; so that the cut may be regarded as an impassable barrier.

[‡] It will be a good exercise for the reader to construct a rigorous proof of the third of these results.

[§] This analysis is due to Gauss. A method more easy to remember but more difficult to justify is given in § 14·6 example 2.

various series, that if $0 \leqslant x < 1$, then

$$c \{c - 1 - (2c - a - b - 1) x\} F(a, b; c; x) + (c - a)(c - b) xF(a, b; c + 1; x)$$
$$= c(c - 1)(1 - x) F(a, b; c - 1; x)$$
$$= c(c - 1) \left\{ 1 + \sum_{n=1}^{\infty} (u_n - u_{n-1}) x^n \right\},$$

where u_n is the coefficient of x^n in $F(a, b; c - 1; x)$.

Now make $x \to 1$. By § 3·71, the right-hand side tends to zero if $1 + \sum_{n=1}^{\infty} (u_n - u_{n-1})$ converges to zero, i.e. if $u_n \to 0$, which is the case when $R(c - a - b) > 0$.

Also, by § 2·38 and § 3·71, the left-hand side tends to

$$c(a + b - c) F(a, b; c; 1) + (c - a)(c - b) F(a, b; c + 1; 1)$$

under the same condition; and therefore

$$F(a, b; c; 1) = \frac{(c - a)(c - b)}{c(c - a - b)} F(a, b; c + 1; 1).$$

Repeating this process, we see that

$$F(a, b; c; 1) = \left\{ \prod_{n=0}^{m-1} \frac{(c - a + n)(c - b + n)}{(c + n)(c - a - b + n)} \right\} F(a, b; c + m; 1)$$
$$= \left\{ \lim_{m \to \infty} \prod_{n=0}^{m-1} \frac{(c - a + n)(c - b + n)}{(c + n)(c - a - b + n)} \right\} \lim_{m \to \infty} F(a, b; c + m; 1),$$

if these two limits exist.

But (§ 12·13) the former limit is $\dfrac{\Gamma(c) \Gamma(c - a - b)}{\Gamma(c - a) \Gamma(c - b)}$, if c is not a negative integer; and, if $u_n(a, b, c)$ be the coefficient of x^n in $F(a, b; c; x)$, and $m > |c|$, we have

$$|F(a, b; c + m; 1) - 1| \leqslant \sum_{n=1}^{\infty} |u_n(a, b, c + m)|$$
$$\leqslant \sum_{n=1}^{\infty} u_n(|a|, |b|, m - |c|)$$
$$< \frac{|ab|}{m - |c|} \sum_{n=0}^{\infty} u_n(|a| + 1, |b| + 1, m + 1 - |c|).$$

Now the last series converges, when $m > |c| + |a| + |b| - 1$, and is a positive decreasing function of m; therefore, since $\{m - |c|\}^{-1} \to 0$, we have

$$\lim_{m \to \infty} F(a, b; c + m; 1) = 1;$$

and therefore, finally,

$$F(a, b; c; 1) = \frac{\Gamma(c) \Gamma(c - a - b)}{\Gamma(c - a) \Gamma(c - b)}.$$

14·2. *The differential equation satisfied by $F(a, b; c; z)$.*

The reader will verify without difficulty, by the methods of § 10·3, that the hypergeometric series is an integral valid near $z = 0$ of the *hypergeometric equation*[*]

$$z(1 - z)\frac{d^2u}{dz^2} + \{c - (a + b + 1)z\}\frac{du}{dz} - abu = 0;$$

from § 10·3, it is apparent that every point is an 'ordinary point' of this equation, with the exception of $0, 1, \infty$, and that these are 'regular points.'

Example. Shew that an integral of the equation

$$z\left(z\frac{d}{dz} + a\right)\left(z\frac{d}{dz} + b\right)u - \left(z\frac{d}{dz} - a\right)\left(z\frac{d}{dz} - \beta\right)u = 0$$

is

$$z^a F(a + a, \ b + a; \ a - \beta + 1; \ z).$$

14·3. *Solutions of Riemann's P-equation by hypergeometric functions.*

In § 10·72 it was observed that Riemann's differential equation[†]

$$\frac{d^2u}{dz^2} + \left\{\frac{1 - \alpha - \alpha'}{z - a} + \frac{1 - \beta - \beta'}{z - b} + \frac{1 - \gamma - \gamma'}{z - c}\right\}\frac{du}{dz}$$

$$+ \left\{\frac{\alpha\alpha'(a - b)(a - c)}{z - a} + \frac{\beta\beta'(b - c)(b - a)}{z - b} + \frac{\gamma\gamma'(c - a)(c - b)}{z - c}\right\}$$

$$\times \frac{u}{(z - a)(z - b)(z - c)} = 0,$$

by a suitable change of variables, could be reduced to a hypergeometric equation; and, carrying out the change, we see that a solution of Riemann's equation is

$$\left(\frac{z - a}{z - b}\right)^a \left(\frac{z - c}{z - b}\right)^\gamma F\left\{\alpha + \beta + \gamma, \ \alpha + \beta' + \gamma; \ 1 + \alpha - \alpha'; \frac{(z - a)(c - b)}{(z - b)(c - a)}\right\},$$

provided that $\alpha - \alpha'$ is not a negative integer; for simplicity, we shall, throughout this section, suppose that no one of the exponent differences $\alpha - \alpha'$, $\beta - \beta'$, $\gamma - \gamma'$ is zero or an integer, as (§ 10·32) in this exceptional case the general solution of the differential equation may involve logarithmic terms; the formulae in the exceptional case will be found in a memoir[‡] by Lindelöf, to which the reader is referred.

Now if α be interchanged with α', or γ with γ', in this expression, it must still satisfy Riemann's equation, since the latter is unaffected by this change.

---

[*] This equation was given by Gauss.

[†] The constants are subject to the condition $\alpha + \alpha' + \beta + \beta' + \gamma + \gamma' = 1$.

[‡] *Acta Soc. Scient. Fennicae*, XIX. (1893). See also Klein's lithographed Lectures, *Ueber die hypergeometrische Funktion* (Leipzig, 1894).

We thus obtain altogether four expressions, namely,

$$u_1 = \left(\frac{z-a}{z-b}\right)^{\alpha} \left(\frac{z-c}{z-b}\right)^{\gamma} F\left\{\alpha+\beta+\gamma, \ \alpha+\beta'+\gamma; \ 1+\alpha-\alpha'; \ \frac{(c-b)(z-a)}{(c-a)(z-b)}\right\},$$

$$u_2 = \left(\frac{z-a}{z-b}\right)^{\alpha'} \left(\frac{z-c}{z-b}\right)^{\gamma} F\left\{\alpha'+\beta+\gamma, \ \alpha'+\beta'+\gamma; \ 1+\alpha'-\alpha; \ \frac{(c-b)(z-a)}{(c-a)(z-b)}\right\},$$

$$u_3 = \left(\frac{z-a}{z-b}\right)^{\alpha} \left(\frac{z-c}{z-b}\right)^{\gamma'} F\left\{\alpha+\beta+\gamma', \ \alpha+\beta'+\gamma'; \ 1+\alpha-\alpha'; \ \frac{(c-b)(z-a)}{(c-a)(z-b)}\right\},$$

$$u_4 = \left(\frac{z-a}{z-b}\right)^{\alpha'} \left(\frac{z-c}{z-b}\right)^{\gamma'} F\left\{\alpha'+\beta+\gamma', \ \alpha'+\beta'+\gamma'; \ 1+\alpha'-\alpha; \ \frac{(c-b)(z-a)}{(c-a)(z-b)}\right\},$$

which are all solutions of the differential equation.

Moreover, the differential equation is unaltered if the triads (α, α', a), (β, β', b), (γ, γ', c) are interchanged in any manner. If therefore we make such changes in the above solutions, they will still be solutions of the differential equation.

There are five such changes possible, for we may write

$$\{b, c, a\}, \ \{c, a, b\}, \ \{a, c, b\}, \ \{c, b, a\}, \ \{b, a, c\}$$

in turn in place of $\{a, b, c\}$, with corresponding changes of $\alpha, \alpha', \beta, \beta', \gamma, \gamma'$.

We thus obtain $4 \times 5 = 20$ new expressions, which with the original four make altogether twenty-four particular solutions of Riemann's equation, in terms of hypergeometric series.

The twenty new solutions may be written down as follows:

$$u_5 = \left(\frac{z-b}{z-c}\right)^{\beta} \left(\frac{z-a}{z-c}\right)^{\alpha} F\left\{\beta+\gamma+\alpha, \ \beta+\gamma'+\alpha; \ 1+\beta-\beta'; \ \frac{(a-c)(z-b)}{(a-b)(z-c)}\right\},$$

$$u_6 = \left(\frac{z-b}{z-c}\right)^{\beta'} \left(\frac{z-a}{z-c}\right)^{\alpha} F\left\{\beta'+\gamma+\alpha, \ \beta'+\gamma'+\alpha; \ 1+\beta'-\beta; \ \frac{(a-c)(z-b)}{(a-b)(z-c)}\right\},$$

$$u_7 = \left(\frac{z-b}{z-c}\right)^{\beta} \left(\frac{z-a}{z-c}\right)^{\alpha'} F\left\{\beta+\gamma+\alpha', \ \beta+\gamma'+\alpha'; \ 1+\beta-\beta'; \ \frac{(a-c)(z-b)}{(a-b)(z-c)}\right\},$$

$$u_8 = \left(\frac{z-b}{z-c}\right)^{\beta'} \left(\frac{z-a}{z-c}\right)^{\alpha'} F\left\{\beta'+\gamma+\alpha', \ \beta'+\gamma'+\alpha'; \ 1+\beta'-\beta; \ \frac{(a-c)(z-b)}{(a-b)(z-c)}\right\},$$

$$u_9 = \left(\frac{z-c}{z-a}\right)^{\gamma} \left(\frac{z-b}{z-a}\right)^{\beta} F\left\{\gamma+\alpha+\beta, \ \gamma+\alpha'+\beta; \ 1+\gamma-\gamma'; \ \frac{(b-a)(z-c)}{(b-c)(z-a)}\right\},$$

$$u_{10} = \left(\frac{z-c}{z-a}\right)^{\gamma'} \left(\frac{z-b}{z-a}\right)^{\beta} F\left\{\gamma'+\alpha+\beta, \ \gamma'+\alpha'+\beta; \ 1+\gamma'-\gamma; \ \frac{(b-a)(z-c)}{(b-c)(z-a)}\right\},$$

$$u_{11} = \left(\frac{z-c}{z-a}\right)^{\gamma} \left(\frac{z-b}{z-a}\right)^{\beta'} F\left\{\gamma+\alpha+\beta', \ \gamma+\alpha'+\beta'; \ 1+\gamma-\gamma'; \ \frac{(b-a)(z-c)}{(b-c)(z-a)}\right\},$$

$$u_{12} = \left(\frac{z-c}{z-a}\right)^{\gamma'} \left(\frac{z-b}{z-a}\right)^{\beta'} F\left\{\gamma'+\alpha+\beta', \ \gamma'+\alpha'+\beta'; \ 1+\gamma'-\gamma; \ \frac{(b-a)(z-c)}{(b-c)(z-a)}\right\},$$

$$u_{13} = \left(\frac{z-a}{z-c}\right)^{\alpha} \left(\frac{z-b}{z-c}\right)^{\beta} F\left\{\alpha+\gamma+\beta,\ \alpha+\gamma'+\beta;\ 1+\alpha-\alpha';\ \frac{(b-c)(z-a)}{(b-a)(z-c)}\right\},$$

$$u_{14} = \left(\frac{z-a}{z-c}\right)^{\alpha'} \left(\frac{z-b}{z-c}\right)^{\beta} F\left\{\alpha'+\gamma+\beta,\ \alpha'+\gamma'+\beta;\ 1+\alpha'-\alpha;\ \frac{(b-c)(z-a)}{(b-a)(z-c)}\right\},$$

$$u_{15} = \left(\frac{z-a}{z-c}\right)^{\alpha} \left(\frac{z-b}{z-c}\right)^{\beta'} F\left\{\alpha+\gamma+\beta',\ \alpha+\gamma'+\beta';\ 1+\alpha-\alpha';\ \frac{(b-c)(z-a)}{(b-a)(z-c)}\right\},$$

$$u_{16} = \left(\frac{z-a}{z-c}\right)^{\alpha'} \left(\frac{z-b}{z-c}\right)^{\beta'} F\left\{\alpha'+\gamma+\beta',\ \alpha'+\gamma'+\beta';\ 1+\alpha'-\alpha;\ \frac{(b-c)(z-a)}{(b-a)(z-c)}\right\},$$

$$u_{17} = \left(\frac{z-c}{z-b}\right)^{\gamma} \left(\frac{z-a}{z-b}\right)^{\alpha} F\left\{\gamma+\beta+\alpha,\ \gamma+\beta'+\alpha;\ 1+\gamma-\gamma';\ \frac{(a-b)(z-c)}{(a-c)(z-b)}\right\},$$

$$u_{18} = \left(\frac{z-c}{z-b}\right)^{\gamma'} \left(\frac{z-a}{z-b}\right)^{\alpha} F\left\{\gamma'+\beta+\alpha,\ \gamma'+\beta'+\alpha;\ 1+\gamma'-\gamma;\ \frac{(a-b)(z-c)}{(a-c)(z-b)}\right\},$$

$$u_{19} = \left(\frac{z-c}{z-b}\right)^{\gamma} \left(\frac{z-a}{z-b}\right)^{\alpha'} F\left\{\gamma+\beta+\alpha',\ \gamma+\beta'+\alpha';\ 1+\gamma-\gamma';\ \frac{(a-b)(z-c)}{(a-c)(z-b)}\right\},$$

$$u_{20} = \left(\frac{z-c}{z-b}\right)^{\gamma'} \left(\frac{z-a}{z-b}\right)^{\alpha'} F\left\{\gamma'+\beta+\alpha',\ \gamma'+\beta'+\alpha';\ 1+\gamma'-\gamma;\ \frac{(a-b)(z-c)}{(a-c)(z-b)}\right\},$$

$$u_{21} = \left(\frac{z-b}{z-a}\right)^{\beta} \left(\frac{z-c}{z-a}\right)^{\gamma} F\left\{\beta+\alpha+\gamma,\ \beta+\alpha'+\gamma;\ 1+\beta-\beta';\ \frac{(c-a)(z-b)}{(c-b)(z-a)}\right\},$$

$$u_{22} = \left(\frac{z-b}{z-a}\right)^{\beta'} \left(\frac{z-c}{z-a}\right)^{\gamma} F\left\{\beta'+\alpha+\gamma,\ \beta'+\alpha'+\gamma;\ 1+\beta'-\beta;\ \frac{(c-a)(z-b)}{(c-b)(z-a)}\right\},$$

$$u_{23} = \left(\frac{z-b}{z-a}\right)^{\beta} \left(\frac{z-c}{z-a}\right)^{\gamma'} F\left\{\beta+\alpha+\gamma',\ \beta+\alpha'+\gamma';\ 1+\beta-\beta';\ \frac{(c-a)(z-b)}{(c-b)(z-a)}\right\},$$

$$u_{24} = \left(\frac{z-b}{z-a}\right)^{\beta'} \left(\frac{z-c}{z-a}\right)^{\gamma'} F\left\{\beta'+\alpha+\gamma',\ \beta'+\alpha'+\gamma';\ 1+\beta'-\beta;\ \frac{(c-a)(z-b)}{(c-b)(z-a)}\right\},$$

By writing 0, $1-C$, A, B, 0, $C-A-B$, x for α, α', β, β', γ, γ', $\frac{(z-a)(c-b)}{(z-b)(c-a)}$ respectively, we obtain 24 solutions of the hypergeometric equation satisfied by $F(A, B; C; x)$.

The existence of these 24 solutions was first shewn by Kummer*.

14·4. *Relations between particular solutions of the hypergeometric equation.*

It has just been shewn that 24 expressions involving hypergeometric series are solutions of the hypergeometric equation; and, from the general theory of linear differential equations of the second order, it follows that, if any three have a common domain of existence, there must be a linear relation with constant coefficients connecting those three solutions.

If we simplify u_1, u_2, u_3, u_4; u_{17}, u_{18}; u_{21}, u_{22} in the manner indicated at

* *Journal für Math.* xv. (1836), pp. 39–83, 127–172. They are obtained in a different manner in Forsyth's *Treatise on Differential Equations*, Chap. vi.

the end of § 14·3, we obtain the following solutions of the hypergeometric equation with elements A, B, C, x:

$$y_1 = F(A, B; C; x),$$

$$y_2 = (-x)^{1-C} F(A - C + 1, B - C + 1; 2 - C; x),$$

$$y_3 = (1 - x)^{C-A-B} F(C - B, C - A; C; x),$$

$$y_4 = (-x)^{1-C} (1 - x)^{C-A-B} F(1 - B, 1 - A; 2 - C; x),$$

$$y_{17} = F(A, B; A + B - C + 1; 1 - x),$$

$$y_{18} = (1 - x)^{C-A-B} F(C - B, C - A; C - A - B + 1; 1 - x),$$

$$y_{21} = (-x)^{-B} F(A, A - C + 1; A - B + 1; x^{-1}),$$

$$y_{22} = (-x)^{-A} F(B, B - C + 1; B - A + 1; x^{-1}).$$

If $|\arg(1 - x)| < \pi$, it is easy to see from § 2·53 that, when $|x| < 1$, the relations connecting y_1, y_2, y_3, y_4 must be $y_1 = y_3$, $y_2 = y_4$, by considering the form of the expansions near $x = 0$ of the series involved.

In this manner we can group the functions $u_1, \ldots u_{24}$ into six sets of four[*], viz. $u_1, u_3, u_{13}, u_{15}; u_2, u_4, u_{14}, u_{16}; u_5, u_7, u_{21}, u_{23}; u_6, u_8, u_{22}, u_{24}; u_9, u_{11}, u_{17}, u_{19}; u_{10}, u_{12}, u_{18}, u_{20}$, such that members of the same set are constant multiples of one another throughout a suitably chosen domain.

In particular, we observe that u_1, u_3, u_{13}, u_{15} are constant multiples of a function which (by §§ 5·4, 2·53) can be expanded in the form

$$(z - a)^a \left\{ 1 + \sum_{n=1}^{\infty} e_n (z - a)^n \right\}$$

when $|z - a|$ is sufficiently small; when $\arg(z - a)$ is so restricted that $(z - a)^a$ is one-valued, this solution of Riemann's equation is usually written $P^{(a)}$. And $P^{(a')}$; $P^{(\beta)}, P^{(\beta')}$; $P^{(\gamma)}, P^{(\gamma')}$ are defined in a similar manner when $|z - a|, |z - b|, |z - c|$ respectively are sufficiently small.

To obtain the relations which connect three members of separate sets of solutions is much more difficult. The relations have been obtained by elaborate transformations of the double circuit integrals which will be obtained later in § 14·61; but a more simple and singularly elegant method has recently been discovered by Barnes; of his investigation we shall give a brief account.

14·5. *Barnes' contour integrals for the hypergeometric function*[†].

Consider
$$\frac{1}{2\pi i} \int_{-\infty i}^{\infty i} \frac{\Gamma(a + s) \Gamma(b + s) \Gamma(-s)}{\Gamma(c + s)} (- z)^s ds,$$

where $|\arg(-z)| < \pi$, and the path of integration is curved (if necessary) to ensure that the poles of $\Gamma(a + s)\Gamma(b + s)$, viz. $s = -a - n, -b - n$ $(n = 0, 1, 2, \ldots)$,

---

* The special formula
$$F(A, 1; C; x) = \frac{1}{1 - x} F\left(C - A, 1; C; \frac{x}{x - 1}\right),$$
which is derivable from the relation connecting u_1 with u_{13}, was discovered in 1730 by Stirling, *Methodus Differentialis*, prop. VII.

† *Proc. London Math. Soc.* (2), VI. (1908), pp. 141–177. References to previous work on similar topics by Pincherle, Mellin and Barnes are there given.

lie on the left of the path and the poles of $\Gamma(-s)$, viz. $s = 0, 1, 2, \ldots$, lie on the right of the path*.

From § 13·6 it follows that the integrand is

$$O\left[|s|^{a+b-c-1}\exp\{-\arg(-z)\,.\,I(s) - \pi|I(s)|\}\right]$$

as $s \to \infty$ on the contour, and hence it is easily seen (§ 5·32) that the integrand is an analytic function of z throughout the domain defined by the inequality $|\arg z| \leqslant \pi - \delta$, where δ is any positive number.

Now, taking note of the relation $\Gamma(-s)\,\Gamma(1+s) = -\pi\operatorname{cosec} s\pi$, consider

$$\frac{1}{2\pi i}\int_C \frac{\Gamma(a+s)\,\Gamma(b+s)}{\Gamma(c+s)\,\Gamma(1+s)}\frac{\pi(-z)^s}{\sin s\pi}\,ds,$$

where C is the semicircle of radius $N + \frac{1}{2}$ on the right of the imaginary axis with centre at the origin, and N is an integer.

Now, by § 13·6, we have

$$\frac{\Gamma(a+s)\,\Gamma(b+s)}{\Gamma(c+s)\,\Gamma(1+s)}\frac{\pi(-z)^s}{\sin s\pi} = O\left(N^{a+b-c-1}\right).\frac{(-z)^s}{\sin s\pi}$$

as $N \to \infty$, the constant implied in the symbol O being independent of $\arg s$ when s is on the semicircle; and, if $s = \left(N + \frac{1}{2}\right)e^{i\theta}$ and $|z| < 1$, we have

$$(-z)^s\operatorname{cosec} s\pi = O\left[\exp\left\{\left(N + \tfrac{1}{2}\right)\cos\theta\log|z| - \left(N + \tfrac{1}{2}\right)\sin\theta\arg(-z)\right.\right.$$
$$\left.\left. - \left(N + \tfrac{1}{2}\right)\pi|\sin\theta|\right\}\right]$$
$$= O\left[\exp\left\{\left(N + \tfrac{1}{2}\right)\cos\theta\log|z| - \left(N + \tfrac{1}{2}\right)\delta|\sin\theta|\right\}\right]$$
$$= \begin{cases} O\left[\exp\left\{2^{-\frac{1}{2}}\left(N + \tfrac{1}{2}\right)\log|z|\right\}\right] & 0 \leqslant|\theta| \leqslant\tfrac{1}{4}\pi, \\[2mm] O\left[\exp\left\{-2^{-\frac{1}{2}}\delta\left(N + \tfrac{1}{2}\right)\right\}\right] & \tfrac{1}{4}\pi \leqslant|\theta| \leqslant\tfrac{1}{2}\pi. \end{cases}$$

Hence *if* $\log|z|$ *is negative* (i.e. $|z| < 1$), the integrand tends to zero sufficiently rapidly (for all values of θ under consideration) to ensure that $\int_C \to 0$ as $N \to \infty$.

Now

$$\int_{-\infty i}^{\infty i} - \left\{\int_{-\infty i}^{-(N+\frac{1}{2})i} + \int_C + \int_{(N+\frac{1}{2})i}^{\infty i}\right\},$$

by Cauchy's theorem, is equal to minus $2\pi i$ times the sum of the residues of the integrand at the points $s = 0, 1, 2, \ldots N$. Make $N \to \infty$, and the last

---

* It is assumed that a and b are such that the contour can be drawn, i.e. that a and b are not negative integers (in which case the hypergeometric series is merely a polynomial).

three integrals tend to zero when $|\arg(-z)| \leqslant \pi - \delta$, and $|z| < 1$, and so, in these circumstances,

$$\frac{1}{2\pi i} \int_{-\infty i}^{\infty i} \frac{\Gamma(a+s)\,\Gamma(b+s)\,\Gamma(-s)}{\Gamma(c+s)} (-z)^s ds = \lim_{N \to \infty} \sum_{n=0}^{N} \frac{\Gamma(a+n)\,\Gamma(b+n)}{\Gamma(c+n).\,n!} z^n,$$

the general term in this summation being the residue of the integrand at $s = n$.

Thus, an analytic function (namely the integral under consideration) exists throughout the domain defined by the inequality $|\arg z| < \pi$, and, when $|z| < 1$, this analytic function may be represented by the series

$$\sum_{n=0}^{\infty} \frac{\Gamma(a+n)\,\Gamma(b+n)}{\Gamma(c+n).\,n!} z^n.$$

The symbol $F(a, b; c; z)$ will, in future, be used to denote this function divided by $\Gamma(a)\,\Gamma(b)/\Gamma(c)$.

14·51.   *The continuation of the hypergeometric series.*

To obtain a representation of the function $F(a, b; c; z)$ in the form of series convergent when $|z| > 1$, we shall employ the integral obtained in § 14·5. If D be the semicircle of radius ρ on the left of the imaginary axis with centre at the origin, it may be shewn* by the methods of § 14·5 that

$$\frac{1}{2\pi i} \int_{D} \frac{\Gamma(a+s)\,\Gamma(b+s)\,\Gamma(-s)}{\Gamma(c+s)} (-z)^s ds \to 0$$

as $\rho \to \infty$, provided that $|\arg(-z)| < \pi$, $|z| > 1$ and $\rho \to \infty$ in such a way that the lower bound of the distance of D from poles of the integrand is a *positive* number (not zero).

Hence it can be proved (as in the corresponding work of § 14·5) that, when $|\arg(-z)| < \pi$ and $|z| > 1$,

$$\frac{1}{2\pi i} \int \frac{\Gamma(a+s)\,\Gamma(b+s)\,\Gamma(-s)}{\Gamma(c+s)} (-z)^s ds$$

$$= \sum_{n=0}^{\infty} \frac{\Gamma(a+n)\,\Gamma(1-c+a+n)}{\Gamma(1+n)\,\Gamma(1-b+a+n)} \frac{\sin(c-a-n)\pi}{\cos n\pi \sin(b-a-n)\pi} (-z)^{-a-n}$$

$$+ \sum_{n=0}^{\infty} \frac{\Gamma(b+n)\,\Gamma(1-c+b+n)}{\Gamma(1+n)\,\Gamma(1-a+b+n)} \frac{\sin(c-b-n)\pi}{\cos n\pi \sin(a-b-n)\pi} (-z)^{-b-n},$$

the expressions in these summations being the residues of the integrand at the points $s = -a-n$, $s = -b-n$ respectively.

It then follows at once on simplifying these series that the analytic

---

* In considering the asymptotic expansion of the integrand when $|s|$ is large on the contour or on D, it is simplest to transform $\Gamma(a+s)$, $\Gamma(b+s)$, $\Gamma(c+s)$ by the relation of § 12·14.

continuation of the series, by which the hypergeometric function was originally defined, is given by the equation

$$\frac{\Gamma(a)\Gamma(b)}{\Gamma(c)} F(a,b;c;z) = \frac{\Gamma(a)\Gamma(a-b)}{\Gamma(a-c)}(-z)^{-a} F(a,1-c+a;1-b+a;z^{-1})$$

$$+ \frac{\Gamma(b)\Gamma(b-a)}{\Gamma(b-c)}(-z)^{-b} F(b,1-c+b;1-a+b;z^{-1}),$$

where $|\arg(-z)| < \pi$.

It is readily seen that each of the three terms in this equation is a solution of the hypergeometric equation (see § 14·4).

This result has to be modified when $a-b$ is an integer or zero, as some of the poles of $\Gamma(a+s)\Gamma(b+s)$ are double poles, and the right-hand side then may involve logarithmic terms, in accordance with § 14·3.

Corollary. Putting $b=c$, we see that, if $|\arg(-z)| < \pi$,

$$\Gamma(a)(1-z)^{-a} = \frac{1}{2\pi i}\int_{-\infty i}^{\infty i}\Gamma(a+s)\Gamma(-s)(-z)^s ds,$$

where $(1-z)^{-a} \to 1$ as $z \to 0$, and so the value of $|\arg(1-z)|$ which is less than π always has to be taken in this equation, in virtue of the *cut* (see § 14·1) from 0 to $+\infty$ caused by the inequality $|\arg(-z)| < \pi$.

14·52. *Barnes' lemma that, if the path of integration is curved so that the poles of $\Gamma(\gamma-s)\Gamma(\delta-s)$ lie on the right of the path and the poles of $\Gamma(a+s)\Gamma(\beta+s)$ lie on the left*, then*

$$\frac{1}{2\pi i}\int_{-\infty i}^{\infty i}\Gamma(a+s)\Gamma(\beta+s)\Gamma(\gamma-s)\Gamma(\delta-s)ds = \frac{\Gamma(a+\gamma)\Gamma(a+\delta)\Gamma(\beta+\gamma)\Gamma(\beta+\delta)}{\Gamma(a+\beta+\gamma+\delta)}.$$

Write I for the expression on the left.

If C be defined to be the semicircle of radius ρ on the right of the imaginary axis with centre at the origin, and if $\rho \to \infty$ in such a way that the lower bound of the distance of C from the poles of $\Gamma(\gamma-s)\Gamma(\delta-s)$ is *positive* (not zero), it is readily seen that

$$\Gamma(a+s)\Gamma(\beta+s)\Gamma(\gamma-s)\Gamma(\delta-s) = \frac{\Gamma(a+s)\Gamma(\beta+s)}{\Gamma(1-\gamma+s)\Gamma(1-\delta+s)}\pi^2\operatorname{cosec}(\gamma-s)\pi\operatorname{cosec}(\delta-s)\pi$$

$$= O[s^{a+\beta+\gamma+\delta-2}\exp\{-2\pi|I(s)|\}],$$

as $|s| \to \infty$ on the imaginary axis or on C.

Hence the original integral converges; and $\int_C \to 0$ as $\rho \to \infty$, when $R(a+\beta+\gamma+\delta-1) < 0$. Thus, as in § 14·5, the integral involved in I is $-2\pi i$ times the sum of the residues of the integrand at the poles of $\Gamma(\gamma-s)\Gamma(\delta-s)$; evaluating these residues we get†

$$I = \sum_{n=0}^{\infty}\frac{\Gamma(a+\gamma+n)\Gamma(\beta+\gamma+n)}{\Gamma(n+1)\Gamma(1+\gamma-\delta+n)}\frac{\pi}{\sin(\delta-\gamma)\pi} + \sum_{n=0}^{\infty}\frac{\Gamma(a+\delta+n)\Gamma(\beta+\delta+n)}{\Gamma(n+1)\Gamma(1+\delta-\gamma+n)}\frac{\pi}{\sin(\gamma-\delta)\pi}.$$

---

* It is supposed that a,β,γ,δ are such that no pole of the first set coincides with any pole of the second set.

† These two series converge (§ 2·38).

And so, using the result of § 12·14 freely, by § 14·11 :

$$I = \frac{\pi}{\sin(\gamma - \delta)\pi} \left\{ \frac{\Gamma(a+\delta)\,\Gamma(\beta+\delta)}{\Gamma(1-\gamma+\delta)} F(a+\delta, \beta+\delta; 1-\gamma+\delta; 1) \right.$$

$$\left. - \frac{\Gamma(a+\gamma)\,\Gamma(\beta+\gamma)}{\Gamma(1-\delta+\gamma)} F(a+\gamma, \beta+\gamma; 1-\delta+\gamma; 1) \right\}$$

$$= \frac{\pi\Gamma(1-a-\beta-\gamma-\delta)}{\sin(\gamma-\delta)\pi} \left\{ \frac{\Gamma(a+\delta)\,\Gamma(\beta+\delta)}{\Gamma(1-a-\gamma)\,\Gamma(1-\beta-\gamma)} - \frac{\Gamma(a+\gamma)\,\Gamma(\beta+\gamma)}{\Gamma(1-a-\delta)\,\Gamma(1-\beta-\delta)} \right\}$$

$$= \frac{\Gamma(a+\gamma)\,\Gamma(\beta+\gamma)\,\Gamma(a+\delta)\,\Gamma(\beta+\delta)}{\Gamma(a+\beta+\gamma+\delta)\sin(a+\beta+\gamma+\delta)\pi\sin(\gamma-\delta)\pi} \{\sin(a+\gamma)\pi\sin(\beta+\gamma)\pi$$

$$- \sin(a+\delta)\pi\sin(\beta+\delta)\pi\}.$$

But $\quad 2\sin(a+\gamma)\pi\sin(\beta+\gamma)\pi - 2\sin(a+\delta)\pi\sin(\beta+\delta)\pi$

$$= \cos(a-\beta)\pi - \cos(a+\beta+2\gamma)\pi - \cos(a-\beta)\pi + \cos(a+\beta+2\delta)\pi$$

$$= 2\sin(\gamma-\delta)\pi\sin(a+\beta+\gamma+\delta)\pi.$$

Therefore $\qquad I = \dfrac{\Gamma(a+\gamma)\,\Gamma(\beta+\gamma)\,\Gamma(a+\delta)\,\Gamma(\beta+\delta)}{\Gamma(a+\beta+\gamma+\delta)},$

which is the required result; it has, however, only been proved when

$$R(a+\beta+\gamma+\delta-1) < 0;$$

but, by the theory of analytic continuation, it is true throughout the domain through which both sides of the equation are analytic functions of, say, a; and hence it is true for all values of a, β, γ, δ for which none of the poles of $\Gamma(a+s)\,\Gamma(\beta+s)$, *qua* function of s, coincide with any of the poles of $\Gamma(\gamma-s)\,\Gamma(\delta-s)$.

Corollary. Writing $s+k$, $a-k$, $\beta-k$, $\gamma+k$, $\delta+k$ in place of s, a, β, γ, δ, we see that the result is still true when the limits of integration are $-k \pm \infty i$, where k is any real constant.

14·53. *The connexion between hypergeometric functions of z and of $1-z$.*

We have seen that, if $|\arg(-z)| < \pi$,

$$\frac{\Gamma(a)\,\Gamma(b)}{\Gamma(c)} F(a, b; c; z) = \frac{1}{2\pi i} \int_{-\infty i}^{\infty i} \frac{\Gamma(a+s)\,\Gamma(b+s)\,\Gamma(-s)}{\Gamma(c+s)} (-z)^s \, ds$$

$$= \frac{1}{2\pi i} \int_{-\infty i}^{\infty i} \left\{ \frac{1}{2\pi i} \int_{-k-\infty i}^{-k+\infty i} \Gamma(a+t)\,\Gamma(b+t)\,\Gamma(s-t)\,\Gamma(c-a-b-t)\,dt \right\}$$

$$\times \frac{\Gamma(-s)(-z)^s}{\Gamma(c-a)\,\Gamma(c-b)}\,ds,$$

by Barnes' lemma.

If k be so chosen that the lower bound of the distance between the s contour and the t contour is positive (not zero), it may be shewn that the order of the integrations[*] may be interchanged.

Carrying out the interchange, we see that if $\arg(1-z)$ be given its principal value,

$$\Gamma(c-a)\,\Gamma(c-b)\,\Gamma(a)\,\Gamma(b)\,F(a, b; c; z)/\Gamma(c)$$

$$= \frac{1}{2\pi i} \int_{-k-\infty i}^{-k+\infty i} \Gamma(a+t)\,\Gamma(b+t)\,\Gamma(c-a-b-t) \left\{ \frac{1}{2\pi i} \int_{-\infty i}^{\infty i} \Gamma(s-t)\,\Gamma(-s)(-z)^s\,ds \right\} dt$$

$$= \frac{1}{2\pi i} \int_{-k-\infty i}^{-k+\infty i} \Gamma(a+t)\,\Gamma(b+t)\,\Gamma(c-a-b-t)\,\Gamma(-t)(1-z)^t\,dt.$$

---

[*] Methods similar to those of § 4·51 may be used, or it may be proved without much difficulty that conditions established by Bromwich, *Infinite Series*, § 177, are satisfied.

Now, when $|\arg(1-z)| < 2\pi$ and $|1-z| < 1$, this last integral may be evaluated by the methods of Barnes' lemma (§ 14·52); and so we deduce that

$$\Gamma(c-a)\,\Gamma(c-b)\,\Gamma(a)\,\Gamma(b)\,F(a,\,b\,;\;c\,;\;z)$$

$$=\Gamma(c)\,\Gamma(a)\,\Gamma(b)\,\Gamma(c-a-b)\,F(a,\,b\,;\;a+b-c+1\,;\;1-z)$$

$$+\Gamma(c)\,\Gamma(c-a)\,\Gamma(c-b)\,\Gamma(a+b-c)\,(1-z)^{c-a-b}\,F(c-a,\,c-b\,;\;c-a-b+1\,;\;1-z),$$

a result which shews the nature of the singularity of $F(a,\,b\,;\;c\,;\;z)$ at $z=1$.

This result has to be modified if $c-a-b$ is an integer or zero, as then

$$\Gamma(a+t)\,\Gamma(b+t)\,\Gamma(c-a-b-t)\,\Gamma(-t)$$

has double poles, and logarithmic terms may appear. With this exception, the result is valid when $|\arg(-z)| < \pi$, $|\arg(1-z)| < \pi$.

Taking $|z| < 1$, we may make z tend to a real value, and we see that the result still holds for real values of z such that $0 < z < 1$.

14·6. *Solution of Riemann's equation by a contour integral.*

We next proceed to establish a result relating to the expression of the hypergeometric function by means of contour integrals.

Let the dependent variable u in Riemann's equation (§ 10·7) be replaced by a new dependent variable I, defined by the relation

$$u = (z-a)^\alpha\,(z-b)^\beta\,(z-c)^\gamma\,I.$$

The differential equation satisfied by I is easily found to be

$$\frac{d^2I}{dz^2} + \left\{\frac{1+\alpha-\alpha'}{z-a} + \frac{1+\beta-\beta'}{z-b} + \frac{1+\gamma-\gamma'}{z-c}\right\}\frac{dI}{dz}$$

$$+ \frac{(\alpha+\beta+\gamma)\,\{(\alpha+\beta+\gamma+1)\,z + \Sigma a\,(\alpha+\beta'+\gamma'-1)\}}{(z-a)(z-b)(z-c)}\,I = 0,$$

which can be written in the form

$$Q(z)\frac{d^2I}{dz^2} - \{(\lambda-2)\,Q'(z) + R(z)\}\frac{dI}{dz}$$

$$+ \{\tfrac{1}{2}(\lambda-2)(\lambda-1)\,Q''(z) + (\lambda-1)\,R'(z)\}\,I = 0,$$

where

$$\begin{cases} \lambda = 1-\alpha-\beta-\gamma = \alpha'+\beta'+\gamma', \\ Q(z) = (z-a)(z-b)(z-c), \\ R(z) = \Sigma\,(\alpha'+\beta+\gamma)(z-b)(z-c). \end{cases}$$

It must be observed that the function I is not analytic at ∞, and consequently the above differential equation in I is not a case of the generalised hypergeometric equation.

We shall now shew that this differential equation can be satisfied by an integral of the form

$$I = \int_C (t-a)^{\alpha'+\beta+\gamma-1}\,(t-b)^{\alpha+\beta'+\gamma-1}\,(t-c)^{\alpha+\beta+\gamma'-1}\,(z-t)^{-\alpha-\beta-\gamma}\,dt,$$

provided that C, the contour of integration, is suitably chosen.

For, if we substitute this value of I in the differential equation, the condition* that the equation should be satisfied becomes

$$\int_C (t-a)^{a'+\beta+\gamma-1}(t-b)^{a+\beta'+\gamma-1}(t-c)^{a+\beta+\gamma'-1}(z-t)^{-a-\beta-\gamma-2}K\,dt = 0,$$

where

$$K = (\lambda-2)\left\{Q(z) + (t-z)\,Q'(z) + \frac{1}{2}(t-z)^2\,Q''(z)\right\}$$

$$+ (t-z)\{R(z) + (t-z)\,R'(z)\}$$

$$= (\lambda-2)\{Q(t) - (t-z)^3\} + (t-z)\{R(t) - (t-z)^2\,\Sigma(a'+\beta+\gamma)\}$$

$$= -(1+a+\beta+\gamma)(t-a)(t-b)(t-c)$$

$$+ \Sigma(a'+\beta+\gamma)(t-b)(t-c)(t-z).$$

It follows that the condition to be satisfied reduces to $\displaystyle\int_C \frac{dV}{dt}\,dt = 0$, where

$$V = (t-a)^{a'+\beta+\gamma}(t-b)^{a+\beta'+\gamma}(t-c)^{a+\beta+\gamma'}(t-z)^{-(1+a+\beta+\gamma)}.$$

The integral I is therefore a solution of the differential equation, when C is such that V resumes its initial value after t has described C.

Now

$$V = (t-a)^{a'+\beta+\gamma-1}(t-b)^{a+\beta'+\gamma-1}(t-c)^{a+\beta+\gamma'-1}(z-t)^{-a-\beta-\gamma}U,$$

where

$$U = (t-a)(t-b)(t-c)(z-t)^{-1}.$$

Now U is a one-valued function of t; hence, if C be a closed contour, it must be such that the integrand in the integral I resumes its original value after t has described the contour.

Hence finally *any integral of the type*

$$(z-a)^a(z-b)^\beta(z-c)^\gamma\int_C (t-a)^{\beta+\gamma+a'-1}(t-b)^{\gamma+a+\beta'-1}(t-c)^{a+\beta+\gamma'-1}(z-t)^{-a-\beta-\gamma}\,dt,$$

where C is either a closed contour in the t-plane such that the integrand resumes its initial value after t has described it, or else is a simple curve such that V has the same value at its termini, is a solution of the differential equation of the general hypergeometric function.

The reader is referred to the memoirs of Pochhammer, *Math. Ann.* xxxv. (1890), pp. 495–526, and Hobson, *Phil. Trans.* 187 A (1896), pp. 443–531, for an account of the methods by which integrals of this type are transformed so as to give rise to the relations of §§ 14·51 and 14·53.

Example 1. To deduce a real definite integral which, in certain circumstances, represents the hypergeometric series.

---

* The differentiations under the sign of integration are legitimate (§ 4·2) if the path C does not depend on z and does not pass through the points a, b, c, z; if C be an infinite contour or if C passes through the points a, b, c or z, further conditions are necessary.

The hypergeometric series $F(a, b; c; z)$ is, as already shewn, a solution of the differential equation defined by the scheme

$$P \left\{ \begin{array}{ccc} 0 & \infty & 1 \\ 0 & a & 0 \\ 1-c & b & c-a-b \end{array} \quad z \right\}.$$

If in the integral

$$(z-a)^a \left(1 - \frac{z}{b}\right)^\beta (z-c)^\gamma \int_C (t-a)^{\beta+\gamma+a'-1} \left(1 - \frac{t}{b}\right)^{\gamma+a+\beta'-1} (t-c)^{a+\beta+\gamma'-1} (t-z)^{-a-\beta-\gamma} dt,$$

which is a constant multiple of that just obtained, we make $b \to \infty$ (without paying attention to the validity of this process), we are led to consider

$$\int_C t^{a-c} (t-1)^{c-b-1} (t-z)^{-a} dt.$$

Now the limiting form of V in question is

$$t^{1-c+a} (t-1)^{c-b} (t-z)^{-1-a},$$

and this tends to zero at $t = 1$ and $t = \infty$, provided $R(c) > R(b) > 0$.

We accordingly consider $\int_1^\infty t^{a-c} (t-1)^{c-b-1} (t-z)^{-a} dt$, where z is not* positive and greater than 1.

In this integral, write $t = u^{-1}$; the integral becomes

$$\int_0^1 u^{b-1} (1-u)^{c-b-1} (1-uz)^{-a} du.$$

We are therefore led to expect that this integral may be a solution of the differential equation for the hypergeometric series.

The reader will easily see that if $R(c) > R(b) > 0$, and if $\arg u = \arg(1-u) = 0$, while the branch of $1-uz$ is specified by the fact that $(1-uz)^{-a} \to 1$ as $u \to 0$, the integral just found is

$$\frac{\Gamma(b) \Gamma(c-b)}{\Gamma(c)} F(a, b; c; z).$$

This can be proved by expanding† $(1-uz)^{-a}$ in ascending powers of z when $|z| < 1$ and using § 12·41.

Example 2. Deduce the result of § 14·11 from the preceding example.

14·61. *Determination of an integral which represents $P^{(a)}$.*

We shall now shew how an integral which represents the particular solution $P^{(a)}$ (§ 14·3) of the hypergeometric differential equation can be found.

We have seen (§ 14·6) that the integral

$$I = (z-a)^a (z-b)^\beta (z-c)^\gamma \int_C (t-a)^{\beta+\gamma+a'-1} (t-b)^{\gamma+a+\beta'-1} (t-c)^{a+\beta+\gamma'-1} (t-z)^{-a-\beta-\gamma} dt$$

satisfies the differential equation of the hypergeometric function, provided C is a closed contour such that the integrand resumes its initial value after t has described C. Now the singularities of this integrand in the t-plane are the points a, b, c, z; and after describing the double circuit contour (§ 12·43) symbolised by $(b+, c+, b-, c-)$ the integrand returns to its original value.

---

* This ensures that the point $t = 1/z$ is not on the path of integration.

† The justification of this process by § 4·7 is left to the reader.

Now, if z lie in a circle whose centre is a, the circle not containing either of the points b and c, we can choose the path of integration so that t is outside this circle, and so $|z-a| < |t-a|$ for all points t on the path.

Now choose $\arg(z-a)$ to be numerically less than π and $\arg(z-b)$, $\arg(z-c)$ so that they reduce to* $\arg(a-b)$, $\arg(a-c)$ when $z \to a$; fix $\arg(t-a)$, $\arg(t-b)$, $\arg(t-c)$ at the point N at which the path of integration starts and ends; also choose $\arg(t-z)$ to reduce to $\arg(t-a)$ when $z \to a$.

Then
$$(z-b)^\beta = (a-b)^\beta \left\{ 1 + \beta \left(\frac{z-a}{a-b} \right) + \dots \right\},$$

$$(z-c)^\gamma = (a-c)^\gamma \left\{ 1 + \gamma \left(\frac{z-a}{a-c} \right) + \dots \right\},$$

and since we can expand $(t-z)^{-a-\beta-\gamma}$ into an absolutely and uniformly convergent series

$$(t-a)^{-a-\beta-\gamma} \left\{ 1 - (a+\beta+\gamma) \frac{a-z}{t-a} + \dots \right\},$$

we may expand the integral into a series which converges absolutely.

Multiplying up the absolutely convergent series, we get a series of integer powers of $z-a$ multiplied by $(z-a)^a$. Consequently we must have

$$I = (a-b)^\beta (a-c)^\gamma P^{(a)} \int_N^{(b+, c+, b--, c-)} (t-a)^{\beta+\gamma+a'-1} (t-b)^{\gamma+a+\beta'-1} (t-c)^{a+\beta+\gamma'-1} dt.$$

We can define $P^{(a')}$, $P^{(\beta)}$, $P^{(\beta')}$, $P^{(\gamma)}$, $P^{(\gamma')}$ by double circuit integrals in a similar manner.

14·7. *Relations between contiguous hypergeometric functions.*

Let $P(z)$ be a solution of Riemann's equation with argument z, singularities a, b, c, and exponents α, α', β, β', γ, γ'. Further let $P(z)$ be a constant multiple of one of the six functions $P^{(a)}$, $P^{(a')}$, $P^{(\beta)}$, $P^{(\beta')}$, $P^{(\gamma)}$, $P^{(\gamma')}$. Let $P_{l+1, m-1}(z)$ denote the function which is obtained by replacing two of the exponents, l and m, in $P(z)$ by $l+1$ and $m-1$ respectively. Such functions $P_{l+1, m-1}(z)$ are said to be *contiguous* to $P(z)$. There are $6 \times 5 = 30$ contiguous functions, since l and m may be any two of the six exponents.

It was first shewn by Riemann† that *the function $P(z)$ and any two of its contiguous functions are connected by a linear relation, the coefficients in which are polynomials in z.*

There will clearly be $\frac{1}{2} \times 30 \times 29 = 435$ of these relations. To shew how to obtain them, we shall take $P(z)$ in the form

$$P(z) = (z-a)^a (z-b)^\beta (z-c)^\gamma \int_C (t-a)^{\beta+\gamma+a'-1} (t-b)^{\gamma+a+\beta'-1}$$
$$(t-c)^{a+\beta+\gamma'-1} (t-z)^{a-\beta-\gamma} dt,$$

where C is a double circuit contour of the type considered in § 14·61.

---

* The values of $\arg(a-b)$, $\arg(a-c)$ being fixed.

† *Abh. der k. Ges. der Wiss. zu Göttingen*, 1857; Gauss had previously obtained 15 relations between contiguous hypergeometric functions.

First, since the integral round C of the differential of any function which resumes its initial value after t has described C is zero, we have

$$0 = \int_C \frac{d}{dt} \{(t-a)^{\alpha'+\beta+\gamma}(t-b)^{\alpha+\beta'+\gamma-1}(t-c)^{\alpha+\beta+\gamma'-1}(t-z)^{-\alpha-\beta-\gamma}\} \, dt.$$

On performing the differentiation by differentiating each factor in turn, we get

$$(\alpha'+\beta+\gamma) P + (\alpha+\beta'+\gamma-1) P_{\alpha'+1,\beta'-1} + (\alpha+\beta+\gamma'-1) P_{\alpha'+1,\gamma'-1}$$

$$= \frac{(\alpha+\beta+\gamma)}{z-b} P_{\beta+1,\gamma'-1}.$$

Considerations of symmetry shew that the right-hand side of this equation can be replaced by

$$\frac{(\alpha+\beta+\gamma)}{z-c} P_{\beta'-1,\gamma+1}.$$

These, together with the analogous formulae obtained by cyclical interchange* of (a, α, α') with (b, β, β') and (c, γ, γ'), are six linear relations connecting the hypergeometric function P with the twelve contiguous functions

$$P_{\alpha+1,\beta'-1}, \quad P_{\beta+1,\gamma'-1}, \quad P_{\gamma+1,\alpha'-1}, \quad P_{\alpha+1,\gamma'-1}, \quad P_{\beta+1,\alpha'-1}, \quad P_{\gamma+1,\beta'-1},$$
$$P_{\alpha'+1,\beta'-1}, \quad P_{\alpha'+1,\gamma'-1}, \quad P_{\beta'+1,\gamma'-1}, \quad P_{\beta'+1,\alpha'-1}, \quad P_{\gamma'+1,\alpha'-1}, \quad P_{\gamma'+1,\beta'-1}.$$

Next, writing $t-a = (t-b)+(b-a)$, and using† $P_{\alpha'-1}$ to denote the result of writing $\alpha'-1$ for α' in P, we have

$$P = P_{\alpha'-1,\beta'+1} + (b-a) P_{\alpha'-1}.$$

Similarly $$P = P_{\alpha'-1,\gamma'+1} + (c-a) P_{\alpha'-1}.$$

Eliminating $P_{\alpha'-1}$ from these equations, we have

$$(c-b) P + (a-c) P_{\alpha'-1,\beta'+1} + (b-a) P_{\alpha'-1,\gamma'+1} = 0.$$

This and the analogous formulae are three more linear relations connecting P with the last six of the twelve contiguous functions written above.

Next, writing $(t-z) = (t-a)-(z-a)$, we readily find the relation

$$P = \frac{1}{z-b} P_{\beta+1,\gamma'-1} - (z-a)^{\alpha+1}(z-b)^\beta(z-c)^\gamma$$

$$\times \int_C (t-a)^{\beta+\gamma+\alpha'-1}(t-b)^{\gamma+\alpha+\beta'-1}(t-c)^{\alpha+\beta+\gamma'-1}(t-z)^{-\alpha-\beta-\gamma-1} \, dt,$$

which gives the equations

$$(z-a)^{-1}\{P-(z-b)^{-1} P_{\beta+1,\gamma'-1}\} = (z-b)^{-1}\{P-(z-c)^{-1} P_{\gamma+1,\alpha'-1}\}$$
$$= (z-c)^{-1}\{P-(z-a)^{-1} P_{\alpha+1,\beta'-1}\}.$$

---

* The interchange is to be made only in the integrands; the contour C is to remain unaltered.

† $P_{\alpha'-1}$ is not a function of Riemann's type since the sum of its exponents at a, b, c is not unity.

These are two more linear equations between P and the above twelve contiguous functions.

We have therefore now altogether found eleven linear relations between P and these twelve functions, the coefficients in these relations being rational functions of z. Hence each of these functions can be expressed linearly in terms of P and some selected one of them; that is, *between P and any two of the above functions there exists a linear relation*. The coefficients in this relation will be rational functions of z, and therefore will become polynomials in z when the relation is multiplied throughout by the least common multiple of their denominators.

The theorem is therefore proved, so far as the above twelve contiguous functions are concerned. It can, without difficulty, be extended so as to be established for the rest of the thirty contiguous functions.

Corollary. If functions be derived from P by replacing the exponents a, a', β, β', γ, γ' by $a+p$, $a'+q$, $\beta+r$, $\beta'+s$, $\gamma+t$, $\gamma'+u$, where p, q, r, s, t, u are integers satisfying the relation

$$p+q+r+s+t+u=0,$$

then between P and any two such functions there exists a linear relation, the coefficients in which are polynomials in z.

This result can be obtained by connecting P with the two functions by a chain of intermediate contiguous functions, writing down the linear relations which connect them with P and the two functions, and from these relations eliminating the intermediate contiguous functions.

Many theorems which will be established subsequently, e.g. the recurrence-formulae for the Legendre functions (§ 15·21), are really cases of the theorem of this article.

REFERENCES.

C. F. GAUSS, *Ges. Werke*, III. pp. 123–163, 207–229.

E. E. KUMMER, *Journal für Math.* XV. (1836), pp. 39–83, 127–172.

G. F. B. RIEMANN, *Ges. Math. Werke*, pp. 67–84.

E. PAPPERITZ, *Math. Ann.* XXV. (1885), pp. 212–221.

S. PINCHERLE, *Rend. Accad. Lincei* (4), IV. (1888), pp. 694–700, 792–799.

E. W. BARNES, *Proc. London Math. Soc.* (2), VI. (1908), pp. 141–177.

HJ. MELLIN, *Acta Soc. Fennicae*, XX. (1895), No. 12.

MISCELLANEOUS EXAMPLES.

1. Shew that

$$F(a,\ b+1\ ;\ c\ ;\ z)-F(a,\ b\ ;\ c\ ;\ z)=\frac{az}{c}\,F(a+1,\ b+1\ ;\ c+1\ ;\ z).$$

2. Shew that if a is a negative integer while β and γ are not integers, then the ratio $F(a,\ \beta\ ;\ a+\beta+1-\gamma\ ;\ 1-x)\div F(a,\ \beta\ ;\ \gamma\ ;\ x)$ is independent of x, and find its value.

3. If $P(z)$ be a hypergeometric function, express its derivates $\dfrac{dP}{dz}$ and $\dfrac{d^2P}{dz^2}$ linearly in terms of P and contiguous functions, and hence find the linear relation between P, $\dfrac{dP}{dz}$, and $\dfrac{d^2P}{dz^2}$, i.e. verify that P satisfies the hypergeometric differential equation.

4. Shew that $F\{\frac{1}{4}, \frac{1}{4}; 1; 4z(1-z)\}$ satisfies the hypergeometric equation satisfied by $F(\frac{1}{2}, \frac{1}{2}; 1; z)$. Shew that, in the left-hand half of the lemniscate $|z(1-z)|=\frac{1}{4}$, these two functions are equal; and in the right-hand half of the lemniscate, the former function is equal to $F(\frac{1}{2}, \frac{1}{2}; 1; 1-z)$.

5. If $F_{a+}=F(a+1, b; c; x)$, $F_{a-}=F(a-1, b; c; x)$, determine the 15 linear relations with polynomial coefficients which connect $F(a, b; c; x)$ with pairs of the six functions F_{a+}, F_{a-}, F_{b+}, F_{b-}, F_{c+}, F_{c-}. (Gauss.)

6. Shew that the hypergeometric equation

$$x(x-1)\frac{d^2y}{dx^2}-\{\gamma-(a+\beta+1)x\}\frac{dy}{dx}+a\beta y=0$$

is satisfied by the two integrals (supposed convergent)

$$\int_0^1 z^{\beta-1}(1-z)^{\gamma-\beta-1}(1-xz)^{-a}\,dz$$

and

$$\int_0^1 z^{\beta-1}(1-z)^{a-\gamma}\{1-(1-x)z\}^{-a}\,dz.$$

7. Shew that, for values of x between 0 and 1, the solution of the equation

$$x(1-x)\frac{d^2y}{dx^2}+\frac{1}{2}(a+\beta+1)(1-2x)\frac{dy}{dx}-a\beta y=0$$

is

$$AF\{\tfrac{1}{2}a, \tfrac{1}{2}\beta; \tfrac{1}{2}; (1-2x)^2\}+B(1-2x)F\{\tfrac{1}{2}(a+1), \tfrac{1}{2}(\beta+1); \tfrac{3}{2}; (1-2x)^2\},$$

where A, B are arbitrary constants and $F(a, \beta; \gamma; x)$ represents the hypergeometric series. (Math. Trip. 1896.)

8. Shew that

$$\lim_{x\to1-0}\left[F(a, \beta; \gamma; x)-\sum_{n=0}^{k}(-)^n\frac{\Gamma(a+\beta-\gamma-n)\Gamma(\gamma-a+n)\Gamma(\gamma-\beta+n)\Gamma(\gamma)}{n!\,\Gamma(\gamma-a)\Gamma(\gamma-\beta)\Gamma(a)\Gamma(\beta)}(1-x)^{n+\gamma-a-\beta}\right]$$
$$=\frac{\Gamma(\gamma-a-\beta)\Gamma(\gamma)}{\Gamma(\gamma-a)\Gamma(\gamma-\beta)}$$

where k is the integer such that $k\leqslant R(a+\beta-\gamma)<k+1$.

(This specifies the manner in which the hypergeometric function becomes infinite when $x\to1-0$ provided that $a+\beta-\gamma$ is not an integer.) (Hardy.)

9. Shew that, when $R(\gamma-a-\beta)<0$, then

$$S_n\div\frac{\Gamma(\gamma)n^{a+\beta-\gamma}}{(a+\beta-\gamma)\Gamma(a)\Gamma(\beta)}\to1$$

as $n\to\infty$; where S_n denotes the sum of the first n terms of the series for $F(a, \beta; \gamma; 1)$.

(M. J. M. Hill, *Proc. London Math. Soc.* (2), v.)

10.   Shew that, if y_1, y_2 be independent solutions of

$$\frac{d^2y}{dx^2} + P\frac{dy}{dx} + Qy = 0,$$

then the general solution of

$$\frac{d^3z}{dx^3} + 3P\frac{d^2z}{dx^2} + \left\{2P^2 + \frac{dP}{dx} + 4Q\right\}\frac{dz}{dx} + \left\{4PQ + 2\frac{dQ}{dx}\right\}z = 0$$

is $z = Ay_1^2 + By_1y_2 + Cy_2^2$, where A, B, C are constants.

(Appell, *Comptes Rendus*, XCI.)

11.   Deduce from example 10 that, if $a + b + \frac{1}{2} = c$,

$$\{F(a,\,b;\,c;\,x)\}^2 = \frac{\Gamma(c)\,\Gamma(2c-1)}{\Gamma(2a)\,\Gamma(2b)\,\Gamma(a+b)} \sum_{n=0}^{\infty} \frac{\Gamma(2a+n)\,\Gamma(a+b+n)\,\Gamma(2b+n)}{n!\,\Gamma(c+n)\,\Gamma(2c-1+n)} x^n.$$

(Clausen, *Journal für Math.* III.)

12.   Shew that, if $|x| < \frac{1}{2}$ and $|x(1-x)| < \frac{1}{4}$,

$$F\{2a,\,2\beta;\,a+\beta+\tfrac{1}{2};\,x\} = F\{a,\,\beta;\,a+\beta+\tfrac{1}{2};\,4x(1-x)\}. \qquad \text{(Kummer.)}$$

13.   Deduce from example 12 that

$$F\{2a,\,2\beta;\,a+\beta+\tfrac{1}{2};\,\tfrac{1}{2}\} = \frac{\Gamma(a+\beta+\tfrac{1}{2})\,\Gamma(\tfrac{1}{2})}{\Gamma(a+\tfrac{1}{2})\,\Gamma(\beta+\tfrac{1}{2})}.$$

14.   Shew that, if $\omega = e^{\frac{2}{3}\pi i}$ and $R(a) < 1$,

$$F(a,\,3a-1;\,2a;\,-\omega^2) = 3^{\frac{3}{2}a-\frac{3}{2}} \exp\{\tfrac{1}{6}\pi i(3a-1)\}\frac{\Gamma(2a)\,\Gamma(a-\tfrac{1}{3})}{\Gamma(3a-1)\,\Gamma(\tfrac{2}{3})},$$

$$F(a,\,3a-1;\,2a;\,-\omega) = 3^{\frac{3}{2}a-\frac{3}{2}} \exp\{\tfrac{1}{6}\pi i(1-3a)\}\frac{\Gamma(2a)\,\Gamma(a-\tfrac{1}{3})}{\Gamma(3a-1)\,\Gamma(\tfrac{2}{3})}.$$

(Watson, *Quarterly Journal*, XLI.)

15.   Shew that

$$F(-\tfrac{1}{2}n,\,-\tfrac{1}{2}n+\tfrac{1}{2};\,n+\tfrac{3}{2};\,-\tfrac{1}{3}) = (\tfrac{8}{9})^n \frac{\Gamma(\tfrac{4}{3})\,\Gamma(n+\tfrac{3}{2})}{\Gamma(\tfrac{3}{2})\,\Gamma(n+\tfrac{4}{3})}.$$

(Heymann, *Zeitschrift für Math. und Phys.* XLIV.)

16.   If $\qquad (1-x)^{a+\beta-\gamma}\,F(2a,\,2\beta;\,2\gamma;\,x) = 1 + Bx + Cx^2 + Dx^3 + \ldots,$

shew that

$$F(a,\,\beta;\,\gamma+\tfrac{1}{2};\,x)\,F(\gamma-a,\,\gamma-\beta;\,\gamma+\tfrac{1}{2};\,x)$$

$$= 1 + \frac{\gamma}{\gamma+\tfrac{1}{2}}\,Bx + \frac{\gamma\cdot\gamma+1}{(\gamma+\tfrac{1}{2})(\gamma+\tfrac{3}{2})}\,Cx^2 + \frac{\gamma(\gamma+1)(\gamma+2)}{(\gamma+\tfrac{1}{2})(\gamma+\tfrac{3}{2})(\gamma+\tfrac{5}{2})}\,Dx^3 + \ldots.$$

(Cayley, *Phil. Mag.* (4), XVI. (1858), pp. 356–357.   See also Orr, *Camb. Phil. Trans.* XVII. (1899), pp. 1–15.)

17.   If the function $F'(a,\,\beta,\,\beta',\,\gamma;\,x,\,y)$ be defined by the equation

$$F(a,\,\beta,\,\beta',\,\gamma;\,x,\,y) = \frac{\Gamma(\gamma)}{\Gamma(a)\,\Gamma(\gamma-a)} \int_0^1 u^{a-1}(1-u)^{\gamma-a-1}(1-ux)^{-\beta}(1-uy)^{-\beta'}\,du,$$

then shew that between F and any three of its eight contiguous functions

$$F(a\pm 1), \quad F(\beta\pm 1), \quad F(\beta'\pm 1), \quad F(\gamma\pm 1),$$

there exists a homogeneous linear equation, whose coefficients are polynomials in x and y.

(Le Vavasseur.)

18. If $\gamma - a - \beta < 0$, shew that, as $x \to 1 - 0$,

$$F(a, \beta; \gamma; x) \div \left\{ \frac{\Gamma(\gamma)\,\Gamma(a + \beta - \gamma)}{\Gamma(a)\,\Gamma(\beta)} (1 - x)^{\gamma - a - \beta} \right\} \to 1,$$

and that, if $\gamma - a - \beta = 0$, the corresponding approximate formula is

$$F(a, \beta; \gamma; x) \div \left\{ \frac{\Gamma(a + \beta)}{\Gamma(a)\,\Gamma(\beta)} \log \frac{1}{1 - x} \right\} \to 1.$$

(Math. Trip. 1893.)

19. Shew that, when $|x| < 1$,

$$\int_c^{(x+, 0+, x-, 0-)} x^{1-\gamma} (\nu - x)^{\gamma - a - 1} \nu^{a-1} (1 - \nu)^{-\beta} \, d\nu$$

$$= -4 e^{\pi \gamma i} \sin a\pi \sin(\gamma - a)\, \pi \cdot \frac{\Gamma(\gamma - a)\,\Gamma(a)}{\Gamma(\gamma)} F(a, \beta; \gamma; x),$$

where c denotes a point on the straight line joining the points 0, x, the initial arguments of $\nu - x$ and of ν are the same as that of x, and $\arg(1 - \nu) \to 0$ as $\nu \to 0$.

(Pochhammer.)

20. If, when $|\arg(1 - x)| < 2\pi$,

$$K(x) = \frac{1}{2\pi i} \int_{-\infty i}^{\infty i} \{\Gamma(-s)\,\Gamma(\tfrac{1}{2} + s)\}^2 (1 - x)^s \, ds,$$

and, when $|\arg x| < 2\pi$,

$$K'(x) = \frac{1}{2\pi i} \int_{-\infty i}^{\infty i} \{\Gamma(-s)\,\Gamma(\tfrac{1}{2} + s)\}^2 x^s \, ds,$$

by changing the variable s in the integral or otherwise, obtain the following relations:

$$K(x) = K'(1 - x), \qquad\qquad \text{if } |\arg(1 - x)| < \pi.$$

$$K(1 - x) = K'(x), \qquad\qquad \text{if } |\arg x| < \pi.$$

$$K(x) = (1 - x)^{-\frac{1}{2}} K\left(\frac{x}{x - 1}\right), \qquad \text{if } |\arg(1 - x)| < \pi.$$

$$K(1 - x) = x^{-\frac{1}{2}} K\left(\frac{x - 1}{x}\right), \qquad \text{if } |\arg x| < \pi.$$

$$K'(x) = x^{-\frac{1}{2}} K'(1/x), \qquad\qquad \text{if } |\arg x| < \pi.$$

$$K'(1 - x) = (1 - x)^{-\frac{1}{2}} K'\left(\frac{1}{1 - x}\right), \text{ if } |\arg(1 - x)| < \pi. \qquad \text{(Barnes.)}$$

21. With the notation of the preceding example, obtain the following results:

$$2K(x) = \sum_{n=0}^{\infty} \left\{ \frac{\Gamma(\tfrac{1}{2} + n)}{n!} \right\}^2 x^n,$$

$$2\pi K'(x) = -\sum_{n=0}^{\infty} \left\{ \frac{\Gamma(\tfrac{1}{2} + n)}{n!} \right\}^2 x^n \left\{ \log x - 4\log 2 + 4\left(\frac{1}{1} - \frac{1}{2} + \ldots - \frac{1}{2n}\right) \right\},$$

when $|x| < 1$, $|\arg x| < \pi$; and

$$K(x) = \mp i(-x)^{-\frac{1}{2}} K(1/x) + (-x)^{-\frac{1}{2}} K'(1/x),$$

when $|\arg(-x)| < \pi$, the ambiguous sign being the same as the sign of $I(x)$.

(Barnes.)

22. Hypergeometric series in two variables are defined by the equations

$$F_1(a ; \beta, \beta' ; \gamma ; x, y) = \underset{m, n}{\Sigma} \frac{a_{m+n}\, \beta_m \beta_n'}{m!\, n!\, \gamma_{m+n}} x^m y^n,$$

$$F_2(a ; \beta, \beta' ; \gamma, \gamma' ; x, y) = \underset{m, n}{\Sigma} \frac{a_{m+n}\, \beta_m \beta_n'}{m!\, n!\, \gamma_m \gamma_n} x^m y^n,$$

$$F_3(a, a', \beta, \beta' ; \gamma ; x, y) = \underset{m, n}{\Sigma} \frac{a_m a_n'\, \beta_m \beta_n'}{m!\, n!\, \gamma_{m+n}} x^m y^n,$$

$$F_4(a, \beta ; \gamma, \gamma' ; x, y) = \underset{m, n}{\Sigma} \frac{a_{m+n}\beta_{m+n}}{m!\, n!\, \gamma_m \gamma_n} x^m y^n,$$

where $a_m = a(a+1)\ldots(a+m-1)$, and $\underset{m, n}{\Sigma}$ means $\overset{\infty}{\underset{m=0}{\Sigma}}\, \overset{\infty}{\underset{n=0}{\Sigma}}$.

Obtain the differential equations

$$x(1-x)\frac{\partial^2 F_1}{\partial x^2} + y(1-x)\frac{\partial^2 F_1}{\partial x \partial y} + \{\gamma - (a+\beta+1)\, x\}\frac{\partial F_1}{\partial x} - \beta y \frac{\partial F_1}{\partial y} - a\beta F_1 = 0,$$

$$x(1-x)\frac{\partial^2 F_2}{\partial x^2} - xy\frac{\partial^2 F_2}{\partial x \partial y} + \{\gamma - (a+\beta+1)\, x\}\frac{\partial F_2}{\partial x} - \beta y \frac{\partial F_2}{\partial y} - a\beta F_2 = 0,$$

$$x(1-x)\frac{\partial^2 F_3}{\partial x^2} + y\frac{\partial^2 F_3}{\partial x \partial y} + \{\gamma - (a+\beta+1)\, x\}\frac{\partial F_3}{\partial x} - a\beta F_3 = 0,$$

$$x(1-x)\frac{\partial^2 F_4}{\partial x^2} - 2xy\frac{\partial^2 F_4}{\partial x \partial y} - y^2\frac{\partial^2 F_4}{\partial y^2} + \{\gamma - (a+\beta+1)\, x\}\frac{\partial F_4}{\partial x} - (a+\beta+1)\, y \frac{\partial F_4}{\partial y} - a\beta F_4 = 0,$$

and four similar equations, derived from these by interchanging x with y and a, β, γ with a', β', γ' when a', β', γ' occur in the corresponding series.

(Appell, *Comptes Rendus*, XC.)

23. If a is negative, and if

$$a = -\nu + a,$$

where ν is an integer and a is positive, shew that

$$\frac{\Gamma(x)\, \Gamma(a)}{\Gamma(x+a)} = \overset{\infty}{\underset{n=1}{\Sigma}} \left\{ \frac{R_n}{x+n} + G_n(x) \right\},$$

where

$$R_n = \frac{(-)^n (a-1)(a-2)\ldots(a-n)}{n!}\, G(-n),$$

$$G(x) = \left(1 + \frac{x}{a-1}\right)\left(1 + \frac{x}{a-2}\right)\ldots\left(1 + \frac{x}{a-\nu}\right)$$

$$G_n(x) = \frac{G(x) - G(-n)}{x+n}.$$ (Hermite, *Journal für Math.* XCII.)

24. When $a < 1$, shew that

$$\frac{\Gamma(x)\, \Gamma(a-x)}{\Gamma(a)} = \overset{\infty}{\underset{n=1}{\Sigma}} \frac{R_n}{x+n} - \overset{\infty}{\underset{n=1}{\Sigma}} \frac{R_n}{x-a-n},$$

where

$$R_n = \frac{(-)^n a(a+1)\ldots(a+n-1)}{n!}.$$

25. When $a > 1$, and ν and a are respectively the integral and fractional parts of a, shew that

$$\frac{\Gamma(x)\, \Gamma(a-x)}{\Gamma(a)} = \overset{\infty}{\underset{n=1}{\Sigma}} \frac{G(x)\, \rho_n}{x+n} - \overset{\infty}{\underset{n=1}{\Sigma}} \frac{G(x)\, \rho_{\nu+n}}{x-a-n}$$

$$- G(x)\left[\frac{\rho_0}{x-a} + \frac{\rho_1}{x-a-1} + \ldots + \frac{\rho_{\nu-1}}{x-a-\nu+1}\right],$$

where
$$G(x) = \left(1 - \frac{x}{a}\right)\left(1 - \frac{x}{a+1}\right) \cdots \left(1 - \frac{x}{a+\nu-1}\right)$$

and
$$\rho_n = \frac{(-)^n\, a\,(a+1) \cdots (a+n-1)}{n\,!}.$$

(Hermite, *Journal für Math.* XCII.)

26. If

$$f_n(x, y, v) = 1 - {}_nC_1 \frac{x(y+v+n-1)}{y(x+v)} + {}_nC_2 \frac{x(x+1)(y+v+n-1)(y+v+n)}{y(y+1)(x+v)(x+v+1)} - \cdots,$$

where n is a positive integer and ${}_nC_1$, ${}_nC_2$, ... are binomial coefficients, shew that

$$f_n(x, y, v) = \frac{\Gamma(y)\,\Gamma(y-x+n)\,\Gamma(x+v)\,\Gamma(v+n)}{\Gamma(y-x)\,\Gamma(y+n)\,\Gamma(v)\,\Gamma(x+v+n)}.$$

(Saalschütz, *Zeitschrift für Math.* XXXV; a number of similar results are given by Dougall, *Proc. Edinburgh Math. Soc.* XXV.)

27. If $\quad F(a, \beta, \gamma;\ \delta, \epsilon;\ x) = 1 + \frac{a\beta\gamma}{\delta\epsilon\,1}\,x + \frac{a(a+1)\,\beta(\beta+1)\,\gamma(\gamma+1)}{\delta(\delta+1)\,\epsilon(\epsilon+1)\,1\,.\,2}\,x^2 + \cdots,$

shew that, when $R\,(\delta + \epsilon - \tfrac{3}{2}a - 1) > 0$, then

$$F(a, a-\delta+1, a-\epsilon+1;\ \delta, \epsilon;\ 1) = 2^{-a}\,\frac{\Gamma(\tfrac{1}{2})\,\Gamma(\delta)\,\Gamma(\epsilon)\,\Gamma(\delta+\epsilon-\tfrac{3}{2}a-1)}{\Gamma(\delta-\tfrac{1}{2}a)\,\Gamma(\epsilon-\tfrac{1}{2}a)\,\Gamma(\tfrac{1}{2}+\tfrac{1}{2}a)\,\Gamma(\delta+\epsilon-a-1)}.$$

(A. C. Dixon, *Proc. London Math. Soc.* XXXV.)

28. Shew that, if $R\,(a) < \tfrac{2}{3}$, then

$$1 + \sum_{n=1}^{\infty} \left\{ \frac{a(a+1) \cdots (a+n-1)}{n\,!} \right\}^3 = \cos\left(\tfrac{1}{2}\pi a\right) \frac{\Gamma(1-\tfrac{3}{2}a)}{\{\Gamma(1-\tfrac{1}{2}a)\}^3}.$$

(Morley, *Proc. London Math. Soc.* XXXIV.)

29. If

$$\int_0^1 \int_0^1 x^{i-1}(1-x)^{j-1}y^{l-1}(1-y)^{k-1}(1-xy)^{m-j-k}\,dx\,dy = B\,(i, j, k, l, m),$$

shew, by integrating with respect to x, and also with respect to y, that $B\,(i, j, k, l, m)$ is a symmetric function of $i+j$, $j+k$, $k+l$, $l+m$, $m+i$.

Deduce that

$$F(a, \beta, \gamma;\ \delta, \epsilon;\ 1) \div \Gamma(\delta)\,\Gamma(\epsilon)\,\Gamma(\delta+\epsilon-a-\beta-\gamma)$$

is a symmetric function of δ, ϵ, $\delta+\epsilon-a-\beta$, $\delta+\epsilon-\beta-\gamma$, $\delta+\epsilon-\gamma-a$.

(A. C. Dixon, *Proc. London Math. Soc.* (2), II. (1905), pp. 8–16. For a proof of a special case by Barnes' methods, see Barnes, *Quarterly Journal*, XLI. (1910), pp. 136–140.)

30. If

$$F_n = F(-n, a+n;\ \gamma;\ x) = \frac{x^{1-\gamma}(1-x)^{\gamma-a}}{\gamma(\gamma+1) \cdots (\gamma+n-1)}\,\frac{d^n}{dx^n}\left\{x^{\gamma+n-1}(1-x)^{a+n-\gamma}\right\},$$

shew that, when n is a large positive integer, and $0 < x < 1$,

$$F_n = \frac{\Gamma(\gamma)}{n^{\gamma-\frac{1}{2}}\sqrt{\pi}}\,(\sin\phi)^{\frac{1}{2}-\gamma}(\cos\phi)^{\gamma-a-\frac{1}{2}}\cos\left\{(2n+a)\phi - \tfrac{1}{4}\pi\,(2\gamma-1)\right\} + O\left(\frac{1}{n^{\gamma+\frac{1}{2}}}\right),$$

where $x = \sin^2\phi$.

(This result is contained in the great memoir by Darboux, "Sur l'approximation des fonctions de très grands nombres," *Journal de Math.* (3), IV. (1878), pp. 5–56, 377–416. For a systematic development of hypergeometric functions in which one (or more) of the constants is large, see *Camb. Phil. Trans.* XXII. (1918), pp. 277–308.)

CHAPTER XV

LEGENDRE FUNCTIONS

15·1. *Definition of Legendre polynomials.*

Consider the expression $(1 - 2zh + h^2)^{-\frac{1}{2}}$; when $|2zh - h^2| < 1$, it can be expanded in a series of ascending powers of $2zh - h^2$. If, in addition, $|2zh| + |h|^2 < 1$, these powers can be multiplied out and the resulting series rearranged in any manner (§ 2·52) since the expansion of $[1 - \{|2zh| + |h|^2\}]^{-\frac{1}{2}}$ in powers of $|2zh| + |h|^2$ then converges absolutely. In particular, if we rearrange in powers of h, we get

$$(1 - 2zh + h^2)^{-\frac{1}{2}} = P_0(z) + hP_1(z) + h^2 P_2(z) + h^3 P_3(z) + \dots,$$

where

$$P_0(z) = 1, \quad P_1(z) = z, \quad P_2(z) = \tfrac{1}{2}(3z^2 - 1), \quad P_3(z) = \tfrac{1}{2}(5z^3 - 3z),$$

$$P_4(z) = \tfrac{1}{8}(35z^4 - 30z^2 + 3), \quad P_5(z) = \tfrac{1}{8}(63z^5 - 70z^3 + 15z),$$

and generally

$$P_n(z) = \frac{(2n)!}{2^n \cdot (n!)^2} \left\{ z^n - \frac{n(n-1)}{2(2n-1)} z^{n-2} + \frac{n(n-1)(n-2)(n-3)}{2 \cdot 4 \cdot (2n-1)(2n-3)} z^{n-4} - \dots \right\}$$

$$= \sum_{r=0}^{m} (-)^r \frac{(2n-2r)!}{2^n \cdot r! (n-r)! (n-2r)!} z^{n-2r},$$

where $m = \tfrac{1}{2} n$ or $\tfrac{1}{2}(n-1)$, whichever is an integer.

If a, b and δ be positive constants, b being so small that $2ab + b^2 \leqslant 1 - \delta$, the expansion of $(1 - 2zh + h^2)^{-\frac{1}{2}}$ converges uniformly with respect to z and h when $|z| \leqslant a$, $|h| \leqslant b$.

The expressions $P_0(z)$, $P_1(z)$, ..., which are clearly all polynomials in z, are known as *Legendre polynomials**, $P_n(z)$ being called the *Legendre polynomial of degree n.*

It will appear later (§ 15·2) that these polynomials are particular cases of a more extensive class of functions known as *Legendre functions.*

Example 1. By giving z special values in the expression $(1 - 2zh + h^2)^{-\frac{1}{2}}$, shew that

$$P_n(1) = 1, \qquad P_n(-1) = (-1)^n,$$

$$P_{2n+1}(0) = 0, \quad P_{2n}(0) = (-)^n \frac{1 \cdot 3 \dots (2n-1)}{2 \cdot 4 \dots (2n)}.$$

---

* Other names are *Legendre coefficients* and *Zonal Harmonics*. They were introduced into analysis in 1784 by Legendre, *Mémoires par divers savans*, x. (1785).

Example 2.　From the expansion

$$(1 - 2h \cos \theta + h^2)^{-\frac{1}{2}} = \left(1 + \frac{1}{2} h e^{i\theta} + \frac{1\cdot3}{2\cdot4} h^2 e^{2i\theta} + \dots\right)$$

$$\times \left(1 + \frac{1}{2} h e^{-i\theta} + \frac{1\cdot3}{2\cdot4} h^2 e^{-2i\theta} + \dots\right),$$

shew that

$$P_n(\cos\theta) = \frac{1\cdot3\dots(2n-1)}{2\cdot4\dots(2n)} \left\{ 2 \cos n\theta + \frac{1\cdot(2n)}{2\cdot(2n-1)} 2 \cos(n-2)\theta \right.$$

$$\left. + \frac{1\cdot3\cdot(2n)(2n-2)}{2\cdot4\cdot(2n-1)(2n-3)} 2 \cos(n-4)\theta + \dots \right\}.$$

Deduce that, if θ be a real angle,

$$|P_n(\cos\theta)| \leqslant \frac{1\cdot3\dots2n-1}{2\cdot4\dots2n} \left\{ 2 + \frac{1\cdot(2n)}{2\cdot(2n-1)}\cdot2 + \frac{1\cdot3\cdot(2n)(2n-2)}{2\cdot4\cdot(2n-1)(2n-3)}\cdot2 + \dots \right\}$$

$$= P_n(1),$$

so that $|P_n(\cos\theta)| \leqslant 1.$　　　　　　　　　　　　　　　　(Legendre.)

Example 3.　Shew that, when $z = -\frac{1}{2}$,

$$P_n = P_0 P_{2n} - P_1 P_{2n-1} + P_2 P_{2n-2} - \dots + P_{2n} P_0.$$　　　(Clare, 1905.)

15·11.　*Rodrigues'* [*] *formula for the Legendre polynomials.*

It is evident that, when n is an integer,

$$\frac{d^n}{dz^n}(z^2 - 1)^n = \frac{d^n}{dz^n} \left\{ \sum_{r=0}^{n} (-)^r \frac{n!}{r!\,(n-r)!} z^{2n-2r} \right\}$$

$$= \sum_{r=0}^{m} (-)^r \frac{n!}{r!\,(n-r)!} \frac{(2n-2r)!}{(n-2r)!} z^{n-2r},$$

where $m = \frac{1}{2}n$ or $\frac{1}{2}(n-1)$, the coefficients of negative powers of z vanishing. From the general formula for $P_n(z)$ it follows at once that

$$P_n(z) = \frac{1}{2^n\cdot n!} \frac{d^n}{dz^n}(z^2-1)^n;$$

this result is known as Rodrigues' formula.

Example.　Shew that $P_n(z) = 0$ has n real roots, all lying between ± 1.

15·12.　*Schläfli's* [†] *integral for $P_n(z)$.*

From the result of § 15·11 combined with § 5·22, it follows at once that

$$P_n(z) = \frac{1}{2\pi i} \int_C \frac{(t^2-1)^n}{2^n (t-z)^{n+1}} dt,$$

where C is a contour which encircles the point z once counter-clockwise; this result is called *Schläfli's integral formula* for the Legendre polynomials.

---

[*] *Corresp. sur l'École polytechnique*, III. (1814–1816), pp. 361–385.

[†] Schläfli, *Ueber die zwei Heine'schen Kugelfunctionen* (Bern, 1881).

15·13. *Legendre's differential equation.*

We shall now prove that the function $u = P_n(z)$ is a solution of the differential equation

$$(1 - z^2) \frac{d^2u}{dz^2} - 2z \frac{du}{dz} + n(n+1)u = 0,$$

which is called *Legendre's differential equation for functions of degree n.*

For, substituting Schläfli's integral in the left-hand side, we have, by § 5·22,

$$(1 - z^2) \frac{d^2 P_n(z)}{dz^2} - 2z \frac{dP_n(z)}{dz} + n(n+1) P_n(z)$$

$$= \frac{(n+1)}{2\pi i} \int_C \frac{(t^2 - 1)^n \, dt}{2^n (t - z)^{n+3}} \{-(n+2)(t^2 - 1) + 2(n+1)t(t-z)\}$$

$$= \frac{(n+1)}{2\pi i \cdot 2^n} \int_C \frac{d}{dt} \left\{ \frac{(t^2 - 1)^{n+1}}{(t - z)^{n+2}} \right\} dt,$$

and this integral is zero, since $(t^2 - 1)^{n+1}(t - z)^{-n-2}$ resumes its original value after describing C when n is an integer. The Legendre polynomial therefore satisfies the differential equation.

The result just obtained can be written in the form

$$\frac{d}{dz} \left\{ (1 - z^2) \frac{dP_n(z)}{dz} \right\} + n(n+1) P_n(z) = 0.$$

It will be observed that Legendre's equation is a particular case of Riemann's equation, defined by the scheme

$$P \left\{ \begin{matrix} -1 & \infty & 1 \\ 0 & n+1 & 0 \\ 0 & -n & 0 \end{matrix} \; z \right\}.$$

Example 1.   Shew that the equation satisfied by $\dfrac{d^r P_n(z)}{dz^r}$ is defined by the scheme

$$P \left\{ \begin{matrix} -1 & \infty & 1 \\ -r & n+r+1 & -r \\ 0 & -n+r & 0 \end{matrix} \; z \right\}.$$

Example 2.   If $z^2 = \eta$, shew that Legendre's differential equation takes the form

$$\frac{d^2y}{d\eta^2} + \left\{ \frac{1}{2\eta} - \frac{1}{1-\eta} \right\} \frac{dy}{d\eta} + \frac{n(n+1)y}{4\eta(1-\eta)} = 0.$$

Shew that this is a hypergeometric equation.

Example 3.   Deduce Schläfli's integral for the Legendre functions, as a limiting case of the general hypergeometric integral of § 14·6.

[Since Legendre's equation is given by the scheme

$$P \left\{ \begin{matrix} -1 & \infty & 1 \\ 0 & n+1 & 0 \\ 0 & -n & 0 \end{matrix} \; z \right\},$$

the integral suggested is

$$\lim_{b\to\infty}\left(1-\frac{z}{b}\right)^{n+1}\int_C (t+1)^n (t-1)^n \lim_{b\to\infty}\left(1-\frac{t}{b}\right)^{-n}(t-z)^{-n-1}dt$$

$$=\int_C (t^2-1)^n (t-z)^{-n-1}dt,$$

taken round a contour C such that the integrand resumes its initial value after describing it ; and this gives Schläfli's integral.]

15·14. *The integral properties of the Legendre polynomials.*

We shall now shew that *

$$\int_{-1}^{1} P_m(z)\, P_n(z)\, dz \begin{cases} = 0 & (m \neq n), \\ = \dfrac{2}{2n+1} & (m = n). \end{cases}$$

Let $\{u\}_r$ denote $\dfrac{d^r u}{dz^r}$; then, if $r \leqslant n$, $\{(z^2-1)^n\}_r$ is divisible by $(z^2-1)^{n-r}$; and so, if $r < n$, $\{(z^2-1)^n\}_r$ vanishes when $z=1$ and when $z=-1$.

Now, of the two numbers m, n, let m be that one which is equal to or greater than the other.

Then, integrating by parts continually,

$$\int_{-1}^{1} \{(z^2-1)^m\}_m \{(z^2-1)^n\}_n \, dz$$

$$= \left[\{(z^2-1)^m\}_{m-1} \{(z^2-1)^n\}_n \right]_{-1}^{1} - \int_{-1}^{1} \{(z^2-1)^m\}_{m-1} \{(z^2-1)^n\}_{n+1} \, dz$$

$$= \dots\dots\dots\dots\dots\dots\dots\dots\dots\dots\dots\dots\dots\dots\dots\dots$$

$$= (-)^m \int_{-1}^{1} (z^2-1)^m \{(z^2-1)^n\}_{n+m} \, dz,$$

since $\{(z^2-1)^m\}_{m-1}, \{(z^2-1)^m\}_{m-2}, \dots$ vanish at both limits.

Now, when $m > n$, $\{(z^2-1)^n\}_{m+n} = 0$, since differential coefficients of $(z^2-1)^n$ of order higher than $2n$ vanish ; and so, *when m is greater than n*, it follows from Rodrigues' formula that

$$\int_{-1}^{1} P_m(z)\, P_n(z)\, dz = 0.$$

When $m = n$, we have, by the transformation just obtained,

$$\int_{-1}^{1} \{(z^2-1)^n\}_n \{(z^2-1)^n\}_n \, dz = (-)^n \int_{-1}^{1} (z^2-1)^n \frac{d^{2n}}{dz^{2n}} (z^2-1)^n \, dz$$

$$= (2n)! \int_{-1}^{1} (1-z^2)^n \, dz$$

$$= 2 \cdot (2n)! \int_{0}^{1} (1-z^2)^n \, dz$$

$$= 2 \cdot (2n)! \int_{0}^{\frac{1}{2}\pi} \sin^{2n+1}\theta \, d\theta$$

$$= 2 \cdot (2n)! \frac{2 \cdot 4 \dots (2n)}{3 \cdot 5 \dots (2n+1)},$$

* These two results were given by Legendre in 1784 and 1789.

where $\cos\theta$ has been written for z in the integral; hence, by Rodrigues' formula,

$$\int_{-1}^{1} \{P_n(z)\}^2 \, dz = \frac{2 \cdot (2n)!}{(2^n \cdot n!)^2} \frac{(2^n \cdot n!)^2}{(2n+1)!} = \frac{2}{2n+1}.$$

We have therefore obtained both the required results.

It follows that, in the language of Chapter XI, the functions $(n+\frac{1}{2})^{\frac{1}{2}} P_n(z)$ are normal orthogonal functions for the interval $(-1, 1)$.

Example 1. Shew that, if $x > 0$,

$$\int_{-1}^{1} (\cosh 2x - z)^{-\frac{1}{2}} P_n(z) \, dz = 2^{\frac{1}{2}} (n+\tfrac{1}{2})^{-1} e^{-(2n+1)x}.$$

(Clare, 1908.)

Example 2. If $I = \int_0^1 P_m(z) P_n(z) \, dz$, then

(i) $I = 1/(2n+1)$ $(m = n)$,

(ii) $I = 0$ $(m - n \text{ even})$,

(iii) $I = \dfrac{(-)^{\mu+\nu}}{2^{m+n-1}(n-m)(n+m+1)} \dfrac{n! \, m!}{(\nu!)^2 (\mu!)^2}$ $(n = 2\nu+1, \, m = 2\mu)$.

(Clare, 1902.)

15·2. *Legendre functions.*

Hitherto we have supposed that the degree n of $P_n(z)$ is a positive integer; in fact, $P_n(z)$ has not been defined except when n is a positive integer. We shall now see how $P_n(z)$ can be defined for values of n which are not necessarily integers.

An analogy can be drawn from the theory of the Gamma-function. The expression $z!$ as ordinarily defined (viz. as $z(z-1)(z-2)\ldots 2 \cdot 1$) has a meaning only for positive integral values of z; but when the Gamma-function has been introduced, $z!$ can be defined to be $\Gamma(z+1)$, and so a function $z!$ will exist for values of z which are not integers.

Referring to § 15·13, we see that the differential equation

$$(1 - z^2) \frac{d^2 u}{dz^2} - 2z \frac{du}{dz} + n(n+1) u = 0$$

is satisfied by the expression

$$u = \frac{1}{2\pi i} \int_C \frac{(t^2 - 1)^n}{2^n (t - z)^{n+1}} \, dt,$$

even when n *is not a positive integer*, provided that C is a contour such that $(t^2 - 1)^{n+1} (t - z)^{-n-2}$ resumes its original value after describing C.

Suppose then that n is no longer taken to be a positive integer.

The function $(t^2 - 1)^{n+1} (t - z)^{-n-2}$ has three singularities, namely the points $t = 1$, $t = -1$, $t = z$; and it is clear that after describing a circuit round the point $t = 1$ counter-clockwise, the function resumes its original value multiplied by $e^{2\pi i(n+1)}$; while after describing a circuit round the point $t = z$ counter-clockwise, the function resumes its original value multiplied by

$e^{2\pi i(-n-2)}$. If therefore C be a contour enclosing the points $t = 1$ and $t = z$, but not enclosing the point $t = -1$, then the function $(t^2 - 1)^{n+1} (t - z)^{-n-2}$ will resume its original value after t has described the contour C. Hence, *Legendre's differential equation for functions of degree n,*

$$(1 - z^2) \frac{d^2 u}{dz^2} - 2z \frac{du}{dz} + n(n+1) u = 0,$$

is satisfied by the expression

$$u = \frac{1}{2\pi i} \int_A^{(1+, z+)} \frac{(t^2 - 1)^n}{2^n (t - z)^{n+1}} dt,$$

for all values of n; the many-valued functions will be specified precisely by taking A on the real axis on the right of the point $t = 1$ (and on the right of z if z be real), and by taking $\arg(t-1) = \arg(t+1) = 0$ and $|\arg(t-z)| < \pi$ at A.

This expression will be denoted by $P_n(z)$, and will be termed the Legendre function of degree n of the first kind.

We have thus defined a function $P_n(z)$, the definition being valid whether n is an integer or not.

The function $P_n(z)$ thus defined is not a one-valued function of z; for we might take two contours as shewn in the figure, and the integrals along them would not be the same;

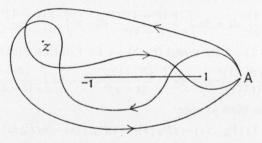

to make the contour integral unique, make a cut in the t plane from -1 to $-\infty$ along the real axis; this involves making a similar cut in the z plane, for if the cut were not made, then, as z varied continuously across the negative part of the real axis, the contour would not vary continuously.

It follows, by § 5·31, that $P_n(z)$ is analytic throughout the cut plane.

15·21. *The Recurrence Formulae.*

We proceed to establish a group of formulae (which are really particular cases of the relations between contiguous Riemann P-functions which were shewn to exist in § 14·7) connecting Legendre functions of different degrees.

If C be the contour of § 15·2, we have*

$$P_n(z) = \frac{1}{2^{n+1} \pi i} \int_C \frac{(t^2 - 1)^n}{(t - z)^{n+1}} dt, \quad P_n'(z) = \frac{n+1}{2^{n+1} \pi i} \int_C \frac{(t^2 - 1)^n}{(t - z)^{n+2}} dt.$$

---

* We write $P_n'(z)$ for $\frac{d}{dz} P_n(z)$.

20—2

Now $\dfrac{d}{dt}\dfrac{(t^2-1)^{n+1}}{(t-z)^{n+1}}=\dfrac{2(n+1)t(t^2-1)^n}{(t-z)^{n+1}}-\dfrac{(n+1)(t^2-1)^{n+1}}{(t-z)^{n+2}},$

and so, integrating,

$$0=2\int_C \frac{t(t^2-1)^n}{(t-z)^{n+1}}\,dt-\int_C \frac{(t^2-1)^{n+1}}{(t-z)^{n+2}}\,dt.$$

Therefore

$$\frac{1}{2^{n+1}\pi i}\int_C \frac{(t^2-1)^n}{(t-z)^n}\,dt=\frac{1}{2^{n+2}\pi i}\int_C \frac{(t^2-1)^{n+1}}{(t-z)^{n+2}}\,dt-\frac{z}{2^{n+1}\pi i}\int_C \frac{(t^2-1)^n}{(t-z)^{n+1}}\,dt.$$

Consequently

$$P_{n+1}(z)-zP_n(z)=\frac{1}{2^{n+1}\pi i}\int_C \frac{(t^2-1)^n}{(t-z)^n}\,dt \quad\ldots\ldots\ldots\ldots(A).$$

Differentiating*, we get

$$P'_{n+1}(z)-zP'_n(z)-P_n(z)=nP_n(z),$$

and so $\qquad P'_{n+1}(z)-zP'_n(z)=(n+1)P_n(z) \quad\ldots\ldots\ldots\ldots\ldots(I).$

This is the first of the required formulae.

Next, expanding the equation

$$\int_C \frac{d}{dt}\left\{\frac{t(t^2-1)^n}{(t-z)^n}\right\}\,dt=0,$$

we find that

$$\int_C \frac{(t^2-1)^n}{(t-z)^n}\,dt+2n\int_C \frac{t^2(t^2-1)^{n-1}}{(t-z)^n}\,dt-n\int_C \frac{t(t^2-1)^n}{(t-z)^{n+1}}\,dt=0.$$

Writing $(t^2-1)+1$ for t^2 and $(t-z)+z$ for t in this equation, we get

$$(n+1)\int_C \frac{(t^2-1)^n}{(t-z)^n}\,dt+2n\int_C \frac{(t^2-1)^{n-1}}{(t-z)^n}\,dt-nz\int_C \frac{(t^2-1)^n}{(t-z)^{n+1}}\,dt=0.$$

Using (A), we have at once

$$(n+1)\{P_{n+1}(z)-zP_n(z)\}+nP_{n-1}(z)-nzP_n(z)=0.$$

That is to say

$$(n+1)P_{n+1}(z)-(2n+1)zP_n(z)+nP_{n-1}(z)=0 \quad\ldots\ldots\ldots(II),$$

a relation† connecting three Legendre functions of consecutive degrees. This is the second of the required formulae.

We can deduce the remaining formulae from (I) and (II) thus:

Differentiating (II), we have

$$(n+1)\{P'_{n+1}(z)-zP'_n(z)\}-n\{zP'_n(z)-P'_{n-1}(z)\}-(2n+1)P_n(z)=0.$$

Using (I) to eliminate $P'_{n+1}(z)$, and then dividing by‡ n, we get

$$zP'_n(z)-P'_{n-1}(z)=nP_n(z) \quad\ldots\ldots\ldots\ldots\ldots(III).$$

---

* The process of differentiating under the sign of integration is readily justified by § 4·2.

† This relation was given in substance by Lagrange in a memoir on Probability, *Misc. Taurinensia*, v. (1770–1773), pp. 167–232.

‡ If $n=0$, we have $P_0(z)=1$, $P_{-1}(z)=1$, and the result (III) is true but trivial.

Adding (I) and (III) we get

$$P'_{n+1}(z) - P'_{n-1}(z) = (2n+1) P_n(z) \quad \dots\dots\dots\dots(IV).$$

Lastly, writing $n-1$ for n in (I) and eliminating $P'_{n-1}(z)$ between the equation so obtained and (III), we have

$$(z^2 - 1) P'_n(z) = nzP_n(z) - nP_{n-1}(z)\dots\dots\dots\dots(V).$$

The formulae (I)—(V) are called the *recurrence formulae*.

The above proof holds whether n is an integer or not, i.e. it is applicable to the general Legendre functions.   Another proof which, however, only applies to the case when n is a positive integer (i.e. is only applicable to the Legendre polynomials) is as follows :

Write
$$V = (1 - 2hz + h^2)^{-\frac{1}{2}}.$$

Then, equating coefficients* of powers of h in the expansions on each side of the equation

$$(1 - 2hz + h^2)\frac{\partial V}{\partial h} = (z - h) V,$$

we have
$$nP_n(z) - (2n-1) zP_{n-1}(z) + (n-1) P_{n-2}(z) = 0,$$

which is the formula (II).

Similarly, equating coefficients* of powers of h in the expansions on each side of the equation

$$h\frac{\partial V}{\partial h} = (z - h) \frac{\partial V}{\partial z},$$

we have
$$z\frac{dP_n(z)}{dz} - \frac{dP_{n-1}(z)}{dz} = nP_n(z),$$

which is the formula (III).   The others can be deduced from these.

Example 1.   Shew that, for all values of n,

$$\frac{d}{dz}\{z(P_n{}^2 + P^2{}_{n+1}) - 2P_n P_{n+1}\} = (2n+3) P^2{}_{n+1} - (2n+1) P_n{}^2.$$

(Hargreaves.)

Example 2.   If
$$M_n(x) = \left[\left(\frac{d}{dz}\right)^n (ze^{xz} \operatorname{cosech} z)\right]_{z=0},$$

shew that
$$\frac{dM_n(x)}{dx} = nM_{n-1}(x) \quad \text{and} \quad \int_{-1}^{1} M_n(x)\, dx = 0. \qquad \text{(Trinity, 1900.)}$$

Example 3.   Prove that if m and n are integers such that $m \leqslant n$, both being even or both odd,

$$\int_{-1}^{1} \frac{dP_m(z)}{dz} \frac{dP_n(z)}{dz}\, dz = m(m+1). \qquad \text{(Clare, 1898.)}$$

Example 4.   Prove that, if m, n are integers and $m \geqslant n$,

$$\int_{-1}^{1} \frac{d^2 P_m(z)}{dz^2} \frac{d^2 P_n(z)}{dz^2}\, dz = \frac{(n-1)\, n\, (n+1)\, (n+2)}{48} \{3m(m+1) - n(n+1) + 6\}$$
$$\times \{1 + (-)^{n+m}\}.$$

(Math. Trip. 1897.)

* The reader is recommended to justify these processes.

15·211. *The expression of any polynomial as a series of Legendre polynomials.*

Let $f_n(z)$ be a polynomial of degree n in z.

Then it is always possible to choose a_0, a_1, ... a_n so that

$$f_n(z) \equiv a_0 P_0(z) + a_1 P_1(z) + \ldots + a_n P_n(z),$$

for, on equating coefficients of z^n, z^{n-1}, ... on each side, we obtain equations which determine a_n, a_{n-1}, ... uniquely in turn, in terms of the coefficients of powers of z in $f_n(z)$.

To determine a_0, a_1, ... a_n in the most simple manner, multiply the identity by $P_r(z)$, and integrate. Then, by § 15·14,

$$\int_{-1}^{1} f_n(z) P_r(z)\, dz = \frac{2a_r}{2r+1},$$

when $r = 0, 1, 2, \ldots n$; when $r > n$, the integral on the left vanishes.

Example 1. Given $z^n = a_0 P_0(z) + a_1 P_1(z) + \ldots + a_n P_n(z)$, to determine a_0, a_1, ... a_n.

(Legendre, *Exercices de Calc. Int.* II. p. 352.)

[Equate coefficients of z^n on both sides; this gives

$$a_n = \frac{2^n \cdot (n\,!)^2}{(2n)\,!}.$$

Let $I_{n,m} = \int_{-1}^{1} z^n P_m(z)\, dz$, so that, by the result just given,

$$I_{m,m} = \frac{2^{m+1}(m\,!)^2}{(2m+1)\,!}.$$

Now when $n - m$ is odd, $I_{n,m}$ is the integral of an odd function with limits ± 1, and so vanishes; and $I_{n,m}$ also vanishes when $n - m$ is negative and even.

To evaluate $I_{n,m}$ when $n - m$ is a positive even integer, we have from Legendre's equation

$$m(m+1)\int_{-1}^{1} z^n P_m(z)\, dz = -\int_{-1}^{1} z^n \frac{d}{dz}\{(1-z^2) P_m'(z)\}\, dz$$

$$= -\left[z^n(1-z^2) P_m'(z) \right]_{-1}^{1} + n\int_{-1}^{1} z^{n-1}(1-z^2) P_m'(z)\, dz$$

$$= n\left[z^{n-1}(1-z^2) P_m(z) \right]_{-1}^{1} - n\int_{-1}^{1}\{(n-1)z^{n-2} - (n+1)z^n\} P_m(z)\, dz,$$

on integrating by parts twice; and so

$$m(m+1) I_{n,m} = n(n+1) I_{n,m} - n(n-1) I_{n-2,m}.$$

Therefore

$$I_{n,m} = \frac{n(n-1)}{(n-m)(n+m+1)} I_{n-2,m}$$

$$= \frac{n(n-1)\ldots(m+1)}{(n-m)(n-2-m)\ldots 2 \cdot (n+m+1)(n+m-1)\ldots(2m+3)} I_{m,m},$$

by carrying on the process of reduction.

Consequently
$$I_{n,\,m}=\frac{2^{m+1}.\,n\,!\,(\frac{1}{2}n+\frac{1}{2}m)\,!}{(\frac{1}{2}n-\frac{1}{2}m)\,!\,(n+m+1)\,!}\,,$$

and so $\quad a_m = 0$, when $n-m$ is odd or negative,

$$a_m = \frac{(2m+1)\,2^m\,n\,!\,(\frac{1}{2}n+\frac{1}{2}m)\,!}{(\frac{1}{2}n-\frac{1}{2}m)\,!\,(n+m+1)\,!}\ \text{when } n-m \text{ is even and positive.}]$$

Example 2. Express $\cos n\theta$ as a series of Legendre polynomials of $\cos\theta$ when n is an integer.

Example 3. Evaluate the integrals

$$\int_{-1}^{1} z P_n(z)\,P_{n+1}(z)\,dz, \quad \int_{-1}^{1} z^2 P_n(z)\,P_{n+1}(z)\,dz.$$

(St John's, 1899.)

Example 4. Shew that

$$\int_{-1}^{1} (1-z^2)\,\{P_n{}'(z)\}^2\,dz = \frac{2n\,(n+1)}{2n+1}\,.$$
(Trinity, 1894.)

Example 5. Shew that

$$nP_n(\cos\theta) = \sum_{r=1}^{n} \cos r\theta\, P_{n-r}(\cos\theta).$$
(St John's, 1898.)

Example 6. If $u_n = \displaystyle\int_{-1}^{1} (1-z^2)^n\, P_{2m}(z)\,dz$, where $m < n$, shew that

$$(n-m)\,(2n+2m+1)\,u_n = 2n^2 u_{n-1}.$$
(Trinity, 1895.)

15·22. *Murphy's expression* of $P_n(z)$ as a hypergeometric function.*

Since (§ 15·13) Legendre's equation is a particular case of Riemann's equation, it is to be expected that a formula can be obtained giving $P_n(z)$ in terms of hypergeometric functions. To determine this formula, take the integral of § 15·2 for the Legendre function and suppose that $|1-z| < 2$; to fix the contour C, let δ be any constant such that $0 < \delta < 1$, and suppose that z is such that $|1-z| \leqslant 2(1-\delta)$; and then take C to be the circle†

$$|1-t| = 2-\delta.$$

Since $\left|\dfrac{1-z}{1-t}\right| \leqslant \dfrac{2-2\delta}{2-\delta} < 1$, we may expand $(t-z)^{-n-1}$ into the uniformly convergent series‡

$$(t-z)^{-n-1} = (t-1)^{-n-1}\left\{1 + (n+1)\frac{z-1}{t-1} + \frac{(n+1)(n+2)}{2\,!}\left(\frac{z-1}{t-1}\right)^2 + \dots\right\}.$$

Substituting this result in Schläfli's integral, and integrating term-by-term (§ 4·7), we get

$$P_n(z) = \sum_{r=0}^{\infty} \frac{(z-1)^r}{2^{n+1}\pi i} \frac{(n+1)(n+2)\dots(n+r)}{r\,!} \int_{A}^{(1+,\,z+)} \frac{(t^2-1)^n}{(t-1)^{n+1+r}}\,dt$$

$$= \sum_{r=0}^{\infty} \frac{(z-1)^r.\,(n+1)(n+2)\dots(n+r)}{2^n.\,(r\,!)^2}\left[\frac{d^r}{dt^r}\,(t+1)^n\right]_{t=1},$$

---

* *Electricity* (1833). Murphy's result was obtained only for the Legendre polynomials.

† This circle contains the points $t=1$, $t=z$.

‡ The series terminates if n be a negative integer.

by § 5·22.   Since $\arg(t+1) = 0$ when $t = 1$, we get

$$\left[\frac{d^r}{dt^r}(t+1)^n\right]_{t=1} = 2^{n-r}\, n\,(n-1)\ldots(n-r+1),$$

and so, when $|1-z| \leqslant 2\,(1-\delta) < 2$, we have

$$P_n(z) = \sum_{r=0}^{\infty} \frac{(n+1)(n+2)\ldots(n+r)\cdot(-n)(1-n)\ldots(r-1-n)}{(r!)^2}\left(\tfrac{1}{2} - \tfrac{1}{2}z\right)^r$$

$$= F\left(n+1,\; -n;\; 1;\; \tfrac{1}{2} - \tfrac{1}{2}z\right).$$

This is the required expression; it supplies a reason (§ 14·53) why the cut from -1 to $-\infty$ could not be avoided in § 15·2.

Corollary.   From this result, it is obvious that, for all values of n,

$$P_n(z) = P_{-n-1}(z).$$

NOTE.   When n is a positive integer, the result gives the Legendre polynomial as a polynomial in $1-z$ with simple coefficients.

Example 1.   Shew that, if m be a positive integer,

$$\left\{\frac{d^{m+1} P_{m+n}(z)}{dz^{m+1}}\right\}_{z=1} = \frac{\Gamma(2m+n+2)}{2^{m+1}(m+1)!\,\Gamma(n)}.$$ (Trinity, 1907.)

Example 2.   Shew that the Legendre polynomial $P_n(\cos\theta)$ is equal to

$$(-)^n F(n+1,\; -n;\; 1;\; \cos^2 \tfrac{1}{2}\theta),$$

and to

$$\cos^n \tfrac{1}{2}\theta\, F(-n,\; -n;\; 1;\; \tan^2 \tfrac{1}{2}\theta).$$ (Murphy.)

15·23.   *Laplace's integrals* for $P_n(z)$.*

We shall next shew that, for all values of n and for certain values of z, the Legendre function $P_n(z)$ can be represented by the integral (called *Laplace's first integral*)

$$\frac{1}{\pi}\int_0^\pi \{z + (z^2-1)^{\frac{1}{2}}\cos\phi\}^n\, d\phi.$$

(A)   *Proof applicable only to the Legendre polynomials.*

When n is a positive integer, we have, by § 15·12,

$$P_n(z) = \frac{1}{2^{n+1}\pi i}\int_C \frac{(t^2-1)^n}{(t-z)^{n+1}}\, dt,$$

where C is any contour which encircles the point z counter-clockwise. Take C to be the circle with centre z and radius $|z^2-1|^{\frac{1}{2}}$, so that, on C, $t = z + (z^2-1)^{\frac{1}{2}} e^{i\phi}$, where ϕ may be taken to increase from $-\pi$ to π.

---

* *Mécanique Céleste*, Livre xi. Ch. 2.   For the contour employed in this section, and for some others introduced later in the chapter, we are indebted to Mr J. Hodgkinson.

Making the substitution, we have, for *all* values of z,

$$P_n(z) = \frac{1}{2^{n+1}\pi i} \int_{-\pi}^{\pi} \left(\frac{\{z - 1 + (z^2 - 1)^{\frac{1}{2}} e^{i\phi}\} \{z + 1 + (z^2 - 1)^{\frac{1}{2}} e^{i\phi}\}}{(z^2 - 1)^{\frac{1}{2}} e^{i\phi}} \right)^n i \, d\phi$$

$$= \frac{1}{2\pi} \int_{-\pi}^{\pi} \{z + (z^2 - 1)^{\frac{1}{2}} \cos \phi\}^n \, d\phi$$

$$= \frac{1}{\pi} \int_{0}^{\pi} \{z + (z^2 - 1)^{\frac{1}{2}} \cos \phi\}^n \, d\phi,$$

since the integrand is an even function of ϕ. The choice of the branch of the two-valued function $(z^2 - 1)^{\frac{1}{2}}$ is obviously a matter of indifference.

(B) *Proof applicable to the Legendre functions, where n is unrestricted.*

Make the same substitution as in (A) in Schläfli's integral defining $P_n(z)$; it is, however, necessary in addition to verify that $t = 1$ is inside the contour and $t = -1$ outside it, and it is also necessary that we should specify the branch of $\{z + (z^2 - 1)^{\frac{1}{2}} \cos \phi\}^n$, which is now a many-valued function of ϕ.

The conditions that $t = 1$, $t = -1$ should be inside and outside C respectively are that the distances of z from these points should be less and greater than $|z^2 - 1|^{\frac{1}{2}}$. These conditions are both satisfied if $|z - 1| < |z + 1|$, which gives $R(z) > 0$, and so (giving $\arg z$ its principal value) *we must have* $|\arg z| < \frac{1}{2}\pi$.

Therefore $P_n(z) = \frac{1}{2\pi} \int_{-\pi}^{\pi} \{z + (z^2 - 1)^{\frac{1}{2}} \cos \phi\}^n \, d\phi,$

where the value of $\arg \{z + (z^2 - 1)^{\frac{1}{2}} \cos \phi\}$ is specified by the fact that it [being equal to $\arg(t^2 - 1) - \arg(t - z)$] is numerically less than π when t is on the real axis and on the right of z (see § 15·2).

Now as ϕ increases from $-\pi$ to π, $z + (z^2 - 1)^{\frac{1}{2}} \cos \phi$ describes a straight line in the Argand diagram going from $z - (z^2 - 1)^{\frac{1}{2}}$ to $z + (z^2 - 1)^{\frac{1}{2}}$ and back again; and since this line does not pass through the origin*, $\arg \{z + (z^2 - 1)^{\frac{1}{2}} \cos \phi\}$ does not change by so much as π on the range of integration.

Now suppose that the branch of $\{z + (z^2 - 1)^{\frac{1}{2}} \cos \phi\}^n$ which has to be taken is such that it reduces to $z^n e^{n \cdot 2k\pi i}$ (where k is an integer) when $\phi = \frac{1}{2}\pi$.

Then $P_n(z) = \frac{e^{2nk\pi i}}{2\pi} \int_{-\pi}^{\pi} \{z + (z^2 - 1)^{\frac{1}{2}} \cos \phi\}^n \, d\phi,$

where now that branch of the many-valued function is taken which is equal to z^n when $\phi = \frac{1}{2}\pi$.

Now make $z \to 1$ by a path which avoids the zeros of $P_n(z)$; since $P_n(z)$ and the integral are analytic functions of z when $|\arg z| < \frac{1}{2}\pi$, k does not change as z describes the path. And so we get $e^{2nk\pi i} = 1$.

---

* It only does so if z is a pure imaginary; and such values of z have been excluded.

Therefore, when $|\arg z| < \frac{1}{2}\pi$ and n is unrestricted,

$$P_n(z) = \frac{1}{2\pi} \int_{-\pi}^{\pi} \{z + (z^2 - 1)^{\frac{1}{2}} \cos \phi\}^n \, d\phi,$$

where $\arg \{z + (z^2 - 1)^{\frac{1}{2}} \cos \phi\}$ is to be taken equal to $\arg z$ when $\phi = \frac{1}{2}\pi$.

This expression for $P_n(z)$, which may, again, obviously be written

$$\frac{1}{\pi} \int_0^{\pi} \{z + (z^2 - 1)^{\frac{1}{2}} \cos \phi\}^n \, d\phi,$$

is known as *Laplace's first integral* for $P_n(z)$.

Corollary. From § 15·22 corollary, it is evident that, when $|\arg z| < \frac{1}{2}\pi$,

$$P_n(z) = \frac{1}{\pi} \int_0^{\pi} \frac{d\phi}{\{z + (z^2 - 1)^{\frac{1}{2}} \cos \phi\}^{n+1}},$$

a result, due to Jacobi, *Journal für Math.* XXVI. (1843), pp. 81–87, known as *Laplace's second integral* for $P_n(z)$.

Example 1. Obtain Laplace's first integral by considering

$$\sum_{n=0}^{\infty} h^n \int_0^{\pi} \{z + (z^2 - 1)^{\frac{1}{2}} \cos \phi\}^n \, d\phi,$$

and using § 6·21 example 1.

Example 2. Shew, by direct differentiation, that Laplace's integral is a solution of Legendre's equation.

Example 3. If $s < 1$, $|h| < 1$ and

$$(1 - 2h \cos \theta + h^2)^{-s} = \sum_{n=0}^{\infty} b_n \cos n\theta,$$

shew that $\qquad b_n = \dfrac{2 \sin s\pi}{\pi} \displaystyle\int_0^1 \dfrac{h^n x^{n+s-1}}{(1-x)^s (1 - xh^2)^s} \, dx.$ (Binet.)

Example 4. When $z > 1$, deduce Laplace's second integral from his first integral by the substitution

$$\{z - (z^2 - 1)^{\frac{1}{2}} \cos \theta\} \{z + (z^2 - 1)^{\frac{1}{2}} \cos \phi\} = 1.$$

Example 5. By expanding in powers of $\cos \phi$, shew that for a certain range of values of z,

$$\frac{1}{\pi} \int_0^{\pi} \{z + (z^2 - 1)^{\frac{1}{2}} \cos \phi\}^n \, d\phi = z^n F\left(-\tfrac{1}{2}n, \tfrac{1}{2} - \tfrac{1}{2}n; \ 1; \ 1 - z^{-2}\right).$$

Example 6. Shew that Legendre's equation is defined by the scheme

$$P \left\{ \begin{matrix} 0 & \infty & 1 & \\ -\tfrac{1}{2}n & \tfrac{1}{2} + \tfrac{1}{2}n & 0 & \xi \\ \tfrac{1}{2} + \tfrac{1}{2}n & -\tfrac{1}{2}n & 0 & \end{matrix} \right\},$$

where $z = \frac{1}{2}(\xi^{\frac{1}{2}} + \xi^{-\frac{1}{2}})$.

15·231. *The Mehler-Dirichlet integral* [*] *for* $P_n(z)$.

Another expression for the Legendre function as a definite integral may be obtained in the following way:

[*] Dirichlet, *Journal für Math.* XVII. (1837), p. 35; Mehler, *Math. Ann.* v. (1872), p. 141.

For all values of n, we have, by the preceding theorem,

$$P_n(z) = \frac{1}{\pi} \int_0^\pi \{z + \cos\phi\, (z^2 - 1)^{\frac{1}{2}}\}^n\, d\phi.$$

In this integral, replace the variable ϕ by a new variable h, defined by the equation

$$h = z + (z^2 - 1)^{\frac{1}{2}} \cos\phi,$$

and we get

$$P_n(z) = \frac{i}{\pi} \int_{z-(z^2-1)^{\frac{1}{2}}}^{z+(z^2-1)^{\frac{1}{2}}} h^n (1 - 2hz + h^2)^{-\frac{1}{2}}\, dh;$$

the path of integration is a straight line, $\arg h$ is determined by the fact that $h = z$ when $\phi = \frac{1}{2}\pi$, and $(1 - 2hz + h^2)^{-\frac{1}{2}} = -i (z^2 - 1)^{\frac{1}{2}} \sin\phi$.

Now let $z = \cos\theta$; then

$$P_n(\cos\theta) = \frac{i}{\pi} \int_{e^{-i\theta}}^{e^{i\theta}} h^n (1 - 2hz + h^2)^{-\frac{1}{2}}\, dh.$$

Now (θ being restricted so that $-\frac{1}{2}\pi < \theta < \frac{1}{2}\pi$ when n is not a positive integer) the path of integration may be deformed* into that arc of the circle $|h| = 1$ which passes through $h = 1$, and joins the points $h = e^{-i\theta}$, $h = e^{i\theta}$, since the integrand is analytic throughout the region between this arc and its chord†.

Writing $h = e^{i\phi}$ we get

$$P_n(\cos\theta) = \frac{1}{\pi} \int_{-\theta}^{\theta} \frac{e^{(n+\frac{1}{2})i\phi}}{(2\cos\phi - 2\cos\theta)^{\frac{1}{2}}}\, d\phi,$$

and so

$$P_n(\cos\theta) = \frac{2}{\pi} \int_0^\theta \frac{\cos(n+\frac{1}{2})\phi}{\{2(\cos\phi - \cos\theta)\}^{\frac{1}{2}}}\, d\phi;$$

it is easy to see that the positive value of the square root is to be taken.

This is known as *Mehler's simplified form of Dirichlet's integral*. The result is valid for all values of n.

Example 1. Prove that, when n is a positive integer,

$$P_n(\cos\theta) = \frac{2}{\pi} \int_\theta^\pi \frac{\sin(n+\frac{1}{2})\phi\, d\phi}{\{2(\cos\theta - \cos\phi)\}^{\frac{1}{2}}}.$$

(Write $\pi - \theta$ for θ and $\pi - \phi$ for ϕ in the result just obtained.)

Example 2. Prove that

$$P_n(\cos\theta) = \frac{1}{2\pi i} \int \frac{h^n}{(h^2 - 2h\cos\theta + 1)^{\frac{1}{2}}}\, dh,$$

the integral being taken along a closed path which encircles the two points $h = e^{\pm i\theta}$, and a suitable meaning being assigned to the radical.

---

* If θ be complex and $R(\cos\theta) > 0$ the deformation of the contour presents slightly greater difficulties. The reader will easily modify the analysis given to cover this case.

† The integrand is not analytic at the ends of the arc but behaves like $(h - e^{\pm i\theta})^{-\frac{1}{2}}$ near them; but if the region be indented (§ 6·23) at $e^{\pm i\theta}$ and the radii of the indentations be made to tend to zero, we see that the deformation is legitimate.

Hence (or otherwise) prove that, if θ lie between $\frac{1}{8}\pi$ and $\frac{5}{8}\pi$,

$$P_n(\cos\theta) = \frac{4}{\pi} \frac{2.4\ldots 2n}{3.5\ldots(2n+1)} \left(\frac{\cos(n\theta+\phi)}{(2\sin\theta)^{\frac{1}{2}}} + \frac{1^2}{2(2n+3)} \frac{\cos(n\theta+3\phi)}{(2\sin\theta)^{\frac{3}{2}}} \right.$$
$$\left. + \frac{1^2.3^2}{2.4.(2n+3)(2n+5)} \frac{\cos(n\theta+5\phi)}{(2\sin\theta)^{\frac{5}{2}}} \right.$$
$$\left. + \ldots\ldots\ldots\ldots\ldots\ldots\ldots\ldots\ldots \right),$$

where ϕ denotes $\frac{1}{2}\theta - \frac{1}{4}\pi$.

Shew also that the first few terms of the series give an approximate value of $P_n(\cos\theta)$ for all values of θ between 0 and π which are not nearly equal to either 0 or π. And explain how this theorem may be used to approximate to the roots of the equation $P_n(\cos\theta)=0$.

(See Heine, *Kugelfunktionen*, I. p. 178 ; Darboux, *Comptes Rendus*, LXXXII. (1876), pp. 365, 404.)

15·3. *Legendre functions of the second kind.*

We have hitherto considered only one solution of Legendre's equation, namely $P_n(z)$. We proceed to find a second solution.

We have seen (§ 15·2) that Legendre's equation is satisfied by

$$\int (t^2-1)^n (t-z)^{-n-1} dt,$$

taken round any contour such that the integrand returns to its initial value after describing it. Let D be a figure-of-eight contour formed in the following way: let z be not a real number between ± 1; draw an ellipse in the t-plane with the points ± 1 as foci, the ellipse being so small that the point $t=z$ is outside. Let A be the end of the major axis of the ellipse on the right of $t=1$.

Let the contour D start from A and describe the circuits $(1-,-1+)$, returning to A (cf. § 12·43), and lying wholly inside the ellipse.

Let $|\arg z| \leqslant \pi$ and let $|\arg(z-t)| \to \arg z$ as $t \to 0$ on the contour. Let $\arg(t+1) = \arg(t-1) = 0$ at A.

Then a solution of Legendre's equation valid in the plane (cut along the real axis from 1 to $-\infty$) is

$$Q_n(z) = \frac{1}{4i\sin n\pi} \int_D \frac{(t^2-1)^n}{2^n(z-t)^{n+1}} dt,$$

if n is not an integer.

When $R(n+1) > 0$, we may deform the path of integration as in § 12·43, and get

$$Q_n(z) = \frac{1}{2^{n+1}} \int_{-1}^{1} (1-t^2)^n (z-t)^{-n-1} dt$$

(where $\arg(1-t) = \arg(1+t) = 0$); this will be taken as the definition of $Q_n(z)$ when n is a positive integer or zero. When n is a negative integer $(=-m-1)$ Legendre's differential equation for functions of degree n is identical with that for functions of degree m, and accordingly we shall take the two fundamental solutions to be $P_m(z)$, $Q_m(z)$.

$Q_n(z)$ *is called the Legendre function of degree n of the second kind.*

15·31. *Expansion of $Q_n(z)$ as a power-series.*

We now proceed to express the Legendre function of the second kind as a power-series in z^{-1}.

We have, when the real part of $n+1$ is positive,

$$Q_n(z) = \frac{1}{2^{n+1}} \int_{-1}^{1} (1-t^2)^n (z-t)^{-n-1} dt.$$

Suppose that $|z| > 1$. Then the integrand can be expanded in a series uniformly convergent with regard to t, so that

$$Q_n(z) = \frac{1}{2^{n+1} z^{n+1}} \int_{-1}^{1} (1-t^2)^n \left(1 - \frac{t}{z}\right)^{-n-1} dt$$

$$= \frac{1}{2^{n+1} z^{n+1}} \int_{-1}^{1} (1-t^2)^n \left\{1 + \sum_{r=1}^{\infty} \left(\frac{t}{z}\right)^r \frac{(n+1)(n+2)\ldots(n+r)}{r!}\right\} dt$$

$$= \frac{1}{2^n z^{n+1}} \left[\int_0^1 (1-t^2)^n dt + \sum_{s=1}^{\infty} \frac{(n+1)\ldots(n+2s)}{2s! \, z^{2s}} \int_0^1 (1-t^2)^n t^{2s} dt\right],$$

where $r = 2s$, the integrals arising from odd values of r vanishing.

Writing $t^2 = u$, we get without difficulty, from § 12·41,

$$Q_n(z) = \frac{\pi^{\frac{1}{2}} \Gamma(n+1)}{2^{n+1} \Gamma(n+\frac{3}{2})} \frac{1}{z^{n+1}} F\left(\tfrac{1}{2}n + \tfrac{1}{2}, \tfrac{1}{2}n + 1; n + \tfrac{3}{2}; z^{-2}\right).$$

The proof given above applies only when the real part of $(n+1)$ is positive (see § 4·5); but a similar process can be applied to the integral

$$Q_n(z) = \frac{1}{4i \sin n\pi} \int_D \frac{1}{2^n} (t^2-1)^n (z-t)^{-n-1} dt,$$

the coefficients being evaluated by writing $\int_D (t^2-1)^n t^r dt$ in the form

$$e^{n\pi i} \int_0^{(1-)} (1-t^2)^n t^r dt + e^{n\pi i} \int_0^{(-1+)} (1-t^2)^n t^r dt;$$

and then, writing $t^2 = u$ and using § 12·43, the same result is reached, so that the formula

$$Q_n(z) = \frac{\pi^{\frac{1}{2}}}{2^{n+1}} \frac{\Gamma(n+1)}{\Gamma(n+\frac{3}{2})} \frac{1}{z^{n+1}} F\left(\tfrac{1}{2}n + \tfrac{1}{2}, \tfrac{1}{2}n + 1; n + \tfrac{3}{2}; \frac{1}{z^2}\right)$$

is true for unrestricted values of n (negative integer values excepted) and for all values* of z, such that $|z| > 1$, $|\arg z| < \pi$.

Example 1. Shew that, when n is a positive integer,

$$Q_n(z) = \frac{(-2)^n n!}{2n!} \frac{d^n}{dz^n} \left\{(z^2-1)^n \int_z^{\infty} (v^2-1)^{-n-1} dv\right\}.$$

* When n is a positive integer it is unnecessary to restrict the value of arg z.

[It is easily verified that Legendre's equation can be derived from the equation

$$(1 - z^2)\frac{d^2w}{dz^2} + 2(n-1)z\frac{dw}{dz} + 2nw = 0,$$

by differentiating n times and writing $u = \dfrac{d^n w}{dz^n}$.

Two independent solutions of this equation are found to be

$$(z^2 - 1)^n \quad \text{and} \quad (z^2 - 1)^n \int_z^\infty (v^2 - 1)^{-n-1}\, dv.$$

It follows that

$$\frac{d^n}{dz^n}\left\{(z^2 - 1)^n \int_z^\infty (v^2 - 1)^{-n-1}\, dv\right\}$$

is a solution of Legendre's equation. As this expression, when expanded in ascending powers of z^{-1}, commences with a term in z^{-n-1}, it must be a constant multiple* of $Q_n(z)$; and on comparing the coefficient of z^{-n-1} in this expression with the coefficient of z^{-n-1} in the expansion of $Q_n(z)$, as found above, we obtain the required result.]

Example 2. Shew that, when n is a positive integer, the Legendre function of the second kind can be expressed by the formula

$$Q_n(z) = 2^n n! \int_z^\infty \int_v^\infty \int_v^\infty \cdots \int_v^\infty (v^2 - 1)^{-n-1}\, (dv)^{n+1}.$$

Example 3. Shew that, when n is a positive integer,

$$Q_n(z) = \sum_{t=0}^n \frac{2^n \cdot n!}{t!\,(n-t)!}\,(-z)^{n-t}\int_z^\infty v^t (v^2 - 1)^{-n-1}\, dv.$$

[This result can be obtained by applying the general integration-theorem

$$\int_z^\infty\int_v^\infty\int_v^\infty\cdots\int_v^\infty f(v)\,(dv)^{n+1} = \sum_{t=0}^n \frac{(-z)^{n-t}}{t!\,(n-t)!}\int_z^\infty v^t f(v)\, dv$$

to the preceding result.]

15·32. *The recurrence-formulae for* $Q_n(z)$.

The functions $P_n(z)$ and $Q_n(z)$ have been defined by means of integrals of precisely the same form, namely

$$\int (t^2 - 1)^n (t - z)^{-n-1}\, dt,$$

taken round different contours.

It follows that the general proof of the recurrence-formulae for $P_n(z)$, given in § 15·21, is equally applicable to the function $Q_n(z)$; and hence that *the Legendre function of the second kind satisfies the recurrence-formulae*

$$Q'_{n+1}(z) - zQ'_n(z) = (n+1)\,Q_n(z),$$
$$(n+1)\,Q_{n+1}(z) - (2n+1)\,zQ_n(z) + nQ_{n-1}(z) = 0,$$
$$zQ'_n(z) - Q'_{n-1}(z) = nQ_n(z),$$
$$Q'_{n+1}(z) - Q'_{n-1}(z) = (2n+1)\,Q_n(z),$$
$$(z^2 - 1)\,Q'_n(z) = nzQ_n(z) - nQ_{n-1}(z).$$

Example 1. Shew that

$$Q_0(z) = \tfrac12 \log\frac{z+1}{z-1}, \quad Q_1(z) = \tfrac12 z \log\frac{z+1}{z-1} - 1,$$

and deduce that

$$Q_2(z) = \tfrac12 P_2(z)\log\frac{z+1}{z-1} - \tfrac32 z,$$

and that

$$\frac{Q_n(z)}{P_n(z)} = \tfrac12 \log\frac{z+1}{z-1} - \frac{1}{z} - \frac{1^2}{3z} - \frac{2^2}{5z} - \frac{3^2}{7z} - \ldots - \frac{(n-1)^2}{(2n-1)z}.$$

* $P_n(z)$ contains *positive* powers of z when n is an integer.

Example 2. Shew by the recurrence-formulae that, when n is a positive integer*,

$$\tfrac{1}{2} P_n(z) \log \frac{z+1}{z-1} - Q_n(z) = f_{n-1}(z),$$

where $f_{n-1}(z)$ consists of the positive (and zero) powers of z in the expansion of $\tfrac{1}{2} P_n(z) \log \frac{z+1}{z-1}$ in descending powers of z.

[This example shews the nature of the singularities of $Q_n(z)$ at ± 1, when n is an integer, which make the cut from -1 to $+1$ necessary. For the connexion of the result with the theory of continued fractions, see Gauss, *Werke*, III. pp. 165–206, and Frobenius, *Journal für Math.* LXXIII. (1871), p. 16 ; the formulae of example 1 are due to them.]

15·33.　*The Laplacian integral† for Legendre functions of the second kind.*

It will now be proved that, when $R(n+1) > 0$,

$$Q_n(z) = \int_0^\infty \{z + (z^2-1)^{\frac{1}{2}} \cosh \theta\}^{-n-1} \, d\theta,$$

where $\arg \{z + (z^2-1)^{\frac{1}{2}} \cosh \theta\}$ has its principal value when $\theta = 0$, if n be not an integer.

First suppose that $z > 1$. In the integral of § 15·3, viz.

$$Q_n(z) = \frac{1}{2^{n+1}} \int_{-1}^1 (1-t^2)^n (z-t)^{-n-1} \, dt,$$

write
$$t = \frac{e^\theta (z+1)^{\frac{1}{2}} - (z-1)^{\frac{1}{2}}}{e^\theta (z+1)^{\frac{1}{2}} + (z-1)^{\frac{1}{2}}},$$

so that the range $(-1, 1)$ of real values of t corresponds to the range $(-\infty, \infty)$ of real values of θ. It then follows (as in § 15·23 A) by straightforward substitution that

$$Q_n(z) = \frac{1}{2} \int_{-\infty}^\infty \{z + (z^2-1)^{\frac{1}{2}} \cosh \theta\}^{-n-1} \, d\theta$$

$$= \int_0^\infty \{z + (z^2-1)^{\frac{1}{2}} \cosh \theta\}^{-n-1} \, d\theta,$$

since the integrand is an even function of θ.

To prove the result for values of z not comprised in the range of real values greater than 1, we observe that the branch points of the integrand, *qua* function of z, are at the points ± 1 and at points where $z + (z^2-1)^{\frac{1}{2}} \cosh \theta$ vanishes ; the latter are the points at which $z = \pm \coth \theta$.

Hence $Q_n(z)$ and $\int_0^\infty \{z + (z^2-1)^{\frac{1}{2}} \cosh \theta\}^{-n-1} \, d\theta$ are both analytic ‡ at all points of the plane when cut along the line joining the points $z = \pm 1$.

---

* If $-1 < z < 1$, it is apparent from these formulae that $Q_n(z+0i) - Q_n(z-0i) = -\pi i P_n(z)$.

It is convenient to *define* $Q_n(z)$ for such values of z to be $\tfrac{1}{2} Q_n(z+0i) + \tfrac{1}{2} Q_n(z-0i)$. The reader will observe that this function satisfies Legendre's equation for real values of z.

† This formula was first given by Heine ; see his *Kugelfunktionen*, p. 147.

‡ It is easy to shew that the integral has a unique derivate in the cut plane.

By the theory of analytic continuation the equation proved for positive values of $z-1$ persists for all values of z in the cut plane, provided that $\arg \{z + (z^2 - 1)^{\frac{1}{2}} \cosh \theta\}$ is given a suitable value, namely that one which reduces to zero when $z - 1$ is positive.

The integrand is one-valued in the cut plane [and so is $Q_n(z)$] when n is a positive integer; but $\arg \{z + (z^2 - 1)^{\frac{1}{2}} \cosh \theta\}$ increases by 2π as $\arg z$ does so, and therefore if n be not a positive integer, a further cut has to be made from $z = -1$ to $z = -\infty$.

These cuts give the necessary limitations on the value of z; and the cut when n is not an integer ensures that $\arg \{z + (z^2 - 1)^{\frac{1}{2}}\} = 2 \arg \{(z+1)^{\frac{1}{2}} + (z-1)^{\frac{1}{2}}\}$ has its principal value.

Example 1. Obtain this result for complex values of z by taking the path of integration to be a certain circular arc before making the substitution

$$t = \frac{e^\theta (z+1)^{\frac{1}{2}} - (z-1)^{\frac{1}{2}}}{e^\theta (z+1)^{\frac{1}{2}} + (z-1)^{\frac{1}{2}}},$$

where θ is real.

Example 2. Shew that, if $z > 1$ and $\coth a = z$,

$$Q_n(z) = \int_0^a \{z - (z^2 - 1)^{\frac{1}{2}} \cosh u\}^n \, du,$$

where $\arg \{z - (z^2 - 1)^{\frac{1}{2}} \cosh u\} = 0$.   (Trinity, 1893.)

15·34. *Neumann's* [*] *formula for $Q_n(z)$, when n is an integer.*

When n is a positive integer, and z is not a real number between 1 and -1, the function $Q_n(z)$ is expressed in terms of the Legendre function of the first kind by the relation

$$Q_n(z) = \frac{1}{2} \int_{-1}^1 P_n(y) \frac{dy}{z-y},$$

which we shall now establish.

When $|z| > 1$ we can expand the integrand in the uniformly convergent series

$$P_n(y) \sum_{m=0}^\infty \frac{y^m}{z^{m+1}}.$$

Consequently

$$\frac{1}{2} \int_{-1}^1 P_n(y) \frac{dy}{z-y} = \frac{1}{2} \sum_{m=0}^\infty z^{-m-1} \int_{-1}^1 y^m P_n(y) \, dy.$$

The integrals for which $m - n$ is odd or negative vanish (§ 15·211); and so

$$\frac{1}{2} \int_{-1}^1 P_n(y) \frac{dy}{z-y} = \frac{1}{2} \sum_{m=0}^\infty z^{-n-2m-1} \int_{-1}^1 y^{n+2m} P_n(y) \, dy$$

$$= \frac{1}{2} \sum_{m=0}^\infty z^{-n-2m-1} \frac{2^{n+1} (n+2m)! \, (n+m)!}{m! \, (2n+2m+1)!}$$

$$= \frac{2^n (n!)^2}{(2n+1)!} z^{-n-1} F(\tfrac{1}{2}n + \tfrac{1}{2}, \tfrac{1}{2}n + 1; n + \tfrac{3}{2}; z^{-2})$$

$$= Q_n(z),$$

by § 15·31. The theorem is thus established for the case in which $|z| > 1$. Since each side of the equation

$$Q_n(z) = \frac{1}{2} \int_{-1}^1 P_n(y) \frac{dy}{z-y}$$

represents an analytic function, even when $|z|$ is not greater than unity, provided that z is not a real number between -1 and $+1$, it follows that, with this exception, the result is true (§ 5·5) for all values of z.

[*] F. Neumann, *Journal für Math.* xxxvii. (1848), p. 24.

The reader should notice that Neumann's formula apparently expresses $Q_n(z)$ as a one-valued function of z, whereas it is known to be many-valued (§ 15·32 example 2). The reason for the apparent discrepancy is that Neumann's formula has been established when the z plane is cut from -1 to $+1$, and $Q_n(z)$ is *one-valued in the cut plane*.

Example 1. Shew that, when $-1 \leqslant R(z) \leqslant 1$, $|Q_n(z)| \leqslant |I(z)|^{-1}$; and that for other values of z, $|Q_n(z)|$ does not exceed the larger of $|z-1|^{-1}$, $|z+1|^{-1}$.

Example 2. Shew that, when n is a positive integer, $Q_n(z)$ is the coefficient of h^n in the expansion of $(1 - 2hz + h^2)^{-\frac{1}{2}} \operatorname{arc\,cosh} \left\{ \dfrac{h-z}{(z^2-1)^{\frac{1}{2}}} \right\}$.

[For, when $|h|$ is sufficiently small,

$$\sum_{n=0}^{\infty} h^n Q_n(z) = \sum_{n=0}^{\infty} \frac{h^n}{2} \int_{-1}^{1} \frac{P_n(y)\,dy}{z-y} = \frac{1}{2} \int_{-1}^{1} \frac{(1 - 2hy + h^2)^{-\frac{1}{2}}\,dy}{(z-y)}$$

$$= (1 - 2hz + h^2)^{-\frac{1}{2}} \operatorname{arc\,cosh} \left\{ \frac{h-z}{(z^2-1)^{\frac{1}{2}}} \right\}.$$

This result has been investigated by Heine, *Kugelfunktionen*, I. p. 134, and Laurent, *Journal de Math.* (3), I. p. 373.]

15·4. *Heine's* development of $(t-z)^{-1}$ as a series of Legendre polynomials in z.*

We shall now obtain an expansion which will serve as the basis of a general class of expansions involving Legendre polynomials.

The reader will readily prove by induction from the recurrence-formulae

$$(2m+1)\, tQ_m(t) - (m+1)\, Q_{m+1}(t) - mQ_{m-1}(t) = 0,$$
$$(2m+1)\, zP_m(z) - (m+1)\, P_{m+1}(z) - mP_{m-1}(z) = 0,$$

that

$$\frac{1}{t-z} = \sum_{m=0}^{n} (2m+1)\, P_m(z)\, Q_m(t) + \frac{n+1}{t-z} \{ P_{n+1}(z)\, Q_n(t) - P_n(z)\, Q_{n+1}(t) \}.$$

Using Laplace's integrals, we have

$$P_{n+1}(z)\, Q_n(t) - P_n(z)\, Q_{n+1}(t)$$

$$= \frac{1}{\pi} \int_0^\pi \int_0^\infty \frac{\{z + (z^2-1)^{\frac{1}{2}} \cos\phi\}^n}{\{t + (t^2-1)^{\frac{1}{2}} \cosh u\}^{n+1}}$$

$$\times [z + (z^2-1)^{\frac{1}{2}} \cos\phi - \{t + (t^2-1)^{\frac{1}{2}} \cosh u\}^{-1}]\, d\phi\, du.$$

Now consider $\left| \dfrac{z + (z^2-1)^{\frac{1}{2}} \cos\phi}{t + (t^2-1)^{\frac{1}{2}} \cosh u} \right|$.

Let $\cosh\alpha$, $\cosh a$ be the semi-major axes of the ellipses with foci ± 1 which pass through z and t respectively. Let θ be the eccentric angle of z; then

$$z = \cosh(a + i\theta),$$
$$|z \pm (z^2-1)^{\frac{1}{2}} \cos\phi| = |\cosh(a+i\theta) \pm \sinh(a+i\theta) \cos\phi|$$
$$= \{\cosh^2 a - \sin^2\theta + (\cosh^2 a - \cos^2\theta)\cos^2\phi \pm 2 \sinh a \cosh a \cos\phi\}^{\frac{1}{2}}.$$

This is a maximum for real values of ϕ when $\cos\phi = \mp 1$; and hence

$$|z \pm (z^2-1)^{\frac{1}{2}} \cos\phi|^2 \leqslant 2 \cosh^2 a - 1 + 2 \cosh a (\cosh^2 a - 1)^{\frac{1}{2}} = \exp(2a).$$

Similarly $\qquad\qquad\qquad |t + (t^2-1)^{\frac{1}{2}} \cosh u| \geqslant \exp a.$

* *Journal für Math.* XLII. (1851), p. 72.

Therefore

$$| P_{n+1}(z) Q_n(t) - P_n(z) Q_{n+1}(t) | \leqslant \pi^{-1} \exp \{n(a-\alpha)\} \int_0^\pi \int_0^\infty V d\phi du,$$

where

$$| V | = \left| \frac{z + (z^2-1)^{\frac{1}{2}} \cos\phi}{t + (t^2-1)^{\frac{1}{2}} \cosh u} \right| + | \{t + (t^2-1)^{\frac{1}{2}} \cosh u\} |^{-2}.$$

Therefore $| P_{n+1}(z) Q_n(t) - P_n(z) Q_{n+1}(t) | \to 0$, as $n \to \infty$, provided $a < \alpha$.

And further, if t varies, α remaining constant, it is easy to see that the upper bound of $\int_0^\pi \int_0^\infty V d\phi du$ is independent of t, and so

$$P_{n+1}(z) Q_n(t) - P_n(z) Q_{n+1}(t)$$

tends to zero uniformly with regard to t.

Hence *if the point z is in the interior of the ellipse which passes through the point t and has the points ± 1 for its foci, then the expansion*

$$\frac{1}{t-z} = \sum_{n=0}^\infty (2n+1) P_n(z) Q_n(t)$$

is valid; and if t be a variable point on an ellipse with foci ± 1 such that z is a fixed point inside it, the expansion converges uniformly with regard to t.

15·41. *Neumann's* expansion of an arbitrary function in a series of Legendre polynomials.*

We proceed now to discuss the expansion of a function in a series of Legendre polynomials. The expansion is of special interest, as it stands next in simplicity to Taylor's series, among expansions in series of polynomials.

Let $f(z)$ be any function which is analytic inside and on an ellipse C, whose foci are the points $z = \pm 1$. We shall shew that

$$f(z) = a_0 P_0(z) + a_1 P_1(z) + a_2 P_2(z) + a_3 P_3(z) + \dots,$$

where a_0, a_1, a_2, ... are independent of z, this expansion being valid for all points z in the interior of the ellipse C.

Let t be any point on the circumference of the ellipse.

Then, since $\sum_{n=0}^\infty (2n+1) P_n(z) Q_n(t)$ converges uniformly with regard to t,

$$f(z) = \frac{1}{2\pi i} \int_C \frac{f(t)\,dt}{t-z} = \frac{1}{2\pi i} \sum_{n=0}^\infty \int_C (2n+1) P_n(z) Q_n(t) f(t)\,dt$$

$$= \sum_{n=0}^\infty a_n P_n(z),$$

where

$$a_n = \frac{2n+1}{2\pi i} \int_C f(t) Q_n(t)\,dt.$$

---

* K. Neumann, *Ueber die Entwickelung einer Funktion nach den Kugelfunktionen* (Halle, 1862). See also Thomé, *Journal für Math.* LXVI. (1866), pp. 337–343. Neumann also gives an expansion, in Legendre functions of both kinds, valid in the annulus bounded by two ellipses.

This is the required expansion; since $\sum\limits_{n=0}^{\infty} (2n+1) P_n(z) Q_n(t)$ may be proved *
to converge uniformly with regard to z when z lies in any domain C' lying wholly inside C, the expansion converges uniformly throughout C'.

Another form for a_n can therefore be obtained by integrating, as in § 15·211, so that

$$a_n = \left(n + \tfrac{1}{2}\right) \int_{-1}^{1} f(x) P_n(x)\, dx.$$

A form of this equation which is frequently useful is

$$a_n = \frac{n + \tfrac{1}{2}}{2^n \cdot n!} \int_{-1}^{1} f^{(n)}(x) \cdot (1 - x^2)^n\, dx,$$

which is obtained by substituting for $P_n(x)$ from Rodrigues' formula and integrating by parts.

The theorem which bears the same relation to Neumann's expansion as Fourier's theorem bears to the expansion of § 9·11 is as follows :

Let $f(t)$ be defined when $-1 \leqslant t \leqslant 1$, and let the integral of $(1-t^2)^{-\frac{1}{4}} f(t)$ exist and be absolutely convergent; also let

$$a_n = (n + \tfrac{1}{2}) \int_{-1}^{1} f(t) P_n(t)\, dt.$$

Then $\sum a_n P_n(x)$ is convergent and has the sum $\tfrac{1}{2}\{f(x+0) + f(x-0)\}$ at any point x, for which $-1 < x < 1$, if any condition of the type stated at the end of § 9·43 is satisfied.

For a proof, the reader is referred to memoirs by Hobson† and Burkhardt‡.

Example 1. Shew that, if $\rho\ (\geqslant 1)$ be the radius of convergence of the series $\sum c_n z^n$, then $\sum c_n P_n(z)$ converges inside an ellipse whose semi-axes are $\tfrac{1}{2}(\rho + \rho^{-1})$, $\tfrac{1}{2}(\rho - \rho^{-1})$.

Example 2. If $\quad z = \left(\dfrac{y-1}{y+1}\right)^{\frac{1}{2}}, \quad k^2 = \dfrac{(x-1)(y+1)}{(x+1)(y-1)}$, where $y > x > 1$,

prove that $\quad \displaystyle\int_{z}^{1} \frac{dz}{\{(1-z^2)(1-k^2 z^2)\}^{\frac{1}{2}}} = \{(x+1)(y-1)\}^{\frac{1}{2}} \sum_{n=0}^{\infty} P_n(x) Q_n(y).$

[Substitute Laplace's integrals on the right and integrate with regard to ϕ.]

Example 3. Shew that

$$\frac{1}{2(y-x)} \log \frac{(x+1)(y-1)}{(x-1)(y+1)} = \sum_{n=0}^{\infty} (2n+1) Q_n(x) Q_n(y).$$

(Frobenius, *Journal für Math.* LXXIII. (1871), p. 1.)

15·5. *Ferrers' associated Legendre functions $P_n^m(z)$ and $Q_n^m(z)$.*

We shall now introduce a more extended class of Legendre functions.

If m be a positive integer and $-1 < z < 1$, n being unrestricted§, the functions

$$P_n^m(z) = (1 - z^2)^{\frac{1}{2}m} \frac{d^m P_n(z)}{dz^m}, \qquad Q_n^m(z) = (1 - z^2)^{\frac{1}{2}m} \frac{d^m Q_n(z)}{dz^m}$$

---

* The proof is similar to the proof in § 15·4 that that convergence is uniform with regard to t.
† *Proc. London Math. Soc.* (2), VI. (1908), pp. 388–395; (2), VII. (1909), pp. 24–39.
‡ *Münchener Sitzungsberichte*, XXXIX. (1909), No. 10.
§ See p. 317, footnote. Ferrers writes $T_n^m(z)$ for $P_n^m(z)$.

will be called Ferrers' associated Legendre functions of degree n and order m of the first and second kinds respectively.

It may be shewn that these functions satisfy a differential equation analogous to Legendre's equation.

For, differentiate Legendre's equation

$$(1 - z^2) \frac{d^2y}{dz^2} - 2z \frac{dy}{dz} + n(n+1) y = 0$$

m times and write v for $\dfrac{d^m y}{dz^m}$. We obtain the equation

$$(1 - z^2) \frac{d^2v}{dz^2} - 2z(m+1) \frac{dv}{dz} + (n-m)(n+m+1) v = 0.$$

Write $w = (1 - z^2)^{\frac{1}{2} m} v$, and we get

$$(1 - z^2) \frac{d^2w}{dz^2} - 2z \frac{dw}{dz} + \left\{ n(n+1) - \frac{m^2}{1 - z^2} \right\} w = 0.$$

This is the differential equation satisfied by $P_n{}^m(z)$ and $Q_n{}^m(z)$.

From the definitions given above, several expressions for the associated Legendre functions may be obtained.

Thus, from Schläfli's formula we have

$$P_n{}^m(z) = \frac{(n+1)(n+2) \dots (n+m)}{2^{n+1} \pi i} (1 - z^2)^{\frac{1}{2} m} \int_A^{(1+,\, z+)} (t^2 - 1)^n (t - z)^{-n-m-1} dt,$$

where the contour does not enclose the point $t = -1$.

Further, when n is a positive integer, we have, by Rodrigues' formula,

$$P_n{}^m(z) = \frac{(1 - z^2)^{\frac{1}{2} m}}{2^n n!} \frac{d^{n+m} (z^2 - 1)^n}{dz^{n+m}}.$$

Example. Shew that Legendre's associated equation is defined by the scheme

$$P \left\{ \begin{matrix} 0 & \infty & 1 & \\ \frac{1}{2}m & n+1 & \frac{1}{2}m & \frac{1}{2} - \frac{1}{2}z \\ -\frac{1}{2}m & -n & -\frac{1}{2}m & \end{matrix} \right\}. \qquad \text{(Olbricht.)}$$

15·51. *The integral properties of the associated Legendre functions.*

The generalisation of the theorem of § 15·14 is the following:

When n, r, m are positive integers and $n > m$, $r > m$, then

$$\int_{-1}^{1} P_n{}^m(z) P_r{}^m(z) \, dz \begin{cases} = 0 & (r \neq n), \\ = \dfrac{2}{2n+1} \dfrac{(n+m)!}{(n-m)!} & (r = n). \end{cases}$$

To obtain the first result, multiply the differential equations for $P_n{}^m(z)$, $P_r{}^m(z)$ by $P_r{}^m(z)$, $P_n{}^m(z)$ respectively and subtract; this gives

$$\frac{d}{dz} \left[(1 - z^2) \left\{ P_r{}^m(z) \frac{dP_n{}^m(z)}{dz} - P_n{}^m(z) \frac{dP_r{}^m(z)}{dz} \right\} \right]$$
$$+ (n - r)(n + r + 1) P_r{}^m(z) P_n{}^m(z) = 0.$$

On integrating between the limits -1, $+1$, the result follows when n and r are unequal, since the expression in square brackets vanishes at each limit.

To obtain the second result, we observe that

$$P_n{}^{m+1}(z) = (1 - z^2)^{\frac{1}{2}} \frac{dP_n{}^m(z)}{dz} + mz(1 - z^2)^{-\frac{1}{2}} P_n{}^m(z);$$

squaring and integrating, we get

$$\int_{-1}^{1} \{P_n{}^{m+1}(z)\}^2 \, dz = \int_{-1}^{1} \left[(1 - z^2) \left\{ \frac{dP_n{}^m(z)}{dz} \right\}^2 + 2mz\, P_n{}^m(z) \frac{dP_n{}^m(z)}{dz} \right.$$

$$\left. + \frac{m^2 z^2}{1 - z^2} \{P_n{}^m(z)\}^2 \right] dz$$

$$= -\int_{-1}^{1} P_n{}^m(z) \frac{d}{dz} \left\{ (1 - z^2) \frac{dP_n{}^m(z)}{dz} \right\} dz - m \int_{-1}^{1} \{P_n{}^m(z)\}^2 \, dz$$

$$+ \int_{-1}^{1} \frac{m^2 z^2}{1 - z^2} \{P_n{}^m(z)\}^2 \, dz,$$

on integrating the first two terms in the first line on the right by parts. If now we use the differential equation for $P_n{}^m(z)$ to simplify the first integral in the second line, we at once get

$$\int_{-1}^{1} \{P_n{}^{m+1}(z)\}^2 \, dz = (n - m)(n + m + 1) \int_{-1}^{1} \{P_n{}^m(z)\}^2 \, dz.$$

By repeated applications of this result we get

$$\int_{-1}^{1} \{P_n{}^m(z)\}^2 \, dz = (n - m + 1)(n - m + 2) \dots n$$

$$\times (n + m)(n + m - 1) \dots (n + 1) \int_{-1}^{1} \{P_n(z)\}^2 \, dz,$$

and so

$$\int_{-1}^{1} \{P_n{}^m(z)\}^2 \, dz = \frac{2}{2n + 1} \frac{(n + m)!}{(n - m)!}.$$

15·6. *Hobson's definition of the associated Legendre functions.*

So far it has been taken for granted that the function $(1 - z^2)^{\frac{1}{2}m}$ which occurs in Ferrers' definition of the associated functions is purely real; and since, in the more elementary physical applications of Legendre functions, it usually happens that $-1 < z < 1$, no complications arise. But as we wish to consider the associated functions as functions of a complex variable, it is undesirable to introduce an additional cut in the z-plane by giving $\arg(1 - z)$ its principal value.

Accordingly, in future, when z is not a real number such that $-1 < z < 1$, we shall follow Hobson in defining the associated functions by the equations

$$P_n{}^m(z) = (z^2 - 1)^{\frac{1}{2}m} \frac{d^m P_n(z)}{dz^m}, \quad Q_n{}^m(z) = (z^2 - 1)^{\frac{1}{2}m} \frac{d^m Q_n(z)}{dz^m},$$

where m is a positive integer, n is unrestricted and $\arg z$, $\arg(z + 1)$, $\arg(z - 1)$ have their principal values.

When m is unrestricted, $P_n^m(z)$ is defined by Hobson to be

$$\frac{1}{\Gamma(1-m)} \left(\frac{z+1}{z-1}\right)^{\frac{1}{2}m} F(-n,\ n+1;\ 1-m;\ \tfrac{1}{2}-\tfrac{1}{2}z);$$

and Barnes has given a definition of $Q_n^m(z)$ from which the formula

$$Q_n^m(z) = \frac{\sin(n+m)\pi}{\sin n\pi}\ \frac{\Gamma(n+m+1)\,\Gamma(\tfrac{1}{2})}{2^{n+1}\,\Gamma(n+\tfrac{3}{2})}\ \frac{(z^2-1)^{\frac{1}{2}m}}{z^{n+m+1}}$$
$$\times F(\tfrac{1}{2}n+\tfrac{1}{2}m+1,\ \tfrac{1}{2}n+\tfrac{1}{2}m+\tfrac{1}{2};\ n+\tfrac{3}{2};\ z^{-2})$$

may be obtained.

Throughout this work we shall take m to be a positive integer.

15·61. *Expression of $P_n^m(z)$ as an integral of Laplace's type.*

If we make the necessary modification in the Schläfli integral of § 15·5, in accordance with the definition of § 15·6, we have

$$P_n^m(z) = \frac{(n+1)(n+2)\dots(n+m)}{2^{n+1}\pi i}\ (z^2-1)^{\frac{1}{2}m} \int_A^{(1+,\,z+)} (t^2-1)^n\,(t-z)^{-n-m-1}\,dt.$$

Write $t = z + (z^2-1)^{\frac{1}{2}} e^{i\phi}$, as in § 15·23; then

$$P_n^m(z) = \frac{(n+1)(n+2)\dots(n+m)}{2\pi}\ (z^2-1)^{\frac{1}{2}m} \int_\alpha^{2\pi+\alpha} \frac{\{z+(z^2-1)^{\frac{1}{2}}\cos\phi\}^n}{\{(z^2-1)^{\frac{1}{2}} e^{i\phi}\}^m}\,d\phi,$$

where α is the value of ϕ when t is at A, so that

$$|\arg(z^2-1)^{\frac{1}{2}} + \alpha| < \pi.$$

Now, as in § 15·23, the integrand is a one-valued periodic function of the real variable ϕ with period 2π, and so

$$P_n^m(z) = \frac{(n+1)(n+2)\dots(n+m)}{2\pi} \int_{-\pi}^{\pi} \{z+(z^2-1)^{\frac{1}{2}}\cos\phi\}^n\, e^{-mi\phi}\,d\phi.$$

Since $\{z+(z^2-1)^{\frac{1}{2}}\cos\phi\}^n$ is an even function of ϕ, we get, on dividing the range of integration into the parts $(-\pi, 0)$ and $(0, \pi)$,

$$P_n^m(z) = \frac{(n+1)(n+2)\dots(n+m)}{\pi} \int_0^{\pi} \{z+(z^2-1)^{\frac{1}{2}}\cos\phi\}^n \cos m\phi\,d\phi.$$

The ranges of validity of this formula, which is due to Heine (according as n is or is not an integer), are precisely those of the formula of § 15·23.

Example. Shew that, if $|\arg z| < \tfrac{1}{2}\pi$,

$$P_n^m(z) = (-)^m \frac{n(n-1)\dots(n-m+1)}{\pi} \int_0^{\pi} \frac{\cos m\phi\,d\phi}{\{z+(z^2-1)^{\frac{1}{2}}\cos\phi\}^{n+1}},$$

where the many-valued functions are specified as in § 15·23.

15·7. *The addition theorem for the Legendre polynomials*.*

Let $z = xx' - (x^2-1)^{\frac{1}{2}}(x'^2-1)^{\frac{1}{2}}\cos\omega$, where $x,\ x',\ \omega$ are unrestricted complex numbers.

---

* Legendre, *Calc. Int.* II. pp. 262–269. An investigation of the theorem based on physical reasoning will be given subsequently (§ 18·4).

Then we shall shew that

$$P_n(z) = P_n(x) P_n(x') + 2 \sum_{m=1}^{n} (-)^m \frac{(n-m)!}{(n+m)!} P_n^m(x) P_n^m(x') \cos m\omega.$$

First let $R(x') > 0$, so that $\left| \dfrac{x + (x^2-1)^{\frac{1}{2}} \cos(\omega - \phi)}{x' + (x'^2 - 1)^{\frac{1}{2}} \cos \phi} \right|$ is a bounded function of ϕ in the range $0 < \phi < 2\pi$. If M be its upper bound and if $|h| < M^{-1}$, then

$$\sum_{n=0}^{\infty} h^n \frac{\{x + (x^2-1)^{\frac{1}{2}} \cos(\omega - \phi)\}^n}{\{x' + (x'^2 - 1)^{\frac{1}{2}} \cos \phi\}^{n+1}}$$

converges uniformly with regard to ϕ, and so (§ 4·7)

$$\sum_{n=0}^{\infty} h^n \int_{-\pi}^{\pi} \frac{\{x + (x^2-1)^{\frac{1}{2}} \cos(\omega - \phi)\}^n}{\{x' + (x'^2 - 1)^{\frac{1}{2}} \cos \phi\}^{n+1}} d\phi = \int_{-\pi}^{\pi} \sum_{n=0}^{\infty} \frac{h^n \{x + (x^2-1)^{\frac{1}{2}} \cos(\omega - \phi)\}^n}{\{x' + (x'^2 - 1)^{\frac{1}{2}} \cos \phi\}^{n+1}} d\phi$$

$$= \int_{-\pi}^{\pi} \frac{d\phi}{x' + (x'^2 - 1)^{\frac{1}{2}} \cos \phi - h\{x + (x^2-1)^{\frac{1}{2}} \cos(\omega - \phi)\}}.$$

Now, by a slight modification of example 1 of § 6·21, it follows that

$$\int_{-\pi}^{\pi} \frac{d\phi}{A + B \cos \phi + C \sin \phi} = \frac{2\pi}{(A^2 - B^2 - C^2)^{\frac{1}{2}}},$$

where that value of the radical is taken which makes

$$|A - (A^2 - B^2 - C^2)^{\frac{1}{2}}| < |(B^2 + C^2)^{\frac{1}{2}}|.$$

Therefore

$$\int_{-\pi}^{\pi} \frac{d\phi}{x' + (x'^2 - 1)^{\frac{1}{2}} \cos \phi - h\{x + (x^2-1)^{\frac{1}{2}} \cos(\omega - \phi)\}}$$

$$= \frac{2\pi}{[(x' - hx)^2 - \{(x'^2 - 1)^{\frac{1}{2}} - h(x^2-1)^{\frac{1}{2}} \cos \omega\}^2 - \{h(x^2-1)^{\frac{1}{2}} \sin \omega\}^2]^{\frac{1}{2}}}$$

$$= \frac{2\pi}{(1 - 2hz + h^2)^{\frac{1}{2}}};$$

and when $h \to 0$, this expression has to tend to $2\pi P_0(x')$ by § 15·23. Expanding in powers of h and equating coefficients, we get

$$P_n(z) = \frac{1}{2\pi} \int_{-\pi}^{\pi} \frac{\{x + (x^2-1)^{\frac{1}{2}} \cos(\omega - \phi)\}^n}{\{x' + (x'^2 - 1)^{\frac{1}{2}} \cos \phi\}^{n+1}} d\phi.$$

Now $P_n(z)$ is a polynomial of degree n in $\cos \omega$, and can consequently be expressed in the form $\frac{1}{2} A_0 + \sum_{m=1}^{n} A_m \cos m\omega$, where the coefficients $A_0, A_1, \ldots A_n$ are independent of ω; to determine them, we use Fourier's rule (§ 9·12), and we get

$$A_m = \frac{1}{\pi} \int_{-\pi}^{\pi} P_n(z) \cos m\omega \, d\omega$$

$$= \frac{1}{2\pi^2} \int_{-\pi}^{\pi} \left[\int_{-\pi}^{\pi} \frac{\{x + (x^2-1)^{\frac{1}{2}} \cos(\omega - \phi)\}^n \cos m\omega}{\{x' + (x'^2 - 1)^{\frac{1}{2}} \cos \phi\}^{n+1}} d\phi \right] d\omega$$

$$= \frac{1}{2\pi^2} \int_{-\pi}^{\pi} \left[\int_{-\pi}^{\pi} \frac{\{x + (x^2-1)^{\frac{1}{2}} \cos(\omega - \phi)\}^n \cos m\omega}{\{x' + (x'^2 - 1)^{\frac{1}{2}} \cos \phi\}^{n+1}} d\omega \right] d\phi$$

$$= \frac{1}{2\pi^2} \int_{-\pi}^{\pi} \left[\int_{-\pi}^{\pi} \frac{\{x + (x^2-1)^{\frac{1}{2}} \cos \psi\}^n \cos m(\phi + \psi)}{\{x' + (x'^2 - 1)^{\frac{1}{2}} \cos \phi\}^{n+1}} d\psi \right] d\phi,$$

on changing the order of integration, writing $\omega = \phi + \psi$ and changing the limits for ψ from $\pm \pi - \phi$ to $\pm \pi$.

Now $\int_{-\pi}^{\pi} \{x+(x^2-1)^{\frac{1}{2}}\cos\psi\}^n \sin m\psi\,d\psi = 0$, since the integrand is an odd function; and so, by § 15·61,

$$A_m = \frac{n\,!}{\pi\,(n+m)\,!}\int_{-\pi}^{\pi}\frac{\cos m\phi \cdot P_n{}^m(x)}{\{x'+(x'^2-1)^{\frac{1}{2}}\cos\phi\}^{n+1}}\,d\phi$$

$$=2\,(-)^m\frac{(n-m)\,!}{(n+m)\,!}\,P_n{}^m(x)\,P_n{}^m(x').$$

Therefore, when $|\arg z'|<\tfrac{1}{2}\pi$,

$$P_n(z) = P_n(x)\,P_n(x') + 2\sum_{m=1}^{n}(-)^m\frac{(n-m)\,!}{(n+m)\,!}\,P_n{}^m(x)\,P_n{}^m(x')\cos m\omega.$$

But this is a mere algebraical identity in x, x' and $\cos\omega$ (since n is a positive integer) and so is true independently of the sign of $R(x')$.

The result stated has therefore been proved.

The corresponding theorem with Ferrers' definition is

$$P_n\{xx'+(1-x^2)^{\frac{1}{2}}(1-x'^2)^{\frac{1}{2}}\cos\omega\} = P_n(x)\,P_n(x') + 2\sum_{m=1}^{n}\frac{(n-m)\,!}{(n+m)\,!}\,P_n{}^m(x)\,P_n{}^m(x')\cos m\omega.$$

15·71. The addition theorem for the Legendre functions.

Let x, x' be two constants, real or complex, whose arguments are numerically less than $\tfrac{1}{2}\pi$; and let $(x\pm1)^{\frac{1}{2}}$, $(x'\pm1)^{\frac{1}{2}}$ be given their principal values; let ω be real and let

$$z = xx' - (x^2-1)^{\frac{1}{2}}(x'^2-1)^{\frac{1}{2}}\cos\omega.$$

Then we shall shew that, if $|\arg z|<\tfrac{1}{2}\pi$ for all values of the real variable ω, and n be not a positive integer,

$$P_n(z) = P_n(x)\,P_n(x') + 2\sum_{m=1}^{\infty}(-)^m\frac{\Gamma(n-m+1)}{\Gamma(n+m+1)}\,P_n{}^m(x)\,P_n{}^m(x')\cos m\omega.$$

Let $\cosh a$, $\cosh a'$ be the semi-major axes of the ellipses with foci ±1 passing through x, x' respectively. Let β, β' be the eccentric angles of x, x' on these ellipses so that

$$-\tfrac{1}{2}\pi < \beta < \tfrac{1}{2}\pi, \quad -\tfrac{1}{2}\pi < \beta' < \tfrac{1}{2}\pi.$$

Let $a+i\beta = \xi$, $a'+i\beta' = \xi'$, so that $x=\cosh\xi$, $x'=\cosh\xi'$.

Now as ω passes through all real values, $R(z)$ oscillates between

$$R(xx')\pm R(x^2-1)^{\frac{1}{2}}(x'^2-1)^{\frac{1}{2}} = \cosh(a\pm a')\cos(\beta\pm\beta'),$$

so that *it is necessary that $\beta\pm\beta'$ be acute angles positive or negative*.

Now take Schläfli's integral

$$P_n(z) = \frac{1}{2^{n+1}\pi i}\int_A^{(1+,\,z+)}\frac{(t^2-1)^n}{(t-z)^{n+1}}\,dt,$$

and write

$$t = \frac{e^{i\phi}\{e^{-i\omega}\sinh\xi\cosh\tfrac{1}{2}\xi' - \cosh\xi\sinh\tfrac{1}{2}\xi'\} + \cosh\xi\cosh\tfrac{1}{2}\xi' - e^{i\omega}\sinh\xi\sinh\tfrac{1}{2}\xi'}{\cosh\tfrac{1}{2}\xi' + e^{i\phi}\sinh\tfrac{1}{2}\xi'}.$$

The path of t, as ϕ increases from $-\pi$ to π, may be shewn to be a circle; and the reader will verify that

$$t-1 = \frac{2\{e^{i(\phi-\omega)}\cosh\tfrac{1}{2}\xi + \sinh\tfrac{1}{2}\xi\}\{\sinh\tfrac{1}{2}\xi\cosh\tfrac{1}{2}\xi' - e^{i\omega}\cosh\tfrac{1}{2}\xi\sinh\tfrac{1}{2}\xi'\}}{\cosh\tfrac{1}{2}\xi' + e^{i\phi}\sinh\tfrac{1}{2}\xi'},$$

$$t+1 = \frac{2\{e^{i(\phi-\omega)}\sinh\tfrac{1}{2}\xi + \cosh\tfrac{1}{2}\xi\}\{\cosh\tfrac{1}{2}\xi\cosh\tfrac{1}{2}\xi' - e^{i\omega}\sinh\tfrac{1}{2}\xi\sinh\tfrac{1}{2}\xi'\}}{\cosh\tfrac{1}{2}\xi' + e^{i\phi}\sinh\tfrac{1}{2}\xi'},$$

$$t-z = \frac{\{e^{i\phi}\cosh\tfrac{1}{2}\xi' + \sinh\tfrac{1}{2}\xi'\}\{e^{i\omega}\sinh\xi\sinh^2\tfrac{1}{2}\xi' + e^{-i\omega}\sinh\xi\cosh^2\tfrac{1}{2}\xi' - \cosh\xi\sinh\xi'\}}{\cosh\tfrac{1}{2}\xi' + e^{i\phi}\sinh\tfrac{1}{2}\xi'}.$$

Since* $|\cosh \tfrac{1}{2}\xi'|>|\sinh \tfrac{1}{2}\xi'|$, the argument of the denominators does not change when ϕ increases by 2π; for similar reasons, the arguments of the first and third numerators increase by 2π, and the argument of the second does not change; therefore the circle contains the points $t=1$, $t=z$, and not $t=-.1$, so it is a possible contour.

Making these substitutions it is readily found that

$$P_n(z)=\frac{1}{2\pi}\int_{-\pi}^{\pi}\frac{\{x+(x^2-1)^{\frac{1}{2}}\cos(\omega-\phi)\}^n}{\{x'+(x'^2-1)^{\frac{1}{2}}\cos\phi\}^{n+1}}d\phi,$$

and the rest of the work follows the course of § 15·7 except that the general form of Fourier's theorem has to be employed.

Example. Shew that, if n be a positive integer,

$$Q_n\{xx'+(x^2-1)^{\frac{1}{2}}(x'^2-1)^{\frac{1}{2}}\cos\omega\}=Q_n(x)\,P_n(x')+2\sum_{m=1}^{\infty}Q_n{}^m(x)\,P_n{}^{-m}(x')\cos m\omega,$$

when ω is real, $R(x')\geqslant 0$, and $|(x'-1)(x+1)|<|(x-1)(x'+1)|$.

(Heine, *Kugelfunktionen*; K. Neumann, *Leipziger Abh.* 1886.)

15·8. *The function† $C_n{}^\nu(z)$.*

A function connected with the associated Legendre function $P_n{}^m(z)$ is the function $C_n{}^\nu(z)$, which for integral values of n is defined to be the coefficient of h^n in the expansion of $(1-2hz+h^2)^{-\nu}$ in ascending powers of h.

It is easily seen that $C_n{}^\nu(z)$ satisfies the differential equation

$$\frac{d^2y}{dz^2}+\frac{(2\nu+1)z}{z^2-1}\frac{dy}{dz}-\frac{n(n+2\nu)}{z^2-1}y=0.$$

For all values of n and ν, it may be shewn that we can define a function, satisfying this equation, by a contour integral of the form

$$(1-z^2)^{\frac{1}{2}-\nu}\int_C\frac{(1-t^2)^{n+\nu-\frac{1}{2}}}{(t-z)^{n+1}}dt,$$

where C is the contour of § 15·2; this corresponds to Schläfli's integral.

The reader will easily prove the following results :

(I)   When n is an integer

$$C_n{}^\nu(z)=\frac{(-2)^n\,\nu(\nu+1)\ldots(\nu+n-1)}{n!\,(2n+2\nu-1)(2n+2\nu-2)\ldots(n+2\nu)}(1-z^2)^{\frac{1}{2}-\nu}\frac{d^n}{dz^n}\{(1-z^2)^{n+\nu-\frac{1}{2}}\};$$

since $P_n(z)=C_n{}^{\frac{1}{2}}(z)$, Rodrigues' formula is a particular case of this result.

(II)   When r is an integer,

$$C_{n-r}^{r+\frac{1}{2}}(z)=\frac{1}{(2r-1)(2r-3)\ldots 3.1}\frac{d^r}{dz^r}P_n(z),$$

whence

$$C_{n-r}^{r+\frac{1}{2}}(z)=\frac{(z^2-1)^{-\frac{1}{2}r}}{(2r-1)(2r-3)\ldots 3.1}P_n{}^r(z).$$

The last equation gives the connexion between the functions $C_n{}^\nu(z)$ and $P_n{}^r(z)$.

---

* This follows from the fact that $\cos\beta'>0$.

† This function has been studied by Gegenbauer, *Wiener Sitzungsberichte*, LXX. (1874), pp. 434–443; LXXV. (1877), pp. 891–896; XCVII. (1888), pp. 259–316; CII. (1893), p. 942.

(III)   Modifications of the recurrence-formulae for $P_n(z)$ are the following :

$$zC_{n-1}^{\nu+1}(z) - C_{n-2}^{\nu+1}(z) - \frac{n}{2\nu}\, C_n^{\nu}(z) = 0, \quad C_n^{\nu+1}(z) - zC_{n-1}^{\nu+1}(z) = \frac{n+2\nu}{2\nu}\, C_n^{\nu}(z),$$

$$\frac{dC_n^{\nu}(z)}{dz} = 2\nu C_{n-1}^{\nu+1}(z), \quad nC_n^{\nu}(z) = (n-1+2\nu)\, zC_{n-1}^{\nu}(z) - 2\nu\,(1-z^2)\, C_{n-2}^{\nu-1}(z).$$

REFERENCES.

A. M. LEGENDRE, *Calcul Intégral*, II. (Paris, 1817).

H. E. HEINE*, *Handbuch der Kugelfunktionen* (Berlin, 1878).

N. M. FERRERS, *Spherical Harmonics* (1877).

I. TODHUNTER, *Functions of Laplace, Lamé and Bessel* (1875).

L. SCHLÄFLI, *Ueber die zwei Heine'schen Kugelfunktionen* (Bern, 1881).

E. W. HOBSON, *Phil. Trans. of the Royal Society*, 187 A (1896), pp. 443–531.

E. W. BARNES, *Quarterly Journal*, XXXIX. (1908), pp. 97–204.

R. OLBRICHT, *Studien ueber die Kugel- und Cylinder-funktionen* (Halle, 1887).   [*Nova Acta Acad. Leop.* LII. (1888), pp. 1–48.]

N. NIELSEN, *Théorie des fonctions métasphériques* (Paris, 1911).

MISCELLANEOUS EXAMPLES†.

1.   Prove that when n is a positive integer,

$$P_n(z) = \sum_0^n \frac{(n+p)!\,(-)^p}{(n-p)!\,p!\,p!\,2^{p+1}}\{(1-z)^p + (-)^n(1+z)^p\}.$$

(Math. Trip. 1898.)

2.   Prove that

$$\int_{-1}^1 z\,(1-z^2)\,\frac{dP_n}{dz}\frac{dP_m}{dz}\,dz$$

is zero unless $m - n = \pm 1$, and determine its value in these cases.

(Math. Trip. 1896.)

3.   Shew (by induction or otherwise) that when n is a positive integer,

$$(2n+1)\int_z^1 P_n^2(z)\,dz = 1 - zP_n^2 - 2z\,(P_1^2 + P_2^2 + \dots + P_{n-1}^2) + 2\,(P_1 P_2 + P_2 P_3 + \dots + P_{n-1} P_n).$$

(Math. Trip. 1899.)

4.   Shew that

$$zP_n'(z) = nP_n(z) + (2n-3)\,P_{n-2}(z) + (2n-7)\,P_{n-4}(z) + \dots.$$

(Clare, 1906.)

5.   Shew that

$$z^2 P_n''(z) = n\,(n-1)\,P_n(z) + \sum_{r=1}^p (2n-4r+1)\,\{r\,(2n-2r+1)-2\}\,P_{n-2r}(z),$$

where $p = \frac{1}{2}n$ or $\frac{1}{2}(n-1)$.

(Math. Trip. 1904.)

* Before studying the Legendre function $P_n(z)$ in this treatise, the reader should consult Hobson's memoir, as some of Heine's work is incorrect.

† The functions involved in examples 1–30 are Legendre *polynomials*.

6.   Shew that the Legendre polynomial satisfies the relation

$$(z^2-1)^2 \frac{d^2 P_n}{dz^2} = n\,(n-1)\,(n+1)\,(n+2) \int_1^z dz \int_1^z P_n(z)\,dz.$$

(Trin. Coll. Dublin.)

7.   Shew that

$$\int_0^1 z^2 P_{n+1}(z)\,P_{n-1}(z)\,dz = \frac{n\,(n+1)}{(2n-1)\,(2n+1)\,(2n+3)}.$$

(Peterhouse, 1905.)

8.   Shew that the values of $\displaystyle\int_{-1}^1 (1-z^2)^2\, P_m'''(z)\, P_n'(z)\, dz$ are as follows:

(i) $8n\,(n+1)$ when $m-n$ is positive and even,

(ii) $-2n\,(n^2-1)\,(n-2)/(2n+1)$ when $m=n$,

(iii)   0 for other values of m and n.   (Peterhouse, 1907.)

9.   Shew that

$$\sin^n \theta P_n(\sin \theta) = \sum_{r=0}^n (-)^r \frac{n!}{r!\,(n-r)!} \cos^r \theta P_r(\cos \theta).$$

(Math. Trip. 1907.)

10.   Shew, by evaluating $\displaystyle\int_0^\pi P_n(\cos \theta)\, d\theta$ (§ 15·1 example 2), and then integrating by parts, that $\displaystyle\int_{-1}^1 P_n(\mu)$ arc $\sin \mu \cdot d\mu$ is zero when n is even and is equal to $\pi \left\{\dfrac{1\cdot 3\dots(n-2)}{2\cdot 4\dots(n+1)}\right\}^2$ when n is odd.   (Clare, 1903.)

11.   If m and n be positive integers, and $m \leqslant n$, shew by induction that

$$P_m(z)\,P_n(z) = \sum_{r=0}^m \frac{A_{m-r}A_r A_{n-r}}{A_{n+m-r}} \left(\frac{2n+2m-4r+1}{2n+2m-2r+1}\right) P_{n+m-2r}(z),$$

where

$$A_m = \frac{1\cdot 3\cdot 5\dots(2m-1)}{m!}.$$

(Adams, Proc. Royal Soc. XXVII.)

12.   By expanding in ascending powers of u shew that

$$P_n(z) = \frac{(-)^n}{n!} \frac{d^n}{dz^n} (u^2+z^2)^{-\frac{1}{2}},$$

where u^2 is to be replaced by $(1-z^2)$ after the differentiation has been performed.

13.   Shew that $P_n(z)$ can be expressed as a constant multiple of a determinant in which all elements parallel to the auxiliary diagonal are equal (i.e. all elements are equal for which the sum of the row-index and column-index is the same); the determinant containing n rows, and its elements being

$$z,\quad -\frac{1}{3},\quad \frac{1}{3}z,\quad -\frac{1}{5},\quad \frac{1}{5}z,\dots \frac{1}{2n-1}z.$$

(Heun, Gött. Nach. 1881.)

14.   Shew that, if the path of integration passes above $t=1$,

$$P_n(z) = \frac{2}{\pi i} \cdot \int_0^\infty \frac{\{z(1-t^2)-2t(1-z^2)^{\frac{1}{2}}\}^n}{(1-t^2)^{n+1}}\, dt.$$

(Silva.)

15.   By writing $\cot \theta' = \cot \theta - h\,\mathrm{cosec}\,\theta$ and expanding $\sin \theta'$ in powers of h by Taylor's theorem, shew that

$$P_n(\cos \theta) = \frac{(-)^n}{n!} \mathrm{cosec}^{n+1}\theta \frac{d^n (\sin \theta)}{d(\cot \theta)^n}.$$

(Math. Trip. 1893.)

16.   By considering $\sum\limits_{n=0}^{\infty} h^n P_n(z)$, shew that

$$P_n(z) = \frac{1}{n! \sqrt{\pi}} \int_{-\infty}^{\infty} e^{-(1-z^2) t^2} \left(-\frac{d}{dz}\right)^n e^{-z^2 t^2} dt.$$

(Glaisher, *Proc. London Math. Soc.* VI.)

17.   The equation of a nearly spherical surface of revolution is

$$r = 1 + a\{P_1(\cos\theta) + P_3(\cos\theta) + \dots + P_{2n-1}(\cos\theta)\},$$

where a is small; shew that if a^2 be neglected the radius of curvature of the meridian is

$$1 + a \sum_{m=0}^{n-1} \{n(4m+3) - (m+1)(8m+3)\} P_{2m+1}(\cos\theta).$$

(Math. Trip. 1894.)

18.   The equation of a nearly spherical surface of revolution is

$$r = a\{1 + \epsilon P_n(\cos\theta)\},$$

where ϵ is small.

Shew that if ϵ^3 be neglected, its area is

$$4\pi a^2 \left\{1 + \tfrac{1}{2}\epsilon^2 \frac{n^2 + n + 2}{2n+1}\right\}.$$

(Trinity, 1894.)

19.   Shew that, if k is an integer and

$$(1 - 2hz + h^2)^{-\frac{1}{2}k} = \sum_{n=0}^{\infty} a_n P_n(z),$$

then

$$a_n = \frac{h^n}{(1-h^2)^{k-2}} \frac{2^{\frac{1}{2}(k-3)}(2n+1)}{1\,.\,3\,.\,5\dots(k-2)} \left(h^2 \frac{\partial}{\partial x} + \frac{\partial}{\partial y}\right)^{\frac{1}{2}(k-3)} \times x^{-n+\frac{1}{2}k-2} y^{n+\frac{1}{2}k-2},$$

where x and y are to be replaced by unity after the differentiations have been performed.

(Routh, *Proc. London Math. Soc.* XXVI.)

20.   Shew that

$$\int_{-1}^{1} \frac{1}{z-x} \{P_n(x) P_{n-1}(z) - P_{n-1}(x) P_n(z)\}\, dx = -\frac{2}{n},$$

$$\sum_{n=1}^{\infty} \frac{1}{2n+1} \frac{d}{dz} \left[P_n(z) \left(\frac{1}{n} P_{n-1}(z) + \frac{1}{n+1} P_{n+1}(z)\right)\right] = -1.$$ (Catalan.)

21.   Let $x^2 + y^2 + z^2 = r^2$, $z = \mu r$, the numbers involved being real, so that $-1 < \mu < 1$. Shew that

$$P_n(\mu) = \frac{(-)^n r^{n+1}}{n!} \frac{\partial^n}{\partial z^n} \left(\frac{1}{r}\right),$$

where r is to be treated as a function of the independent variables x, y, z in performing the differentiations.

22.   With the notation of the preceding example (cf. p. 319, footnote *), shew that

$$Q_n(\mu) = \frac{(-)^n r^{n+1}}{n!} \frac{\partial^n}{\partial z^n} \left\{\frac{1}{2r} \log\left(\frac{r-z}{r+z}\right)\right\},$$

$$(n+1) P_n(\mu) + \mu P_n'(\mu) = \frac{(-)^n r^{n+3}}{n!} \frac{\partial^n}{\partial z^n} \left(\frac{1}{r^3}\right).$$

23.   Shew that, if $|h|$ and $|z|$ are sufficiently small,

$$\frac{1-h^2}{(1-2hz+h^2)^{\frac{3}{2}}} = \sum_{n=0}^{\infty} (2n+1) h^n P_n(z).$$

24. Prove that

$$P_{n+1}(z)\,Q_{n-1}(z) - P_{n-1}(z)\,Q_{n+1}(z) = \frac{2n+1}{n\,(n+1)}\,z.$$

(Math. Trip. 1894.)

25. If the arbitrary function $f(x)$ can be expanded in the series

$$f(x) = \sum_{n=0}^{\infty} a_n P_n(x),$$

converging uniformly in a domain which includes the point $x=1$, shew that the expansion of the integral of this function is

$$\int_1^x f(x)\,dx = -a_0 - \frac{1}{3}a_1 + \sum_{n=1}^{\infty} \left(\frac{a_{n-1}}{2n-1} - \frac{a_{n+1}}{2n+3} \right) P_n(x). \qquad \text{(Bauer.)}$$

26. Determine the coefficients in Neumann's expansion of e^{az} in a series of Legendre polynomials. (Bauer, *Journal für Math.* LVI.)

27. Deduce from example 25 that

$$\arcsin z = \frac{\pi}{2} \sum_0^{\infty} \left\{ \frac{1\,.\,3\,.\,5 \dots (2n-1)}{2\,.\,4\,.\,6 \dots 2n} \right\}^2 \{P_{2n+1}(z) - P_{2n-1}(z)\}.$$

(Catalan.)

28. Shew that

$$Q_n(z) = \frac{1}{2} \log\left(\frac{z+1}{z-1}\right) . \, P_n(z) - \left\{ P_{n-1}(z)\,P_0(z) + \frac{1}{2} P_{n-2}(z)\,P_1(z) \right.$$
$$\left. + \frac{1}{3} P_{n-3}(z)\,P_2(z) + \dots + \frac{1}{n} P_0(z)\,P_{n-1}(z) \right\}.$$

(Schläfli; Hermite, *Teixeira J. de Sci. Math.* VI. (1884), pp. 81–84.)

29. Shew that

$$Q_n(z) = \frac{1}{2^n\,n!} \frac{d^n}{dz^n} \left\{ (z^2-1)^n \log\frac{z+1}{z-1} \right\} - \frac{1}{2} P_n(z) \log\frac{z+1}{z-1}.$$

Prove also that

$$Q_n(z) = \frac{1}{2} P_n(z) \log\frac{z+1}{z-1} - f_{n-1}(z),$$

where*

$$f_{n-1}(z) = \frac{2n-1}{1\,.\,n} P_{n-1}(z) + \frac{2n-5}{3\,(n-1)} P_{n-3}(z) + \frac{2n-9}{5\,(n-2)} P_{n-5}(z) + \dots$$

$$= \left\{ k_n + (k_n-1)\frac{n\,(n+1)}{1^2}\left(\frac{z-1}{2}\right) + \left(k_n - 1 - \frac{1}{2}\right)\frac{n\,(n-1)\,(n+1)\,(n+2)}{1^2 2^2}\left(\frac{z-1}{2}\right)^2 \right.$$
$$\left. + \left(k_n - 1 - \frac{1}{2} - \frac{1}{3}\right)\frac{n\,(n-1)\,(n-2)\,(n+1)\,(n+2)\,(n+3)}{1^2 2^2 3^2}\left(\frac{z-1}{2}\right)^3 + \dots \right\},$$

where $k_n = 1 + \frac{1}{2} + \frac{1}{3} + \dots + \frac{1}{n}.$

(Math. Trip. 1898.)

30. Shew that the complete solution of Legendre's differential equation is

$$y = A P_n(z) + B P_n(z) \int_z^{\infty} \frac{dt}{(t^2-1)\{P_n(t)\}^2},$$

the path of integration being the straight line which when produced backwards passes through the point $t=0$.

---

* The first of these expressions for $f_{n-1}(z)$ was given by Christoffel, *Journal für Math.* LV. (1858), p. 68, and he also gives (*Ibid.* p. 72) a generalisation of example 28; the second was given by Stieltjes, *Corresp. d'Hermite et de Stieltjes*, II. p. 59.

31. Shew that
$$\{z+(z^2-1)^{\frac{1}{2}}\}^a = \sum_{m=0}^{\infty} B_m Q_{2m-a-1}(z),$$

where
$$B_m = -\frac{a(a-2m+\frac{1}{2})}{2\pi} \frac{\Gamma(m-\frac{1}{2})\,\Gamma(m-a-\frac{1}{2})}{m!\,\Gamma(m-a+1)}. \tag{Schläfli.}$$

32. Shew that, when $R(n+1)>0$,
$$Q_n(z) = \int_{z+(z^2-1)^{\frac{1}{2}}}^{\infty} \frac{h^{-n-1}}{(1-2hz+h^2)^{\frac{1}{2}}}\,dh,$$

and
$$Q_n(z) = \int_0^{z-(z^2-1)^{\frac{1}{2}}} \frac{h^n}{(1-2hz+h^2)^{\frac{1}{2}}}\,dh.$$

33. Shew that
$$Q_n^m(z) = e^{m\pi i}\frac{\Gamma(n+1)}{\Gamma(n-m+1)} \int_0^{\infty} \frac{\cosh mu}{\{z+(z^2-1)^{\frac{1}{2}}\cosh u\}^{n+1}}\,du,$$

where the real part of $(n+1)$ is greater than m.   (Hobson.)

34. Obtain the expansion of $P_n(z)$ when $|\arg z|<\pi$ as a series of powers of $1/z$, when n is not an integer, namely
$$P_n(z) = \frac{\tan n\pi}{\pi}\{Q_n(z)-Q_{-n-1}(z)\}$$
$$= \frac{2^n\Gamma(n+\frac{1}{2})}{\Gamma(n+1)\Gamma(\frac{1}{2})} z^n F\left(\frac{1-n}{2},\ -\frac{n}{2},\ \frac{1}{2}-n,\ \frac{1}{z^2}\right)$$
$$+ \frac{2^{-n-1}\Gamma(-n-\frac{1}{2})}{\Gamma(-n)\Gamma(\frac{1}{2})} z^{-n-1} F\left(\frac{n}{2}+1,\ \frac{n+1}{2},\ n+\frac{3}{2},\ \frac{1}{z^2}\right).$$

[This is most easily obtained by the method of § 14·51.]

35. Shew that the differential equation for the associated Legendre function $P_n^m(z)$ is defined by the schemes*
$$P\left\{\begin{matrix} 0 & \infty & 1 \\ -\frac{1}{2}n & m & -\frac{1}{2}n & \dfrac{z+(z^2-1)^{\frac{1}{2}}}{z-(z^2-1)^{\frac{1}{2}}} \\ \frac{1}{2}n+\frac{1}{2} & -m & \frac{1}{2}n+\frac{1}{2} \end{matrix}\right\}, \quad P\left\{\begin{matrix} 0 & \infty & 1 \\ -\frac{1}{2}n & \frac{1}{2}m & 0 & \dfrac{1}{1-z^2} \\ \frac{1}{2}n+\frac{1}{2} & -\frac{1}{2}m & \frac{1}{2} \end{matrix}\right\}.$$

(Olbricht.)

36. Shew that the differential equation for $C_n^\nu(z)$ is defined by the scheme
$$P\left\{\begin{matrix} -1 & \infty & 1 \\ \frac{1}{2}-\nu & n+2\nu & \frac{1}{2}-\nu & z \\ 0 & -n & 0 \end{matrix}\right\}.$$

37. Prove that, if
$$y_s = \frac{(2n+1)(2n+3)\dots(2n+2s-1)}{n(n^2-1)(n^2-4)\dots\{n^2-(s-1)^2\}(n+s)}(z^2-1)^s \frac{d^s P_n}{dz^s},$$

then
$$y_2 = P_{n+2} - \frac{2(2n+1)}{2n-1}P_n + \frac{2n+3}{2n-1}P_{n-2},$$

$$y_3 = P_{n+3} - \frac{3(2n+3)}{2n-1}P_{n+1} + \frac{3(2n+5)}{2n-3}P_{n-1} - \frac{(2n+3)(2n+5)}{(2n-1)(2n-3)}P_{n-3},$$

and find the general formula.   (Math. Trip. 1896.)

* See also § 15·5 example.

38. Shew that

$$P_n{}^m (\cos\theta) = \frac{2}{\sqrt{\pi}} \frac{\Gamma(n+m+1)}{\Gamma(n+\tfrac{3}{2})} \left[\frac{\cos\{(n+\tfrac{1}{2})\theta - \tfrac{1}{4}\pi + \tfrac{1}{2}m\pi\}}{(2\sin\theta)^{\tfrac{1}{2}}} + \frac{1^2 - 4m^2}{2(2n+3)} \frac{\cos\{(n+\tfrac{3}{2})\theta - \tfrac{3}{4}\pi + \tfrac{1}{2}m\pi\}}{(2\sin\theta)^{\tfrac{3}{2}}} \right.$$

$$\left. + \frac{(1^2 - 4m^2)(3^2 - 4m^2)}{2.4.(2n+3)(2n+5)} \frac{\cos\{(n+\tfrac{5}{2})\theta - \tfrac{5}{4}\pi + \tfrac{1}{2}m\pi\}}{(2\sin\theta)^{\tfrac{5}{2}}} + \ldots \right],$$

obtaining the ranges of values of m, n and θ for which it is valid.

(Math. Trip. 1901.)

39. Shew that the values of n, for which $P_n{}^{-m}(\cos\theta)$ vanishes, decrease as θ increases from 0 to π when m is positive; and that the number of real zeros of $P_n{}^{-m}(\cos\theta)$ for values of θ between $-\pi$ and π is the greatest integer less than $n-m+1$.

(Macdonald, Proc. London Math. Soc. XXXI, XXXIV.)

40. Obtain the formula

$$\frac{1}{2\pi} \int_{-\pi}^{\pi} [1 - 2h\{\cos\omega\cos\phi + \sin\omega\sin\phi\cos(\theta' - \theta)\} + h^2]^{-\tfrac{1}{2}} \, d\theta = \sum_{n=0}^{\infty} h^n P_n(\cos\omega) P_n(\cos\phi).$$

(Legendre.)

41. If $f(x) = x^2 \ (x \geqslant 0)$ and $f(x) = -x^2 \ (x < 0)$, shew that, if $f(x)$ can be expanded into a uniformly convergent series of Legendre polynomials in the range $(-1, 1)$, the expansion is

$$f(x) = \tfrac{3}{4} P_1(x) - \sum_{r=1}^{\infty} (-)^r \frac{1.3 \ldots (2r-3)}{4.6.8 \ldots 2r} \frac{4r+3}{2r+4} P_{2r+1}(x).$$

(Trinity, 1893.)

42. If

$$\frac{1}{(1 - 2hz + h^2)^\nu} = \sum_{n=0}^{\infty} h^n C_n{}^\nu(z),$$

shew that

$$C_n{}^\nu \{xx_1 - (x^2 - 1)^{\tfrac{1}{2}}(x_1{}^2 - 1)^{\tfrac{1}{2}} \cos\phi\}$$

$$= \frac{\Gamma(2\nu - 1)}{\{\Gamma(\nu)\}^2} \sum_{\lambda=0}^{n} (-)^\lambda \frac{4^\lambda \Gamma(n - \lambda + 1)\{\Gamma(\nu + \lambda)\}^2 (2\nu + 2\lambda - 1)}{\Gamma(n + 2\nu + \lambda)}$$

$$\times (x^2 - 1)^{\tfrac{1}{2}\lambda}(x_1{}^2 - 1)^{\tfrac{1}{2}\lambda} C_{n-\lambda}^{\nu+\lambda}(x) C_{n-\lambda}^{\nu+\lambda}(x_1) C_\lambda^{\nu-\tfrac{1}{2}}(\cos\phi)$$

(Gegenbauer, Wiener Sitzungsberichte, CII. (1893), p. 942.)

43. If

$$\sigma_n(z) = \int_0^{e_1} (t^3 - 3tz + 1)^{-\tfrac{1}{2}} t^n dt,$$

where e_1 is the least root of $t^3 - 3tz + 1 = 0$, shew that

$$(2n+1)\sigma_{n+1} - 3(2n-1)z\sigma_{n-1} + 2(n-1)\sigma_{n-2} = 0,$$

and

$$4(4z^3 - 1)\sigma_n{}''' + 144z^2\sigma_n{}'' - z(12n^2 - 24n - 291)\sigma_n{}' - (n-3)(2n-7)(2n+5)\sigma_n = 0,$$

where

$$\sigma_n{}''' = \frac{d^3\sigma_n(z)}{dz^3}, \text{ etc.}$$

(Pincherle, Rendiconti Lincei (4), VII. (1891), p. 74.)

44. If

$$(h^3 - 3hz + 1)^{-\tfrac{1}{2}} = \sum_{n=0}^{\infty} R_n(z) h^n,$$

shew that

$$2(n+1)R_{n+1} - 3(2n+1)zR_n + (2n-1)R_{n-2} = 0,$$

$$nR_n + R'_{n-2} - zR_n{}' = 0,$$

and

$$4(4z^3 - 1)R_n{}''' + 96z^2 R_n{}'' - z(12n^2 + 24n - 91)R_n{}' - n(2n+3)(2n+9)R_n = 0,$$

where

$$R_n{}''' = \frac{d^3 R_n}{dz^3}, \text{ etc.}$$

(Pincherle, Mem. Ist. Bologna (5), I. (1889), p. 337.)

45. If
$$A_n(x) = \frac{1}{2^n \, n! \, (x-1)} \frac{d^n}{dx^n} \{(x^2-1)^n (x-1)\},$$

obtain the recurrence-formula

$$(n+1)(2n-1) A_n(x) - \{(4n^2-1)x+1\} A_{n-1}(x) + (n-1)(2n+1) A_{n-2}(x) = 0.$$

(Schendel, *Journal für Math.* LXXX.)

46. If n is not negative and m is a positive integer, shew that the equation

$$(x^2-1)\frac{d^2y}{dx^2} + (2n+2)x\frac{dy}{dx} = m(m+2n+1)y$$

has the two solutions

$$K_m(x) = (x^2-1)^{-n}\frac{d^m}{dx^m}(x^2-1)^{m+n}, \quad L_m(x) = (x^2-1)^{-n}\int_{-1}^{1}\frac{(t^2-1)^n}{x-t} K_m(t)\,dt,$$

when x is not a real number such that $-1 \leqslant x \leqslant 1$.

47. Prove that

$$\{1-hx-(1-2hx+h^2)^{\frac{1}{2}}\}^m = m(x^2-1)^m \sum_{n=m}^{\infty} \frac{h^{n+m}}{(n+m)!} \frac{1}{n} \frac{d^{n+m}}{dx^{n+m}} \left(\frac{x^2-1}{2}\right)^n.$$

(Clare, 1901.)

48. If
$$F_{a,\,n}(x) = \sum_{m=0}^{\infty} \frac{(m+a)^n}{m!} x^m,$$

shew that
$$F_{a,\,n}(x) = \left\{\frac{d^n}{dt^n}(e^{at+xe^t})\right\}_{t=0} = e^x P_n(x, a),$$

where $P_n(x, a)$ is a polynomial of degree n in x; and deduce that

$$P_{n+1}(x, a) = (x+a) P_n(x, a) + x\frac{d}{dx} P_n(x, a).$$

(Trinity, 1905.)

49. If $F_n(x)$ be the coefficient of z^n in the expansion of

$$\frac{2hz}{e^{hz} - e^{-hz}} e^{xz}$$

in ascending powers of z, so that

$$F_0(x) = 1, \quad F_1(x) = x, \quad F_2(x) = \frac{3x^2 - h^2}{6}, \text{ etc.},$$

shew that

(1) $F_n(x)$ is a homogeneous polynomial of degree n in x and h,

(2) $\dfrac{dF_n(x)}{dx} = F_{n-1}(x)$ $(n \geqslant 1)$,

(3) $\displaystyle\int_{-h}^{h} F_n(x)\,dx = 0$ $(n \geqslant 1)$,

(4) If $y = a_0 F_0(x) + a_1 F_1(x) + a_2 F_2(x) + \dots$, where $a_0, a_1, a_2, \dots$ are real constants, then the mean value of $\dfrac{d^r y}{dx^r}$ in the interval from $x = -h$ to $x = +h$ is a_r.   (Léauté.)

50. If $F_u(x)$ be defined as in the preceding example, shew that, when $-h < x < h$,

$$F_{2m}(x) = (-)^m \, 2\frac{h^{2m}}{\pi^{2m}} \left(\cos\frac{\pi x}{h} - \frac{1}{2^{2m}}\cos\frac{2\pi x}{h} + \frac{1}{3^{2m}}\cos\frac{3\pi x}{h} + \dots\right),$$

$$F_{2m+1}(x) = (-)^m \, 2\frac{h^{2m+1}}{\pi^{2m+1}} \left(\sin\frac{\pi x}{h} - \frac{1}{2^{2m+1}}\sin\frac{2\pi x}{h} + \frac{1}{3^{2m+1}}\sin\frac{3\pi x}{h} + \dots\right).$$

(Appell.)

CHAPTER XVI

THE CONFLUENT HYPERGEOMETRIC FUNCTION

16·1. *The confluence of two singularities of Riemann's equation.*

We have seen (§ 10·8) that the linear differential equation with two regular singularities only can be integrated in terms of elementary functions; while the solution of the linear differential equation with three regular singularities is substantially the topic of Chapter XIV. As the next type in order of complexity, we shall consider a modified form of the differential equation which is obtained from Riemann's equation by the confluence of two of the singularities. This confluence gives an equation with an irregular singularity (corresponding to the confluent singularities of Riemann's equation) and a regular singularity corresponding to the third singularity of Riemann's equation.

The confluent equation is obtained by making $c \to \infty$ in the equation defined by the scheme

$$P \left\{ \begin{matrix} 0 & \infty & c \\ \frac{1}{2}+m & -c & c-k & z \\ \frac{1}{2}-m & 0 & k \end{matrix} \right\}.$$

The equation in question is readily found to be

$$\frac{d^2u}{dz^2} + \frac{du}{dz} + \left(\frac{k}{z} + \frac{\frac{1}{4}-m^2}{z^2} \right) u = 0 \quad \ldots\ldots\ldots\ldots\ldots(A).$$

We modify this equation by writing $u = e^{-\frac{1}{2}z} W_{k,m}(z)$ and obtain as the equation* for $W_{k,m}(z)$

$$\frac{d^2W}{dz^2} + \left\{ -\frac{1}{4} + \frac{k}{z} + \frac{\frac{1}{4}-m^2}{z^2} \right\} W = 0 \quad \ldots\ldots\ldots\ldots(B).$$

The reader will verify that the singularities of this equation are at 0 and ∞, the former being regular and the latter irregular; and when $2m$ is *not an integer*, two integrals of equation (B) which are regular near 0 and valid for all finite values of z are given by the series

$$M_{k,m}(z) = z^{\frac{1}{2}+m} e^{-\frac{1}{2}z} \left\{ 1 + \frac{\frac{1}{2}+m-k}{1!(2m+1)} z + \frac{(\frac{1}{2}+m-k)(\frac{3}{2}+m-k)}{2!(2m+1)(2m+2)} z^2 + \ldots \right\},$$

---

* This equation was given by Whittaker, *Bulletin American Math. Soc.* x. (1904), pp. 125–134.

$$M_{k,-m}(z) = z^{\frac{1}{2}-m} e^{-\frac{1}{2}z} \left\{ 1 + \frac{\frac{1}{2}-m-k}{1!(1-2m)} z + \frac{(\frac{1}{2}-m-k)(\frac{3}{2}-m-k)}{2!(1-2m)(2-2m)} z^2 + \ldots \right\}.$$

These series obviously form a fundamental system of solutions.

[NOTE. Series of the type in { } have been considered by Kummer* and more recently by Jacobsthal† and Barnes‡; the special series in which $k=0$ had been investigated by Lagrange in 1762–1765 (*Oeuvres*, I. p. 480). In the notation of Kummer, modified by Barnes, they would be written $_1F_1\{\frac{1}{2} \pm m - k;\ \pm 2m+1;\ z\}$; the reason for discussing solutions of equation (B) rather than those of the equation $z \dfrac{d^2y}{dz^2} - (z-\rho)\dfrac{dy}{dz} - ay = 0$, of which $_1F_1(a;\ \rho;\ z)$ is a solution, is the greater appearance of symmetry in the formulae, together with a simplicity in the equations giving various functions of Applied Mathematics (see § 16·2) in terms of solutions of equation (B).]

16·11. *Kummer's formulae.*

(I)   We shall now shew that, if $2m$ is not a negative integer, then

$$z^{-\frac{1}{2}-m} M_{k,m}(z) = (-z)^{-\frac{1}{2}-m} M_{-k,m}(-z),$$

that is to say,

$$e^{-z}\left\{ 1 + \frac{\frac{1}{2}+m-k}{1!(2m+1)} z + \frac{(\frac{1}{2}+m-k)(\frac{3}{2}+m-k)}{2!(2m+1)(2m+2)} z^2 + \ldots \right\}$$

$$= 1 - \frac{\frac{1}{2}+m+k}{1!(2m+1)} z + \frac{(\frac{1}{2}+m+k)(\frac{3}{2}+m+k)}{2!(2m+1)(2m+2)} z^2 - \ldots.$$

For, replacing e^{-z} by its expansion in powers of z, the coefficient of z^n in the product of absolutely convergent series on the left is

$$\frac{(-)^n}{n!} F\left(\frac{1}{2}+m-k,\ -n;\ 2m+1;\ 1\right) = \frac{(-)^n}{n!} \frac{\Gamma(2m+1)\,\Gamma(m+\frac{1}{2}+k+n)}{\Gamma(m+\frac{1}{2}+k)\,\Gamma(2m+1+n)},$$

by § 14·11, and this is the coefficient of z^n on the right§; we have thus obtained the required result.

This will be called *Kummer's first formula.*

(II)   The equation

$$M_{0,m}(z) = z^{\frac{1}{2}+m}\left\{ 1 + \sum_{p=1}^{\infty} \frac{z^{2p}}{2^{4p} \cdot p!\,(m+1)(m+2)\ldots(m+p)} \right\},$$

valid when $2m$ is not a negative integer, will be called *Kummer's second formula.*

To prove it we observe that the coefficient of $z^{n+m+\frac{1}{2}}$ in the product

$$z^{m+\frac{1}{2}} e^{-\frac{1}{2}z}\,_1F_1(m+\tfrac{1}{2};\ 2m+1;\ z),$$

---

* *Journal für Math.* XV. (1836), p. 139.
† *Math. Ann.* LVI. (1903), pp. 129–154.
‡ *Trans. Camb. Phil. Soc.* XX. (1908), pp. 253–279.
§ The result is still true when $m+\frac{1}{2}+k$ is a negative integer, by a slight modification of the analysis of § 14·11.

of which the second and third factors possess absolutely convergent expansions, is (§ $3\cdot73$)

$$\frac{(\tfrac{1}{2}+m)(\tfrac{3}{2}+m)\dots(n-m+\tfrac{1}{2})}{n!\,(2m+1)(2m+2)\dots(2m+n)}\,F(-n,\,-2m-n;\,-n+\tfrac{1}{2}-m;\,\tfrac{1}{2})$$

$$=\frac{(\tfrac{1}{2}+m)(\tfrac{3}{2}+m)\dots(n-m+\tfrac{1}{2})}{n!\,(2m+1)(2m+2)\dots(2m+n)}\,F(-\tfrac{1}{2}n,\,-m-\tfrac{1}{2}n;\,-n+\tfrac{1}{2}-m;\,1),$$

by Kummer's relation*

$$F(2a,\,2\beta;\,a+\beta+\tfrac{1}{2};\,x)=F\{a,\,\beta;\,a+\beta+\tfrac{1}{2};\,4x(1-x)\},$$

valid when $0\leqslant x\leqslant\tfrac{1}{2}$; and so the coefficient of $z^{n+m+\frac{1}{2}}$ (by § $14\cdot11$) is

$$\frac{(\tfrac{1}{2}+m)(\tfrac{3}{2}+m)\dots(n-m+\tfrac{1}{2})}{n!\,(2m+1)(2m+2)\dots(2m+n)}\,\frac{\Gamma(-n+\tfrac{1}{2}-m)\,\Gamma(\tfrac{1}{2})}{\Gamma(\tfrac{1}{2}-m-\tfrac{1}{2}n)\,\Gamma(\tfrac{1}{2}-\tfrac{1}{2}n)}$$

$$=\frac{\Gamma(\tfrac{1}{2}-m)\,\Gamma(\tfrac{1}{2})}{n!\,(2m+1)(2m+2)\dots(2m+n)\,\Gamma(\tfrac{1}{2}-m-\tfrac{1}{2}n)\,\Gamma(\tfrac{1}{2}-\tfrac{1}{2}n)},$$

and when n is odd this vanishes; for even values of $n\,(=2p)$ it is

$$\frac{\Gamma(\tfrac{1}{2}-m)(-\tfrac{1}{2})(-\tfrac{3}{2})\dots(\tfrac{1}{2}-p)}{2p!\,2^{2p}\,(m+\tfrac{1}{2})(m+\tfrac{3}{2})\dots(m+p-\tfrac{1}{2})(m+1)(m+2)\dots(m+p)\,\Gamma(\tfrac{1}{2}-m-p)}$$

$$=\frac{1\cdot3\dots(2p-1)}{2p!\,2^{3p}\,(m+1)(m+2)\dots(m+p)}=\frac{1}{2^{4p}\cdot p!\,(m+1)(m+2)\dots(m+p)}.$$

$16\cdot12$. *Definition† of the function* $W_{k,m}(z)$.

The solutions $M_{k,\pm m}(z)$ of equation (B) of § $16\cdot1$ are not, however, the most convenient to take as the standard solutions, on account of the disappearance of one of them when $2m$ is an integer.

The integral obtained by confluence from that of § $14\cdot6$, when multiplied by a constant multiple of $e^{\frac{1}{2}z}$, is‡

$$W_{k,m}(z)$$
$$=-\frac{1}{2\pi i}\,\Gamma\left(k+\tfrac{1}{2}-m\right)e^{-\frac{1}{2}z}z^k\int_\infty^{(0+)}(-t)^{-k-\frac{1}{2}+m}\left(1+\frac{t}{z}\right)^{k-\frac{1}{2}+m}e^{-t}\,dt.$$

It is supposed that $\arg z$ has its principal value and that the contour is so chosen that the point $t=-z$ is outside it. The integrand is rendered one-valued by taking $|\arg(-t)|\leqslant\pi$ and taking that value of $\arg(1+t/z)$ which tends to zero as $t\to0$ by a path lying inside the contour.

Under these circumstances it follows from § $5\cdot32$ that the integral is an analytic function of z. To shew that it satisfies equation (B), write

$$v=\int_\infty^{(0+)}(-t)^{-k-\frac{1}{2}+m}(1+t/z)^{k-\frac{1}{2}+m}e^{-t}\,dt;$$

---

* See Chapter xiv, examples 12 and 13, p. 298.

† The function $W_{k,m}(z)$ was defined by means of an integral in this manner by Whittaker, *loc. cit.* p. 125.

‡ A suitable contour has been chosen and the variable t of § $14\cdot6$ replaced by $-t$.

and we have without difficulty *

$$\frac{d^2v}{dz^2} + \left(\frac{2k}{z} - 1\right)\frac{dv}{dz} + \frac{\frac{1}{4} - m^2 + k(k-1)}{z^2}\, v$$

$$= -\frac{(k - \frac{1}{2} + m)}{z^2} \int_\infty^{(0+)} \frac{d}{dt}\left\{ t^{-k+\frac{1}{2}+m}\left(1 + \frac{t}{z}\right)^{k-\frac{3}{2}+m} e^{-t}\right\} dt$$

$$= 0,$$

since the expression in $\{\ \}$ tends to zero as $t \to +\infty$; and this is the condition that $e^{-\frac{1}{2}z} z^k v$ should satisfy (B).

Accordingly the function $W_{k,m}(z)$ defined by the integral

$$-\frac{1}{2\pi i}\, \Gamma\left(k + \frac{1}{2} - m\right) e^{-\frac{1}{2}z}\, z^k \int_\infty^{(0+)} (-t)^{-k-\frac{1}{2}+m}\left(1 + \frac{t}{z}\right)^{k-\frac{1}{2}+m} e^{-t}\, dt$$

is a solution of the differential equation (B).

The formula for $W_{k,m}(z)$ becomes nugatory when $k - \frac{1}{2} - m$ is a negative integer. To overcome this difficulty, we observe that *whenever*

$$R\left(k - \frac{1}{2} - m\right) \leqslant 0$$

and $k - \frac{1}{2} - m$ *is not an integer*, we may transform the contour integral into an infinite integral, after the manner of § 12·22; and so, when

$$R\left(k - \frac{1}{2} - m\right) \leqslant 0,$$

$$W_{k,m}(z) = \frac{e^{-\frac{1}{2}z} z^k}{\Gamma(\frac{1}{2} - k + m)} \int_0^\infty t^{-k-\frac{1}{2}+m}\left(1 + \frac{t}{z}\right)^{k-\frac{1}{2}+m} e^{-t}\, dt.$$

This formula suffices to define $W_{k,m}(z)$ in the critical cases when $m + \frac{1}{2} - k$ is a positive integer, and so $W_{k,m}(z)$ is defined for all values of k and m and all values of z except negative real values †.

Example. Solve the equation

$$\frac{d^2u}{dz^2} + \left(a + \frac{b}{z} + \frac{c}{z^2}\right) u = 0$$

in terms of functions of the type $W_{k,m}(z)$, where a, b, c are any constants.

16·2. *Expression of various functions by functions of the type $W_{k,m}(z)$.*

It has been shewn ‡ that various functions employed in Applied Mathematics are expressible by means of the function $W_{k,m}(z)$; the following are a few examples:

---

* The differentiations under the sign of integration are legitimate by § 4·44 corollary.

† When z is real and negative, $W_{k,m}(z)$ may be defined to be either $W_{k,m}(z+0i)$ or $W_{k,m}(z-0i)$, whichever is more convenient.

‡ Whittaker, *Bulletin American Math. Soc.* x; this paper contains a more complete account than is given here.

(I) *The Error function** which occurs in connexion with the theories of Probability, Errors of Observation, Refraction and Conduction of Heat is defined by the equation

$$\text{Erfc}\,(x) = \int_x^\infty e^{-t^2}\,dt,$$

where x is real.

Writing $t = x^2(w^2 - 1)$ and then $w = s/x$ in the integral for $W_{-\frac{1}{4},\,\frac{1}{4}}(x^2)$, we get

$$W_{-\frac{1}{4},\,\frac{1}{4}}(x^2) = x^{-\frac{1}{2}} e^{-\frac{1}{2}x^2} \int_0^\infty \left(1 + \frac{t}{x^2}\right)^{-\frac{1}{2}} e^{-t}\,dt$$

$$= 2x^{\frac{3}{2}} e^{-\frac{1}{2}x^2} \int_1^\infty e^{x^2(1-w^2)}\,dw$$

$$= 2x^{\frac{1}{2}} e^{\frac{1}{2}x^2} \int_x^\infty e^{-s^2}\,ds,$$

and so the error function is given by the formula

$$\text{Erfc}\,(x) = \frac{1}{2} x^{-\frac{1}{2}} e^{-\frac{1}{2}x^2} W_{-\frac{1}{4},\,\frac{1}{4}}(x^2).$$

Other integrals which occur in connexion with the theory of Conduction of Heat, e.g. $\int_a^b e^{-t^2 - x^2/t^2}\,dt$, can be expressed in terms of error functions, and so in terms of $W_{k,\,m}$ functions.

Example. Shew that the formula for the error function is true for complex values of x.

(II) *The Incomplete Gamma function*, studied by Legendre and others[†], is defined by the equation

$$\gamma\,(n,\,x) = \int_0^x t^{n-1} e^{-t}\,dt.$$

By writing $t = s - x$ in the integral for $W_{\frac{1}{2}(n-1),\,\frac{1}{2}n}(x)$, the reader will verify that

$$\gamma\,(n,\,x) = \Gamma\,(n) - x^{\frac{1}{2}(n-1)} e^{-\frac{1}{2}x} W_{\frac{1}{2}(n-1),\,\frac{1}{2}n}(x).$$

(III) *The Logarithmic-integral function*, which has been discussed by Euler and others[‡], is defined, when $|\arg\{-\log z\}| < \pi$, by the equation

$$\text{li}\,(z) = \int_0^z \frac{dt}{\log t}.$$

---

* This name is also applied to the function

$$\text{Erf}\,(x) = \int_0^x e^{-t^2}\,dt = \frac{\sqrt{\pi}}{2} - \text{Erfc}\,(x).$$

† Legendre, *Exercices*, I. p. 339; Hočevar, *Zeitschrift für Math. und Phys.* XXI. (1876), p. 449; Schlömilch, *Zeitschrift für Math. und Phys.* XVI. (1871), p. 261; Prym, *Journal für Math.* LXXXII. (1877), p. 165.

‡ Euler, *Inst. Calc. Int.* I.; Soldner, *Monatliche Correspondenz*, von Zach (1811), p. 182; *Briefwechsel zwischen Gauss und Bessel* (1880), pp. 114–120; Bessel, *Königsberger Archiv*, I. (1812), pp. 369–405; Laguerre, *Bulletin de la Soc. Math. de France*, VII. (1879), p. 72; Stieltjes, *Ann. de l'École norm. sup.* (3), III. (1886). The logarithmic-integral function is of considerable importance in the higher parts of the Theory of Prime Numbers. See Landau, *Primzahlen*, p. 11.

On writing $s - \log z = u$ and then $u = - \log t$ in the integral for

$$W_{-\frac{1}{2}, 0} (- \log z),$$

it may be verified that

$$\mathrm{li}\,(z) = - (- \log z)^{-\frac{1}{2}} z^{\frac{1}{2}} W_{-\frac{1}{2}, 0} (- \log z).$$

It will appear later that Weber's Parabolic Cylinder functions (§ 16·5) and Bessel's Circular Cylinder functions (Chapter XVII) are particular cases of the $W_{k, m}$ function. Other functions of like nature are given in the Miscellaneous Examples at the end of this chapter.

[NOTE. The error function has been tabulated by Encke, *Berliner ast. Jahrbuch*, 1834, pp. 248–304, and Burgess, *Trans. Roy. Soc. Edin.* XXXIX. (1900), p. 257. The logarithmic-integral function has been tabulated by Bessel and by Soldner. Jahnke und Emde, *Funktionentafeln* (Leipzig, 1909), and Glaisher, *Factor Tables* (London, 1883), should also be consulted.]

16·3. *The asymptotic expansion of $W_{k, m}(z)$, when $|z|$ is large.*

From the contour integral by which $W_{k, m}(z)$ was defined, it is possible to obtain an asymptotic expansion for $W_{k, m}(z)$ valid when $|\arg z| < \pi$.

For this purpose, we employ the result given in Chap. V, example 6, that

$$\left(1 + \frac{t}{z}\right)^{\lambda} = 1 + \frac{\lambda}{1} \frac{t}{z} + \dots + \frac{\lambda (\lambda - 1) \dots (\lambda - n + 1)}{n!} \frac{t^n}{z^n} + R_n (t, z),$$

where

$$R_n (t, z) = \frac{\lambda (\lambda - 1) \dots (\lambda - n)}{n!} \left(1 + \frac{t}{z}\right)^{\lambda} \int_0^{t/z} u^n (1 + u)^{-\lambda - 1} du.$$

Substituting this in the formula of § 16·12, and integrating term-by-term, it follows from the result of § 12·22 that

$$W_{k, m}(z) = e^{-\frac{1}{2}z} z^k \left\{ 1 + \frac{m^2 - (k - \frac{1}{2})^2}{1!\,z} + \frac{\{m^2 - (k - \frac{1}{2})^2\} \{m^2 - (k - \frac{3}{2})^2\}}{2!\,z^2} + \dots \right.$$

$$+ \frac{\{m^2 - (k - \frac{1}{2})^2\} \{m^2 - (k - \frac{3}{2})^2\} \dots \{m^2 - (k - n + \frac{1}{2})^2\}}{n!\,z^n}$$

$$\left. + \frac{1}{\Gamma (- k + \frac{1}{2} + m)} \int_0^{\infty} t^{-k - \frac{1}{2} + m} R_n (t, z)\, e^{-t}\, dt \right\}$$

provided that n be taken so large that $R \left(n - k - \frac{1}{2} + m \right) > 0$.

Now, if $|\arg z| \leqslant \pi - \alpha$ and $|z| > 1$, then

$$\begin{aligned} 1 &\leqslant |(1 + t/z)| \leqslant 1 + t & R(z) &\geqslant 0 \\ |(1 + t/z)| &\geqslant \sin \alpha & R(z) &\leqslant 0 \end{aligned} \Bigg\} ,$$

and so*

$$|R_n (t, z)| \leqslant \left| \frac{\lambda (\lambda - 1) \dots (\lambda - n)}{n!} \right| (1 + t)^{|\lambda|} (\operatorname{cosec} \alpha)^{|\lambda|} \int_0^{|(t/z)|} u^n (1 + u)^{|\lambda|} du.$$

---

* It is supposed that λ is real; the inequality has to be slightly modified for complex values of λ.

Therefore

$$|R_n(t, z)|$$
$$< \left| \frac{\lambda(\lambda-1)\dots(\lambda-n)}{n!} \right| (1+t)^{|\lambda|} (\operatorname{cosec} \alpha)^{|\lambda|} |(t/z)|^{n+1} (1+t)^{|\lambda|} (n+1)^{-1},$$

since
$$1 + u < 1 + t.$$

Therefore, when $|z| > 1$,

$$\left| \frac{1}{\Gamma(-k+\frac{1}{2}+m)} \int_0^\infty t^{-k-\frac{1}{2}+m} R_n(t, z) e^{-t} dt \right|$$

$$= O \left\{ \int_0^\infty t^{-k+\frac{1}{2}+m+n} (1+t)^{2|\lambda|} |z|^{-n-1} e^{-t} dt \right\}$$

$$= O(z^{-n-1}),$$

since the integral converges. The constant implied in the symbol O is independent of $\arg z$, but depends on α, and tends to infinity as $\alpha \to 0$.

That is to say, the asymptotic expansion of $W_{k,m}(z)$ *is given by the formula*

$$W_{k,m}(z) \sim e^{-\frac{1}{2}z} z^k \left\{ 1 + \sum_{n=1}^\infty \frac{\{m^2 - (k-\frac{1}{2})^2\} \{m^2 - (k-\frac{3}{2})^2\} \dots \{m^2 - (k-n+\frac{1}{2})^2\}}{n! z^n} \right\}$$

for large values of $|z|$ *when* $|\arg z| \leqslant \pi - \alpha < \pi$.

16·31. *The second solution of the equation for* $W_{k,m}(z)$.

The differential equation (B) of § 16·1 satisfied by $W_{k,m}(z)$ is unaltered if the signs of z and k are changed throughout.

Hence, if $|\arg(-z)| < \pi$, $W_{-k,m}(-z)$ is a solution of the equation.

Since, when $|\arg z| < \pi$,

$$W_{k,m}(z) = e^{-\frac{1}{2}z} z^k \{1 + O(z^{-1})\},$$

whereas, when $|\arg(-z)| < \pi$,

$$W_{-k,m}(-z) = e^{\frac{1}{2}z} (-z)^{-k} \{1 + O(z^{-1})\},$$

the ratio $W_{k,m}(z)/W_{-k,m}(-z)$ cannot be a constant, and so $W_{k,m}(z)$ and $W_{-k,m}(-z)$ form a fundamental system of solutions of the differential equation.

16·4. *Contour integrals of the Mellin-Barnes type for* $W_{k,m}(z)$.

Consider now

$$I = \frac{e^{-\frac{1}{2}z} z^k}{2\pi i} \int_{-\infty i}^{\infty i} \frac{\Gamma(s) \Gamma(-s-k-m+\frac{1}{2}) \Gamma(-s-k+m+\frac{1}{2})}{\Gamma(-k-m+\frac{1}{2}) \Gamma(-k+m+\frac{1}{2})} z^s ds \dots (C),$$

where $|\arg z| < \frac{3}{2}\pi$, and neither of the numbers $k \pm m + \frac{1}{2}$ is a positive integer or zero*; the contour has loops if necessary so that the poles of $\Gamma(s)$ and those of $\Gamma\left(-s-k-m+\frac{1}{2}\right)\Gamma\left(-s-k+m+\frac{1}{2}\right)$ are on opposite sides of it.

It is easily verified, by § 13·6, that, as $s \to \infty$ on the contour,

$$\Gamma(s)\,\Gamma\left(-s-k-m+\frac{1}{2}\right)\Gamma\left(-s-k+m+\frac{1}{2}\right) = O\left(e^{-\frac{3}{2}\pi|s|}|s|^{-2k-\frac{1}{2}}\right),$$

and so the integral represents a function of z which is analytic at all points† in the domain $|\arg z| \leqslant \frac{3}{2}\pi - \alpha < \frac{3}{2}\pi$.

Now choose N so that the poles of $\Gamma\left(-s-k-m+\frac{1}{2}\right)\Gamma\left(-s-k+m+\frac{1}{2}\right)$ are on the right of the line $R(s) = -N-\frac{1}{2}$; and consider the integral taken round the rectangle whose corners are $\pm \xi i, -N-\frac{1}{2}\pm\xi i$, where ξ is positive‡ and large.

The reader will verify that, when $|\arg z| \leqslant \frac{3}{2}\pi - \alpha$, the integrals

$$\int_{-\xi i}^{-N-\frac{1}{2}-\xi i}, \qquad \int_{\xi i}^{-N-\frac{1}{2}+\xi i}$$

tend to zero as $\xi \to \infty$; and so, by Cauchy's theorem,

$$\frac{e^{-\frac{1}{2}z}z^k}{2\pi i}\int_{-\infty i}^{\infty i} \frac{\Gamma(s)\,\Gamma\left(-s-k-m+\frac{1}{2}\right)\Gamma\left(-s-k+m+\frac{1}{2}\right)}{\Gamma\left(-k-m+\frac{1}{2}\right)\Gamma\left(-k+m+\frac{1}{2}\right)} z^s\,ds$$

$$= e^{-\frac{1}{2}z}z^k\left\{\sum_{n=0}^{N} R_n\right.$$

$$\left. + \frac{1}{2\pi i}\int_{-N-\frac{1}{2}-\infty i}^{-N-\frac{1}{2}+\infty i} \frac{\Gamma(s)\,\Gamma\left(-s-k-m+\frac{1}{2}\right)\Gamma\left(-s-k+m+\frac{1}{2}\right)}{\Gamma\left(-k-m+\frac{1}{2}\right)\Gamma\left(-k+m+\frac{1}{2}\right)} z^s\,ds\right\},$$

where R_n is the residue of the integrand at $s = -n$.

Write $s = -N-\frac{1}{2}+it$, and the modulus of the last integrand is

$$|z|^{-N-\frac{1}{2}}O\left\{e^{-\alpha|t|}|t|^{N-2k}\right\},$$

where the constant implied in the symbol O is independent of z.

Since $\displaystyle\int^{\pm\infty} e^{-\alpha|t|}|t|^{N-2k}\,dt$ converges, we find that

$$I = e^{-\frac{1}{2}z}z^k\left\{\sum_{n=0}^{N} R_n + O\left(|z|^{-N-\frac{1}{2}}\right)\right\}.$$

---

* In these cases the series of § 16·3 terminates and $W_{k,\,m}(z)$ is a combination of elementary functions.

† The integral is rendered one-valued when $R(z) < 0$ by specifying $\arg z$.

‡ The line joining $\pm \xi i$ may have loops to avoid poles of the integrand as explained above.

But, on calculating the residue R_n, we get

$$R_n = \frac{\Gamma(n-k-m+\frac{1}{2})\,\Gamma(n-k+m+\frac{1}{2})}{n!\,\Gamma(-k-m+\frac{1}{2})\,\Gamma(-k+m+\frac{1}{2})}\,(-)^n\,z^{-n}$$

$$= \frac{\{m^2-(k-\frac{1}{2})^2\}\,\{m^2-(k-\frac{3}{2})^2\}\,\ldots\,\{m^2-(k-n+\frac{1}{2})^2\}}{n!\,z^n},$$

and so *I has the same asymptotic expansion as* $W_{k,m}(z)$.

Further I satisfies the differential equation for $W_{k,m}(z)$; for, on substituting $\displaystyle\int_{-\infty i}^{\infty i} \Gamma(s)\,\Gamma\left(-s-k-m+\frac{1}{2}\right)\Gamma\left(-s-k+m+\frac{1}{2}\right)z^s\,ds$ for v in the expression (given in § 16·12)

$$z^2\frac{d^2v}{dz^2} + 2kz\frac{dv}{dz} + \left(k-m-\frac{1}{2}\right)\left(k+m-\frac{1}{2}\right)v - z^2\frac{dv}{dz},$$

we get

$$\int_{-\infty i}^{\infty i} \Gamma(s)\,\Gamma\left(-s-k-m+\frac{3}{2}\right)\Gamma\left(-s-k+m+\frac{3}{2}\right)z^s\,ds$$

$$-\int_{-\infty i}^{\infty i} \Gamma(s+1)\,\Gamma\left(-s-k-m+\frac{1}{2}\right)\Gamma\left(-s-k+m+\frac{1}{2}\right)z^{s+1}\,ds$$

$$= \left(\int_{-\infty i}^{\infty i} - \int_{1-\infty i}^{1+\infty i}\right)\Gamma(s)\,\Gamma\left(-s-k-m+\frac{3}{2}\right)\Gamma\left(-s-k+m+\frac{3}{2}\right)z^s\,ds.$$

Since there are no poles of the last integrand between the contours, and since the integrand tends to zero as $|s|\to\infty$, s being between the contours, the expression under consideration vanishes, by Cauchy's theorem; and so I satisfies the equation for $W_{k,m}(z)$.

Therefore $I = A\,W_{k,m}(z) + B\,W_{-k,m}(-z),$

where A and B are constants. Making $|z|\to\infty$ when $R(z)>0$ we see, from the asymptotic expansions obtained for I and $W_{\pm k,m}(\pm z)$, that

$$A = 1, \quad B = 0.$$

Accordingly, by the theory of analytic continuation, the equality

$$I = W_{k,m}(z)$$

persists for all values of z such that $|\arg z| < \pi$; and, for values* of $\arg z$ such that $\pi \leqslant |\arg z| < \frac{3}{2}\pi$, $W_{k,m}(z)$ may be *defined* to be the expression I.

Example 1. Shew that

$$W_{k,m}(z) = \frac{e^{-\frac{1}{2}z}}{2\pi i}\int_{-\infty i}^{\infty i} \frac{\Gamma(s-k)\,\Gamma(-s-m+\frac{1}{2})\,\Gamma(-s+m+\frac{1}{2})}{\Gamma(-k-m+\frac{1}{2})\,\Gamma(-k+m+\frac{1}{2})}\,z^s\,ds,$$

taken along a suitable contour.

---

* It would have been possible, by modifying the path of integration in § 16·3, to have shewn that that integral could be made to define an analytic function when $|\arg z| < \frac{3}{2}\pi$. But the reader will see that it is unnecessary to do so, as Barnes' integral affords a simpler definition of the function.

Example 2. Obtain Barnes' integral for $W_{k,m}(z)$ by writing

$$\frac{1}{2\pi i}\int_{-\infty i}^{\infty i}\frac{\Gamma(s)\,\Gamma(-s-k-m+\frac{1}{2})}{\Gamma(-k-m+\frac{1}{2})}z^{s}t^{-s}\,ds$$

for $(1+t/z)^{k-\frac{1}{2}+m}$ in the integral of § 16·12 and changing the order of integration.

16·41. *Relations between* $W_{k,m}(z)$ *and* $M_{k,\pm m}(z)$.

If we take the expression

$$F(s)\equiv\Gamma(s)\,\Gamma\left(-s-k-m+\frac{1}{2}\right)\Gamma\left(-s-k+m+\frac{1}{2}\right)$$

which occurs in Barnes' integral for $W_{k,m}(z)$, and write it in the form

$$\frac{\pi^{2}\Gamma(s)}{\Gamma(s+k+m+\frac{1}{2})\,\Gamma(s+k-m+\frac{1}{2})\cos(s+k+m)\pi\cos(s+k-m)\pi},$$

we see, by § 13·6, that, when $R(s)\geqslant 0$, we have, as $|s|\to\infty$,

$$F(s)=O\left[\exp\left\{\left(-s-\frac{1}{2}-2k\right)\log s+s\right\}\right]\sec(s+k+m)\pi\sec(s+k-m)\pi.$$

Hence, if $|\arg z|<\frac{3}{2}\pi$, $\int F(s)\,z^{s}\,ds$, taken round a semicircle on the right of the imaginary axis, tends to zero as the radius of the semicircle tends to infinity, provided the lower bound of the distance of the semicircle from the poles of the integrand is positive (not zero).

Therefore $$W_{k,m}(z)=-\frac{e^{-\frac{1}{2}z}z^{k}\cdot(\Sigma R')}{\Gamma(-k-m+\frac{1}{2})\,\Gamma(-k+m+\frac{1}{2})},$$

where $\Sigma R'$ denotes the sum of the residues of $F(s)$ at its poles on the right of the contour (cf. § 14·5) which occurs in equation (C) of § 16·4.

Evaluating these residues we find without difficulty that, when

$$|\arg z|<\frac{3}{2}\pi,$$

and $2m$ is not an integer*,

$$W_{k,m}(z)=\frac{\Gamma(-2m)}{\Gamma(\frac{1}{2}-m-k)}M_{k,m}(z)+\frac{\Gamma(2m)}{\Gamma(\frac{1}{2}+m-k)}M_{k,-m}(z).$$

Example 1. Shew that, when $|\arg(-z)|<\frac{3}{2}\pi$ and $2m$ is not an integer,

$$W_{-k,m}(-z)=\frac{\Gamma(-2m)}{\Gamma(\frac{1}{2}-m+k)}M_{-k,m}(-z)+\frac{\Gamma(2m)}{\Gamma(\frac{1}{2}+m+k)}M_{-k,-m}(-z).$$

(Barnes†.)

Example 2. When $-\frac{1}{2}\pi<\arg z<\frac{3}{2}\pi$ and $-\frac{3}{2}\pi<\arg(-z)<\frac{1}{2}\pi$, shew that

$$M_{k,m}(z)=\frac{\Gamma(2m+1)}{\Gamma(\frac{1}{2}+m-k)}e^{k\pi i}W_{-k,m}(-z)+\frac{\Gamma(2m+1)}{\Gamma(\frac{1}{2}+m+k)}e^{(\frac{1}{2}+m+k)\pi i}W_{k,m}(z).$$

---

* When $2m$ is an integer some of the poles are generally double poles, and their residues involve logarithms of z. The result has not been proved when $k-\frac{1}{2}\pm m$ is a positive integer or zero, but may be obtained for such values of k and m by comparing the terminating series for $W_{k,m}(z)$ with the series for $M_{k,\pm m}(z)$.

† Barnes' results are given in the notation explained in § 16·1.

Example 3.   Obtain Kummer's first formula (§ 16·11) from the result

$$z^n e^{-z} = \frac{1}{2\pi i} \int_{-\infty i}^{\infty i} \Gamma(n-s) z^s \, ds.$$

(Barnes.)

16·5.   *The parabolic cylinder functions.   Weber's equation.*

Consider the differential equation satisfied by $w = z^{-\frac{1}{2}} W_{k,-\frac{1}{4}}\left(\frac{1}{2} z^2\right)$; it is

$$\frac{d}{z\,dz}\left\{\frac{d\,(wz^{\frac{1}{2}})}{z\,dz}\right\} + \left\{-\frac{1}{4} + \frac{2k}{z^2} + \frac{\frac{3}{4}}{z^4}\right\} wz^{\frac{1}{2}} = 0;$$

this reduces to

$$\frac{d^2 w}{dz^2} + \left\{2k - \frac{1}{4} z^2\right\} w = 0.$$

Therefore the function

$$D_n(z) = 2^{\frac{1}{2}n + \frac{1}{4}} z^{-\frac{1}{2}} W_{\frac{1}{2}n + \frac{1}{4}, -\frac{1}{4}}\left(\frac{1}{2} z^2\right)$$

satisfies the differential equation

$$\frac{d^2 D_n(z)}{dz^2} + \left(n + \frac{1}{2} - \frac{1}{4} z^2\right) D_n(z) = 0.$$

Accordingly $D_n(z)$ is one of the functions associated with the parabolic cylinder in harmonic analysis[*]; the equation satisfied by it will be called Weber's equation.

From § 16·41, it follows that

$$D_n(z) = \frac{\Gamma\left(\frac{1}{2}\right) 2^{\frac{1}{2}n + \frac{1}{4}} z^{-\frac{1}{2}}}{\Gamma\left(\frac{1}{2} - \frac{1}{2} n\right)} M_{\frac{1}{2}n + \frac{1}{4}, -\frac{1}{4}}\left(\frac{1}{2} z^2\right) + \frac{\Gamma\left(-\frac{1}{2}\right) 2^{\frac{1}{2}n + \frac{1}{4}} z^{-\frac{1}{2}}}{\Gamma\left(-\frac{1}{2} n\right)} M_{\frac{1}{2}n + \frac{1}{4}, \frac{1}{4}}\left(\frac{1}{2} z^2\right)$$

when $|\arg z| < \frac{3}{4}\pi$.

But

$$z^{-\frac{1}{2}} M_{\frac{1}{2}n + \frac{1}{4}, -\frac{1}{4}}\left(\frac{1}{2} z^2\right) = 2^{-\frac{1}{4}} e^{-\frac{1}{4}z^2} {}_1F_1\left\{-\frac{1}{2}n;\ \frac{1}{2};\ \frac{1}{2} z^2\right\},$$

$$z^{-\frac{1}{2}} M_{\frac{1}{2}n + \frac{1}{4}, \frac{1}{4}}\left(\frac{1}{2} z^2\right) = 2^{-\frac{3}{4}} z e^{-\frac{1}{4}z^2} {}_1F_1\left\{\frac{1}{2} - \frac{1}{2}n;\ \frac{3}{2};\ \frac{1}{2} z^2\right\},$$

and these are *one-valued* analytic functions of z throughout the z-plane. Accordingly $D_n(z)$ is a one-valued function of z throughout the z-plane; and, by § 16·4, its asymptotic expansion when $|\arg z| < \frac{3}{4}\pi$ is

$$e^{-\frac{1}{4}z^2} z^n \left\{1 - \frac{n(n-1)}{2z^2} + \frac{n(n-1)(n-2)(n-3)}{2 \cdot 4z^4} - \ldots\right\}.$$

16·51.   *The second solution of Weber's equation.*

Since Weber's equation is unaltered if we simultaneously replace n and z by $-n-1$ and $\pm iz$ respectively, it follows that $D_{-n-1}(iz)$ and $D_{-n-1}(-iz)$ are solutions of Weber's equation, as is also $D_n(-z)$.

---

[*] Weber, *Math. Ann.* I. (1869), pp. 1–36; Whittaker, *Proc. London Math. Soc.* XXXV. (1903), pp. 417–427.

It is obvious from the asymptotic expansions of $D_n(z)$ and $D_{-n-1}(ze^{\frac{1}{2}\pi i})$, valid in the range $-\frac{3}{4}\pi < \arg z < \frac{1}{4}\pi$, that the ratio of these two solutions is not a constant.

16·511.   *The relation between the functions $D_n(z)$, $D_{-n-1}(\pm iz)$.*

From the theory of linear differential equations, a relation of the form
$$D_n(z) = a\,D_{-n-1}(iz) + b\,D_{-n-1}(-iz)$$
must hold when the ratio of the functions on the right is not a constant.

To obtain this relation, we observe that if the functions involved be expanded in ascending powers of z, the expansions are
$$\frac{\Gamma(\frac{1}{2})\,2^{\frac{1}{2}n}}{\Gamma(\frac{1}{2}-\frac{1}{2}n)} + \frac{\Gamma(-\frac{1}{2})\,2^{\frac{1}{2}n-\frac{1}{2}}}{\Gamma(-\frac{1}{2}n)}\,z + \dots$$

and
$$a\left\{ \frac{\Gamma(\frac{1}{2})\,2^{-\frac{1}{2}n-\frac{1}{2}}}{\Gamma(1+\frac{1}{2}n)} + \frac{\Gamma(-\frac{1}{2})\,2^{-\frac{1}{2}n-1}}{\Gamma(\frac{1}{2}+\frac{1}{2}n)}\,iz + \dots \right\}$$
$$+ b\left\{ \frac{\Gamma(\frac{1}{2})\,2^{-\frac{1}{2}n-\frac{1}{2}}}{\Gamma(1+\frac{1}{2}n)} - \frac{\Gamma(-\frac{1}{2})\,2^{-\frac{1}{2}n-1}}{\Gamma(\frac{1}{2}+\frac{1}{2}n)}\,iz + \dots \right\}.$$

Comparing the first two terms we get
$$a = (2\pi)^{-\frac{1}{2}}\,\Gamma(n+1)\,e^{\frac{1}{2}n\pi i}, \quad b = (2\pi)^{-\frac{1}{2}}\,\Gamma(n+1)\,e^{-\frac{1}{2}n\pi i},$$
and so
$$D_n(z) = \frac{\Gamma(n+1)}{\sqrt{(2\pi)}}\left[e^{\frac{1}{2}n\pi i}\,D_{-n-1}(iz) + e^{-\frac{1}{2}n\pi i}\,D_{-n-1}(-iz) \right].$$

16·52.   *The general asymptotic expansion of $D_n(z)$.*

So far the asymptotic expansion of $D_n(z)$ for large values of z has only been given (§ 16·5) in the sector $|\arg z| < \frac{3}{4}\pi$. To obtain its form for values of $\arg z$ not comprised in this range we write $-iz$ for z and $-n-1$ for n in the formula of the preceding section, and get
$$D_n(z) = e^{n\pi i}\,D_n(-z) + \frac{\sqrt{(2\pi)}}{\Gamma(-n)}\,e^{\frac{1}{2}(n+1)\pi i}\,D_{-n-1}(-iz).$$

Now, if $\frac{5}{4}\pi > \arg z > \frac{1}{4}\pi$, we can assign to $-z$ and $-iz$ arguments between $\pm\frac{3}{4}\pi$; and $\arg(-z) = \arg z - \pi$, $\arg(-iz) = \arg z - \frac{1}{2}\pi$; and then, applying the asymptotic expansion of § 16·5 to $D_n(-z)$ and $D_{-n-1}(-iz)$, we see that, if $\frac{5}{4}\pi > \arg z > \frac{1}{4}\pi$,
$$D_n(z) \sim e^{-\frac{1}{4}z^2}\,z^n\left\{ 1 - \frac{n(n-1)}{2z^2} + \frac{n(n-1)(n-2)(n-3)}{2\,.\,4z^4} - \dots \right\}$$
$$- \frac{\sqrt{(2\pi)}}{\Gamma(-n)}\,e^{n\pi i}\,e^{\frac{1}{4}z^2}\,z^{-n-1}\left\{ 1 + \frac{(n+1)(n+2)}{2z^2} \right.$$
$$\left. + \frac{(n+1)(n+2)(n+3)(n+4)}{2\,.\,4z^4} + \dots \right\}.$$

This formula is not inconsistent with that of § $16 \cdot 5$ since in their common range of validity, viz. $\frac{1}{4}\pi < \arg z < \frac{3}{4}\pi$, $e^{\frac{1}{2}z^2} z^{-2n-1}$ is $o(z^{-m})$ for all positive values of m.

To obtain a formula valid in the range $-\frac{1}{4}\pi > \arg z > -\frac{5}{4}\pi$, we use the formula

$$D_n(z) = e^{-n\pi i} D_n(-z) + \frac{\surd(2\pi)}{\Gamma(-n)} e^{-\frac{1}{2}(n+1)\pi i} D_{-n-1}(iz),$$

and we get an asymptotic expansion which differs from that which has just been obtained only in containing $e^{-n\pi i}$ in place of $e^{n\pi i}$.

Since $D_n(z)$ is one-valued and one or other of the expansions obtained is valid for all values of $\arg z$ in the range $-\pi \leqslant \arg z \leqslant \pi$, the complete asymptotic expansion of $D_n(z)$ has been obtained.

16·6. *A contour integral for $D_n(z)$.*

Consider $\displaystyle\int_\infty^{(0+)} e^{-zt-\frac{1}{2}t^2}(-t)^{-n-1} dt$, where $|\arg(-t)| \leqslant \pi$; it represents a one-valued analytic function of z throughout the z-plane (§ $5 \cdot 32$) and further

$$\left\{\frac{d^2}{dz^2} - z\frac{d}{dz} + n\right\} \int_\infty^{(0+)} e^{-zt-\frac{1}{2}t^2}(-t)^{-n-1} dt = \int_\infty^{(0+)} \frac{d}{dt}\{e^{-zt-\frac{1}{2}t^2}(-t)^{-n}\} dt = 0,$$

the differentiations under the sign of integration being easily justified; accordingly the integral satisfies the differential equation satisfied by $e^{\frac{1}{4}z^2} D_n(z)$; and therefore

$$e^{-\frac{1}{4}z^2} \int_\infty^{(0+)} e^{-zt-\frac{1}{2}t^2}(-t)^{-n-1} dt = aD_n(z) + bD_{-n-1}(iz),$$

where a and b are constants.

Now, if the expression on the right be called $E_n(z)$, we have

$$E_n(0) = \int_\infty^{(0+)} e^{-\frac{1}{2}t^2}(-t)^{-n-1} dt, \quad E_n'(0) = \int_\infty^{(0+)} e^{-\frac{1}{2}t^2}(-t)^{-n} dt.$$

To evaluate these integrals, which are analytic functions of n, we suppose first that $R(n) < 0$; then, deforming the paths of integration, we get

$$E_n(0) = -2i \sin(n+1)\pi \int_0^\infty e^{-\frac{1}{2}t^2} t^{-n-1} dt$$

$$= 2^{-\frac{1}{2}n} i \sin n\pi \int_0^\infty e^{-u} u^{-\frac{1}{2}n-1} du$$

$$= 2^{-\frac{1}{2}n} i \sin(n\pi) \Gamma(-\frac{1}{2}n).$$

Similarly $\qquad E_n'(0) = -2^{\frac{1}{2}-\frac{1}{2}n} i \sin(n\pi) \Gamma(\frac{1}{2}-\frac{1}{2}n).$

Both sides of these equations being analytic functions of n, the equations are true for all values of n; and therefore

$$b = 0, \quad a = \frac{\Gamma(\frac{1}{2}-\frac{1}{2}n)}{\Gamma(\frac{1}{2}) 2^{\frac{1}{2}n}} 2^{-\frac{1}{2}n} i \sin(n\pi) \Gamma(-\frac{1}{2}n)$$

$$= 2i\Gamma(-n) \sin n\pi.$$

Therefore $\qquad D_n(z) = -\dfrac{\Gamma(n+1)}{2\pi i} e^{-\frac{1}{4}z^2} \displaystyle\int_\infty^{(0+)} e^{-zt-\frac{1}{2}t^2}(-t)^{-n-1} dt.$

16·61.   *Recurrence formulae for $D_n(z)$.*

From the equation

$$0 = \int_{\infty}^{(0+)} \frac{d}{dt} \left\{ e^{-zt - \frac{1}{2}t^2} (-t)^{-n-1} \right\} dt$$

$$= \int_{\infty}^{(0+)} \left\{ -z(-t)^{-n-1} + (-t)^{-n} + (n+1)(-t)^{-n-2} \right\} e^{-zt - \frac{1}{2}t^2} dt,$$

after using § 16·6, we see that

$$D_{n+1}(z) - z D_n(z) + n D_{n-1}(z) = 0.$$

Further, by differentiating the integral of § 16·6, it follows that

$$D_n'(z) + \frac{1}{2} z D_n(z) - n D_{n-1}(z) = 0.$$

Example.   Obtain these results from the ascending power series of § 16·5.

16·7.   *Properties of $D_n(z)$ when n is an integer.*

When n is an integer, we may write the integral of § 16·6 in the form

$$D_n(z) = -\frac{n! \, e^{-\frac{1}{4}z^2}}{2\pi i} \int_{\infty}^{(0+)} \frac{e^{-zt - \frac{1}{2}t^2}}{(-t)^{n+1}} dt.$$

If now we write $t = v - z$, we get

$$D_n(z) = (-)^n \frac{n! \, e^{\frac{1}{4}z^2}}{2\pi i} \int_{}^{(z+)} \frac{e^{-\frac{1}{2}v^2}}{(v-z)^{n+1}} dv$$

$$= (-)^n e^{\frac{1}{4}z^2} \frac{d^n}{dz^n} (e^{-\frac{1}{2}z^2}),$$

a result due to Hermite*.

Also, if m and n be unequal integers, we see from the differential equations that

$$D_n(z) D_m''(z) - D_m(z) D_n''(z) + (m-n) D_m(z) D_n(z) = 0,$$

and so

$$(m-n) \int_{-\infty}^{\infty} D_m(z) D_n(z) \, dz = \left[D_n(z) D_m'(z) - D_m(z) D_n'(z) \right]_{-\infty}^{\infty}$$

$$= 0,$$

by the expansion of § 16·5 in descending powers of z (which terminates and is valid for all values of arg z when n is a positive integer).

Therefore if m and n are unequal positive integers

$$\int_{-\infty}^{\infty} D_m(z) D_n(z) \, dz = 0.$$

---

*   *Comptes Rendus*, LVIII. (1864), pp. 266–273.

On the other hand, when $m = n$, we have

$$(n+1)\int_{-\infty}^{\infty} \{D_n(z)\}^2\, dz$$

$$= \int_{-\infty}^{\infty} D_n(z) \left\{ D'_{n+1}(z) + \tfrac{1}{2} z D_{n+1}(z) \right\} dz$$

$$= \left[D_n(z) D_{n+1}(z) \right]_{-\infty}^{\infty} + \int_{-\infty}^{\infty} \left\{ \tfrac{1}{2} z D_n(z) D_{n+1}(z) - D_{n+1}(z) D_n'(z) \right\} dz$$

$$= \int_{-\infty}^{\infty} \{D_{n+1}(z)\}^2\, dz,$$

on using the recurrence formula, integrating by parts and then using the recurrence formula again.

It follows by induction that

$$\int_{-\infty}^{\infty} \{D_n(z)\}^2\, dz = n! \int_{-\infty}^{\infty} \{D_0(z)\}^2\, dz$$

$$= n! \int_{-\infty}^{\infty} e^{-\frac{1}{2}z^2}\, dz$$

$$= (2\pi)^{\frac{1}{2}} n!,$$

by § 12·14 corollary 1 and § 12·2.

It follows at once that if, for a function $f(z)$, an expansion of the form

$$f(z) = a_0 D_0(z) + a_1 D_1(z) + \dots + a_n D_n(z) + \dots$$

exists, and if it is legitimate to integrate term-by-term between the limits $-\infty$ and ∞, then

$$a_n = \frac{1}{(2\pi)^{\frac{1}{2}} n!} \int_{-\infty}^{\infty} D_n(t) f(t)\, dt.$$

REFERENCES.

A. ERDÉLYI, *Math. ZS.* XLII (1936), p. 125: XLII (1937), p. 641: *Math. Ann.* CXIII (1936), p. 347: *Mon. f. M. u. P.* XLV (1936), p. 31: XLVI (1937), pp. 1, 132: *Proc. Amst. Ac.* XXXIX (1936), p. 1092: XLI (1938), p. 481: *Wien Sitz IIa*, CXLVI (1937), p. 431: *Proc. Camb. Phil. Soc.* XXXIV (1938), p. 28.

C. S. MEIJER, *Nieuw. Arch. v. Wisk.*(2) XVIII (Heft 2) (1934), p. 36: (2) XVIII (Heft 4) (1936), p. 10: *Proc. Amst. Ac.* XXXVII (1934), p. 805: XXXVIII (1935), p. 528: XXXIX (1936), pp. 394, 519: XL (1937), pp. 133, 259, 871: XLI (1938), p. 42: *Quart. J. M.* VI (1935), p. 241: *Math. Ann.* CXII (1936), p. 469.

MISCELLANEOUS EXAMPLES.

1. Shew that, if the integral is convergent, then

$$M_{k,m}(z) = \frac{\Gamma(2m+1)\, z^{m+\frac{1}{2}}\, 2^{-2m}}{\Gamma(\frac{1}{2}+m+k)\,\Gamma(\frac{1}{2}+m-k)} \int_{-1}^{1} (1+u)^{-\frac{1}{2}+m-k}\,(1-u)^{-\frac{1}{2}+m+k}\, e^{\frac{1}{2}zu}\, du.$$

2. Shew that $M_{k,m}(z) = z^{\frac{1}{2}+m}\, e^{-\frac{1}{2}z} \lim_{\rho\to\infty} F(\tfrac{1}{2}+m-k,\ \tfrac{1}{2}+m-k+\rho;\ 2m+1;\ z/\rho).$

3. Obtain the recurrence formulae

$$W_{k,m}(z) = z^{\frac{1}{2}}\, W_{k-\frac{1}{2},\, m-\frac{1}{2}}(z) + (\tfrac{1}{2}-k+m)\, W_{k-1,\, m}(z),$$

$$W_{k,m}(z) = z^{\frac{1}{2}}\, W_{k-\frac{1}{2},\, m+\frac{1}{2}}(z) + (\tfrac{1}{2}-k-m)\, W_{k-1,\, m}(z),$$

$$z\, W'_{k,m}(z) = (k-\tfrac{1}{2}z)\, W_{k,m}(z) - \{m^2-(k-\tfrac{1}{2})^2\}\, W_{k-1,\, m}(z).$$

4. Prove that $W_{k,m}(z)$ is the integral of an elementary function when either of the numbers $k-\frac{1}{2}\pm m$ is a negative integer.

5. Shew that, by a suitable change of variables, the equation

$$(a_2+b_2 x)\frac{d^2y}{dx^2} + (a_1+b_1 x)\frac{dy}{dx} + (a_0+b_0 x)\, y = 0$$

can be brought to the form

$$\xi\frac{d^2\eta}{d\xi^2} + (c-\xi)\frac{d\eta}{d\xi} - a\eta = 0\ ;$$

derive this equation from the equation for $F(a,\, b\,;\, c\,;\, x)$ by writing $x=\xi/b$ and making $b\to\infty$.

6. Shew that the cosine integral of Schlömilch and Besso (*Giornale di Matematiche*, VI), defined by the equation

$$\mathrm{Ci}\,(z) = \int_z^\infty \frac{\cos t}{t}\, dt,$$

is equal to $\quad \frac{1}{2}z^{-\frac{1}{2}} e^{\frac{1}{2}iz+\frac{1}{4}\pi i}\, W_{-\frac{1}{2},\, 0}(-iz) + \frac{1}{2}z^{-\frac{1}{2}} e^{-\frac{1}{2}iz-\frac{1}{4}\pi i}\, W_{-\frac{1}{2},\, 0}(iz).$

Shew also that Schlömilch's function, defined (*Zeitschrift für Math. und Physik*, IV. (1859), p. 390) by the equations

$$S(\nu,\, z) = \int_0^\infty (1+t)^{-\nu}\, e^{-zt}\, dt = z^{\nu-1} e^z \int_z^\infty \frac{e^{-u}}{u^\nu}\, du,$$

is equal to $\quad z^{\frac{1}{2}\nu-1} e^{\frac{1}{2}z}\, W_{-\frac{1}{2}\nu,\, \frac{1}{2}-\frac{1}{2}\nu}(z).$

7. Express in terms of $W_{k,m}$ functions the two functions

$$\mathrm{Si}\,(z) \equiv \int_0^z \frac{\sin t}{t}\, dt,\quad \mathrm{Ei}\,(z) \equiv \int_z^\infty \frac{e^{-t}}{t}\, dt.$$

8. Shew that Sonine's polynomial, defined (*Math. Ann.* XVI. p. 41) by the equation

$$T_m{}^n(z) = \frac{z^n}{n!\,(m+n)!\,0!} - \frac{z^{n-1}}{(n-1)!\,(m+n-1)!\,1!} + \frac{z^{n-2}}{(n-2)!\,(m+n-2)!\,2!} - \cdots,$$

is equal to $\quad \dfrac{1}{n!\,(m+n)!}\, z^{-\frac{1}{2}(m+1)}\, e^{\frac{1}{2}z}\, W_{n+\frac{1}{2}m+\frac{1}{2},\, \frac{1}{2}m}(z).$

9. Shew that the function $\phi_m(z)$ defined by Lagrange in 1762–1765 (*Oeuvres*, I. p. 520) and by Abel (*Oeuvres*, 1881, p. 284) as the coefficient of h^m in the expansion of $(1-h)^{-1} e^{-hz/(1-h)}$ is equal to

$$(-)^m z^{-\frac{1}{2}} e^{\frac{1}{2}z} W_{m+\frac{1}{2},\,0}(z)/m!.$$

10*. Shew that the Pearson-Cunningham function (*Proc. Royal Soc.* LXXXI. p. 310), $\omega_{n,\,m}(z)$, defined as

$$\frac{e^{-z}(-z)^{n-\frac{1}{2}m}}{\Gamma(n-\frac{1}{2}m+1)}\left\{1 - \frac{(n+\frac{1}{2}m)(n-\frac{1}{2}m)}{z} + \frac{(n+\frac{1}{2}m)(n+\frac{1}{2}m-1)(n-\frac{1}{2}m)(n-\frac{1}{2}m-1)}{2!\,z^2} - \cdots\right\},$$

is equal to

$$\frac{(-)^{n-\frac{1}{2}m}}{\Gamma(n-\frac{1}{2}m+1)} z^{-\frac{1}{2}(m+1)} e^{-\frac{1}{2}z} W_{n+\frac{1}{2},\,\frac{1}{2}m}(z).$$

11. Shew that, if $|\arg z| < \frac{1}{4}\pi$, and $|\arg(1+t)| \leqslant \pi$,

$$D_n(z) = \frac{\Gamma(\frac{1}{2}n+1)}{2^{-\frac{1}{2}(n-1)}\pi i} \int_{-\infty}^{(-1+)} e^{\frac{1}{4}z^2 t}(1+t)^{-\frac{1}{2}n-1}(1-t)^{\frac{1}{2}(n-1)}\,dt.$$

(Whittaker.)

12. Shew that, if n be not a positive integer and if $|\arg z| < \frac{3}{4}\pi$, then

$$D_n(z) = \frac{1}{2\pi i}\cdot e^{-\frac{1}{4}z^2} \int_{-\infty i}^{\infty i} \frac{\Gamma(\frac{1}{2}t-\frac{1}{2}n)\,\Gamma(-t)}{\Gamma(-n)}(\sqrt{2})^{t-n-2} z^t\,dt,$$

and that this result holds for all values of $\arg z$ if the integral be $\int_{\infty}^{(0-)}$, the contours enclosing the poles of $\Gamma(-t)$ but not those of $\Gamma(\frac{1}{2}t-\frac{1}{2}n)$.

13. Shew that, if $|\arg a| < \frac{1}{2}\pi$,

$$\int_{\infty}^{(0+)} e^{(\frac{1}{4}-a)z^2} z^m D_n(z)\,dz$$
$$= \frac{\pi^{\frac{3}{2}} 2^{\frac{1}{2}n-m} e^{\pi i(m-\frac{1}{2})}}{\Gamma(-m)\,\Gamma(\frac{1}{2}m-\frac{1}{2}n+1)\,a^{\frac{1}{2}(m+1)}} F(-\frac{1}{2}n,\,\frac{1}{2}m+\frac{1}{2};\,\frac{1}{2}m-\frac{1}{2}n+1;\,1-\frac{1}{2}a^{-1}).$$

14. Deduce from example 13 that, if the integral is convergent, then

$$\int_0^{\infty} e^{-\frac{3}{4}z^2} z^m D_{m+1}(z)\,dz = (\sqrt{2})^{-1-m}\,\Gamma(m+1)\sin(\frac{1}{4}-\frac{1}{4}m)\,\pi.$$

(Watson.)

15. Shew that, if n be a positive integer, and if

$$E_n(x) = \int_{-\infty}^{\infty} e^{-\frac{1}{4}z^2}(z-x)^{-1} D_n(z)\,dz,$$

then

$$E_n(x) = \pm i e^{\mp n\pi i}\sqrt{(2\pi)}\,\Gamma(n+1)\,e^{-\frac{1}{4}x^2} D_{-n-1}(\mp ix),$$

the upper or lower signs being taken according as the imaginary part of x is positive or negative.

(Watson.)

16. Shew that, if n be a positive integer,

$$D_n(x) = (-)^\mu 2^{n+2}(2\pi)^{-\frac{1}{2}} e^{\frac{1}{4}x^2} \int_0^{\infty} u^n e^{-2u^2} {\textstyle\genfrac{}{}{0pt}{}{\cos}{\sin}}(2xu)\,du,$$

where μ is $\frac{1}{2}n$ or $\frac{1}{2}(n-1)$, whichever is an integer, and the cosine or sine is taken as n is even or odd.

(Adamoff.)

---

* The results of examples 8, 9, 10 were communicated to us by Mr Bateman.

17.   Shew that, if n be a positive integer,

$$D_n(x) = (-)^\mu (\tfrac{1}{2}\pi)^{-\frac{1}{2}} (\surd n)^{n+1} e^{\frac{1}{4}x^2} e^{-\frac{1}{2}n} (J_1 + J_2 - J_3),$$

where

$$J_1 = \int_{-\infty}^{\infty} e^{-n(v-1)^2} {\cos \atop \sin} (xv\surd n)\, dv,$$

$$J_2 = \int_{0}^{\infty} \sigma(v) {\cos \atop \sin} (xv\surd n)\, dv,$$

$$J_3 = \int_{-\infty}^{0} e^{-n(v-1)^2} {\cos \atop \sin} (xv\surd n)\, dv,$$

and

$$\sigma(v) = e^{\frac{1}{2}n(1-v^2)} v^n - e^{-n(v-1)^2}. \qquad \text{(Adamoff.)}$$

18.   With the notation of the preceding examples, shew that, when x is real,

$$J_1 = \pi^{\frac{1}{2}} n^{-\frac{1}{2}} e^{-\frac{1}{4}x^2} {\cos \atop \sin} (x\surd n);$$

while J_3 satisfies both the inequalities

$$|J_3| < 2e^{-n} \div \{|x|\surd n\}, \quad |J_3| < \left(\frac{\pi}{2n}\right)^{\frac{1}{2}} e^{-n}.$$

Shew also that as v increases from 0 to 1, $\sigma(v)$ decreases from 0 to a minimum at $v = 1 - h_1$ and then increases to 0 at $v = 1$; and as v increases from 1 to ∞, $\sigma(v)$ increases to a maximum at $1 + h_2$ and then decreases, its limit being zero ; where

$$\frac{1}{2}\surd\left(\frac{3}{2n}\right) < h_1 < \surd\left(\frac{3}{2n}\right), \quad \frac{1}{2}\surd\left(\frac{3}{2n}\right) < h_2 < \surd\left(\frac{3}{2n}\right),$$

and $|\sigma(1-h_1)| < An^{-\frac{1}{3}}$, $\sigma(1+h_2) < An^{-\frac{1}{3}}$, where $A = 0\cdot0742\dots$ (Adamoff.)

19.   By employing the second mean value theorem when necessary, shew that

$$D_n(x) = \surd 2 . (\surd n)^n e^{-\frac{1}{2}n} \left[\cos(xn^{\frac{1}{2}} - \tfrac{1}{2}n\pi) + \frac{\omega_n(x)}{\surd n} \right],$$

where $\omega_n(x)$ satisfies both the inequalities

$$|\omega_n(x)| < \frac{3\cdot35\dots}{|x|\surd\pi} e^{\frac{1}{4}x^2}, \quad |\omega_n(0)| < \frac{1}{6} n^{-\frac{1}{2}},$$

when x is real and n is an integer greater than 2.   (Adamoff.)

20.   Shew that, if n be positive but otherwise unrestricted, and if m be a *positive integer* (or zero), then the equation in z

$$D_n(z) = 0$$

has m positive roots when $2m - 1 < n < 2m + 1$.   (Milne.)

CHAPTER XVII

BESSEL FUNCTIONS

17·1. *The Bessel coefficients.*

In this chapter we shall consider a class of functions known as *Bessel functions* or *cylindrical functions* which have many analogies with the Legendre functions of Chapter XV. Just as the Legendre functions proved to be particular forms of the hypergeometric function with three regular singularities, so the Bessel functions are particular forms of the confluent hypergeometric function with one regular and one irregular singularity. As in the case of the Legendre functions, we first introduce* a certain set of the Bessel functions as coefficients in an expansion.

For all values of z and t ($t = 0$ excepted), the function

$$e^{\frac{1}{2}z\left(t - \frac{1}{t}\right)}$$

can be expanded by Laurent's theorem in a series of positive and negative powers of t. If the coefficient of t^n, where n is any integer positive or negative, be denoted by $J_n(z)$, it follows, from § 5·6, that

$$J_n(z) = \frac{1}{2\pi i} \int^{(0+)} u^{-n-1} e^{\frac{1}{2}z\left(u - \frac{1}{u}\right)} du.$$

To express $J_n(z)$ as a power series in z, write $u = 2t/z$; then

$$J_n(z) = \frac{1}{2\pi i} \left(\frac{1}{2}z\right)^n \int^{(0+)} t^{-n-1} \exp\left\{t - \frac{z^2}{4t}\right\} dt;$$

since the contour is any one which encircles the origin once counter-clockwise, we may take it to be the circle $|t| = 1$; as the integrand can be expanded in a series of powers of z uniformly convergent on this contour, it follows from § 4·7 that

$$J_n(z) = \frac{1}{2\pi i} \sum_{r=0}^{\infty} \frac{(-)^r}{r!} \left(\frac{1}{2}z\right)^{n+2r} \int^{(0+)} t^{-n-r-1} e^t dt.$$

Now the residue of the integrand at $t = 0$ is $\{(n+r)!\}^{-1}$ by § 6·1, when $n + r$ is a positive integer or zero; when $n + r$ is a negative integer the residue is zero.

Therefore, if n is a positive integer or zero,

$$J_n(z) = \sum_{r=0}^{\infty} \frac{(-)^r \left(\frac{1}{2}z\right)^{n+2r}}{r!\,(n+r)!}$$

$$= \frac{z^n}{2^n n!} \left\{1 - \frac{z^2}{2^2 \cdot 1\,(n+1)} + \frac{z^4}{2^4 \cdot 1 \cdot 2\,(n+1)(n+2)} - \cdots\right\};$$

* This procedure is due to Schlömilch, *Zeitschrift für Math. und Phys.* II. (1857), pp. 137–165.

whereas, when n is a negative integer equal to $-m$,

$$J_n(z) = \sum_{r=m}^{\infty} \frac{(-)^r (\tfrac{1}{2}z)^{2r-m}}{r!\,(r-m)!} = \sum_{s=0}^{\infty} \frac{(-)^{m+s}(\tfrac{1}{2}z)^{m+2s}}{(m+s)!\,s!},$$

and so $J_n(z) = (-)^m J_m(z)$.

The function $J_n(z)$, which has now been defined for all integral values of n, positive and negative, is called the *Bessel coefficient* of order n; the series defining it converges for all values of z.

We shall see later (§ 17·2) that Bessel coefficients are a particular case of a class of functions known as *Bessel functions*.

The series by which $J_n(z)$ is defined occurs in a memoir by Euler, on the vibrations of a stretched circular membrane, *Novi Comm. Acad. Petrop.* x. (1764) [Published 1766], pp. 243–260, an investigation dealt with below in § 18·51; it also occurs in a memoir by Lagrange on elliptic motion, *Hist. de l'Acad. R. des Sci. de Berlin*, xxv. (1769) [Published 1771], p. 223.

The earliest systematic study of the functions was made in 1824 by Bessel in his *Untersuchung des Theils der planetarischen Störungen welcher aus der Bewegung der Sonne entsteht (Berliner Abh.* 1824); special cases of Bessel coefficients had, however, appeared in researches published before 1769; the earliest of these is in a letter, dated Oct. 3, 1703, from Jakob Bernoulli to Leibniz[*], in which occurs a series which is now described as a Bessel function of order $\tfrac{1}{3}$; the Bessel coefficient of order zero occurs in 1732 in Daniel Bernoulli's memoir on the oscillations of heavy chains, *Comm. Acad. Sci. Imp. Petrop.* VI. (1732–1733) [Published 1738], pp. 108–122.

In reading some of the earlier papers on the subject, it should be remembered that the notation has changed, what was formerly written $J_n(z)$ being now written $J_n(2z)$.

Example 1.   Prove that if

$$\frac{2b\,(1+\theta^2)}{(1-2u\theta-\theta^2)^2 + 4b^2\theta^2} = A_1 + A_2\theta + A_3\theta^2 + \ldots,$$

then $e^{az}\sin bz = A_1 J_1(z) + A_2 J_2(z) + A_3 J_3(z) + \ldots$.

(Math. Trip. 1896.)

[For, if the contour D in the u-plane be a circle with centre $u=0$ and radius large enough to include the zeros of the denominator, we have

$$e^{\frac{1}{2}z\left(u-\frac{1}{u}\right)} \frac{2b\left(\dfrac{1}{u^2}+\dfrac{1}{u^4}\right)}{\left(1-\dfrac{2a}{u}-\dfrac{1}{u^2}\right)^2 + \dfrac{4b^2}{u^2}} = \sum_{n=1}^{\infty} e^{\frac{1}{2}z\left(u-\frac{1}{u}\right)} A_n u^{-n-1},$$

the series on the right converging uniformly on the contour; and so, using § 4·7 and replacing the integrals by Bessel coefficients, we have

$$\frac{1}{2\pi i}\int_D e^{\frac{1}{2}z\left(u-\frac{1}{u}\right)} \frac{2b\left(\dfrac{1}{u^2}+\dfrac{1}{u^4}\right)}{\left(1-\dfrac{2a}{u}-\dfrac{1}{u^2}\right)^2 + \dfrac{4b^2}{u^2}}\,du = \frac{1}{2\pi i}\int_D e^{\frac{1}{2}z\left(u-\frac{1}{u}\right)} \left(\frac{A_1}{u^2}+\frac{A_2}{u^3}+\frac{A_3}{u^4}+\ldots\right) du$$

$$= A_1 J_1(z) + A_2 J_2(z) + A_3 J_3(z) + \ldots.$$

* Published in *Leibnizens Ges. Werke*, Dritte Folge, III. (Halle, 1855), p. 75.

In the integral on the left write $\frac{1}{2}(u-u^{-1})-a=t$, so that as u describes a circle of radius e^{β}, t describes an ellipse with semiaxes $\cosh\beta$ and $\sinh\beta$ with foci at $-a\pm i$; then we have

$$\sum_{n=1}^{\infty} A_n J_n(z) = \frac{1}{2\pi i} \int \frac{e^{z(t+a)} b\, dt}{t^2+b^2},$$

the contour being the ellipse just specified, which contains the zeros of t^2+b^2. Evaluating the integral by § 6·1, we have the required result.]

Example 2. Shew that, when n is an integer,

$$J_n(y+z) = \sum_{m=-\infty}^{\infty} J_m(y) J_{n-m}(z).$$

(K. Neumann and Schläfli.)

[Consider the expansion of each side of the equation

$$\exp\left\{\tfrac{1}{2}(y+z)\left(t-\frac{1}{t}\right)\right\} = \exp\left\{\tfrac{1}{2}y\left(t-\frac{1}{t}\right)\right\}.\exp\left\{\tfrac{1}{2}z\left(t-\frac{1}{t}\right)\right\}.]$$

Example 3. Shew that

$$e^{iz\cos\phi} = J_0(z) + 2i\cos\phi J_1(z) + 2i^2\cos 2\phi J_2(z) + \dots.$$

Example 4. Shew that if $r^2 = x^2 + y^2$

$$J_0(r) = J_0(x)J_0(y) - 2J_2(x)J_2(y) + 2J_4(x)J_4(y) - \dots.$$

(K. Neumann and Lommel.)

17·11. *Bessel's differential equation.*

We have seen that, when n is an integer, the Bessel coefficient of order n is given by the formula

$$J_n(z) = \frac{1}{2\pi i}\left(\tfrac{1}{2}z\right)^n \int^{(0+)} t^{-n-1}\exp\left(t-\frac{z^2}{4t}\right) dt.$$

From this formula we shall now shew that $J_n(z)$ is a solution of the linear differential equation

$$\frac{d^2y}{dz^2} + \frac{1}{z}\frac{dy}{dz} + \left(1-\frac{n^2}{z^2}\right)y = 0,$$

which is called Bessel's equation for functions of order n.

For we find on performing the differentiations (§ 4·2) that

$$\frac{d^2 J_n(z)}{dz^2} + \frac{1}{z}\frac{dJ_n(z)}{dz} + \left(1-\frac{n^2}{z^2}\right)J_n(z)$$

$$= \frac{1}{2\pi i}\left(\tfrac{1}{2}z\right)^n \int^{(0+)} t^{-n-1}\left\{1-\frac{n+1}{t}+\frac{z^2}{4t^2}\right\}\exp\left(t-\frac{z^2}{4t}\right) dt$$

$$= -\frac{1}{2\pi i}\left(\tfrac{1}{2}z\right)^n \int^{(0+)} \frac{d}{dt}\left\{t^{-n-1}\exp\left(t-\frac{z^2}{4t}\right)\right\} dt$$

$$= 0,$$

since $t^{-n-1}\exp(t-z^2/4t)$ is one-valued. *Thus we have proved that*

$$\frac{d^2 J_n(z)}{dz^2} + \frac{1}{z}\frac{dJ_n(z)}{dz} + \left(1-\frac{n^2}{z^2}\right)J_n(z) = 0.$$

The reader will observe that $z=0$ is a regular point and $z=\infty$ an irregular point, all other points being ordinary points of this equation.

Example 1.   By differentiating the expansion

$$e^{\frac{1}{2}z\left(t-\frac{1}{t}\right)} = \sum_{n=-\infty}^{\infty} t^n J_n(z)$$

with regard to z and with regard to t, shew that the Bessel coefficients satisfy Bessel's equation.   (St John's, 1899.)

Example 2.   The function $P_n{}^m\left(1-\dfrac{z^2}{2n^2}\right)$ satisfies the equation defined by the scheme

$$P\left\{\begin{array}{ccc} 4n^2 & \infty & 0 \\ \frac{1}{2}m & n+1 & \frac{1}{2}m \quad z^2 \\ -\frac{1}{2}m & -n & -\frac{1}{2}m \end{array}\right\};$$

shew that $J_m(z)$ satisfies the confluent form of this equation obtained by making $n \to \infty$.

17·2.   *The solution of Bessel's equation when n is not necessarily an integer.*

We now proceed, after the manner of § 15·2, to extend the definition of $J_n(z)$ to the case when n is any number, real or complex.   It appears by methods similar to those of § 17·11 that, for all values of n, the equation

$$\frac{d^2y}{dz^2} + \frac{1}{z}\frac{dy}{dz} + \left(1-\frac{n^2}{z^2}\right)y = 0$$

is satisfied by an integral of the form

$$y = z^n \int_C t^{-n-1} \exp\left(t-\frac{z^2}{4t}\right)dt$$

provided that $t^{-n-1}\exp(t-z^2/4t)$ resumes its initial value after describing C and that differentiations under the sign of integration are justified.

Accordingly, we define $J_n(z)$ by the equation

$$J_n(z) = \frac{z^n}{2^{n+1}\pi i}\int_{-\infty}^{(0+)} t^{-n-1}\exp\left(t-\frac{z^2}{4t}\right)dt,$$

the expression being rendered precise by giving $\arg z$ its principal value and taking $|\arg t| \leqslant \pi$ on the contour.

To express this integral as a power series, we observe that it is an analytic function of z; and we may obtain the coefficients in the Taylor's series in powers of z by differentiating under the sign of integration (§§ 5·32 and 4·44).   Hence we deduce that

$$J_n(z) = \frac{z^n}{2^{n+1}\pi i}\sum_{r=0}^{\infty}\frac{(-)^r z^{2r}}{2^{2r}r!}\int_{-\infty}^{(0+)} e^t t^{-n-r-1}dt$$

$$= \sum_{r=0}^{\infty}\frac{(-)^r z^{n+2r}}{2^{n+2r}r!\,\Gamma(n+r+1)},$$

by § 12·22.   This is the expansion in question.

Accordingly, for general values of n, we define the Bessel function $J_n(z)$ *by the equations*

$$J_n(z) = \frac{1}{2\pi i} \cdot \left(\frac{1}{2}z\right)^n \int_{-\infty}^{(0+)} t^{-n-1} \exp\left(t - \frac{z^2}{4t}\right) dt$$

$$= \sum_{r=0}^{\infty} \frac{(-)^r z^{n+2r}}{2^{n+2r} r! \, \Gamma(n+r+1)}.$$

This function reduces to a Bessel coefficient when n is an integer; it is sometimes called a Bessel function *of the first kind.*

The reader will observe that since Bessel's equation is unaltered by writing $-n$ for n, fundamental· solutions are $J_n(z)$, $J_{-n}(z)$, except when n is an integer, in which case the solutions are not independent. With this exception *the general solution of Bessel's equation is*

$$\alpha J_n(z) + \beta J_{-n}(z),$$

where α *and* β *are arbitrary constants.*

A second solution of Bessel's equation when n is an integer will be given later (§ 17·6).

17·21. *The recurrence formulae for the Bessel functions.*

As the Bessel function satisfies a confluent form of the hypergeometric equation, it is to be expected that recurrence formulae will exist, corresponding to the relations between contiguous hypergeometric functions indicated in § 14·7.

To establish these relations for general values of n, real or complex, we have recourse to the result of § 17·2. On writing the equation

$$0 = \int_{-\infty}^{(0+)} \frac{d}{dt}\left\{t^{-n} \exp\left(t - \frac{z^2}{4t}\right)\right\} dt$$

at length, we have

$$0 = \int_{-\infty}^{(0+)} \left(t^{-n} + \frac{1}{4}z^2 t^{-n-2} - nt^{-n-1}\right) \exp\left(t - \frac{z^2}{4t}\right) dt$$

$$= 2\pi i \left\{(2z^{-1})^{n-1} J_{n-1}(z) + \frac{1}{4}z^2 (2z^{-1})^{n+1} J_{n+1}(z) - n(2z^{-1})^n J_n(z)\right\},$$

and so
$$J_{n-1}(z) + J_{n+1}(z) = \frac{2n}{z} J_n(z) \quad\quad\quad\quad \text{(A).}$$

Next we have, by § 4·44,

$$\frac{d}{dz}\{z^{-n} J_n(z)\} = \frac{1}{2^{n+1}\pi i} \frac{d}{dz} \int_{-\infty}^{(0+)} t^{-n-1} \exp\left(t - \frac{z^2}{4t}\right) dt$$

$$= -\frac{z}{2^{n+2}\pi i} \int_{-\infty}^{(0+)} t^{-n-2} \exp\left(t - \frac{z^2}{4t}\right) dt$$

$$= -z^{-n} J_{n+1}(z),$$

and consequently, if primes denote differentiations with regard to z,

$$J_n'(z) = \frac{n}{z} J_n(z) - J_{n+1}(z) \dots\dots\dots\dots\dots(B).$$

From (A) and (B) it is easy to derive the other recurrence formulae

$$J_n'(z) = \frac{1}{2} \{J_{n-1}(z) - J_{n+1}(z)\} \dots\dots\dots\dots(C),$$

and

$$J_n'(z) = J_{n-1}(z) - \frac{n}{z} J_n(z) \dots\dots\dots\dots(D).$$

Example 1. Obtain these results from the power series for $J_n(z)$.

Example 2. Shew that $\quad \dfrac{d}{dz} \{z^n J_n(z)\} = z^n J_{n-1}(z).$

Example 3. Shew that $\quad J_0'(z) = -J_1(z).$

Example 4. Shew that
$$16 J_n^{\mathrm{iv}}(z) = J_{n-4}(z) - 4J_{n-2}(z) + 6J_n(z) - 4J_{n+2}(z) + J_{n+4}(z).$$

Example 5. Shew that
$$J_2(z) - J_0(z) = 2J_0''(z).$$

Example 6. Shew that
$$J_2(z) = J_0''(z) - z^{-1} J_0'(z).$$

17·211. *Relation between two Bessel functions whose orders differ by an integer.*

From the last article can be deduced an equation connecting any two Bessel functions whose orders differ by an integer, namely

$$z^{-n-r} J_{n+r}(z) = (-)^r \frac{d^r}{(z\,dz)^r} \{z^{-n} J_n(z)\},$$

where n is unrestricted and r is any positive integer. This result follows at once by induction from formula (B), when it is written in the form

$$z^{-n-1} J_{n+1}(z) = -\frac{d}{z\,dz} \{z^{-n} J_n(z)\}.$$

17·212. *The connexion between $J_n(z)$ and $W_{k,m}$ functions.*

The reader will verify without difficulty that, if in Bessel's equation we write $y = z^{-\frac{1}{2}} v$ and then write $z = x/2i$, we get

$$\frac{d^2 v}{dx^2} + \left(-\frac{1}{4} + \frac{\frac{1}{4} - n^2}{x^2} \right) v = 0,$$

which is the equation satisfied by $W_{0,n}(x)$; it follows that

$$J_n(z) = A z^{-\frac{1}{2}} M_{0,n}(2iz) + B z^{-\frac{1}{2}} M_{0,-n}(2iz).$$

Comparing the coefficients of $z^{\pm n}$ on each side we see that

$$J_n(z) = \frac{z^{-\frac{1}{2}}}{2^{2n+\frac{1}{2}} i^{n+\frac{1}{2}} \Gamma(n+1)} M_{0,n}(2iz),$$

except in the critical cases when $2n$ is a negative integer; when n is half of a negative odd integer, the result follows from Kummer's second formula (§ 16·11).

17·22. *The zeros of Bessel functions whose order n is real.*

The relations of § 17·21 enable us to deduce the interesting theorem that *between any two consecutive real zeros of $z^{-n} J_n(z)$, there lies one and only one zero* of $z^{-n} J_{n+1}(z)$.

For, from relation (B) when written in the form

$$z^{-n} J_{n+1}(z) = -\frac{d}{dz}\{z^{-n} J_n(z)\},$$

it follows from Rolle's theorem† that between each consecutive pair of zeros of $z^{-n} J_n(z)$ there is at least one zero of $z^{-n} J_{n+1}(z)$.

Similarly, from relation (D) when written in the form

$$z^{n+1} J_n(z) = \frac{d}{dz}\{z^{n+1} J_{n+1}(z)\},$$

it follows that between each consecutive pair of zeros of $z^{n+1} J_{n+1}(z)$ there is at least one zero of $z^{n+1} J_n(z)$.

Further $z^{-n} J_n(z)$ and $\dfrac{d}{dz}\{z^{-n} J_n(z)\}$ have no common zeros; for the former function satisfies the equation

$$z\frac{d^2 y}{dz^2} + (2n+1)\frac{dy}{dz} + zy = 0,$$

and it is easily verified by induction on differentiating this equation that if both y and $\dfrac{dy}{dz}$ vanish for any value of z, all differential coefficients of y vanish, and y is zero by § 5·4.

The theorem required is now obvious except for the numerically smallest zeros $\pm \xi$ of $z^{-n} J_n(z)$, since (except for $z = 0$), $z^{-n} J_n(z)$ and $z^{n+1} J_n(z)$ have the same zeros. But $z = 0$ is a zero of $z^{-n} J_{n+1}(z)$, and if there were any other positive zero of $z^{-n} J_{n+1}(z)$, say ξ_1, which was less than ξ, then $z^{n+1} J_n(z)$ would have a zero between 0 and ξ_1, which contradicts the hypothesis that there were no zeros of $z^{n+1} J_n(z)$ between 0 and ξ.

The theorem is therefore proved.

[See also § 17·3 examples 3 and 4, and example 19 at the end of the chapter.]

---

* Proofs of this theorem have been given by Bôcher, *Bull. American Math. Soc.* IV. (1897), p. 206; Gegenbauer, *Monatshefte für Math.* VIII. (1897), p. 383; and Porter, *Bull. American Math. Soc.* IV. (1898), p. 274.

† This is proved in Burnside and Panton's *Theory of Equations* (I. p. 157) for polynomials. It may be deduced for any functions with continuous differential coefficients by using the First Mean Value Theorem (§ 4·14).

17·23. *Bessel's integral for the Bessel coefficients.*

We shall next obtain an integral first given by Bessel in the particular case of the Bessel functions for which n is a positive integer; in some respects the result resembles Laplace's integrals given in § 15·23 and § 15·33 for the Legendre functions.

In the integral of § 17·1, viz.

$$J_n(z) = \frac{1}{2\pi i} \int^{(0+)} u^{-n-1} e^{\frac{1}{2}z\left(u - \frac{1}{u}\right)} du,$$

take the contour to be the circle $|u| = 1$ and write $u = e^{i\theta}$, so that

$$J_n(z) = \frac{1}{2\pi} \int_{-\pi}^{\pi} e^{-ni\theta + iz\sin\theta} d\theta.$$

Bisect the range of integration and in the former part write $-\theta$ for θ; we get

$$J_n(z) = \frac{1}{2\pi} \int_0^{\pi} e^{ni\theta - iz\sin\theta} d\theta + \frac{1}{2\pi} \int_0^{\pi} e^{-ni\theta + iz\sin\theta} d\theta,$$

and so
$$J_n(z) = \frac{1}{\pi} \int_0^{\pi} \cos(n\theta - z\sin\theta)\, d\theta,$$

which is the formula in question.

Example 1. Shew that, when z is real and n is an integer,
$$|J_n(z)| \leqslant 1.$$

Example 2. Shew that, for all values of n (real or complex), the integral
$$y = \frac{1}{\pi} \int_0^{\pi} \cos(n\theta - z\sin\theta)\, d\theta$$
satisfies
$$\frac{d^2 y}{dz^2} + \frac{1}{z}\frac{dy}{dz} + \left(1 - \frac{n^2}{z^2}\right) y = \frac{\sin n\pi}{\pi}\left(\frac{1}{z} - \frac{n}{z^2}\right),$$
which reduces to Bessel's equation when n is an integer.

[It is easy to shew, by differentiating under the integral sign, that the expression on the left is equal to
$$-\frac{1}{\pi} \int_0^{\pi} \frac{d}{d\theta}\left\{\left(\frac{n}{z^2} + \frac{\cos\theta}{z}\right) \sin(n\theta - z\sin\theta)\right\} d\theta.]$$

17·231. *The modification of Bessel's integral when n is not an integer.*

We shall now shew that[*], for general values of n,

$$J_n(z) = \frac{1}{\pi} \int_0^{\pi} \cos(n\theta - z\sin\theta)\, d\theta - \frac{\sin n\pi}{\pi} \int_0^{\infty} e^{-n\theta - z\sinh\theta}\, d\theta \quad \ldots(A),$$

when $R(z) > 0$. This obviously reduces to the result of § 17·23 when n is an integer.

Taking the integral of § 17·2, viz.

$$J_n(z) = \frac{z^n}{2^{n+1}\pi i} \int_{-\infty}^{(0+)} t^{-n-1} \exp\left(t - \frac{z^2}{4t}\right) dt,$$

---

[*] This result is due to Schläfli, *Math. Ann.* III. (1871), p. 148.

and supposing that z is positive, we have, on writing $t = \frac{1}{2} uz$,

$$J_n(z) = \frac{1}{2\pi i} \int_{-\infty}^{(0+)} u^{-n-1} \exp\left\{\frac{1}{2} z \left(u - \frac{1}{u}\right)\right\} du.$$

But, if the contour be taken to be that of the figure consisting of the real axis from -1 to $-\infty$ taken twice and the circle $|u| = 1$, this integral represents an analytic function of z when $R(zu)$ is negative as $|u| \to \infty$ on the path, i.e. when $|\arg z| < \frac{1}{2}\pi$; and so, by the theory of analytic continuation, the formula (which has been proved by a direct transformation for *positive* values of z) is true whenever $R(z) > 0$.

Hence

$$J_n(z) = \frac{1}{2\pi i} \left\{ \int_{-\infty}^{-1} + \int_C + \int_{-1}^{-\infty} \right\} u^{-n-1} \exp\left\{\frac{1}{2} z \left(u - \frac{1}{u}\right)\right\} du,$$

where C denotes the circle $|u| = 1$, and $\arg u = -\pi$ on the first path of integration while $\arg u = +\pi$ on the third path.

Writing $u = te^{\mp\pi i}$ in the first and third integrals respectively (so that in each case $\arg t = 0$), and $u = e^{i\theta}$ in the second, we have

$$J_n(z) = \frac{1}{2\pi} \int_{-\pi}^{\pi} e^{-ni\theta + iz\sin\theta} d\theta + \left\{\frac{e^{(n+1)\pi i}}{2\pi i} - \frac{e^{-(n+1)\pi i}}{2\pi i}\right\} \int_1^\infty t^{-n-1} e^{\frac{1}{2} z \left(-t + \frac{1}{t}\right)} dt.$$

Modifying the former of these integrals as in § 17·23 and writing e^θ for t in the latter, we have at once

$$J_n(z) = \frac{1}{\pi} \int_0^\pi \cos(n\theta - z\sin\theta) d\theta + \frac{\sin(n+1)\pi}{\pi} \int_0^\infty e^{-n\theta - z\sinh\theta} d\theta,$$

which is the required result, when $|\arg z| < \frac{1}{2}\pi$.

When $|\arg z|$ lies between $\frac{1}{2}\pi$ and π, since $J_n(z) = e^{\pm n\pi i} J_n(-z)$, we have

$$J_n(z) = \frac{e^{\pm n\pi i}}{\pi} \left\{ \int_0^\pi \cos(n\theta + z\sin\theta) d\theta - \sin n\pi \int_0^\infty e^{-n\theta + z\sinh\theta} d\theta \right\} \quad \ldots\ldots \text{(B)},$$

the upper or lower sign being taken as $\arg z > \frac{1}{2}\pi$ or $< -\frac{1}{2}\pi$.

When n is an integer (A) reduces at once to Bessel's integral, and (B) does so when we make use of the equation $J_n(z) = (-)^n J_{-n}(z)$, which is true for integer values of n.

Equation (A), as already stated, is due to Schläfli, *Math. Ann.* III. (1871), p. 148, and equation (B) was given by Sonine, *Math. Ann.* XVI. (1880), p. 14.

These trigonometric integrals for the Bessel functions may be regarded as corresponding to Laplace's integrals for the Legendre functions. For (§ 17·11 example 2) $J_m(z)$ satisfies the confluent form (obtained by making $n \to \infty$) of the equation for $P_n{}^m (1 - z^2/2n^2)$.

But Laplace's integral for this function is a multiple of

$$\int_0^\pi \left[1 - \frac{z^2}{2n^2} + \left\{ \left(1 - \frac{z^2}{2n^2} \right)^2 - 1 \right\}^{\frac{1}{2}} \cos \phi \right]^n \cos m\phi \, d\phi$$

$$= \int_0^\pi \left\{ 1 + \frac{iz}{n} \cos \phi + O\left(n^{-2}\right) \right\}^n \cos m\phi \, d\phi.$$

The limit of the integrand as $n \to \infty$ is $e^{iz\cos\phi} \cos m\phi$, and this exhibits the similarity of Laplace's integral for $P_n{}^m(z)$ to the Bessel-Schläfli integral for $J_m(z)$.

Example 1. From the formula $J_0(x) = \dfrac{1}{2\pi} \displaystyle\int_{-\pi}^\pi e^{-ix\cos\phi} \, d\phi$, by a change of order of integration, shew that, when n is a positive integer and $\cos\theta > 0$,

$$P_n(\cos\theta) = \frac{1}{\Gamma(n+1)} \int_0^\infty e^{-x\cos\theta} J_0(x\sin\theta)\, x^n \, dx.$$

(Callandreau, *Bull. des Sci. Math.* (2), XV. (1891), p. 121.)

Example 2. Shew that, with Ferrers' definition of $P_n{}^m(\cos\theta)$,

$$P_n{}^m(\cos\theta) = \frac{1}{\Gamma(n-m+1)} \int_0^\infty e^{-x\cos\theta} J_m(x\sin\theta)\, x^n \, dx$$

when n and m are positive integers and $\cos\theta > 0$.

(Hobson, *Proc. London Math. Soc.* XXV. (1894), p. 49.)

17·24. *Bessel functions whose order is half an odd integer.*

We have seen (§ 17·2) that when the order n of a Bessel function $J_n(z)$ is half an odd integer, the difference of the roots of the indicial equation at $z = 0$ is $2n$, which is an integer. We now shew that, in such cases, $J_n(z)$ is expressible in terms of elementary functions.

For $\qquad J_{\frac{1}{2}}(z) = \dfrac{2^{\frac{1}{2}} z^{\frac{1}{2}}}{\pi^{\frac{1}{2}}} \left\{ 1 - \dfrac{z^2}{2 \cdot 3} + \dfrac{z^4}{2 \cdot 3 \cdot 4 \cdot 5} - \ldots \right\} = \left(\dfrac{2}{\pi z} \right)^{\frac{1}{2}} \sin z,$

and therefore (§ 17·211) if k is a positive integer

$$J_{k+\frac{1}{2}}(z) = \frac{(-)^k (2z)^{k+\frac{1}{2}}}{\pi^{\frac{1}{2}}} \frac{d^k}{d(z^2)^k} \left(\frac{\sin z}{z} \right).$$

On differentiating out the expression on the right, we obtain the result that

$$J_{k+\frac{1}{2}}(z) = P_k \sin z + Q_k \cos z,$$

where P_k, Q_k are polynomials in $z^{-\frac{1}{2}}$.

Example 1. Shew that $J_{-\frac{1}{2}}(z) = \left(\dfrac{2}{\pi z} \right)^{\frac{1}{2}} \cos z.$

Example 2. Prove by induction that if k be an integer and $n = k + \frac{1}{2}$, then

$$J_n(z) = \left(\frac{2}{\pi z}\right)^{\frac{1}{2}} \left[\cos\left(z - \tfrac{1}{2}n\pi - \tfrac{1}{4}\pi\right) \left\{ 1 + \sum_{r=1} \frac{(-)^r (4n^2 - 1^2)(4n^2 - 3^2) \dots \{4n^2 - (4r-1)^2\}}{(2r)! \ 2^{6r} z^{2r}} \right\}\right.$$

$$\left. + \sin\left(z - \tfrac{1}{2}n\pi - \tfrac{1}{4}\pi\right) \sum_{r=1} \frac{(-)^r (4n^2 - 1^2)(4n^2 - 3^2) \dots \{4n^2 - (4r-3)^2\}}{(2r-1)! \ 2^{6r-3} z^{2r-1}} \right],$$

the summations being continued as far as the terms with the vanishing factors in the numerators.

Example 3. Shew that $z^{k+\frac{1}{2}} \dfrac{d^k}{d(z^2)^k}\left(\dfrac{\cos z}{z}\right)$ is a solution of Bessel's equation for $J_{k+\frac{1}{2}}(z)$.

Example 4. Shew that the solution of $z^{m+\frac{1}{2}} \dfrac{d^{2m+1} y}{dz^{2m+1}} + y = 0$ is

$$y = z^{\frac{1}{2}m + \frac{1}{4}} \sum_{p=0}^{2m} c_p \{ J_{-m-\frac{1}{2}}(2a_p z^{\frac{1}{2}}) + i J_{m+\frac{1}{2}}(2a_p z^{\frac{1}{2}}) \},$$

where $c_0, c_1, \dots c_{2m}$ are arbitrary and $a_0, a_1, \dots a_{2m}$ are the roots of

$$a^{2m+1} = i. \qquad\qquad\qquad \text{(Lommel.)}$$

17·3. *Hankel's contour integral* for $J_n(z)$.

Consider the integral

$$y = z^n \int_A^{(1+, -1-)} (t^2 - 1)^{n - \frac{1}{2}} \cos(zt)\, dt,$$

where A is a point on the right of the point $t = 1$, and

$$\arg(t - 1) = \arg(t + 1) = 0$$

at A; the contour may conveniently be regarded as being in the shape of a figure of eight.

We shall shew that this integral is a constant multiple of $J_n(z)$. It is easily seen that the integrand returns to its initial value after t has described the path of integration; for $(t - 1)^{n - \frac{1}{2}}$ is multiplied by the factor $e^{(2n-1)\pi i}$ after the circuit $(1+)$ has been described, and $(t + 1)^{n - \frac{1}{2}}$ is multiplied by the factor $e^{-(2n-1)\pi i}$ after the circuit $(-1-)$ has been described.

Since

$$\sum_{r=0}^{\infty} \frac{(-)^r (zt)^{2r}}{(2r)!} (t^2 - 1)^{n - \frac{1}{2}}$$

converges uniformly on the contour, we have (§ 4·7)

$$y = \sum_{r=0}^{\infty} \frac{(-)^r z^{n+2r}}{(2r)!} \int_A^{(1+, -1-)} t^{2r} (t^2 - 1)^{n - \frac{1}{2}}\, dt.$$

To evaluate these integrals, we observe firstly that they are analytic functions of n for all values of n, and secondly that, when $R\left(n + \frac{1}{2}\right) > 0$, we may deform the contour into the circles $|t - 1| = \delta$, $|t + 1| = \delta$ and the real axis joining the points $t = \pm(1 - \delta)$ taken twice, and then we may make $\delta \to 0$; the integrals round the circles tend to zero and, assigning to $t - 1$

---

* *Math. Ann.* i. (1869), pp. 467–501.

and $t + 1$ their appropriate arguments on the modified path of integration, we get, if $\arg(1 - t^2) = 0$ and $t^2 = u$,

$$\int_A^{(1+, -1-)} t^{2r} (t^2 - 1)^{n - \frac{1}{2}} dt$$

$$= e^{(n - \frac{1}{2})\pi i} \int_1^{-1} t^{2r} (1 - t^2)^{n - \frac{1}{2}} dt + e^{-(n - \frac{1}{2})\pi i} \int_{-1}^1 t^{2r} (1 - t^2)^{n - \frac{1}{2}} dt$$

$$= -4i \sin \left(n - \frac{1}{2} \right) \pi \int_0^1 t^{2r} (1 - t^2)^{n - \frac{1}{2}} dt$$

$$= -2i \sin \left(n - \frac{1}{2} \right) \pi \int_0^1 u^{r - \frac{1}{2}} (1 - u)^{n - \frac{1}{2}} du$$

$$= 2i \sin \left(n + \frac{1}{2} \right) \pi \Gamma \left(r + \frac{1}{2} \right) \Gamma \left(n + \frac{1}{2} \right) \Big/ \Gamma (n + r + 1).$$

Since the initial and final expressions are analytic functions of n for all values of n, it follows from § 5·5 that this equation, proved when

$$R \left(n + \frac{1}{2} \right) > 0,$$

is true for all values of n.

Accordingly

$$y = \sum_{r=0}^{\infty} \frac{(-)^r z^{n+2r} 2i \sin \left(n + \frac{1}{2} \right) \pi \Gamma \left(r + \frac{1}{2} \right) \Gamma \left(n + \frac{1}{2} \right)}{(2r)! \, \Gamma (n + r + 1)}$$

$$= 2^{n+1} i \sin \left(n + \frac{1}{2} \right) \pi \Gamma \left(n + \frac{1}{2} \right) \Gamma \left(\frac{1}{2} \right) J_n (z),$$

on reduction.

Accordingly, when $\left\{ \Gamma \left(\frac{1}{2} - n \right) \right\}^{-1} \neq 0$, *we have*

$$J_n (z) = \frac{\Gamma \left(\frac{1}{2} - n \right) \left(\frac{1}{2} z \right)^n}{2\pi i \Gamma \left(\frac{1}{2} \right)} \int_A^{(1+, -1-)} (t^2 - 1)^{n - \frac{1}{2}} \cos (zt) \, dt.$$

Corollary. When $R \left(n + \frac{1}{2} \right) > 0$, we may deform the path of integration, and obtain the result

$$J_n (z) = \frac{\left(\frac{1}{2} z \right)^n}{\Gamma \left(n + \frac{1}{2} \right) \Gamma \left(\frac{1}{2} \right)} \int_{-1}^1 (1 - t^2)^{n - \frac{1}{2}} \cos (zt) \, dt$$

$$= \frac{2 \cdot \left(\frac{1}{2} z \right)^n}{\Gamma \left(n + \frac{1}{2} \right) \Gamma \left(\frac{1}{2} \right)} \int_0^{\frac{1}{2}\pi} \sin^{2n} \phi \cos (z \cos \phi) \, d\phi.$$

Example 1. Shew that, when $R \left(n + \frac{1}{2} \right) > 0$,

$$J_n (z) = \frac{\left(\frac{1}{2} z \right)^n}{\Gamma \left(n + \frac{1}{2} \right) \Gamma \left(\frac{1}{2} \right)} \int_0^{\pi} e^{\pm iz \cos \phi} \sin^{2n} \phi \, d\phi.$$

Example 2. Obtain the result

$$J_n (z) = \frac{\left(\frac{1}{2} z \right)^n}{\Gamma \left(n + \frac{1}{2} \right) \Gamma \left(\frac{1}{2} \right)} \int_0^{\pi} \cos (z \cos \phi) \sin^{2n} \phi \, d\phi,$$

when $R (n) > 0$, by expanding in powers of z and integrating (§ 4·7) term-by-term.

Example 3. Shew that when $-\frac{1}{2} < n < \frac{1}{2}$, $J_n(z)$ has an infinite number of real zeros.

[Let $z = (m + \frac{1}{2})\pi$ where m is zero or a positive integer; then by the corollary above

$$J_n(m\pi + \tfrac{1}{2}\pi) = \frac{z^n}{2^{n-1}\,\Gamma(n + \frac{1}{2})\,\Gamma(\frac{1}{2})}\,\{\tfrac{1}{2}u_0 - u_1 + u_2 - \ldots + (-)^m u_m\},$$

where

$$u_r = \left| \int_{\frac{2r-1}{2m+1}}^{\frac{2r+1}{2m+1}} (1 - t^2)^{n-\frac{1}{2}} \cos\{(m + \tfrac{1}{2})\pi t\}\,dt \right|$$

$$= \int_0^{1/(m+\frac{1}{2})} \left\{ 1 - \left(t + \frac{2r-1}{2m+1} \right)^2 \right\}^{n-\frac{1}{2}} \sin\{(m + \tfrac{1}{2})\pi t\}\,dt,$$

so, since $n - \frac{1}{2} < 0$, $u_m > u_{m-1} > u_{m-2} > \ldots$, and hence $J_n(m\pi + \tfrac{1}{2}\pi)$ has the sign of $(-)^m$. This method of proof for $n = 0$ is due to Bessel.]

Example 4. Shew that if n be real, $J_n(z)$ has an infinite number of real zeros; and find an upper limit to the numerically smallest of them.

[Use example 3 combined with § 17·22.]

17·4. *Connexion between Bessel coefficients and Legendre functions.*

We shall now establish a result due to Heine* which renders precise the statement of § 17·11 example 2, concerning the expression of Bessel coefficients as limiting forms of hypergeometric functions.

When $|\arg(1 \pm z)| < \pi$, n is unrestricted and m is a positive integer, it follows by differentiating the formula of § 15·22 that, with Ferrers' definition of $P_n{}^m(z)$,

$$P_n{}^m(z) = \frac{\Gamma(n + m + 1)}{2^m \cdot m!\,\Gamma(n - m + 1)} (1 - z)^{\frac{1}{2}m} (1 + z)^{\frac{1}{2}m}\,F(-n + m,\ n + 1 + m;\ m + 1;\ \tfrac{1}{2} - \tfrac{1}{2}z),$$

and so, if $|\arg z| < \frac{1}{2}\pi$, $|\arg(1 - \frac{1}{4}z^2/n^2)| < \pi$, we have

$$P_n{}^m\left(1 - \frac{z^2}{2n^2}\right) = \frac{\Gamma(n + m + 1)\,z^m\,n^{-m}}{2^m \cdot m!\,\Gamma(n - m + 1)} \left(1 - \frac{z^2}{4n^2}\right)^{\frac{1}{2}m} F(-n + m,\ n + 1 + m;\ m + 1;\ \tfrac{1}{4}z^2 n^{-2}).$$

Now make $n \to +\infty$ (n being positive, but not necessarily integral), so that, if $\delta = n^{-1}$, $\delta \to 0$ continuously through positive values.

Then $\dfrac{\Gamma(n + m + 1)\,n^{-m}}{\Gamma(n - m + 1)\,n^m} \to 1$, by § 13·6, and $\left(1 - \dfrac{z^2}{4n^2}\right)^{\frac{1}{2}m} \to 1$.

Further, the $(r + 1)$th term of the hypergeometric series is

$$\frac{(-)^r(1 - m\delta)(1 + m\delta + r\delta)\{1 - (m+1)^2\delta^2\}\{1 - (m+2)^2\delta^2\}\ldots\{1 - (m + r - 1)^2\delta^2\}}{(m+1)(m+2)\ldots(m+r) \cdot r!}\,(\tfrac{1}{2}z)^{2r};$$

this is a continuous function of δ and the series of which this is the $(r + 1)$th term is easily seen to converge uniformly in a range of values of δ including the point $\delta = 0$; so, by § 3·32, we have

$$\lim_{n \to \infty} \left[n^{-m} P_n{}^m\left(1 - \frac{z^2}{2n^2}\right) \right] = \frac{z^m}{2^m \cdot m!} \sum_{r=0}^{\infty} \frac{(-)^r(\tfrac{1}{2}z)^r}{(m+1)(m+2)\ldots(m+r)\,r!}$$

$$= J_m(z),$$

which is the relation required.

Example 1. Shew that†

$$\lim_{n \to \infty} \left[n^{-m} P_n{}^m\left(\cos \frac{z}{n}\right) \right] = J_m(z).$$

---

* The apparently different result given in Heine's *Kugelfunktionen* is due to the difference between Heine's associated Legendre function and Ferrers' function.

† The special case of this when $m = 0$ was given by Mehler, *Journal für Math.* LXVIII. (1868), p. 140; see also *Math. Ann.* v. (1872), pp. 141–144.

Example 2. Shew that Bessel's equation is the confluent form of the equations defined by the schemes

$$P \left\{ \begin{matrix} 0 & \infty & c \\ n & ic & \frac{1}{2}+ic & z \\ -n & -ic & \frac{1}{2}-ic \end{matrix} \right\}, \quad e^{iz} P \left\{ \begin{matrix} 0 & \infty & c \\ n & \frac{1}{2} & 0 & z \\ -n & \frac{3}{2}-2ic & 2ic-1 \end{matrix} \right\}, \quad P \left\{ \begin{matrix} 0 & \infty & c^2 \\ \frac{1}{2}n & \frac{1}{2}(c-n) & 0 & z^2 \\ -\frac{1}{2}n & -\frac{1}{2}(c+n) & n+1 \end{matrix} \right\},$$

the confluence being obtained by making $c \to \infty$.

17·5. *Asymptotic series for $J_n(z)$ when $|z|$ is large.*

We have seen (§ 17·212) that

$$J_n(z) = \frac{z^{-\frac{1}{2}}}{2^{2n+\frac{1}{2}} e^{\frac{1}{2}(n+\frac{1}{2})\pi i} \Gamma(n+1)} M_{0,n}(2iz),$$

where it is supposed that $|\arg z| < \pi$, $-\frac{1}{2}\pi < \arg(2iz) < \frac{3}{2}\pi$.

But for this range of values of z

$$M_{0,n}(2iz) = \frac{\Gamma(2n+1)}{\Gamma(\frac{1}{2}+n)} e^{(n+\frac{1}{2})\pi i} W_{0,n}(2iz) + \frac{\Gamma(2n+1)}{\Gamma(\frac{1}{2}+n)} W_{0,n}(-2iz)$$

by § 16·41 example 2, if $-\frac{3}{2}\pi < \arg(-2iz) < \frac{1}{2}\pi$; and so, when $|\arg z| < \pi$,

$$J_n(z) = \frac{1}{(2\pi z)^{\frac{1}{2}}} \{ e^{\frac{1}{2}(n+\frac{1}{2})\pi i} W_{0,n}(2iz) + e^{-\frac{1}{2}(n+\frac{1}{2})\pi i} W_{0,n}(-2iz) \}.$$

But, for the values of z under consideration, the asymptotic expansion of $W_{0,n}(\pm 2iz)$ is

$$e^{\mp iz} \left\{ 1 \pm \frac{(4n^2-1^2)}{8iz} + \frac{(4n^2-1^2)(4n^2-3^2)}{2!(8iz)^2} \pm \cdots \right.$$

$$\left. + \frac{(\pm 1)^r \{4n^2-1^2\}\{4n^2-3^2\} \cdots \{4n^2-(2r-1)^2\}}{r!(8iz)^r} + O(z^{-r}) \right\},$$

and therefore, combining the series, the asymptotic expansion of $J_n(z)$, when $|z|$ is large and $|\arg z| < \pi$, is

$$J_n(z) \sim \left(\frac{2}{\pi z}\right)^{\frac{1}{2}} \left[\cos\left(z - \frac{1}{2}n\pi - \frac{1}{4}\pi\right) \right.$$

$$\times \left\{ 1 + \sum_{r=1}^{\infty} \frac{(-)^r \{4n^2-1^2\}\{4n^2-3^2\} \cdots \{4n^2-(4r-1)^2\}}{(2r)! \, 2^{6r} \, z^{2r}} \right\}$$

$$\left. + \sin\left(z - \frac{1}{2}n\pi - \frac{1}{4}\pi\right) \sum_{r=1}^{\infty} \frac{(-)^r \{4n^2-1^2\}\{4n^2-3^2\} \cdots \{4n^2-(4r-3)^2\}}{(2r-1)! \, 2^{6r-3} \, z^{2r-1}} \right]$$

$$= \left(\frac{2}{\pi z}\right)^{\frac{1}{2}} \left[\cos\left(z - \frac{1}{2}n\pi - \frac{1}{4}\pi\right).U_n(z) - \sin\left(z - \frac{1}{2}n\pi - \frac{1}{4}\pi\right).V_n(z) \right],$$

where $U_n(z)$, $-V_n(z)$ have been written in place of the series.

The reader will observe that if n is half an odd integer these series terminate and give the result of § 17·24 example 2.

Even when z is not very large, the value of $J_n(z)$ can be computed with great accuracy from this formula. Thus, for all positive values of z greater than 8, the first three terms of the asymptotic expansion give the value of $J_0(z)$ and $J_1(z)$ to six places of decimals.

This asymptotic expansion was given by Poisson* (for $n=0$) and by Jacobi† (for general integral values of n) for real values of z. Complex values of z were considered by Hankel‡ and several subsequent writers. The method of obtaining the expansion here given is due to Barnes§.

Asymptotic expansions for $J_n(z)$ when the order n is large have been given by Debye (*Math. Ann.* LXVII. (1909), pp. 535–558, *Münchener Sitzungsberichte*, XL. (1910), no. 5) and Nicholson (*Phil. Mag.* 1907).

An approximate formula for $J_n(nx)$ when n is large and $0 < x < 1$, namely

$$\frac{x^n \exp\{n \sqrt{(1-x^2)}\}}{(2\pi n)^{\frac{1}{2}} (1-x^2)^{\frac{1}{4}} \{1+\sqrt{(1-x^2)}\}^n},$$

was obtained by Carlini in 1817 in a memoir reprinted in Jacobi's *Ges. Werke*, VII. pp. 189–245. The formula was also investigated by Laplace in 1827 in his *Mécanique Céleste* v. supplément [*Oeuvres*, v. (1882)] on the hypothesis that x is purely imaginary.

A more extended account of researches on Bessel functions of large order is given in *Proc. London Math. Soc.* (2), XVI. (1917), pp. 150–174.

Example 1.   By suitably modifying Hankel's contour integral (§ 17·3), shew that, when $|\arg z| < \frac{1}{2}\pi$ and $R(n+\frac{1}{2}) > 0$,

$$J_n(z) = \frac{1}{\Gamma(n+\frac{1}{2})(2\pi z)^{\frac{1}{2}}} \left[e^{i(z-\frac{1}{2}n\pi-\frac{1}{4}\pi)} \int_0^\infty e^{-u} u^{n-\frac{1}{2}} \left(1+\frac{iu}{2z}\right)^{n-\frac{1}{2}} du \right.$$
$$\left. + e^{-i(z-\frac{1}{2}n\pi-\frac{1}{4}\pi)} \int_0^\infty e^{-u} u^{n-\frac{1}{2}} \left(1-\frac{iu}{2z}\right)^{n-\frac{1}{2}} du \right];$$

and deduce the asymptotic expansion of $J_n(z)$ when $|z|$ is large and $|\arg z| < \frac{1}{2}\pi$.

[Take the contour to be the rectangle whose corners are ± 1, $\pm 1 + iN$, the rectangle being indented at ± 1, and make $N \to \infty$; the integrand being $(1-t^2)^{n-\frac{1}{2}} e^{izt}$.]

Example 2.   Shew that, when $|\arg z| < \frac{1}{2}\pi$ and $R(n+\frac{1}{2}) > 0$,

$$J_n(z) = \frac{2^{n+1} z^n}{\Gamma(n+\frac{1}{2})\pi^{\frac{1}{2}}} \int_0^{\frac{1}{2}\pi} e^{-2z\cot\phi} \cos^{n-\frac{1}{2}}\phi \operatorname{cosec}^{2n+1}\phi \sin\{z-(n-\frac{1}{2})\phi\} d\phi.$$

[Write $u = 2z\cot\phi$ in the preceding example.]

Example 3.   Shew that, if $|\arg z| < \frac{1}{2}\pi$ and $R(n+\frac{1}{2}) > 0$, then

$$A e^{iz} z^n \int_0^\infty v^{n-\frac{1}{2}} (1+iv)^{n-\frac{1}{2}} e^{-2vz} dv + B e^{-iz} z^n \int_0^\infty v^{n-\frac{1}{2}} (1-iv)^{n-\frac{1}{2}} e^{-2vz} dv$$

is a solution of Bessel's equation.

Further, determine A and B so that this may represent $J_n(z)$.

(Schafheitlin, *Journal für Math.* CXIV.)

17·6.   *The second solution of Bessel's equation when the order is an integer.*

We have seen in § 17·2 that, when the order n of Bessel's differential equation is not an integer, the general solution of the equation is

$$\alpha J_n(z) + \beta J_{-n}(z),$$

where α and β are arbitrary constants.

* *Journal de l'École Polytechnique* (1), cah. 19 (1823), p. 350.
† *Astr. Nach.* XXVIII. p. 94.
‡ *Math. Ann.* I. (1869), pp. 467–501.
§ *Trans. Camb. Phil. Soc.* XX. (1908), p. 274.

When, however, n is an integer, we have seen that

$$J_n(z) = (-)^n J_{-n}(z),$$

and consequently the two solutions $J_n(z)$ and $J_{-n}(z)$ are not really distinct. We therefore require in this case to find another particular solution of the differential equation, distinct from $J_n(z)$, in order to have the general solution.

We shall now consider the function

$$\mathsf{Y}_n(z) = 2\pi e^{n\pi i} \frac{J_n(z)\cos n\pi - J_{-n}(z)}{\sin 2n\pi},$$

which is a solution of Bessel's equation when $2n$ is not an integer. The introduction of this function $\mathsf{Y}_n(z)$ is due to Hankel*.

When n is an integer, $\mathsf{Y}_n(z)$ is defined by the limiting form of this equation, namely

$$\mathsf{Y}_n(z) = \lim_{\epsilon \to 0} 2\pi e^{(n+\epsilon)\pi i} \frac{J_{n+\epsilon}(z)\cos(n\pi + \epsilon\pi) - J_{-n-\epsilon}(z)}{\sin 2(n+\epsilon)\pi}$$

$$= \lim_{\epsilon \to 0} \frac{2\pi e^{n\pi i}}{\sin 2\epsilon\pi} \{J_{n+\epsilon}(z).(-)^n - J_{-n-\epsilon}(z)\}$$

$$= \lim_{\epsilon \to 0} \epsilon^{-1} \{J_{n+\epsilon}(z) - (-)^n J_{-n-\epsilon}(z)\}.$$

To express $\mathsf{Y}_n(z)$ in terms of $W_{k,m}$ functions, we have recourse to the result of § 17·5, which gives

$$\mathsf{Y}_n(z) = \lim_{\epsilon \to 0} \frac{\epsilon^{-1}}{(2\pi z)^{\frac{1}{2}}} \left[\{e^{\frac{1}{2}(n+\epsilon+\frac{1}{2})\pi i} W_{0,n+\epsilon}(2iz) + e^{-\frac{1}{2}(n+\epsilon+\frac{1}{2})\pi i} W_{0,n+\epsilon}(-2iz)\} \right.$$

$$\left. -(-)^n \{e^{\frac{1}{2}(-n-\epsilon+\frac{1}{2})\pi i} W_{0,n+\epsilon}(2iz) + e^{-\frac{1}{2}(-n-\epsilon+\frac{1}{2})\pi i} W_{0,n+\epsilon}(-2iz)\} \right],$$

remembering that $W_{k,m} = W_{k,-m}$.

Hence, since† $\lim\limits_{\epsilon \to 0} W_{0,n+\epsilon}(2iz) = W_{0,n}(2iz)$, we have

$$\mathsf{Y}_n(z) = \left(\frac{\pi}{2z}\right)^{\frac{1}{2}} \{e^{(\frac{1}{2}n+\frac{3}{4})\pi i} W_{0,n}(2iz) + e^{-(\frac{1}{2}n+\frac{3}{4})\pi i} W_{0,n}(-2iz)\}.$$

This function (n being an integer) is obviously a solution of Bessel's equation; it is called a *Bessel function of the second kind*.

Another function (also called a function of the second kind) was first used by Weber, *Math. Ann.* VI. (1873), p. 148 and by Schläfli, *Ann. di Mat.* (2), VI. (1875), p. 17 ; it is defined by the equation

$$Y_n(z) = \frac{J_n(z)\cos n\pi - J_{-n}(z)}{\sin n\pi} = \frac{\mathsf{Y}_n(z)\cos n\pi}{\pi e^{n\pi i}},$$

* *Math. Ann.* I. (1869), p. 472.

† This is most easily seen from the uniformity of the convergence with regard to ϵ of Barnes' contour integral (§ 16·4) for $W_{0,n+\epsilon}(2iz)$.

or by the limits of these expressions when n is an integer. This function which exists for *all* values of n is taken as the canonical function of the second kind by Nielsen, *Handbuch der Cylinderfunktionen* (Leipzig, 1904), and formulae involving it are generally (but not always) simpler than the corresponding formulae involving Hankel's function.

The asymptotic expansion for $Y_n(z)$, corresponding to that of § 17·5 for $J_n(z)$, is that, when $|\arg z| < \pi$ and n is an integer,

$$Y_n(z) \sim \left(\frac{2}{\pi z}\right)^{\frac{1}{2}} \left[\sin\left(z - \tfrac{1}{2} n\pi - \tfrac{1}{4}\pi\right) . U_n(z) + \cos\left(z - \tfrac{1}{2} n\pi - \tfrac{1}{4}\pi\right) . V_n(z) \right],$$

where $U_n(z)$ and $V_n(z)$ are the asymptotic expansions defined in § 17·5, their leading terms being 1 and $(4n^2 - 1)/8z$ respectively.

Example 1.   Prove that

$$\mathbf{Y}_n(z) = \frac{dJ_n(z)}{dn} - (-)^n \frac{dJ_{-n}(z)}{dn},$$

where n is made an integer after differentiation.   (Hankel.)

Example 2.   Shew that if $\mathbf{Y}_n(z)$ be defined by the equation of example 1, it is a solution of Bessel's equation when n is an integer.

17·61.   *The ascending series for* $\mathbf{Y}_n(z)$.

The series of § 17·6 is convenient for calculating $\mathbf{Y}_n(z)$ when $|z|$ is large. To obtain a convenient series for small values of $|z|$, we observe that, since the ascending series for $J_{\pm(n+\epsilon)}(z)$ are uniformly convergent series of analytic functions* of ϵ, each term may be expanded in powers of ϵ and this double series may then be arranged in powers of ϵ (§§ 5·3, 5·4).

Accordingly, to obtain $\mathbf{Y}_n(z)$, we have to sum the coefficients of the first power of ϵ in the terms of the series

$$\sum_{r=0}^{\infty} \frac{(-)^r (\tfrac{1}{2}z)^{n+2r+\epsilon}}{r! \, \Gamma(n+\epsilon+r+1)} - (-)^n \sum_{r=0}^{\infty} \frac{(-)^r (\tfrac{1}{2}z)^{-n+2r-\epsilon}}{r! \, \Gamma(-n-\epsilon+r+1)}.$$

Now, if s be a positive integer or zero and t a negative integer, the following expansions in powers of ϵ are valid:

$$\left(\tfrac{1}{2}z\right)^{n+\epsilon+2r} = \left(\tfrac{1}{2}z\right)^{n+2r} \left\{1 + \epsilon \log\left(\tfrac{1}{2}z\right) + \dots\right\},$$

$$\frac{1}{\Gamma(s+\epsilon+1)} = \frac{1}{\Gamma(s+1)} \left\{1 - \epsilon \frac{\Gamma'(s+1)}{\Gamma(s+1)} + \dots\right\}$$

$$= \frac{1}{\Gamma(s+1)} \left\{1 - \epsilon\left(-\gamma + \sum_{m=1}^{s} m^{-1}\right) + \dots\right\},$$

$$\frac{1}{\Gamma(t+\epsilon+1)} = -\frac{\sin(t+\epsilon)\pi}{\pi} \Gamma(-t-\epsilon) = (-)^{t+1} \epsilon \, \Gamma(-t) + \dots,$$

where γ is Euler's constant (§ 12·1).

---

* The proof of this is left to the reader.

Accordingly, picking out the coefficient of ϵ, we see that

$$\mathsf{Y}_n(z) = \log\left(\tfrac{1}{2}z\right)\left[\sum_{r=0}^{\infty}\frac{(-)^r(\tfrac{1}{2}z)^{n+2r}}{r!\,\Gamma(n+r+1)} + (-)^n\sum_{r=n}^{\infty}\frac{(-)^r(\tfrac{1}{2}z)^{-n+2r}}{r!\,\Gamma(-n+r+1)}\right]$$
$$+ \sum_{r=0}^{\infty}\frac{(-)^r(\tfrac{1}{2}z)^{n+2r}}{r!\,\Gamma(n+r+1)}\left(\gamma - \sum_{m=1}^{n+r}m^{-1}\right)$$
$$+ (-)^n\sum_{r=n}^{\infty}\frac{(-)^r(\tfrac{1}{2}z)^{-n+2r}}{r!\,\Gamma(-n+r+1)}\left(\gamma - \sum_{m=1}^{r-n}m^{-1}\right)$$
$$+ (-)^n\sum_{r=0}^{n-1}\frac{(-)^r(\tfrac{1}{2}z)^{-n+2r}}{r!}(-)^{r-n+1}\,\Gamma(n-r),$$

and so

$$\mathsf{Y}_n(z) = \sum_{r=0}^{\infty}\frac{(-)^r(\tfrac{1}{2}z)^{n+2r}}{r!\,(n+r)!}\left\{2\log\left(\tfrac{1}{2}z\right) + 2\gamma - \sum_{m=1}^{n+r}m^{-1} - \sum_{m=1}^{r}m^{-1}\right\}$$
$$- \sum_{r=0}^{n-1}\frac{(\tfrac{1}{2}z)^{-n+2r}(n-r-1)!}{r!}.$$

When n is an integer, fundamental solutions* of Bessel's equations, regular near $z = 0$, are $J_n(z)$ and $Y_n(z)$ or $\mathsf{Y}_n(z)$.

Karl Neumann† took as the second solution the function $Y^{(n)}(z)$ defined by the equation

$$Y^{(n)}(z) = \tfrac{1}{2}\mathsf{Y}_n(z) + J_n(z)\,.\,(\log 2 - \gamma);$$

but $Y_n(z)$ and $\mathsf{Y}_n(z)$ are more useful for physical applications.

Example 1.   Shew that the function $Y_n(z)$ satisfies the recurrence formulae
$$nY_n(z) = \tfrac{1}{2}z\{Y_{n+1}(z) + Y_{n-1}(z)\},$$
$$Y_n'(z) = \tfrac{1}{2}\{Y_{n-1}(z) - Y_{n+1}(z)\}.$$

Shew also that Hankel's function $\mathsf{Y}_n(z)$ and Neumann's function $Y^{(n)}(z)$ satisfy the same recurrence formulae.

[These are the same as the recurrence formulae satisfied by $J_n(z)$.]

Example 2.   Shew that, when $|\arg z| < \tfrac{1}{2}\pi$,
$$\pi Y_n(z) = \int_0^{\pi}\sin(z\sin\theta - n\theta)\,d\theta - \int_0^{\infty}e^{-z\sinh\theta}\{e^{n\theta} + (-)^n e^{-n\theta}\}\,d\theta.$$

(Schläfli, *Math. Ann.* III.)

Example 3.   Shew that
$$Y^{(0)}(z) = J_0(z)\log z + 2\{J_2(z) - \tfrac{1}{2}J_4(z) + \tfrac{1}{3}J_6(z) - \dots\}.$$

17·7.   *Bessel functions with purely imaginary argument.*

The function‡

$$I_n(z) = i^{-n}J_n(iz) = \sum_{r=0}^{\infty}\frac{(\tfrac{1}{2}z)^{n+2r}}{r!\,(n+r)!}$$

---

* Euler gave a second solution (involving a logarithm) of the equation in the special cases $n=0$, $n=1$, *Inst. Calc. Int.* II. (Petersburg, 1769), pp. 187, 233.

† *Theorie der Bessel'schen Funktionen* (Leipzig, 1867), p. 41.

‡ This notation was introduced by Basset, *Hydrodynamics* II. (1888), p. 17; in 1886 he had defined $I_n(z)$ as $i^n J_n(iz)$; see *Proc. Camb. Phil. Soc.* VI. (1889), p. 11.

is of frequent occurrence in various branches of applied mathematics; in these applications z is usually positive.

The reader should have no difficulty in obtaining the following formulae:

(i) $\quad I_{n-1}(z) - I_{n+1}(z) = \dfrac{2n}{z} I_n(z)$.

(ii) $\quad \dfrac{d}{dz}\{z^n I_n(z)\} = z^n I_{n-1}(z)$.

(iii) $\quad \dfrac{d}{dz}\{z^{-n} I_n(z)\} = z^{-n} I_{n+1}(z)$.

(iv) $\quad \dfrac{d^2 I_n(z)}{dz^2} + \dfrac{1}{z}\dfrac{dI_n(z)}{dz} - \left(1 + \dfrac{n^2}{z^2}\right) I_n(z) = 0$.

(v) $\quad$ When $R\left(n + \dfrac{1}{2}\right) > 0$,

$$I_n(z) = \frac{z^n}{2^n\,\Gamma\left(\tfrac{1}{2}\right)\,\Gamma\left(n + \tfrac{1}{2}\right)} \int_0^\pi \cosh(z\cos\phi)\sin^{2n}\phi\,d\phi.$$

(vi) $\quad$ When $-\dfrac{3}{2}\pi < \arg z < \dfrac{1}{2}\pi$, the asymptotic expansion of $I_n(z)$ is

$$I_n(z) \sim \frac{e^z}{(2\pi z)^{\frac{1}{2}}}\left[1 + \sum_{r=1}^\infty (-)^r\,\frac{\{4n^2 - 1^2\}\{4n^2 - 3^2\}\dots\{4n^2 - (2r-1)^2\}}{r!\,2^{3r}z^r}\right]$$

$$+ \frac{e^{-(n+\frac{1}{2})\pi i}\,e^{-z}}{(2\pi z)^{\frac{1}{2}}}\left[1 + \sum_{r=1}^\infty \frac{\{4n^2 - 1^2\}\{4n^2 - 3^2\}\dots\{4n^2 - (2r-1)^2\}}{r!\,2^{3r}z^r}\right],$$

the second series being negligible when $|\arg z| < \dfrac{1}{2}\pi$. The result is easily seen to be valid over the extended range $-\dfrac{3}{2}\pi < \arg z < \dfrac{3}{2}\pi$ if we write $e^{\pm(n+\frac{1}{2})\pi i}$ for $e^{-(n+\frac{1}{2})\pi i}$, the upper or lower sign being taken according as $\arg z$ is positive or negative.

17·71. *Modified Bessel functions of the second kind.*

When n is a positive integer or zero, $I_{-n}(z) = I_n(z)$; to obtain a second solution of the modified Bessel equation (iv) of § 17·7, we define* the function $K_n(z)$ for all values of n by the equation

$$K_n(z) = \left(\frac{\pi}{2z}\right)^{\frac{1}{2}} \cos n\pi\, W_{0,n}(2z),$$

so that $\qquad K_n(z) = \dfrac{1}{2}\pi\{I_{-n}(z) - I_n(z)\}\cot n\pi.$

---

* The notation $K_n(z)$ was used by Basset in 1886, *Proc. Camb. Phil. Soc.* VI. (1889), p. 11, to denote a function which differed from the function now defined by the omission of the factor $\cos n\pi$, and Basset's notation has since been used by various writers, notably Macdonald. The object of the insertion of the factor is to make $I_n(z)$ and $K_n(z)$ satisfy the same recurrence formulae. Subsequently Basset, *Hydrodynamics* II. (1888), p. 19, used the notation $K_n(z)$ to denote a slightly different function, but the latter usage has not been followed by other writers. The definition of $K_n(z)$ for *integral* values of n which is given here is due to Gray and Mathews, *Bessel Functions*, p. 68, and is now common (see example 40, p. 384), but the corresponding definition for non-integral values has the serious disadvantage that the function vanishes identically when $2n$ is an odd integer. The function was considered by Riemann, *Ann. der Phys.* XCV. (1855), pp. 130–139 and Hankel, *Math. Ann.* I. (1869), p. 498.

Whether n be an integer or not, this function is a solution of the modified Bessel equation, and when $|\arg z| < \frac{3}{2}\pi$ it possesses the asymptotic expansion

$$K_n(z) \sim \left(\frac{\pi}{2z}\right)^{\frac{1}{2}} e^{-z} \cos(n\pi) \left[1 + \sum_{r=1}^{\infty} \frac{\{4n^2 - 1^2\}\{4n^2 - 3^2\} \ldots \{4n^2 - (2r-1)^2\}}{r!\, 2^{3r} z^r} \right]$$

for large values of $|z|$.

When n is an integer, $K_n(z)$ is defined by the equation

$$K_n(z) = \lim_{\epsilon \to 0} \frac{1}{2}\pi \left\{ I_{-n-\epsilon}(z) - I_{n+\epsilon}(z) \right\} \cot \pi\epsilon,$$

which gives (cf. § 17·61)

$$K_n(z) = - \sum_{r=0}^{\infty} \frac{(\frac{1}{2}z)^{n+2r}}{r!\,(n+r)!} \left\{ \log \frac{1}{2}z + \gamma - \frac{1}{2}\sum_{m=1}^{n+r} m^{-1} - \frac{1}{2}\sum_{m=1}^{r} m^{-1} \right\}$$
$$+ \frac{1}{2}\sum_{r=0}^{n-1} \left(\frac{1}{2}z\right)^{-n+2r} \frac{(-)^{n-r}(n-r-1)!}{r!}$$

as an ascending series.

Example. Shew that $K_n(z)$ satisfies the same recurrence formulae as $I_n(z)$.

17·8. *Neumann's expansion* of an analytic function in a series of Bessel coefficients.*

We shall now consider the expansion of an arbitrary function $f(z)$, analytic in a domain including the origin, in a series of Bessel coefficients, in the form

$$f(z) = \alpha_0 J_0(z) + \alpha_1 J_1(z) + \alpha_2 J_2(z) + \ldots,$$

where $\alpha_0, \alpha_1, \alpha_2, \ldots$ are independent of z.

Assuming the possibility of expansions of this type, let us first consider the expansion of $1/(t-z)$; let it be

$$\frac{1}{t-z} = O_0(t) J_0(z) + 2O_1(t) J_1(z) + 2O_2(t) J_2(z) + \ldots,$$

where the functions $O_n(t)$ are independent of z.

We shall now determine conditions which $O_n(t)$ must satisfy if the series on the right is to be a uniformly convergent series of analytic functions; by these conditions $O_n(t)$ will be determined, and it will then be shewn that, if $O_n(t)$ is so determined, then the series on the right actually converges to the sum $1/(t-z)$ when $|z| < |t|$.

Since $$\left(\frac{\partial}{\partial t} + \frac{\partial}{\partial z}\right) \frac{1}{t-z} = 0,$$

we have

$$O_0'(t) J_0(z) + 2\sum_{n=1}^{\infty} O_n'(t) J_n(z) + O_0(t) J_0'(z) + 2\sum_{n=1}^{\infty} O_n(t) J_n'(z) \equiv 0,$$

so that, on replacing $2J_n'(z)$ by $J_{n-1}(z) - J_{n+1}(z)$, we find

$$\{O_0'(t) + O_1(t)\} J_0(z) + \sum_{n=1}^{\infty} \{2O_n'(t) + O_{n+1}(t) - O_{n-1}(t)\} J_n(z) \equiv 0.$$

---

* K. Neumann, *Journal für Math.* LXVII. (1867), p. 310; see also Kapteyn, *Ann. de l'École norm. sup.* (3), x. (1893), p. 106.

Accordingly the successive functions $O_1(t), O_2(t), O_3(t), \ldots$ *are determined by the recurrence formulae*

$$O_1(t) = -O_0'(t), \quad O_{n+1}(t) = O_{n-1}(t) - 2O_n'(t),$$

and, putting $z = 0$ in the original expansion, we see that $O_0(t)$ *is to be defined by the equation*

$$O_0(t) = 1/t.$$

These formulae shew without difficulty that $O_n(t)$ is a polynomial of degree n in $1/t$.

We shall next prove by induction that $O_n(t)$, so defined, is equal to

$$\tfrac{1}{2} \int_0^\infty e^{-tu} \left[\{u + \sqrt{(u^2+1)}\}^n + \{u - \sqrt{(u^2+1)}\}^n\right] du$$

when $R(t) > 0$. For the expression is obviously equal to $O_0(t)$ or $O_1(t)$ when n is equal to 0 or 1 respectively; and

$$\tfrac{1}{2} \int_0^\infty e^{-tu} \{u \pm \sqrt{(u^2+1)}\}^{n-1} du - \frac{d}{dt} \int_0^\infty e^{-tu} \{u \pm \sqrt{(u^2+1)}\}^n du$$

$$= \tfrac{1}{2} \int_0^\infty e^{-tu} \{u \pm \sqrt{(u^2+1)}\}^{n-1} \{1 + 2u^2 \pm 2u \sqrt{(u^2+1)}\} du$$

$$= \tfrac{1}{2} \int_0^\infty e^{-tu} \{u \pm \sqrt{(u^2+1)}\}^{n+1} du,$$

whence the induction is obvious.

Writing $u = \sinh \theta$, we see that, according as n is even or odd[*],

$$\tfrac{1}{2} [\{u + \sqrt{(u^2+1)}\}^n + \{u - \sqrt{(u^2+1)}\}^n] = \frac{\cosh}{\sinh} n\theta$$

$$= 2^{n-1} \left\{ \sinh^n \theta + \frac{n(n-1)}{2(2n-2)} \sinh^{n-2} \theta + \frac{n(n-1)(n-2)(n-3)}{2 \cdot 4 (2n-2)(2n-4)} \sinh^{n-4} \theta + \ldots \right\},$$

and hence, when $R(t) > 0$, we have on integration,

$$O_n(t) = \frac{2^{n-1} n!}{t^{n+1}} \left\{ 1 + \frac{t^2}{2(2n-2)} + \frac{t^4}{2 \cdot 4 (2n-2)(2n-4)} + \ldots \right\},$$

the series terminating with the term in t^n or t^{n-1}; now, whether $R(t)$ be positive or not, $O_n(t)$ is defined as a polynomial in $1/t$; and so the expansion obtained for $O_n(t)$ is the value of $O_n(t)$ for *all* values of t.

Example. Shew that, for all values of t,

$$O_n(t) = \frac{1}{2t^{n+1}} \int_0^\infty e^{-x} [\{x + \sqrt{(x^2+t^2)}\}^n + \{x - \sqrt{(x^2+t^2)}\}^n] \, dx,$$

and verify that the expression on the right satisfies the recurrence formulae for $O_n(t)$.

17·81. *Proof of Neumann's expansion.*

The method of § 17·8 merely determined the coefficients in Neumann's expansion of $1/(t-z)$, on the hypothesis that the expansion existed and that the rearrangements were legitimate.

To obtain a proof of the validity of the expansion, we observe that

$$J_n(z) = \frac{(\tfrac{1}{2}z)^n}{n!} \{1 + \theta_n\}, \quad O_n(t) = \frac{2^{n-1} n!}{t^{n+1}} \{1 + \phi_n\},$$

[*] Cf. Hobson, *Plane Trigonometry* (1918), §§ 79, 264.

where $\theta_n \to 0$, $\phi_n \to 0$ as $n \to \infty$, when z and t are fixed. Hence the series

$$O_0(t) J_0(z) + 2 \sum_{n=1}^{\infty} O_n(t) J_n(z) \equiv F(z, t)$$

is comparable with the geometrical progression whose general term is z^n/t^{n+1}, and this progression is absolutely convergent when $|z| < |t|$, and so the expansion for $F(z, t)$ is absolutely convergent (§ 2·34) in the same circumstances.

Again if $|z| \leqslant r$, $|t| \geqslant R$, where $r < R$, the series is comparable with the geometrical progression whose general term is r^n/R^{n+1}, and so the expansion for $F(z, t)$ converges uniformly throughout the domains $|z| \leqslant r$ and $|t| \geqslant R$ by § 3·34. Hence, by § 5·3, term-by-term differentiations are permissible, and so

$$\left(\frac{\partial}{\partial t} + \frac{\partial}{\partial z}\right) F(z, t) = O_0'(t) J_0(z) + 2 \sum_{n=1}^{\infty} O_n'(t) J_n(z)$$

$$+ O_0(t) J_0'(z) + 2 \sum_{n=1}^{\infty} O_n(t) J_n'(z)$$

$$= \{O_0'(t) + O_1(t)\} J_0(z) + \sum_{n=1}^{\infty} \{2O_n'(t) + O_{n+1}(t) - O_{n-1}(t)\} J_n(z)$$

$$= 0,$$

by the recurrence formulae.

Since
$$\left(\frac{\partial}{\partial t} + \frac{\partial}{\partial z}\right) F(z, t) = 0,$$

it follows that $F(z, t)$ is expressible as a function of $t - z$; and since

$$F(0, t) = O_0(t) = 1/t,$$

it is clear that $F(z, t) = 1/(t - z)$.

It is therefore proved that

$$\frac{1}{t - z} = O_0(t) J_0(z) + 2 \sum_{n=1}^{\infty} O_n(t) J_n(z),$$

provided that $|z| < |t|$.

Hence, if $f(z)$ be analytic when $|z| \leqslant r$, we have, when $|z| < r$,

$$f(z) = \frac{1}{2\pi i} \int \frac{f(t)}{t - z} dt$$

$$= \frac{1}{2\pi i} \int f(t) \left\{ O_0(t) J_0(z) + 2 \sum_{n=1}^{\infty} O_n(t) J_n(z) \right\} dt$$

$$= J_0(z) f(0) + \sum_{n=1}^{\infty} \frac{J_n(z)}{\pi i} \int O_n(t) f(t) dt,$$

by § 4·7, the paths of integration being the circle $|t| = r$; and this establishes the validity of Neumann's expansion when $|z| < r$ and $f(z)$ is analytic when $|z| \leqslant r$.

Example 1. Shew that

$$\cos z = J_0(z) - 2J_2(z) + 2J_4(z) - \dots,$$

$$\sin z = 2J_1(z) - 2J_3(z) + 2J_5(z) - \dots. \qquad \text{(K. Neumann.)}$$

Example 2. Shew that

$$(\tfrac{1}{2}z)^n = \sum_{r=0}^{\infty} \frac{(n+2r) \cdot (n+r-1)!}{r!} J_{n+2r}(z). \qquad \text{(K. Neumann.)}$$

Example 3. Shew that, when $|z| < |t|$,

$$O_0(t) J_0(z) + 2 \sum_{n=1}^{\infty} O_n(t) J_n(z) = \sum_{n=-\infty}^{\infty} J_n(z) \int_0^{\infty} t^{-n-1} e^{-x} \{x + \surd(x^2+t^2)\}^n \, dx$$

$$= \int_0^{\infty} \frac{e^{-x}}{t^{n+1}} \sum_{n=-\infty}^{\infty} J_n(z) \{x + \surd(x^2+t^2)\}^n \, dx$$

$$= \frac{1}{t} \int_0^{\infty} \exp\left(\frac{zx}{t} - x\right) dx$$

$$= \frac{1}{t-z}. \qquad \text{(Kapteyn.)}$$

17·82. *Schlömilch's expansion of an arbitrary function in a series of Bessel coefficients of order zero.*

Schlömilch[*] has given an expansion of quite a different character from that of Neumann. His result may be stated thus :

Any function $f(x)$, which has a continuous differential coefficient with limited total fluctuation for all values of x in the closed range $(0, \pi)$, may be expanded in the series

$$f(x) = a_0 + a_1 J_0(x) + a_2 J_0(2x) + a_3 J_0(3x) + \dots,$$

valid in this range; where

$$a_0 = f(0) + \frac{1}{\pi} \int_0^{\pi} u \int_0^{\frac{1}{2}\pi} f'(u \sin\theta) \, d\theta \, du,$$

$$a_n = \frac{2}{\pi} \int_0^{\pi} u \cos nu \int_0^{\frac{1}{2}\pi} f'(u \sin\theta) \, d\theta \, du \qquad (n > 0).$$

Schlömilch's proof is substantially as follows :

Let $F(x)$ be the continuous solution of the integral equation

$$f(x) = \frac{2}{\pi} \int_0^{\frac{1}{2}\pi} F(x \sin\phi) \, d\phi.$$

Then (§ 11·81)

$$F(x) = f(0) + x \int_0^{\frac{1}{2}\pi} f'(x \sin\theta) \, d\theta.$$

In order to obtain Schlömilch's expansion, it is merely necessary to apply Fourier's theorem to the function $F(x \sin\phi)$. We thus have

$$f(x) = \frac{2}{\pi} \int_0^{\frac{1}{2}\pi} d\phi \left\{ \frac{1}{\pi} \int_0^{\pi} F(u) \, du + \frac{2}{\pi} \sum_{n=1}^{\infty} \int_0^{\pi} \cos nu \cos(nx \sin\phi) F(u) \, du \right\}$$

$$= \frac{1}{\pi} \int_0^{\pi} F(u) \, du + \frac{2}{\pi} \sum_{n=1}^{\infty} \int_0^{\pi} \cos nu \, F(u) J_0(nx) \, du,$$

the interchange of summation and integration being permissible by §§ 4·7 and 9·44.

---

[*] *Zeitschrift für Math. und Phys.* II. (1857), pp. 137–165. See Chapman, *Quarterly Journal*, XLIII. (1912), pp. 34–37.

In this equation, replace $F(u)$ by its value in terms of $f(u)$. Thus we have

$$f(x) = \frac{1}{\pi} \int_0^\pi \left\{ f(0) + u \int_0^{\frac{1}{2}\pi} f'(u \sin \theta) \, d\theta \right\} du$$

$$+ \frac{2}{\pi} \sum_{n=1}^\infty J_0(nx) \int_0^\pi \cos nu \left\{ f(0) + u \int_0^{\frac{1}{2}\pi} f'(u \sin \theta) \, d\theta \right\} du,$$

which gives Schlömilch's expansion.

Example. Shew that, if $0 \leqslant x \leqslant \pi$, the expression

$$\frac{\pi^2}{4} - 2 \left\{ J_0(x) + \frac{1}{9} J_0(3x) + \frac{1}{25} J_0(5x) + \ldots \right\}$$

is equal to x; but that, if $\pi \leqslant x \leqslant 2\pi$, its value is

$$x + 2\pi \arccos(\pi x^{-1}) - 2 \sqrt{(x^2 - \pi^2)},$$

where $\arccos(\pi x^{-1})$ is taken between 0 and $\frac{\pi}{3}$.

Find the value of the expression when x lies between 2π and 3π.

(Math. Trip. 1895.)

17·9. *Tabulation of Bessel functions.*

Hansen used the asymptotic expansion (§ 17·5) to calculate tables of $J_n(x)$ which are given in Lommel's *Studien über die Bessel'schen Funktionen.*

Meissel tabulated $J_0(x)$ and $J_1(x)$ to 12 places of decimals from $x = 0$ to $x = 15\cdot5$ (*Abh. der Akad. zu Berlin*, 1888), while the *British Assoc. Report* (1909), p. 33 gives tables by which $J_n(x)$ and $Y_n(x)$ may be calculated when $x > 10$.

Tables of $J_{\frac{1}{3}}(x)$, $J_{\frac{2}{3}}(x)$, $J_{-\frac{1}{3}}(x)$, $J_{-\frac{2}{3}}(x)$ are given by Dinnik, *Archiv der Math. und Phys.* XVIII. (1911), p. 337.

Tables of the second solution of Bessel's equation have been given by the following writers: B. A. Smith, *Messenger*, XXVI. (1897), p. 98; *Phil. Mag.* (5), XLV. (1898), p. 106; Aldis, *Proc. Royal Soc.* LXVI. (1900), p. 32; Airey, *Phil. Mag.* (6), XXII. (1911), p. 658.

The functions $I_n(x)$ have been tabulated in the *British Assoc. Reports*, (1889) p. 28, (1893) p. 223, (1896) p. 98, (1907) p. 94; also by Aldis, *Proc. Royal Soc.* LXIV. (1899); by Isherwood, *Proc. Manchester Lit. and Phil. Soc.* XLVIII. (1904); and by E. Anding, *Sechs-stellige Tafeln der Bessel'schen Funktionen imaginären Argumentes* (Leipzig, 1911).

Tables of $J_n(x\sqrt{i})$, a function employed in the theory of alternating currents in wires, have been given in the *British Assoc. Reports*, 1889, 1893, 1896 and 1912; by Kelvin, *Math. and Phys. Papers*, III. p. 493; by Aldis, *Proc. Royal Soc.* LXVI. (1900), p. 32; and by Savidge, *Phil. Mag.* (6), XIX. (1910), p. 49.

Formulae for computing the zeros of $J_0(z)$ were given by Stokes, *Camb. Phil. Trans.* IX. and the 40 smallest zeros were tabulated by Willson and Peirce, *Bull. American Math. Soc.* III. (1897), p. 153. The roots of an equation involving Bessel functions were computed by Kalähne, *Zeitschrift für Math. und Phys.* LIV. (1907), p. 55.

A number of tables connected with Bessel functions are given in *British Assoc. Reports*, 1910–1914, and also by Jahnke und Emde, *Funktionentafeln* (Leipzig, 1909).

REFERENCES.

R. LIPSCHITZ, *Journal für Math.* LVI. (1859), pp. 189–196.

H. HANKEL, *Math. Ann.* I. (1869), pp. 467–501.

K. NEUMANN, *Theorie der Bessel'schen Funktionen.* (Leipzig, 1867.)

E. Lommel, *Studien über die Bessel'schen Funktionen.* (Leipzig, 1868.) *Math. Ann.* III. IV.

H. E. Heine, *Handbuch der Kugelfunktionen.* (Berlin, 1878.)

R. Olbricht, *Studien über die Kugel- und Cylinder-funktionen.* (Halle, 1887.)

A. Sommerfeld, *Math. Ann.* XLVII. (1896), pp. 317–374.

N. Nielsen, *Handbuch der Theorie der Cylinderfunktionen.* (Leipzig, 1904.)

A. Gray and G. B. Mathews, *A Treatise on Bessel Functions.* (London, 1895.)

J. W. Nicholson, *Quarterly Journal,* XLII. (1911), pp. 216–224.

G. N. Watson, *Theory of Bessel Functions.* (Cambridge, 1922.)

Miscellaneous Examples.

1. Shew that
$$\cos (z \sin \theta) = J_0 (z) + 2 J_2 (z) \cos 2\theta + 2 J_4 (z) \cos 4\theta + \dots,$$
$$\sin (z \sin \theta) = 2 J_1 (z) \sin \theta + 2 J_3 (z) \sin 3\theta + 2 J_5 (z) \sin 5\theta + \dots.$$

(K. Neumann.)

2. By expanding each side of the equations of example 1 in powers of $\sin \theta$, express z^n as a series of Bessel coefficients.

3. By multiplying the expansions for $\exp \left\{ \frac{1}{2} z \left(t - \frac{1}{t} \right) \right\}$ and $\exp \left\{ -\frac{1}{2} z \left(t - \frac{1}{t} \right) \right\}$ and considering the terms independent of t, shew that

$$\{ J_0 (z) \}^2 + 2 \{ J_1 (z) \}^2 + 2 \{ J_2 (z) \}^2 + 2 \{ J_3 (z) \}^2 + \dots = 1.$$

Deduce that, for the Bessel coefficients,

$$| J_0 (z) | \leqslant 1, \quad | J_n (z) | \leqslant 2^{-\frac{1}{2}}, \quad (n \geqslant 1)$$

when z is real.

4. If
$$J_m^k (z) = \frac{1}{\pi} \int_0^\pi 2^k \cos^k u \cos (mu - z \sin u) \, du$$

(this function reduces to a Bessel coefficient when k is zero and m an integer), shew that

$$J_m^k (z) = \sum_{p=0}^\infty \frac{1}{p!} (\tfrac{1}{2} z)^p N_{-m, k, p},$$

where $N_{-m, k, p}$ is the 'Cauchy's number' defined by the equation

$$N_{-m, k, p} = \frac{1}{2\pi} \int_{-\pi}^\pi e^{-miu} (e^{iu} + e^{-iu})^k (e^{iu} - e^{-iu})^p \, du.$$

Shew further that
$$J_m^k (z) = J_{m-1}^{k-1} (z) + J_{m+1}^{k-1} (z),$$

and
$$z J_m^{k+2} (z) = 2m J_m^{k+1} (z) - 2 (k+1) \{ J_{m-1}^k (z) - J_{m+1}^k (z) \}.$$

(Bourget, *Journal de Math.* (2), VI.)

5. If v and M are connected by the equations

$$M = E - e \sin E, \quad \cos v = \frac{\cos E - e}{1 - e \cos E}, \quad \text{where } | e | < 1,$$

shew that
$$v = M + 2 (1 - e^2)^{\frac{1}{2}} \sum_{m=1}^\infty \sum_{k=0}^\infty (\tfrac{1}{2} e)^k J_m^k (me) \frac{1}{m} \sin mM,$$

where $J_m^k (z)$ is defined as in example 4.

(Bourget.)

6. Prove that, if m and n are integers,

$$P_n{}^m (\cos \theta) = \frac{c_n{}^m}{r^n} J_m \left\{ (x^2 + y^2)^{\frac{1}{2}} \frac{\partial}{\partial z} \right\} z^n,$$

where $z = r \cos \theta$, $x^2 + y^2 = r^2 \sin^2 \theta$, and $c_n{}^m$ is independent of z.

(Math. Trip. 1893.)

7. Shew that the solution of the differential equation

$$\frac{d^2 y}{dz^2} - \frac{\phi'}{\phi} \frac{dy}{dz} + \left\{ \frac{1}{4} \left(\frac{\phi'}{\phi} \right)^2 - \frac{1}{2} \frac{d}{dz} \left(\frac{\phi'}{\phi} \right) - \frac{1}{4} \left(\frac{\psi''}{\psi'} \right)^2 + \frac{1}{2} \frac{d}{dz} \left(\frac{\psi''}{\psi'} \right) + \left(\psi^2 - \frac{4\nu^2 - 1}{4} \right) \left(\frac{\psi'}{\psi} \right)^2 \right\} y = 0,$$

where ϕ and ψ are arbitrary functions of z, is

$$y = \left(\frac{\phi \psi}{\psi'} \right)^{\frac{1}{2}} \{ A J_\nu (\psi) + B J_{-\nu} (\psi) \}.$$

8. Shew that

$$J_1 (x) + J_3 (x) + J_5 (x) + \ldots = \frac{1}{2} \left[J_0 (x) + \int_0^x \{ J_0 (t) + J_1 (t) \} \, dt - 1 \right].$$

(Trinity, 1908.)

9. Shew that

$$J_\mu (z) J_\nu (z) = \sum_{n=0}^{\infty} \frac{(-)^n \Gamma (\mu + \nu + 2n + 1) (\frac{1}{2} z)^{\mu + \nu + 2n}}{n! \, \Gamma (\mu + n + 1) \Gamma (\nu + n + 1) \Gamma (\mu + \nu + n + 1)}$$

for all values of μ and ν.

(Schläfli, *Math. Ann.* III. (1871), p. 142; and Schönholzer, Bern dissertation, 1877.)

10. Shew that, if n is a positive integer and $m + 2n + 1$ is positive,

$$(m - 1) \int_0^x x^m J_{n+1} (x) J_{n-1} (x) \, dx = x^{m+1} \{ J_{n+1} (x) J_{n-1} (x) - J_n{}^2 (x) \} + (m + 1) \int_0^x x^m J_n{}^2 (x) \, dx.$$

(Math. Trip. 1899.)

11. Shew that

$$J_3 (z) + 3 \frac{d J_0 (z)}{dz} + 4 \frac{d^3 J_0 (z)}{dz^3} = 0.$$

12. Shew that

$$\frac{J_{n+1} (z)}{J_n (z)} = \frac{\frac{1}{2} z}{n + 1} - \frac{(\frac{1}{2} z)^2}{n + 2} - \frac{(\frac{1}{2} z)^2}{n + 3} - \ldots.$$

13. Shew that

$$J_{-n} (z) J_{n-1} (z) + J_{-n+1} (z) J_n (z) = \frac{2 \sin n\pi}{\pi z}.$$

(Lommel.)

14. If $\dfrac{J_{n+1} (z)}{z J_n (z)}$ be denoted by $Q_n (z)$, shew that

$$\frac{d Q_n (z)}{dz} = \frac{1}{z} - \frac{2 (n + 1)}{z} Q_n (z) + z \{ Q_n (z) \}^2.$$

15. Shew that, if $R^2 = r^2 + r_1{}^2 - 2 r r_1 \cos \theta$ and $r_1 > r > 0$,

$$J_0 (R) = J_0 (r) J_0 (r_1) + 2 \sum_{n=1}^{\infty} J_n (r) J_n (r_1) \cos n\theta,$$

$$Y_0 (R) = J_0 (r) Y_0 (r_1) + 2 \sum_{n=1}^{\infty} J_n (r) Y_n (r_1) \cos n\theta.$$

(K. Neumann.)

16. Shew that, if $R (n + \frac{1}{2}) > 0$,

$$\int_0^{\frac{1}{2}\pi} J_{2n} (2z \cos \theta) \, d\theta = \frac{1}{2} \pi \{ J_n (z) \}^2.$$

(K. Neumann.)

17. Shew how to express $z^{2n} J_{2n}(z)$ in the form $A J_2(z) + B J_0(z)$, where A, B are polynomials in z; and prove that

$$J_4(6^{\frac{1}{2}}) + 3 J_0(6^{\frac{1}{2}}) = 0, \quad 3 J_6(30^{\frac{1}{2}}) + 5 J_2(30^{\frac{1}{2}}) = 0.$$

(Math. Trip. 1896.)

18. Shew that, if $a \neq \beta$ and $n > -1$,

$$(a^2 - \beta^2) \int_0^x x J_n(ax) J_n(\beta x) \, dx = x \left\{ J_n(ax) \frac{d}{dx} J_n(\beta x) - J_n(\beta x) \frac{d}{dx} J_n(ax) \right\},$$

$$2a^2 \int_0^x x \{ J_n(ax) \}^2 \, dx = (a^2 x^2 - n^2) \{ J_n(ax) \}^2 + \left\{ x \frac{d}{dx} J_n(ax) \right\}^2.$$

19. Prove that, if $n > -1$, and $J_n(a) = J_n(\beta) = 0$ while $a \neq \beta$,

$$\int_0^1 x J_n(ax) J_n(\beta x) \, dx = 0, \quad \text{and} \quad \int_0^1 x \{ J_n(ax) \}^2 \, dx = \tfrac{1}{2} \{ J_{n+1}(a) \}^2.$$

Hence prove that, when $n > -1$, the roots of $J_n(x) = 0$, other than zero, are all real and unequal.

[If a could be complex, take β to be the conjugate complex.]

(Lommel, *Studien über die Bessel'schen Funktionen*, p. 69.)

20. Let $x^{\frac{1}{2}} f(x)$ have an absolutely convergent integral in the range $0 \leqslant x \leqslant 1$; let H be a real constant and let $n \geqslant 0$. Then, if $k_1, k_2, \ldots$ denote the positive roots of the equation

$$k^{-n} \{ k J_n'(k) + H J_n(k) \} = 0,$$

shew that, at any point x for which $0 < x < 1$ and $f(x)$ satisfies one of the conditions of § 9·43, $f(x)$ can be expanded in the form

$$f(x) = \sum_{r=1}^{\infty} A_r J_n(k_r x),$$

where

$$A_r = \left[\int_0^1 x \{ J_n(k_r x) \}^2 \, dx \right]^{-1} \int_0^1 x f(x) J_n(k_r x) \, dx.$$

In the special case when $H = -n$, k_1 is to be taken to be zero, the equation determining $k_1, k_2, \ldots$ being $J_{n+1}(k) = 0$, and the first term of the expansion is $A_0 x^n$ where

$$A_0 = (2n + 2) \int_0^1 x^{n+1} f(x) \, dx.$$

Discuss, in particular, the case when H is infinite, so that $J_n(k) = 0$, shewing that

$$A_r = 2 \{ J_{n+1}(k_r) \}^{-2} \int_0^1 x f(x) J_n(k_r x) \, dx.$$

[This result is due to Hobson, *Proc. London Math. Soc.* (2), VII. (1909), p. 349; see also W. H. Young, *Proc. London Math. Soc.* (2), XVIII. (1920), pp. 163–200. The formal expansion was given with H infinite (when $n = 0$) by Fourier and (for general values of n) by Lommel; proofs were given by Hankel and Schläfli. The formula when $H = -n$ was given incorrectly by Dini, *Serie di Fourier* (Pisa, 1880), the term $A_0 x^n$ being printed as A_0, and this error was not corrected by Nielsen. See Bridgeman, *Phil. Mag.* (6), XVI. (1908), p. 947 and Chree, *Phil. Mag.* (6), XVII. (1909), p. 330. The expansion is usually called the *Fourier-Bessel expansion*.]

21. Prove that, if the expansion

$$a^2 - x^2 = A_1 J_0(\lambda_1 x) + A_2 J_0(\lambda_2 x) + \ldots$$

exists as a uniformly convergent series when $-a \leqslant x \leqslant a$, where $\lambda_1, \lambda_2, \ldots$ are the positive roots of $J_0(\lambda a) = 0$, then

$$A_n = 8 \{ a \lambda_n^3 J_1(\lambda_n a) \}^{-1}.$$

(Clare, 1900.)

22.   If k_1, k_2, ... are the positive roots of $J_n(ka)=0$, and if

$$x^{n+2}=\sum_{r=1}^{\infty} A_r J_n(k_r x),$$

this series converging uniformly when $0 \leqslant x \leqslant a$, then

$$A_r=\frac{2a^{n-1}}{k_r^2}(4n+4-a^2 k_r^2)\div\frac{dJ_n(k_r a)}{da}.$$

(Math. Trip. 1906.)

23.   Shew that

$$J_n(x)=\frac{x^{n-m}}{2^{n-m-1}\,\Gamma(n-m)}\int_0^{\frac{1}{2}\pi} J_m(x\sin\theta)\cos^{2n-2m-1}\theta\sin^{m+1}\theta\,d\theta$$

when $n>m>-1$.   (Sonine, *Math. Ann.* XVI.)

24.   Shew that, if $\sigma>0$,

$$\int_0^{\infty}\cos(t^3-\sigma t)\,dt=\frac{\pi\sigma^{\frac{1}{2}}}{3\sqrt{3}}\left\{J_{\frac{1}{3}}\left(\frac{2\sigma^{\frac{3}{2}}}{3^{\frac{3}{2}}}\right)+J_{-\frac{1}{3}}\left(\frac{2\sigma^{\frac{3}{2}}}{3^{\frac{3}{2}}}\right)\right\}.$$

(Nicholson, *Phil. Mag.* (6), XVIII. (1909), p. 6.)

25.   If m be a positive integer and $u>0$, deduce from Bessel's integral formula that

$$\int_0^{\infty} e^{-x\sinh u}J_m(x)\,dx=e^{-mu}\operatorname{sech} u.$$

(Math. Trip. 1904.)

26.   Prove that, when $x>0$,

$$J_0(x)=\frac{2}{\pi}\int_0^{\infty}\sin(x\cosh t)\,dt,\qquad Y_0(x)=-\frac{2}{\pi}\int_0^{\infty}\cos(x\cosh t)\,dt.$$

[Take the contour of § 17·1 to be the imaginary axis indented at the origin and a semicircle on the left of this line.]

(Sonine, *Math. Ann.* XVI.)

27.   Shew that

$$\int_0^{\infty} x^{-1}J_0(xt)\sin x\,dx=\tfrac{1}{2}\pi \qquad\qquad 0<t<1\left.\right\}$$
$$=\text{arc cosec } t \qquad\qquad t>1 \quad\,$$

and that

$$\int_0^{\infty} x^{-1}J_1(xt)\sin x\,dx=t^{-1}\{1-(1-t^2)^{\frac{1}{2}}\}\qquad 0<t<1\left.\right\}$$
$$=t^{-1}\qquad\qquad t>1 \quad\,$$

(Weber, *Journal für Math.* LXXV.)

28.   Shew that

$$u=\int_0^{\pi} e^{nr\cos\theta}\{A+B\log(r\sin^2\theta)\}\,d\theta$$

is the solution of

$$\frac{d^2 u}{dr^2}+\frac{1}{r}\frac{du}{dr}-n^2 u=0.$$

(Poisson, *Journal de l'École Polytechnique*, XII. (1823), p. 476; see also Stokes, *Camb. Phil. Trans.* IX. (1856), p. [38].)

29.   Prove that no relation of the form

$$\sum_{s=0}^{k} N_s J_{n+s}(x)=0$$

can exist for rational values of N_s, n and x except relations which are satisfied when the Bessel functions are replaced by arbitrary solutions of the recurrence formula of § 17·21 (A).

(Math. Trip. 1901.)

[Express the left-hand side in terms of $J_n(x)$ and $J_{n+1}(x)$, and shew by example 12 that $J_{n+1}(x)/J_n(x)$ is irrational when n and x are rational.]

30. Prove that, when $R(n) > -\frac{1}{2}$,

$$J_n(z) = \frac{z^n}{2^{n-1}\,\Gamma(n+\frac{1}{2})\,\Gamma(\frac{1}{2})}\left(1+\frac{d^2}{dz^2}\right)^{n-\frac{1}{2}}\left(\frac{\sin z}{z}\right),$$

$$-Y_n(z) = \frac{z^n}{2^{n-1}\,\Gamma(n+\frac{1}{2})\,\Gamma(\frac{1}{2})}\left(1+\frac{d^2}{dz^2}\right)^{n-\frac{1}{2}}\left(\frac{\cos z}{z}\right).$$

$$\left[\left(1+\frac{d^2}{dz^2}\right)^{n-\frac{1}{2}}\text{ means }1+\frac{n-\frac{1}{2}}{1\,!}\frac{d^2}{dz^2}+\frac{(n-\frac{1}{2})(n-\frac{3}{2})}{2\,!}\frac{d^4}{dz^4}+\dots.\quad\text{Write }\frac{e^{iz}}{z}=\int_{\infty i}^{1}ie^{izt}\,dt.\right]$$

(Hargreave, *Phil. Trans.* 1848 ; Macdonald, *Proc. London Math. Soc.* XXIX.)

31. Shew that, when $R(m+\frac{1}{2}) > 0$,

$$\left(\frac{2}{\pi}\right)^{\frac{1}{2}}\int_0^{\frac{1}{2}\pi}J_m(z\sin\theta)\sin^{m+1}\theta\,d\theta = z^{-\frac{1}{2}}J_{m+\frac{1}{2}}(z).\qquad\text{(Hobson.)}$$

32. Shew that, if $2n+1 > m > -1$,

$$\int_0 x^{-n+m}J_n(ax)\,dx = 2^{-n+m}a^{n-m-1}\frac{\Gamma(\frac{1}{2}m+\frac{1}{2})}{\Gamma(n-\frac{1}{2}m+\frac{1}{2})}.$$

(Weber, *Journal für Math.* LXIX. ; Math. Trip. 1898.)

33. Shew that

$$\frac{z}{\pi} = \sum_{p=0}^{\infty}\frac{2p+1}{2}\{J_{p+\frac{1}{2}}(z)\}^2.\qquad\text{(Lommel.)}$$

34. In the equation

$$\frac{d^2y}{dz^2}+\frac{1}{z}\frac{dy}{dz}+\left(1+\frac{n^2}{z^2}\right)y = 0,$$

n is real ; shew that a solution is given by

$$\cos(n\log z)-\sum_{m=1}^{\infty}\frac{(-)^m z^{2m}\cos(u_m - n\log z)}{2^{2m}\,m\,!\,(1+n^2)^{\frac{1}{2}}(4+n^2)^{\frac{1}{2}}\dots\dots(m^2+n^2)^{\frac{1}{2}}},$$

where u_m denotes $\sum\limits_{r=1}^{m}\arctan(n/r)$.   (Math. Trip. 1894.)

35. Shew that, when n is large and positive,

$$J_n(n) = 2^{-\frac{2}{3}}3^{-\frac{1}{6}}\pi^{-1}\Gamma(\tfrac{1}{3})\,n^{-\frac{1}{3}}+o(n^{-1}).$$

(Cauchy, *Comptes Rendus*, XXXVIII. (1854), p. 993 ; Nicholson, *Phil. Mag.* (6), XVI. (1908), p. 276.)

36. Shew that

$$K_0(x) = \int_0^{\infty}\frac{tJ_0(tx)}{1+t^2}\,dt.$$

(Mehler, *Journal für Math.* LXVIII.)

37. Shew that

$$e^{\lambda\cos\theta} = 2^{n-1}\Gamma(n)\sum_{k=0}^{\infty}(n+k)\,C_k^n(\cos\theta)\lambda^{-n}I_{n+k}(\lambda).$$

(Math. Trip. 1900.)

38. Shew that, if

$$W = \int_0^{\infty}J_m(ax)\,J_m(bx)\,J_m(cx)\,x^{1-m}\,dx,$$

a, b, c being positive, and m is a positive integer or zero, then

$$W = 0 \qquad (a-b)^2 > c^2,$$

$$W = \frac{a^{-m}b^{-m}c^{-m}}{2^{3m-1}\pi^{\frac{1}{2}}\Gamma(m+\frac{1}{2})}\{2\Sigma b^2c^2-\Sigma a^4\}^{m-\frac{1}{2}}\qquad (a+b)^2 > c^2 > (a-b)^2,$$

$$W = 0 \qquad (a+b)^2 > c^2.\qquad\text{(Sonine, *Math. Ann.* XVI.)}$$

39. Shew that, if $n > -1$, $m > -\frac{1}{2}$ and

$$W = \int_0^\infty J_n(ax) J_n(bx) J_m(cx) x^{1-m} dx,$$

a, b, c being positive, then

$$W = 0 \qquad (a-b)^2 > c^2,$$

$$W = (2\pi)^{-\frac{1}{2}} a^{m-1} b^{m-1} c^{-m} (1-\mu^2)^{\frac{1}{4}(2m-1)} P_{n-\frac{1}{2}}^{\frac{1}{2}-m}(\mu) \qquad (a+b)^2 > c^2 > (a-b)^2,$$

$$W = (\tfrac{1}{2}\pi)^{-\frac{1}{2}} a^{m-1} b^{m-1} c^{-m} \frac{\sin(m-n)\pi}{\pi} e^{(m-\frac{1}{2})\pi i} (\mu_1^2-1)^{\frac{1}{4}(2m-1)} Q_{n-\frac{1}{2}}^{\frac{1}{2}-m}(\mu_1)$$

$$c^2 > (a+b)^2,$$

where $$\mu = (a^2+b^2-c^2)/2ab, \quad \mu_1 = -\mu.$$

(Macdonald, *Proc. London Math. Soc.* (2), VII.)

40. Shew that, if $R(m+\frac{1}{2}) > 0$,

$$I_m(z) = \frac{z^m}{2^m \Gamma(m+\frac{1}{2}) \Gamma(\frac{1}{2})} \int_0^\pi \cosh(z \cos\phi) \sin^{2m}\phi \, d\phi,$$

and, if $|\arg z| < \frac{1}{2}\pi$;

$$K_m(z) = \frac{z^m \Gamma(\frac{1}{2}) \cos m\pi}{2^m \Gamma(m+\frac{1}{2})} \int_0^\infty e^{-z \cosh\phi} \sinh^{2m}\phi \, d\phi.$$

Prove also that

$$K_m(z) = \pi^{-\frac{1}{2}} 2^m z^m \Gamma(m+\frac{1}{2}) \cos m\pi \int_0^\infty (u^2+z^2)^{-m-\frac{1}{2}} \cos u \, du.$$

(Math. Trip. 1898. Cf. Basset, *Proc. Camb. Phil. Soc.* VI.)

[The first integral may be obtained by expanding in powers of z and integrating term-by-term. To obtain the second, consider

$$z^m \int_\infty^{(1+, -1+)} e^{-zt} (t^2-1)^{m-\frac{1}{2}} dt,$$

where initially $\arg(t-1) = \arg(t+1) = 0$. Take $|t| > 1$ on the contour, expand $(t^2-1)^{m-\frac{1}{2}}$ in descending powers of t, and integrate term-by-term. The result is

$$2ie^{2m\pi i} \sin(2m\pi) \Gamma(2m) 2^{-m} \Gamma(1-m) I_{-m}(z).$$

Also, deforming the contour by flattening it, the integral becomes

$$2ie^{2m\pi i} z^m \sin 2m\pi \int_1^\infty e^{-zt} (t^2-1)^{m-\frac{1}{2}} dt + 2ie^{2m\pi i} z^m \cos m\pi \int_{-1}^1 e^{-zt} (1-t^2)^{m-\frac{1}{2}} dt;$$

and consequently

$$I_{-m}(z) - I_m(z) = \frac{2^{1-m} \sin(m\pi) z^m}{\Gamma(\frac{1}{2}) \Gamma(m+\frac{1}{2})} \int_1^\infty e^{-zt} (t^2-1)^{m-\frac{1}{2}} dt.]$$

41. Shew that $O_n(z)$ satisfies the differential equation

$$\frac{d^2 O_n(z)}{dz^2} + \frac{3}{z} \frac{dO_n(z)}{dz} + \left\{1 - \frac{n^2-1}{z^2}\right\} O_n(z) = g_n,$$

where $$g_n = z^{-1} \ (n \text{ even}), \quad g_n = nz^{-2} \ (n \text{ odd}).$$ (K. Neumann.)

42. If $f(z)$ be analytic throughout the ring-shaped region bounded by the circles c, C whose centres are at the origin, establish the expansion

$$f(z) = \tfrac{1}{2} a_0 J_0(z) + a_1 J_1(z) + a_2 J_2(z) + \dots$$
$$+ \tfrac{1}{2} \beta_0 O_0(z) + \beta_1 O_1(z) + \beta_2 O_2(z) + \dots,$$

where $$a_n = \frac{1}{\pi i} \int_C f(t) O_n(t) dt, \quad \beta_n = \frac{1}{\pi i} \int_c f(t) J_n(t) dt. \quad \text{(K. Neumann.)}$$

43. Shew that, if x and y are positive,

$$\int_0^\infty \frac{e^{-\beta x}}{\beta} J_0(ky) k \, dk = \frac{e^{-ir}}{r},$$

where $r = +\sqrt{(x^2+y^2)}$ and $\beta = +\sqrt{(k^2-1)}$ or $i\sqrt{(1-k^2)}$ according as $k > 1$ or $k < 1$.

(Math. Trip. 1905.)

44. Shew that, with suitable restrictions on n and on the form of the function $f(x)$,

$$f(x) = \int_0^\infty J_n(tx)\, t \left\{ \int_0^\infty f(x')\, J_n(tx')\, x'\, dx' \right\} dt.$$

[A proof with an historical account of this important theorem is given by Nielsen, *Cylinderfunktionen*, pp. 360–363. It is due to Hankel, but (in view of the result of § 9·7) it is often called the *Fourier-Bessel integral*.]

45. If C be any closed contour, and m and n are integers, shew that

$$\int_C J_m(z)\, J_n(z)\, dz = \int_C O_m(z)\, O_n(z)\, dz = \int_C J_m(z)\, O_n(z)\, dz = 0,$$

unless C contains the origin and $m = n$; in which case the first two integrals are still zero, but the third is equal to πi (or $2\pi i$ if $m = 0$) if C encircles the origin once counterclockwise. (K. Neumann.)

46. Shew that, if

$$\frac{(-)^p}{p!\, q!} = a_{p,\,q},$$

and if n be a positive integer, then

$$z^{-2n} = \sum_{m=1}^{n} a_{n-m,\, n+m-1}\, O_{2m-1}(z),$$

while

$$z^{1-2n} = a_{n-1,\, n-1}\, O_0(z) + 2 \sum_{m=1}^{n-1} a_{n-m-1,\, n+m-1}\, O_{2m}(z).$$

(K. Neumann.)

47. If

$$\Omega_n(y) = \sum_{m=0}^{n} \frac{2^{2m}(m!)^2}{2m!} \frac{n^2 \{n^2 - 1^2\}\{n^2 - 2^2\} \dots \{n^2 - (m-1)^2\}}{y^{2m+2}},$$

shew that

$$(y^2 - x^2)^{-1} = \Omega_0(y)\, \{J_0(x)\}^2 + 2 \sum_{n=1}^{\infty} \Omega_n(y)\, \{J_n(x)\}^2$$

when the series on the right converges. (K. Neumann, *Math. Ann.* III.)

48. Shew that, if $c > 0$, $R(n) > -1$ and $R(a \pm b)^2 > 0$, then

$$J_n(a)\, J_n(b) = \frac{1}{2\pi i} \int_{c-\infty i}^{c+\infty i} t^{-1} \exp\{(t^2 - a^2 - b^2)/(2t)\} \cdot I_n(ab/t)\, dt.$$

(Macdonald, *Proc. London Math. Soc.* XXXII.)

49. Deduce from example 48, or otherwise prove, that

$$(a^2 + b^2 - 2ab\cos\theta)^{-\frac{1}{2}n}\, J_n\{(a^2 + b^2 - 2ab\cos\theta)^{\frac{1}{2}}\}$$

$$= 2^n\, \Gamma(n) \sum_{m=0}^{\infty} (m+n)\, a^{-n} b^{-n}\, J_{m+n}(a)\, J_{m+n}(b)\, C_m^n(\cos\theta).$$

(Gegenbauer, *Wiener Sitzungsberichte*, LXIX. LXXIV.)

50. Shew that

$$y = \int_C J_m(t)\, J_n(tz^{\frac{1}{2}})\, t^{k-1}\, dt$$

satisfies the equation

$$\frac{d^2 y}{dz^2} + \left(\frac{1}{z} + \frac{k}{z-1}\right) \frac{dy}{dz} + \left(k^2 - m^2 + \frac{n^2}{z}\right) \frac{y}{4z(z-1)} = 0$$

if

$$k t^k\, J_m(t)\, J_n(tz^{\frac{1}{2}}) - t^{k+1}\, J_m{}'(t)\, J_n(tz^{\frac{1}{2}}) + z^{\frac{1}{2}}\, t^{k+1}\, J_m(t)\, J_n{}'(tz^{\frac{1}{2}})$$

resumes its initial value after describing the contour.

Deduce that, when $0 < z < 1$,

$$\int_0^\infty J_{a-\beta}(t)\, J_{\gamma-1}(tz^{\frac{1}{2}})\, t^{a+\beta-\gamma}\, dt = \frac{\Gamma(a)\, z^{\frac{1}{2}(\gamma-1)}}{2^{\gamma-a-\beta}\, \Gamma(1-\beta)\, \Gamma(\gamma)}\, F(a,\, \beta;\, \gamma;\, z).$$

(Schafheitlin, *Math. Ann.* XXX.; Math. Trip. 1903.)

CHAPTER XVIII

THE EQUATIONS OF MATHEMATICAL PHYSICS

18·1. *The differential equations of mathematical physics.*

The functions which have been introduced in the preceding chapters are of importance in the applications of mathematics to physical investigations. Such applications are outside the province of this book; but most of them depend essentially on the fact that, by means of these functions, it is possible to construct solutions of certain partial differential equations, of which the following are among the most important:

(I) *Laplace's equation*

$$\frac{\partial^2 V}{\partial x^2} + \frac{\partial^2 V}{\partial y^2} + \frac{\partial^2 V}{\partial z^2} = 0,$$

which was originally introduced in a memoir* on Saturn's rings.

If (x, y, z) be the rectangular coordinates of any point in space, this equation is satisfied by the following functions which occur in various branches of mathematical physics:

(i)   The gravitational potential in regions not occupied by attracting matter.

(ii)   The electrostatic potential in a uniform dielectric. in the theory of electrostatics.

(iii)   The magnetic potential in free aether, in the theory of magnetostatics.

(iv)   The electric potential, in the theory of the steady flow of electric currents in solid conductors.

(v)   The temperature, in the theory of thermal equilibrium in solids.

(vi)   The velocity potential at points of a homogeneous liquid moving irrotationally, in hydrodynamical problems.

Notwithstanding the physical differences of these theories, the mathematical investigations are much the same for all of them: thus, the problem of thermal equilibrium in a solid when the points of its surface are maintained at given temperatures is mathematically identical with the problem of determining the electric intensity in a region when the points of its boundary are maintained at given potentials.

(II) *The equation of wave motions*

$$\frac{\partial^2 V}{\partial x^2} + \frac{\partial^2 V}{\partial y^2} + \frac{\partial^2 V}{\partial z^2} = \frac{1}{c^2} \frac{\partial^2 V}{\partial t^2}.$$

This equation is of general occurrence in investigations of undulatory disturbances propagated with velocity c independent of the wave length; for example, in the theory of electric waves and the electro-magnetic theory of light, it is the equation satisfied by each component of the electric or magnetic vector; in the theory of elastic vibrations, it is the equation satisfied by each component of the displacement; and in the theory of sound, it is the equation satisfied by the velocity potential in a perfect gas.

* *Mém. de l'Acad. des Sciences,* 1787 (published 1789), p. 252.

(III)   *The equation of conduction of heat*

$$\frac{\partial^2 V}{\partial x^2} + \frac{\partial^2 V}{\partial y^2} + \frac{\partial^2 V}{\partial z^2} = \frac{1}{k}\frac{\partial V}{\partial t}.$$

This is the equation satisfied by the temperature at a point of a homogeneous isotropic body; the constant k is proportional to the heat conductivity of the body and inversely proportional to its specific heat and density.

(IV)   A particular case of the preceding equation (II), when the variable z is absent, is

$$\frac{\partial^2 V}{\partial x^2} + \frac{\partial^2 V}{\partial y^2} = \frac{1}{c^2}\frac{\partial^2 V}{\partial t^2}.$$

This is the equation satisfied by the displacement in the theory of transverse vibrations of a membrane; the equation also occurs in the theory of wave motion in two dimensions.

(V)   *The equation of telegraphy*

$$LK\frac{\partial^2 V}{\partial t^2} + KR\frac{\partial V}{\partial t} = \frac{\partial^2 V}{\partial x^2}.$$

This is the equation satisfied by the potential in a telegraph cable when the inductance L, the capacity K, and the resistance R per unit length are taken into account.

It would not be possible, within the limits of this chapter, to attempt an exhaustive account of the theories of these and the other differential equations of mathematical physics; but, by considering selected typical cases, we shall expound some of the principal methods employed, with special reference to the uses of the transcendental functions.

18·2.   *Boundary conditions.*

A problem which arises very frequently is the determination, for one of the equations of § 18·1, of a solution which is subject to certain boundary conditions; thus we may desire to find the temperature at any point inside a homogeneous isotropic conducting solid in thermal equilibrium when the points of its outer surface are maintained at given temperatures. This amounts to finding a solution of Laplace's equation at points inside a given surface, when the value of the solution at points on the surface is given.

A more complicated problem of a similar nature occurs in discussing small oscillations of a liquid in a basin, the liquid being exposed to the atmosphere; in this problem we are given, effectively, the velocity potential at points of the free surface and the normal derivate of the velocity potential where the liquid is in contact with the basin.

The nature of the boundary conditions, necessary to determine a solution uniquely, varies very much with the form of differential equation considered, even in the case of equations which, at first sight, seem very much alike. Thus a solution of the equation

$$\frac{\partial^2 V}{\partial x^2} + \frac{\partial^2 V}{\partial y^2} = 0$$

(which occurs in the problem of thermal equilibrium in a conducting cylinder) is uniquely determined at points inside a closed curve in the xy-plane by a knowledge of the value of V at points on the curve; but in the case of the equation

$$\frac{\partial^2 V}{\partial x^2} - \frac{1}{c^2}\frac{\partial^2 V}{\partial t^2} = 0$$

(which effectively only differs from the former in a change of sign), occurring in connexion with transverse vibrations of a stretched string, where V denotes the displacement at time t at distance x from the end of the string, it is physically evident that a solution is determined uniquely only if both V and $\dfrac{\partial V}{\partial t}$ are given for all values of x such that $0 \leqslant x \leqslant l$, when $t = 0$ (where l denotes the length of the string).

Physical intuitions will usually indicate the nature of the boundary conditions which are necessary to determine a solution of a differential equation uniquely; but the existence theorems which are necessary from the point of view of the pure mathematician are usually very tedious and difficult*.

18·3. *A general solution of Laplace's equation†.*

It is possible to construct a general solution of Laplace's equation in the form of a definite integral. This solution can be employed to solve various problems involving boundary conditions.

Let $V(x, y, z)$ be a solution of Laplace's equation which can be expanded into a power series in three variables valid for points of (x, y, z) sufficiently near a given point (x_0, y_0, z_0). Accordingly we write

$$x = x_0 + X, \quad y = y_0 + Y, \quad z = z_0 + Z;$$

and we assume the expansion

$$V = a_0 + a_1 X + b_1 Y + c_1 Z + a_2 X^2 + b_2 Y^2 + c_2 Z^2$$
$$+ 2d_2 YZ + 2e_2 ZX + 2f_2 XY + \ldots,$$

it being supposed that this series is absolutely convergent whenever

$$|X|^2 + |Y|^2 + |Z|^2 \leqslant a,$$

where a is some positive constant‡. If this expansion exists, V is said to be analytic at (x_0, y_0, z_0). It can be proved by the methods of §§ 3·7, 4·7

---

* See e.g. Forsyth, *Theory of Functions* (1918), §§ 216–220, where an apparently simple problem is discussed.

† Whittaker, *Math. Ann.* LVII. (1902), p. 333.

‡ The functions of applied mathematics satisfy this condition.

that the series converges uniformly throughout the domain indicated and may be differentiated term-by-term with regard to X, Y or Z any number of times at points inside the domain.

If we substitute the expansion in Laplace's equation, which may be written

$$\frac{\partial^2 V}{\partial X^2} + \frac{\partial^2 V}{\partial Y^2} + \frac{\partial^2 V}{\partial Z^2} = 0,$$

and equate to zero (§ 3·73) the coefficients of the various powers of X, Y and Z, we get an infinite set of linear relations between the coefficients, of which

$$a_2 + b_2 + c_2 = 0$$

may be taken as typical.

There are $\frac{1}{2} n(n-1)$ of these relations* between the $\frac{1}{2}(n+2)(n+1)$ coefficients of the terms of degree n in the expansion of V, so that there are only $\frac{1}{2}(n+2)(n+1) - \frac{1}{2} n(n-1) = 2n+1$ independent coefficients in the terms of degree n in V. Hence the terms of degree n in V must be a linear combination of $2n+1$ linearly independent particular solutions of Laplace's equation, these solutions being each of degree n in X, Y and Z.

To find a set of such solutions, consider $(Z + iX \cos u + iY \sin u)^n$; it is a solution of Laplace's equation which may be expanded in a series of sines and cosines of multiples of u, thus:

$$\sum_{m=0}^{n} g_m(X, Y, Z) \cos mu + \sum_{m=1}^{n} h_m(X, Y, Z) \sin mu,$$

the functions $g_m(X, Y, Z)$ and $h_m(X, Y, Z)$ being independent of u. The highest power of Z in $g_m(X, Y, Z)$ and $h_m(X, Y, Z)$ is Z^{n-m} and the former function is an even function of Y, the latter an odd function; hence the functions are linearly independent. They therefore form a set of $2n+1$ functions of the type sought.

Now by Fourier's rule† (§ 9·12)

$$\pi g_m(X, Y, Z) = \int_{-\pi}^{\pi} (Z + iX \cos u + iY \sin u)^n \cos mu \, du,$$

$$\pi h_m(X, Y, Z) = \int_{-\pi}^{\pi} (Z + iX \cos u + iY \sin u)^n \sin mu \, du,$$

---

* If $a_{r,s,t}$ (where $r+s+t=n$) be the coefficient of $X^r Y^s Z^t$ in V, and if the terms of degree $n-2$ in $\frac{\partial^2 V}{\partial X^2} + \frac{\partial^2 V}{\partial Y^2} + \frac{\partial^2 V}{\partial Z^2}$ be arranged primarily in powers of X and secondarily in powers of Y, the coefficient $a_{r,s,t}$ does not occur in any term after $X^{r-2} Y^s Z^t$ (or $X^r Y^{s-2} Z^t$ if $r=0$ or 1), and hence the relations are all linearly independent.

† 2π must be written for π in the coefficient of $g_0(X, Y, Z)$.

and so any linear combination of the $2n+1$ solutions can be written in the form

$$\int_{-\pi}^{\pi} (Z + iX \cos u + iY \sin u)^n f_n(u)\, du,$$

where $f_n(u)$ is a rational function of e^{iu}.

Now it is readily verified that, if the terms of degree n in the expression assumed for V be written in this form, the series of terms under the integral sign converges uniformly if $|X|^2 + |Y|^2 + |Z|^2$ be sufficiently small, and so (§ 4·7) we may write

$$V = \int_{-\pi}^{\pi} \sum_{n=0}^{\infty} (Z + iX \cos u + iY \sin u)^n f_n(u)\, du.$$

But any expression of this form may be written

$$V = \int_{-\pi}^{\pi} F(Z + iX \cos u + iY \sin u,\, u)\, du,$$

where F is a function such that differentiations with regard to X, Y or Z under the sign of integration are permissible. And, conversely, if F be any function of this type, V is a solution of Laplace's equation.

This result may be written

$$V = \int_{-\pi}^{\pi} f(z + ix \cos u + iy \sin u,\, u)\, du,$$

on absorbing the terms $-z_0 - ix_0 \cos u - iy_0 \sin u$ into the second variable; and, if differentiations under the sign of integration are permissible, this gives a general solution of Laplace's equation; that is to say, every solution of Laplace's equation which is analytic throughout the interior of some sphere is expressible by an integral of the form given.

This result is the three-dimensional analogue of the theorem that

$$V = f(x + iy) + g(x - iy)$$

is the general solution of

$$\frac{\partial^2 V}{\partial x^2} + \frac{\partial^2 V}{\partial y^2} = 0.$$

[NOTE. A distinction has to be drawn between the primitive of an ordinary differential equation and general integrals of a partial differential equation of order higher than the first[*].

Two apparently distinct primitives are always directly transformable into one another by means of suitable relations between the constants; thus in the case of $\frac{d^2 y}{dx^2} + y = 0$, we can obtain the primitive $C \sin(x + \epsilon)$ from $A \cos x + B \sin x$ by defining C and ϵ by the equations $C \sin \epsilon = A$, $C \cos \epsilon = B$. On the other hand, every solution of Laplace's equation is expressible in each of the forms

$$\int_{-\pi}^{\pi} f(x \cos t + y \sin t + iz,\, t)\, dt, \qquad \int_{-\pi}^{\pi} g(y \cos u + z \sin u + ix,\, u)\, du\,;$$

* For a discussion of general integrals of such equations, see Forsyth, *Theory of Differential Equations*, vi. (1906), Ch. xii.

but if these are known to be the same solution, there appears to be no general analytical relation, connecting the functions f and g, which will directly transform one form of the solution into the other.]

Example 1.   Shew that the potential of a particle of unit mass at (a, b, c) is

$$\frac{1}{2\pi} \int_{-\pi}^{\pi} \frac{du}{(z-c)+i\,(x-a)\cos u + i\,(y-b)\sin u}$$

at all points for which $z > c$.

Example 2.   Shew that a general solution of Laplace's equation of zero degree in x, y, z is

$$\int_{-\pi}^{\pi} \log\,(x\cos t + y\sin t + iz)\,g\,(t)\,dt, \text{ if } \int_{-\pi}^{\pi} g\,(t)\,dt = 0.$$

Express the solutions $\dfrac{x}{z+r}$ and $\log\dfrac{r+z}{r-z}$ in this form, where $r^2 = x^2 + y^2 + z^2$.

Example 3.   Shew that, in the case of the equation

$$p^{\frac{1}{2}} + q^{\frac{1}{2}} = x + y$$

$\left(\text{where } p = \dfrac{\partial z}{\partial x}, q = \dfrac{\partial z}{\partial y}\right)$, integrals of Charpit's subsidiary equations (see Forsyth, *Differential Equations*, Chap. IX.) are

(i) $p^{\frac{1}{2}} - x = y - q^{\frac{1}{2}} = a,$

(ii) $p = q + a^2.$

Deduce that the corresponding general integrals are derived from

(i) $z = \tfrac{1}{3}\,(x+a)^3 + \tfrac{1}{3}\,(y-a)^3 + F\,(a)$
      $0 = (x+a)^2 - (y-a)^2 + F'\,(a)$,

(ii) $4z = \tfrac{1}{3}\,(x+y)^3 + 2a^2\,(x-y) - a^4\,(x+y)^{-1} + G\,(a)$
       $0 = 4a\,(x-y) - 4a^3\,(x+y)^{-1} + G'\,(a)$,

and thence obtain a differential equation determining the function $G\,(a)$ in terms of the function $F\,(a)$ when the two general integrals are the same.

18·31.   *Solutions of Laplace's equation involving Legendre functions.*

If an expansion for V, of the form assumed in § 18·3, exists when

$$x_0 = y_0 = z_0 = 0,$$

we have seen that we can express V as a series of expressions of the type

$$\int_{-\pi}^{\pi} (z + ix\cos u + iy\sin u)^n \cos mu\,du, \quad \int_{-\pi}^{\pi} (z + ix\cos u + iy\sin u)^n \sin mu\,du,$$

where n and m are integers such that $0 \leqslant m \leqslant n$.

We shall now examine these expressions more closely.

If we take polar coordinates, defined by the equations

$$x = r\sin\theta\cos\phi, \quad y = r\sin\theta\sin\phi, \quad z = r\cos\theta,$$

we have

$$\int_{-\pi}^{\pi} (z + ix \cos u + iy \sin u)^n \cos m u \, du$$

$$= r^n \int_{-\pi}^{\pi} \{\cos \theta + i \sin \theta \cos (u - \phi)\}^n \cos m u \, du$$

$$= r^n \int_{-\pi - \phi}^{\pi - \phi} \{\cos \theta + i \sin \theta \cos \psi\}^n \cos m (\phi + \psi) \, d\psi$$

$$= r^n \int_{-\pi}^{\pi} \{\cos \theta + i \sin \theta \cos \psi\}^n \cos m (\phi + \psi) \, d\psi$$

$$= r^n \cos m\phi \int_{-\pi}^{\pi} \{\cos \theta + i \sin \theta \cos \psi\}^n \cos m\psi \, d\psi,$$

since the integrand is a periodic function of ψ and

$$(\cos \theta + i \sin \theta \cos \psi)^n \sin m\psi$$

is an odd function of ψ. Therefore (§ 15·61), with Ferrers' definition of the associated Legendre function,

$$\int_{-\pi}^{\pi} (z + ix \cos u + iy \sin u)^n \cos m u \, du = \frac{2\pi i^m \cdot n!}{(n + m)!} r^n P_n^m (\cos \theta) \cos m\phi.$$

Similarly

$$\int_{-\pi}^{\pi} (z + ix \cos u + iy \sin u)^n \sin m u \, du = \frac{2\pi i^m \cdot n!}{(n + m)!} r^n P_n^m (\cos \theta) \sin m\phi.$$

Therefore $r^n P_n^m (\cos \theta) \cos m\phi$ *and* $r^n P_n^m (\cos \theta) \sin m\phi$ *are polynomials in* x, y, z *and are particular solutions of Laplace's equation. Further, by* § 18·3, *every solution of Laplace's equation, which is analytic near the origin, can be expressed in the form*

$$V = \sum_{n=0}^{\infty} r^n \left\{ A_n P_n (\cos \theta) + \sum_{m=1}^{n} (A_n^{(m)} \cos m\phi + B_n^{(m)} \sin m\phi) P_n^m (\cos \theta) \right\}.$$

Any expression of the form

$$A_n P_n (\cos \theta) + \sum_{m=1}^{n} (A_n^{(m)} \cos m\phi + B_n^{(m)} \sin m\phi) P_n^m (\cos \theta),$$

where n is a positive integer, is called a *surface harmonic* of degree n; a surface harmonic of degree n multiplied by r^n is called a *solid harmonic* (or a *spherical harmonic*) of degree n.

The curves on a unit sphere (with centre at the origin) on which $P_n (\cos \theta)$ vanishes are n parallels of latitude which divide the surface of the sphere into zones, and so $P_n (\cos \theta)$ is called (see § 15·1) a *zonal harmonic*; and the curves on which $\frac{\cos}{\sin} m\phi \cdot P_n^m (\cos \theta)$ vanishes are $n - m$ parallels of latitude and $2m$ meridians, which divide the surface of the sphere into quadrangles whose angles are right angles, and so these functions are called *tesseral harmonics*.

A solid harmonic of degree n is evidently a homogeneous polynomial of degree n in x, y, z and it satisfies Laplace's equation.

It is evident that, if a change of rectangular coordinates* is made by rotating the axes about the origin, a solid harmonic (or a surface harmonic) of degree n transforms into a solid harmonic (or a surface harmonic) of degree n in the new coordinates.

Spherical harmonics were investigated with the aid of Cartesian coordinates by W. Thomson in 1862, see *Phil. Trans.* (1863), pp. 573–582, and Thomson and Tait, *Treatise on Natural Philosophy* I. (1879), pp. 171–218; they were also investigated independently in the same manner at about the same time by Clebsch, *Journal für Math.* LXI. (1863), pp. 195–262.

Example. If coordinates r, θ, ϕ are defined by the equations

$$x = r \cos \theta, \quad y = (r^2 - 1)^{\frac{1}{2}} \sin \theta \cos \phi, \quad z = (r^2 - 1)^{\frac{1}{2}} \sin \theta \sin \phi,$$

shew that $P_n{}^m(r) P_n{}^m(\cos \theta) \cos m\phi$ satisfies Laplace's equation.

18·4. *The solution of Laplace's equation which satisfies assigned boundary conditions at the surface of a sphere.*

We have seen (§ 18·31) that any solution of Laplace's equation which is analytic near the origin can be expanded in the form

$$V(r, \theta, \phi) = \sum_{n=0}^{\infty} r^n \left\{ A_n P_n(\cos \theta) \right.$$
$$\left. + \sum_{m=1}^{n} (A_n{}^{(m)} \cos m\phi + B_n{}^{(m)} \sin m\phi) P_n{}^m(\cos \theta) \right\};$$

and, from § 3·7, it is evident that if it converges for a given value of r, say a, for all values of θ and ϕ such that $0 \leqslant \theta \leqslant \pi$, $-\pi \leqslant \phi \leqslant \pi$, it converges absolutely and uniformly when $r < a$.

To determine the constants, we must know the boundary conditions which V must satisfy. A boundary condition of frequent occurrence is that V is a given bounded integrable function of θ and ϕ, say $f(\theta, \phi)$, on the surface of a given sphere, which we take to have radius a, and V is analytic at points inside this sphere.

We then have to determine the coefficients A_n, $A_n{}^{(m)}$, $B_n{}^{(m)}$ from the equation

$$f(\theta, \phi) = \sum_{n=0}^{\infty} a^n \left\{ A_n P_n(\cos \theta) + \sum_{m=1}^{n} (A_n{}^{(m)} \cos m\phi + B_n{}^{(m)} \sin m\phi) P_n{}^m(\cos \theta) \right\}.$$

Assuming that this series converges uniformly† throughout the domain

$$0 \leqslant \theta \leqslant \pi, \quad -\pi \leqslant \phi \leqslant \pi,$$

multiplying by

$$P_n{}^m(\cos \theta) \frac{\cos}{\sin} m\phi,$$

---

* Laplace's operator $\frac{\partial^2}{\partial x^2} + \frac{\partial^2}{\partial y^2} + \frac{\partial^2}{\partial z^2}$ is invariant for changes of rectangular axes.

† This is usually the case in physical problems.

integrating term-by-term (§ 4·7) and using the results of §§ 15·14, 15·51 on the integral properties of Legendre functions, we find that

$$\int_{-\pi}^{\pi} \int_{0}^{\pi} f(\theta', \phi') \, P_n{}^m (\cos \theta') \cos m\phi' \sin \theta' d\theta' d\phi' = \pi a^n \frac{2}{2n+1} \cdot \frac{(n+m)!}{(n-m)!} A_n{}^{(m)},$$

$$\int_{-\pi}^{\pi} \int_{0}^{\pi} f(\theta', \phi') \, P_n{}^m (\cos \theta') \sin m\phi' \sin \theta' d\theta' d\phi' = \pi a^n \frac{2}{2n+1} \cdot \frac{(n+m)!}{(n-m)!} B_n{}^{(m)},$$

$$\int_{-\pi}^{\pi} \int_{0}^{\pi} f(\theta', \phi') \, P_n (\cos \theta') \sin \theta' d\theta' d\phi' = 2\pi a^n \frac{2}{2n+1} A_n.$$

Therefore, when $r < a$,

$$V(r, \theta, \phi) = \sum_{n=0}^{\infty} \frac{2n+1}{4\pi} \left(\frac{r}{a}\right)^n \int_{-\pi}^{\pi} \int_{0}^{\pi} f(\theta', \phi') \left\{ P_n(\cos \theta) \, P_n(\cos \theta') \right.$$

$$\left. + 2 \sum_{m=1}^{n} \frac{(n-m)!}{(n+m)!} P_n{}^m (\cos \theta) \, P_n{}^m (\cos \theta') \cos m(\phi - \phi') \right\} \sin \theta' d\theta' d\phi'.$$

The series which is here integrated term-by-term converges uniformly when $r < a$, since the expression under the integral sign is a bounded function of $\theta, \theta', \phi, \phi'$, and so (§ 4·7)

$$4\pi V(r, \theta, \phi) = \int_{-\pi}^{\pi} \int_{0}^{\pi} f(\theta', \phi') \sum_{n=0}^{\infty} (2n+1) \left(\frac{r}{a}\right)^n \left\{ P_n(\cos \theta) \, P_n(\cos \theta') \right.$$

$$\left. + 2 \sum_{m=1}^{n} \frac{(n-m)!}{(n+m)!} P_n{}^m (\cos \theta) \, P_n{}^m (\cos \theta') \cos m(\phi - \phi') \right\} \sin \theta' d\theta' d\phi'.$$

Now suppose that we take the line (θ, ϕ) as a new polar axis and let (θ_1', ϕ_1') be the new coordinates of the line whose old coordinates were (θ', ϕ'); we consequently have to replace $P_n(\cos \theta)$ by 1 and $P_n{}^m(\cos \theta)$ by zero; and so we get

$$4\pi V(r, \theta, \phi) = \int_{-\pi}^{\pi} \int_{0}^{\pi} f(\theta', \phi') \sum_{n=0}^{\infty} (2n+1) \left(\frac{r}{a}\right)^n P_n(\cos \theta_1') \sin \theta_1' d\theta_1' d\phi_1'$$

$$= \int_{-\pi}^{\pi} \int_{0}^{\pi} f(\theta', \phi') \sum_{n=0}^{\infty} (2n+1) \left(\frac{r}{a}\right)^n P_n(\cos \theta_1') \sin \theta' d\theta' d\phi'.$$

If, in this formula, we make use of the result of example 23 of Chapter xv (p. 332), we get

$$4\pi V(r, \theta, \phi) = \int_{-\pi}^{\pi} \int_{0}^{\pi} f(\theta', \phi') \frac{a(a^2 - r^2) \sin \theta' d\theta' d\phi'}{(r^2 - 2ar \cos \theta_1' + a^2)^{\frac{3}{2}}},$$

and so

$$4\pi V(r, \theta, \phi)$$

$$= a(a^2 - r^2) \int_{-\pi}^{\pi} \int_{0}^{\pi} \frac{f(\theta', \phi') \sin \theta' d\theta' d\phi'}{[r^2 - 2ar \{\cos \theta \cos \theta' + \sin \theta \sin \theta' \cos (\phi - \phi')\} + a^2]^{\frac{3}{2}}}.$$

In this compact formula the Legendre functions have ceased to appear explicitly.

The last formula can be obtained by the theory of *Green's functions*. For properties of such functions the reader is referred to Thomson and Tait, *Natural Philosophy*, §§ 499–519.

[NOTE. From the integrals for $V(r, \theta, \phi)$ involving Legendre functions of $\cos \theta_1'$ and of $\cos \theta$, $\cos \theta'$ respectively, we can obtain a new proof of the addition theorem for the Legendre polynomial.

For let

$$\chi_n(\theta', \phi') = P_n(\cos \theta_1') - \bigg\{ P_n(\cos \theta) P_n(\cos \theta')$$
$$+ 2 \sum_{m=1}^{n} \frac{(n-m)!}{(n+m)!} P_n{}^m(\cos \theta) P_n{}^m(\cos \theta') \cos m(\phi - \phi') \bigg\},$$

and we get, on comparing the two formulae for $V(r, \theta, \phi)$,

$$0 = \int_{-\pi}^{\pi} \int_0^{\pi} f(\theta', \phi') \sum_{n=0}^{\infty} (2n+1) \left(\frac{r}{a}\right)^n \chi_n(\theta', \phi') \sin \theta' d\theta' d\phi'.$$

If we take $f(\theta', \phi')$ to be a surface harmonic of degree n, the term involving r^n is the only one which occurs in the integrated series; and in particular, if we take $f(\theta', \phi') = \chi_n(\theta', \phi')$, we get

$$\int_{-\pi}^{\pi} \int_0^{\pi} \{\chi_n(\theta', \phi')\}^2 \sin \theta' d\theta' d\phi' = 0.$$

Since the integrand is continuous and is not negative it must be zero; and so $\chi_n(\theta', \phi') \equiv 0$; that is to say we have proved the formula

$$P_n(\cos \theta_1') = P_n(\cos \theta) P_n(\cos \theta') + 2 \sum_{m=1}^{n} \frac{(n-m)!}{(n+m)!} P_n{}^m(\cos \theta) P_n{}^m(\cos \theta') \cos m(\phi - \phi'),$$

wherein it is obvious that

$$\cos \theta_1' = \cos \theta \cos \theta' + \sin \theta \sin \theta' \cos (\phi - \phi'),$$

from geometrical considerations.

We have thus obtained a physical proof of a theorem proved elsewhere* (§ 15·7) by purely analytical reasoning.]

Example 1. Find the solution of Laplace's equation analytic inside the sphere $r = 1$ which has the value $\sin 3\theta \cos \phi$ at the surface of the sphere.

$$[\tfrac{8}{15} r^3 P_3{}^1(\cos \theta) \cos \phi - \tfrac{1}{5} r P_1{}^1(\cos \theta) \cos \phi.]$$

Example 2. Let $f_n(r, \theta, \phi)$ be equal to a homogeneous polynomial of degree n in x, y, z. Shew that

$$\int_{-\pi}^{\pi} \int_0^{\pi} f_n(a, \theta, \phi) P_n \{\cos \theta \cos \theta' + \sin \theta \sin \theta' \cos (\phi - \phi')\} a^2 \sin \theta \, d\theta \, d\phi$$
$$= \frac{4\pi a^2}{2n+1} f_n(a, \theta', \phi').$$

[Take the direction (θ', ϕ') as a new polar axis.]

18·5. *Solutions of Laplace's equation which involve Bessel coefficients.*

A particular case of the result of § 18·3 is that

$$\int_{-\pi}^{\pi} e^{k(z + ix \cos u + iy \sin u)} \cos mu \, du$$

is a solution of Laplace's equation, k being any constant and m being any integer.

* The absence of the factor $(-)^m$ which occurs in § 15·7 is due to the fact that the functions now employed are Ferrers' associated functions.

Taking cylindrical-polar coordinates (ρ, ϕ, z) defined by the equations

$$x = \rho \cos \phi, \quad y = \rho \sin \phi,$$

the above solution becomes

$$e^{kz} \int_{-\pi}^{\pi} e^{ik\rho \cos (u-\phi)} \cos mu\,du = e^{kz} \int_{-\pi}^{\pi} e^{ik\rho \cos v} \cos m\,(v + \phi)\,.\,dv$$

$$= 2e^{kz} \int_{0}^{\pi} e^{ik\rho \cos v} \cos mv \cos m\phi\,dv$$

$$= 2e^{kz} \cos (m\phi) \int_{0}^{\pi} e^{ik\rho \cos v} \cos mv\,dv,$$

and so, using § 17·1 example 3, *we see that* $2\pi i^m e^{kz} \cos (m\phi)\,.\,J_m(k\rho)$ *is a solution of Laplace's equation analytic near the origin.*

Similarly, from the expression

$$\int_{-\pi}^{\pi} e^{k(z+ix\cos u+iy\sin u)} \sin mu\,du,$$

where m is an integer, *we deduce that* $2\pi i^m e^{kz} \sin (m\phi)\,.\,J_m(k\rho)$ *is a solution of Laplace's equation.*

18·51.   *The periods of vibration of a uniform membrane*.*

The equation satisfied by the displacement V at time t of a point (x, y) of a uniform plane membrane vibrating harmonically is

$$\frac{\partial^2 V}{\partial x^2} + \frac{\partial^2 V}{\partial y^2} = \frac{1}{c^2} \frac{\partial^2 V}{\partial t^2},$$

where c is a constant depending on the tension and density of the membrane. The equation can be reduced to Laplace's equation by the change of variable given by $z = cti$. It follows, from § 18·5, that expressions of the form

$$J_m(k\rho) \,\frac{\cos}{\sin}\, m\phi \,\frac{\cos}{\sin}\, ckt$$

satisfy the equation of motion of the membrane.

Take as a particular case a drum, that is to say a membrane with a fixed circular boundary of radius R.

Then one possible type of vibration is given by the equation

$$V = J_m(k\rho) \cos m\phi \cos ckt,$$

provided that $V = 0$ when $\rho = R$; so that we have to choose k to satisfy the equation

$$J_m(kR) = 0.$$

This equation to determine k has an infinite number of real roots (§ 17·3 example 3), $k_1, k_2, k_3, \dots$ say.   A possible type of vibration is then given by

$$V = J_m(k_r\rho) \cos m\phi \cos ck_r t \qquad (r = 1, 2, 3, \dots).$$

This is a periodic motion with period $2\pi/(ck_r)$; and so the calculation of the periods depends essentially on calculating the zeros of Bessel coefficients (see § 17·9).

---

* Euler, *Novi Comm. Acad. Petrop.* x. (1764) [published 1766], pp. 243–260; Poisson, *Mém. de l'Académie*, VIII. (1829), pp. 357–570; Bourget, *Ann. de l'École norm. sup.* III. (1866), pp. 55–95. For a detailed discussion of vibrations of membranes, see also Rayleigh, *Theory of Sound*, Chapter IX.

Example. The equation of motion of air in a circular cylinder vibrating perpendicularly to the axis OZ of the cylinder is

$$\frac{\partial^2 V}{\partial x^2} + \frac{\partial^2 V}{\partial y^2} = \frac{1}{c^2}\frac{\partial^2 V}{\partial t^2},$$

V denoting the velocity potential. If the cylinder have radius R, the boundary condition is that $\frac{\partial V}{\partial \rho} = 0$ when $\rho = R$. Shew that the determination of the free periods depends on finding the zeros of $J_m'(\zeta) = 0$.

18·6. *A general solution of the equation of wave motions.*

It may be shewn* by the methods of § 18·3 that *a general solution of the equation of wave motions*

$$\frac{\partial^2 V}{\partial x^2} + \frac{\partial^2 V}{\partial y^2} + \frac{\partial^2 V}{\partial z^2} = \frac{1}{c^2}\frac{\partial^2 V}{\partial t^2}$$

is $\quad V = \int_{-\pi}^{\pi}\int_{-\pi}^{\pi} f(x\sin u\cos v + y\sin u\sin v + z\cos u + ct,\ u,\ v)\,du\,dv,$

where f is a function (of three variables) of the type considered in § 18·3.

Regarding an integral as a limit of a sum, we see that a physical interpretation of this equation is that the velocity potential V is produced by a number of plane waves, the disturbance represented by the element

$$f(x\sin u\cos v + y\sin u\sin v + z\cos u + ct,\ u,\ v)\,\delta u\,\delta v$$

being propagated in the direction $(\sin u\cos v,\ \sin u\sin v,\ \cos u)$ with velocity c. *The solution therefore represents an aggregate of plane waves travelling in all directions with velocity* c.

18·61. *Solutions of the equation of wave motions which involve Bessel functions.*

We shall now obtain a class of particular solutions of the equation of wave motions, useful for the solution of certain special problems.

In physical investigations, it is desirable to have the time occurring by means of a factor $\sin ckt$ or $\cos ckt$, where k is constant. This suggests that we should consider solutions of the type

$$V = \int_{-\pi}^{\pi}\int_{0}^{\pi} e^{ik(x\sin u\cos v + y\sin u\sin v + z\cos u + ct)}\,f(u,\ v)\,du\,dv.$$

Physically this means that we consider motions in which all the elementary waves have the same period.

Now let the polar coordinates of (x, y, z) be (r, θ, ϕ) and let (ω, ψ) be the polar coordinates of the direction (u, v) referred to new axes such that the polar axis is the direction (θ, ϕ), and the plane $\psi = 0$ passes through OZ; so that

$$\cos\omega = \cos\theta\cos u + \sin\theta\sin u\cos(\phi - v),$$
$$\sin u\sin(\phi - v) = \sin\omega\sin\psi.$$

* See the paper previously cited, *Math. Ann.* LVII. (1902), pp. 342–345, or *Messenger of Mathematics*, XXXVI. (1907), pp. 98–106.

Also, take the arbitrary function $f(u, v)$ to be $S_n(u, v) \sin u$, where S_n denotes a surface harmonic in u, v of degree n; so that we may write

$$S_n(u, v) = \bar{S}_n(\theta, \phi; \omega, \psi),$$

where (§ 18·31) $\bar{S}_n$ is a surface harmonic in ω, ψ of degree n.

We thus get

$$V = e^{ikct} \int_{-\pi}^{\pi} \int_0^{\pi} e^{ikr\cos\omega} \bar{S}_n(\theta, \phi; \omega, \psi) \sin \omega\, d\omega\, d\psi.$$

Now we may write (§ 18·31)

$$\bar{S}_n(\theta, \phi; \omega, \psi) = A_n(\theta, \phi) . P_n(\cos\omega)$$

$$+ \sum_{m=1}^{n} \{A_n{}^{(m)}(\theta, \phi) \cos m\psi + B_n{}^{(m)}(\theta, \phi) \sin m\psi\} P_n{}^m(\cos\omega),$$

where $A_n(\theta, \phi)$, $A_n{}^{(m)}(\theta, \phi)$ and $B_n{}^{(m)}(\theta, \phi)$ are independent of ψ and ω.

Performing the integration with respect to ψ, we get

$$V = 2\pi e^{ikct} A_n(\theta, \phi) \int_0^{\pi} e^{ikr\cos\omega} P_n(\cos\omega) \sin \omega\, d\omega$$

$$= 2\pi e^{ikct} A_n(\theta, \phi) \int_{-1}^{1} e^{ikr\mu} P_n(\mu)\, d\mu$$

$$= 2\pi e^{ikct} A_n(\theta, \phi) \int_{-1}^{1} e^{ikr\mu} \frac{1}{2^n . n!} \frac{d^n}{d\mu^n} (\mu^2 - 1)^n\, d\mu,$$

by Rodrigues' formula (§ 15·11); on integrating by parts n times and using Hankel's integral (§ 17·3 corollary), we obtain the equation

$$V = \frac{2\pi}{2^n . n!} e^{ikct} A_n(\theta, \phi) (ikr)^n \int_{-1}^{1} e^{ikr\mu} (1 - \mu^2)^n\, d\mu$$

$$= (2\pi)^{\frac{3}{2}} i^n e^{ikct} (kr)^{-\frac{1}{2}} J_{n+\frac{1}{2}}(kr) A_n(\theta, \phi),$$

and so V is a constant multiple of $e^{ikct} r^{-\frac{1}{2}} J_{n+\frac{1}{2}}(kr) A_n(\theta, \phi)$.

Now the equation of wave motions is unaffected if we multiply x, y, z and t by the same constant factor, i.e. if we multiply r and t by the same constant factor leaving θ and ϕ unaltered; so that $A_n(\theta, \phi)$ may be taken to be independent of the arbitrary constant k which multiplies r and t.

Hence $\lim_{k \to 0} e^{ikct} r^{-\frac{1}{2}} k^{-n-\frac{1}{2}} J_{n+\frac{1}{2}}(kr) A_n(\theta, \phi)$ is a solution of the equation of wave motions; and therefore $r^n A_n(\theta, \phi)$ is a solution (independent of t) of the equation of wave motions, and is consequently a solution of Laplace's equation; it is, accordingly, permissible to take $A_n(\theta, \phi)$ to be any surface harmonic of degree n; *and so we obtain the result that*

$$r^{-\frac{1}{2}} J_{n+\frac{1}{2}}(kr) P_n{}^m(\cos\theta) \begin{array}{c} \cos \\ \sin \end{array} m\phi \begin{array}{c} \cos \\ \sin \end{array} ckt$$

is a particular solution of the equation of wave motions.

18·611. *Application of* § 18·61 *to a physical problem.*

The solution just obtained for the equation of wave motions may be used in the following manner to determine the periods of free vibration of air contained in a rigid sphere.

The velocity potential V satisfies the equation of wave motions and the boundary condition is that $\dfrac{\partial V}{\partial r} = 0$ when $r = a$, where a is the radius of the sphere. Hence

$$V = r^{-\frac{1}{2}} J_{n+\frac{1}{2}}(kr) \, P_n{}^m(\cos\theta) \, {\cos \atop \sin} \, m\phi \, {\cos \atop \sin} \, ckt$$

gives a possible motion if k is so chosen that

$$\frac{d}{dr} \{ r^{-\frac{1}{2}} J_{n+\frac{1}{2}}(kr) \}_{r=a} = 0.$$

This equation determines k; on using § 17·24, we see that it may be written in the form

$$\tan ka = f_n(ka),$$

where $f_n(ka)$ is a rational function of ka.

In particular the radial vibrations, in which V is independent of θ and ϕ, are given by taking $n = 0$; then the equation to determine k becomes simply

$$\tan ka = ka ;$$

and the pitches of the fundamental radial vibrations correspond to the roots of this equation.

REFERENCES.

J. Fourier, *La théorie analytique de la Chaleur.* (Translated by A. Freeman.)

W. Thomson and P. G. Tait, *Natural Philosophy.* (1879.)

Lord Rayleigh, *Theory of Sound.* (London, 1894–1896.)

F. Pockels, *Über die partielle Differentialgleichung* $\Delta u + k^2 u = 0$. (Leipzig, 1891.)

H. Burkhardt, *Entwickelungen nach oscillirenden Funktionen.* (Leipzig, 1908.)

H. Bateman, *Electrical and Optical Wave-motion.* (1915.)

E. T. Whittaker, *History of the Theories of Aether and Electricity.* (Dublin, 1910.)

A. E. H. Love, *Proc. London Math. Soc.* xxx. (1899), pp. 308–321.

H. Bateman, *Proc. London Math. Soc.* (2), i. (1904), pp. 451–458.

L. N. G. Filon, *Philosophical Magazine* (6), vi. (1903), pp. 193–213.

H. Bateman, *Proc. London Math. Soc.* (2), vii. (1909), pp. 70–89.

Miscellaneous Examples.

1. If V be a solution of Laplace's equation which is symmetrical with respect to OZ, and if $V = f\{z\}$ on OZ, shew that if $f\{\zeta\}$ be a function which is analytic in a domain of values (which contains the origin) of the complex variable ζ, then

$$V = \frac{1}{\pi} \int_0^\pi f\{ z + i\,(x^2 + y^2)^{\frac{1}{2}} \cos\phi \} \, d\phi$$

at any point of a certain three-dimensional region.

Deduce that the potential of a uniform circular ring of radius c and of mass M lying in the plane XOY with its centre at the origin is

$$\frac{M}{\pi} \int_0^\pi [c^2 + \{ z + i\,(x^2 + y^2)^{\frac{1}{2}} \cos\phi \}^2]^{-\frac{1}{2}} \, d\phi.$$

2. If V be a solution of Laplace's equation, which is of the form $e^{mi\phi} F(\rho, z)$, where (ρ, ϕ, z) are cylindrical coordinates, and if this solution is approximately equal to $\rho^m e^{mi\phi} f(z)$ near the axis of z, where $f(\zeta)$ is of the character described in example 1, shew that

$$V = \frac{m! \, \rho^m e^{mi\phi}}{\Gamma(m+\frac{1}{2}) \, \Gamma(\frac{1}{2})} \int_0^{\pi} f(z + i\rho \cos t) \sin^{2m} t \, dt. \qquad \text{(Dougall.)}$$

3. If u be determined as a function of x, y and z by means of the equation

$$Ax + By + Cz = 1,$$

where A, B, C are functions of u such that

$$A^2 + B^2 + C^2 = 0,$$

shew that (subject to certain general conditions) any function of u is a solution of Laplace's equation.

(Forsyth, *Messenger*, XXVII. (1898), pp. 99–118.)

4. A, B are two points outside a sphere whose centre is C. A layer of attracting matter on the surface of the sphere is such that its surface density σ_P at P is given by the formula

$$\sigma_P \propto (AP \cdot BP)^{-1}.$$

Shew that the total quantity of matter is unaffected by varying A and B so long as $CA \cdot CB$ and $A\hat{C}B$ are unaltered; and prove that this result is equivalent to the theorem that the surface integral of two harmonics of different degrees taken over the sphere is zero.

(Sylvester, *Phil. Mag.* (5), II. (1876), pp. 291–307.)

5. Let $V(x, y, z)$ be the potential function defined analytically as due to particles of masses $\lambda + i\mu$, $\lambda - i\mu$ at the points $(a + ia', \ b + ib', \ c + ic')$ and $(a - ia', \ b - ib', \ c - ic')$ respectively. Shew that $V(x, y, z)$ is infinite at all points of a certain real circle, and if the point (x, y, z) describes a circuit intertwined once with this circle the initial and final values of $V(x, y, z)$ are numerically equal, but opposite in sign.

(Appell, *Math. Ann.* XXX. (1887), pp. 155–156.)

6. Find the solution of Laplace's equation analytic in the region for which $a < r < A$, it being given that on the spheres $r = a$ and $r = A$ the solution reduces to

$$\sum_{n=0}^{\infty} c_n P_n(\cos\theta), \qquad \sum_{n=0}^{\infty} C_n P_n(\cos\theta),$$

respectively.

7. Let O' have coordinates $(0, 0, c)$, and let

$$P\hat{O}Z = \theta, \quad P\hat{O}'Z = \theta', \quad PO = r, \quad PO' = r'.$$

Shew that

$$\frac{P_n(\cos\theta')}{r'^{n+1}} = \frac{P_n(\cos\theta)}{r^{n+1}} + (n+1)\frac{cP_{n+1}(\cos\theta)}{r^{n+2}} + \frac{(n+1)(n+2)}{2!}\frac{c^2 P_{n+2}(\cos\theta)}{r^{n+3}} + \cdots,$$

or

$$= (-)^n \left\{ \frac{1}{c^{n+1}} + (n+1)\frac{rP_1(\cos\theta)}{c^{n+2}} + \frac{(n+1)(n+2)}{2!}\frac{r^2 P_2(\cos\theta)}{c^{n+3}} + \cdots \right\},$$

according as $r > c$ or $r < c$.

Obtain a similar expansion for $r'^n P_n'(\cos\theta)$. (Trinity, 1893.)

8. At a point (r, θ, ϕ) outside a uniform oblate spheroid whose semi-axes are a, b and whose density is ρ, shew that the potential is

$$4\pi\rho a^2 b\left[\frac{1}{3r} - \frac{m^2}{3 \cdot 5}\frac{P_2(\cos\theta)}{r^3} + \frac{m^4}{5 \cdot 7}\frac{P_4(\cos\theta)}{r^5} - \cdots\right],$$

where $m^2 = a^2 - b^2$ and $r > m$. Obtain the potential at points for which $r < m$.

(St John's, 1899.)

9. Shew that

$$e^{ir\cos\theta} = (\tfrac{1}{2}\pi)^{\frac{1}{2}} \sum_{n=0}^{\infty} i^n (2n+1) r^{-\frac{1}{2}} P_n(\cos\theta) J_{n+\frac{1}{2}}(r).$$

(Bauer, *Journal für Math.* LVI.)

10*. Shew that if $x \pm iy = h \cosh(\xi \pm i\eta)$, the equation of two-dimensional wave motions in the coordinates ξ and η is

$$\frac{\partial^2 V}{\partial \xi^2} + \frac{\partial^2 V}{\partial \eta^2} = \frac{h^2}{c^2}(\cosh^2\xi - \cos^2\eta)\frac{\partial^2 V}{\partial t^2}.$$

(Lamé.)

11. Let $x = (c + r\cos\theta)\cos\phi, \quad y = (c + r\cos\theta)\sin\phi, \quad z = r\sin\theta;$

shew that the surfaces for which r, θ, ϕ respectively are constant form an orthogonal system; and shew that Laplace's equation in the coordinates r, θ, ϕ is

$$\frac{\partial}{\partial r}\left\{ r(c + r\cos\theta)\frac{\partial V}{\partial r}\right\} + \frac{1}{r}\frac{\partial}{\partial\theta}\left\{ (c + r\cos\theta)\frac{\partial V}{\partial\theta}\right\} + \frac{r}{c + r\cos\theta}\frac{\partial^2 V}{\partial\phi^2} = 0.$$

(W. D. Niven, *Messenger,* X.)

12. Let P have Cartesian coordinates (x, y, z) and polar coordinates (r, θ, ϕ). Let the plane POZ meet the circle $x^2 + y^2 = k^2$, $z = 0$ in the points a, γ; and let

$$a\hat{P}\gamma = \omega, \quad \log(Pa/P\gamma) = \sigma.$$

Shew that Laplace's equation in the coordinates σ, ω, ϕ is

$$\frac{\partial}{\partial\sigma}\left\{ \frac{\sinh\sigma}{\cosh\sigma - \cos\omega}\frac{\partial V}{\partial\sigma}\right\} + \frac{\partial}{\partial\omega}\left\{ \frac{\sinh\sigma}{\cosh\sigma - \cos\omega}\frac{\partial V}{\partial\omega}\right\} + \frac{1}{\sinh\sigma(\cosh\sigma - \cos\omega)}\frac{\partial^2 V}{\partial\phi^2} = 0;$$

and shew that a solution is

$$V = (\cosh\sigma - \cos\omega)^{\frac{1}{2}}\cos n\omega \cos m\phi \, P_{n-\frac{1}{2}}^{m}(\cosh\sigma).$$

(Hicks, *Phil. Trans.* CLXXII. pp. 617 et seq.)

13. Shew that

$$(R^2 + \rho^2 - 2R\rho\cos\phi + c^2)^{-\frac{1}{2}} = \sum_{m=0}^{\infty}\frac{e^{-\frac{1}{2}m\pi i}}{\pi}\int_0^\infty dk \int_{-\pi}^{\pi} e^{-ck}J_m(k\rho)e^{ikR\cos u}\cos mu \, du,$$

and deduce an expression for the potential of a particle in terms of Bessel functions.

14. Shew that if a, b, c are constants and λ, μ, ν are confocal coordinates, defined as the roots of the equation in ϵ

$$\frac{x^2}{a^2 + \epsilon} + \frac{y^2}{b^2 + \epsilon} + \frac{z^2}{c^2 + \epsilon} = 1,$$

then Laplace's equation may be written

$$\Delta_\lambda(\mu - \nu)\frac{\partial}{\partial\lambda}\left\{ \Delta_\lambda\frac{\partial V}{\partial\lambda}\right\} + \Delta_\mu(\nu - \lambda)\frac{\partial}{\partial\mu}\left\{ \Delta_\mu\frac{\partial V}{\partial\mu}\right\} + \Delta_\nu(\lambda - \mu)\frac{\partial}{\partial\nu}\left\{ \Delta_\nu\frac{\partial V}{\partial\nu}\right\} = 0,$$

where $\Delta_\lambda = \sqrt{\{(a^2 + \lambda)(b^2 + \lambda)(c^2 + \lambda)\}}.$

(Lamé.)

* Examples 10, 11, 12 and 14 are most easily proved by using Lamé's result (*Journal de l'École Polyt.* XIV. cahier 23 (1834), pp. 191–288) that if (λ, μ, ν) be orthogonal coordinates for which the line-element is given by the formula $(\delta x)^2 + (\delta y)^2 + (\delta z)^2 = (H_1\delta\lambda)^2 + (H_2\delta\mu)^2 + (H_3\delta\nu)^2$, Laplace's equation in these coordinates is

$$\frac{\partial}{\partial\lambda}\left(\frac{H_2 H_3}{H_1}\frac{\partial V}{\partial\lambda}\right) + \frac{\partial}{\partial\mu}\left(\frac{H_3 H_1}{H_2}\frac{\partial V}{\partial\mu}\right) + \frac{\partial}{\partial\nu}\left(\frac{H_1 H_2}{H_3}\frac{\partial V}{\partial\nu}\right) = 0.$$

A simple method (due to W. Thomson, *Camb. Math. Journal,* IV. (1845), pp. 33–42) of proving this result, by means of arguments of a physical character, is reproduced by Lamb, *Hydrodynamics* (1916), § 111. Analytical proofs, based on Lamé's proof, are given by Bertrand, *Traité de Calcul Différentielle* (1864), pp. 181–187, and Goursat, *Cours d'Analyse,* I. (1910), pp. 155–159; and a most compact proof is due to Neville, *Quarterly Journal,* XLIX. (1923), pp. 338–352. Another proof is given by Heine, *Theorie der Kugelfunctionen,* I. (1878), pp. 303–306.

15.   Shew that a general solution of the equation of wave motions is

$$V = \int_{-\pi}^{\pi} F\left(x \cos\theta + y \sin\theta + iz,\; y + iz \sin\theta + ct \cos\theta,\; \theta\right) d\theta.$$

(Bateman, *Proc. London Math. Soc.* (2) I. (1904), p. 457.)

16.   If $U = f(x, y, z, t)$ be a solution of

$$\frac{1}{a^2}\frac{\partial U}{\partial t} = \frac{\partial^2 U}{\partial x^2} + \frac{\partial^2 U}{\partial y^2} + \frac{\partial^2 U}{\partial z^2},$$

prove that another solution of the equation is

$$U = t^{-\frac{3}{2}} f\left(\frac{x}{t},\; \frac{y}{t},\; \frac{z}{t},\; -\frac{1}{t}\right) \exp\left(-\frac{x^2 + y^2 + z^2}{4a^2 t}\right).$$

17.   Shew that a general solution of the equation of wave motions, when the motion is independent of ϕ, is

$$\int_{-\pi}^{\pi} f\left(z + i\rho \cos\theta,\; ct + \rho \sin\theta\right) d\theta$$

$$+ \int_0^b \int_{-\pi}^{\pi} \operatorname{arc\,sinh}\left(\frac{a + z + ct \cos\theta}{\rho \sin\theta}\right) F(a, \theta)\, d\theta\, da,$$

where ρ, ϕ, z are cylindrical coordinates and a, b are arbitrary constants.

(Bateman, *Proc. London Math. Soc.* (2) I. (1904), p. 458.)

18.   If $V = f(x, y, z)$ is a solution of Laplace's equation, shew that

$$V = \frac{1}{(x - iy)^{\frac{1}{2}}} f\left(\frac{r^2 - a^2}{2(x - iy)},\; \frac{r^2 + a^2}{2i(x - iy)},\; \frac{az}{x - iy}\right)$$

is another solution.

(Bateman, *Proc. London Math. Soc.* (2) VII. (1909), p. 77.)

19.   If $U = f(x, y, z, t)$ is a solution of the equation of wave motions, shew that another solution is

$$U = \frac{1}{z - ct} f\left(\frac{x}{z - ct},\; \frac{y}{z - ct},\; \frac{r^2 - 1}{2(z - ct)},\; \frac{r^2 + 1}{2c(z - ct)}\right).$$

(Bateman, *Proc. London Math. Soc.* (2) VII. (1909), p. 77.)

20.   If $l = x - iy,\quad m = z + iw,\quad n = x^2 + y^2 + z^2 + w^2,$

$\lambda = x + iy,\quad \mu = z - iw,\quad \nu = -1,$

so that $l\lambda + m\mu + n\nu = 0,$

shew that any homogeneous solution, of degree zero, of

$$\frac{\partial^2 U}{\partial x^2} + \frac{\partial^2 U}{\partial y^2} + \frac{\partial^2 U}{\partial z^2} + \frac{\partial^2 U}{\partial w^2} = 0$$

satisfies

$$\frac{\partial^2 U}{\partial l\,\partial\lambda} + \frac{\partial^2 U}{\partial m\,\partial\mu} + \frac{\partial^2 U}{\partial n\,\partial\nu} = 0;$$

and obtain a solution of this equation in the form

$$l^{-a}\lambda^{-a'} m^{-\beta}\mu^{-\beta'} n^{-\gamma}\nu^{-\gamma'} P\left\{\begin{matrix} a, & b, & c & \\ \alpha, & \beta, & \gamma, & \zeta \\ \alpha', & \beta', & \gamma' & \end{matrix}\right\},$$

where $l\lambda = (b - c)(\zeta - a),\quad m\mu = (c - a)(\zeta - b),\quad n\nu = (a - b)(\zeta - c).$

(Bateman, *Proc. London Math. Soc.* (2) VII. (1909), pp. 78–82.)

21*.   If (r, θ, ϕ) are spheroidal coordinates, defined by the equations

$$x = c\,(r^2+1)^{\frac{1}{2}} \sin\theta \cos\phi, \quad y = c\,(r^2+1)^{\frac{1}{2}} \sin\theta \sin\phi, \quad z = cr\cos\theta,$$

where x, y, z are rectangular coordinates and c is a constant, shew that, when n and m are integers,

$$\int_{-\pi}^{\pi} P_n\left(\frac{x\cos t + y\sin t + iz}{c}\right) \frac{\cos}{\sin} mt\,dt = 2\pi\,\frac{(n-m)\,!}{(n+m)\,!}\,P_n{}^m\,(ir)\,P_n{}^m\,(\cos\theta)\,\frac{\cos}{\sin}\,m\phi.$$

$$\text{(Blades, } \textit{Proc. Edinburgh Math. Soc.} \text{ XXXIII.)}$$

22.   With the notation of example 21, shew that, if $z \neq 0$,

$$\int_{-\pi}^{\pi} Q_n\left(\frac{x\cos t + y\sin t + iz}{c}\right) \frac{\cos}{\sin} mt\,dt = 2\pi\,\frac{(n-m)\,!}{(n+m)\,!}\,Q_n{}^m\,(ir)\,P_n{}^m\,(\cos\theta)\,\frac{\cos}{\sin}\,m\phi.$$

$$\text{(Jeffery, } \textit{Proc. Edinburgh Math. Soc.} \text{ XXXIII.)}$$

23.   Prove that the most general solution of Laplace's equation which is of degree zero in x, y, z is expressible in the form

$$V = f\left(\frac{x+iy}{r+z}\right) + F\left(\frac{x-iy}{r+z}\right),$$

where f and F are arbitrary functions.

     (Donkin, *Phil. Trans.* 1857 ; Hobson, *Proc. London Math. Soc.* (1) XXII. p. 422.)

* The functions introduced in examples 21 and 22 are known as *internal* and *external* *spheroidal harmonics* respectively.

CHAPTER XIX

MATHIEU FUNCTIONS

19·1. *The differential equation of Mathieu.*

The preceding five chapters have been occupied with the discussion of functions which belong to what may be generally described as the hypergeometric type, and many simple properties of these functions are now well known.

In the present chapter we enter upon a region of Analysis which lies beyond this, and which is, as yet, only very imperfectly explored.

The functions which occur in Mathematical Physics and which come next in order of complication to functions of hypergeometric type are called *Mathieu functions*; these functions are also known as *the functions associated with the elliptic cylinder*. They arise from the equation of two-dimensional wave motion, namely

$$\frac{\partial^2 V}{\partial x^2} + \frac{\partial^2 V}{\partial y^2} = \frac{1}{c^2} \frac{\partial^2 V}{\partial t^2}.$$

This partial differential equation occurs in the theory of the propagation of electromagnetic waves; if the electric vector in the wave-front is parallel to OZ and if E denotes the electric force, while $(H_x, H_y, 0)$ are the components of magnetic force, Maxwell's fundamental equations are

$$\frac{1}{c^2} \frac{\partial E}{\partial t} = \frac{\partial H_y}{\partial x} - \frac{\partial H_x}{\partial y}, \quad \frac{\partial H_x}{\partial t} = -\frac{\partial E}{\partial y}, \quad \frac{\partial H_y}{\partial t} = \frac{\partial E}{\partial x},$$

c denoting the velocity of light; and these equations give at once

$$\frac{1}{c^2} \frac{\partial^2 E}{\partial t^2} = \frac{\partial^2 E}{\partial x^2} + \frac{\partial^2 E}{\partial y^2}.$$

In the case of the scattering of waves, propagated parallel to OX, incident on an elliptic cylinder for which OX and OY are axes of a principal section, the boundary condition is that E should vanish at the surface of the cylinder.

The same partial differential equation occurs in connexion with the vibrations of a uniform plane membrane, the dependent variable being the displacement perpendicular to the membrane; if the membrane be in the shape of an ellipse with a rigid boundary, the boundary condition is the same as in the electromagnetic problem just discussed.

The differential equation was discussed by Mathieu [*] in 1868 in connexion with the problem of vibrations of an elliptic membrane in the following manner:

[*] *Journal de Math.* (2), XIII. (1868), p. 137.

Suppose that the membrane, which is in the plane XOY when it is in equilibrium, is vibrating with frequency p. Then, if we write

$$V = u(x, y) \cos(pt + \epsilon),$$

the equation becomes

$$\frac{\partial^2 u}{\partial x^2} + \frac{\partial^2 u}{\partial y^2} + \frac{p^2}{c^2} u = 0.$$

Let the foci of the elliptic membrane be $(\pm h, 0, 0)$, and introduce new real variables* ξ, η defined by the complex equation

$$x + iy = h \cosh(\xi + i\eta),$$

so that

$$x = h \cosh \xi \cos \eta, \quad y = h \sinh \xi \sin \eta.$$

The curves, on which ξ or η is constant, are evidently ellipses or hyperbolas confocal with the boundary; if we take $\xi \geqslant 0$ and $-\pi < \eta \leqslant \pi$, to each point $(x, y, 0)$ of the plane corresponds one and only one† value of (ξ, η).

The differential equation for u transforms into‡

$$\frac{\partial^2 u}{\partial \xi^2} + \frac{\partial^2 u}{\partial \eta^2} + \frac{h^2 p^2}{c^2} (\cosh^2 \xi - \cos^2 \eta) u = 0.$$

If we assume a solution of this equation of the form

$$u = F(\xi) G(\eta),$$

where the factors are functions of ξ only and of η only respectively, we see that

$$\left\{ \frac{1}{F(\xi)} \frac{d^2 F(\xi)}{d\xi^2} + \frac{h^2 p^2}{c^2} \cosh^2 \xi \right\} = -\left\{ \frac{1}{G(\eta)} \frac{d^2 G(\eta)}{d\eta^2} - \frac{h^2 p^2}{c^2} \cos^2 \eta \right\}.$$

Since the left-hand side contains ξ but not η, while the right-hand side contains η but not ξ, $F(\xi)$ and $G(\eta)$ must be such that each side is a constant, A, say, since ξ and η are independent variables.

We thus arrive at the equations

$$\frac{d^2 F(\xi)}{d\xi^2} + \left(\frac{h^2 p^2}{c^2} \cosh^2 \xi - A \right) F(\xi) = 0,$$

$$\frac{d^2 G(\eta)}{d\eta^2} - \left(\frac{h^2 p^2}{c^2} \cos^2 \eta - A \right) G(\eta) = 0.$$

By a slight change of independent variable in the former equation, we see that *both of these equations are linear differential equations, of the second order, of the form*

$$\frac{d^2 u}{dz^2} + (a + 16q \cos 2z) u = 0,$$

---

* The introduction of these variables is due to Lamé, who called ξ the *thermometric parameter*. They are more usually known as *confocal coordinates*. See Lamé, *Sur les fonctions inverses des transcendantes*, 1ère Leçon.

† This may be seen most easily by considering the ellipses obtained by giving ξ various positive values. If the ellipse be drawn through a definite point (ξ, η) of the plane, η is the eccentric angle of that point on the ellipse.

‡ A proof of this result, due to Lamé, is given in numerous text-books; see p. 401, footnote.

where a and q are constants*. It is obvious that every point (infinity excepted) is a regular point of this equation.

This is the equation which is known as *Mathieu's equation* and, in certain circumstances (§ 19·2), particular solutions of it are called *Mathieu functions*.

19·11. *The form of the solution of Mathieu's equation.*

In the physical problems which suggested Mathieu's equation, the constant a is not given *a priori*, and we have to consider how it is to be determined. It is obvious from physical considerations in the problem of the membrane that $u(x, y)$ is a *one-valued* function of position, and is consequently unaltered by increasing η by 2π; and the condition† $G(\eta + 2\pi) = G(\eta)$ is sufficient to determine a set of values of a in terms of q. And it will appear later (§§ 19·4, 19·41) that, when a has not one of these values, the equation

$$G(\eta + 2\pi) = G(\eta)$$

is no longer true.

When a is thus determined, q (and thence p) is determined by the fact that $F(\xi) = 0$ on the boundary; and so the periods of the free vibrations of the membrane are obtained.

Other problems of Mathematical Physics which involve Mathieu functions in their solution are (i) Tidal waves in a cylindrical vessel with an elliptic boundary, (ii) Certain forms of steady vortex motion in an elliptic cylinder, (iii) The decay of magnetic force in a metal cylinder‡. The equation also occurs in a problem of Rigid Dynamics which is of general interest§.

19·12. *Hill's equation.*

A differential equation, similar to Mathieu's but of a more general nature, arises in G. W. Hill's‖ method of determining the motion of the Lunar Perigee, and in Adams'¶ determination of the motion of the Lunar Node. Hill's equation is

$$\frac{d^2u}{dz^2} + \left(\theta_0 + 2\sum_{n=1}^{\infty}\theta_n\cos 2nz\right)u = 0.$$

The theory of Hill's equation is very similar to that of Mathieu's (in spite of the increase in generality due to the presence of the infinite series), so the two equations will, to some extent, be considered together.

---

* Their actual values are $a = A - h^2p^2/(2c^2)$, $q = h^2p^2/(32c^2)$; the factor 16 is inserted to avoid powers of 2 in the solution.

† An elementary analogue of this result is that a solution of $\dfrac{d^2u}{dz^2} + au = 0$ has period 2π if, and only if, a is the square of an integer.

‡ R. C. Maclaurin, *Trans. Camb. Phil. Soc.* XVII. p. 41.

§ A. W. Young, *Proc. Edinburgh Math. Soc.* XXXII. p. 81.

‖ *Acta Math.* VIII. (1886). Hill's memoir was originally published in 1877 at Cambridge, U.S.A.

¶ *Monthly Notices R.A.S.* XXXVIII. p. 43.

In the astronomical applications θ_0, θ_1, ... are *known* constants, so the problem of choosing them in such a way that the solution may be periodic does not arise. The solution of Hill's equation in the Lunar Theory is, in fact, not periodic.

19·2. *Periodic solutions of Mathieu's equation.*

We have seen that in physical (as distinguished from astronomical) problems the constant a in Mathieu's equation has to be chosen to be such a function of q that the equation possesses a periodic solution.

Let this solution be $G(z)$; then $G(z)$, in addition to being periodic, is an integral function of z. Three possibilities arise as to the nature of $G(z)$: (i) $G(z)$ may be an *even* function of z, (ii) $G(z)$ may be an *odd* function of z, (iii) $G(z)$ may be neither even nor odd.

In case (iii), $$\tfrac{1}{2}\{G(z) + G(-z)\}$$

is an *even* periodic solution and

$$\tfrac{1}{2}\{G(z) - G(-z)\}$$

is an *odd* periodic solution of Mathieu's equation, these two solutions forming a fundamental system. It is therefore sufficient to confine our attention to periodic solutions of Mathieu's equation which are either even or odd. These solutions, *and these only*, will be called *Mathieu functions*.

It will be observed that, since the roots of the indicial equation at $z=0$ are 0 and 1, two even (or two odd) periodic solutions of Mathieu's equation cannot form a fundamental system. But, so far, there seems to be no reason why Mathieu's equation, for special values of a and q, should not have one even and one odd periodic solution; for comparatively small values of $|q|$ it can be seen [§ 19·3 example 2, (ii) and (iii)] that Mathieu's equation has two periodic solutions only in the trivial case in which $q=0$; the result that there are never pairs of periodic solutions for larger values of $|q|$ is a special case of a theorem due to Hille, *Proc. London Math. Soc.* (2) XXIII. (1924), p. 224. See also Ince, *Proc. Camb. Phil. Soc.* XXI. (1922), p. 117.

19·21. *An integral equation satisfied by even Mathieu functions*.*

It will now be shewn that, if $G(\eta)$ is any even Mathieu function, *then $G(\eta)$ satisfies the homogeneous integral equation*

$$G(\eta) = \lambda \int_{-\pi}^{\pi} e^{k\cos\eta\cos\theta} G(\theta)\,d\theta,$$

where $k = \surd(32q)$. This result is suggested by the solution of Laplace's equation given in § 18·3.

---

* This integral equation and the expansions of § 19·3 were published by Whittaker, *Proc. Int. Congress of Math.* 1912. The integral equation was known to him as early as 1904; see *Trans. Camb. Phil. Soc.* XXI. (1912), p. 193.

For, if $x + iy = h \cosh(\xi + i\eta)$ and if $F(\xi)$ and $G(\eta)$ are solutions of the differential equations

$$\frac{d^2 F(\xi)}{d\xi^2} - (A + m^2 h^2 \cosh^2 \xi)\, F(\xi) = 0,$$

$$\frac{d^2 G(\eta)}{d\eta^2} + (A + m^2 h^2 \cos^2 \eta)\, G(\eta) = 0,$$

then, by § 19·1, $F(\xi)\, G(\eta)\, e^{miz}$ is a particular solution of Laplace's equation. If this solution is a special case of the general solution

$$\int_{-\pi}^{\pi} f(h \cosh \xi \cos \eta \cos \theta + h \sinh \xi \sin \eta \sin \theta + iz,\ \theta)\, d\theta,$$

given in § 18·3, it is natural to expect that*

$$f(v,\ \theta) \equiv F(0)\, e^{mv}\, \phi(\theta),$$

where $\phi(\theta)$ is a function of θ to be determined. Thus

$$F(\xi)\, G(\eta)\, e^{miz} = \int_{-\pi}^{\pi} F(0)\, \phi(\theta) \exp\{mh \cosh \xi \cos \eta \cos \theta$$
$$+ mh \sinh \xi \sin \eta \sin \theta + miz\}\, d\theta.$$

Since ξ and η are independent, we may put $\xi = 0$; and we are thus led to consider the possibility of Mathieu's equation possessing a solution of the form

$$G(\eta) = \int_{-\pi}^{\pi} e^{mh \cos \eta \cos \theta}\, \phi(\theta)\, d\theta.$$

19·22. *Proof that the even Mathieu functions satisfy the integral equation.*

It is readily verified (§ 5·31) that, if $\phi(\theta)$ be analytic in the range $(-\pi, \pi)$ and if $G(\eta)$ be *defined* by the equation

$$G(\eta) = \int_{-\pi}^{\pi} e^{mh \cos \eta \cos \theta}\, \phi(\theta)\, d\theta,$$

then $G(\eta)$ is an even periodic integral function of η and

$$\frac{d^2 G(\eta)}{d\eta^2} + (A + m^2 h^2 \cos^2 \eta)\, G(\eta)$$

$$= \int_{-\pi}^{\pi} \{m^2 h^2 (\sin^2 \eta \cos^2 \theta + \cos^2 \eta) - mh \cos \eta \cos \theta + A\}\, e^{mh \cos \eta \cos \theta}\, \phi(\theta)\, d\theta$$

$$= - \left[\{mh \sin \theta \cos \eta\, \phi(\theta) + \phi'(\theta)\}\, e^{mh \cos \eta \cos \theta} \right]_{-\pi}^{\pi}$$

$$+ \int_{-\pi}^{\pi} \{\phi''(\theta) + (A + m^2 h^2 \cos^2 \theta)\, \phi(\theta)\}\, e^{mh \cos \eta \cos \theta}\, d\theta,$$

on integrating by parts.

* The constant $F(0)$ is inserted to simplify the algebra.

But if $\phi(\theta)$ be a periodic *function (with period 2π) such that*

$$\phi''(\theta) + (A + m^2h^2\cos^2\theta)\,\phi(\theta) = 0,$$

both the integral and the integrated part vanish; that is to say, $G(\eta)$, defined by the integral, is a periodic solution of Mathieu's equation.

Consequently $G(\eta)$ is an even periodic solution of Mathieu's equation if $\phi(\theta)$ is a periodic solution of Mathieu's equation formed with the same constants; and therefore $\phi(\theta)$ is a constant multiple of $G(\theta)$; let it be $\lambda G(\theta)$.

[In the case when the Mathieu equation has two periodic solutions, if this case exist, we have $\phi(\theta) = \lambda G(\theta) + G_1(\theta)$ where $G_1(\theta)$ is an odd periodic function; but

$$\int_{-\pi}^{\pi} e^{mh\cos\eta\cos\theta}\,G_1(\theta)\,d\theta$$

vanishes, so the subsequent work is unaffected.]

If we take a and q as the parameters of the Mathieu equation instead of A and mh, it is obvious that $mh = \sqrt{(32q)} = k$.

We have thus proved that, if $G(\eta)$ be an even periodic solution of Mathieu's equation, then

$$G(\eta) = \lambda \int_{-\pi}^{\pi} e^{k\cos\eta\cos\theta}\,G(\theta)\,d\theta,$$

which is the result stated in § 19·21.

From § 11·23, it is known that this integral equation has a solution only when λ has one of the 'characteristic values.' It will be shewn in § 19·3 that for such values of λ, the integral equation affords a simple means of constructing the even Mathieu functions.

Example 1.　Shew that the odd Mathieu functions satisfy the integral equation

$$G(\eta) = \lambda \int_{-\pi}^{\pi} \sin(k\sin\eta\sin\theta)\,G(\theta)\,d\theta.$$

Example 2.　Shew that both the even and the odd Mathieu functions satisfy the integral equation

$$G(\eta) = \lambda \int_{-\pi}^{\pi} e^{ik\sin\eta\sin\theta}\,G(\theta)\,d\theta.$$

Example 3.　Shew that when the eccentricity of the fundamental ellipse tends to zero, the confluent form of the integral equation for the even Mathieu functions is

$$J_n(x) = \frac{1}{2\pi i^n} \int_{-\pi}^{\pi} e^{ix\cos\theta}\cos n\theta\,d\theta.$$

19·3.　*The construction of Mathieu functions.*

We shall now make use of the integral equation of § 19·21 to construct Mathieu functions; the canonical form of Mathieu's equation will be taken as

$$\frac{d^2u}{dz^2} + (a + 16q\cos 2z)\,u = 0.$$

In the special case when q is zero, the periodic solutions are obtained by taking $a = n^2$, where n is any integer; the solutions are then

$$1, \quad \cos z, \quad \cos 2z, \quad \ldots,$$
$$\sin z, \quad \sin 2z, \quad \ldots.$$

The Mathieu functions, which reduce to these when $q \to 0$, will be called

$$ce_0(z, q), \quad ce_1(z, q), \quad ce_2(z, q), \quad \ldots,$$
$$se_1(z, q), \quad se_2(z, q), \quad \ldots.$$

To make the functions precise, we take the coefficients of $\cos nz$ and $\sin nz$ in the respective Fourier series for $ce_n(z, q)$ and $se_n(z, q)$ to be unity. The functions $ce_n(z, q)$, $se_n(z, q)$ will be called *Mathieu functions of order n.*

Let us now construct $ce_0(z, q)$.

Since $ce_0(z, 0) = 1$, we see that $\lambda \to (2\pi)^{-1}$ as $q \to 0$. Accordingly we suppose that, for general values of q, the characteristic value of λ which gives rise to $ce_0(z, q)$ can be expanded in the form

$$(2\pi\lambda)^{-1} = 1 + \alpha_1 q + \alpha_2 q^2 + \ldots,$$

and that

$$ce_0(z, q) = 1 + q\beta_1(z) + q^2\beta_2(z) + \ldots,$$

where α_1, α_2, ... are numerical constants and $\beta_1(z)$, $\beta_2(z)$, ... are periodic functions of z which are independent of q and which contain no constant term.

On substituting in the integral equation, we find that

$$(1 + \alpha_1 q + \alpha_2 q^2 + \ldots)\{1 + q\beta_1(z) + q^2\beta_2(z) + \ldots\}$$
$$= \frac{1}{2\pi} \int_{-\pi}^{\pi} \{1 + \sqrt{(32q)} . \cos z \cos \theta + 16q \cos^2 z \cos^2 \theta + \ldots\}$$
$$\times \{1 + q\beta_1(\theta) + q^2\beta_2(\theta) + \ldots\}\, d\theta.$$

Equating coefficients of successive powers of q in this result and making use of the fact that $\beta_1(z)$, $\beta_2(z)$, ... contain no constant term, we find in succession

$$\alpha_1 = 4, \qquad \beta_1(z) = 4 \cos 2z,$$
$$\alpha_2 = 14, \qquad \beta_2(z) = 2 \cos 4z,$$
$$\cdots\cdots\cdots\cdots\cdots\cdots\cdots\cdots,$$

and we thus obtain the following expansion:

$$ce_0(z, q) = 1 + \left(4q - 28q^3 + \frac{2^7 . 29}{9} q^5 - \ldots\right)\cos 2z + \left(2q^2 - \frac{160}{9} q^4 + \ldots\right)\cos 4z$$

$$+ \left(\frac{4}{9}q^3 - \frac{13}{3} q^5 + \ldots\right)\cos 6z + \left(\frac{1}{18} q^4 - \ldots\right)\cos 8z$$

$$+ \left(\frac{1}{225} q^5 - \ldots\right)\cos 10z + \ldots,$$

the terms not written down being $O(q^6)$ as $q \to 0$.

The value of a is $-32q^2 + 224q^4 - \dfrac{2^{10} . 29}{9} q^6 + O(q^8)$; it will be observed that the coefficient of $\cos 2z$ in the series for $ce_0(z, q)$ is $-a/(8q)$.

The Mathieu functions of higher order may be obtained in a similar manner from the same integral equation and from the integral equation of § 19·22 example 1. The consideration of the convergence of the series thus obtained is postponed to § 19·61.

Example 1. Obtain the following expansions*:

(i) $ce_0(z, q) = 1 + \sum\limits_{r=1}^{\infty} \left\{ \dfrac{2^{r+1}q^r}{r!\,r!} - \dfrac{2^{r+3}r\,(3r+4)\,q^{r+2}}{(r+1)!\,(r+1)!} + O\,(q^{r+4}) \right\} \cos 2rz,$

(ii) $ce_1(z, q) = \cos z + \sum\limits_{r=1}^{\infty} \left\{ \dfrac{2^r q^r}{(r+1)!\,r!} - \dfrac{2^{r+1}r q^{r+1}}{(r+1)!\,(r+1)!} \right.$

$$\left. + \dfrac{2^r q^{r+2}}{(r-1)!\,(r+2)!} + O\,(q^{r+3}) \right\} \cos (2r+1)\,z,$$

(iii) $se_1(z, q) = \sin z + \sum\limits_{r=1}^{\infty} \left\{ \dfrac{2^r q^r}{(r+1)!\,r!} + \dfrac{2^{r+1}r q^{r+1}}{(r+1)!\,(r+1)!} \right.$

$$\left. + \dfrac{2^r q^{r+2}}{(r-1)!\,(r+2)!} + O\,(q^{r+3}) \right\} \sin (2r+1)\,z,$$

(iv) $ce_2(z, q) = \left\{ -2q + \dfrac{40}{3} q^3 + O\,(q^5) \right\} + \cos 2z$

$$+ \sum\limits_{r=1}^{\infty} \left\{ \dfrac{2^{r+1}q^r}{r!\,(r+2)!} + \dfrac{2^{r+1}r\,(47r^2+222r+247)\,q^{r+2}}{3^2 \cdot (r+2)!\,(r+3)!} + O\,(q^{r+4}) \right\} \cos (2r+2)\,z,$$

where, in each case, the constant implied in the symbol O depends on r but not on z.

(Whittaker.)

Example 2. Shew that the values of a associated with (i) $ce_0(z, q)$, (ii) $ce_1(z, q)$, (iii) $se_1(z, q)$, (iv) $ce_2(z, q)$ are respectively:

(i) $-32q^2 + 224q^4 - \dfrac{2^{10} \cdot 29}{9} q^6 + O\,(q^8),$

(ii) $1 - 8q - 8q^2 + 8q^3 - \dfrac{8}{3} q^4 + O\,(q^5),$

(iii) $1 + 8q - 8q^2 - 8q^3 - \dfrac{8}{3} q^4 + O\,(q^5),$

(iv) $4 + \dfrac{80}{3} q^2 - \dfrac{6104}{27} q^4 + O\,(q^6).$ (Mathieu.)

Example 3. Shew that, if n be an integer,

$$ce_{2n+1}(z, q) = (-)^n\, se_{2n+1}(z+\tfrac{1}{2}\pi, -q).$$

19·31. *The integral formulae for the Mathieu functions.*

Since all the Mathieu functions satisfy a homogeneous integral equation with a symmetrical nucleus (§ 19·22 example 3), it follows (§ 11·61) that

$$\int_{-\pi}^{\pi} ce_m(z, q)\, ce_n(z, q)\, dz = 0 \qquad (m \neq n),$$

$$\int_{-\pi}^{\pi} se_m(z, q)\, se_n(z, q)\, dz = 0 \qquad (m \neq n),$$

$$\int_{-\pi}^{\pi} ce_m(z, q)\, se_n(z, q)\, dz = 0.$$

---

* The leading terms of these series, as given in example 4 at the end of the chapter (p. 427), were obtained by Mathieu.

Example 1.   Obtain expansions of the form :

$$\text{(i)} \qquad e^{k \cos z \cos \theta} = \sum_{n=0}^{\infty} A_n ce_n(z, q)\, ce_n(\theta, q),$$

$$\text{(ii)} \quad \cos(k \sin z \sin \theta) = \sum_{n=0}^{\infty} B_n ce_n(z, q)\, ce_n(\theta, q),$$

$$\text{(iii)} \quad \sin(k \sin z \sin \theta) = \sum_{n=0}^{\infty} C_n se_n(z, q)\, se_n(\theta, q),$$

where $k = \sqrt{(32q)}$.

Example 2.   Obtain the expansion

$$e^{iz \sin \phi} = \sum_{n=-\infty}^{\infty} J_n(z)\, e^{ni\phi}$$

as a confluent form of expansions (ii) and (iii) of example 1.

19·4.   *The nature of the solution of Mathieu's general equation; Floquet's theory.*

We shall now discuss the nature of the solution of Mathieu's equation when the parameter a is no longer restricted so as to give rise to periodic solutions; this is the case which is of importance in astronomical problems, as distinguished from other physical applications of the theory.

The method is applicable to any linear equation with *periodic* coefficients which are one-valued functions of the independent variable; the nature of the general solution of particular equations of this type has long been perceived by astronomers, by inference from the circumstances in which the equations arise. These inferences have been confirmed by the following analytical investigation which was published in 1883 by Floquet[*].

Let $g(z)$, $h(z)$ be a fundamental system of solutions of Mathieu's equation (or, indeed, of any linear equation in which the coefficients have period 2π); then, if $F(z)$ be any other integral of such an equation, we must have

$$F(z) = Ag(z) + Bh(z),$$

where A and B are definite constants.

Since $g(z + 2\pi)$, $h(z + 2\pi)$ are obviously solutions of the equation[†], they can be expressed in terms of the continuations of $g(z)$ and $h(z)$ by equations of the type

$$g(z + 2\pi) = \alpha_1 g(z) + \alpha_2 h(z), \quad h(z + 2\pi) = \beta_1 g(z) + \beta_2 h(z),$$

where $\alpha_1, \alpha_2, \beta_1, \beta_2$ are definite constants; and then

$$F(z + 2\pi) = (A\alpha_1 + B\beta_1)\, g(z) + (A\alpha_2 + B\beta_2)\, h(z).$$

---

[*] *Ann. de l'École norm. sup.* (2), XII. (1883), p. 47.   Floquet's analysis is a natural sequel to Picard's theory of differential equations with doubly-periodic coefficients (§ 20·1), and to the theory of the fundamental equation due to Fuchs and Hamburger.

[†] These solutions may not be identical with $g(z)$, $h(z)$ respectively, as the solution of an equation with periodic coefficients is not necessarily periodic.   To take a simple case, $u = e^z \sin z$ is a solution of $\dfrac{du}{dz} - (1 + \cot z)\, u = 0$.

Consequently $F(z + 2\pi) = kF(z)$, *where k is a constant*, if A and B are chosen so that*

$$A\alpha_1 + B\beta_1 = kA, \quad A\alpha_2 + B\beta_2 = kB.$$

These equations will have a solution, other than $A = B = 0$, if, and only if,

$$\begin{vmatrix} \alpha_1 - k, & \beta_1 \\ \alpha_2, & \beta_2 - k \end{vmatrix} = 0 ;$$

and if k be taken to be either root of this equation, the function $F(z)$ can be constructed so as to be a solution of the differential equation such that

$$F(z + 2\pi) = kF(z).$$

Defining μ by the equation $k = e^{2\pi\mu}$ and writing $\phi(z)$ for $e^{-\mu z} F(z)$, we see that

$$\phi(z + 2\pi) = e^{-\mu(z+2\pi)} F(z + 2\pi) = \phi(z).$$

Hence the differential equation has a particular solution of the form $e^{\mu z} \phi(z)$, where $\phi(z)$ is a periodic function with period 2π.

We have seen that in physical problems, the parameters involved in the differential equation have to be so chosen that $k = 1$ is a root of the quadratic, and a solution is periodic. In general, however, in astronomical problems, in which the parameters are given, $k \neq 1$ and there is no periodic solution.

In the particular case of Mathieu's general equation or Hill's equation, a fundamental system of solutions† is then $e^{\mu z} \phi(z)$, $e^{-\mu z} \phi(-z)$, since the equation is unaltered by writing $-z$ for z; so that the complete solution of Mathieu's general equation is then

$$u = c_1 e^{\mu z} \phi(z) + c_2 e^{-\mu z} \phi(-z),$$

where c_1, c_2 are arbitrary constants, and μ is a definite function of a and q.

Example. Shew that the roots of the equation

$$\begin{vmatrix} a_1 - k, & \beta_1 \\ a_2, & \beta_2 - k \end{vmatrix} = 0$$

are independent of the particular pair of solutions, $g(z)$ and $h(z)$, chosen.

19·41. *Hill's method of solution.*

Now that the general functional character of the solution of equations with periodic coefficients has been found by Floquet's theory, it might be expected that the determination of an explicit expression for the solutions of Mathieu's and Hill's equations would be a comparatively easy matter; this however is not the case. For example, in the particular case of Mathieu's general equation, a solution has to be obtained in the form

$$y = e^{\mu z} \phi(z),$$

---

* The symbol k is used in this particular sense only in this section. It must not be confused with the constant k of § 19·21, which was associated with the parameter q of Mathieu's equation.

† The ratio of these solutions is not even periodic; still less is it a constant.

where $\phi(z)$ is periodic and μ is a function of the parameters a and q. The crux of the problem is to determine μ; when this is done, the determination of $\phi(z)$ presents comparatively little difficulty.

The first successful method of attacking the problem was published by Hill in the memoir cited in § 19·12; since the method for Hill's equation is no more difficult than for the special case of Mathieu's general equation, we shall discuss the case of Hill's equation, viz.

$$\frac{d^2u}{dz^2} + J(z)\,u = 0,$$

where $J(z)$ is an even function of z with period π. Two cases are of interest, the analysis being the same in each:

(I)   The astronomical case when z is real and, for real values of z, $J(z)$ can be expanded in the form

$$J(z) = \theta_0 + 2\theta_1 \cos 2z + 2\theta_2 \cos 4z + 2\theta_3 \cos 6z + \dots;$$

the coefficients θ_n are known constants and $\sum\limits_{n=0}^{\infty} \theta_n$ converges absolutely.

(II)   The case when z is a complex variable and $J(z)$ is analytic in a strip of the plane (containing the real axis), whose sides are parallel to the real axis.   The expansion of $J(z)$ in the Fourier series $\theta_0 + 2\sum\limits_{n=1}^{\infty} \theta_n \cos 2nz$ is then valid (§ 9·11) throughout the interior of the strip, and, as before, $\sum\limits_{n=0}^{\infty} \theta_n$ converges absolutely.

Defining θ_{-n} to be equal to θ_n, we assume

$$u = e^{\mu z} \sum_{n=-\infty}^{\infty} b_n e^{2niz}$$

as a solution of Hill's equation.

[In case (II) this is the solution analytic in the strip (§§ 10·2, 19·4); in case (I) it will have to be shewn ultimately (see the note at the end of § 19·42) that the values of b_n which will be determined are such as to make $\sum\limits_{n=-\infty}^{\infty} n^2 b_n$ absolutely convergent, in order to justify the processes which we shall now carry out.]

On substitution in the equation, we find

$$\sum_{n=-\infty}^{\infty} (\mu + 2ni)^2 b_n e^{(\mu+2ni)z} + \left(\sum_{n=-\infty}^{\infty} \theta_n e^{2niz}\right)\left(\sum_{n=-\infty}^{\infty} b_n e^{(\mu+2ni)z}\right) = 0.$$

Multiplying out the absolutely convergent series and equating coefficients of powers of e^{2iz} to zero (§§ 9·6–9·632), we obtain the system of equations

$$(\mu + 2ni)^2 b_n + \sum_{m=-\infty}^{\infty} \theta_m b_{n-m} = 0 \qquad (n = \dots, -2, -1, 0, 1, 2, \dots).$$

If we eliminate the coefficients b_n determinantally (after dividing the typical equation by $\theta_0 - 4n^2$ to secure convergence) we obtain* Hill's determinantal equation:

$$
\left|
\begin{array}{ccccc}
\cdots & & & & & =0. \\
\cdots \; \dfrac{(i\mu+4)^2-\theta_0}{4^2-\theta_0} & \dfrac{-\theta_1}{4^2-\theta_0} & \dfrac{-\theta_2}{4^2-\theta_0} & \dfrac{-\theta_3}{4^2-\theta_0} & \dfrac{-\theta_4}{4^2-\theta_0} \; \cdots \\[2ex]
\cdots \; \dfrac{-\theta_1}{2^2-\theta_0} & \dfrac{(i\mu+2)^2-\theta_0}{2^2-\theta_0} & \dfrac{-\theta_1}{2^2-\theta_0} & \dfrac{-\theta_2}{2^2-\theta_0} & \dfrac{-\theta_3}{2^2-\theta_0} \; \cdots \\[2ex]
\cdots \; \dfrac{-\theta_2}{0^2-\theta_0} & \dfrac{-\theta_1}{0^2-\theta_0} & \dfrac{(i\mu)^2-\theta_0}{0^2-\theta_0} & \dfrac{-\theta_1}{0^2-\theta_0} & \dfrac{-\theta_2}{0^2-\theta_0} \; \cdots \\[2ex]
\cdots \; \dfrac{-\theta_3}{2^2-\theta_0} & \dfrac{-\theta_2}{2^2-\theta_0} & \dfrac{-\theta_1}{2^2-\theta_0} & \dfrac{(i\mu-2)^2-\theta_0}{2^2-\theta_0} & \dfrac{-\theta_1}{2^2-\theta_0} \; \cdots \\[2ex]
\cdots \; \dfrac{-\theta_4}{4^2-\theta_0} & \dfrac{-\theta_3}{4^2-\theta_0} & \dfrac{-\theta_2}{4^2-\theta_0} & \dfrac{-\theta_1}{4^2-\theta_0} & \dfrac{(i\mu-4)^2-\theta_0}{4^2-\theta_0} \; \cdots \\[2ex]
\cdots & & & & &
\end{array}
\right|
$$

We write $\Delta(i\mu)$ for the determinant, so the equation determining μ is

$$\Delta(i\mu) = 0.$$

19·42. *The evaluation of Hill's determinant.*

We shall now obtain an extremely simple expression for Hill's determinant, namely

$$\Delta(i\mu) \equiv \Delta(0) - \sin^2\left(\tfrac{1}{2}\pi i\mu\right)\operatorname{cosec}^2\left(\tfrac{1}{2}\pi\sqrt{\theta_0}\right).$$

Adopting the notation of § 2·8, we write

$$\Delta(i\mu) \equiv [A_{m,n}],$$

where $A_{m,m} = \dfrac{(i\mu-2m)^2-\theta_0}{4m^2-\theta_0}$, $A_{m,n} = \dfrac{-\theta_{m-n}}{4m^2-\theta_0}$ $(m \neq n)$.

The determinant $[A_{m,n}]$ is only *conditionally* convergent, since the product of the principal diagonal elements does not converge absolutely (§§ 2·81, 2·7). We can, however, obtain an *absolutely* convergent determinant, $\Delta_1(i\mu)$, by dividing the linear equations of § 19·41 by $\theta_0 - (i\mu-2n)^2$ instead of dividing by $\theta_0 - 4n^2$. We write this determinant $\Delta_1(i\mu)$ in the form $[B_{m,n}]$, where

$$B_{m,m} = 1, \quad B_{m,n} = \dfrac{-\theta_{m-n}}{(2m-i\mu)^2-\theta_0} \quad (m \neq n).$$

The absolute convergence of $\overset{\infty}{\underset{n=0}{\Sigma}} \theta_n$ secures the convergence of the determinant $[B_{m,n}]$, except when μ has such a value that the denominator of one of the expressions $B_{m,n}$ vanishes.

---

* Since the coefficients b_n are not all zero, we may obtain the infinite determinant as the eliminant of the system of linear equations by multiplying these equations by suitably chosen cofactors and adding up.

From the definition of an infinite determinant (§ 2·8) it follows that

$$\Delta(i\mu) = \Delta_1(i\mu) \lim_{p \to \infty} \prod_{n=-p}^{p} \left\{ \frac{\theta_0 - (i\mu - 2n)^2}{\theta_0 - 4n^2} \right\},$$

and so

$$\Delta(i\mu) = -\Delta_1(i\mu) \frac{\sin \tfrac{1}{2}\pi (i\mu - \sqrt{\theta_0}) \sin \tfrac{1}{2}\pi (i\mu + \sqrt{\theta_0})}{\sin^2 (\tfrac{1}{2}\pi \sqrt{\theta_0})}.$$

Now, if the determinant $\Delta_1(i\mu)$ be written out in full, it is easy to see (i) that $\Delta_1(i\mu)$ is an even periodic function of μ with period $2i$, (ii) that $\Delta_1(i\mu)$ is an analytic function (cf. §§ 2·81, 3·34, 5·3) of μ (except at its obvious simple poles), which tends to unity as the real part of μ tends to $\pm \infty$.

If now we choose the constant K so that the function $D(\mu)$, defined by the equation

$$D(\mu) \equiv \Delta_1(i\mu) - K \{ \cot \tfrac{1}{2}\pi (i\mu + \sqrt{\theta_0}) - \cot \tfrac{1}{2}\pi (i\mu - \sqrt{\theta_0}) \},$$

has no pole at the point $\mu = i\sqrt{\theta_0}$, then, since $D(\mu)$ is an even periodic function of μ, it follows that $D(\mu)$ has no pole at any of the points

$$2ni \pm i\sqrt{\theta_0},$$

where n is any integer.

The function $D(\mu)$ is therefore a periodic function of μ (with period $2i$) which has no poles, and which is obviously bounded as $R(\mu) \to \pm \infty$. The conditions postulated in Liouville's theorem (§ 5·63) are satisfied, and so $D(\mu)$ is a constant; making $\mu \to +\infty$, we see that this constant is unity.

Therefore

$$\Delta_1(i\mu) = 1 + K \{ \cot \tfrac{1}{2}\pi (i\mu + \sqrt{\theta_0}) - \cot \tfrac{1}{2}\pi (i\mu - \sqrt{\theta_0}) \},$$

and so

$$\Delta(i\mu) = -\frac{\sin \tfrac{1}{2}\pi (i\mu - \sqrt{\theta_0}) \sin \tfrac{1}{2}\pi (i\mu + \sqrt{\theta_0})}{\sin^2 (\tfrac{1}{2}\pi \sqrt{\theta_0})} + 2K \cot (\tfrac{1}{2}\pi \sqrt{\theta_0}).$$

To determine K, put $\mu = 0$; then

$$\Delta(0) = 1 + 2K \cot (\tfrac{1}{2}\pi \sqrt{\theta_0}).$$

Hence, on subtraction,

$$\Delta(i\mu) = \Delta(0) - \frac{\sin^2 (\tfrac{1}{2}\pi i\mu)}{\sin^2 (\tfrac{1}{2}\pi \sqrt{\theta_0})},$$

which is the result stated.

The roots of Hill's determinantal equation are therefore the roots of the equation

$$\sin^2 (\tfrac{1}{2}\pi i\mu) = \Delta(0) . \sin^2 (\tfrac{1}{2}\pi \sqrt{\theta_0}).$$

When μ has thus been determined, the coefficients b_n can be determined in terms of b_0 and cofactors of $\Delta(i\mu)$; and the solution of Hill's differential equation is complete.

[In case (I) of § 19·41, the convergence of $\Sigma \,|\, b_n \,|$ follows from the rearrangement theorem of § 2·82; for $\Sigma n^2 \,|\, b_n \,|$ is equal to $|\, b_0 \,| \sum\limits_{m=-\infty}^{\infty} |\, C_{m,0} \,| \div |\, C_{0,0} \,|$, where $C_{m,n}$ is the cofactor of $B_{m,n}$ in $\Delta_1 (i\mu)$; and $\Sigma \,|\, C_{m,0} \,|$ is the determinant obtained by replacing the elements of the row through the origin by numbers whose moduli are bounded.]

It was shewn by Hill that, for the purposes of his astronomical problem, a remarkably good approximation to the value of μ could be obtained by considering only the three central rows and columns of his determinant.

19·5. *The Lindemann-Stieltjes' theory of Mathieu's general equation.*

Up to the present, Mathieu's equation has been treated as a linear differential equation with periodic coefficients. Some extremely interesting properties of the equation have been obtained by Lindemann[*] by the substitution $\zeta = \cos^2 z$, which transforms the equation into an equation with rational coefficients, namely

$$4\zeta (1 - \zeta) \frac{d^2 u}{d\zeta^2} + 2 (1 - 2\zeta) \frac{du}{d\zeta} + (a - 16q + 32q\zeta) u = 0.$$

This equation, though it somewhat resembles the hypergeometric equation, is of higher type than the equations dealt with in Chapters XIV and XVI, inasmuch as it has two regular singularities at 0 and 1 and an irregular singularity at ∞; whereas the three singularities of the hypergeometric equation are all regular, while the equation for $W_{k,m}(z)$ has one irregular singularity and only one regular singularity.

We shall now give a short account of Lindemann's analysis, with some modifications due to Stieltjes[†].

19·51. *Lindemann's form of Floquet's theorem.*

Since Mathieu's equation (in Lindemann's form) has singularities at $\zeta = 0$ and $\zeta = 1$, the exponents at each being $0, \frac{1}{2}$, there exist solutions of the form

$$y_{00} = \sum_{n=0}^{\infty} a_n \zeta^n, \qquad\qquad y_{01} = \zeta^{\frac{1}{2}} \sum_{n=0}^{\infty} b_n \zeta^n,$$

$$y_{10} = \sum_{n=0}^{\infty} a_n' (1 - \zeta)^n, \qquad y_{11} = (1 - \zeta)^{\frac{1}{2}} \sum_{n=0}^{\infty} b_n' (1 - \zeta)^n;$$

the first two series converge when $|\, \zeta \,| < 1$, the last two when $|\, 1 - \zeta \,| < 1$.

When the ζ-plane is cut along the real axis from 1 to $+ \infty$ and from 0 to $- \infty$, the four functions defined by these series are one-valued in the cut plane; and so relations of the form

$$y_{10} = \alpha y_{00} + \beta y_{01}, \quad y_{11} = \gamma y_{00} + \delta y_{01}$$

will exist throughout the cut plane.

Now suppose that ζ describes a closed circuit round the origin, so that the circuit crosses the cut from $- \infty$ to 0; the analytic continuation of y_{10} is

---

[*] *Math. Ann.* XXIII. (1883), p. 117.

[†] *Astr. Nach.* CIX. (1884), cols. 145–152, 261–266. The analysis is very similar to that employed by Hermite in his lectures at the École Polytechnique in 1872–1873 [*Oeuvres*, III. (Paris, 1912), pp. 118–122] in connexion with Lamé's equation. See § 23·7.

$\alpha y_{00} - \beta y_{01}$ (since y_{00} is unaffected by the description of the circuit, but y_{01} changes sign) and the continuation of y_{11} is $\gamma y_{00} - \delta y_{01}$; *and so $A y_{10}{}^2 + B y_{11}{}^2$ will be unaffected by the description of the circuit if*

$$A (\alpha y_{00} + \beta y_{01})^2 + B (\gamma y_{00} + \delta y_{01})^2 \equiv A (\alpha y_{00} - \beta y_{01})^2 + B (\gamma y_{00} - \delta y_{01})^2,$$

i.e. if　　　　　　　　　　$A \alpha \beta + B \gamma \delta = 0.$

Also $A y_{10}{}^2 + B y_{11}{}^2$ obviously has not a branch-point at $\zeta = 1$, and so, if $A \alpha \beta + B \gamma \delta = 0$, this function has no branch-points at 0 or 1, and, as it has no other possible singularities in the finite part of the plane, *it must be an integral function of ζ.*

The two expressions

$$A^{\frac{1}{2}} y_{10} + i B^{\frac{1}{2}} y_{11}, \quad A^{\frac{1}{2}} y_{10} - i B^{\frac{1}{2}} y_{11}$$

are consequently two solutions of Mathieu's equation whose product is an integral function of ζ.

[This amounts to the fact (§ 19·4) that the product of $\epsilon^{\mu z} \phi (z)$ and $e^{-\mu z} \phi (- z)$ is a *periodic integral* function of z.]

19·52. *The determination of the integral function associated with Mathieu's general equation.*

The integral function $F(z) \equiv A y_{10}{}^2 + B y_{11}{}^2$, just introduced, can be determined without difficulty; for, if y_{10} and y_{11} are any solutions of

$$\frac{d^2 u}{d\zeta^2} + P (\zeta) \frac{du}{d\zeta} + Q (\zeta) u = 0,$$

their squares (and consequently any linear combination of their squares) satisfy the equation*

$$\frac{d^3 y}{d\zeta^3} + 3P (\zeta) \frac{d^2 y}{d\zeta^2} + [P' (\zeta) + 4Q (\zeta) + 2 \{P (\zeta)\}^2] \frac{dy}{d\zeta}$$
$$+ 2 [Q' (\zeta) + 2P (\zeta) Q (\zeta)] y = 0;$$

in the case under consideration, this result reduces to

$$\zeta (1 - \zeta) \frac{d^3 F (\zeta)}{d\zeta^3} + \tfrac{3}{2} (1 - 2\zeta) \frac{d^2 F (\zeta)}{d\zeta^2}$$
$$+ (a - 1 - 16q + 32q\zeta) \frac{dF (\zeta)}{d\zeta} + 16q F (\zeta) = 0.$$

Let the Maclaurin series for $F (\zeta)$ be $\sum_{n=0}^{\infty} c_n \zeta^n$; on substitution, we easily obtain the recurrence formula for the coefficients c_n, namely

$$v_{n+1} c_{n+2} = u_n c_{n+1} + c_n,$$

where

$$u_n = - \frac{(n + 1) \{(n + 1)^2 - a + 16q\}}{16q (2n + 1)}, \quad v_n = - \frac{n (n + 1) (2n + 1)}{32q (2n - 1)}.$$

* Appell, *Comptes Rendus*, XCI. (1880), pp. 211–214 ; cf. example 10, p. 298 *supra*.

At first sight, it appears from the recurrence formula that c_0 and c_1 can be chosen arbitrarily, and the remaining coefficients c_2, c_3, ... calculated in terms of them; but the third order equation has a singularity at $\zeta = 1$, and the series thus obtained would have only unit radius of convergence. It is necessary to choose the value of the ratio c_1/c_0 so that the series may converge for all values of ζ.

The recurrence formula, when written in the form

$$(c_n/c_{n+1}) = u_n + \frac{v_{n+1}}{(c_{n+1}/c_{n+2})},$$

suggests the consideration of the infinite continued fraction

$$u_n + \frac{v_{n+1}}{u_{n+1}} + \frac{v_{n+2}}{u_{n+2}} + \ldots = \lim_{m \to \infty} \left\{ u_n + \frac{v_{n+1}}{u_{n+1}} + \ldots + \frac{v_{n+m}}{u_{n+m}} \right\}.$$

The continued fraction on the right can be written*

$$u_n K(n, n+m)/K(n+1, n+m),$$

where $K(n, n+m) = \begin{vmatrix} 1 & , & v_{n+1}/u_n, & 0 & , & \ldots\ldots\ldots \\ -u_{n+1}^{-1}, & 1 & , & v_{n+2}/u_{n+1}, & \ldots\ldots\ldots \\ 0 & , & -u_{n+2}^{-1}, & 1 & , & \ldots\ldots\ldots \\ \ldots\ldots\ldots\ldots\ldots\ldots\ldots\ldots\ldots \\ \ldots\ldots\ldots\ldots\ldots\ldots\ldots -u_{n+m}^{-1}, & 1 \end{vmatrix}.$

The limit of this, as $m \to \infty$, is a convergent determinant of von Koch's type (by the example of § 2·82); and since

$$\sum_{r=n}^{\infty} \left| \frac{v_{r+1}}{u_r u_{r+1}} \right| \to 0 \text{ as } n \to \infty,$$

it is easily seen that $K(n, \infty) \to 1$ as $n \to \infty$.

Therefore, if

$$\frac{c_n}{c_{n+1}} = \frac{u_n K(n, \infty)}{K(n+1, \infty)},$$

then c_n satisfies the recurrence formula and, since $c_{n+1}/c_n \to 0$ as $n \to \infty$, the resulting series for $F(\zeta)$ is an integral function. From the recurrence formula it is obvious that all the coefficients c_n are finite, since they are finite when n is sufficiently large. The construction of the integral function $F(\zeta)$ has therefore been effected.

19·53. *The solution of Mathieu's equation in terms of $F(\zeta)$.*

If w_1 and w_2 be two particular solutions of

$$\frac{d^2u}{d\zeta^2} + P(\zeta)\frac{du}{d\zeta} + Q(\zeta)u = 0,$$

then†

$$w_2 w_1' - w_1 w_2' = C \exp\left\{ -\int_0^\zeta P(\zeta)\,d\zeta \right\},$$

---

* Sylvester, *Phil. Mag.* (4), v. (1853), p. 446 [*Math. Papers*, I. p. 609].

† Abel, *Journal für Math.* II. (1827), p. 22.　Primes denote differentiations with regard to ζ.

where C is a definite constant. Taking w_1 and w_2 to be those two solutions of Mathieu's general equation whose product is $F(\zeta)$, we have

$$\frac{w_1'}{w_1} - \frac{w_2'}{w_2} = \frac{C}{\zeta^{\frac{1}{2}}(1-\zeta)^{\frac{1}{2}} F(\zeta)}, \quad \frac{w_1'}{w_1} + \frac{w_2'}{w_2} = \frac{F'(\zeta)}{F(\zeta)},$$

the latter following at once from the equation $w_1 w_2 = F(\zeta)$.

Solving these equations for w_1'/w_1 and w_2'/w_2, and then integrating, we at once get

$$w_1 = \gamma_1 \{F(\zeta)\}^{\frac{1}{2}} \exp\left\{\frac{1}{2} C \int_0^\zeta \frac{d\zeta}{\zeta^{\frac{1}{2}}(1-\zeta)^{\frac{1}{2}} F(\zeta)}\right\},$$

$$w_2 = \gamma_2 \{F(\zeta)\}^{\frac{1}{2}} \exp\left\{-\frac{1}{2} C \int_0^\zeta \frac{d\zeta}{\zeta^{\frac{1}{2}}(1-\zeta)^{\frac{1}{2}} F(\zeta)}\right\},$$

where γ_1, γ_2 are constants of integration; obviously no real generality is lost by taking $c_0 = \gamma_1 = \gamma_2 = 1$.

From the former result we have, for small values of $|\zeta|$,

$$w_1 = 1 + C\zeta^{\frac{1}{2}} + \frac{1}{2}(c_1 + C^2)\zeta + O(\zeta^{\frac{3}{2}}),$$

while, in the notation of § 19·51, we have $a_1/a_0 = -\frac{1}{2}a + 8q$.

Hence $\qquad\qquad C^2 = 16q - a - c_1.$

This equation determines C in terms of a, q and c_1, the value of c_1 being

$$K(1, \infty) \div \{u_0 K(0, \infty)\}.$$

Example 1. If the solutions of Mathieu's equation be $e^{\pm \mu z}\phi(\pm z)$, where $\phi(z)$ is periodic, shew that

$$\pi\mu = \pm C \int_0^\pi \frac{dz}{F(\cos^2 z)}.$$

Example 2. Shew that the zeros of $F(\zeta)$ are all simple, unless $C=0$.

(Stieltjes.)

[If $F(\zeta)$ could have a repeated zero, w_1 and w_2 would then have an essential singularity.]

19·6. *A second method of constructing the Mathieu function.*

So far, it has been assumed that all the various series of § 19·3 involved in the expressions for $ce_N(z, q)$ and $se_N(z, q)$ are convergent. *It will now be shewn that $ce_N(z, q)$ and $se_N(z, q)$ are integral functions of z and that the coefficients in their expansions as Fourier series are power series in q which converge absolutely when $|q|$ is sufficiently small*[*].

To obtain this result for the functions $ce_N(z, q)$, we shall shew how to determine a particular integral of the equation

$$\frac{d^2u}{dz^2} + (a + 16q \cos 2z)u = \psi(a, q) \cos Nz$$

---

[*] The essential part of this theorem is the proof of the *convergence of the series which occur in the coefficients*; it is already known (§§ 10·2, 10·21) that solutions of Mathieu's equation are integral functions of z, and (in the case of *periodic* solutions) the existence of the Fourier expansion follows from § 9·11.

in the form of a Fourier series converging over the whole z-plane, where $\psi(a, q)$ is a function of the parameters a and q. The equation $\psi(a, q) = 0$ then determines a relation between a and q which gives rise to a Mathieu function. The reader who is acquainted with the method of Frobenius* as applied to the solution of linear differential equations in power series will recognise the resemblance of the following analysis to his work.

Write $a = N^2 + 8p$, where N is zero or a positive or negative integer.

Mathieu's equation becomes

$$\frac{d^2u}{dz^2} + N^2 u = -8(p + 2q \cos 2z) u.$$

If p and q are neglected, a solution of this equation is $u = \cos Nz = U_0(z)$, say.

To obtain a closer approximation, write $-8(p + 2q \cos 2z) U_0(z)$ as a sum of cosines, i.e. in the form

$$-8\{q \cos(N-2)z + p \cos Nz + q \cos(N+2)z\} = V_1(z), \text{ say.}$$

Then, instead of solving $\dfrac{d^2u}{dz^2} + N^2 u = V_1(z)$, suppress the terms† in $V_1(z)$ which involve $\cos Nz$; i.e. consider the function $W_1(z)$ where‡

$$W_1(z) = V_1(z) + 8p \cos Nz.$$

A particular integral of

$$\frac{d^2u}{dz^2} + N^2 u = W_1(z)$$

is

$$u = 2\left\{\frac{q}{1(1-N)} \cos(N-2)z + \frac{q}{1(1+N)} \cos(N+2)z\right\} = U_1(z), \text{ say.}$$

Now express $-8(p + 2q \cos 2z) U_1(z)$ as a sum of cosines; calling this sum $V_2(z)$, choose α_2 to be such a function of p and q that $V_2(z) + \alpha_2 \cos Nz$ contains no term in $\cos Nz$; and let $V_2(z) + \alpha_2 \cos Nz = W_2(z)$.

Solve the equation $\qquad \dfrac{d^2u}{dz^2} + N^2 u = W_2(z)$,

and continue the process. Three sets of functions $U_m(z)$, $V_m(z)$, $W_m(z)$ are thus obtained, such that $U_m(z)$ and $W_m(z)$ contain no term in $\cos Nz$ when $m \neq 0$, and

$$W_m(z) = V_m(z) + \alpha_m \cos Nz, \quad V_m(z) = -8(p + 2q \cos 2z) U_{m-1}(z),$$
$$\frac{d^2 U_m(z)}{dz^2} + N^2 U_m(z) = W_m(z),$$

where α_m is a function of p and q but not of z.

---

* *Journal für Math.* LXXVI. (1873), pp. 214–224.

† The reason for this suppression is that the particular integral of $\dfrac{d^2u}{dz^2} + N^2 u = \cos Nz$ contains non-periodic terms.

‡ Unless $N = 1$, in which case $W_1(z) = V_1(z) + 8(p+q)\cos z$.

It follows that

$$\left\{\frac{d^2}{dz^2} + N^2\right\} \sum_{m=0}^{n} U_m(z) = \sum_{m=1}^{n} W_m(z)$$

$$= \sum_{m=1}^{n} V_m(z) + \left(\sum_{m=1}^{n} \alpha_m\right) \cos Nz$$

$$= -8(p + 2q \cos 2z) \sum_{m=0}^{n-1} U_{m-1}(z) + \left(\sum_{m=1}^{n} \alpha_m\right) \cos Nz.$$

Therefore, if $U(z) = \sum\limits_{m=0}^{\infty} U_m(z)$ be a uniformly convergent series of analytic functions throughout a two-dimensional region in the z-plane, we have (§ 5·3)

$$\frac{d^2 U(z)}{dz^2} + (a + 16q \cos 2z) U(z) = \psi(a, q) \cos Nz,$$

where

$$\psi(a, q) = \sum_{m=1}^{\infty} \alpha_m.$$

It is obvious that, if a be so chosen that $\psi(a, q) = 0$, then $U(z)$ reduces to $ce_N(z)$.

A similar process can obviously be carried out for the functions $se_N(z, q)$ by making use of sines of multiples of z.

19·61.   *The convergence of the series defining Mathieu functions.*

We shall now examine the expansion of § 19·6 more closely, with a view to investigating the convergence of the series involved.

When $n \geqslant 1$, we may obviously write

$$U_n(z) = \sum_{r=1}^{n} {}^*\beta_{n, r} \cos(N - 2r) z + \sum_{r=1}^{n} a_{n, r} \cos(N + 2r) z,$$

the asterisk denoting that the first summation ceases at the greatest value of r for which $r \leqslant \frac{1}{2} N$.

Since $\left\{\dfrac{d^2}{dz^2} + N^2\right\} U_{n+1}(z) = a_{n+1} \cos Nz - 8(p + 2q \cos 2z) U_n(z),$

it follows on equating coefficients of $\cos(N \pm 2r) z$ on each side of the equation† that

$$a_{n+1} = 8q(a_{n,1} + \beta_{n,1}),$$

$$r(r + N) a_{n+1, r} = 2\{pa_{n, r} + q(a_{n, r-1} + a_{n, r+1})\} \qquad (r = 1, 2, \ldots),$$

$$r(r - N) \beta_{n+1, r} = 2\{p\beta_{n, r} + q(\beta_{n, r-1} + \beta_{n, r+1})\} \qquad (r \leqslant \tfrac{1}{2} N).$$

These formulae hold universally with the following conventions‡:

(i) $a_{n, 0} = \beta_{n, 0} = 0$ $(n = 1, 2, \ldots)$; $a_{n, r} = \beta_{n, r} = 0$ $(r > n)$,

(ii) $\beta_{n, \frac{1}{2} N + 1} = \beta_{n, \frac{1}{2} N - 1}$ when N is even and $r = \frac{1}{2} N$,

(iii) $\beta_{n, \frac{1}{2}(N+1)} = \beta_{n, \frac{1}{2}(N-1)}$ when N is odd and $r = \frac{1}{2}(N - 1)$.

† When $N = 0$ or 1 these equations must be modified by the suppression of all the coefficients $\beta_{n, r}$.

‡ The conventions (ii) and (iii) are due to the fact that $\cos z = \cos(-z)$, $\cos 2z = \cos(-2z)$.

The reader will easily obtain the following special formulae:

(I) $a_1 = 8p$, $(N \neq 1)$; $a_1 = 8(p+q)$, $(N=1)$,

(II) $a_{n,n} = \dfrac{(2q)^n \cdot N!}{n!(N+n)!}$, $(N \neq 0)$; $a_{n,n} = \dfrac{2^{n+1} q^n}{(n!)^2}$, $(N=0)$.

(III) $a_{n,r}$ and $\beta_{n,r}$ are homogeneous polynomials of degree n in p and q.

If $\sum\limits_{n=r}^{\infty} a_{n,r} = A_r$, $\sum\limits_{n=r}^{\infty} \beta_{n,r} = B_r$,

we have $\psi(a, q) = 8p + 8q(A_1 + B_1)$ $(N \neq 1)$,

$$r(r+N) A_r = 2\{pA_r + q(A_{r-1} + A_{r+1})\} \dots\dots\dots\dots\dots\dots(A),$$

$$r(r-N) B_r = 2\{pB_r + q(B_{r-1} + B_{r+1})\} \dots\dots\dots\dots\dots\dots(B),$$

where $A_0 = B_0 = 1$ and B_r is subject to conventions due to (ii) and (iii) above.

Now write $w_r = -q\{r(r+N) - 2p\}^{-1}$, $w_r' = -q\{r(r-N) - 2p\}^{-1}$.

The result of eliminating $A_1, A_2, \dots A_{r-1}, A_{r+1}, \dots$ from the set of equations (A) is

$$A_r \Delta_0 = (-)^r w_1 w_2 \dots w_r \Delta_r,$$

where Δ_r is the infinite determinant of von Koch's type (§ 2·82)

$$\Delta_r = \begin{vmatrix} 1, & w_{r+1}, & 0, & 0, & \dots \\ w_{r+2}, & 1, & w_{r+2}, & 0, & \dots \\ 0, & w_{r+3}, & 1, & w_{r+3}, & \dots \\ \hdotsfor{5} \end{vmatrix}.$$

The determinant converges absolutely (§ 2·82 example) if no denominator vanishes; and $\Delta_r \to 1$ as $r \to \infty$ (cf. § 19·52). If p and q be given such values that $\Delta_0 \neq 0$, $2p \neq r(r+N)$, where $r = 1, 2, 3, \dots$, the series

$$\sum_{r=1}^{\infty} (-)^r w_1 w_2 \dots w_r \Delta_r \Delta_0^{-1} \cos(N+2r)z$$

represents an integral function of z.

In like manner $B_r D_0 = (-)^r w_1' w_2' \dots w_r' D_r$, where D_r is the finite determinant

$$\begin{vmatrix} 1, & w'_{r+1}, & 0, & \dots \\ w'_{r+2}, & 1, & w'_{r+2}, & \dots \\ \hdotsfor{4} \end{vmatrix},$$

the last row being $0, 0, \dots 0, 2w'_{\frac{1}{2}N}, 1$ or $0, 0, \dots 0, w'_{\frac{1}{2}(N-1)}, 1 + w'_{\frac{1}{2}(N-1)}$ according as N is even or odd.

The series $\sum\limits_{n=0}^{\infty} U_n(z)$ is therefore

$$\cos Nz + \Delta_0^{-1} \sum_{r=1}^{\infty} (-)^r w_1 w_2 \dots w_r \Delta_r \cos(N+2r)z$$

$$+ D_0^{-1} \sum_{r=1}^{r \leqslant \frac{1}{2}N} (-)^r w_1' w_2' \dots w_r' D_r \cos(N-2r)z,$$

these series converging uniformly in any bounded domain of values of z, so that term-by-term differentiations are permissible.

Further, the condition $\psi(a, q) = 0$ is equivalent to

$$p = q\left(\frac{w_1 \Delta_1}{\Delta_0} + \frac{w_1' D_1}{D_0}\right),$$

i.e. $p\Delta_0 D_0 - q(w_1 \Delta_1 D_0 + w_1' D_1 \Delta_0) = 0.$

If we multiply by

$$\prod_{r=1}^{\infty} \left\{1 - \frac{2p}{r(r+N)}\right\} \prod_{r=1}^{r \leqslant \frac{1}{2}N} \left\{1 - \frac{2p}{r(r-N)}\right\},$$

the expression on the left becomes an integral function of both p and q, $\Psi(a, q)$, say; the terms of $\Psi(a, q)$, which are of lowest degrees in p and q, are respectively p and

$$q^2 \left\{ \frac{1}{N-1} - \frac{1}{N+1} \right\}.$$

Now expand
$$\frac{1}{2\pi i} \int \frac{p}{\Psi(N^2 + 8p, q)} \frac{\partial \Psi(N^2 + 8p, q)}{\partial p} dp$$

in ascending powers of q (cf. § 7·31), the contour being a small circle in the p-plane, with centre at the origin, and $|q|$ being so small that $\Psi(N^2 + 8p, q)$ has only one zero inside the contour. Then it follows, just as in § 7·31, that, for sufficiently small values of $|q|$, we may expand p as a power series in q commencing* with a term in q^2; and if $|q|$ be sufficiently small D_0 and Δ_0 will not vanish, since both are equal to 1 when $q = 0$.

On substituting for p in terms of q throughout the series for $U(z)$, we see that the series involved in $ce_N(z, q)$ are absolutely convergent when $|q|$ is sufficiently small.

The series involved in $se_N(z, q)$ may obviously be investigated in a similar manner.

19·7. *The method of change of parameter†.*

The methods of Hill and of Lindemann-Stieltjes are effective in determining μ, but only after elaborate analysis. Such analysis is inevitable, as μ is by no means a simple function of q; this may be seen by giving q an assigned real value and making a vary from $-\infty$ to $+\infty$; then μ alternates between real and complex values, the changes taking place when, with the Hill-Mathieu notation, $\Delta(0) \sin^2(\frac{1}{2}\pi \sqrt{a})$ passes through the values 0 and 1; the complicated nature of this condition is due to the fact that $\Delta(0)$ is an elaborate expression involving both a and q.

It is, however, possible to express μ and a in terms of q and of a new parameter σ, and the results are very well adapted for purposes of numerical computation when $|q|$ is small‡.

The introduction of the parameter σ is suggested by the series for $ce_1(z, q)$ and $se_1(z, q)$ given in § 19·3 example 1; a consideration of these series leads us to investigate the potentialities of a solution of Mathieu's general equation in the form $y = e^{\mu z} \phi(z)$, where

$$\phi(z) = \sin(z - \sigma) + a_3 \cos(3z - \sigma) + b_3 \sin(3z - \sigma) + a_5 \cos(5z - \sigma) + b_5 \sin(5z - \sigma) + \dots,$$

the parameter σ being rendered definite by the fact that no term in $\cos(z - \sigma)$ is to appear in $\phi(z)$; the special functions $se_1(z, q)$, $ce_1(z, q)$ are the cases of this solution in which σ is 0 or $\frac{1}{2}\pi$.

On substituting this expression in Mathieu's equation, the reader will have no difficulty in obtaining the following approximations, valid for § small values of q and real values of σ:

$$\mu = 4q \sin 2\sigma - 12q^3 \sin 2\sigma - 12q^4 \sin 4\sigma + O(q^5),$$
$$a = 1 + 8q \cos 2\sigma + (-16 + 8 \cos 4\sigma) q^2 - 8q^3 \cos 2\sigma + (\tfrac{256}{3} - 88 \cos 4\sigma) q^4 + O(q^5),$$
$$a_3 = 3q^2 \sin 2\sigma + 3q^3 \sin 4\sigma + (-\tfrac{274}{9} \sin 2\sigma + 9 \sin 6\sigma) q^4 + O(q^5),$$
$$b_3 = q + q^2 \cos 2\sigma + (-\tfrac{14}{3} + 5 \cos 4\sigma) q^3 + (-\tfrac{74}{9} \cos 2\sigma + 7 \cos 6\sigma) q^4 + O(q^5),$$
$$a_5 = \tfrac{14}{9} q^3 \sin 2\sigma + \tfrac{44}{27} q^4 \sin 4\sigma + O(q^5),$$
$$b_5 = \tfrac{1}{3} q^2 + \tfrac{4}{9} q^3 \cos 2\sigma + (-\tfrac{155}{54} + \tfrac{83}{27} \cos 4\sigma) q^4 + O(q^5),$$
$$a_7 = \tfrac{35}{108} q^4 \sin 2\sigma + O(q^5), \quad b_7 = \tfrac{1}{18} q^3 + \tfrac{1}{12} q^4 \cos 2\sigma + O(q^5),$$
$$a_9 = O(q^5), \quad b_9 = \tfrac{1}{180} q^4 + O(q^5),$$

the constants involved in the various functions $O(q^5)$ depending on σ.

---

* If $N = 1$ this result has to be modified, since there is an additional term q on the right and the term $q^2/(N-1)$ does not appear.

† Whittaker, *Proc. Edinburgh Math. Soc.* XXXII. (1914), pp. 75–80.

‡ They have been applied to Hill's problem by Ince, *Monthly Notices of the R. A. S.* LXXV. (1915), pp. 436–448.

§ The parameters q and σ are to be regarded as fundamental in this analysis, instead of a and q as hitherto.

The domains of values of q and σ for which these series converge have not yet been determined*.

If the solution thus obtained be called $\Lambda(z, \sigma, q)$, then $\Lambda(z, \sigma, q)$ and $\Lambda(z, -\sigma, q)$ form a fundamental system of solutions of Mathieu's general equation if $\mu \neq 0$.

Example 1. Shew that, if $\sigma = i \times 0·5$ and $q = 0·01$, then

$$a = 1·124,841,4 \dots, \qquad \mu = i \times 0·046,993,5 \dots;$$

shew also that, if $\sigma = i$ and $q = 0·01$, then

$$a = 1·321,169,3 \dots, \qquad \mu = i \times 0·145,027,6 \dots.$$

Example 2. Obtain the equations

$$\mu = 4q \sin 2\sigma - 4qa_3,$$
$$a = 1 + 8q \cos 2\sigma - \mu^2 - 8qb_3,$$

expressing μ and a in finite terms as functions of q, σ, a_3 and b_3.

Example 3. Obtain the recurrence formulae

$$\{-4n(n+1) + 8q \cos 2\sigma - 8qb_3 \pm 8qi(2n+1)(a_3 - \sin 2\sigma)\} z_{2n+1} + 8q(z_{2n-1} + z_{2n+3}) = 0,$$

where z_{2n+1} denotes $b_{2n+1} + ia_{2n+1}$ or $b_{2n+1} - ia_{2n+1}$, according as the upper or lower sign is taken.

19·8. *The asymptotic solution of Mathieu's equation.*

If in Mathieu's equation

$$\frac{d^2u}{dz^2} + \left(a + \frac{1}{2}k^2 \cos 2z\right)u = 0$$

we write $k \sin z = \xi$, we get

$$(\xi^2 - k^2)\frac{d^2u}{d\xi^2} + \xi\frac{du}{d\xi} + (\xi^2 - M^2)u = 0,$$

where $M^2 \equiv a + \frac{1}{2}k^2$.

This equation has an irregular singularity at infinity. From its resemblance to Bessel's equation, we are led to write $u = e^{i\xi}\xi^{-\frac{1}{2}}v$, and substitute

$$v = 1 + (a_1/\xi) + (a_2/\xi^2) + \dots$$

in the resulting equation for v; we then find that

$$a_1 = -\tfrac{1}{2}i\left(\tfrac{1}{4} - M^2 + k^2\right), \quad a_2 = -\tfrac{1}{8}\left(\tfrac{1}{4} - M^2 + k^2\right)\left(\tfrac{9}{4} - M^2 + k^2\right) + \tfrac{1}{4}k^2,$$

the general coefficient being given by the recurrence formula

$$2i(r+1)a_{r+1} = \{\tfrac{1}{4} - M^2 + k^2 + r(r+1)\} + (2r-1)ik^2 a_{r-1} - (r^2 - 2r + \tfrac{3}{4})k^2 a_{r-2}.$$

The two series

$$e^{i\xi}\xi^{-\frac{1}{2}}\left(1 + \frac{a_1}{\xi} + \frac{a_2}{\xi^2} + \dots\right), \quad e^{-i\xi}\xi^{-\frac{1}{2}}\left(1 - \frac{a_1}{\xi} + \frac{a_2}{\xi^2} - \dots\right)$$

are formal solutions of Mathieu's equation, reducing to the well-known asymptotic solutions of Bessel's equation (§ 17·5) when $k \to 0$. The complete formulae which connect them with the solutions $e^{\pm\mu z}\phi(\pm z)$ have not yet been published, though some steps towards obtaining them have been made by Dougall, *Proc. Edinburgh Math. Soc.* XXXIV. (1916), pp. 176–196.

---

* It seems highly probable that, if $|q|$ is sufficiently small, the series converge for all real values of σ, and also for complex values of σ for which $|I(\sigma)|$ is sufficiently small. It may be noticed that, when q is real, real and purely imaginary values of σ correspond respectively to real and purely imaginary values of μ.

REFERENCES*.

E. L. MATHIEU, *Journal de Math.* (2), XIII. (1868), pp. 137–203.

G. W. HILL, *Acta Mathematica*, VIII. (1886), pp. 1–36.

G. FLOQUET, *Ann. de l'École norm. sup.* (2), XII. (1883), pp. 47–88.

C. L. F. LINDEMANN, *Math. Ann.* XXII. (1883), pp. 117–123.

T. J. STIELTJES, *Astr. Nach.* CIX. (1884), cols. 145–152, 261–266.

A. LINDSTEDT, *Astr. Nach.* CIII. (1882), cols. 211–220, 257–268; CIV. (1883), cols. 145–150; CV. (1883), cols. 97–112.

H. BRUNS, *Astr. Nach.* CVI. (1883), cols. 193–204; CVII. (1884), cols. 129–132.

R. C. MACLAURIN, *Trans. Camb. Phil. Soc.* XVII. (1899), pp. 41–108.

K. AICHI, *Proc. Tōkyō Math. and Phys. Soc.* (2), IV. (1908), pp. 266–278.

E. T. WHITTAKER, *Proc. International Congress of Mathematicians*, Cambridge, 1912, I. pp. 366–371.

E. T. WHITTAKER, *Proc. Edinburgh Math. Soc.* XXXII. (1914), pp. 75–80.

G. N. WATSON, *Proc. Edinburgh Math. Soc.* XXXIII. (1915), pp. 25–30.

A. W. YOUNG, *Proc. Edinburgh Math. Soc.* XXXII. (1914), pp. 81–90.

E. LINDSAY INCE, *Proc. Edinburgh Math. Soc.* XXXIII. (1915), pp. 2–15.

J. DOUGALL, *Proc. Edinburgh Math. Soc.* XXXIV. (1916), pp. 176–196.

MISCELLANEOUS EXAMPLES.

1. Shew that, if $k = \sqrt{(32q)}$,

$$2\pi c e_0(z, q) = c e_0(0, q) \int_{-\pi}^{\pi} \cos(k \sin z \sin \theta) \, c e_0(\theta, q) \, d\theta.$$

2. Shew that the even Mathieu functions satisfy the integral equation

$$G(z) = \lambda \int_{-\pi}^{\pi} J_0 \{ik(\cos z + \cos \theta)\} \, G(\theta) \, d\theta.$$

3. Shew that the equation

$$(az^2 + c) \frac{d^2u}{dz^2} + 2az \frac{du}{dz} + (\lambda^2 cz^2 + m) \, u = 0$$

(where a, c, λ, m are constants) is satisfied by

$$u = \int e^{\lambda zs} \nu(s) \, ds$$

taken round an appropriate contour, provided that $\nu(s)$ satisfies

$$(as^2 + c) \frac{d^2 \nu(s)}{ds^2} + 2as \frac{d\nu(s)}{ds} + (\lambda^2 cs^2 + m) \, \nu(s) = 0,$$

which is the same as the equation for u.

Derive the integral equations satisfied by the Mathieu functions as particular cases of this result.

* A complete bibliography is given by Humbert, *Fonctions de Mathieu et fonctions de Lamé* (Paris, 1926).

4. Shew that, if powers of q above the fourth are neglected, then

$$ce_1 (z, q) = \cos z + q \cos 3z + q^2 \left(\tfrac{1}{3} \cos 5z - \cos 3z\right)$$
$$+ q^3 \left(\tfrac{1}{18} \cos 7z - \tfrac{4}{9} \cos 5z + \tfrac{1}{3} \cos 3z\right)$$
$$+ q^4 \left(\tfrac{1}{180} \cos 9z - \tfrac{1}{12} \cos 7z + \tfrac{1}{6} \cos 5z + \tfrac{11}{9} \cos 3z\right),$$

$$se_1 (z, q) = \sin z + q \sin 3z + q^2 \left(\tfrac{1}{3} \sin 5z + \sin 3z\right)$$
$$+ q^3 \left(\tfrac{1}{18} \sin 7z + \tfrac{4}{9} \sin 5z + \tfrac{1}{3} \sin 3z\right)$$
$$+ q^4 \left(\tfrac{1}{180} \sin 9z + \tfrac{1}{12} \sin 7z + \tfrac{1}{6} \sin 5z - \tfrac{11}{9} \sin 3z\right),$$

$$ce_2 (z, q) = \cos 2z + q \left(\tfrac{2}{3} \cos 4z - 2\right) + \tfrac{1}{6} q^2 \cos 6z$$
$$+ q^3 \left(\tfrac{1}{45} \cos 8z + \tfrac{43}{27} \cos 4z + \tfrac{40}{3}\right)$$
$$+ q^4 \left(\tfrac{1}{540} \cos 10z + \tfrac{293}{540} \cos 6z\right).$$

(Mathieu.)

5. Shew that

$$ce_3 (z, q) = \cos 3z + q \left(- \cos z + \tfrac{1}{2} \cos 5z\right)$$
$$+ q^2 \left(\cos z + \tfrac{1}{10} \cos 7z\right) + q^3 \left(- \tfrac{1}{2} \cos z + \tfrac{7}{40} \cos 5z + \tfrac{1}{90} \cos 9z\right) + O (q^4),$$

and that, in the case of this function

$$a = 9 + 4q^2 - 8q^3 + O (q^4).$$

(Mathieu.)

6. Shew that, if $y (z)$ be a Mathieu function, then a second solution of the corresponding differential equation is

$$y (z) \int^z \{y (t)\}^{-2} dt.$$

Shew that a second solution* of the equation for $ce_0 (z, q)$ is

$$z ce_0 (z, q) - 4q \sin 2z - 3q^2 \sin 4z - \ldots.$$

7. If $y (z)$ be a solution of Mathieu's general equation, shew that

$$\{y (z + 2\pi) + y (z - 2\pi)\} / y (z)$$

is constant.

8. Express the Mathieu functions as series of Bessel functions in which the coefficients are multiples of the coefficients in the Fourier series for the Mathieu functions.

[Substitute the Fourier series under the integral sign in the integral equations of § 19·22.]

9. Shew that the confluent form of the equations for $ce_n (z, q)$ and $se_n (z, q)$, when the eccentricity of the fundamental ellipse tends to zero, is, in each case, the equation satisfied by $J_n (ik \cos z)$.

10. Obtain the parabolic cylinder functions of Chapter XVI as confluent forms of the Mathieu functions, by making the eccentricity of the fundamental ellipse tend to unity.

11. Shew that $ce_n (z, q)$ can be expanded in series of the form

$$\sum_{m=0}^{\infty} A_m \cos^{2m} z \quad \text{or} \quad \sum_{m=0}^{\infty} B_m \cos^{2m+1} z,$$

according as n is even or odd; and that these series converge when $| \cos z | < 1$.

---

* This solution is called $in_0 (z, q)$; the second solutions of the equations satisfied by Mathieu functions have been investigated by Ince, *Proc. Edinburgh Math. Soc.* xxxiii. (1915), pp. 2–15. See also § 19·2.

12. With the notation of example 11, shew that, if

$$ce_n\,(z,\,q) = \lambda_n \int_{-\pi}^{\pi} e^{k\cos z \cos \theta}\,ce_n\,(\theta,\,q)\,d\theta,$$

then λ_n is given by one or other of the series

$$A_0 = 2\pi\lambda_n \sum_{m=0}^{\infty} \frac{2m}{2^{2m}\,(m\,!)^2}\,A_m, \quad B_0 = 2\pi\lambda_n k \sum_{m=0}^{\infty} \frac{(2m+1)\,!}{2^{2m+1}\,m\,!\,(m+1)\,!}\,B_m,$$

provided that these series converge.

13. Shew that the differential equation satisfied by the product of any two solutions of Bessel's equation for functions of order n is

$$\vartheta\,(\vartheta - 2n)\,(\vartheta + 2n)\,u + 4z^2\,(\vartheta + 1)\,u = 0,$$

where ϑ denotes $z\dfrac{d}{dz}$.

Shew that one solution of this equation is an integral function of z; and thence, by the methods of §§ 19·5–19·53, obtain the Bessel functions, discussing particularly the case in which n is an integer.

14. Shew that an approximate solution of the equation

$$\frac{d^2u}{dz^2} + (A + k^2 \sinh^2 z)\,u = 0$$

is

$$u = C\,(\operatorname{cosech} z)^{\frac{1}{2}} \sin\,(k \cosh z + \epsilon),$$

where C and ϵ are constants of integration; it is to be assumed that k is large, A is not very large and z is not small.

CHAPTER XX

ELLIPTIC FUNCTIONS. GENERAL THEOREMS AND THE WEIERSTRASSIAN FUNCTIONS

20·1. *Doubly-periodic functions.*

A most important property of the circular functions $\sin z$, $\cos z$, $\tan z$, ... is that, if $f(z)$ denote any one of them,

$$f(z + 2\pi) = f(z),$$

and hence $f(z + 2n\pi) = f(z)$, for all integer values of n. It is on account of this property that the circular functions are frequently described as *periodic functions* with period 2π. To distinguish them from the functions which will be discussed in this and the two following chapters, they are called *singly-periodic functions*.

Let ω_1, ω_2 be any two numbers (real or complex) *whose ratio* is not purely real*. A function which satisfies the equations

$$f(z + 2\omega_1) = f(z), \quad f(z + 2\omega_2) = f(z),$$

for all values of z for which $f(z)$ exists, is called a *doubly-periodic* function of z, with periods $2\omega_1$, $2\omega_2$. A doubly-periodic function which is analytic (except at poles), and which has no singularities other than poles in the finite part of the plane, is called an *elliptic function*.

[NOTE. What is now known as an *elliptic integral*† occurs in the researches of Jakob Bernoulli on the Elastica. Maclaurin, Fagnano, Legendre, and others considered such integrals in connexion with the problem of rectifying an arc of an ellipse; the idea of 'inverting' an elliptic integral (§ 21·7) to obtain an elliptic function is due to Abel, Jacobi and Gauss.]

The periods $2\omega_1$, $2\omega_2$ play much the same part in the theory of elliptic functions as is played by the single period in the case of the circular functions.

Before actually constructing any elliptic functions, and, indeed, before establishing the existence of such functions, it is convenient to prove some general theorems (§§ 20·11–20·14) concerning properties common to all elliptic functions; this procedure, though not strictly logical, is convenient

---

* If ω_2/ω_1 is real, the parallelograms defined in § 20·11 collapse, and the function reduces to a singly-periodic function when ω_2/ω_1 is rational; and when ω_2/ω_1 is irrational, it has been shewn by Jacobi, *Journal für Math.* XIII. (1835), pp. 55–56 [*Ges. Werke*, II. (1882), pp. 25–26] that the function reduces to a constant.

† A brief discussion of elliptic integrals will be found in §§ 22·7–22·741.

because a large number of the properties of particular elliptic functions can be obtained at once by an appeal to these theorems.

Example. The differential coefficient of an elliptic function is itself an elliptic function.

20·11. *Period-parallelograms.*

The study of elliptic functions is much facilitated by the geometrical representation afforded by the Argand diagram.

Suppose that in the plane of the variable z we mark the points 0, $2\omega_1$, $2\omega_2$, $2\omega_1 + 2\omega_2$, and, generally, all the points whose complex coordinates are of the form $2m\omega_1 + 2n\omega_2$, where m and n are integers.

Join in succession consecutive points of the set 0, $2\omega_1$, $2\omega_1 + 2\omega_2$, $2\omega_2$, 0, and we obtain a parallelogram. If there is no point ω inside or on the boundary of this parallelogram (the vertices excepted) such that

$$f(z + \omega) = f(z)$$

for all values of z, this parallelogram is called a *fundamental period-parallelogram* for an elliptic function with periods $2\omega_1$, $2\omega_2$.

It is clear that the z-plane may be covered with a network of parallelograms equal to the fundamental period-parallelogram and similarly situated, each of the points $2m\omega_1 + 2n\omega_2$ being a vertex of four parallelograms.

These parallelograms are called *period-parallelograms*, or *meshes*; for all values of z, the points z, $z + 2\omega_1$, ... $z + 2m\omega_1 + 2n\omega_2$, ... manifestly occupy corresponding positions in the meshes; any pair of such points are said to be *congruent* to one another. The congruence of two points z, z' is expressed by the notation $z' \equiv z$ (mod. $2\omega_1$, $2\omega_2$).

From the fundamental property of elliptic functions, it follows that an elliptic function assumes the same value at every one of a set of congruent points; and so *its values in any mesh are a mere repetition of its values in any other mesh.*

For purposes of integration it is not convenient to deal with the actual meshes if they have singularities of the integrand on their boundaries; on account of the periodic properties of elliptic functions nothing is lost by taking as a contour, not an actual mesh, but a parallelogram obtained by translating a mesh (without rotation) in such a way that none of the poles of the integrands considered are on the sides of the parallelogram. Such a parallelogram is called a *cell*. Obviously the values assumed by an elliptic function in a cell are a mere repetition of its values in any mesh.

A set of poles (or zeros) of an elliptic function in any given cell is called an *irreducible* set; all other poles (or zeros) of the function are congruent to one or other of them.

20·12. *Simple properties of elliptic functions.*

(I) *The number of poles of an elliptic function in any cell is finite.*

For, if not, the poles would have a limit point, by the two-dimensional analogue of § 2·21. This point is (§ 5·61) an essential singularity of the function; and so, by definition, the function is not an elliptic function.

(II) *The number of zeros of an elliptic function in any cell is finite.*

For, if not, the reciprocal of the function would have an infinite number of poles in the cell, and would therefore have an essential singularity; and this point would be an essential singularity of the original function, which would therefore not be an elliptic function. [This argument presupposes that the function is not identically zero.]

(III) *The sum of the residues of an elliptic function, $f(z)$, at its poles in any cell is zero.*

Let C be the contour formed by the edges of the cell, and let the corners of the cell be t, $t + 2\omega_1$, $t + 2\omega_1 + 2\omega_2$, $t + 2\omega_2$.

[NOTE. In future, the periods of an elliptic function will not be called $2\omega_1$, $2\omega_2$ indifferently; but that one will be called $2\omega_1$ which makes the ratio ω_2/ω_1 *have a positive imaginary part*; and then, if C be described in the sense indicated by the order of the corners given above, the description of C is *counter-clockwise*.

Throughout the chapter, we shall denote by the symbol C the contour formed by the edges of a cell.]

The sum of the residues of $f(z)$ at its poles inside C is

$$\frac{1}{2\pi i} \int_C f(z)\, dz = \frac{1}{2\pi i} \left\{ \int_t^{t+2\omega_1} + \int_{t+2\omega_1}^{t+2\omega_1+2\omega_2} + \int_{t+2\omega_1+2\omega_2}^{t+2\omega_2} + \int_{t+2\omega_2}^{t} \right\} f(z)\, dz.$$

In the second and third integrals write $z + 2\omega_1$, $z + 2\omega_2$ respectively for z, and the right-hand side becomes

$$\frac{1}{2\pi i} \int_t^{t+2\omega_1} \{f(z) - f(z + 2\omega_2)\}\, dz - \frac{1}{2\pi i} \int_t^{t+2\omega_2} \{f(z) - f(z + 2\omega_1)\}\, dz,$$

and each of these integrals vanishes in virtue of the periodic properties of $f(z)$; and so $\int_C f(z)\, dz = 0$, and the theorem is established.

(IV) *Liouville's theorem*.* *An elliptic function, $f(z)$, with no poles in a cell is merely a constant.*

For if $f(z)$ has no poles inside the cell, it is analytic (and consequently bounded) inside and on the boundary of the cell (§ 3·61 corollary ii); that is to say, there is a number K such that $|f(z)| < K$ when z is inside or on the boundary of the cell. From the periodic properties of $f(z)$ it follows that

---

* This modification of the theorem of § 5·63 is the result on which Liouville based his lectures on elliptic functions.

$f(z)$ is analytic and $|f(z)| < K$ for all values of z; and so, by § 5·63, $f(z)$ is a constant.

It will be seen later that a very large number of theorems concerning elliptic functions can be proved by the aid of this result.

20·13. *The order of an elliptic function.*

It will now be shewn that, if $f(z)$ be an elliptic function and c be any constant, *the number of roots of the equation*

$$f(z) = c$$

which lie in any cell depends only on $f(z)$, and not on c; this number is called the *order* of the elliptic function, and is equal to the number of poles of $f(z)$ in the cell.

By § 6·31, the difference between the number of zeros and the number of poles of $f(z) - c$ which lie in the cell C is

$$\frac{1}{2\pi i} \int_C \frac{f'(z)}{f(z) - c} \, dz.$$

Since $f'(z + 2\omega_1) = f'(z + 2\omega_2) = f'(z)$, by dividing the contour into four parts, precisely as in § 20·12 (III), we find that this integral is zero.

Therefore the number of zeros of $f(z) - c$ is equal to the number of poles of $f(z) - c$; but any pole of $f(z) - c$ is obviously a pole of $f(z)$ and conversely; hence the number of zeros of $f(z) - c$ is equal to the number of poles of $f(z)$, which is independent of c; the required result is therefore established.

[NOTE. In determining the order of an elliptic function by counting the number of its irreducible poles, it is obvious, from § 6·31, that each pole has to be reckoned according to its multiplicity.]

The order of an elliptic function is *never less than* 2; for an elliptic function of order 1 would have a single irreducible pole; and if this point actually were a pole (and not an ordinary point) the residue there would not be zero, which is contrary to the result of § 20·12 (III).

So far as singularities are concerned, the simplest elliptic functions are those of order 2. Such functions may be divided into two classes, (i) those which have a single irreducible double pole, at which the residue is zero in accordance with § 20·12 (III); (ii) those which have two simple poles at which, by § 20·12 (III), the residues are numerically equal but opposite in sign.

Functions belonging to these respective classes will be discussed in this chapter and in Chapter XXII under the names of Weierstrassian and Jacobian elliptic functions respectively; and it will be shewn that any elliptic function is expressible in terms of functions of either of these types.

20·14. *Relation between the zeros and poles of an elliptic function.*

We shall now shew that *the sum of the affixes of a set of irreducible zeros of an elliptic function is congruent to the sum of the affixes of a set of irreducible poles.*

For, with the notation previously employed, it follows, from § 6·3, that the difference between the sums in question is

$$\frac{1}{2\pi i}\int_C \frac{zf'(z)}{f(z)}\,dz = \frac{1}{2\pi i}\left\{\int_t^{t+2\omega_1} + \int_{t+2\omega_1}^{t+2\omega_1+2\omega_2} + \int_{t+2\omega_1+2\omega_2}^{t+2\omega_2} + \int_{t+2\omega_2}^{t}\right\}\frac{zf'(z)}{f(z)}\,dz$$

$$= \frac{1}{2\pi i}\int_t^{t+2\omega_1}\left\{\frac{zf'(z)}{f(z)} - \frac{(z+2\omega_2)f'(z+2\omega_2)}{f(z+2\omega_2)}\right\}dz$$

$$- \frac{1}{2\pi i}\int_t^{t+2\omega_2}\left\{\frac{zf'(z)}{f(z)} - \frac{(z+2\omega_1)f'(z+2\omega_1)}{f(z+2\omega_1)}\right\}dz$$

$$= \frac{1}{2\pi i}\left\{-2\omega_2\int_t^{t+2\omega_1}\frac{f'(z)}{f(z)}\,dz + 2\omega_1\int_t^{t+2\omega_2}\frac{f'(z)}{f(z)}\,dz\right\}$$

$$= \frac{1}{2\pi i}\left\{-2\omega_2\left[\log f(z)\right]_t^{t+2\omega_1} + 2\omega_1\left[\log f(z)\right]_t^{t+2\omega_2}\right\},$$

on making use of the substitutions used in § 20·12 (III) and of the periodic properties of $f(z)$ and $f'(z)$.

Now $f(z)$ has the same values at the points $t+2\omega_1$, $t+2\omega_2$ as at t, so the values of $\log f(z)$ at these points can only differ from the value of $\log f(z)$ at t by integer multiples of $2\pi i$, say $-2n\pi i$, $2m\pi i$; then we have

$$\frac{1}{2\pi i}\int_C \frac{zf'(z)}{f(z)}\,dz = 2m\omega_1 + 2n\omega_2,$$

and so the sum of the affixes of the zeros minus the sum of the affixes of the poles is a period; and this is the result which had to be established.

20·2. *The construction of an elliptic function.   Definition of $\wp(z)$.*

It was seen in § 20·1 that elliptic functions may be expected to have some properties analogous to those of the circular functions.   It is therefore natural to introduce elliptic functions into analysis by some definition analogous to one of the definitions which may be made the foundation of the theory of circular functions.

One mode of developing the theory of the circular functions is to start from the series $\sum\limits_{m=-\infty}^{\infty} (z - m\pi)^{-2}$; calling this series $(\sin z)^{-2}$, it is possible to deduce all the known properties of $\sin z$; the method of doing so is briefly indicated in § 20·222.

The analogous method of founding the theory of elliptic functions· is to define the function $\wp(z)$ by the equation*

$$\wp(z) = \frac{1}{z^2} + \sum_{m,\,n}' \left\{ \frac{1}{(z - 2m\omega_1 - 2n\omega_2)^2} - \frac{1}{(2m\omega_1 + 2n\omega_2)^2} \right\},$$

where ω_1, ω_2 satisfy the conditions laid down in §§ 20·1, 20·12 (III); the summation extends over all integer values (positive, negative and zero) of m and n, simultaneous zero values of m and n excepted.

For brevity, we write $\Omega_{m,n}$ in place of $2m\omega_1 + 2n\omega_2$, so that

$$\wp(z) = z^{-2} + \sum_{m,\,n}' \left\{ (z - \Omega_{m,n})^{-2} - \Omega_{m;\,n}^{-2} \right\}.$$

When m and n are such that $|\Omega_{m,n}|$ is large, the general term of the series defining $\wp(z)$ is $O(|\Omega_{m,\,n}|^{-3})$, and so (§ 3·4) the series converges absolutely and uniformly (with regard to z) except near its poles, namely the points $\Omega_{m,\,n}$.

Therefore (§ 5·3), $\wp(z)$ is analytic throughout the whole z-plane except at the points $\Omega_{m,\,n}$, where it has double poles.

The introduction of this function $\wp(z)$ is due to Weierstrass†; we now proceed to discuss properties of $\wp(z)$, and in the course of the investigation it will appear that $\wp(z)$ is an elliptic function with periods $2\omega_1$, $2\omega_2$.

For purposes of numerical computation the series for $\wp(z)$ is useless on account of the slowness of its convergence. Elliptic functions free from this defect will be obtained in Chapter XXI.

Example. Prove that

$$\wp(z) = \left(\frac{\pi}{2\omega_1}\right)^2 \left[-\frac{1}{3} + \sum_{n=-\infty}^{\infty} \operatorname{cosec}^2\left(\frac{z - 2n\omega_2}{2\omega_1}\pi\right) - \sum_{n=-\infty}^{\infty}{}' \operatorname{cosec}^2 \frac{n\omega_2}{\omega_1}\pi \right].$$

20·21. *Periodicity and other properties of $\wp(z)$.*

Since the series for $\wp(z)$ is a uniformly convergent series of analytic functions, term-by-term differentiation is legitimate (§ 5·3), and so

$$\wp'(z) = \frac{d}{dz}\wp(z) = -2 \sum_{m,\,n} \frac{1}{(z - \Omega_{m,n})^3}.$$

The function $\wp'(z)$ *is an* odd *function of* z; for, from the definition of $\wp'(z)$, we at once get

$$\wp'(-z) = 2 \sum_{m,\,n} (z + \Omega_{m,n})^{-3}.$$

* Throughout the chapter $\Sigma\limits_{m,\,n}$ will be written to denote a summation over all integer values of m and n, a prime being inserted $(\Sigma'\limits_{m,\,n})$ when the term for which $m = n = 0$ has to be omitted from the summation. It is also customary to write $\wp'(z)$ for the derivate of $\wp(z)$. The use of the prime in two senses will not cause confusion.

† *Werke*, II. (1895), pp. 245–255. The subject-matter of the greater part of this chapter is due to Weierstrass, and is contained in his lectures, of which an account has been published by Schwarz, *Formeln und Lehrsätze zum Gebrauche der elliptischen Funktionen, Nach Vorlesungen und Aufzeichnungen des Herrn Prof. K. Weierstrass* (Berlin, 1893). See also Cayley, *Journal de Math.* x. (1845), pp. 385–420 [*Math. Papers*, I. pp. 156–182], and Eisenstein, *Journal für Math.* xxxv. (1847), pp. 137–184, 185–274.

But the set of points $-\Omega_{m, n}$ is the same as the set $\Omega_{m, n}$ and so the terms of $\wp'(-z)$ are just the same as those of $-\wp'(z)$, but in a different order. But, the series for $\wp'(z)$ being absolutely convergent (§ 3·4), the derangement of the terms does not affect its sum, and therefore

$$\wp'(-z) = -\wp'(z).$$

In like manner, the terms of the absolutely convergent series

$$\underset{m, n}{\Sigma'} \{(z + \Omega_{m, n})^{-2} - \Omega_{m, n}^{-2}\}$$

are the terms of the series

$$\underset{m, n}{\Sigma'} \{(z - \Omega_{m, n})^{-2} - \Omega_{m, n}^{-2}\}$$

in a different order, and hence

$$\wp(-z) = \wp(z);$$

that is to say, $\wp(z)$ is an even function of z.

Further, $\qquad \wp'(z + 2\omega_1) = -2 \underset{m, n}{\Sigma} (z - \Omega_{m, n} + 2\omega_1)^{-3};$

but the set of points $\Omega_{m, n} - 2\omega_1$ is the same as the set $\Omega_{m, n}$, so the series for $\wp'(z + 2\omega_1)$ is a derangement of the series for $\wp'(z)$. The series being absolutely convergent, we have

$$\wp'(z + 2\omega_1) = \wp'(z);$$

that is to say, $\wp'(z)$ *has the period* $2\omega_1$; in like manner it has the period $2\omega_2$.

Since $\wp'(z)$ is analytic except at its poles, it follows from this result that $\wp'(z)$ *is an elliptic function.*

If now we integrate the equation $\wp'(z + 2\omega_1) = \wp'(z)$, we get

$$\wp(z + 2\omega_1) = \wp(z) + A,$$

where A is constant. Putting $z = -\omega_1$ and using the fact that $\wp(z)$ is an even function, we get $A = 0$, so that

$$\wp(z + 2\omega_1) = \wp(z);$$

in like manner $\wp(z + 2\omega_2) = \wp(z)$.

Since $\wp(z)$ has no singularities but poles, it follows from these two results that $\wp(z)$ *is an elliptic function.*

There are other methods of introducing both the circular and elliptic functions into analysis; for the circular functions the following may be noticed:

(1) The geometrical definition in which $\sin z$ is the ratio of the side opposite the angle z to the hypotenuse in a right-angled triangle of which one angle is z. This is the definition given in elementary text-books on Trigonometry; from our point of view it has various disadvantages, some of which are stated in the Appendix.

(2) The definition by the power series

$$\sin z = z - \frac{z^3}{3!} + \frac{z^5}{5!} - \dots.$$

(3)   The definition by the product

$$\sin z = z \left(1 - \frac{z^2}{\pi^2}\right)\left(1 - \frac{z^2}{2^2 \pi^2}\right)\left(1 - \frac{z^2}{3^2 \pi^2}\right)\cdots$$

(4)   The definition by 'inversion' of an integral

$$z = \int_0^{\sin z} (1 - t^2)^{-\frac{1}{2}}\, dt.$$

The periodicity properties may be obtained easily from (4) by taking suitable paths of integration (cf. Forsyth, *Theory of Functions*, (1918), § 104), but it is extremely difficult to prove that $\sin z$ defined in this way is an analytic function.

The reader will see later (§§ 22·82, 22·1, 20·42, 20·22 and § 20·53 example 4) that elliptic functions may be defined by definitions analogous to each of these, with corresponding disadvantages in the cases of the first and fourth.

Example.   Deduce the periodicity of $\wp(z)$ directly from its definition as a double series. [It is not difficult to justify the necessary derangement.]

20·22.   *The differential equation satisfied by $\wp(z)$.*

We shall now obtain an equation satisfied by $\wp(z)$, which will prove to be of great importance in the theory of the function.

The function $\wp(z) - z^{-2}$, which is equal to $\sum'_{m,n}\{(z - \Omega_{m,n})^{-2} - \Omega_{m,n}^{-2}\}$, is analytic in a region of which the origin is an internal point, and it is an even function of z.   Consequently, by Taylor's theorem, we have an expansion of the form

$$\wp(z) - z^{-2} = \frac{1}{20}g_2 z^2 + \frac{1}{28}g_3 z^4 + O(z^6)$$

valid for sufficiently small values of $|z|$.   It is easy to see that

$$g_2 = 60 \sum'_{m,n} \Omega_{m,n}^{-4}, \quad g_3 = 140 \sum'_{m,n} \Omega_{m,n}^{-6}.$$

Thus

$$\wp(z) = z^{-2} + \frac{1}{20}g_2 z^2 + \frac{1}{28}g_3 z^4 + O(z^6);$$

differentiating this result, we have

$$\wp'(z) = -2z^{-3} + \frac{1}{10}g_2 z + \frac{1}{7}g_3 z^3 + O(z^5).$$

Cubing and squaring these respectively, we get

$$\wp^3(z) = z^{-6} + \frac{3}{20}g_2 z^{-2} + \frac{3}{28}g_3 + O(z^2),$$

$$\wp'^2(z) = 4z^{-6} - \frac{2}{5}g_2 z^{-2} - \frac{4}{7}g_3 + O(z^2).$$

Hence

$$\wp'^2(z) - 4\wp^3(z) = -g_2 z^{-2} - g_3 + O(z^2),$$

and so

$$\wp'^2(z) - 4\wp^3(z) + g_2\wp(z) + g_3 = O(z^2).$$

That is to say, the function $\wp'^2(z) - 4\wp^3(z) + g_2\wp(z) + g_3$, which is obviously an elliptic function, is analytic at the origin, and consequently it is also analytic at all congruent points.   But such points are the only possible singularities of the function, *and so it is an elliptic function with no singularities*; it is therefore a constant (§ 20·12, IV).

On making $z \to 0$, we see that this constant is zero.

Thus, finally, the function $\wp(z)$ satisfies the differential equation

$$\wp'^2(z) = 4\wp^3(z) - g_2\wp(z) - g_3,$$

where g_2 and g_3 (called the *invariants*) are given by the equations

$$g_2 = 60 \sum_{m,n}{}' \Omega_{m,n}^{-4}, \quad g_3 = 140 \sum_{m,n}{}' \Omega_{m,n}^{-6}.$$

Conversely, given the equation

$$\left(\frac{dy}{dz}\right)^2 = 4y^3 - g_2 y - g_3,$$

if numbers ω_1, ω_2 can be determined * *such that*

$$g_2 = 60 \sum_{m,n}{}' \Omega_{m,n}^{-4}, \quad g_3 = 140 \sum_{m,n}{}' \Omega_{m,n}^{-6},$$

then the general solution of the differential equation is

$$y = \wp(\pm z + \alpha),$$

where α is the constant of integration. This may be seen by taking a new dependent variable u defined by the equation† $y = \wp(u)$, when the differential equation reduces to $\left(\dfrac{du}{dz}\right)^2 = 1$.

Since $\wp(z)$ is an even function of z, we have $y = \wp(z \pm \alpha)$, and so the solution of the equation can be written in the form

$$y = \wp(z + \alpha)$$

without loss of generality.

Example. Deduce from the differential equation that, if

$$\wp(z) = z^{-2} + \sum_{n=1}^{\infty} c_{2n} z^{2n},$$

then $c_2 = g_2/2^2 \cdot 5,$ $c_4 = g_3/2^2 \cdot 7,$ $c_6 = g_2^2/2^4 \cdot 3 \cdot 5^2,$

$$c_8 = \frac{3 g_2 g_3}{2^4 \cdot 5 \cdot 7 \cdot 11}, \quad c_{10} = \frac{g_2^3}{2^5 \cdot 3 \cdot 5^3 \cdot 13} + \frac{g_3^2}{2^4 \cdot 7^2 \cdot 13}, \quad c_{12} = \frac{g_2^2 g_3}{2^5 \cdot 3 \cdot 5^2 \cdot 7 \cdot 11}.$$

20·221. *The integral formula for $\wp(z)$.*

Consider the equation

$$z = \int_{\zeta}^{\infty} (4t^3 - g_2 t - g_3)^{-\frac{1}{2}} dt,$$

determining z in terms of ζ; the path of integration may be any curve which does not pass through a zero of $4t^3 - g_2 t - g_3$.

On differentiation, we get

$$\left(\frac{d\zeta}{dz}\right)^2 = 4\zeta^3 - g_2\zeta - g_3,$$

and so $\zeta = \wp(z + \alpha),$

where α is a constant.

---

* The difficult problem of establishing the existence of such numbers ω_1 and ω_2 when g_2 and g_3 are given is solved in § 21·73.

† This equation in u always has solutions, by § 20·13.

Make $\zeta \to \infty$; then $z \to 0$, since the integral converges, and so α is a pole of the function $\wp$; i.e., α is of the form $\Omega_{m,n}$, and so $\zeta = \wp(z + \Omega_{m,n}) = \wp(z)$.

The result that the equation $z = \int_{\zeta}^{\infty} (4t^3 - g_2 t - g_3)^{-\frac{1}{2}} dt$ is equivalent to the equation $\zeta = \wp(z)$ is sometimes written in the form

$$z = \int_{\wp(z)}^{\infty} (4t^3 - g_2 t - g_3)^{-\frac{1}{2}} dt.$$

20·222. *An illustration from the theory of the circular functions.*

The theorems obtained in §§ 20·2–20·221 may be illustrated by the corresponding results in the theory of the circular functions. Thus we may deduce the properties of the function $\operatorname{cosec}^2 z$ from the series $\sum\limits_{m=-\infty}^{\infty} (z - m\pi)^{-2}$ in the following manner:

Denote the series by $f(z)$; the series converges absolutely and uniformly* (with regard to z) except near the points $m\pi$ at which it obviously has double poles. Except at these points, $f(z)$ is analytic. The effect of adding any multiple of π to z is to give a series whose terms are the same as those occurring in the original series; since the series converges absolutely, the sum of the series is unaffected, and so $f(z)$ *is a periodic function of z with period π.*

Now consider the behaviour of $f(z)$ in the strip for which $-\frac{1}{2}\pi \leqslant R(z) \leqslant \frac{1}{2}\pi$. From the periodicity of $f(z)$, the value of $f(z)$ at any point in the plane is equal to its value at the corresponding point of the strip. In the strip $f(z)$ has one singularity, namely $z = 0$; and $f(z)$ is bounded as $z \to \infty$ in the strip, because the terms of the series for $f(z)$ are small compared with the corresponding terms of the comparison series $\sum\limits_{m=-\infty}^{\infty}{}' m^{-2}$.

In a domain including the point $z = 0$, $f(z) - z^{-2}$ is analytic, and is an even function; and consequently there is a Maclaurin expansion

$$f(z) - z^{-2} = \sum_{n=0}^{\infty} a_{2n} z^{2n},$$

valid when $|z| < \pi$. It is easily seen that

$$a_{2n} = 2\pi^{-2n-2}(2n+1) \sum_{m=1}^{\infty} m^{-2n-2},$$

and so

$$a_0 = \tfrac{1}{3}, \quad a_2 = 6\pi^{-4} \sum_{m=1}^{\infty} m^{-4} = \tfrac{1}{15}.$$

Hence, for small values of $|z|$,

$$f(z) = z^{-2} + \tfrac{1}{3} + \tfrac{1}{15} z^2 + O(z^4).$$

Differentiating this result twice, and also squaring it, we have

$$f''(z) = 6z^{-4} + \tfrac{2}{15} + O(z^2),$$
$$f^2(z) = z^{-4} + \tfrac{2}{3}z^{-2} + \tfrac{11}{45} + O(z^2).$$

It follows that

$$f''(z) - 6f^2(z) + 4f(z) = O(z^2).$$

That is to say, the function $f''(z) - 6f^2(z) + 4f(z)$ is analytic at the origin and it is obviously periodic. Since its only possible singularities are at the points $m\pi$, it follows from the periodic property of the function that it is an integral function.

---

* By comparison with the series $\sum\limits_{m=-\infty}^{\infty}{}' m^{-2}$.

Further, it is bounded as $z \to \infty$ in the strip $-\frac{1}{2}\pi \leqslant R(z) \leqslant \frac{1}{2}\pi$, since $f(z)$ is bounded and so is* $f''(z)$. Hence $f''(z) - 6f^2(z) + 4f(z)$ is bounded in the strip, and therefore from its periodicity it is bounded everywhere. By Liouville's theorem (§ 5·63) it is therefore a constant. By making $z \to 0$, we see that the constant is zero. Hence the function $\operatorname{cosec}^2 z$ satisfies the equation

$$f''(z) = 6f^2(z) - 4f(z).$$

Multiplying by $2f'(z)$ and integrating, we get

$$f'^2(z) = 4f^2(z)\{f(z) - 1\} + c,$$

where c is a constant, which is easily seen to be zero on making use of the power series for $f'(z)$ and $f(z)$.

We thence deduce that

$$2z = \int_{f(z)}^{\infty} t^{-1}(t-1)^{-\frac{1}{2}}\,dt,$$

when an appropriate path of integration is chosen.

Example 1. If $y = \wp(z)$ and primes denote differentiations with regard to z, shew that

$$\frac{3y''^2}{4y'^4} - \frac{y'''}{2y'^3} = \tfrac{3}{16}\{(y-e_1)^{-2} + (y-e_2)^{-2} + (y-e_3)^{-2}\} - \tfrac{3}{8}y(y-e_1)^{-1}(y-e_2)^{-1}(y-e_3)^{-1},$$

where e_1, e_2, e_3 are the roots of the equation $4t^3 - g_2 t - g_3 = 0$.

[We have
$$\begin{aligned} y'^2 &= 4y^3 - g_2 y - g_3 \\ &= 4(y-e_1)(y-e_2)(y-e_3). \end{aligned}$$

Differentiating logarithmically and dividing by y', we have

$$2y''/y'^2 = \sum_{r=1}^{3}(y-e_r)^{-1}.$$

Differentiating again, we have

$$\frac{2y'''}{y'^3} - \frac{4y''^2}{y'^4} = -\sum_{r=1}^{3}(y-e_r)^{-2}.$$

Adding this equation multiplied by $\tfrac{1}{4}$ to the square of the preceding equation, multiplied by $\tfrac{1}{16}$, we readily obtain the desired result.

It should be noted that the left-hand side of the equation is half the Schwarzian derivative† of z with respect to y; and so z is the quotient of two solutions of the equation

$$\frac{d^2v}{dy^2} + \left\{\tfrac{3}{16}\sum_{r=1}^{3}(y-e_r)^{-2} - \tfrac{3}{8}y\prod_{r=1}^{3}(y-e_r)^{-1}\right\}v = 0.]$$

Example 2. Obtain the 'properties of homogeneity' of the function $\wp(z)$; namely that

$$\wp\left(\lambda z \,\middle|\, \begin{matrix} \lambda\omega_1 \\ \lambda\omega_2 \end{matrix}\right) = \lambda^{-2}\,\wp\left(z \,\middle|\, \begin{matrix} \omega_1 \\ \omega_2 \end{matrix}\right), \qquad \wp(\lambda z;\ \lambda^{-4}g_2,\ \lambda^{-6}g_3) = \lambda^{-2}\,\wp(z;\ g_2,\ g_3),$$

where $\wp\left(z \,\middle|\, \begin{matrix} \omega_1 \\ \omega_2 \end{matrix}\right)$ denotes the function formed with periods $2\omega_1$, $2\omega_2$ and $\wp(z;\ g_2,\ g_3)$ denotes the function formed with invariants g_2, g_3.

[The former is a direct consequence of the definition of $\wp(z)$ by a double series; the latter may then be derived from the double series defining the g invariants.]

---

* The series for $f''(z)$ may be compared with $\displaystyle\sum_{m=-\infty}^{\infty}{}' m^{-4}$.

† Cayley, *Camb. Phil. Trans.* XIII. (1883), p. 5 [*Math. Papers*, XI. p. 148].

20·3.　*The addition-theorem for the function $\wp(z)$.*

The function $\wp(z)$ possesses what is known as an *addition-theorem*; that is to say, there exists a formula expressing $\wp(z+y)$ as an algebraic function of $\wp(z)$ and $\wp(y)$ for general values* of z and y.

Consider the equations

$$\wp'(z) = A\wp(z) + B, \quad \wp'(y) = A\wp(y) + B,$$

which determine A and B in terms of z and y unless $\wp(z) = \wp(y)$, i.e. unless† $z \equiv \pm y \pmod{2\omega_1, 2\omega_2}$.

Now consider　　　　　$\wp'(\zeta) - A\wp(\zeta) - B,$

qua function of ζ. It has a triple pole at $\zeta = 0$ and consequently it has three, and only three, irreducible zeros, by § 20·13; the sum of these is a period, by § 20·14, and as $\zeta = z$, $\zeta = y$ are two zeros, the third irreducible zero must be congruent to $-z - y$. Hence $-z - y$ is a zero of $\wp'(\zeta) - A\wp(\zeta) - B$, and so

$$\wp'(-z - y) = A\wp(-z - y) + B.$$

Eliminating A and B from this equation and the equations by which A and B were defined, we have

$$\begin{vmatrix} \wp(z) & \wp'(z) & 1 \\ \wp(y) & \wp'(y) & 1 \\ \wp(z+y) & -\wp'(z+y) & 1 \end{vmatrix} = 0.$$

Since the derived functions occurring in this result can be expressed algebraically in terms of $\wp(z)$, $\wp(y)$, $\wp(z+y)$ respectively (§ 20·22), this result really expresses $\wp(z+y)$ algebraically in terms of $\wp(z)$ and $\wp(y)$. It is therefore an *addition-theorem*.

Other methods of obtaining the addition-theorem are indicated in § 20·311 examples 1 and 2, and § 20·312.

A symmetrical form of the addition-theorem may be noticed, namely that, if $u + v + w = 0$, then

$$\begin{vmatrix} \wp(u) & \wp'(u) & 1 \\ \wp(v) & \wp'(v) & 1 \\ \wp(w) & \wp'(w) & 1 \end{vmatrix} = 0.$$

20·31.　*Another form of the addition-theorem.*

Retaining the notation of § 20·3, we see that the values of ζ, which make $\wp'(\zeta) - A\wp(\zeta) - B$ vanish, are congruent to one of the points z, y, $-z - y$.

---

* It is, of course, unnecessary to consider the special cases when y, or z, or $y + z$ is a period.

† The function $\wp(z) - \wp(y)$, *qua* function of z, has double poles at points congruent to $z = 0$, and no other singularities; it therefore (§ 20·13) has only two irreducible zeros; and the points congruent to $z = \pm y$ therefore give *all* the zeros of $\wp(z) - \wp(y)$.

Hence $\wp'^2(\zeta) - \{A\wp(\zeta) + B\}^2$ vanishes when ζ is congruent to any of the points z, y, $-z-y$.   And so

$$4\wp^3(\zeta) - A^2\wp^2(\zeta) - (2AB + g_2)\wp(\zeta) - (B^2 + g_3)$$

vanishes when $\wp(\zeta)$ is equal to any one of $\wp(z)$, $\wp(y)$, $\wp(z+y)$.

For general values of z and y, $\wp(z)$, $\wp(y)$ and $\wp(z+y)$ are unequal and so they are all the roots of the equation

$$4Z^3 - A^2Z^2 - (2AB + g_2)Z - (B^2 + g_3) = 0.$$

Consequently, by the ordinary formula for the sum of the roots of a cubic equation,

$$\wp(z) + \wp(y) + \wp(z+y) = \tfrac{1}{4}A^2,$$

and so

$$\wp(z+y) = \frac{1}{4}\left\{\frac{\wp'(z) - \wp'(y)}{\wp(z) - \wp(y)}\right\}^2 - \wp(z) - \wp(y),$$

on solving the equations by which A and B were defined.

This result expresses $\wp(z+y)$ explicitly in terms of functions of z and of y.

20·311.   *The duplication formula for $\wp(z)$.*

The forms of the addition-theorem which have been obtained are both nugatory when $y = z$.   But the result of § 20·31 is true, in the case of any given value of z, for general values of y.   Taking the limiting form of the result when y approaches z, we have

$$\lim_{y \to z} \wp(z+y) = \tfrac{1}{4}\lim_{y \to z}\left\{\frac{\wp'(z) - \wp'(y)}{\wp(z) - \wp(y)}\right\}^2 - \wp(z) - \lim_{y \to z}\wp(y).$$

From this equation, we see that, if $2z$ is not a period, we have

$$\wp(2z) = \tfrac{1}{4}\lim_{h \to 0}\left\{\frac{\wp'(z) - \wp'(z+h)}{\wp(z) - \wp(z+h)}\right\}^2 - 2\wp(z)$$

$$= \tfrac{1}{4}\lim_{h \to 0}\left\{\frac{-h\wp''(z) + O(h^2)}{-h\wp'(z) + O(h^2)}\right\}^2 - 2\wp(z),$$

on applying Taylor's theorem to $\wp(z+h)$, $\wp'(z+h)$; and so

$$\wp(2z) = \tfrac{1}{4}\left\{\frac{\wp''(z)}{\wp'(z)}\right\}^2 - 2\wp(z),$$

unless $2z$ is a period.   This result is called the *duplication formula*.

Example 1.   Prove that

$$\frac{1}{4}\left\{\frac{\wp'(z) - \wp'(y)}{\wp(z) - \wp(y)}\right\}^2 - \wp(z) - \wp(z+y),$$

qua function of z, has no singularities at points congruent with $z = 0$, $\pm y$; and, by making use of Liouville's theorem, deduce the addition-theorem.

Example 2. Apply the process indicated in example 1 to the function

$$\begin{vmatrix} \wp(z) & \wp'(z) & 1 \\ \wp(y) & \wp'(y) & 1 \\ \wp(z+y) & -\wp'(z+y) & 1 \end{vmatrix},$$

and deduce the addition-theorem.

Example 3. Shew that

$$\wp(z+y) + \wp(z-y) = \{\wp(z) - \wp(y)\}^{-2} \left[\{2\wp(z)\wp(y) - \tfrac{1}{2}g_2\} \{\wp(z) + \wp(y)\} - g_3 \right].$$

[By the addition-theorem we have

$$\wp(z+y) + \wp(z-y) = \frac{1}{4} \left\{ \frac{\wp'(z) - \wp'(y)}{\wp(z) - \wp(y)} \right\}^2 - \wp(z) - \wp(y) + \frac{1}{4} \left\{ \frac{\wp'(z) + \wp'(y)}{\wp(z) - \wp(y)} \right\}^2 - \wp(z) - \wp(y)$$

$$= \frac{1}{2} \frac{\wp'^2(z) + \wp'^2(y)}{\{\wp(z) - \wp(y)\}^2} - 2\{\wp(z) + \wp(y)\}.$$

Replacing $\wp'^2(z)$ and $\wp'^2(y)$ by $4\wp^3(z) - g_2\wp(z) - g_3$ and $4\wp^3(y) - g_2\wp(y) - g_3$ respectively, and reducing, we obtain the required result.]

Example 4. Shew, by Liouville's theorem, that

$$\frac{d}{dz} \{\wp(z-a)\wp(z-b)\} = \wp(a-b)\{\wp'(z-a) + \wp'(z-b)\} - \wp'(a-b)\{\wp(z-a) - \wp(z-b)\}.$$

(Trinity, 1905.)

20·312. *Abel's* method of proving the addition-theorem for $\wp(z)$.*

The following outline of a method of establishing the addition-theorem for $\wp(z)$ is instructive, though a completely rigorous proof would be long and tedious.

Let the invariants of $\wp(z)$ be g_2, g_3; take rectangular axes OX, OY in a plane, and consider the intersections of the cubic curve

$$y^2 = 4x^3 - g_2x - g_3$$

with a variable line

$$y = mx + n.$$

If any point (x_1, y_1) be taken on the cubic, the equation in z

$$\wp(z) - x_1 = 0$$

has two solutions $+z_1$, $-z_1$ (§ 20·13) and all other solutions are congruent to these two.

Since $\wp'^2(z) = 4\wp^3(z) - g_2\wp(z) - g_3$, we have $\wp'^2(z) = y_1^2$; choose z_1 to be the solution for which $\wp'(z_1) = +y_1$, not $-y_1$.

A number z_1 thus chosen will be called the *parameter* of (x_1, y_1) on the cubic.

Now the abscissae x_1, x_2, x_3 of the intersections of the cubic with the variable line are the roots of

$$\phi(x) \equiv 4x^3 - g_2x - g_3 - (mx + n)^2 = 0,$$

and so

$$\phi(x) \equiv 4(x - x_1)(x - x_2)(x - x_3).$$

The variation δx_r in one of these abscissae due to the variation in position of the line consequent on small changes δm, δn in the coefficients m, n is given by the equation

$$\phi'(x_r)\,\delta x_r + \frac{\partial \phi}{\partial m}\,\delta m + \frac{\partial \phi}{\partial n}\,\delta n = 0,$$

and so

$$\phi'(x_r)\,\delta x_r = 2(mx_r + n)(x_r\delta m + \delta n),$$

whence

$$\sum_{r=1}^{3} \frac{\delta x_r}{mx_r + n} = 2 \sum_{r=1}^{3} \frac{x_r\delta m + \delta n}{\phi'(x_r)},$$

provided that x_1, x_2, x_3 are unequal, so that $\phi'(x_r) \neq 0$.

* *Journal für Math.* II. (1827), pp. 101–181; III. (1828), pp. 160–190 [*Oeuvres*, I. (Christiania, 1839), pp. 141–252].

Now, if we put $x\,(x\,\delta m + \delta n)/\phi\,(x)$, *qua* function of x, into partial fractions, the result is

$$\sum_{r=1}^{3} A_r/(x - x_r),$$

where
$$A_r = \lim_{x \to x_r} x\,(x\,\delta m + \delta n)\,\frac{x - x_r}{\phi\,(x)}$$

$$= x_r\,(x_r\,\delta m + \delta n)\,\lim_{x \to x_r}\,(x - x_r)/\phi\,(x)$$

$$= x_r\,(x_r\,\delta m + \delta n)/\phi'\,(x_r),$$

by Taylor's theorem.

Putting $x = 0$, we get $\displaystyle\sum_{r=1}^{3} \delta x_r/y_r = 0$, i.e. $\displaystyle\sum_{r=1}^{3} \delta z_r = 0$.

That is to say, *the sum of the parameters of the points of intersection is a constant independent of the position of the line.*

Vary the line so that all the points of intersection move off to infinity (no two points coinciding during this process), and it is evident that $z_1 + z_2 + z_3$ is equal to the sum of the parameters when the line is the line at infinity; but when the line is at infinity, each parameter is a period of $\wp\,(z)$ and therefore $z_1 + z_2 + z_3$ is a period of $\wp\,(z)$.

Hence the sum of the parameters of three collinear points on the cubic is congruent to zero. This result having been obtained, the determinantal form of the addition-theorem follows as in § 20·3.

20·32. *The constants e_1, e_2, e_3.*

It will now be shewn that $\wp\,(\omega_1)$, $\wp\,(\omega_2)$, $\wp\,(\omega_3)$, (where $\omega_3 = -\omega_1 - \omega_2$), are all unequal; and, if their values be e_1, e_2, e_3, then e_1, e_2, e_3 are the roots of the equation $4t^3 - g_2 t - g_3 = 0$.

First consider $\wp'\,(\omega_1)$. Since $\wp'\,(z)$ is an odd periodic function, we have

$$\wp'\,(\omega_1) = -\wp'\,(-\omega_1) = -\wp'\,(2\omega_1 - \omega_1) = -\wp'\,(\omega_1),$$

and so
$$\wp'\,(\omega_1) = 0.$$

Similarly
$$\wp'\,(\omega_2) = \wp'\,(\omega_3) = 0.$$

Since $\wp'\,(z)$ is an elliptic function whose only singularities are triple poles at points congruent to the origin, $\wp'\,(z)$ has three, and only three (§ 20·13), irreducible zeros. Therefore the only zeros of $\wp'\,(z)$ are points congruent to ω_1, ω_2, ω_3.

Next consider $\wp\,(z) - e_1$. This vanishes at ω_1 and, since $\wp'\,(\omega_1) = 0$, it has a double zero at ω_1. Since $\wp\,(z)$ has only two irreducible poles, it follows from § 20·13 that the only zeros of $\wp\,(z) - e_1$ are congruent to ω_1. In like manner, the only zeros of $\wp\,(z) - e_2$, $\wp\,(z) - e_3$ are double zeros at points congruent to ω_2, ω_3 respectively.

Hence $e_1 \neq e_2 \neq e_3$. For if $e_1 = e_2$, then $\wp\,(z) - e_1$ has a zero at ω_2, which is a point not congruent to ω_1.

Also, since $\wp'^2\,(z) = 4\wp^3\,(z) - g_2\wp\,(z) - g_3$ and since $\wp'\,(z)$ vanishes at ω_1, ω_2, ω_3, it follows that $4\wp^3\,(z) - g_2\wp\,(z) - g_3$ vanishes when $\wp\,(z) = e_1$, e_2 or e_3.

That is to say, e_1, e_2, e_3 are the roots of the equation

$$4t^3 - g_2 t - g_3 = 0.$$

From the well-known formulae connecting roots of equations with their coefficients, it follows that

$$e_1 + e_2 + e_3 = 0,$$

$$e_2 e_3 + e_3 e_1 + e_1 e_2 = -\frac{1}{4} g_2,$$

$$e_1 e_2 e_3 = \frac{1}{4} g_3.$$

Example 1. When g_2 and g_3 are real and the discriminant $g_2{}^3 - 27 g_3{}^2$ is positive, shew that e_1, e_2, e_3 are all real; choosing them so that $e_1 > e_2 > e_3$, shew that

$$\omega_1 = \int_{e_1}^{\infty} (4t^3 - g_2 t - g_3)^{-\frac{1}{2}} \, dt,$$

and

$$\omega_3 = -i \int_{-\infty}^{e_3} (g_3 + g_2 t - 4t^3)^{-\frac{1}{2}} \, dt,$$

so that ω_1 is real and ω_3 a pure imaginary.

Example 2. Shew that, in the circumstances of example 1, $\wp(z)$ is real on the perimeter of the rectangle whose corners are 0, ω_3, $\omega_1 + \omega_3$, ω_1.

20·33. *The addition of a half-period to the argument of* $\wp(z)$.

From the form of the addition-theorem given in § 20·31, we have

$$\wp(z + \omega_1) + \wp(z) + \wp(\omega_1) = \frac{1}{4} \left\{ \frac{\wp'(z) - \wp'(\omega_1)}{\wp(z) - \wp(\omega_1)} \right\}^2,$$

and so, since

$$\wp'^2(z) = 4 \prod_{r=1}^{3} \{\wp(z) - e_r\},$$

we have

$$\wp(z + \omega_1) = \frac{\{\wp(z) - e_2\} \{\wp(z) - e_3\}}{\wp(z) - e_1} - \wp(z) - e_1$$

i.e.

$$\wp(z + \omega_1) = e_1 + \frac{(e_1 - e_2)(e_1 - e_3)}{\wp(z) - e_1},$$

on using the result

$$\sum_{r=1}^{3} e_r = 0;$$

this formula expresses $\wp(z + \omega_1)$ in terms of $\wp(z)$.

Example 1. Shew that

$$\wp(\tfrac{1}{2}\omega_1) = e_1 \pm \{(e_1 - e_2)(e_1 - e_3)\}^{\frac{1}{2}}.$$

Example 2. From the formula for $\wp(z + \omega_2)$ combined with the result of example 1, shew that

$$\wp(\tfrac{1}{2}\omega_1 + \omega_2) = e_1 \mp \{(e_1 - e_2)(e_1 - e_3)\}^{\frac{1}{2}}.$$

(Math. Trip. 1913.)

Example 3. Shew that the value of $\wp'(z) \, \wp'(z + \omega_1) \, \wp'(z + \omega_2) \, \wp'(z + \omega_3)$ is equal to the discriminant of the equation $4t^3 - g_2 t - g_3 = 0$.

[Differentiating the result of § 20·33, we have

$$\wp'(z + \omega_1) = -(e_1 - e_2)(e_1 - e_3) \, \wp'(z) \, \{\wp(z) - e_1\}^{-2};$$

from this and analogous results, we have

$$\wp'(z) \, \wp'(z + \omega_1) \, \wp'(z + \omega_2) \, \wp'(z + \omega_3)$$

$$= (e_1 - e_2)^2 (e_2 - e_3)^2 (e_3 - e_1)^2 \, \wp'^4(z) \prod_{r=1}^{3} \{\wp(z) - e_r\}^{-2}$$

$$= 16 (e_1 - e_2)^2 (e_2 - e_3)^2 (e_3 - e_1)^2,$$

which is the discriminant $g_2{}^3 - 27 g_3{}^2$ in question.]

Example 4. Shew that, with appropriate interpretations of the radicals,

$$\wp'\left(\tfrac{1}{2}\omega_1\right) = -2\left\{(e_1-e_2)(e_1-e_3)\right\}^{\frac{1}{2}}\left\{(e_1-e_2)^{\frac{1}{2}}+(e_1-e_3)^{\frac{1}{2}}\right\}.$$

(Math. Trip. 1913.)

Example 5. Shew that, with appropriate interpretations of the radicals,

$$\{\wp(2z)-e_2\}^{\frac{1}{2}}\{\wp(2z)-e_3\}^{\frac{1}{2}}+\{\wp(2z)-e_3\}^{\frac{1}{2}}\{\wp(2z)-e_1\}^{\frac{1}{2}}$$
$$+\{\wp(2z)-e_1\}^{\frac{1}{2}}\{\wp(2z)-e_2\}^{\frac{1}{2}}=\wp(z)-\wp(2z).$$

20·4. *Quasi-periodic functions. The function* * $\zeta(z)$.

We shall next introduce the function $\zeta(z)$ defined by the equation

$$\frac{d\zeta(z)}{dz} = -\wp(z),$$

coupled with the condition $\lim_{z\to 0}\{\zeta(z)-z^{-1}\}=0$.

Since the series for $\wp(z)-z^{-2}$ converges uniformly throughout any domain from which the neighbourhoods of the points† $\Omega'_{m,n}$ are excluded, we may integrate term-by-term (§ 4·7) and get

$$\zeta(z)-z^{-1} = -\int_0^z \{\wp(z)-z^{-2}\}\, dz$$

$$= -\underset{m,n}{\Sigma'}\int_0^z \{(z-\Omega_{m,n})^{-2}-\Omega_{m,n}^{-2}\}\, dz,$$

and so

$$\zeta(z) = \frac{1}{z}+\underset{m,n}{\Sigma'}\left\{\frac{1}{z-\Omega_{m,n}}+\frac{1}{\Omega_{m,n}}+\frac{z}{\Omega_{m,n}^2}\right\}.$$

The reader will easily see that the general term of this series is

$$O\left(|\Omega_{m,n}|^{-3}\right) \quad\text{as}\quad |\Omega_{m,n}|\to\infty;$$

and hence (cf. § 20·2), $\zeta(z)$ is an analytic function of z over the whole z-plane except at simple poles (the residue at each pole being $+1$) at all the points of the set $\Omega_{m,n}$.

It is evident that

$$-\zeta(-z) = \frac{1}{z}+\underset{m,n}{\Sigma'}\left\{\frac{1}{z+\Omega_{m,n}}-\frac{1}{\Omega_{m,n}}+\frac{z}{\Omega_{m,n}^2}\right\},$$

and, since this series consists of the terms of the series for $\zeta(z)$, deranged in the same way as in the corresponding series of § 20·21, we have, by § 2·52,

$$\zeta(-z) = -\zeta(z),$$

that is to say, $\zeta(z)$ *is an odd function of* z.

---

* This function should not, of course, be confused with the Zeta-function of Riemann, discussed in Chapter XIII.

† The symbol $\Omega'_{m,n}$ is used to denote all the points $\Omega_{m,n}$ with the exception of the origin (cf. § 20·2).

Following up the analogy of § 20·222, we may compare $\zeta(z)$ with the function $\cot z$ defined by the series $z^{-1} + \sum_{m=-\infty}^{\infty} {}' \{(z - m\pi)^{-1} + (m\pi)^{-1}\}$, the equation $\dfrac{d}{dz} \cot z = -\operatorname{cosec}^2 z$ corresponding to $\dfrac{d}{dz} \zeta(z) = -\wp(z)$.

20·41. *The quasi-periodicity of the function* $\zeta(z)$.

The heading of § 20·4 was an anticipation of the result, which will now be proved, that $\zeta(z)$ is not a doubly-periodic function of z; and the effect on $\zeta(z)$ of increasing z by $2\omega_1$ or by $2\omega_2$ will be considered. It is evident from § 20·12 (III) that $\zeta(z)$ cannot be an elliptic function, in view of the fact that the residue of $\zeta(z)$ at every pole is $+1$.

If now we integrate the equation

$$\wp(z + 2\omega_1) = \wp(z),$$

we get

$$\zeta(z + 2\omega_1) = \zeta(z) + 2\eta_1,$$

where $2\eta_1$ is the constant introduced by integration; putting $z = -\omega_1$, and taking account of the fact that $\zeta(z)$ is an odd function, we have

$$\eta_1 = \zeta(\omega_1).$$

In like manner, $\zeta(z + 2\omega_2) = \zeta(z) + 2\eta_2,$

where $\eta_2 = \zeta(\omega_2).$

Example 1. Prove by Liouville's theorem that, if $x + y + z = 0$, then

$$\{\zeta(x) + \zeta(y) + \zeta(z)\}^2 + \zeta'(x) + \zeta'(y) + \zeta'(z) = 0.$$

(Frobenius u. Stickelberger, *Journal für Math.* LXXXVIII.)

[This result is a pseudo-addition theorem. It is not a true addition-theorem since $\zeta'(x)$, $\zeta'(y)$, $\zeta'(z)$ are not algebraic functions of $\zeta(x)$, $\zeta(y)$, $\zeta(z)$.]

Example 2. Prove by Liouville's theorem that

$$2 \begin{vmatrix} 1 & \wp(x) & \wp^2(x) \\ 1 & \wp(y) & \wp^2(y) \\ 1 & \wp(z) & \wp^2(z) \end{vmatrix} \div \begin{vmatrix} 1 & \wp(x) & \wp'(x) \\ 1 & \wp(y) & \wp'(y) \\ 1 & \wp(z) & \wp'(z) \end{vmatrix} = \zeta(x + y + z) - \zeta(x) - \zeta(y) - \zeta(z).$$

Obtain a generalisation of this theorem involving n variables.

(Math. Trip. 1894.)

20·411. *The relation between* η_1 *and* η_2.

We shall now shew that

$$\eta_1 \omega_2 - \eta_2 \omega_1 = \frac{1}{2} \pi i.$$

To obtain this result consider $\displaystyle\int_C \zeta(z)\, dz$ taken round the boundary of a cell. There is one pole of $\zeta(z)$ inside the cell, the residue there being $+1$. Hence $\displaystyle\int_C \zeta(z)\, dz = 2\pi i.$

Modifying the contour integral in the manner of § 20·12, we get

$$2\pi i = \int_t^{t+2\omega_1} \{\zeta(z) - \zeta(z+2\omega_2)\}\, dz - \int_t^{t+2\omega_2} \{\zeta(z) - \zeta(z+2\omega_1)\}\, dz$$

$$= -2\eta_2 \int_t^{t+2\omega_1} dt + 2\eta_1 \int_t^{t+2\omega_2} dt,$$

and so $2\pi i = -4\eta_2\omega_1 + 4\eta_1\omega_2,$

which is the required result.

20·42.   *The function $\sigma(z)$.*

We shall next introduce the function $\sigma(z)$, defined by the equation

$$\frac{d}{dz} \log \sigma(z) = \zeta(z)$$

coupled with the condition $\lim_{z\to 0} \{\sigma(z)/z\} = 1$.

On account of the uniformity of convergence of the series for $\zeta(z)$, except near the poles of $\zeta(z)$, we may integrate the series term-by-term. Doing so, and taking the exponential of each side of the resulting equation, we get

$$\sigma(z) = z \prod_{m,n}' \left\{ \left(1 - \frac{z}{\Omega_{m,n}}\right) \exp\left(\frac{z}{\Omega_{m,n}} + \frac{z^2}{2\Omega_{m,n}^2}\right) \right\};$$

the constant of integration has been adjusted in accordance with the condition stated.

By the methods employed in §§ 20·2, 20·21, 20·4, the reader will easily obtain the following results:

(I)   The product for $\sigma(z)$ converges absolutely and uniformly in any bounded domain of values of z.

(II)   The function $\sigma(z)$ is an odd integral function of z with simple zeros at all the points $\Omega_{m,n}$.

The function $\sigma(z)$ may be compared with the function $\sin z$ defined by the product

$$z \prod_{m=-\infty}^{\infty}{}' \left\{ \left(1 - \frac{z}{m\pi}\right) e^{z/(m\pi)} \right\},$$

the relation $\dfrac{d}{dz} \log \sin z = \cot z$ corresponding to $\dfrac{d}{dz} \log \sigma(z) = \zeta(z)$.

20·421.   *The quasi-periodicity of the function $\sigma(z)$.*

If we integrate the equation

$$\zeta(z+2\omega_1) = \zeta(z) + 2\eta_1,$$

we get $\sigma(z+2\omega_1) = ce^{2\eta_1 z}\sigma(z),$

where c is the constant of integration; to determine c, we put $z = -\omega_1$, and then

$$\sigma(\omega_1) = -ce^{-2\eta_1\omega_1}\sigma(\omega_1).$$

Consequently $\qquad\qquad\qquad c = -e^{2\eta_1\omega_1},$

and $\qquad\qquad\qquad \sigma(z + 2\omega_1) = -e^{2\eta_1(z+\omega_1)}\sigma(z).$

In like manner $\qquad \sigma(z + 2\omega_2) = -e^{2\eta_2(z+\omega_2)}\sigma(z).$

These results exhibit the behaviour of $\sigma(z)$ when z is increased by a period of $\wp(z)$.

If, as in § 20·32, we write $\omega_3 = -\omega_1 - \omega_2$, then three other Sigma-functions are defined by the equations

$$\sigma_r(z) = e^{-\eta_r z}\sigma(z + \omega_r)/\sigma(\omega_r) \qquad (r = 1, 2, 3).$$

The four Sigma-functions are analogous to the four Theta-functions discussed in Chapter XXI (see § 21·9).

Example 1. Shew that, if m and n are any integers,

$$\sigma(z + 2m\omega_1 + 2n\omega_2) = (-)^{m+n}\sigma(z)\exp\{(2m\eta_1 + 2n\eta_2)z + 2m^2\eta_1\omega_1 + 4mn\eta_1\omega_2 + 2n^2\eta_2\omega_2\},$$

and deduce that $\eta_1\omega_2 - \eta_2\omega_1$ is an integer multiple of $\frac{1}{2}\pi i$.

Example 2. Shew that, if $q = \exp(\pi i\omega_2/\omega_1)$, so that $|q| < 1$, and if

$$F(z) = \exp\left(\frac{\eta_1 z^2}{2\omega_1}\right)\sin\left(\frac{\pi z}{2\omega_1}\right)\prod_{n=1}^{\infty}\left\{1 - 2q^{2n}\cos\frac{\pi z}{\omega_1} + q^{4n}\right\},$$

then $F(z)$ is an integral function with the same zeros as $\sigma(z)$ and also $F(z)/\sigma(z)$ is a doubly-periodic function of z with periods $2\omega_1$, $2\omega_2$.

Example 3. Deduce from example 2, by using Liouville's theorem, that

$$\sigma(z) = \frac{2\omega_1}{\pi}\exp\left(\frac{\eta_1 z^2}{2\omega_1}\right)\sin\left(\frac{\pi z}{2\omega_1}\right)\prod_{n=1}^{\infty}\left\{\frac{1 - 2q^{2n}\cos(\pi z/\omega_1) + q^{4n}}{(1 - q^{2n})^2}\right\}.$$

Example 4. Obtain the result of example 3 by expressing each factor on the right as a singly infinite product.

20·5. *Formulae expressing any elliptic function in terms of Weierstrassian functions with the same periods.*

There are various formulae analogous to the expression of any rational fraction as (I) a quotient of two sets of products of linear factors, (II) a sum of partial fractions; of the first type there are two formulae involving Sigma-functions and Weierstrassian elliptic functions respectively; of the second type there is a formula involving derivates of Zeta-functions. These formulae will now be obtained.

20·51. *The expression of any elliptic function in terms of $\wp(z)$ and $\wp'(z)$.*

Let $f(z)$ be any elliptic function, and let $\wp(z)$ be the Weierstrassian elliptic function formed with the same periods $2\omega_1$, $2\omega_2$.

We first write

$$f(z) = \tfrac{1}{2}[f(z) + f(-z)] + \tfrac{1}{2}[\{f(z) - f(-z)\}\{\wp'(z)\}^{-1}]\wp'(z).$$

The functions
$$f(z) + f(-z), \quad \{f(z) - f(-z)\} \{\wp'(z)\}^{-1}$$
are both *even* functions, and they are obviously elliptic functions when $f(z)$ is an elliptic function.

The solution of the problem before us is therefore effected *if we can express any even elliptic function $\phi(z)$, say, in terms of $\wp(z)$.*

Let a be a zero of $\phi(z)$ in any cell; then the point in the cell congruent to $-a$ will also be a zero. The irreducible zeros of $\phi(z)$ may therefore be arranged in two sets, say $a_1, a_2, \ldots a_n$ and certain points congruent to $-a_1, -a_2, \ldots -a_n$.

In like manner, the irreducible poles may be arranged in two sets, say $b_1, b_2, \ldots b_n$, and certain points congruent to $-b_1, -b_2, \ldots -b_n$.

Consider now the function *
$$\frac{1}{\phi(z)} \prod_{r=1}^{n} \left\{ \frac{\wp(z) - \wp(a_r)}{\wp(z) - \wp(b_r)} \right\}.$$

It is an elliptic function of z, and clearly it has no poles; for the zeros of $\phi(z)$ are zeros† of the numerator of the product, and the zeros of the denominator of the product are poles† of $\phi(z)$. Consequently by Liouville's theorem it is a constant, A_1, say.

Therefore
$$\phi(z) = A_1 \prod_{r=1}^{n} \left\{ \frac{\wp(z) - \wp(a_r)}{\wp(z) - \wp(b_r)} \right\},$$
that is to say, $\phi(z)$ has been expressed as a rational function of $\wp(z)$.

Carrying out this process with each of the functions
$$f(z) + f(-z), \quad \{f(z) - f(-z)\} \{\wp'(z)\}^{-1},$$
we obtain the theorem that *any elliptic function $f(z)$ can be expressed in terms of the Weierstrassian elliptic functions $\wp(z)$ and $\wp'(z)$ with the same periods, the expression being rational in $\wp(z)$ and linear in $\wp'(z)$.*

20·52. *The expression of any elliptic function as a linear combination of Zeta-functions and their derivates.*

Let $f(z)$ be any elliptic function with periods $2\omega_1, 2\omega_2$. Let a set of irreducible poles of $f(z)$ be $a_1, a_2, \ldots a_n$, and let the principal part (§ 5·61) of $f(z)$ near the pole a_k be
$$\frac{c_{k,1}}{z - a_k} + \frac{c_{k,2}}{(z - a_k)^2} + \ldots + \frac{c_{k,r_k}}{(z - a_k)^{r_k}}.$$

---

* If any one of the points a_r or b_r is congruent to the origin, we omit the corresponding factor $\wp(z) - \wp(a_r)$ or $\wp(z) - \wp(b_r)$. The zero (or pole) of the product and the zero (or pole) of $\phi(z)$ at the origin are then of the same order of multiplicity. In this product, and in that of § 20·53, factors corresponding to multiple zeros and poles have to be repeated the appropriate number of times.

† Of the same order of multiplicity.

Then we can shew that

$$f(z) = A_2 + \sum_{k=1}^{n} \left\{ c_{k,1} \zeta(z - a_k) - c_{k,2} \zeta'(z - a_k) + \dots \right.$$
$$\left. + \frac{(-)^{r_k-1} c_{k,r_k}}{(r_k - 1)!} \zeta^{(r_k-1)}(z - a_k) \right\},$$

where A_2 is a constant, and $\zeta^{(s)}(z)$ denotes $\dfrac{d^s}{dz^s} \zeta(z)$.

Denoting the summation on the right by $F(z)$, we see that

$$F(z + 2\omega_1) - F(z) = \sum_{k=1}^{n} 2\eta_1 c_{k,1},$$

by § 20·41, since all the derivates of the Zeta-functions are periodic.

But $\sum\limits_{k=1}^{n} c_{k,1}$ is the sum of the residues of $f(z)$ at all of its poles in a cell, and is consequently (§ 20·12) zero.

Therefore $F(z)$ has period $2\omega_1$, and similarly it has period $2\omega_2$; and so $f(z) - F(z)$ is an elliptic function.

Moreover $F(z)$ has been so constructed that $f(z) - F(z)$ has no poles at the points $a_1, a_2, \dots a_n$; and hence it has no poles in a certain cell. It is consequently a constant, A_2, by Liouville's theorem.

Thus the function $f(z)$ can be expanded in the form

$$A_2 + \sum_{k=1}^{n} \sum_{s=1}^{r_k} \frac{(-)^{s-1}}{(s-1)!} c_{k,s} \zeta^{(s-1)}(z - a_k).$$

This result is of importance in the problem of integrating an elliptic function $f(z)$ when the principal part of its expansion at each of its poles is known; for we obviously have

$$\int^z f(z)\, dz = A_2 z + \sum_{k=1}^{n} \left[c_{k,1} \log \sigma(z - a_k) \right.$$
$$\left. + \sum_{s=2}^{r_k} \frac{(-)^{s-1}}{(s-1)!} c_{k,s} \zeta^{(s-2)}(z - a_k) \right] + C,$$

where C is a constant of integration.

Example. Shew by the method of this article that

$$\wp^2(z) = \tfrac{1}{6} \wp''(z) + \tfrac{1}{12} g_2,$$

and deduce that

$$\int^z \wp^2(z)\, dz = \tfrac{1}{6} \wp'(z) + \tfrac{1}{12} g_2 z + C,$$

where C is a constant of integration.

20·53. *The expression of any elliptic function as a quotient of Sigma-functions.*

Let $f(z)$ be any elliptic function, with periods $2\omega_1$ and $2\omega_2$, and let a set of irreducible zeros of $f(z)$ be $a_1, a_2, \dots a_n$. Then (§ 20·14) we can choose a set of poles b_1, b_2, ... b_n such that all poles of $f(z)$ are congruent to one or other of them and†

$$a_1 + a_2 + \ldots + a_n = b_1 + b_2 + \ldots + b_n.$$

Consider now the function

$$\prod_{r=1}^{n} \frac{\sigma(z - a_r)}{\sigma(z - b_r)}.$$

This product obviously has the same poles and zeros as $f(z)$; also the effect of increasing z by $2\omega_1$ is to multiply the function by

$$\prod_{r=1}^{n} \frac{\exp\{2\eta_1(z - a_r)\}}{\exp\{2\eta_1(z - b_r)\}} = 1.$$

The function therefore has period $2\omega_1$ (and in like manner it has period $2\omega_2$), and so the quotient

$$f(z) \div \prod_{r=1}^{n} \frac{\sigma(z - a_r)}{\sigma(z - b_r)}$$

is an elliptic function with no zeros or poles. By Liouville's theorem, it must be a constant, A_3 say.

Thus the function $f(z)$ can be expressed in the form

$$f(z) = A_3 \prod_{r=1}^{n} \frac{\sigma(z - a_r)}{\sigma(z - b_r)}.$$

An elliptic function is consequently determinate (save for a multiplicative constant) when its periods and a set of irreducible zeros and poles are known.

Example 1. Shew that

$$\wp(z) - \wp(y) = -\frac{\sigma(z+y)\,\sigma(z-y)}{\sigma^2(z)\,\sigma^2(y)}.$$

Example 2. Deduce by differentiation, from example 1, that

$$\frac{1}{2} \frac{\wp'(z) - \wp'(y)}{\wp(z) - \wp(y)} = \zeta(z+y) - \zeta(z) - \zeta(y),$$

and by further differentiation obtain the addition-theorem for $\wp(z)$.

Example 3. If $\sum_{r=1}^{n} a_r = \sum_{r=1}^{n} b_r$, shew that

$$\sum_{r=1}^{n} \frac{\sigma(a_r - b_1)\,\sigma(a_r - b_2)\ldots\sigma(a_r - b_n)}{\sigma(a_r - a_1)\,\sigma(a_r - a_2)\ldots*\ldots\sigma(a_r - a_n)} = 0,$$

the * denoting that the vanishing factor $\sigma(a_r - a_r)$ is to be omitted.

Example 4. Shew that

$$\wp(z) - e_r = \sigma_r^2(z)/\sigma^2(z) \qquad (r = 1, 2, 3).$$

[It is customary to *define* $\{\wp(z) - e_r\}^{\frac{1}{2}}$ to mean $\sigma_r(z)/\sigma(z)$, not $-\sigma_r(z)/\sigma(z)$.]

Example 5. Establish, by example 1, the 'three-term equation,' namely,

$$\sigma(z+a)\,\sigma(z-a)\,\sigma(b+c)\,\sigma(b-c) + \sigma(z+b)\,\sigma(z-b)\,\sigma(c+a)\,\sigma(c-a)$$
$$+ \sigma(z+c)\,\sigma(z-c)\,\sigma(a+b)\,\sigma(a-b) = 0.$$

† Multiple zeros or poles are, of course, to be reckoned according to their degree of multiplicity; to determine b_1, b_2, ... b_n, we choose b_1, b_2, ... b_{n-1}, b_n' to be the set of poles in the cell in which a_1, a_2, ... a_n lie, and then choose b_n, congruent to b_n', in such a way that the required equation is satisfied.

[This result is due to Weierstrass ; see p. 47 of the edition of his lectures by Schwarz.]

The equation is characteristic of the Sigma-function ; it has been proved by Halphen, *Fonctions Elliptiques*, I. (Paris, 1886), p. 187, that no function essentially different from the Sigma-function satisfies an equation of this type. See p. 461, example 38.

20·54. *The connexion between any two elliptic functions with the same periods.*

We shall now prove the important result that *an algebraic relation exists between any two elliptic functions, $f(z)$ and $\phi(z)$, with the same periods.*

For, by § 20·51, we can express $f(z)$ and $\phi(z)$ as rational functions of the Weierstrassian functions $\wp(z)$ and $\wp'(z)$ with the same periods, so that

$$f(z) = R_1\{\wp(z), \wp'(z)\}, \qquad \phi(z) = R_2\{\wp(z), \wp'(z)\},$$

where R_1 and R_2 denote rational functions of two variables.

Eliminating $\wp(z)$ and $\wp'(z)$ algebraically from these two equations and

$$\wp'^2(z) = 4\wp^3(z) - g_2\wp(z) - g_3,$$

we obtain an algebraic relation connecting $f(z)$ and $\phi(z)$; and the theorem is proved.

A particular case of the proposition is that every elliptic function is connected with its derivate by an algebraic relation.

If now we take the orders of the elliptic functions $f(z)$ and $\phi(z)$ to be m and n respectively, then, corresponding to any given value of $f(z)$ there is (§ 20·13) a set of m irreducible values of z, and consequently there are m values (in general distinct) of $\phi(z)$. So, corresponding to each value of f, there are m values of ϕ and, similarly, to each value of ϕ correspond n values of f.

The relation between $f(z)$ and $\phi(z)$ is therefore (in general) of degree m in ϕ and n in f.

The relation *may* be of lower degree. Thus, if $f(z) = \wp(z)$, of order 2, and $\phi(z) = \wp^2(z)$, of order 4, the relation is $f^2 = \phi$.

As an illustration of the general result take $f(z) = \wp(z)$, of order 2, and $\phi(z) = \wp'(z)$, of order 3. The relation should be of degree 2 in ϕ and of degree 3 in f; this is, in fact, the case, for the relation is $\phi^2 = 4f^3 - g_2 f - g_3$.

Example. If u, v, w are three elliptic functions of their argument of the second order with the same periods, shew that, in general, there exist two distinct relations which are linear in each of u, v, w, namely

$$A\,uvw + B\,vw + C\,wu + D\,uv + E\,u + F\,v + G\,w + H = 0,$$
$$A'uvw + B'vw + C'wu + D'uv + E'u + F'v + G'w + H' = 0,$$

where A, B, ..., H' are constants.

20·6. *On the integration of $\{a_0 x^4 + 4a_1 x^3 + 6a_2 x^2 + 4a_3 x + a_4\}^{-\frac{1}{2}}$.*

It will now be shewn that certain problems of integration, which are insoluble by means of elementary functions only, can be solved by the introduction of the function $\wp(z)$.

Let $a_0 x^4 + 4a_1 x^3 + 6a_2 x^2 + 4a_3 x + a_4 \equiv f(x)$ be any quartic polynomial which has no repeated factors; and let its invariants* be

$$g_2 \equiv a_0 a_4 - 4a_1 a_3 + 3a_2{}^2,$$

$$g_3 \equiv a_0 a_2 a_4 + 2a_1 a_2 a_3 - a_2{}^3 - a_0 a_3{}^2 - a_1{}^2 a_4.$$

Let $z = \int_{x_0}^{x} \{f(t)\}^{-\frac{1}{2}} dt$, where x_0 is any root of the equation $f(x) = 0$; then, if the function $\wp(z)$ be constructed† with the invariants g_2 and g_3, *it is possible to express x as a rational function of $\wp(z; g_2, g_3)$.*

[NOTE. The reason for assuming that $f(x)$ has no repeated factors is that, when $f(x)$ has a repeated factor, the integration can be effected with the aid of circular or logarithmic functions only. For the same reason, the case in which $a_0 = a_1 = 0$ need not be considered.]

By Taylor's theorem, we have

$$f(t) = 4A_3(t - x_0) + 6A_2(t - x_0)^2 + 4A_1(t - x_0)^3 + A_0(t - x_0)^4,$$

(since $f(x_0) = 0$), where

$$A_0 = a_0, \quad A_1 = a_0 x_0 + a_1,$$
$$A_2 = a_0 x_0{}^2 + 2a_1 x_0 + a_2,$$
$$A_3 = a_0 x_0{}^3 + 3a_1 x_0{}^2 + 3a_2 x_0 + a_3.$$

On writing $(t - x_0)^{-1} = \tau$, $(x - x_0)^{-1} = \xi$, we have

$$z = \int_{\xi}^{\infty} \{4A_3 \tau^3 + 6A_2 \tau^2 + 4A_1 \tau + A_0\}^{-\frac{1}{2}} d\tau.$$

To remove the second term in the cubic involved, write‡

$$\tau = A_3^{-1}(\sigma - \tfrac{1}{2}A_2), \quad \xi = A_3^{-1}(s - \tfrac{1}{2}A_2),$$

and we get

$$z = \int_{s}^{\infty} \{4\sigma^3 - (3A_2{}^2 - 4A_1 A_3)\sigma - (2A_1 A_2 A_3 - A_2{}^3 - A_0 A_3{}^2)\}^{-\frac{1}{2}} d\sigma.$$

The reader will verify, without difficulty, that

$$3A_2{}^2 - 4A_1 A_3 \quad \text{and} \quad 2A_1 A_2 A_3 - A_2{}^3 - A_0 A_3{}^2$$

are respectively equal to g_2 and g_3, the invariants of the original quartic, and so

$$s = \wp(z; g_2, g_3).$$

Now $x = x_0 + A_3\{s - \tfrac{1}{2}A_2\}^{-1},$

and hence $x = x_0 + \tfrac{1}{4} f'(x_0) \{\wp(z; g_2, g_3) - \tfrac{1}{24} f''(x_0)\}^{-1},$

so that x has been expressed as a rational function of $\wp(z; g_2, g_3)$.

* Burnside and Panton, *Theory of Equations*, II. p. 113.
† See § 21·73.
‡ This substitution is legitimate since $A_3 \neq 0$; for the equation $A_3 = 0$ involves $f(x) = 0$ having $x = x_0$ as a repeated root.

This formula for x is to be regarded as the integral equivalent of the relation

$$z = \int_{x_0}^{x} \{f(t)\}^{-\frac{1}{2}} dt.$$

Example 1. With the notation of this article, shew that

$$\{f(x)\}^{\frac{1}{2}} = \frac{-f'(x_0)\,\wp'(z)}{4\,\{\wp(z) - \frac{1}{24}f''(x_0)\}^2}.$$

Example 2. Shew that, if

$$z = \int_{a}^{x} \{f(t)\}^{-\frac{1}{2}} dt,$$

where a is *any* constant, not necessarily a zero of $f(x)$, and $f(x)$ is a quartic polynomial with no repeated factors, then

$$x = a + \frac{\{f(a)\}^{\frac{1}{2}}\,\wp'(z) + \frac{1}{2}f'(a)\,\{\wp(z) - \frac{1}{24}f''(a)\} + \frac{1}{24}f(a)f'''(a)}{2\,\{\wp(z) - \frac{1}{24}f''(a)\}^2 - \frac{1}{48}f(a)f^{\mathrm{iv}}(a)},$$

the function $\wp(z)$ being formed with the invariants of the quartic $f(x)$.

(Weierstrass.)

[This result was first published in 1865, in an Inaugural-dissertation at Berlin by Biermann, who ascribed it to Weierstrass. An alternative result, due to Mordell, *Messenger*, XLIV. (1915), pp. 138–141, is that, if

$$z = \int_{a,\,b}^{x,\,y} \frac{y\,dx - x\,dy}{\sqrt{f(x,y)}},$$

where $f(x, y)$ is a homogeneous quartic whose Hessian is $h(x, y)$, then we may take

$$x = a\wp'(z)\sqrt{f} + \tfrac{1}{2}\wp(z)f_b + \tfrac{1}{2}h_b,$$
$$y = b\wp'(z)\sqrt{f} - \tfrac{1}{2}\wp(z)f_a - \tfrac{1}{2}h_a,$$

where f and h stand for $f(a, b)$ and $h(a, b)$, and suffixes denote partial differentiations.]

Example 3. Shew that, with the notation of example 2,

$$\wp(z) = \frac{\{f(x)f(a)\}^{\frac{1}{2}} + f(a)}{2\,(x-a)^2} + \frac{f'(a)}{4\,(x-a)} + \frac{f''(a)}{24},$$

and

$$\wp'(z) = -\left\{\frac{f(x)}{(x-a)^3} - \frac{f'(x)}{4\,(x-a)^2}\right\}\{f(a)\}^{\frac{1}{2}} - \left\{\frac{f(a)}{(x-a)^3} + \frac{f'(a)}{4\,(x-a)^2}\right\}\{f(x)\}^{\frac{1}{2}}.$$

20·7. *The uniformisation* of curves of genus unity.*

The theorem of § 20·6 may be stated somewhat differently thus :

If the variables x and y are connected by an equation of the form

$$y^2 = a_0 x^4 + 4a_1 x^3 + 6a_2 x^2 + 4a_3 x + a_4,$$

then they can be expressed as one-valued functions of a variable z by the equations

$$\left.\begin{array}{l} x = x_0 + \tfrac{1}{4}f'(x_0)\,\{\wp(z) - \tfrac{1}{24}f''(x_0)\}^{-1} \\[2mm] y = -\tfrac{1}{4}f'(x_0)\,\wp'(z)\,\{\wp(z) - \tfrac{1}{24}f''(x_0)\}^{-2} \end{array}\right\},$$

where $f(x) = a_0 x^4 + 4a_1 x^3 + 6a_2 x^2 + 4a_3 x + a_4$, x_0 *is any zero of* $f(x)$, *and the function* $\wp(z)$ *is formed with the invariants of the quartic; and z is such that*

$$z = \int_{x_0}^{x} \{f(t)\}^{-\frac{1}{2}} dt.$$

* This term employs the word *uniform* in the sense *one-valued*. To prevent confusion with the idea of uniformity as explained in Chapter III, throughout the present work we have used the phrase ' one-valued function ' as being preferable to ' uniform function.'

It is obvious that y is a two-valued function of x and x is a four-valued function of y; and the fact, that x and y can be expressed as *one-valued* functions of the variable z, makes this variable z of considerable importance in the theory of algebraic equations of the type considered; z is called the *uniformising variable* of the equation

$$y^2 = a_0 x^4 + 4a_1 x^3 + 6a_2 x^2 + 4a_3 x + a_4.$$

The reader who is acquainted with the theory of algebraic plane curves will be aware that they are classified according to their *deficiency* or *genus**, a number whose geometrical significance is that it is the difference between the number of double points possessed by the curve and the maximum number of double points which can be possessed by a curve of the same degree as the given curve.

Curves whose deficiency is zero are called *unicursal curves*. If $f(x, y) = 0$ is the equation of a unicursal curve, it is well known† that x and y can be expressed as *rational functions of a parameter*. Since rational functions are one-valued, this parameter is a *uniformising variable* for the curve in question.

Next consider curves of genus unity; let $f(x, y) = 0$ be such a curve; then it has been shewn by Clebsch‡ that x and y can be expressed as rational functions of ξ and η where η^2 is a polynomial in ξ of degree three or four. Hence, by § 20·6, ξ and η can be expressed as rational functions of $\wp(z)$ and $\wp'(z)$, (these functions being formed with suitable invariants), and so x and y can be expressed as one-valued (elliptic) functions of z, which is therefore a uniformising variable for the equation under consideration.

When the genus of the algebraic curve $f(x, y) = 0$ is greater than unity, the uniformisation can be effected by means of what are known as *automorphic functions*. Two classes of such functions of genus greater than unity have been constructed, the first by Weber, *Göttinger Nach.* (1886), pp. 359–370, the other by Whittaker, *Phil. Trans.* CXCII. (1898), pp. 1–32. The analogue of the period-parallelogram is known as the 'fundamental polygon.' In the case of Weber's functions this polygon is 'multiply-connected,' i.e. it consists of a region containing islands which have to be regarded as not belonging to it; whereas in the case of the second class of functions, the polygon is 'simply-connected,' i.e. it contains no such islands. The latter class of functions may therefore be regarded as a more immediate generalisation of elliptic functions. Cf. Ford, *Introduction to theory of Automorphic Functions*, Edinburgh Math. Tracts, No. 6 (1915).

REFERENCES.

K. WEIERSTRASS, *Werke*, I. (1894), pp. 1–49, II. (1895), pp. 245–255, 257–309.

C. BRIOT et J. C. BOUQUET, *Théorie des fonctions elliptiques.* (Paris, 1875.)

H. A. SCHWARZ, *Formeln und Lehrsätze zum Gebrauche der elliptischen Funktionen. Nach Vorlesungen und Aufzeichnungen des Herrn Prof. K. Weierstrass.* (Berlin, 1893.)

A. L. DANIELS, 'Notes on Weierstrass' methods,' *American Journal of Math.* VI. (1884), pp. 177–182, 253–269; VII. (1885), pp. 82–99.

J. LIOUVILLE (Lectures published by C. W. Borchardt), *Journal für Math.* LXXXVIII. (1880), pp. 277–310.

A. ENNEPER, *Elliptische Funktionen.* (Zweite Auflage, von F. Müller, Halle, 1890.)

J. TANNERY et J. MOLK, *Fonctions Elliptiques.* (Paris, 1893–1902.)

* French *genre*, German *Geschlecht*.

† See Salmon, *Higher Plane Curves* (Dublin, 1873), Ch. II.

‡ *Journal für Math.* LXIV. (1865), pp. 210–270. A proof of the result of Clebsch is given by Forsyth, *Theory of Functions* (1918), § 248. See also Cayley, *Proc. London Math. Soc.* IV. (1873), pp. 347–352 [*Math. Papers*, VIII. pp. 181–187].

MISCELLANEOUS EXAMPLES.

1. Shew that
$$\wp(z+y) - \wp(z-y) = -\wp'(z)\,\wp'(y)\,\{\wp(z) - \wp(y)\}^{-2}.$$

2. Prove that
$$\wp(z) - \wp(z+y+w) = 2\frac{\partial}{\partial z}\frac{\Sigma\wp^2(z)\{\wp(y) - \wp(w)\}}{\Sigma\wp'(z)\{\wp(y) - \wp(w)\}},$$

where, on the right-hand side, the subject of differentiation is symmetrical in z, y, and w.

(Math. Trip. 1897.)

3. Shew that
$$\begin{vmatrix} \wp'''(z-y) & \wp'''(y-w) & \wp'''(w-z) \\ \wp''(z-y) & \wp''(y-w) & \wp''(w-z) \\ \wp(z-y) & \wp(y-w) & \wp(w-z) \end{vmatrix} = \tfrac{1}{2}g_2 \begin{vmatrix} \wp'''(z-y) & \wp'''(y-w) & \wp'''(w-z) \\ \wp(z-y) & \wp(y-w) & \wp(w-z) \\ 1 & 1 & 1 \end{vmatrix}.$$

(Trinity, 1898.)

4. If
$$y = \wp(z) - e_1, \quad y' = \frac{dy}{dz};$$

shew that y is one of the values of
$$\left\{ y'\left(y - \frac{1}{4}\frac{d^2}{dz^2}\log y\right)^{\frac{1}{2}} + (e_1 - e_2)(e_1 - e_3) \right\}^{\frac{1}{2}}.$$

(Math. Trip. 1897.)

5. Prove that
$$\Sigma\{\wp(z) - e\}\{\wp(y) - \wp(w)\}^2\{\wp(y+w) - e\}^{\frac{1}{2}}\{\wp(y-w) - e\}^{\frac{1}{2}} = 0,$$

where the sign of summation refers to the three arguments z, y, w, and e is any one of the roots e_1, e_2, e_3.

(Math. Trip. 1896.)

6. Shew that
$$\frac{\wp'(z+\omega_1)}{\wp'(z)} = -\left\{\frac{\wp(\tfrac{1}{2}\omega_1) - \wp(\omega_1)}{\wp(z) - \wp(\omega_1)}\right\}^2.$$

(Math. Trip. 1894.)

7. Prove that
$$\wp(2z) - \wp(\omega_1) = \{\wp'(z)\}^{-2}\{\wp(z) - \wp(\tfrac{1}{2}\omega_1)\}^2\{\wp(z) - \wp(\omega_2 + \tfrac{1}{2}\omega_1)\}^2.$$

(Math. Trip. 1894.)

8. Shew that
$$\wp(u+v)\,\wp(u-v) = \frac{\{\wp(u)\,\wp(v) + \tfrac{1}{4}g_2\}^2 + g_3\{\wp(u) + \wp(v)\}}{\{\wp(u) - \wp(v)\}^2}.$$

(Trinity, 1908.)

9. If $\wp(u)$ have primitive periods $2\omega_1$, $2\omega_2$ and $f(u) = \{\wp(u) - \wp(\omega_2)\}^{\frac{1}{2}}$, while $\wp_1(u)$ and $f_1(u)$ are similarly constructed with periods $2\omega_1/n$ and $2\omega_2$, prove that
$$\wp_1(u) = \wp(u) + \sum_{m=1}^{n-1}\{\wp(u+2m\omega_1/n) - \wp(2m\omega_1/n)\},$$

and
$$f_1(u) = \frac{\prod\limits_{m=0}^{n-1} f(u+2m\omega_1/n)}{\prod\limits_{m=1}^{n-1} f(2m\omega_1/n)}.$$

(Math. Trip. 1914 ; the first of the formulae is due to Kiepert, *Journal für Math.* LXXVI. (1873), p. 39.)

10. If $\qquad x = \wp(u+a), \quad y = \wp(u-a),$

where a is constant, shew that the curve on which (x, y) lies is

$$(xy + cx + cy + \tfrac{1}{4}g_2)^2 = 4(x+y+c)(cxy - \tfrac{1}{4}g_3),$$

where $c = \wp(2a)$.

(Burnside, *Messenger*, XXI.)

11. Shew that

$$2\wp'^3(u) - 3g_2\wp'^2(u) + g_3{}^3 = 27\{\wp'^2(u) + g_3\}^2.$$

(Trinity, 1909.)

12. If $\qquad z = \int_{-\infty}^{x} (x^4 + 6cx^2 + e^2)^{-\frac{1}{2}} dx,$

verify that $\qquad x = \dfrac{\tfrac{1}{2}\wp'(z)}{\wp(z) + c},$

the elliptic function being formed with the roots $-c$, $\tfrac{1}{2}(c+e)$, $\tfrac{1}{2}(c-e)$.

(Trinity, 1905.)

13. If m be any constant, prove that

$$\frac{1}{\wp'(y)} \int \frac{e^{m\{\wp(z)-\wp(y)\}}\,\wp'^2(z)\,dz}{\wp(z)-\wp(y)} + \wp'(z) \int \frac{e^{m\{\wp(z)-\wp(y)\}}\,dy}{\wp(z)-\wp(y)}$$
$$= -\frac{1}{2}\sum_r \int\int \frac{e^{m\{\wp(z)-\wp(y)\}}\,\wp'^2(z)\,dz\,dy}{\{\wp(z)-e_r\}\{\wp(y)-e_r\}},$$

where the summation refers to the values 1, 2, 3 of r; and the integrals are indefinite.

(Math. Trip. 1897.)

14. Let $\qquad R(x) = Ax^4 + Bx^3 + Cx^2 + Dx + E,$

and let $\xi = \phi(x)$ be the function defined by the equation

$$x = \int^{\xi} \{R(\xi)\}^{-\frac{1}{2}}\, d\xi,$$

where the lower limit of the integral is arbitrary. Shew that

$$\frac{2\phi'(a)}{\phi(x+y)-\phi(a)} = \frac{\phi'(a+y)+\phi'(a)}{\phi(a+y)-\phi(a)} + \frac{\phi'(a-y)+\phi'(a)}{\phi(a-y)-\phi(a)} - \frac{\phi'(a+y)-\phi'(x)}{\phi(a+y)-\phi(x)}$$
$$- \frac{\phi'(a-y)-\phi'(x)}{\phi(a-y)-\phi(x)}.$$

[Hermite, *Proc. Math. Congress* (Chicago, 1896), p. 105. This formula is an addition-formula which is satisfied by every elliptic function of order 2.]

15. Shew that, when the change of variables

$$\xi' = \xi/\eta, \quad \eta' = \xi^3/\eta^2$$

is applied to the equations

$$\eta^2 + \eta(1+p\xi) + \xi^3 = 0, \quad du - \frac{d\xi}{2\eta+1+p\xi} = 0,$$

they transform into the similar equations

$$\eta'^2 + \eta'(1+p\xi') + \xi'^3 = 0, \quad du - \frac{d\xi'}{2\eta'+1+p\xi'} = 0.$$

Shew that the result of performing this change of variables three times in succession is a return to the original variables ξ, η; and hence prove that, if ξ and η be denoted as functions of u by $E(u)$ and $F(u)$ respectively, then

$$E(u+A) = \frac{E(u)}{F(u)}, \quad F(u+A) = \frac{E^3(u)}{F^2(u)},$$

where A is one-third of a period of the functions $E(u)$ and $F(u)$.

Shew that $\qquad E(u) = \dfrac{p^2}{12} - \wp(u\,;\,g_2, g_3),$

where $\qquad g_2 = 2p + \dfrac{1}{12}p^4, \quad g_3 = -1 - \dfrac{1}{6}p^3 - \dfrac{1}{216}p^6.$

(De Brun, *Öfversigt af K. Vet. Akad., Stockholm*, LIV.)

16. Shew that

$$\wp'(z) = \frac{2\sigma(z+\omega_1)\,\sigma(z+\omega_2)\,\sigma(z-\omega_1-\omega_2)}{\sigma^3(z)\,\sigma(\omega_1)\,\sigma(\omega_2)\,\sigma(\omega_1+\omega_2)},$$

and

$$\wp''(z) = \frac{6\sigma(z+a)\,\sigma(z-a)\,\sigma(z+c)\,\sigma(z-c)}{\sigma^4(z)\,\sigma^2(a)\,\sigma^2(c)},$$

where

$$\wp(a) = (\tfrac{1}{12}g_2)^{\frac{1}{2}}, \quad \wp(c) = -(\tfrac{1}{12}g_2)^{\frac{1}{2}}.$$

(Math. Trip. 1913.)

17. Prove that

$$\wp(z-a)\,\wp(z-b) = \wp(a-b)\,\{\wp(z-a)+\wp(z-b)-\wp(a)-\wp(b)\}$$
$$+\wp'(a-b)\,\{\zeta(z-a)-\zeta(z-b)+\zeta(a)-\zeta(b)\}$$
$$+\wp(a)\,\wp(b).$$

(Math. Trip. 1895.)

18. Shew that

$$\frac{1}{2}\left\{\frac{\wp'(u)+\wp'(w)}{\wp(u)-\wp(w)} - \frac{\wp'(v)+\wp'(w)}{\wp(v)-\wp(w)}\right\} = -\zeta(w-u)+\zeta(w-v)+\zeta(v)-\zeta(u).$$

(Math. Trip. 1910.)

19. Shew that

$$\zeta(u_1)+\zeta(u_2)+\zeta(u_3)-\zeta(u_1+u_2+u_3)$$
$$= \frac{2\,\{\wp(u_1)-\wp(u_2)\}\,\{\wp(u_2)-\wp(u_3)\}\,\{\wp(u_3)-\wp(u_1)\}}{\wp'(u_1)\,\{\wp(u_2)-\wp(u_3)\}+\wp'(u_2)\,\{\wp(u_3)-\wp(u_1)\}+\wp'(u_3)\,\{\wp(u_1)-\wp(u_2)\}}.$$

(Math. Trip. 1912.)

20. Shew that

$$\frac{\sigma(x+y+z)\,\sigma(x-y)\,\sigma(y-z)\,\sigma(z-x)}{\sigma^3(x)\,\sigma^3(y)\,\sigma^3(z)} = \frac{1}{2}\begin{vmatrix} 1 & \wp(x) & \wp'(x) \\ 1 & \wp(y) & \wp'(y) \\ 1 & \wp(z) & \wp'(z) \end{vmatrix}.$$

Obtain the addition-theorem for the function $\wp(z)$ from this result.

21. Shew by induction, or otherwise, that

$$\begin{vmatrix} 1 & \wp(z_0) & \wp'(z_0) \cdots \wp^{(n-1)}(z_0) \\ 1 & \wp(z_1) & \wp'(z_1) \cdots \wp^{(n-1)}(z_1) \\ \cdots\cdots\cdots\cdots\cdots\cdots \\ \cdots\cdots\cdots\cdots\cdots \\ 1 & \wp(z_n) & \wp'(z_n) \cdots \wp^{(n-1)}(z_n) \end{vmatrix} = (-)^{\frac{1}{2}n(n-1)}\,1!\,2!\ldots n!\,\frac{\sigma(z_0+z_1+\ldots+z_n)\,\Pi\sigma(z_\lambda-z_\mu)}{\sigma^{n+1}(z_0)\ldots\sigma^{n+1}(z_n)},$$

where the product is taken for pairs of all integral values of λ and μ from 0 to n, such that $\lambda < \mu$.

(Frobenius u. Stickelberger*, *Journal für Math.* LXXXIII. (1877), p. 179.)

22. Express

$$\begin{vmatrix} 1 & \wp(x) & \wp^2(x) & \wp'(x) \\ 1 & \wp(y) & \wp^2(y) & \wp'(y) \\ 1 & \wp(z) & \wp^2(z) & \wp'(z) \\ 1 & \wp(u) & \wp^2(u) & \wp'(u) \end{vmatrix}$$

as a fraction whose numerator and denominator are products of Sigma-functions.

* See also Kiepert, *Journal für Math.* LXXVI. (1873), pp. 21–33 ; Hermite, *Journal für Math.* LXXXII. (1877), p. 346.

Deduce that if $a = \wp(x)$, $\beta = \wp(y)$, $\gamma = \wp(z)$, $\delta = \wp(u)$, where $x + y + z + u = 0$, then

$$(e_2 - e_3)\{(a - e_1)(\beta - e_1)(\gamma - e_1)(\delta - e_1)\}^{\frac{1}{2}}$$

$$+ (e_3 - e_1)\{(a - e_2)(\beta - e_2)(\gamma - e_2)(\delta - e_2)\}^{\frac{1}{2}}$$

$$+ (e_1 - e_2)\{(a - e_3)(\beta - e_3)(\gamma - e_3)(\delta - e_3)\}^{\frac{1}{2}} = (e_2 - e_3)(e_3 - e_1)(e_1 - e_2).$$

(Math. Trip. 1911.)

23. Shew that

$$2\zeta(2u) - 4\zeta(u) = \frac{\wp''(u)}{\wp'(u)},$$

$$3\zeta(3u) - 9\zeta(u) = \frac{\wp'^3(u)}{\wp^4(u) - \frac{1}{2}g_2\wp^2(u) - g_3\wp(u) - \frac{1}{48}g_2^2}.$$

(Math. Trip. 1905.)

24. Shew that

$$\frac{\sigma(2u)}{\sigma^4(u)} = -\wp'(u), \quad \frac{\sigma(3u)}{\sigma^9(u)} = 3\wp(u)\wp'^2(u) - \frac{1}{4}\wp''^2(u),$$

and prove that $\sigma(nu)/\{\sigma(u)\}^{n^2}$ is a doubly-periodic function of u.

(Math. Trip. 1912.)

25. Prove that

$$\zeta(z - a) - \zeta(z - b) - \zeta(a - b) + \zeta(2a - 2b) = \frac{\sigma(z - 2a + b)\sigma(z - 2b + a)}{\sigma(2b - 2a)\sigma(z - a)\sigma(z - b)}.$$

(Math. Trip. 1895.)

26. Shew that, if $z_1 + z_2 + z_3 + z_4 = 0$, then

$$\{\Sigma\zeta(z_r)\}^3 = 3\{\Sigma\zeta(z_r)\}\{\Sigma\wp(z_r)\} + \Sigma\wp'(z_r),$$

the summations being taken for $r = 1, 2, 3, 4$. (Math. Trip. 1897.)

27. Shew that every elliptic function of order n can be expressed as the quotient of two expressions of the form

$$a_1\wp(z + b) + a_2\wp'(z + b) + \dots + a_n\wp^{(n-1)}(z + b),$$

where $b, a_1, a_2, \dots a_n$ are constants. (Painlevé, *Bulletin de la Soc. Math.* XXVII.)

28. Taking $\quad e_1 > e_2 > e_3$, $\quad \wp(\omega) = e_1$, $\quad \wp(\omega') = e_3$,

consider the values assumed by

$$\zeta(u) - u\zeta(\omega')/\omega'$$

as u passes along the perimeter of the rectangle whose corners are $-\omega$, ω, $\omega + \omega'$, $-\omega + \omega$.

(Math. Trip. 1914.)

29. Obtain an integral of the equation

$$\frac{1}{w}\frac{d^2w}{dz^2} = 6\wp(z) + 3b$$

in the form

$$\frac{d}{dz}\left[\frac{\sigma(z + c)}{\sigma(z)\sigma(c)}\exp\left\{\frac{z\wp'(c)}{b - 2\wp(c)} - z\zeta(c)\right\}\right],$$

where c is defined by the equation

$$(b^2 - 3g_2)\wp(c) = 3(b^3 + g_3).$$

Also, obtain another integral in the form

$$\frac{\sigma(z + a_1)\sigma(z + a_2)}{\sigma^2(z)}\exp\{-z\zeta(a_1) - z\zeta(a_2)\},$$

where $\quad\wp(a_1) + \wp(a_2) = b$, $\quad \wp'(a_1) + \wp'(a_2) = 0$,

and neither $a_1 + a_2$ nor $a_1 - a_2$ is congruent to a period. (Math. Trip. 1912.)

30. Prove that

$$g(z) = \frac{\sigma(z+z_1)\,\sigma(z+z_2)\,\sigma(z+z_3)\,\sigma(z+z_4)}{\sigma\{2z + \tfrac{1}{2}(z_1+z_2+z_3+z_4)\}}$$

is a doubly-periodic function of z, such that

$$g(z) + g(z+\omega_1) + g(z+\omega_2) + g(z+\omega_1+\omega_2)$$
$$= -2\sigma\{\tfrac{1}{2}(z_2+z_3-z_1-z_4)\}\,\sigma\{\tfrac{1}{2}(z_3+z_1-z_2-z_4)\}\,\sigma\{\tfrac{1}{2}(z_1+z_2-z_3-z_4)\}.$$
(Math. Trip. 1893.)

31. If $f(z)$ be a doubly-periodic function of the third order, with poles at $z=c_1$, $z=c_2$, $z=c_3$, and if $\phi(z)$ be a doubly-periodic function of the second order with the same periods and poles at $z=a$, $z=\beta$, its value in the neighbourhood of $z=a$ being

$$\phi(z) = \frac{\lambda}{z-a} + \lambda_1(z-a) + \lambda_2(z-a)^2 + \dots,$$

prove that

$$\tfrac{1}{2}\lambda^2\{f''(a) - f''(\beta)\} - \lambda\{f'(a) + f'(\beta)\}\overset{3}{\underset{1}{\Sigma}}\phi(c_1) + \{f(a) - f(\beta)\}\left\{3\lambda\lambda_1 + \overset{3}{\underset{1}{\Sigma}}\phi(c_2)\,\phi(c_3)\right\} = 0.$$
(Math. Trip. 1894.)

32. If $\lambda(z)$ be an elliptic function with two poles a_1, a_2, and if $z_1, z_2, \dots z_{2n}$ be $2n$ constants subject only to the condition

$$z_1 + z_2 + \dots + z_{2n} = n(a_1 + a_2),$$

shew that the determinant whose ith row is

$$1,\ \lambda(z_i),\ \lambda^2(z_i),\ \dots\ \lambda^n(z_i),\ \lambda_1(z_i),\ \lambda(z_i)\,\lambda_1(z_i),\ \lambda^2(z_i)\,\lambda_1(z_i),\ \dots\ \lambda^{n-2}(z_i)\,\lambda_1(z_i)$$

[where $\lambda_1(z_i)$ denotes the result of writing z_i for z in the derivate of $\lambda(z)$], vanishes identically.
(Math. Trip. 1893.)

33. Deduce from example 21 by a limiting process, or otherwise prove, that

$$\begin{vmatrix} \wp'(z) & \wp''(z) & \dots & \wp^{(n-1)}(z) \\ \wp''(z) & \wp'''(z) & \dots & \wp^{(n)}(z) \\ \dots\dots\dots\dots\dots\dots\dots\dots\dots\dots \\ \dots\dots\dots\dots\dots\dots\dots\dots\dots\dots \\ \wp^{(n-1)}(z) & \wp^{(n)}(z) & \dots & \wp^{(2n-3)}(z) \end{vmatrix} = (-)^{n-1}\{1!\,2!\dots(n-1)!\}^2\,\sigma(nu)/\{\sigma(u)\}^{n^2}.$$

(Kiepert, *Journal für Math.* LXXVI.)

34. Shew that, provided certain conditions of inequality are satisfied,

$$\frac{\sigma(z+y)}{\sigma(z)\,\sigma(y)}e^{\frac{-\eta_1 zy}{\omega_1}} = \frac{\pi}{2\omega_1}\left(\cot\frac{\pi z}{2\omega_1} + \cot\frac{\pi y}{2\omega_1}\right) + \frac{2\pi}{\omega_1}\Sigma q^{2mn}\sin\frac{\pi}{\omega_1}(mz+ny),$$

where the summation applies to all positive integer values of m and n, and $q = \exp(\pi i\omega_2/\omega_1)$.
(Math. Trip. 1895.)

35. Assuming the formula

$$\sigma(z) = e^{\frac{\eta_1 z^2}{2\omega_1}} \cdot \frac{2\omega_1}{\pi}\sin\frac{\pi z}{2\omega_1}\overset{\infty}{\underset{n=1}{\Pi}}\frac{1 - 2q^{2n}\cos\frac{\pi z}{\omega_1} + q^{4n}}{(1-q^{2n})^2},$$

prove that

$$\wp(z) = -\frac{\eta_1}{\omega_1} + \left(\frac{\pi}{2\omega_1}\right)^2\operatorname{cosec}^2\frac{\pi z}{2\omega_1} - 2\left(\frac{\pi}{\omega_1}\right)^2\overset{\infty}{\underset{n=1}{\Sigma}}\frac{nq^{2n}}{1-q^{2n}}\cos\frac{n\pi z}{\omega_1}$$

when z satisfies the inequalities

$$-2R\left(\frac{\omega_2}{i\omega_1}\right) < R\left(\frac{z}{i\omega_1}\right) < 2R\left(\frac{\omega_2}{i\omega_1}\right).$$
(Math. Trip. 1896.)

36. Shew that if 2ϖ be any expression of the form $2m\omega_1 + 2n\omega_2$ and if

$$x = \wp\left(\tfrac{2}{5}\varpi\right) + \wp\left(\tfrac{4}{5}\varpi\right),$$

then x is a root of the sextic

$$x^6 - 5g_2 x^4 - 40g_3 x^3 - 5g_2{}^2 x^2 - 8g_2 g_3 x - 5g_3{}^2 = 0,$$

and obtain all the roots of the sextic. (Trinity, 1898.)

37. Shew that

$$\int \{(x^2 - a)(x^2 - b)\}^{-\frac{1}{4}} dx = -\frac{1}{2} \log \frac{\sigma(z - z_0)}{\sigma(z + z_0)} + \frac{i}{2} \log \frac{\sigma(z - iz_0)}{\sigma(z + iz_0)},$$

where

$$x^2 = a + \frac{1}{6} \frac{1}{\wp^2(z) - \wp^2(z_0)}, \quad g_2 = \frac{2b}{3a(a - b)}, \quad g_3 = 0, \quad \wp^2(z_0) = \frac{1}{6(a - b)}.$$

(Dolbnia, *Darboux' Bulletin* (2), XIX.)

38. Prove that every analytic function $f(z)$ which satisfies the three-term equation

$$\underset{a, b, c}{\Sigma} f(z + a) f(z - a) f(b + c) f(b - c) = 0,$$

for general values of a, b, c and z, is expressible as a finite combination of elementary functions, together with a Sigma-function (including a circular function or an algebraic function as degenerate cases).

(Hermite, *Fonctions elliptiques*, I. p. 187.)

[Put $z = a = b = c = 0$, and then $f(0) = 0$; put $b = c$, and then $f(a - b) + f(b - a) = 0$, so that $f(z)$ is an odd function.

If $F(z)$ is the logarithmic derivate of $f(z)$, the result of differentiating the relation with respect to b, and then putting $b = c$, is

$$\frac{f(z + a) f(z - a) f(2b) f'(0)}{f(z + b) f(z - b) f(a + b) f(a - b)} = F(z + b) - F(z - b) + F(a - b) - F(a + b).$$

Differentiate with respect to b, and put $b = 0$; then

$$\frac{f(z + a) f(z - a) \{f'(0)\}^2}{\{f(z) f(a)\}^2} = F'(z) - F'(a).$$

If $f'(0)$ were zero, $F'(z)$ would be a constant and, by integration, $f(z)$ would be of the form $A \exp(Bz + Cz^2)$, and this is an odd function only in the trivial case when it is zero.

If $f'(0) \neq 0$, and we write $F'(z) = -\Phi(z)$, it is found that the coefficient of a^4 in the expansion of

$$12 f(z + a) f(z - a) / \{f(z)\}^2$$

is $6 \{\Phi(z)\}^2 - \Phi''(z)$, and the coefficient of a^4 in $12 \{f(a)\}^2 \{\Phi(a) - \Phi(z)\}$ is a linear function of $\Phi(z)$. Hence $\Phi''(z)$ is a quadratic function of $\Phi(z)$; and when we multiply this function by $\Phi'(z)$ and integrate we find that

$$\{\Phi'(z)\}^2 = 4 \{\Phi(z)\}^3 + 12A \{\Phi(z)\}^2 + 12B\Phi(z) + 4C,$$

where A, B, C are constants. If the cubic on the right has no repeated factors, then, by § 20·6, $\Phi(z) = \wp(z + a) + A$, where a is constant, and on integration

$$f(z) = \sigma(z + a) \exp\left(-\tfrac{1}{2} Az^2 - Kz - L\right),$$

where K and L are constants; since $f(z)$ is an odd function $a = K = 0$, and

$$f(z) = \sigma(z) \exp\{-\tfrac{1}{2} Az^2 - L\}.$$

If the cubic has a repeated factor, the Sigma-function is to be replaced (cf. § 20·222) by the sine of a multiple of z, and if the cubic is a perfect cube the Sigma-function is to be replaced by a multiple of z.]

CHAPTER XXI

THE THETA FUNCTIONS

21·1. *The definition of a Theta-function.*

When it is desired to obtain definite numerical results in problems involving Elliptic functions, the calculations are most simply performed with the aid of certain auxiliary functions known as *Theta-functions*. These functions are of considerable intrinsic interest, apart from their connexion with Elliptic functions, and we shall now give an account of their fundamental properties.

The Theta-functions were first systematically studied by Jacobi[*], who obtained their properties by purely algebraical methods; and his analysis was so complete that practically all the results contained in this chapter (with the exception of the discussion of the problem of inversion in §§ 21·7 *et seq.*) are to be found in his works. In accordance with the general scheme of this book, we shall not employ the methods of Jacobi, but the more powerful methods based on the use of Cauchy's theorem. These methods were first employed in the theory of Elliptic and allied functions by Liouville in his lectures and have since been given in several treatises on Elliptic functions, the earliest of these works being that by Briot and Bouquet.

[NOTE. The first function of the Theta-function type to appear in Analysis was the *Partition function*[†] $\prod\limits_{n=1}^{\infty} (1 - x^n z)^{-1}$ of Euler, *Introductio in Analysin Infinitorum*, I. (Lausanne, 1748), § 304; by means of the results given in § 21·3, it is easy to express Theta-functions in terms of Partition functions. Euler also obtained properties of products of the type

$$\prod_{n=1}^{\infty} (1 \pm x^n), \quad \prod_{n=1}^{\infty} (1 \pm x^{2n}), \quad \prod_{n=1}^{\infty} (1 \pm x^{2n-1}).$$

The associated series $\sum\limits_{n=0}^{\infty} m^{\frac{1}{2}n(n+3)}$, $\sum\limits_{n=0}^{\infty} m^{\frac{1}{2}n(n+1)}$ and $\sum\limits_{n=0}^{\infty} m^{n^2}$ had previously occurred in the posthumous work of Jakob Bernoulli, *Ars Conjectandi* (1713), p. 55.

---

[*] *Fundamenta Nova Theoriae Functionum Ellipticarum* (Königsberg, 1829), and *Ges. Werke*, I. pp. 497–538.

[†] The Partition function and associated functions have been studied by Gauss, *Comm. Soc. reg. sci. Gottingensis rec.* I. (1811), pp. 7–12 [*Werke*, II. pp. 16–21] and *Werke*, III. pp. 433–480 and Cauchy, *Comptes Rendus*, X. (1840), pp. 178–181. For a discussion of properties of various functions involving what are known as *Basic numbers* (which are closely connected with Partition functions) see Jackson, *Proc. Royal Soc.* LXXIV. (1905), pp. 64–72, *Proc. London Math. Soc.* (1) XXVIII. (1897), pp. 475–486 and (2) I. (1904), pp. 63–88, II. (1904), pp. 192–220; and Watson, *Camb. Phil. Trans.* XXI. (1912), pp. 281–299. A fundamental formula in the theory of Basic numbers was given by Heine, *Kugelfunktionen* (Berlin, 1878), I. p. 107.

Theta-functions also occur in Fourier's *La Théorie Analytique de la Chaleur* (Paris, 1822), cf. p. 265 of Freeman's translation (Cambridge, 1878).

The theory of Theta-functions was developed from the theory of elliptic functions by Jacobi in his *Fundamenta Nova Theoriae Functionum Ellipticarum* (1829), reprinted in his *Ges. Werke*, I. pp. 49–239; the notation there employed is explained in § 21·62. In his subsequent lectures, he introduced the functions discussed in this chapter; an account of these lectures (1838) is given by Borchardt in Jacobi's *Ges. Werke*, I. pp. 497–538. The most important results contained in them seem to have been discovered in 1835, cf. Kronecker, *Sitzungsberichte der Akad. zu Berlin* (1891), pp. 653–659.]

Let τ be a (constant) complex number whose imaginary part is *positive*; and write $q = e^{\pi i \tau}$, so that $|q| < 1$.

Consider the function $\vartheta(z, q)$, defined by the series

$$\vartheta(z, q) = \sum_{n=-\infty}^{\infty} (-)^n q^{n^2} e^{2niz},$$

qua function of the variable z.

If A be any positive constant, then, when $|z| \leqslant A$, we have

$$|q^{n^2} e^{\pm 2niz}| \leqslant |q|^{n^2} e^{2nA},$$

n being a positive integer.

Now d'Alembert's ratio (§ 2·36) for the series $\sum\limits_{n=-\infty}^{\infty} |q|^{n^2} e^{2nA}$ is $|q|^{2n+1} e^{2A}$, which tends to zero as $n \to \infty$. The series for $\vartheta(z, q)$ is therefore a series of analytic functions, uniformly convergent (§ 3·34) in any bounded domain of values of z, and so it is an integral function (§§ 5·3, 5·64).

It is evident that

$$\vartheta(z, q) = 1 + 2 \sum_{n=1}^{\infty} (-)^n q^{n^2} \cos 2nz,$$

and that

$$\vartheta(z + \pi, q) = \vartheta(z, q);$$

further

$$\vartheta(z + \pi\tau, q) = \sum_{n=-\infty}^{\infty} (-)^n q^{n^2} q^{2n} e^{2niz}$$

$$= -q^{-1} e^{-2iz} \sum_{n=-\infty}^{\infty} (-)^{n+1} q^{(n+1)^2} e^{2(n+1)iz},$$

and so

$$\vartheta(z + \pi\tau, q) = -q^{-1} e^{-2iz} \vartheta(z, q).$$

In consequence of these results, $\vartheta(z, q)$ is called a *quasi doubly-periodic function* of z. The effect of increasing z by π or $\pi\tau$ is the same as the effect of multiplying $\vartheta(z, q)$ by 1 or $-q^{-1} e^{-2iz}$, and accordingly 1 and $-q^{-1} e^{-2iz}$ are called the *multipliers* or *periodicity factors* associated with the *periods* π and $\pi\tau$ respectively.

21·11. *The four types of Theta-functions.*

It is customary to write $\vartheta_4(z, q)$ in place of $\vartheta(z, q)$; the other three types of Theta-functions are then defined as follows:

The function $\vartheta_3(z, q)$ is defined by the equation

$$\vartheta_3(z, q) = \vartheta_4\left(z + \frac{1}{2}\pi, q\right) = 1 + 2\sum_{n=1}^{\infty} q^{n^2} \cos 2nz.$$

Next, $\vartheta_1(z, q)$ is defined in terms of $\vartheta_4(z, q)$ by the equation

$$\vartheta_1(z, q) = -ie^{iz + \frac{1}{4}\pi i\tau} \vartheta_4\left(z + \frac{1}{2}\pi\tau, q\right)$$

$$= -i\sum_{n=-\infty}^{\infty} (-)^n q^{(n+\frac{1}{2})^2} e^{(2n+1)iz},$$

and hence*

$$\vartheta_1(z, q) = 2\sum_{n=0}^{\infty} (-)^n q^{(n+\frac{1}{2})^2} \sin(2n+1)z.$$

Lastly, $\vartheta_2(z, q)$ is defined by the equation

$$\vartheta_2(z, q) = \vartheta_1\left(z + \frac{1}{2}\pi, q\right) = 2\sum_{n=0}^{\infty} q^{(n+\frac{1}{2})^2} \cos(2n+1)z.$$

Writing down the series at length, we have

$$\vartheta_1(z, q) = 2q^{\frac{1}{4}}\sin z - 2q^{\frac{9}{4}}\sin 3z + 2q^{\frac{25}{4}}\sin 5z - \dots,$$

$$\vartheta_2(z, q) = 2q^{\frac{1}{4}}\cos z + 2q^{\frac{9}{4}}\cos 3z + 2q^{\frac{25}{4}}\cos 5z + \dots,$$

$$\vartheta_3(z, q) = 1 + 2q\cos 2z + 2q^4\cos 4z + 2q^9\cos 6z + \dots,$$

$$\vartheta_4(z, q) = 1 - 2q\cos 2z + 2q^4\cos 4z - 2q^9\cos 6z + \dots.$$

It is obvious that $\vartheta_1(z, q)$ is an *odd* function of z and that the other Theta-functions are *even* functions of z.

The notation which has now been introduced is a modified form of that employed in the treatise of Tannery and Molk; the only difference between it and Jacobi's notation is that $\vartheta_4(z, q)$ is written where Jacobi would have written $\vartheta(z, q)$. There are, unfortunately, several notations in use; a scheme, giving the connexions between them, will be found in § 21·9.

For brevity, the parameter q will usually not be specified, so that $\vartheta_1(z), \dots$ will be written for $\vartheta_1(z, q), \dots$. When it is desired to exhibit the dependence of a Theta-function on the parameter τ, it will be written $\vartheta(z \mid \tau)$. Also $\vartheta_2(0), \vartheta_3(0), \vartheta_4(0)$ will be replaced by $\vartheta_2, \vartheta_3, \vartheta_4$ respectively; and ϑ_1' will denote the result of making z equal to zero in the derivate of $\vartheta_1(z)$.

Example 1. Shew that

$$\vartheta_3(z, q) = \vartheta_3(2z, q^4) + \vartheta_2(2z, q^4),$$

$$\vartheta_4(z, q) = \vartheta_3(2z, q^4) - \vartheta_2(2z, q^4).$$

Example 2. Obtain the results

$$\vartheta_1(z) = -\vartheta_2(z + \tfrac{1}{2}\pi) = -iM\vartheta_3(z + \tfrac{1}{2}\pi + \tfrac{1}{2}\pi\tau) = -iM\vartheta_4(z + \tfrac{1}{2}\pi\tau),$$

$$\vartheta_2(z) = M\vartheta_3(z + \tfrac{1}{2}\pi\tau) = M\vartheta_4(z + \tfrac{1}{2}\pi + \tfrac{1}{2}\pi\tau) = \vartheta_1(z + \tfrac{1}{2}\pi),$$

$$\vartheta_3(z) = \vartheta_4(z + \tfrac{1}{2}\pi) = M\vartheta_1(z + \tfrac{1}{2}\pi + \tfrac{1}{2}\pi\tau) = M\vartheta_2(z + \tfrac{1}{2}\pi\tau),$$

$$\vartheta_4(z) = -iM\vartheta_1(z + \tfrac{1}{2}\pi\tau) = iM\vartheta_2(z + \tfrac{1}{2}\pi + \tfrac{1}{2}\pi\tau) = \vartheta_3(z + \tfrac{1}{2}\pi),$$

where $M = q^{\frac{1}{4}} e^{iz}$.

* Throughout the chapter, the many-valued function q^λ is to be interpreted to mean $\exp(\lambda\pi i\tau)$.

Example 3. Shew that the multipliers of the Theta-functions associated with the periods π, $\pi\tau$ are given by the scheme

	$\vartheta_1(z)$	$\vartheta_2(z)$	$\vartheta_3(z)$	$\vartheta_4(z)$
π	-1	-1	1	1
$\pi\tau$	$-N$	N	N	$-N$

where $N = q^{-1} e^{-2iz}$.

Example 4. If $\vartheta(z)$ be any one of the four Theta-functions and $\vartheta'(z)$ its derivate with respect to z, shew that

$$\frac{\vartheta'(z+\pi)}{\vartheta(z+\pi)} = \frac{\vartheta'(z)}{\vartheta(z)}, \qquad \frac{\vartheta'(z+\pi\tau)}{\vartheta(z+\pi\tau)} = -2i + \frac{\vartheta'(z)}{\vartheta(z)}.$$

21·12. *The zeros of the Theta-functions.*

From the quasi-periodic properties of the Theta-functions it is obvious that if $\vartheta(z)$ be any one of them, and if z_0 be any zero of $\vartheta(z)$, then

$$z_0 + m\pi + n\pi\tau$$

is also a zero of $\vartheta(z)$, for all integral values of m and n.

It will now be shewn that if C be a cell with corners t, $t+\pi$, $t+\pi+\pi\tau$, $t+\pi\tau$, then $\vartheta(z)$ has one and only one zero inside C.

Since $\vartheta(z)$ is analytic throughout the finite part of the z-plane, it follows, from § 6·31, that the number of its zeros inside C is

$$\frac{1}{2\pi i} \int_C \frac{\vartheta'(z)}{\vartheta(z)}\, dz.$$

Treating the contour after the manner of § 20·12, we see that

$$\frac{1}{2\pi i} \int_C \frac{\vartheta'(z)}{\vartheta(z)}\, dz$$

$$= \frac{1}{2\pi i} \int_t^{t+\pi} \left\{ \frac{\vartheta'(z)}{\vartheta(z)} - \frac{\vartheta'(z+\pi\tau)}{\vartheta(z+\pi\tau)} \right\} dz - \frac{1}{2\pi i} \int_t^{t+\pi\tau} \left\{ \frac{\vartheta'(z)}{\vartheta(z)} - \frac{\vartheta'(z+\pi)}{\vartheta(z+\pi)} \right\} dz$$

$$= \frac{1}{2\pi i} \int_t^{t+\pi} 2i\, dz,$$

by § 21·11, example 4. Therefore

$$\frac{1}{2\pi i} \int_C \frac{\vartheta'(z)}{\vartheta(z)}\, dz = 1,$$

that is to say, $\vartheta(z)$ has one simple zero only inside C; this is the theorem stated.

W. M. A.

Since one zero of $\vartheta_1(z)$ is obviously $z = 0$, it follows that the zeros of $\vartheta_1(z)$, $\vartheta_2(z)$, $\vartheta_3(z)$, $\vartheta_4(z)$ are the points congruent respectively to 0, $\frac{1}{2}\pi$, $\frac{1}{2}\pi + \frac{1}{2}\pi\tau$, $\frac{1}{2}\pi\tau$. The reader will observe that these four points form the corners of a parallelogram described counter-clockwise.

21·2. *The relations between the squares of the Theta-functions.*

It is evident that, if the Theta-functions be regarded as functions of a single variable z, this variable can be eliminated from the equations defining any pair of Theta-functions, the result being a relation* between the functions which might be expected, on general grounds, to be non-algebraic; there are, however, extremely simple relations connecting any *three* of the Theta-functions; these relations will now be obtained.

Each of the four functions $\vartheta_1{}^2(z)$, $\vartheta_2{}^2(z)$, $\vartheta_3{}^2(z)$, $\vartheta_4{}^2(z)$ is analytic for all values of z and has periodicity factors 1, $q^{-2}e^{-4iz}$ associated with the periods π, $\pi\tau$; and each has a double zero (and no other zeros) in any cell.

From these considerations it is obvious that, if a, b, a' and b' are suitably chosen constants, each of the functions

$$\frac{a\vartheta_1{}^2(z) + b\vartheta_4{}^2(z)}{\vartheta_2{}^2(z)}, \quad \frac{a'\vartheta_1{}^2(z) + b'\vartheta_4{}^2(z)}{\vartheta_3{}^2(z)}$$

is a *doubly-periodic function* (with periods π, $\pi\tau$) having at most only a *simple* pole in each cell. By § 20·13, such a function is merely a constant; and obviously we can adjust a, b, a', b' so as to make the constants, in each of the cases under consideration, equal to unity.

There exist, therefore, relations of the form

$$\vartheta_2{}^2(z) = a\vartheta_1{}^2(z) + b\vartheta_4{}^2(z), \quad \vartheta_3{}^2(z) = a'\vartheta_1{}^2(z) + b'\vartheta_4{}^2(z).$$

To determine a, b, a', b', give z the special values $\frac{1}{2}\pi\tau$ and 0; since

$$\vartheta_2\left(\frac{1}{2}\pi\tau\right) = q^{-\frac{1}{4}}\vartheta_3, \quad \vartheta_4\left(\frac{1}{2}\pi\tau\right) = 0, \quad \vartheta_1\left(\frac{1}{2}\pi\tau\right) = iq^{-\frac{1}{4}}\vartheta_4,$$

we have $\qquad \vartheta_3{}^2 = -a\vartheta_4{}^2, \quad \vartheta_2{}^2 = b\vartheta_4{}^2; \quad \vartheta_2{}^2 = -a'\vartheta_4{}^2, \quad \vartheta_3{}^2 = b'\vartheta_4{}^2.$

Consequently, we have obtained the relations

$$\vartheta_2{}^2(z)\,\vartheta_4{}^2 = \vartheta_4{}^2(z)\,\vartheta_2{}^2 - \vartheta_1{}^2(z)\,\vartheta_3{}^2, \quad \vartheta_3{}^2(z)\,\vartheta_4{}^2 = \vartheta_4{}^2(z)\,\vartheta_3{}^2 - \vartheta_1{}^2(z)\,\vartheta_2{}^2.$$

If we write $z + \frac{1}{2}\pi$ for z, we get the additional relations

$$\vartheta_1{}^2(z)\,\vartheta_4{}^2 = \vartheta_3{}^2(z)\,\vartheta_2{}^2 - \vartheta_2{}^2(z)\,\vartheta_3{}^2, \quad \vartheta_4{}^2(z)\,\vartheta_4{}^2 = \vartheta_3{}^2(z)\,\vartheta_3{}^2 - \vartheta_2{}^2(z)\,\vartheta_2{}^2.$$

By means of these results it is possible to express any Theta-function in terms of any other pair of Theta-functions.

---

* The analogous relation for the functions $\sin z$ and $\cos z$ is, of course, $(\sin z)^2 + (\cos z)^2 = 1$.

Corollary.   Writing $z = 0$ in the last relation, we have

$$\vartheta_2{}^4 + \vartheta_4{}^4 = \vartheta_3{}^4,$$

that is to say

$$16q\,(1 + q^{1.2} + q^{2.3} + q^{3.4} + \ldots)^4 + (1 - 2q + 2q^4 - 2q^9 + \ldots)^4 = (1 + 2q + 2q^4 + 2q^9 + \ldots)^4.$$

21·21.   *The addition-formulae for the Theta-functions.*

The results just obtained are particular cases of formulae containing two variables; these formulae are not addition-theorems in the strict sense, as they do not express Theta-functions of $z + y$ algebraically in terms of Theta-functions of z and y, but all involve Theta-functions of $z - y$ as well as of $z + y$, z and y.

To obtain one of these formulae, consider $\vartheta_3\,(z + y)\,\vartheta_3\,(z - y)$ *qua* function of z. The periodicity factors of this function associated with the periods π and $\pi\tau$ are 1 and $q^{-1}\,e^{-2i(z+y)} \cdot q^{-1}\,e^{-2i(z-y)} = q^{-2}\,e^{-4iz}$.

But the function $a\vartheta_3{}^2\,(z) + b\vartheta_1{}^2\,(z)$ has the same periodicity factors, and we can obviously choose the ratio $a : b$ so that *the doubly-periodic function*

$$\frac{a\vartheta_3{}^2\,(z) + b\vartheta_1{}^2\,(z)}{\vartheta_3\,(z + y)\,\vartheta_3\,(z - y)}$$

has no poles at the zeros of $\vartheta_3\,(z - y)$; it then has, at most, a single simple pole in any cell, namely the zero of $\vartheta_3\,(z + y)$ in that cell, and consequently (§ 20·13) it is a constant, i.e. independent of z; and, as only the ratio $a : b$ is so far fixed, we may choose a and b so that the constant is unity.

We then have to determine a and b from the identity in z,

$$a\vartheta_3{}^2\,(z) + b\vartheta_1{}^2\,(z) \equiv \vartheta_3\,(z + y)\,\vartheta_3\,(z - y).$$

To do this, put z in turn equal to 0 and $\tfrac{1}{2}\pi + \tfrac{1}{2}\pi\tau$, and we get

$$a\vartheta_3{}^2 = \vartheta_3{}^2\,(y), \qquad b\vartheta_1{}^2\left(\tfrac{1}{2}\pi + \tfrac{1}{2}\pi\tau\right) = \vartheta_3\left(\tfrac{1}{2}\pi + \tfrac{1}{2}\pi\tau + y\right)\vartheta_3\left(\tfrac{1}{2}\pi + \tfrac{1}{2}\pi\tau - y\right);$$

and so

$$a = \vartheta_3{}^2\,(y)/\vartheta_3{}^2, \qquad b = \vartheta_1{}^2\,(y)/\vartheta_3{}^2.$$

We have therefore obtained an addition-formula, namely

$$\vartheta_3\,(z + y)\,\vartheta_3\,(z - y)\,\vartheta_3{}^2 = \vartheta_3{}^2\,(y)\,\vartheta_3{}^2\,(z) + \vartheta_1{}^2\,(y)\,\vartheta_1{}^2\,(z).$$

The set of formulae, of which this is typical, will be found in examples 1 and 2 at the end of this chapter.

21·22.   *Jacobi's fundamental formulae* *.

The addition-formulae just obtained are particular cases of a set of identities first given by Jacobi, who obtained them by purely algebraical methods; each identity involves as many as four independent variables, w, x, y, z.

Let w', x', y', z' be defined in terms of w, x, y, z by the set of equations

$$\begin{aligned}
2w' &= -w + x + y + z, \\
2x' &= w - x + y + z, \\
2y' &= w + x - y + z, \\
2z' &= w + x + y - z.
\end{aligned}$$

* *Ges. Werke*, I. p. 505.

The reader will easily verify that the connexion between w, x, y, z and w', x', y', z' is a reciprocal one*.

For brevity†, write $[r]$ for $\vartheta_r(w)\,\vartheta_r(x)\,\vartheta_r(y)\,\vartheta_r(z)$ and $[r]'$ for $\vartheta_r(w')\,\vartheta_r(x')\,\vartheta_r(y')\,\vartheta_r(z')$.

Consider $[3]$, $[1]'$, $[2]'$, $[3]'$, $[4]'$ *qua* functions of z. The effect of increasing z by π or $\pi\tau$ is to transform the functions in the first row of the following table into those in the second or third row respectively.

	$[3]$	$[1]'$	$[2]'$	$[3]'$	$[4]'$
(π)	$[3]$	$-[2]'$	$-[1]'$	$[4]'$	$[3]'$
$(\pi\tau)$	$N[3]$	$-N[4]'$	$N[3]'$	$N[2]'$	$-N[1]'$

For brevity, N has been written in place of $q^{-1}e^{-2iz}$.

Hence both $-[1]'+[2]'+[3]'+[4]'$ and $[3]$ have periodicity factors 1 and N, and so their quotient is a doubly-periodic function with, at most, a single simple pole in any cell, namely the zero of $\vartheta_3(z)$ in that cell.

By § 20·13, this quotient is merely a constant, i.e. independent of z; and considerations of symmetry shew that it is also independent of w, x and y.

We have thus obtained the result

$$A[3] = -[1]'+[2]'+[3]'+[4]',$$

where A is independent of w, x, y, z; to determine A put $w=x=y=z=0$, and we get

$$A\vartheta_3^4 = \vartheta_2^4+\vartheta_3^4+\vartheta_4^4;$$

and so, by § 21·2 corollary, we see that $A=2$.

Therefore
$$2[3] = -[1]'+[2]'+[3]'+[4]' \quad\text{..................................(i).}$$

This is one of Jacobi's formulae; to obtain another, increase w, x, y, z (and therefore also w', x', y', z') by $\tfrac{1}{2}\pi$; and we get

$$2[4] = [1]'-[2]'+[3]'+[4]' \quad\text{..................................(ii).}$$

Increasing all the variables in (i) and (ii) by $\tfrac{1}{2}\pi\tau$, we obtain the further results

$$2[2] = [1]'+[2]'+[3]'-[4]' \quad\text{..................................(iii),}$$
$$2[1] = [1]'+[2]'-[3]'+[4]' \quad\text{..................................(iv).}$$

[NOTE. There are 256 expressions of the form $\vartheta_p(w)\,\vartheta_q(x)\,\vartheta_r(y)\,\vartheta_s(z)$ which can be obtained from $\vartheta_3(w)\,\vartheta_3(x)\,\vartheta_3(y)\,\vartheta_3(z)$ by increasing w, x, y, z by suitable half-periods, but only those in which the suffixes p, q, r, s are either equal in pairs or all different give rise to formulae not containing quarter-periods on the right-hand side.]

Example 1. Shew that

$$[1]+[2]=[1]'+[2]', \quad [2]+[3]=[2]'+[3]', \quad [1]+[4]=[1]'+[4]', \quad [3]+[4]=[3]'+[4]',$$
$$[1]+[3]=[2]'+[4]', \quad [2]+[4]=[1]'+[3]'.$$

* In Jacobi's work the signs of w, x', y', z' are changed throughout so that the complete symmetry of the relations is destroyed; the symmetrical forms just given are due to H. J. S. Smith, *Proc. London Math. Soc.* I. (May 21, 1866, pp. 1–12).

† The idea of this abridged notation is to be traced in H. J. S. Smith's memoir. It seems, however, not to have been used before Kronecker, *Journal für Math.* CII. (1887), pp. 260–272.

Example 2. By writing $w + \frac{1}{2}\pi$, $x + \frac{1}{2}\pi$ for w, x (and consequently $y' + \frac{1}{2}\pi$, $z' + \frac{1}{2}\pi$ for y', z'), shew that

$$[3344] + [2211] = [4433]' + [1122]',$$

where $[3344]$ means $\vartheta_3(w)\,\vartheta_3(x)\,\vartheta_4(y)\,\vartheta_4(z)$, etc.

Example 3. Shew that

$$2[1234] = [3412]' + [2143]' - [1234]' + [4321]'.$$

Example 4. Shew that

$$\vartheta_1^4(z) + \vartheta_3^4(z) = \vartheta_2^4(z) + \vartheta_4^4(z).$$

21·3. *Jacobi's expressions for the Theta-functions as infinite products**.*

We shall now establish the result

$$\vartheta_4(z) = G \prod_{n=1}^{\infty} (1 - 2q^{2n-1} \cos 2z + q^{4n-2}),$$

(where G is independent of z), and three similar formulae.

Let

$$f(z) = \prod_{n=1}^{\infty} (1 - q^{2n-1} e^{2iz}) \prod_{n=1}^{\infty} (1 - q^{2n-1} e^{-2iz});$$

each of the two products converges absolutely and uniformly in any bounded domain of values of z, by § 3·341, on account of the absolute convergence of $\sum_{n=1}^{\infty} q^{2n-1}$; hence $f(z)$ is analytic throughout the finite part of the z-plane, and so it is an integral function.

The zeros of $f(z)$ are simple zeros at the points where

$$e^{2iz} = e^{(2n+1)\pi i\tau}, \qquad (n = \ldots, -2, -1, 0, 1, 2, \ldots)$$

i.e. where $2iz = (2n+1)\,\pi i\tau + 2m\pi i$; so that $f(z)$ and $\vartheta_4(z)$ have the same zeros; consequently the quotient $\vartheta_4(z)/f(z)$ has neither zeros nor poles in the finite part of the plane.

Now, obviously $f(z + \pi) = f(z)$;

and

$$f(z + \pi\tau) = \prod_{n=1}^{\infty} (1 - q^{2n+1} e^{2iz}) \prod_{n=1}^{\infty} (1 - q^{2n-3} e^{-2iz})$$

$$= f(z)(1 - q^{-1} e^{-2iz})/(1 - qe^{2iz})$$

$$= -q^{-1} e^{-2iz} f(z).$$

That is to say $f(z)$ *and* $\vartheta_4(z)$ *have the same periodicity factors* (§ 21·11 example 3). Therefore $\vartheta_4(z)/f(z)$ is a doubly-periodic function with no zeros or poles, and so (§ 20·12) it is a constant G, say; consequently

$$\vartheta_4(z) = G \prod_{n=1}^{\infty} (1 - 2q^{2n-1} \cos 2z + q^{4n-2}).$$

[It will appear in § 21·42 that $G = \prod_{n=1}^{\infty} (1 - q^{2n})$.]

Write $z + \frac{1}{2}\pi$ for z in this result, and we get

$$\vartheta_3(z) = G \prod_{n=1}^{\infty} (1 + 2q^{2n-1} \cos 2z + q^{4n-2}).$$

* Cf. *Fundamenta Nova*, p. 145.

Also $\quad \vartheta_1(z) = -iq^{\frac{1}{4}} e^{iz} \vartheta_4 \left(z + \frac{1}{2}\pi\tau\right)$

$$= -iq^{\frac{1}{4}} e^{iz} \, G \prod_{n=1}^{\infty} (1 - q^{2n} e^{2iz}) \prod_{n=1}^{\infty} (1 - q^{2n-2} e^{-2iz})$$

$$= 2Gq^{\frac{1}{4}} \sin z \prod_{n=1}^{\infty} (1 - q^{2n} e^{2iz}) \prod_{n=1}^{\infty} (1 - q^{2n} e^{-2iz}),$$

and so $\qquad \vartheta_1(z) = 2Gq^{\frac{1}{4}} \sin z \prod_{n=1}^{\infty} (1 - 2q^{2n} \cos 2z + q^{4n})$

while $\qquad \vartheta_2(z) = \vartheta_1 \left(z + \frac{1}{2}\pi\right)$

$$= 2Gq^{\frac{1}{4}} \cos z \prod_{n=1}^{\infty} (1 + 2q^{2n} \cos 2z + q^{4n}).$$

Example. Shew that*

$$\left\{ \prod_{n=1}^{\infty} (1 - q^{2n-1}) \right\}^8 + 16q \left\{ \prod_{n=1}^{\infty} (1 + q^{2n}) \right\}^8 = \left\{ \prod_{n=1}^{\infty} (1 + q^{2n-1}) \right\}^8.$$

(Jacobi.)

21·4. *The differential equation satisfied by the Theta-functions.*

We may regard $\vartheta_3(z \,|\, \tau)$ as a function of two independent variables z and τ; and it is permissible to differentiate the series for $\vartheta_3(z \,|\, \tau)$ any number of times with regard to z or τ, on account of the uniformity of convergence of the resulting series (§ 4·7 corollary); in particular

$$\frac{\partial^2 \vartheta_3(z \,|\, \tau)}{\partial z^2} = -4 \sum_{n=-\infty}^{\infty} n^2 \exp(n^2 \pi i \tau + 2niz)$$

$$= -\frac{4}{\pi i} \frac{\partial \vartheta_3(z \,|\, \tau)}{\partial \tau}.$$

Consequently, the function $\vartheta_3(z \,|\, \tau)$ satisfies the partial differential equation

$$\frac{1}{4}\pi i \frac{\partial^2 y}{\partial z^2} + \frac{\partial y}{\partial \tau} = 0.$$

The reader will readily prove that the other three Theta-functions also satisfy this equation.

21·41. *A relation between Theta-functions of zero argument.*

The remarkable result that

$$\vartheta_1'(0) = \vartheta_2(0)\,\vartheta_3(0)\,\vartheta_4(0)$$

will now be established†. It is first necessary to obtain some formulae for differential coefficients of all the Theta-functions.

---

* Jacobi describes this result (*Fund. Nova*, p. 90) as 'aequatio identica satis abstrusa.'

† Several proofs of this important proposition have been given, but none are simple. Jacobi's original proof (*Ges. Werke*, I. pp. 515–517), though somewhat more difficult than the proof given here, is well worth study. For a different method of proof of the preliminary formula given in the text, see p. 490, example 21.

Since the resulting series converge uniformly, except near the zeros of the respective Theta-functions, we may differentiate the formulae for the logarithms of Theta-functions, obtainable from § 21·3, as many times as we please.

Denoting differentiations with regard to z by primes, we thus get

$$\vartheta_3{}'(z) = \vartheta_3(z)\left[\sum_{n=1}^{\infty}\frac{2iq^{2n-1}e^{2iz}}{1+q^{2n-1}e^{2iz}} - \sum_{n=1}^{\infty}\frac{2iq^{2n-1}e^{-2iz}}{1+q^{2n-1}e^{-2iz}}\right],$$

$$\vartheta_3{}''(z) = \vartheta_3{}'(z)\left[\sum_{n=1}^{\infty}\frac{2iq^{2n-1}e^{2iz}}{1+q^{2n-1}e^{2iz}} - \sum_{n=1}^{\infty}\frac{2iq^{2n-1}e^{-2iz}}{1+q^{2n-1}e^{-2iz}}\right]$$

$$+ \vartheta_3(z)\left[\sum_{n=1}^{\infty}\frac{(2i)^2q^{2n-1}e^{2iz}}{(1+q^{2n-1}e^{2iz})^2} + \sum_{n=1}^{\infty}\frac{(2i)^2q^{2n-1}e^{-2iz}}{(1+q^{2n-1}e^{-2iz})^2}\right].$$

Making $z \to 0$, we get

$$\vartheta_3{}'(0) = 0, \quad \vartheta_3{}''(0) = -8\vartheta_3(0)\sum_{n=1}^{\infty}\frac{q^{2n-1}}{(1+q^{2n-1})^2}.$$

In like manner,

$$\vartheta_4{}'(0) = 0, \quad \vartheta_4{}''(0) = 8\vartheta_4(0)\sum_{n=1}^{\infty}\frac{q^{2n-1}}{(1-q^{2n-1})^2},$$

$$\vartheta_2{}'(0) = 0, \quad \vartheta_2{}''(0) = \vartheta_2(0)\left[-1 - 8\sum_{n=1}^{\infty}\frac{q^{2n}}{(1+q^{2n})^2}\right];$$

and, if we write $\vartheta_1(z) = \sin z \,.\, \phi(z)$, we get

$$\phi'(0) = 0, \quad \phi''(0) = 8\phi(0)\sum_{n=1}^{\infty}\frac{q^{2n}}{(1-q^{2n})^2}.$$

If, however, we differentiate the equation $\vartheta_1(z) = \sin z \,.\, \phi(z)$ three times, we get

$$\vartheta_1{}'(0) = \phi(0), \quad \vartheta_1{}'''(0) = 3\phi''(0) - \phi(0).$$

Therefore
$$\frac{\vartheta_1{}'''(0)}{\vartheta_1{}'(0)} = 24\sum_{n=1}^{\infty}\frac{q^{2n}}{(1-q^{2n})^2} - 1;$$

and

$$1 + \frac{\vartheta_2{}''(0)}{\vartheta_2(0)} + \frac{\vartheta_3{}''(0)}{\vartheta_3(0)} + \frac{\vartheta_4{}''(0)}{\vartheta_4(0)}$$

$$= 8\left[-\sum_{n=1}^{\infty}\frac{q^{2n}}{(1+q^{2n})^2} - \sum_{n=1}^{\infty}\frac{q^{2n-1}}{(1+q^{2n-1})^2} + \sum_{n=1}^{\infty}\frac{q^{2n-1}}{(1-q^{2n-1})^2}\right]$$

$$= 8\left[-\sum_{n=1}^{\infty}\frac{q^{n}}{(1+q^{n})^2} + \sum_{n=1}^{\infty}\frac{q^{n}}{(1-q^{n})^2} - \sum_{n=1}^{\infty}\frac{q^{2n}}{(1-q^{2n})^2}\right],$$

on combining the first two series and writing the third as the difference of two series. If we add corresponding terms of the first two series in the last line, we get at once

$$1 + \frac{\vartheta_2{}''(0)}{\vartheta_2(0)} + \frac{\vartheta_3{}''(0)}{\vartheta_3(0)} + \frac{\vartheta_4{}''(0)}{\vartheta_4(0)} = 24\sum_{n=1}^{\infty}\frac{q^{2n}}{(1-q^{2n})^2} = 1 + \frac{\vartheta_1{}'''(0)}{\vartheta_1{}'(0)}.$$

Utilising the differential equations of § 21·4, this may be written

$$\frac{1}{\vartheta_1'(0\,|\,\tau)}\frac{d\vartheta_1'(0\,|\,\tau)}{d\tau}$$

$$= \frac{1}{\vartheta_2(0\,|\,\tau)}\frac{d\vartheta_2(0\,|\,\tau)}{d\tau} + \frac{1}{\vartheta_3(0\,|\,\tau)}\frac{d\vartheta_3(0\,|\,\tau)}{d\tau} + \frac{1}{\vartheta_4(0\,|\,\tau)}\frac{d\vartheta_4(0\,|\,\tau)}{d\tau}.$$

Integrating with regard to τ, we get

$$\vartheta_1'(0,\,q) = C\vartheta_2(0,\,q)\,\vartheta_3(0,\,q)\,\vartheta_4(0,\,q),$$

where C is a constant (independent of q). To determine C, make $q \to 0$; since

$$\lim_{q\to 0} q^{-\frac{1}{4}}\vartheta_1' = 2, \quad \lim_{q\to 0} q^{-\frac{1}{4}}\vartheta_2 = 2, \quad \lim_{q\to 0}\vartheta_3 = 1, \quad \lim_{q\to 0}\vartheta_4 = 1,$$

we see that $C = 1$; and so

$$\vartheta_1' = \vartheta_2\vartheta_3\vartheta_4,$$

which is the result stated.

21·42. *The value of the constant G.*

From the result just obtained, we can at once deduce the value of the constant G which was introduced in § 21·3.

For, by the formulae of that section,

$$\vartheta_1' = \phi(0) = 2q^{\frac{1}{4}}G\prod_{n=1}^{\infty}(1-q^{2n})^2, \quad \vartheta_2 = 2q^{\frac{1}{4}}G\prod_{n=1}^{\infty}(1+q^{2n})^2,$$

$$\vartheta_3 = G\prod_{n=1}^{\infty}(1+q^{2n-1})^2, \quad \vartheta_4 = G\prod_{n=1}^{\infty}(1-q^{2n-1})^2,$$

and·so, by § 21·41, we have

$$\prod_{n=1}^{\infty}(1-q^{2n})^2 = G^2\prod_{n=1}^{\infty}(1+q^{2n})^2\prod_{n=1}^{\infty}(1+q^{2n-1})^2\prod_{n=1}^{\infty}(1-q^{2n-1})^2.$$

Now all the products converge absolutely, since $|q| < 1$, and so the following rearrangements are permissible:

$$\left\{\prod_{n=1}^{\infty}(1-q^{2n-1})\prod_{n=1}^{\infty}(1-q^{2n})\right\} \cdot \left\{\prod_{n=1}^{\infty}(1+q^{2n-1})\prod_{n=1}^{\infty}(1+q^{2n})\right\}$$

$$= \prod_{n=1}^{\infty}(1-q^n)\prod_{n=1}^{\infty}(1+q^n)$$

$$= \prod_{n=1}^{\infty}(1-q^{2n}),$$

the first step following from the consideration that all positive integers are comprised under the forms $2n-1$ and $2n$.

Hence the equation determining G is

$$\prod_{n=1}^{\infty}(1-q^{2n})^2 = G^2,$$

and so $G = \pm\prod_{n=1}^{\infty}(1-q^{2n})$.

To determine the ambiguity in sign, we observe that G is an analytic function of q (and consequently one-valued) throughout the domain $|q| < 1$; and from the product for $\vartheta_3(z)$, we see that $G \to 1$ as $q \to 0$. Hence the plus sign must always be taken; and so we have established the result

$$G = \prod_{n=1}^{\infty} (1 - q^{2n}).$$

Example 1.   Shew that $\vartheta_1' = 2q^{\frac{1}{4}} G^3.$

Example 2.   Shew that

$$\vartheta_4 = \prod_{n=1}^{\infty} \{(1 - q^{2n-1})(1 - q^n)\}.$$

Example 3.   Shew that

$$1 + 2 \sum_{n=1}^{\infty} q^{n^2} = \prod_{n=1}^{\infty} \{(1 - q^{2n})(1 + q^{2n-1})^2\}.$$

21·43.   *Connexion of the Sigma-function with the Theta-functions.*

It has been seen (§ 20·421 example 3) that the function $\sigma(z \mid \omega_1, \omega_2)$, formed with the periods $2\omega_1$, $2\omega_2$, is expressible in the form

$$\sigma(z) = \frac{2\omega_1}{\pi} \exp\left(\frac{\eta_1 z^2}{2\omega_1}\right) \sin\left(\frac{\pi z}{2\omega_1}\right) \prod_{n=1}^{\infty} \left\{ \left(1 - 2q^{2n} \cos\frac{\pi z}{\omega_1} + q^{4n}\right) (1 - q^{2n})^{-2} \right\},$$

where $q = \exp(\pi i \omega_2 / \omega_1)$.

If we compare this result with the product of § 21·4 for $\vartheta_1(z \mid \tau)$, we see at once that

$$\sigma(z) = \frac{2\omega_1}{\pi} \exp\left(\frac{\eta_1 z^2}{2\omega_1}\right) \cdot \frac{1}{2} q^{-\frac{1}{4}} \prod_{n=1}^{\infty} (1 - q^{2n})^{-3} \vartheta_1\left(\frac{\pi z}{2\omega_1} \,\middle|\, \frac{\omega_2}{\omega_1}\right).$$

To express η_1 in terms of Theta-functions, take logarithms and differentiate twice, so that

$$-\wp(z) = \frac{\eta_1}{\omega_1} - \left(\frac{\pi}{2\omega_1}\right)^2 \operatorname{cosec}^2\left(\frac{\pi z}{2\omega_1}\right) + \left(\frac{\pi}{2\omega_1}\right)^2 \left[\frac{\phi''(\nu)}{\phi(\nu)} - \left\{\frac{\phi'(\nu)}{\phi(\nu)}\right\}^2\right],$$

where $\nu = \frac{1}{2}\pi z/\omega_1$ and the function ϕ is that defined in § 21·41.

Expanding in ascending powers of z and equating the terms independent of z in this result, we get

$$0 = \frac{\eta_1}{\omega_1} - \frac{1}{3}\left(\frac{\pi}{2\omega_1}\right)^2 + \left(\frac{\pi}{2\omega_1}\right)^2 \frac{\phi''(0)}{\phi(0)},$$

and so

$$\eta_1 = -\frac{\pi^2}{12\omega_1} \frac{\vartheta_1'''}{\vartheta_1'}.$$

Consequently $\sigma(z \mid \omega_1, \omega_2)$ can be expressed in terms of Theta-functions by the formula

$$\sigma(z \mid \omega_1, \omega_2) = \frac{2\omega_1}{\pi \vartheta_1'} \exp\left(-\frac{\nu^2 \vartheta_1'''}{6\vartheta_1'}\right) \vartheta_1\left(\nu \,\middle|\, \frac{\omega_2}{\omega_1}\right),$$

where $\nu = \frac{1}{2}\pi z/\omega_1$.

Example.   Prove that

$$\eta_2 = -\left(\frac{\pi^2 \omega_2 \vartheta_1'''}{12\omega_1^2 \vartheta_1'} + \frac{\pi i}{2\omega_1}\right).$$

21·5.   *The expression of elliptic functions by means of Theta-functions.*

It has just been seen that Theta-functions are substantially equivalent to Sigma-functions, and so, corresponding to the formulae of §§ 20·5–20·53, there will exist expressions for elliptic functions in terms of Theta-functions.

From the theoretical point of view, the formulae of §§ 20·5–20·53 are the more important on account of their symmetry in the periods, but in practice the Theta-function formulae have two advantages, (i) that Theta-functions are more readily computed than Sigma-functions, (ii) that the Theta-functions have a specially simple behaviour with respect to the real period, which is generally the significant period in applications of elliptic functions in Applied Mathematics.

Let $f(z)$ be an elliptic function with periods $2\omega_1$, $2\omega_2$; let a fundamental set of zeros $(\alpha_1, \alpha_2, \ldots \alpha_n)$ and poles $(\beta_1, \beta_2, \ldots \beta_n)$ be chosen, so that

$$\sum_{r=1}^{n} (\alpha_r - \beta_r) = 0,$$

as in § 20·53.

Then, by the methods of § 20·53, the reader will at once verify that

$$f(z) = A_3 \prod_{r=1}^{n} \left\{ \vartheta_1 \left(\frac{\pi z - \pi \alpha_r}{2\omega_1} \middle| \frac{\omega_2}{\omega_1} \right) \div \vartheta_1 \left(\frac{\pi z - \pi \beta_r}{2\omega_1} \middle| \frac{\omega_2}{\omega_1} \right) \right\},$$

where A_3 is a constant; and if

$$\sum_{m=1}^{m_r} A_{r,m} (z - \beta_r)^{-m}$$

be the principal part of $f(z)$ at its pole β_r, then, by the methods of § 20·52,

$$f(z) = A_2 + \sum_{r=1}^{n} \left\{ \sum_{m=1}^{m_r} \frac{(-)^{m-1} A_{r,m}}{(m-1)!} \frac{d^m}{dz^m} \log \vartheta_1 \left(\frac{\pi z - \pi \beta_r}{2\omega_1} \middle| \frac{\omega_2}{\omega_1} \right) \right\},$$

where A_2 is a constant.

This formula is important in connexion with the integration of elliptic functions. An example of an application of the formula to a dynamical problem will be found in § 22·741.

Example. Shew that

$$\frac{\vartheta_3^2(z)}{\vartheta_1^2(z)} = -\frac{\vartheta_3^2}{\vartheta_1'^2} \frac{d}{dz} \frac{\vartheta_1'(z)}{\vartheta_1(z)} + \frac{\vartheta_3 \vartheta_3''}{\vartheta_1'^3},$$

and deduce that

$$\int_z^{\frac{1}{2}\pi} \frac{\vartheta_3^2(z)}{\vartheta_1^2(z)} \, dz = \frac{\vartheta_3^2}{\vartheta_1'^2} \frac{\vartheta_1'(z)}{\vartheta_1(z)} + \left(\frac{1}{2}\pi - z \right) \frac{\vartheta_3 \vartheta_3''}{\vartheta_1'^3}.$$

21·51. *Jacobi's imaginary transformation.*

If an elliptic function be constructed with periods $2\omega_1$, $2\omega_2$, such that

$$I(\omega_2/\omega_1) > 0,$$

it might be convenient to regard the periods as being $2\omega_2$, $-2\omega_1$; for these numbers are periods and, if $I(\omega_2/\omega_1) > 0$, then also $I(-\omega_1/\omega_2) > 0$. In the case of the elliptic functions which have been considered up to this point, the periods have appeared in a symmetrical manner and nothing is gained by this point of view. But in the case of the Theta-functions, which are only quasi-periodic, the behaviour of the function with respect to the real period π is quite different from its behaviour with respect to the complex period $\pi\tau$. Consequently, in view of the result of § 21·43, we may expect to obtain transformations of Theta-functions in which the period-ratios of the two Theta-functions involved are respectively τ and $-1/\tau$.

The transformations of the four Theta-functions were first obtained by Jacobi[*], who obtained them from the theory of elliptic functions; but Poisson[†] had previously obtained a formula identical with one of the transformations and the other three transformations can be obtained from this one by elementary algebra. A direct proof of the transformations is due to Landsberg, who used the methods of contour integration[‡]. The investigation of Jacobi's formulae, which we shall now give, is based on Liouville's theorem; the precise formula which we shall establish is

$$\vartheta_3(z \mid \tau) = (-i\tau)^{-\frac{1}{2}} \exp\left(\frac{z^2}{\pi i \tau}\right) \cdot \vartheta_3\left(\frac{z}{\tau} \mid -\frac{1}{\tau}\right),$$

where $(-i\tau)^{-\frac{1}{2}}$ is to be interpreted by the convention $|\arg(-i\tau)| < \frac{1}{2}\pi$.

For brevity, we shall write $-1/\tau \equiv \tau'$, $q' = \exp(\pi i \tau')$.

The only zeros of $\vartheta_3(z \mid \tau)$ and $\vartheta_3(\tau'z \mid \tau')$ are simple zeros at the points at which

$$z = m\pi + n\pi\tau + \tfrac{1}{2}\pi + \tfrac{1}{2}\pi\tau, \quad \tau'z = m'\pi + n'\pi\tau' + \tfrac{1}{2}\pi + \tfrac{1}{2}\pi\tau'$$

respectively, where m, n, m', n' take all integer values; taking $m' = -n-1$, $n' = m$, we see that the quotient

$$\psi(z) \equiv \exp\left(\frac{z^2}{\pi i \tau}\right) \vartheta_3\left(\frac{z}{\tau} \mid -\frac{1}{\tau}\right) \div \vartheta_3(z \mid \tau)$$

is an integral function with no zeros.

Also $\qquad \psi(z + \pi\tau) \div \psi(z) = \exp\left(\frac{2z\pi\tau + \pi^2\tau^2}{\pi i \tau}\right) \div q^{-1}e^{-2iz} = 1,$

while $\qquad \psi(z - \pi) \div \psi(z) = \exp\left(\frac{-2z\pi + \pi^2}{\pi i \tau}\right) \times q'^{-1}e^{-2iz/\tau} = 1.$

Consequently $\psi(z)$ is a doubly-periodic function with no zeros or poles; and so (§ 20·12) $\psi(z)$ must be a constant, A (independent of z).

Thus. $\qquad A\vartheta_3(z \mid \tau) = \exp(i\tau'z^2/\pi)\, \vartheta_3(z\tau' \mid \tau');$

and writing $z + \tfrac{1}{2}\pi$, $z + \tfrac{1}{2}\pi\tau$, $z + \tfrac{1}{2}\pi + \tfrac{1}{2}\pi\tau$ in turn for z, we easily get

$$A\vartheta_4(z \mid \tau) = \qquad \exp(i\tau'z^2/\pi)\, \vartheta_2(z\tau' \mid \tau'),$$
$$A\vartheta_2(z \mid \tau) = \qquad \exp(i\tau'z^2/\pi)\, \vartheta_4(z\tau' \mid \tau'),$$
$$A\vartheta_1(z \mid \tau) = -i \exp(i\tau'z^2/\pi)\, \vartheta_1(z\tau' \mid \tau').$$

---

[*] *Journal für Math.* III. (1828), pp. 403–404 [*Ges. Werke*, I. (1881), pp. 264–265].

[†] *Mém. de l'Acad. des Sci.* VI. (1827), p. 592; the special case of the formula in which $z=0$ had been given earlier by Poisson, *Journal de l'École polytechnique*, XII. (cahier XIX), (1823), p. 420.

[‡] This method is indicated in example 17 of Chapter VI, p. 124. See Landsberg, *Journal für Math.* CXI. (1893), pp. 234–253.

We still have to prove that $A = (-i\tau)^{\frac{1}{2}}$; to do so, differentiate the last equation and then put $z = 0$; we get

$$A\vartheta_1'(0\,|\,\tau) = -i\tau'\,\vartheta_1'(0\,|\,\tau').$$

But $\vartheta_1'(0\,|\,\tau) = \vartheta_2(0\,|\,\tau)\,\vartheta_3(0\,|\,\tau)\,\vartheta_4(0\,|\,\tau)$

and $\vartheta_1'(0\,|\,\tau') = \vartheta_2(0\,|\,\tau')\,\vartheta_3(0\,|\,\tau')\,\vartheta_4(0\,|\,\tau');$

on dividing these results and substituting, we at once get $A^{-2} = -i\tau'$, and so

$$A = \pm\,(-i\tau)^{\frac{1}{2}}.$$

To determine the ambiguity in sign, we observe that

$$A\vartheta_3(0\,|\,\tau) = \vartheta_3(0\,|\,\tau'),$$

both the Theta-functions being analytic functions of τ when $I(\tau) > 0$; thus A is analytic and one-valued in the upper half τ-plane. Since the Theta-functions are both positive when τ is a pure imaginary, the *plus* sign must then be taken. Hence, by the theory of analytic continuation, we *always* have

$$A = +\,(-i\tau)^{\frac{1}{2}};$$

this gives the transformation stated.

It has thus been shewn that

$$\sum_{n=-\infty}^{\infty} e^{n^2\pi i\tau + 2niz} = \frac{1}{\sqrt{(-i\tau)}} \sum_{n=-\infty}^{\infty} e^{(z-n\pi)^2/(\pi i\tau)}.$$

Example 1.   Shew that

$$\frac{\vartheta_4(0\,|\,\tau)}{\vartheta_3(0\,|\,\tau)} = \frac{\vartheta_2(0\,|\,\tau')}{\vartheta_3(0\,|\,\tau')}$$

when $\tau\tau' = -1$.

Example 2.   Shew that

$$\frac{\vartheta_2(0\,|\,\tau+1)}{\vartheta_3(0\,|\,\tau+1)} = e^{\frac{1}{4}\pi i}\frac{\vartheta_2(0\,|\,\tau)}{\vartheta_4(0\,|\,\tau)}.$$

Example 3.   Shew that

$$\prod_{n=1}^{\infty}\left(\frac{1-q^{2n-1}}{1+q^{2n-1}}\right) = \pm 2^{\frac{1}{2}}\,q'^{\frac{1}{8}}\prod_{n=1}^{\infty}\left(\frac{1+q'^{2n}}{1+q'^{2n-1}}\right);$$

and shew that the plus sign should be taken.

21·52.   *Landen's type of transformation.*

A transformation of elliptic integrals (§ 22·7), which is of historical interest, is due to Landen (§ 22·42); this transformation follows at once from a transformation connecting Theta-functions with parameters τ and 2τ, namely

$$\frac{\vartheta_3(z\,|\,\tau)\,\vartheta_4(z\,|\,\tau)}{\vartheta_4(2z\,|\,2\tau)} = \frac{\vartheta_3(0\,|\,\tau)\,\vartheta_4(0\,|\,\tau)}{\vartheta_4(0\,|\,2\tau)},$$

which we shall now prove.

The zeros of $\vartheta_3(z\,|\,\tau)\,\vartheta_4(z\,|\,\tau)$ are simple zeros at the points where $z = \left(m+\frac{1}{2}\right)\pi + \left(n+\frac{1}{2}\right)\pi\tau$ and where $z = m\pi + \left(n+\frac{1}{2}\right)\pi\tau$, where m and n

take all integral values; these are the points where $2z = m\pi + \left(n + \frac{1}{2}\right)\pi \cdot 2\tau$, which are the zeros of $\vartheta_4(2z \,|\, 2\tau)$. Hence the quotient

$$\frac{\vartheta_3(z\,|\,\tau)\,\vartheta_4(z\,|\,\tau)}{\vartheta_4(2z\,|\,2\tau)}$$

has no zeros or poles. Moreover, associated with the periods π and $\pi\tau$, it has multipliers 1 and $(q^{-1}e^{-2iz})\,(-q^{-1}e^{-2iz}) \div (-q^{-2}e^{-4iz}) = 1$; it is therefore a doubly-periodic function, and is consequently (§ 20·12) a constant. The value of this constant may be obtained by putting $z = 0$ and we then have the result stated.

If we write $z + \frac{1}{2}\pi\tau$ for z, we get a corresponding result for the other Theta-functions, namely

$$\frac{\vartheta_2(z\,|\,\tau)\,\vartheta_1(z\,|\,\tau)}{\vartheta_1(2z\,|\,2\tau)} = \frac{\vartheta_3(0\,|\,\tau)\,\vartheta_4(0\,|\,\tau)}{\vartheta_4(0\,|\,2\tau)}.$$

21·6. *The differential equations satisfied by quotients of Theta-functions.*

From § 21·11 example 3, it is obvious that the function

$$\vartheta_1(z) \div \vartheta_4(z)$$

has periodicity factors $-1, +1$ associated with the periods $\pi, \pi\tau$ respectively; and consequently its derivative

$$\{\vartheta_1'(z)\,\vartheta_4(z) - \vartheta_4'(z)\,\vartheta_1(z)\} \div \vartheta_4^2(z)$$

has the same periodicity factors.

But it is easy to verify that $\vartheta_2(z)\,\vartheta_3(z)/\vartheta_4^2(z)$ has periodicity factors -1, $+1$; and consequently, if $\phi(z)$ be defined as the quotient

$$\{\vartheta_1'(z)\,\vartheta_4(z) - \vartheta_4'(z)\,\vartheta_1(z)\} \div \{\vartheta_2(z)\,\vartheta_3(z)\},$$

then $\phi(z)$ is doubly-periodic with periods π and $\pi\tau$; and the only possible poles of $\phi(z)$ are simple poles at points congruent to $\frac{1}{2}\pi$ and $\frac{1}{2}\pi + \frac{1}{2}\pi\tau$.

Now consider $\phi\left(z + \frac{1}{2}\pi\tau\right)$; from the relations of § 21·11, namely

$$\vartheta_1\left(z + \frac{1}{2}\pi\tau\right) = iq^{-\frac{1}{4}}e^{-iz}\vartheta_4(z), \quad \vartheta_4\left(z + \frac{1}{2}\pi\tau\right) = iq^{-\frac{1}{4}}e^{-iz}\vartheta_1(z),$$

$$\vartheta_2\left(z + \frac{1}{2}\pi\tau\right) = q^{-\frac{1}{4}}e^{-iz}\vartheta_3(z), \quad \vartheta_3\left(z + \frac{1}{2}\pi\tau\right) = q^{-\frac{1}{4}}e^{-iz}\vartheta_2(z),$$

we easily see that

$$\phi\left(z + \frac{1}{2}\pi\tau\right) = \{-\vartheta_4'(z)\,\vartheta_1(z) + \vartheta_1'(z)\,\vartheta_4(z)\} \div \{\vartheta_3(z)\,\vartheta_2(z)\}.$$

Hence $\phi(z)$ is doubly-periodic with periods π and $\frac{1}{2}\pi\tau$; *and, relative to these periods, the only possible poles of $\phi(z)$ are simple poles at points congruent to $\frac{1}{2}\pi$.*

Therefore (§ 20·12), $\phi(z)$ is a constant; and making $z \to 0$, we see that the value of this constant is $\{\vartheta_1' \vartheta_4\} \div \{\vartheta_2 \vartheta_3\} = \vartheta_4{}^2$.

We have therefore established the important result that

$$\frac{d}{dz} \left\{ \frac{\vartheta_1(z)}{\vartheta_4(z)} \right\} = \vartheta_4{}^2 \frac{\vartheta_2(z)}{\vartheta_4(z)} \cdot \frac{\vartheta_3(z)}{\vartheta_4(z)};$$

writing $\xi \equiv \vartheta_1(z)/\vartheta_4(z)$ and making use of the results of § 21·2, we see that

$$\left(\frac{d\xi}{dz} \right)^2 = (\vartheta_2{}^2 - \xi^2 \vartheta_3{}^2)(\vartheta_3{}^2 - \xi^2 \vartheta_2{}^2).$$

This differential equation possesses the solution $\vartheta_1(z)/\vartheta_4(z)$. It is not difficult to see that the general solution is $\pm \vartheta_1(z+\alpha)/\vartheta_4(z+\alpha)$ where α is the constant of integration; since this quotient changes sign when α is increased by π, the negative sign may be suppressed without affecting the generality of the solution.

Example 1. Shew that
$$\frac{d}{dz} \left\{ \frac{\vartheta_2(z)}{\vartheta_4(z)} \right\} = -\vartheta_3{}^2 \frac{\vartheta_1(z)}{\vartheta_4(z)} \frac{\vartheta_3(z)}{\vartheta_4(z)}.$$

Example 2. Shew that
$$\frac{d}{dz} \left\{ \frac{\vartheta_3(z)}{\vartheta_4(z)} \right\} = -\vartheta_2{}^2 \frac{\vartheta_1(z)}{\vartheta_4(z)} \frac{\vartheta_2(z)}{\vartheta_4(z)}.$$

21·61. *The genesis of the Jacobian Elliptic function* sn u.

The differential equation

$$\left(\frac{d\xi}{dz} \right)^2 = (\vartheta_2{}^2 - \xi^2 \vartheta_3{}^2)(\vartheta_3{}^2 - \xi^2 \vartheta_2{}^2),$$

which was obtained in § 21·6, may be brought to a canonical form by a slight change of variable.

Write†
$$\xi \vartheta_3 / \vartheta_2 = y, \quad z \vartheta_3{}^2 = u;$$

then, if $k^{\frac{1}{2}}$ be written in place of ϑ_2/ϑ_3, the equation determining y in terms of u is

$$\left(\frac{dy}{du} \right)^2 = (1 - y^2)(1 - k^2 y^2).$$

This differential equation has the particular solution

$$y = \frac{\vartheta_3}{\vartheta_2} \frac{\vartheta_1(u \vartheta_3{}^{-2})}{\vartheta_4(u \vartheta_3{}^{-2})}.$$

The function of u on the right has multipliers $-1, +1$ associated with the periods $\pi \vartheta_3{}^2, \pi\tau \vartheta_3{}^2$; it is therefore a doubly-periodic function with periods $2\pi \vartheta_3{}^2, \pi\tau \vartheta_3{}^2$. In any cell, it has two simple poles at the points congruent to $\frac{1}{2}\pi\tau \vartheta_3{}^2$ and $\pi \vartheta_3{}^2 + \frac{1}{2}\pi\tau \vartheta_3{}^2$; and, on account of the nature of the quasi-periodicity of y, the residues at these points are equal and opposite in sign; the zeros of the function are the points congruent to 0 and $\pi \vartheta_3{}^2$.

---

* Jacobi and other early writers used the notation *sin am* in place of sn.

† Notice, from the formulae of § 21·3, that $\vartheta_2 \neq 0$, $\vartheta_3 \neq 0$ when $|q| < 1$, except when $q = 0$, in which case the Theta-functions degenerate; the substitutions are therefore legitimate.

It is customary to regard y as depending on k rather than on q; and to exhibit y as a function of u and k, we write
$$y = \operatorname{sn}(u, k),$$
or simply
$$y = \operatorname{sn} u.$$

It is now evident that $\operatorname{sn}(u, k)$ is an elliptic function of the second of the types described in § 20·13; when $q \to 0$ (so that $k \to 0$), it is easy to see that $\operatorname{sn}(u, k) \to \sin u$.

The constant k is called the *modulus*; if $k'^{\frac{1}{2}} = \vartheta_4/\vartheta_3$, so that $k^2 + k'^2 = 1$, k' is called the *complementary modulus*. The quasi-periods $\pi\vartheta_3^2$, $\pi\tau\vartheta_3^2$ are usually written $2K$, $2iK'$, so that $\operatorname{sn}(u, k)$ has periods $4K$, $2iK'$.

From § 21·51, we see that $2K' = \pi\vartheta_3^2(0 \mid \tau')$, so that K' is the same function of τ' as K is of τ, when $\tau\tau' = -1$.

Example 1. Shew that
$$\frac{d}{dz} \frac{\vartheta_2(z)}{\vartheta_4(z)} = -\vartheta_3^2 \frac{\vartheta_1(z)}{\vartheta_4(z)} \frac{\vartheta_3(z)}{\vartheta_4(z)};$$
and deduce that, if $y = \dfrac{\vartheta_4}{\vartheta_2} \dfrac{\vartheta_2(z)}{\vartheta_4(z)}$, and $u = z\vartheta_3^2$, then
$$\left(\frac{dy}{du}\right)^2 = (1 - u^2)(k'^2 + k^2 u^2).$$

Example 2. Shew that
$$\frac{d}{dz} \frac{\vartheta_3(z)}{\vartheta_4(z)} = -\vartheta_2^2 \frac{\vartheta_1(z)}{\vartheta_4(z)} \frac{\vartheta_2(z)}{\vartheta_4(z)};$$
and deduce that, if $y = \dfrac{\vartheta_4}{\vartheta_3} \dfrac{\vartheta_3(z)}{\vartheta_4(z)}$, and $u = z\vartheta_3^2$, then
$$\left(\frac{dy}{du}\right)^2 = (1 - u^2)(u^2 - k'^2).$$

Example 3. Obtain the following results :
$$\left(\frac{2kK}{\pi}\right)^{\frac{1}{2}} = \vartheta_2 = 2q^{\frac{1}{4}}(1 + q^2 + q^6 + q^{12} + q^{20} + \dots),$$
$$\left(\frac{2K}{\pi}\right)^{\frac{1}{2}} = \vartheta_3 = 1 + 2q + 2q^4 + 2q^9 + \dots,$$
$$\left(\frac{2k'K}{\pi}\right)^{\frac{1}{2}} = \vartheta_4 = 1 - 2q + 2q^4 + 2q^9 - \dots,$$
$$K' = K\pi^{-1}\log(1/q).$$

[These results are convenient for calculating k, k', K, K' when q is given.]

21·62. *Jacobi's earlier notation*.   The Theta-function $\Theta(u)$ and the Eta-function* H (u).

The presence of the factors ϑ_3^{-2} in the expression for $\operatorname{sn}(u, k)$ renders it sometimes desirable to use the notation which Jacobi employed in the *Fundamenta Nova*, and subsequently discarded. The function which is of primary importance with this notation is $\Theta(u)$, defined by the equation
$$\Theta(u) = \vartheta_4(u\vartheta_3^{-2} \mid \tau),$$
so that the periods associated with $\Theta(u)$ are $2K$ and $2iK'$.

* This is the notation employed throughout the *Fundamenta Nova*.

The function $\Theta(u + K)$ then replaces $\vartheta_3(z)$; and in place of $\vartheta_1(z)$ we have the function $H(u)$ defined by the equation

$$H(u) = -iq^{-\frac{1}{4}}e^{i\pi u/(2K)}\Theta(u + iK') = \vartheta_1(u\vartheta_3^{-2} \mid \tau),$$

and $\vartheta_2(z)$ is replaced by $H(u + K)$.

The reader will have no difficulty in translating the analysis of this chapter into Jacobi's earlier notation.

Example 1. If $\Theta'(u) = \dfrac{d\Theta(u)}{du}$, shew that the singularities of $\dfrac{\Theta'(u)}{\Theta(u)}$ are simple poles at the points congruent to iK' (mod $2K$, $2iK'$); and the residue at each singularity is 1.

Example 2. Shew that

$$H'(0) = \tfrac{1}{2}\pi K^{-1}H(K)\Theta(0)\Theta(K).$$

21·7. *The problem of Inversion.*

Up to the present, the Jacobian elliptic function $\mathrm{sn}(u, k)$ has been implicitly regarded as depending on the parameter q rather than on the modulus k; and it has been shewn that it satisfies the differential equation

$$\left(\frac{d\,\mathrm{sn}\,u}{du}\right)^2 = (1 - \mathrm{sn}^2 u)(1 - k^2\,\mathrm{sn}^2 u),$$

where
$$k^2 = \vartheta_2^4(0, q)/\vartheta_3^4(0, q).$$

But, in those problems of Applied Mathematics in which elliptic functions occur, we have to deal with the solution of the differential equation

$$\left(\frac{dy}{du}\right)^2 = (1 - y^2)(1 - k^2 y^2)$$

in which the *modulus* k is given, and we have no *a priori* knowledge of the value of q; and, to prove the existence of an analytic function $\mathrm{sn}(u, k)$ which satisfies this equation, we have to shew that a number τ exists* such that

$$k^2 = \vartheta_2^4(0 \mid \tau)/\vartheta_3^4(0 \mid \tau).$$

When this number τ has been shewn to exist, the function $\mathrm{sn}(u, k)$ can be constructed as a quotient of Theta-functions, satisfying the differential equation and possessing the properties of being doubly-periodic and analytic except at simple poles; and also

$$\lim_{u \to 0} \mathrm{sn}(u, k)/u = 1.$$

That is to say, we can *invert* the integral

$$u = \int_0^y \frac{dt}{(1 - t^2)^{\frac{1}{2}}(1 - k^2 t^2)^{\frac{1}{2}}},$$

so as to obtain the equation $y = \mathrm{sn}(u, k)$.

---

* The existence of a number τ, for which $I(\tau) > 0$, involves the existence of a number q such that $|q| < 1$. An alternative procedure would be to discuss the differential equation directly, after the manner of Chapter x.

The difficulty, of course, arises in shewing that the equation

$$c = \vartheta_2^4(0 \mid \tau)/\vartheta_3^4(0 \mid \tau),$$

(where c has been written for k^2), has a solution.

When* $0 < c < 1$, it is easy to shew that a solution exists. From the identity given in § 21·2 corollary, it is evident that it is sufficient to prove the existence of a solution of the equation

$$1 - c = \vartheta_4^4(0 \mid \tau)/\vartheta_3^4(0 \mid \tau),$$

which may be written $\quad 1 - c = \prod_{n=1}^{\infty} \left(\dfrac{1 - q^{2n-1}}{1 + q^{2n-1}}\right)^8.$

Now, as q increases from 0 to 1, the product on the right is continuous and steadily decreases from 1 to 0; and so (§ 3·63) it passes through the value $1-c$ once and only once. Consequently a solution of the equation in τ exists and the problem of inversion may be regarded as solved.

21·71. *The problem of inversion for complex values of c. The modular functions* $f(\tau)$, $g(\tau)$, $h(\tau)$.

The problem of inversion may be regarded as a problem of Integral Calculus, and it may be proved, by somewhat lengthy algebraical investigations involving a discussion of the behaviour of $\int_0^y (1 - t^2)^{-\frac{1}{2}} (1 - k^2 t^2)^{-\frac{1}{2}} dt$, when y lies on a 'Riemann surface,' that the problem of inversion possesses a solution. For an exhaustive discussion of this aspect of the problem, the reader is referred to Hancock, *Elliptic Functions*, I. (New York, 1910).

It is, however, more in accordance with the spirit of this work to prove by Cauchy's method (§ 6·31) that the equation $c = \vartheta_2^4(0 \mid \tau)/\vartheta_3^4(0 \mid \tau)$ has one root lying in a certain domain of the τ-plane and that (subject to certain limitations) this root is an analytic function of c, when c is regarded as variable. It has been seen that the existence of this root yields the solution of the inversion problem, so that the existence of the Jacobian elliptic function with given modulus k will have been demonstrated.

The method just indicated has the advantage of exhibiting the potentialities of what are known as *modular functions*. The general theory of these functions (which are of great importance in connexion with the Theories of Transformation of Elliptic Functions) has been considered in a treatise by Klein and Fricke†.

Let
$$f(\tau) = 16 e^{\pi i \tau} \prod_{n=1}^{\infty} \left\{\frac{1 + e^{2n\pi i \tau}}{1 + e^{(2n-1)\pi i \tau}}\right\}^8 = \frac{\vartheta_2^4(0 \mid \tau)}{\vartheta_3^4(0 \mid \tau)},$$

$$g(\tau) = \prod_{n=1}^{\infty} \left\{\frac{1 - e^{(2n-1)\pi i \tau}}{1 + e^{(2n-1)\pi i \tau}}\right\}^8 = \frac{\vartheta_4^4(0 \mid \tau)}{\vartheta_3^4(0 \mid \tau)},$$

$$h(\tau) = -f(\tau)/g(\tau).$$

Then, if $\tau\tau' = -1$, the functions just introduced possess the following properties :

$$f(\tau+2) = f(\tau), \qquad g(\tau+2) = g(\tau), \qquad f(\tau) + g(\tau) = 1,$$
$$f(\tau+1) = h(\tau), \qquad f(\tau') = g(\tau), \qquad g(\tau') = f(\tau),$$

by §§ 21·2 corollary, 21·51 example 1.

* This is the case which is of practical importance.

† F. Klein, *Vorlesungen über die Theorie der elliptischen Modulfunktionen* (ausgearbeitet und vervollständigt von R. Fricke). (Leipzig, 1890.)

It is easy to see that as $I(\tau) \to +\infty$, the functions $\frac{1}{16}e^{-\pi i \tau}f(\tau) = f_1(\tau)$ and $g(\tau)$ tend to unity, uniformly with respect to $R(\tau)$, when $-1 \leqslant R(\tau) \leqslant 1$; and the derivates of these two functions (with regard to τ) tend uniformly to zero[*] in the same circumstances.

21·711.   *The principal solution of* $f(\tau) - c = 0$.

It has been seen in § 6·31 that, if $f(\tau)$ is analytic inside and on any contour, $2\pi i$ times the number of roots of the equation $f(\tau) - c = 0$ inside the contour is equal to

$$\int \frac{1}{f(\tau) - c} \frac{df(\tau)}{d\tau} d\tau,$$

taken round the contour in question.

Take the contour $ABCDEFE'D'C'B'A$ shewn in the figure, it being supposed temporarily[†] that $f(\tau) - c$ has no zero actually on the contour.

The contour is constructed in the following manner :

FE is drawn parallel to the real axis, at a large distance from it.

AB is the inverse of FE with respect to the circle $|\tau| = 1$.

BC is the inverse of ED with respect to $|\tau| = 1$, D being chosen so that $D1 = A0$.

By elementary geometry, it follows that, since C and D are inverse points and 1 is its own inverse, the circle on $D1$ as diameter passes through C; and so the arc CD of this circle is the reflexion of the arc AB in the line $R(\tau) = \frac{1}{2}$.

The left-hand half of the figure is the reflexion of the right-hand half in the line $R(\tau) = 0$.

---

[*] This follows from the expressions for the Theta-functions as power series in q, it being observed that $|q| \to 0$ as $I(\tau) \to +\infty$.

[†] The values of $f(\tau)$ at points on the contour are discussed in § 21·712.

It will now be shewn that, unless* $c \geqslant 1$ or $c \leqslant 0$, the equation $f(\tau) - c = 0$ has one, and only one, root inside the contour, provided that FE is sufficiently distant from the real axis. This root will be called the *principal root* of the equation.

To establish the existence of this root, consider $\int \dfrac{1}{f(\tau) - c} \dfrac{df(\tau)}{d\tau} d\tau$ taken along the various portions of the contour.

Since $f(\tau + 2) = f(\tau)$, we have

$$\left\{ \int_{DE} + \int_{E'D'} \right\} \frac{1}{f(\tau) - c} \frac{df(\tau)}{d\tau} d\tau = 0.$$

Also, as τ describes BC and $B'C'$, $\tau' (= -1/\tau)$ describes $E'D'$ and ED respectively; and so

$$\left\{ \int_{BC} + \int_{C'B'} \right\} \frac{1}{f(\tau) - c} \frac{df(\tau)}{d\tau} d\tau = \left\{ \int_{BC} + \int_{C'B'} \right\} \frac{1}{g(\tau') - c} \frac{dg(\tau')}{d\tau} d\tau$$

$$= \left\{ \int_{E'D'} + \int_{DE} \right\} \frac{1}{g(\tau') - c} \frac{dg(\tau')}{d\tau'} d\tau'$$

$$= 0,$$

because $g(\tau' + 2) = g(\tau')$, and consequently corresponding elements of the integrals cancel.

Since $f(\tau \pm 1) = h(\tau)$, we have

$$\left\{ \int_{D'C'} + \int_{CD} \right\} \frac{1}{f(\tau) - c} \frac{df(\tau)}{d\tau} d\tau = \int_{B'AB} \frac{1}{h(\tau) - c} \frac{dh(\tau)}{d\tau} d\tau ;$$

but, as τ' describes $B'AB$, τ describes EE', and so the integral round the complete contour reduces to

$$\int_{EE'} \left\{ \frac{1}{f(\tau) - c} \frac{df(\tau)}{d\tau} + \frac{1}{h(\tau') - c} \frac{dh(\tau')}{d\tau} + \frac{1}{f(\tau') - c} \frac{df(\tau')}{d\tau} \right\} d\tau$$

$$= \int_{EE'} \left\{ \frac{1}{f(\tau) - c} \frac{df(\tau)}{d\tau} - \frac{1}{h(\tau)\{1 - c \cdot h(\tau)\}} \frac{dh(\tau)}{d\tau} + \frac{1}{g(\tau) - c} \frac{dg(\tau)}{d\tau} \right\} d\tau.$$

Now as EE' moves off to infinity†, $f(\tau) - c \to -c \neq 0$, $g(\tau) - c \to 1 - c \neq 0$, and so the limit of the integral is

$$-\lim \int_{EE'} \frac{1}{1 - c \cdot h(\tau)} \frac{d}{d\tau} \{\log h(\tau)\} d\tau$$

$$= \lim \int_{E'E} \frac{1}{1 - c \cdot h(\tau)} \left\{ \pi i + \frac{d\log f_1(\tau)}{d\tau} - \frac{d\log g(\tau)}{d\tau} \right\} d\tau.$$

But $1 - c \cdot h(\tau) \to 1$, $f_1(\tau) \to 1$, $g_1(\tau) \to 1$, $\dfrac{df_1(\tau)}{d\tau} \to 0$, $\dfrac{dg(\tau)}{d\tau} \to 0$, and so the limit of the integral is

$$\int_{E'E} \pi i \, d\tau = 2\pi i.$$

Now, if we choose EE' to be initially so far from the real axis that $f(\tau) - c$, $1 - c \cdot h(\tau)$, $g(\tau) - c$ have no zeros when τ is above EE', then the contour will pass over no zeros of $f(\tau) - c$ as EE' moves off to infinity and the radii of the arcs CD, $D'C'$, $B'AB$ diminish to zero; and then the integral will not change as the contour is modified, and so the original contour integral will be $2\pi i$, and the number of zeros of $f(\tau) - c$ inside the original contour will be precisely one.

---

* It is shewn in § 21·712 that, if $c \geqslant 1$ or $c \leqslant 0$, then $f(\tau) - c$ has a zero on the contour.

† It has been supposed temporarily that $c \neq 0$ and $c \neq 1$.

21·712. *The values of the modular function $f(\tau)$ on the contour considered.*

We now have to discuss the point mentioned at the beginning of § 21·711, concerning the zeros of $f(\tau)-c$ on the lines* joining ± 1 to $\pm 1+\infty\, i$ and on the semicircles of $OBC1$, $(-1)\, C'B'0$.

As τ goes from 1 to $1+\infty\, i$ or from -1 to $-1+\infty\, i$, $f(\tau)$ goes from $-\infty$ to 0 through real negative values. So, if c is negative, we make an indentation in DE and a corresponding indentation in $D'E'$; and the integrals along the indentations cancel in virtue of the relation $f(\tau+2)+f(\tau)$.

As τ describes the semicircle $OBC1$, τ' goes from $-1+\infty\, i$ to -1, and $f(\tau)=g(\tau')=1-f(\tau')$, and goes from 1 to $+\infty$ through real values; it would be possible to make indentations in BC and $B'C'$ to avoid this difficulty, but we do not do so for the following reason: the effect of changing the sign of the imaginary part of the number c is to change the sign of the real part of τ. Now, if $0 < R(c) < 1$ and $I(c)$ be small, this merely makes τ cross OF by a short path; if $R(c) < 0$, τ goes from DE to $D'E'$ (or *vice versa*) and the value of q alters only slightly; but if $R(c) > 1$, τ goes from BC to $B'C'$, and so q is not a one-valued function of c so far as circuits round $c=+1$ are concerned; to make q a one-valued function of c, we cut the c-plane from $+1$ to $+\infty$; and then for values of c in the cut plane, q is determined as a one-valued analytic function of c, say $q(c)$, by the formula $q(c)=e^{\pi i \cdot \tau(c)}$ where

$$\tau(c) = \frac{1}{2\pi i} \int \frac{\tau}{f(\tau)-c} \frac{df(\tau)}{d\tau}\, d\tau,$$

as may be seen from § 6·3, by using the method of § 5·22.

If c describes a circuit not surrounding the point $c=1$, $q(c)$ is one-valued, but $\tau(c)$ is one-valued only if, in addition, the circuit does not surround the point $c=0$.

21·72. *The periods, regarded as functions of the modulus.*

Since $K=\frac{1}{2}\pi \vartheta_3^2 (0, q)$ we see from § 21·712 that K is a one-valued analytic function of $c\,(=k^2)$ when a cut from 1 to $+\infty$ is made in the c-plane; but since $K'=-i\tau K$, we see that K' is not a one-valued function of c unless an additional cut is made from 0 to $-\infty$; it will appear later (§ 22·32) that the cut from 1 to $+\infty$ which was necessary so far as K is concerned is *not* necessary as regards K'.

21·73. *The inversion-problem associated with Weierstrassian elliptic functions.*

It will now be shewn that, when invariants g_2 and g_3 are given, such that $g_2^3 \neq 27g_3^2$, it is possible to construct the Weierstrassian elliptic function with these invariants; that is to say, we shall shew that *it is possible to construct* † periods $2\omega_1$, $2\omega_2$ *such that the function* $\wp(z\,|\,\omega_1, \omega_2)$ *has invariants g_2 and g_3.*

The problem is solved if we can obtain a solution of the differential equation

$$\left(\frac{dy}{dz}\right)^2 = 4y^3 - g_2 y - g_3$$

of the form $\qquad\qquad y = \wp(z\,|\,\omega_1, \omega_2).$

We proceed to effect the solution of the equation with the aid of Theta-functions.

Let $\nu = Az$, where A is a constant to be determined presently.

* We have seen that EE' can be so chosen that $f(\tau)-c$ has no zeros either on EE' or on the small circular arcs.

† On the actual calculation of the periods, see R. T. A. Innes, *Proc. Edinburgh Royal Soc.* XXVII. (1907), pp. 357–368.

By the methods of § 21·6, it is easily seen that

$$\vartheta_2'(\nu)\,\vartheta_1(\nu) - \vartheta_1'(\nu)\,\vartheta_2(\nu) = -\vartheta_3(\nu)\,\vartheta_4(\nu)\,\vartheta_2{}^2,$$

and hence, using the results of § 21·2, we have

$$\left\{\frac{d}{dz}\,\frac{\vartheta_2{}^2(\nu)}{\vartheta_1{}^2(\nu)}\,\vartheta_3{}^2\,\vartheta_4{}^2\right\}^2 = 4A^2\left(\frac{\vartheta_2{}^2(\nu)}{\vartheta_1{}^2(\nu)}\,\vartheta_3{}^2\,\vartheta_4{}^2\right)\left(\frac{\vartheta_2{}^2(\nu)}{\vartheta_1{}^2(\nu)}\,\vartheta_3{}^2\,\vartheta_4{}^2 + \vartheta_4{}^4\right)\left(\frac{\vartheta_2{}^2(\nu)}{\vartheta_1{}^2(\nu)}\,\vartheta_3{}^2\,\vartheta_4{}^2 + \vartheta_3{}^4\right).$$

Now let e_1, e_2, e_3 be the roots of the equation $4y^3 - g_2 y - g_3 = 0$, chosen in such an order that $(e_1 - e_2)/(e_1 - e_3)$ is not* a real number greater than unity or negative.

In these circumstances the equation

$$\frac{e_1 - e_2}{e_1 - e_3} = \frac{\vartheta_4{}^4(0\,|\,\tau)}{\vartheta_3{}^4(0\,|\,\tau)}$$

possesses a solution (§ 21·712) such that $I(\tau) > 0$; this equation determines the parameter τ of the Theta-functions, which has, up till now, been at our disposal.

Choosing τ in this manner, let A be next chosen so that†

$$A^2\vartheta_4{}^4 = e_1 - e_2.$$

Then the function

$$y = A^2\frac{\vartheta_2{}^2(\nu\,|\,\tau)}{\vartheta_1{}^2(\nu\,|\,\tau)}\,\vartheta_3{}^2(0\,|\,\tau)\,\vartheta_4{}^2(0\,|\,\tau) + e_1$$

satisfies the equation

$$\left(\frac{dy}{dz}\right)^2 = 4\,(y - e_1)\,(y - e_2)\,(y - e_3).$$

The periods of y, *qua* function of z, are πA, $\pi\tau/A$; calling these $2\omega_1$, $2\omega_2$ we have

$$I(\omega_2/\omega_1) > 0.$$

The function $\wp(z\,|\,\omega_1,\ \omega_2)$ may be constructed with these periods, and it is easily seen that $\wp(z) - A^2\dfrac{\vartheta_2{}^2(\nu\,|\,\tau)}{\vartheta_1{}^2(\nu\,|\,\tau)}\,\vartheta_3{}^2(0\,|\,\tau)\,\vartheta_4{}^2(0\,|\,\tau) - e_1$ is an elliptic function with no pole at the origin‡; it is therefore a constant, C, say.

If G_2, G_3 be the invariants of $\wp(z\,|\,\omega_1,\ \omega_2)$, we have

$$4\wp^3(z) - G_2\wp(z) - G_3 = \wp'^2(z) = 4\,\{\wp(z) - C - e_1\}\,\{\wp(z) - C - e_2\}\,\{\wp(z) - C - e_3\},$$

and so, comparing coefficients of powers of $\wp(z)$, we have

$$0 = 12C, \quad G_2 = g_2 - 12C^2, \quad G_3 = g_3 - g_2 C + 4C^3.$$

Hence

$$C = 0, \quad G_2 = g_2, \quad G_3 = g_3;$$

and so the function $\wp(z\,|\,\omega_1,\ \omega_2)$ with the required invariants has been constructed.

21·8. *The numerical computation of elliptic functions.*

The series proceeding in ascending powers of q are convenient for calculating Theta-functions generally, even when $|q|$ is as large as $0·9$. But it usually happens in practice that the modulus k is given and the calculation

---

* If $\dfrac{e_i - e_j}{e_i - e_k} > 1$, then $0 < \dfrac{e_i - e_k}{e_i - e_j} < 1$; and if $\dfrac{e_i - e_j}{e_i - e_k} < 0$, then $1 - \dfrac{e_i - e_j}{e_i - e_k} > 1$, and

$$\frac{e_j - e_i}{e_j - e_k} = \left\{1 - \frac{e_i - e_k}{e_i - e_j}\right\}^{-1} < 1.$$

The values 0, 1, ∞ of $(e_1 - e_2)/(e_1 - e_3)$ are excluded since $g_2{}^3 \neq 27g_3{}^2$.

† The sign attached to A is a matter of indifference, since we deal exclusively with *even* functions of ν and z.

‡ The terms in z^{-2} cancel, and there is no term in z^{-1} because the function is even.

of K, K' and q is necessary. It will be seen later (§§ 22·301, 22·32) that K, K' are expressible in terms of hypergeometric functions, by the equations

$$K = \tfrac{1}{2}\pi F\left(\tfrac{1}{2},\ \tfrac{1}{2};\ 1;\ k^2\right), \quad K' = \tfrac{1}{2}\pi F\left(\tfrac{1}{2},\ \tfrac{1}{2};\ 1;\ k'^2\right);$$

but these series converge slowly except when $|k|$ and $|k'|$ respectively are quite small; so that the series are never simultaneously suitable for numerical calculations.

To obtain more convenient series for numerical work, we first calculate q as a root of the equation $k = \vartheta_2{}^2(0, q)/\vartheta_3{}^2(0, q)$, and then obtain K from the formula $K = \tfrac{1}{2}\pi\vartheta_3{}^2(0, q)$ and K' from the formula

$$K' = \pi^{-1}K\log_e(1/q).$$

The equation $\qquad k = \vartheta_2{}^2(0, q)/\vartheta_3{}^2(0, q)$
is equivalent to* $\qquad \sqrt{k'} = \vartheta_4(0, q)/\vartheta_3(0, q).$

Writing $2\epsilon = \dfrac{1 - \sqrt{k'}}{1 + \sqrt{k'}}$, (so that $0 < \epsilon < \tfrac{1}{2}$ when $0 < k < 1$), we get

$$2\epsilon = \frac{\vartheta_3(0, q) - \vartheta_4(0, q)}{\vartheta_3(0, q) + \vartheta_4(0, q)} = \frac{\vartheta_2(0, q^4)}{\vartheta_3(0, q^4)}.$$

We have seen (§§ 21·71–21·712) that this equation in q^4 possesses a solution which is an analytic function of ϵ^4 when $|\epsilon| < \tfrac{1}{2}$; and so q will be expansible in a Maclaurin series in powers of ϵ in this domain†.

It remains to determine the coefficients in this expansion from the equation

$$\epsilon = \frac{q + q^9 + q^{25} + \ldots}{1 + 2q^4 + 2q^{16} + \ldots},$$

which may be written

$$q = \epsilon + 2q^4\epsilon - q^9 + 2q^{16}\epsilon - q^{25} + \ldots;$$

the reader will easily verify by continually substituting $\epsilon + 2q^4\epsilon - q^9 + \ldots$ for q wherever q occurs on the right that the first two terms‡ are given by

$$q = \epsilon + 2\epsilon^5 + 15\epsilon^9 + 150\epsilon^{13} + O(\epsilon^{17}).$$

It has just been seen that this series converges when $|\epsilon| < \tfrac{1}{2}$.

[NOTE. The first two terms of this expansion usually suffice; thus, even if k be as large as $\sqrt{(0·8704)} = 0·933\ldots$, $\epsilon = \tfrac{1}{8}$, $2\epsilon^5 = 0·0000609$, $15\epsilon^9 = 0·0000002$.]

Example. Given $k = k' = 1/\sqrt{2}$, calculate q, K, K' by means of the expansion just obtained, and also by observing that $\tau = i$, so that $q = e^{-\pi}$.

$$[q = 0·0432139, \quad K = K' = 1·854075.]$$

* In numerical work $0 < k < 1$, and so q is positive and $0 < \sqrt{k'} < 1$.

† The Theta-functions do not vanish when $|q| < 1$ except at $q = 0$, so this gives the only possible branch point.

‡ This expansion was given by Weierstrass, *Werke*, II. (1895), p. 276.

21·9. *The notations employed for the Theta-functions.*

The following scheme indicates the principal systems of notation which have been employed by various writers; the symbols in any one column all denote the same function.

$\vartheta_1(\pi z)$	$\vartheta_2(\pi z)$	$\vartheta_3(\pi z)$	$\vartheta(\pi z)$	Jacobi
$\vartheta_1(z)$	$\vartheta_2(z)$	$\vartheta_3(z)$	$\vartheta_4(z)$	Tannery and Molk
$\theta_1(\omega z)$	$\theta_2(\omega z)$	$\theta_3(\omega z)$	$\theta(\omega z)$	Briot and Bouquet
$\theta_1(z)$	$\theta_2(z)$	$\theta_3(z)$	$\theta_0(z)$	Weierstrass, Halphen, Hancock
$\theta(z)$	$\theta_1(z)$	$\theta_3(z)$	$\theta_2(z)$	Jordan, Harkness and Morley

The notation employed by Hermite, H. J. S. Smith and some other mathematicians is expressed by the equation

$$\theta_{\mu,\nu}(x) = \sum_{n=-\infty}^{\infty} (-)^{n\nu} q^{\frac{1}{4}(2n+\mu)^2} e^{i\pi(2n+\mu)x/a} ; \qquad (\mu = 0, 1 ; \nu = 0, 1)$$

with this notation the results of § 21·11 example 3 take the very concise form

$$\theta_{\mu,\nu}(x+a) = (-)^\mu \theta_{\mu,\nu}(x), \quad \theta_{\mu,\nu}(x+a\tau) = (-)^\nu q^{-1} e^{-2i\pi x/a} \theta_{\mu,\nu}(x).$$

Cayley employs Jacobi's earlier notation (§ 21·62). The advantage of the Weierstrassian notation is that unity (instead of π) is the real period of $\theta_3(z)$ and $\theta_0(z)$.

Jordan's notation exhibits the analogy between the Theta-functions and the three Sigma-functions defined in § 20·421. The reader will easily obtain relations, similar to that of § 21·43, connecting $\theta_r(z)$ with $\sigma_r(2\omega_1 z)$ when $r = 1, 2, 3$.

REFERENCES.

L. Euler, *Opera Omnia*, (1), xx. (Leipzig, 1912).

C. G. J. Jacobi, *Fundamenta Nova** (Königsberg, 1829); *Ges. Math. Werke*, I. pp. 497–538.

C. Hermite, *Oeuvres Mathématiques*. (Paris, 1905–1917.)

F. Klein, *Vorlesungen über die Theorie der elliptischen Modulfunktionen* (Ausgear-beitet und vervollständigt von R. Fricke). (Leipzig, 1890.)

H. Weber, *Elliptische Funktionen und algebraische Zahlen*. (Brunswick, 1891.)

J. Tannery et J. Molk, *Fonctions Elliptiques*. (Paris, 1893–1902.)

Miscellaneous Examples.

1. Obtain the addition-formulae

$$\vartheta_1(y+z)\,\vartheta_1(y-z)\,\vartheta_4^2 = \vartheta_3^2(y)\,\vartheta_2^2(z) - \vartheta_2^2(y)\,\vartheta_3^2(z) = \vartheta_1^2(y)\,\vartheta_4^2(z) - \vartheta_4^2(y)\,\vartheta_1^2(z),$$
$$\vartheta_2(y+z)\,\vartheta_2(y-z)\,\vartheta_4^2 = \vartheta_4^2(y)\,\vartheta_2^2(z) - \vartheta_1^2(y)\,\vartheta_3^2(z) = \vartheta_2^2(y)\,\vartheta_4^2(z) - \vartheta_3^2(y)\,\vartheta_1^2(z),$$
$$\vartheta_3(y+z)\,\vartheta_3(y-z)\,\vartheta_4^2 = \vartheta_4^2(y)\,\vartheta_3^2(z) - \vartheta_1^2(y)\,\vartheta_2^2(z) = \vartheta_3^2(y)\,\vartheta_4^2(z) - \vartheta_2^2(y)\,\vartheta_1^2(z),$$
$$\vartheta_4(y+z)\,\vartheta_4(y-z)\,\vartheta_4^2 = \vartheta_3^2(y)\,\vartheta_3^2(z) - \vartheta_2^2(y)\,\vartheta_2^2(z) = \vartheta_4^2(y)\,\vartheta_4^2(z) - \vartheta_1^2(y)\,\vartheta_1^2(z).$$

(Jacobi.)

* Reprinted in his *Ges. Math. Werke*, I. (1881), pp. 49–239.

2. Obtain the addition-formulae

$$\vartheta_4(y+z)\,\vartheta_4(y-z)\,\vartheta_2{}^2=\vartheta_4{}^2(y)\,\vartheta_2{}^2(z)+\vartheta_3{}^2(y)\,\vartheta_1{}^2(z)=\vartheta_2{}^2(y)\,\vartheta_4{}^2(z)+\vartheta_1{}^2(y)\,\vartheta_3{}^2(z),$$

$$\vartheta_4(y+z)\,\vartheta_4(y-z)\,\vartheta_3{}^2=\vartheta_4{}^2(y)\,\vartheta_3{}^2(z)+\vartheta_2{}^2(y)\,\vartheta_1{}^2(z)=\vartheta_3{}^2(y)\,\vartheta_4{}^2(z)+\vartheta_1{}^2(y)\,\vartheta_2{}^2(z)\;;$$

and, by increasing y by half periods, obtain the corresponding formulae for

$$\vartheta_r(y+z)\,\vartheta_r(y-z)\,\vartheta_2{}^2 \text{ and } \vartheta_r(y+z)\,\vartheta_r(y-z)\,\vartheta_3{}^2,$$

where $r=1,2,3$. (Jacobi.)

3. Obtain the formulae

$$\vartheta_1(y\pm z)\,\vartheta_2(y\mp z)\,\vartheta_3\vartheta_4=\vartheta_1(y)\,\vartheta_2(y)\,\vartheta_3(z)\,\vartheta_4(z)\pm\vartheta_3(y)\,\vartheta_4(y)\,\vartheta_1(z)\,\vartheta_2(z),$$

$$\vartheta_1(y\pm z)\,\vartheta_3(y\mp z)\,\vartheta_2\vartheta_4=\vartheta_1(y)\,\vartheta_3(y)\,\vartheta_2(z)\,\vartheta_4(z)\pm\vartheta_2(y)\,\vartheta_4(y)\,\vartheta_1(z)\,\vartheta_3(z),$$

$$\vartheta_1(y\pm z)\,\vartheta_4(y\mp z)\,\vartheta_2\vartheta_3=\vartheta_1(y)\,\vartheta_4(y)\,\vartheta_2(z)\,\vartheta_3(z)\pm\vartheta_2(y)\,\vartheta_3(y)\,\vartheta_1(z)\,\vartheta_4(z),$$

$$\vartheta_2(y\pm z)\,\vartheta_3(y\mp z)\,\vartheta_2\vartheta_3=\vartheta_2(y)\,\vartheta_3(y)\,\vartheta_2(z)\,\vartheta_3(z)\mp\vartheta_1(y)\,\vartheta_4(y)\,\vartheta_1(z)\,\vartheta_4(z),$$

$$\vartheta_2(y\pm z)\,\vartheta_4(y\mp z)\,\vartheta_2\vartheta_4=\vartheta_2(y)\,\vartheta_4(y)\,\vartheta_2(z)\,\vartheta_4(z)\mp\vartheta_1(y)\,\vartheta_3(y)\,\vartheta_1(z)\,\vartheta_3(z),$$

$$\vartheta_3(y\pm z)\,\vartheta_4(y\mp z)\,\vartheta_3\vartheta_4=\vartheta_3(y)\,\vartheta_4(y)\,\vartheta_3(z)\,\vartheta_4(z)\mp\vartheta_1(y)\,\vartheta_2(y)\,\vartheta_1(z)\,\vartheta_2(z).$$

(Jacobi.)

4. Obtain the duplication-formulae

$$\vartheta_2(2y)\,\vartheta_2\vartheta_4{}^2=\vartheta_2{}^2(y)\,\vartheta_4{}^2(y)-\vartheta_1{}^2(y)\,\vartheta_3{}^2(y),$$

$$\vartheta_3(2y)\,\vartheta_3\vartheta_4{}^2=\vartheta_3{}^2(y)\,\vartheta_4{}^2(y)-\vartheta_1{}^2(y)\,\vartheta_2{}^2(y),$$

$$\vartheta_4(2y)\,\vartheta_4{}^3\;=\vartheta_3{}^4(y)-\vartheta_2{}^4(y)=\vartheta_4{}^4(y)-\vartheta_1{}^4(y).$$

(Jacobi.)

5. Obtain the duplication-formula

$$\vartheta_1(2y)\,\vartheta_2\vartheta_3\vartheta_4=2\vartheta_1(y)\,\vartheta_2(y)\,\vartheta_3(y)\,\vartheta_4(y).$$

(Jacobi.)

6. Obtain duplication-formulae from the results indicated in example 2.

7. Shew that, with the notation of § 21·22,

$$[1]-[2]=[4]'-[3]',\quad [1]-[3]=[1]'-[3]',\quad [1]-[4]=[2]'-[3]',$$

$$[2]-[3]=[1]'-[4]',\quad [2]-[4]=[2]'-[4]',\quad [3]-[4]=[2]'-[1]'.$$

8. Shew that

$$2[1122]=[1122]'+[2211]'-[4433]'+[3344]',$$

$$2[1133]=[1133]'+[3311]'-[4422]'+[2244]',$$

$$2[1144]=[1144]'+[4411]'-[3322]'+[2233]',$$

$$2[2233]=[2233]'+[3322]'-[4411]'+[1144]',$$

$$2[2244]=[2244]'+[4422]'-[3311]'+[1133]',$$

$$2[3344]=[3344]'+[4433]'-[2211]'+[1122]'.$$

(Jacobi.)

9. Obtain the formulae

$$2\pi^{-1}Kk^{\frac12}=2q^{\frac14}\prod_{n=1}^{\infty}\{(1-q^{2n})^2(1-q^{2n-1})^{-2}\},$$

$$k^{\frac12}k'^{-\frac12}=2q^{\frac14}\prod_{n=1}^{\infty}\{(1+q^{2n})^2(1-q^{2n-1})^{-2}\}.$$

10. Deduce the following results from example 9 :

$$\prod_{n=1}^{\infty}(1-q^{2n-1})^6=2q^{\frac14}k'k^{-\frac12},\qquad\qquad\prod_{n=1}^{\infty}(1+q^{2n-1})^6=2q^{\frac14}(kk')^{-\frac12},$$

$$\prod_{n=1}^{\infty}(1-q^{2n})^6=2\pi^{-3}q^{-\frac12}kk'K^3,\qquad\prod_{n=1}^{\infty}(1+q^{2n})^6=\tfrac14q^{-\frac12}kk'^{-\frac12},$$

$$\prod_{n=1}^{\infty}(1-q^n)^6=4\pi^{-3}q^{-\frac14}k^{\frac12}k'^2K^3,\qquad\prod_{n=1}^{\infty}(1+q^n)^6=\tfrac12q^{-\frac14}k^{\frac12}k'^{-1}.$$

(Jacobi.)

11. By considering $\int \frac{\vartheta_4'(z)}{\vartheta_4(z)} e^{2niz}\, dz$ taken along the contour formed by the parallelogram whose corners are $-\frac{1}{2}\pi,\ \frac{1}{2}\pi,\ \frac{1}{2}\pi+\pi\tau,\ -\frac{1}{2}\pi+\pi\tau$, shew that, when n is a positive integer,

$$(1-q^{2n})\int_{-\frac{1}{2}\pi}^{\frac{1}{2}\pi} \frac{\vartheta_4'(z)}{\vartheta_4(z)} e^{2niz}\, dz = 2\pi i q^n,$$

and deduce that, when $|I(z)| < \frac{1}{2}I(\pi\tau)$,

$$\frac{\vartheta_4'(z)}{\vartheta_4(z)} = 4\sum_{n=1}^{\infty} \frac{q^n \sin 2nz}{1-q^{2n}}.$$

12. Obtain the following expansions:

$$\frac{\vartheta_1'(z)}{\vartheta_1(z)} = \cot z + 4\sum_{n=1}^{\infty} \frac{q^{2n} \sin 2nz}{1-q^{2n}},$$

$$\frac{\vartheta_2'(z)}{\vartheta_2(z)} = -\tan z + 4\sum_{n=1}^{\infty} \frac{(-)^n q^{2n} \sin 2nz}{1-q^{2n}},$$

$$\frac{\vartheta_3'(z)}{\vartheta_3(z)} = 4\sum_{n=1}^{\infty} \frac{(-)^n q^n \sin 2nz}{1-q^{2n}},$$

each expansion being valid in the strip of the z-plane in which the series involved is absolutely convergent.

(Jacobi.)

13. Shew that, if $|I(y)| < I(\pi\tau)$ and $|I(z)| < I(\pi\tau)$, then

$$\frac{\vartheta_1(y+z)\,\vartheta_1'}{\vartheta_1(y)\,\vartheta_1(z)} = \cot y + \cot z + 4\sum_{m=1}^{\infty}\sum_{n=1}^{\infty} q^{2mn} \sin(2my+2nz).$$

(Math. Trip. 1908.)

14. Shew that, if $|I(z)| < \frac{1}{2}I(\pi\tau)$, then

$$\frac{Kk^{\frac{1}{2}}}{\pi}\frac{\vartheta_4}{\vartheta_4(z)} = \frac{1}{2}a_0 + \sum_{n=1}^{\infty} a_n \cos 2nz,$$

where

$$a_n = 2\sum_{m=0}^{\infty} (-)^m q^{(m+\frac{1}{2})(2n+m+\frac{1}{2})}.$$

(Math. Trip. 1903.)

[Obtain a reduction formula for a_n by considering $\int \{\vartheta_4(z)\}^{-1} e^{2niz}\, dz$ taken round the contour of example 11.]

15. Shew that

$$\frac{\vartheta_1'(z)}{\vartheta_1(z)} - \left[\cot z + 4\sum_{n=1}^{\infty} \frac{q^{2n}\sin 2z}{1-2q^{2n}\cos 2z + q^{4n}}\right]$$

is a doubly-periodic function of z with no singularities, and deduce that it is zero.

Prove similarly that

$$\frac{\vartheta_2'(z)}{\vartheta_2(z)} = -\tan z - 4\sum_{n=1}^{\infty} \frac{q^{2n}\sin 2z}{1+2q^{2n}\cos 2z + q^{4n}},$$

$$\frac{\vartheta_3'(z)}{\vartheta_3(z)} = -4\sum_{n=1}^{\infty} \frac{q^{2n-1}\sin 2z}{1+2q^{2n-1}\cos 2z + q^{4n-2}},$$

$$\frac{\vartheta_4'(z)}{\vartheta_4(z)} = 4\sum_{n=1}^{\infty} \frac{q^{2n-1}\sin 2z}{1-2q^{2n-1}\cos 2z + q^{4n-2}}.$$

16. Obtain the values of $k,\ k',\ K,\ K'$ correct to six places of decimals when $q = \frac{1}{10}$.

$$[k = 0\cdot895769, \quad k' = 0\cdot444518,$$
$$K = 2\cdot262700, \quad K' = 1\cdot658414.]$$

17.   Shew that, if $w+x+y+z=0$, then, with the notation of § 21·22,

$$[3]+[1]=[2]+[4],$$

$$[1234]+[3412]+[2143]+[4321]=0.$$

18.   Shew that

$$\frac{\vartheta_4'(y)}{\vartheta_4(y)}+\frac{\vartheta_4'(z)}{\vartheta_4(z)}-\frac{\vartheta_4'(y+z)}{\vartheta_4(y+z)}=\vartheta_2\vartheta_3\frac{\vartheta_1(y)\,\vartheta_1(z)\,\vartheta_1(y+z)}{\vartheta_4(y)\,\vartheta_4(z)\,\vartheta_4(y+z)}.$$

19.   By putting $x=y=z$, $w=3x$ in Jacobi's fundamental formulae, obtain the following results :

$$\vartheta_1^3(x)\,\vartheta_1(3x)+\vartheta_4^3(x)\,\vartheta_4(3x)=\vartheta_4^3(2x)\,\vartheta_4,$$

$$\vartheta_3^3(x)\,\vartheta_3(3x)-\vartheta_4^3(x)\,\vartheta_4(3x)=\vartheta_2^3(2x)\,\vartheta_2,$$

$$\vartheta_2^3(x)\,\vartheta_2(3x)+\vartheta_4^3(x)\,\vartheta_4(3x)=\vartheta_3^3(2x)\,\vartheta_3.$$

20.   Deduce from example 19 that

$$\{\vartheta_1^3(x)\,\vartheta_1(3x)\,\vartheta_4^2+\vartheta_4^3(x)\,\vartheta_4(3x)\,\vartheta_4^2\}^{\frac{2}{3}}+\{\vartheta_3^3(x)\,\vartheta_3(3x)\,\vartheta_2^2-\vartheta_4^3(x)\,\vartheta_4(3x)\,\vartheta_2^2\}^{\frac{2}{3}}$$
$$=\{\vartheta_2^3(x)\,\vartheta_2(3x)\,\vartheta_3^2+\vartheta_4^3(x)\,\vartheta_4(3x)\,\vartheta_3^2\}^{\frac{2}{3}}.$$

(Trinity, 1882.)

21.   Deduce from Liouville's theorem that

$$\frac{2\vartheta_1(z)\,\vartheta_2(z)\,\vartheta_3(z)\,\vartheta_4(z)}{\vartheta_1(2z)\,\vartheta_2(0)\,\vartheta_3(0)\,\vartheta_4(0)}$$

is constant, and, by making $z \rightarrow 0$, that it is equal to 1.

Hence, by comparing coefficients of z^2 in the expansions of

$$\log\frac{\vartheta_1(2z)}{2\vartheta_1(z)}\quad\text{and}\quad\log\frac{\vartheta_2(z)}{\vartheta_2(0)}+\log\frac{\vartheta_3(z)}{\vartheta_3(0)}+\log\frac{\vartheta_4(z)}{\vartheta_4(0)}$$

by Maclaurin's theorem, deduce that

$$\frac{\vartheta_1'''(0)}{\vartheta_1'(0)}=\frac{\vartheta_2''(0)}{\vartheta_2(0)}+\frac{\vartheta_3''(0)}{\vartheta_3(0)}+\frac{\vartheta_4''(0)}{\vartheta_4(0)}.$$

Hence, after the manner of § 21·41, deduce that

$$\vartheta_1'(0)=\vartheta_2(0)\,\vartheta_3(0)\,\vartheta_4(0).$$

[This method of obtaining the preliminary formula of § 21·41 was suggested to the authors by Mr C. A. Stewart.]

CHAPTER XXII

THE JACOBIAN ELLIPTIC FUNCTIONS

22·1. *Elliptic functions with two simple poles.*

In the course of proving general theorems concerning elliptic functions at the beginning of Chapter XX, it was shewn that two classes of elliptic functions were simpler than any others so far as their singularities were concerned, namely the elliptic functions of order 2. The first class consists of those with a single double pole (with zero residue) in each cell, the second consists of those with two simple poles in each cell, the sum of the residues at these poles being zero.

An example of the first class, namely $\wp(z)$, was discussed at length in Chapter XX; in the present chapter we shall discuss various examples of the second class, known as *Jacobian elliptic functions**.

It will be seen (§ 22·122, note) that, in certain circumstances, the Jacobian functions degenerate into the ordinary circular functions; accordingly, a notation (invented by Jacobi and modified by Gudermann and Glaisher) will be employed which emphasizes an analogy between the Jacobian functions and the circular functions.

From the theoretical aspect, it is most simple to regard the Jacobian functions as quotients of Theta-functions (§ 21·61). But as many of their fundamental properties can be obtained by quite elementary methods, without appealing to the theory of Theta-functions, we shall discuss the functions without making use of Chapter XXI except when it is desirable to do so for the sake of brevity or simplicity.

22·11. *The Jacobian elliptic functions,* sn u, cn u, dn u.

It was shewn in § 21·61 that if

$$y = \frac{\vartheta_3}{\vartheta_2} \frac{\vartheta_1 (u/\vartheta_3{}^2)}{\vartheta_4 (u/\vartheta_3{}^2)},$$

the Theta-functions being formed with parameter τ, then

$$\left(\frac{dy}{du}\right)^2 = (1 - y^2)(1 - k^2 y^2),$$

where $k^{\frac{1}{2}} = \vartheta_2(0\,|\,\tau)/\vartheta_3(0\,|\,\tau)$. Conversely, if the constant k (called the *modulus†*) be given, then, unless $k^2 \geqslant 1$ or $k^2 \leqslant 0$, a value of τ can be found

---

* These functions were introduced by Jacobi, but many of their properties were obtained independently by Abel, who used a different notation. See the note on p. 512.

† If $0 < k < 1$, and θ is the acute angle such that $\sin \theta = k$, θ is called the *modular angle*.

(§§ 21·7–21·712) for which $\vartheta_2^4(0\,|\,\tau)/\vartheta_3^4(0\,|\,\tau) = k^2$, so that the solution of the differential equation

$$\left(\frac{dy}{du}\right)^2 = (1 - y^2)(1 - k^2 y^2)$$

subject to the condition $\left(\dfrac{dy}{du}\right)_{u=y=0} = 1$ is

$$y = \frac{\vartheta_3}{\vartheta_2} \frac{\vartheta_1(u/\vartheta_3^2)}{\vartheta_4(u/\vartheta_3^2)},$$

the Theta-functions being formed with the parameter τ which has been determined.

The differential equation may be written

$$u = \int_0^y (1 - t^2)^{-\frac{1}{2}} (1 - k^2 t^2)^{-\frac{1}{2}} dt,$$

and, by the methods of § 21·73, it may be shewn that, if y and u are connected by this integral formula, y may be expressed in terms of u as the quotient of two Theta-functions, in the form already given.

Thus, if

$$u = \int_0^y (1 - t^2)^{-\frac{1}{2}} (1 - k^2 t^2)^{-\frac{1}{2}} dt,$$

y may be regarded as the function of u defined by the quotient of the Theta-functions, so that y is an analytic function of u except at its singularities, which are all simple poles; to denote this functional dependence, we write

$$y = \operatorname{sn}(u, k),$$

or simply $y = \operatorname{sn} u$, when it is unnecessary to emphasize the modulus*.

The function $\operatorname{sn} u$ is known as a *Jacobian elliptic function* of u, and

$$\operatorname{sn} u = \frac{\vartheta_3}{\vartheta_2} \frac{\vartheta_1(u/\vartheta_3^2)}{\vartheta_4(u/\vartheta_3^2)} \quad \dots\dots\dots\dots\dots\dots(A).$$

[Unless the theory of the Theta-functions is assumed, it is exceedingly difficult to shew that the integral formula defines y as a function of u which is analytic except at simple poles. Cf. Hancock, *Elliptic Functions*, I. (New York, 1910).]

Now write
$$\operatorname{cn}(u, k) = \frac{\vartheta_4}{\vartheta_2} \frac{\vartheta_2(u/\vartheta_3^2)}{\vartheta_4(u/\vartheta_3^2)} \quad \dots\dots\dots\dots\dots(B),$$

$$\operatorname{dn}(u, k) = \frac{\vartheta_4}{\vartheta_3} \frac{\vartheta_3(u/\vartheta_3^2)}{\vartheta_4(u/\vartheta_3^2)}. \quad \dots\dots\dots\dots\dots\dots(C).$$

Then, from the relation of § 21·6, we have

$$\frac{d}{du} \operatorname{sn} u = \operatorname{cn} u \, \operatorname{dn} u. \quad \dots\dots\dots\dots\dots\dots(I),$$

---

* The modulus will always be inserted when it is not k.

and from the relations of § 21·2, we have

$$\operatorname{sn}^2 u + \operatorname{cn}^2 u = 1 \quad \dots\dots\dots\dots\dots\dots(\mathrm{II}),$$

$$k^2 \operatorname{sn}^2 u + \operatorname{dn}^2 u = 1 \quad \dots\dots\dots\dots\dots\dots(\mathrm{III}),$$

and, obviously, $$\operatorname{cn} 0 = \operatorname{dn} 0 = 1 \quad \dots\dots\dots\dots\dots\dots(\mathrm{IV}).$$

We shall now discuss the properties of the functions sn u, cn u, dn u as defined by the equations (A), (B), (C) by using the four relations (I), (II), (III), (IV); these four relations are sufficient to make sn u, cn u, dn u determinate functions of u. It will be assumed, when necessary, that sn u, cn u, dn u are one-valued functions of u, analytic except at their poles; it will also be assumed that they are one-valued analytic functions of k^2 when cuts are made in the plane of the complex variable k^2 from 1 to $+\infty$ and from 0 to $-\infty$.

22·12. *Simple properties of* sn u, cn u, dn u.

From the integral $u = \int_0^y (1 - t^2)^{-\frac{1}{2}} (1 - k^2 t^2)^{-\frac{1}{2}} dt$, it is evident, on writing $-t$ for t, that, if the sign of y be changed, the sign of u is also changed.

Hence sn u *is an odd function of* u.

Since $\operatorname{sn}(-u) = -\operatorname{sn} u$, it follows from (II) that $\operatorname{cn}(-u) = \pm \operatorname{cn} u$; on account of the one-valuedness of cn u, by the theory of analytic continuation it follows that either the upper sign, or else the lower sign, must always be taken. In the special case $u = 0$, the upper sign has to be taken, and so it has to be taken always; hence $\operatorname{cn}(-u) = \operatorname{cn} u$, *and* cn u *is an even function of* u. In like manner, dn u is an even function of u.

These results are also obvious from the definitions (A), (B) and (C) of § 22·11.

Next, let us differentiate the equation $\operatorname{sn}^2 u + \operatorname{cn}^2 u = 1$; on using equation (I), we get

$$\frac{d \operatorname{cn} u}{du} = -\operatorname{sn} u \operatorname{dn} u;$$

in like manner, from equations (III) and (I) we have

$$\frac{d \operatorname{dn} u}{du} = -k^2 \operatorname{sn} u \operatorname{cn} u.$$

22·121. *The complementary modulus.*

If $k^2 + k'^2 = 1$ and $k' \to +1$ as $k \to 0$, k' is known as the *complementary modulus*. On account of the cut in the k^2-plane from 1 to $+\infty$, k' is a one-valued function of k.

[With the aid of the Theta-functions, we can make $k'^{\frac{1}{2}}$ one-valued, by defining it to be $\vartheta_4(0 \mid \tau)/\vartheta_3(0 \mid \tau)$.]

Example. Shew that, if

$$u = \int_v^1 (1 - t^2)^{-\frac{1}{2}} (k'^2 + k^2 t^2)^{-\frac{1}{2}} dt$$

then $$y = \operatorname{cn}(u, k).$$

Also, shew that, if $\qquad u = \int_y^1 (1-t^2)^{-\frac{1}{2}} (t^2 - k'^2)^{-\frac{1}{2}} dt,$

then $\qquad\qquad\qquad\qquad y = \text{dn}\,(u,\,k).$

[These results are sometimes written in the form

$$u = \int_{\text{cn}\,u}^1 (1-t'^2)^{-\frac{1}{2}} (k'^2 + k^2 t^2)^{-\frac{1}{2}} dt = \int_{\text{dn}\,u}^1 (1-t^2)^{-\frac{1}{2}} (t^2 - k'^2)^{-\frac{1}{2}} dt.]$$

22·122. *Glaisher's notation* for quotients.*

A short and convenient notation has been invented by Glaisher to express reciprocals and quotients of the Jacobian elliptic functions; the reciprocals are denoted by reversing the order of the letters which express the function, thus

$$\text{ns}\,u = 1/\text{sn}\,u, \quad \text{nc}\,u = 1/\text{cn}\,u, \quad \text{nd}\,u = 1/\text{dn}\,u;$$

while quotients are denoted by writing in order the first letters of the numerator and denominator functions, thus

$$\text{sc}\,u = \text{sn}\,u/\text{cn}\,u, \quad \text{sd}\,u = \text{sn}\,u/\text{dn}\,u, \quad \text{cd}\,u = \text{cn}\,u/\text{dn}\,u,$$

$$\text{cs}\,u = \text{cn}\,u/\text{sn}\,u, \quad \text{ds}\,u = \text{dn}\,u/\text{sn}\,u, \quad \text{dc}\,u = \text{dn}\,u/\text{cn}\,u.$$

[NOTE. Jacobi's notation for the functions sn u, cn u, dn u was sinam u, cosam u, Δam u, the abbreviations now in use being due to Gudermann†; who also wrote tn u, as an abbreviation for tanam u, in place of what is now written sc u.

The reason for Jacobi's notation was that he regarded the inverse of the integral

$$u = \int_0^\phi (1 - k^2 \sin^2 \theta)^{-\frac{1}{2}} d\theta$$

as fundamental, and wrote ‡ $\phi = \text{am}\,u$; he also wrote $\Delta\phi = (1 - k^2 \sin^2 \phi)^{\frac{1}{2}}$ for $\dfrac{d\phi}{du}$.]

Example.   Obtain the following results:

$$u = \int_0^{\text{sc}\,u} (1+t^2)^{-\frac{1}{2}} (1 + k'^2 t^2)^{-\frac{1}{2}} dt \qquad = \int_{\text{cs}\,u}^\infty (t^2+1)^{-\frac{1}{2}} (t^2 + k'^2)^{-\frac{1}{2}} dt$$

$$= \int_0^{\text{sd}\,u} (1 - k'^2 t^2)^{-\frac{1}{2}} (1 + k^2 t^2)^{-\frac{1}{2}} dt = \int_{\text{ds}\,u}^\infty (t^2 - k'^2)^{-\frac{1}{2}} (t^2 + k^2)^{-\frac{1}{2}} dt$$

$$= \int_{\text{cd}\,u}^1 (1-t^2)^{-\frac{1}{2}} (1 - k^2 t^2)^{-\frac{1}{2}} dt \qquad = \int_{\text{dc}\,u}^1 (t^2 - 1)^{-\frac{1}{2}} (t^2 - k^2)^{-\frac{1}{2}} dt$$

$$= \int_{\text{ns}\,u}^\infty (t^2 - 1)^{-\frac{1}{2}} (t^2 - k^2)^{-\frac{1}{2}} dt \qquad = \int_1^{\text{nc}\,u} (t^2 - 1)^{-\frac{1}{2}} (k'^2 t^2 + k^2)^{-\frac{1}{2}} dt$$

$$= \int_1^{\text{nd}\,u} (t^2 - 1)^{-\frac{1}{2}} (1 - k'^2 t^2)^{-\frac{1}{2}} dt.$$

22·2. *The addition-theorem for the function* sn u.

We shall now shew how to express $\text{sn}\,(u + v)$ in terms of the Jacobian elliptic functions of u and v; the result will be the addition-theorem for the function sn u; it will be an addition-theorem in the strict sense, as it can be written in the form of an algebraic relation connecting sn u, sn v, sn $(u + v)$.

---

* *Messenger of Mathematics,* XI. (1882), p. 86.
† *Journal für Math.* XVIII. (1838), pp. 12, 20.
‡ *Fundamenta Nova,* p. 30. As $k \to 0$, am $u \to u$.

[There are numerous methods of establishing the result ; the one given is essentially due to Euler*, who was the first to obtain (in 1756, 1757) the integral of

$$\frac{dx}{\sqrt{X}} + \frac{dy}{\sqrt{Y}} = 0$$

in the form of an algebraic relation between x and y, when X denotes a quartic function of x and Y is the same quartic function of y.

Three† other methods are given as examples, at the end of this section.]

Suppose that u and v vary while $u + v$ remains constant and equal to α, say, so that

$$\frac{dv}{du} = -1.$$

Now introduce, as new variables, s_1 and s_2 defined by the equations

$$s_1 = \operatorname{sn} u, \quad s_2 = \operatorname{sn} v,$$

so that‡

$$\dot{s}_1^2 = (1 - s_1^2)(1 - k^2 s_1^2),$$

and

$$\dot{s}_2^2 = (1 - s_2^2)(1 - k^2 s_2^2), \text{ since } \dot{v}^2 = 1.$$

Differentiating with regard to u and dividing by $2\dot{s}_1$ and $2\dot{s}_2$ respectively, we find that, for general values§ of u and v,

$$\ddot{s}_1 = -(1 + k^2) s_1 + 2k^2 s_1^3, \quad \ddot{s}_2 = -(1 + k^2) s_2 + 2k^2 s_2^3.$$

Hence, by some easy algebra,

$$\frac{\ddot{s}_1 s_2 - \ddot{s}_2 s_1}{\dot{s}_1^2 s_2^2 - \dot{s}_2^2 s_1^2} = \frac{2k^2 s_1 s_2 (s_1^2 - s_2^2)}{(s_2^2 - s_1^2)(1 - k^2 s_1^2 s_2^2)},$$

and so

$$(\dot{s}_1 s_2 - \dot{s}_2 s_1)^{-1} \frac{d}{du}(\dot{s}_1 s_2 - \dot{s}_2 s_1) = (1 - k^2 s_1^2 s_2^2)^{-1} \frac{d}{du}(1 - k^2 s_1^2 s_2^2);$$

on integrating this equation we have

$$\frac{\dot{s}_1 s_2 - \dot{s}_2 s_1}{1 - k^2 s_1^2 s_2^2} = C,$$

where C is the constant of integration.

Replacing the expressions on the left by their values in terms of u and v we get

$$\frac{\operatorname{cn} u \operatorname{dn} u \operatorname{sn} v + \operatorname{cn} v \operatorname{dn} v \operatorname{sn} u}{1 - k^2 \operatorname{sn}^2 u \operatorname{sn}^2 v} = C.$$

* *Acta Petropolitana*, VI. (1761), pp. 35–57. Euler had obtained some special cases of this result a few years earlier.

† Another method is given by Legendre, *Fonctions Elliptiques*, I. (Paris, 1825), p. 20, and an interesting geometrical proof was given by Jacobi, *Journal für Math.* III. (1828), p. 376.

‡ For brevity, we shall denote differential coefficients with regard to u by dots, thus

$$\dot{v} \equiv \frac{dv}{du}, \quad \ddot{v} \equiv \frac{d^2 v}{du^2}.$$

§ I.e. those values for which $\operatorname{cn} u \operatorname{dn} u$ and $\operatorname{cn} v \operatorname{dn} v$ do not vanish.

That is to say, we have two integrals of the equation $du + dv = 0$, namely (i) $u + v = \alpha$ and (ii)

$$\frac{\operatorname{sn} u \operatorname{cn} v \operatorname{dn} v + \operatorname{sn} v \operatorname{cn} u \operatorname{dn} u}{1 - k^2 \operatorname{sn}^2 u \operatorname{sn}^2 v} = C,$$

each integral involving an arbitrary constant. By the general theory of differential equations of the first order, these integrals cannot be functionally independent, and so

$$\frac{\operatorname{sn} u \operatorname{cn} v \operatorname{dn} v + \operatorname{sn} v \operatorname{cn} u \operatorname{dn} u}{1 - k^2 \operatorname{sn}^2 u \operatorname{sn}^2 v}$$

is expressible as a function of $u + v$; call this function $f(u + v)$.

On putting $v = 0$, we see that $f(u) = \operatorname{sn} u$; and so the function f is the sn function.

We have thus demonstrated the result that

$$\operatorname{sn}(u + v) = \frac{\operatorname{sn} u \operatorname{cn} v \operatorname{dn} v + \operatorname{sn} v \operatorname{cn} u \operatorname{dn} u}{1 - k^2 \operatorname{sn}^2 u \operatorname{sn}^2 v},$$

which is the addition-theorem.

Using an obvious notation*, we may write

$$\operatorname{sn}(u + v) = \frac{s_1 c_2 d_2 + s_2 c_1 d_1}{1 - k^2 s_1^2 s_2^2}.$$

Example 1.   Obtain the addition-theorem for $\sin u$ by using the results

$$\left(\frac{d \sin u}{du}\right)^2 = 1 - \sin^2 u, \quad \left(\frac{d \sin v}{dv}\right)^2 = 1 - \sin^2 v.$$

Example 2.   Prove from first principles that

$$\left(\frac{\partial}{\partial v} - \frac{\partial}{\partial u}\right) \frac{s_1 c_2 d_2 + s_2 c_1 d_1}{1 - k^2 s_1^2 s_2^2} = 0,$$

and deduce the addition-theorem for sn u.

(Abel, Journal für Math. II. (1827), p. 105.)

Example 3.   Shew that

$$\operatorname{sn}(u + v) = \frac{s_1^2 - s_2^2}{s_1 c_2 d_2 - s_2 c_1 d_1} = \frac{s_1 c_1 d_2 + s_2 c_2 d_1}{c_1 c_2 + s_1 d_1 s_2 d_2} = \frac{s_1 d_1 c_2 + s_2 d_2 c_1}{d_1 d_2 + k^2 s_1 s_2 c_1 c_2}.$$

(Cayley, Elliptic Functions (1876), p. 63.)

Example 4.   Obtain the addition-theorem for sn u from the results

$$\vartheta_1(y+z)\,\vartheta_4(y-z)\,\vartheta_2\vartheta_3 = \vartheta_1(y)\,\vartheta_4(y)\,\vartheta_2(z)\,\vartheta_3(z) + \vartheta_2(y)\,\vartheta_3(y)\,\vartheta_1(z)\,\vartheta_4(z),$$

$$\vartheta_4(y+z)\,\vartheta_4(y-z)\,\vartheta_4^2 = \vartheta_4^2(y)\,\vartheta_4^2(z) - \vartheta_1^2(y)\,\vartheta_1^2(z),$$

given in Chapter XXI, Miscellaneous Examples 1 and 3 (pp. 487, 488).   (Jacobi.)

Example 5.   Assuming that the coordinates of any point on the curve

$$y^2 = (1 - x^2)(1 - k^2 x^2)$$

can be expressed in the form (sn u, cn u dn u), obtain the addition-theorem for sn u by Abel's method (§ 20·312).

---

* This notation is due to Glaisher, *Messenger*, X. (1881), pp. 92, 124.

[Consider the intersections of the given curve with the variable curve $y = 1 + mx + nx^2$; one is $(0, 1)$; let the others have parameters u_1, u_2, u_3, of which u_1, u_2 may be chosen arbitrarily by suitable choice of m and n. Shew that $u_1 + u_2 + u_3$ is constant, by the method of § 20·312, and deduce that this constant is zero by taking

$$m = 0, \quad n = -\tfrac{1}{2}(1 + k^2).$$

Observe also that, by reason of the relations

$$(k^2 - n^2)\, x_1 x_2 x_3 = 2m, \quad (k^2 - n^2)\,(x_1 + x_2 + x_3) = 2mn,$$

we have

$$x_3 (1 - k^2 x_1^2 x_2^2) = x_3 - \left(1 + \frac{n^2}{k^2 - n^2}\right) 2m x_1 x_2 = x_3 - 2m x_1 x_2 - n x_1 x_2 (x_1 + x_2 + x_3)$$

$$= (x_1 + x_2 + x_3 - n x_1 x_2 x_3) - (x_1 + x_2) - 2m x_1 x_2 - n x_1 x_2 (x_1 + x_2)$$

$$= - x_1 y_2 - x_2 y_1.]$$

22·21. *The addition-theorems for* cn u *and* dn u.

We shall now establish the results

$$\operatorname{cn}(u + v) = \frac{\operatorname{cn} u \operatorname{cn} v - \operatorname{sn} u \operatorname{sn} v \operatorname{dn} u \operatorname{dn} v}{1 - k^2 \operatorname{sn}^2 u \operatorname{sn}^2 v},$$

$$\operatorname{dn}(u + v) = \frac{\operatorname{dn} u \operatorname{dn} v - k^2 \operatorname{sn} u \operatorname{sn} v \operatorname{cn} u \operatorname{cn} v}{1 - k^2 \operatorname{sn}^2 u \operatorname{sn}^2 v};$$

the most simple method of obtaining them is from the formula for sn $(u + v)$.

Using the notation introduced at the end of § 22·2, we have

$$(1 - k^2 s_1^2 s_2^2)^2 \operatorname{cn}^2 (u + v) = (1 - k^2 s_1^2 s_2^2)^2 \left\{1 - \operatorname{sn}^2 (u + v)\right\}$$

$$= (1 - k^2 s_1^2 s_2^2)^2 - (s_1 c_2 d_2 + s_2 c_1 d_1)^2$$

$$= 1 - 2k^2 s_1^2 s_2^2 + k^4 s_1^4 s_2^4 - s_1^2 (1 - s_2^2)(1 - k^2 s_2^2)$$

$$\qquad\qquad - s_2^2 (1 - s_1^2)(1 - k^2 s_1^2) - 2 s_1 s_2 c_1 c_2 d_1 d_2$$

$$= (1 - s_1^2)(1 - s_2^2) + s_1^2 s_2^2 (1 - k^2 s_1^2)(1 - k^2 s_2^2)$$

$$\qquad\qquad - 2 s_1 s_2 c_1 c_2 d_1 d_2$$

$$= (c_1 c_2 - s_1 s_2 d_1 d_2)^2$$

and so

$$\operatorname{cn}(u + v) = \pm \frac{c_1 c_2 - s_1 s_2 d_1 d_2}{1 - k^2 s_1^2 s_2^2}.$$

But both of these expressions are one-valued functions of u, analytic except at isolated poles and zeros, and it is inconsistent with the theory of analytic continuation that their ratio should be $+1$ for some values of u, and -1 for other values, so the ambiguous sign is really definite; putting $u = 0$, we see that the plus sign has to be taken. The first formula is consequently proved.

The formula for dn $(u + v)$ follows in like manner from the identity

$$(1 - k^2 s_1^2 s_2^2)^2 - k^2 (s_1 c_2 d_2 + s_2 c_1 d_1)^2$$

$$\equiv (1 - k^2 s_1^2)(1 - k^2 s_2^2) + k^4 s_1^2 s_2^2 (1 - s_1^2)(1 - s_2^2) - 2k^2 s_1 s_2 c_1 c_2 d_1 d_2,$$

the proof of which is left to the reader.

Example 1. Shew that

$$\operatorname{dn}(u+v)\operatorname{dn}(u-v)=\frac{d_2{}^2-k^2 s_1{}^2 c_2{}^2}{1-k^2 s_1{}^2 s_2{}^2}.$$

(Jacobi.)

[A set of 33 formulae of this nature connecting functions of $u+v$ and of $u-v$ is given in the *Fundamenta Nova*, pp. 32–34.]

Example 2. Shew that

$$\frac{\partial}{\partial u}\frac{\operatorname{cn} u+\operatorname{cn} v}{\operatorname{sn} u\operatorname{dn} v+\operatorname{sn} v\operatorname{dn} u}=\frac{\partial}{\partial v}\frac{\operatorname{cn} u+\operatorname{cn} v}{\operatorname{sn} u\operatorname{dn} v+\operatorname{sn} v\operatorname{dn} u},$$

so that $(\operatorname{cn} u+\operatorname{cn} v)/(\operatorname{sn} u\operatorname{dn} v+\operatorname{sn} v\operatorname{dn} u)$ is a function of $u+v$ only; and deduce that it is equal to $\{1+\operatorname{cn}(u+v)\}/\operatorname{sn}(u+v)$.

Obtain a corresponding result for the function $(s_1 c_2 + s_2 c_1)/(d_1 + d_2)$.

(Cayley, *Messenger*, XIV. (1885), pp. 56–61.)

Example 3. Shew that

$$1-k^2\operatorname{sn}^2(u+v)\operatorname{sn}^2(u-v)=(1-k^2\operatorname{sn}^4 u)(1-k^2\operatorname{sn}^4 v)(1-k^2\operatorname{sn}^2 u\operatorname{sn}^2 v)^{-2},$$

$$k'^2+k^2\operatorname{cn}^2(u+v)\operatorname{cn}^2(u-v)=(k'^2+k^2\operatorname{cn}^4 u)(k'^2+k^2\operatorname{cn}^4 v)(1-k^2\operatorname{sn}^2 u\operatorname{sn}^2 v)^{-2}.$$

(Jacobi and Glaisher.)

Example 4. Obtain the addition-theorems for $\operatorname{cn}(u+v)$, $\operatorname{dn}(u+v)$ by the method of § 22·2 example 4.

Example 5. Using Glaisher's abridged notation (*Messenger*, X. (1881), p. 105), namely

$$s,\ c,\ d=\operatorname{sn} u,\ \operatorname{cn} u,\ \operatorname{dn} u,\quad\text{and}\quad S,\ C,\ D=\operatorname{sn} 2u,\ \operatorname{cn} 2u,\ \operatorname{dn} 2u,$$

prove that

$$S=\frac{2scd}{1-k^2 s^4},\quad C=\frac{1-2s^2+k^2 s^4}{1-k^2 s^4},\quad D=\frac{1-2k^2 s^2+k^2 s^4}{1-k^2 s^4},$$

$$s=\frac{(1+S)^{\frac{1}{2}}-(1-S)^{\frac{1}{2}}}{(1+kS)^{\frac{1}{2}}+(1-kS)^{\frac{1}{2}}}.$$

Example 6. With the notation of example 5, shew that

$$s^2=\frac{1-C}{1+D}=\frac{1-D}{k^2(1+C)}=\frac{D-k^2 C-k'^2}{k^2(D-C)}=\frac{D-C}{k'^2+D-k^2 C},$$

$$c^2=\frac{D+C}{1+D}=\frac{D+k^2 C-k'^2}{k^2(1+C)}=\frac{k'^2(1-D)}{k^2(D-C)}=\frac{k'^2(1+C)}{k'^2+D-k^2 C},$$

$$d^2=\frac{k'^2+D+k^2 C}{1+D}=\frac{D+C}{1+C}=\frac{k'^2(1-C)}{D-C}=\frac{k'^2(1+D)}{k'^2+D-k^2 C}.$$

(Glaisher.)

22·3. *The constant K.*

We have seen that, if

$$u=\int_0^y (1-t^2)^{-\frac{1}{2}}(1-k^2 t^2)^{-\frac{1}{2}}\,dt,$$

then

$$y=\operatorname{sn}(u,k).$$

If we take the upper limit to be unity (the path of integration being a straight line), it is customary to denote the value of the integral by the symbol K, so that $\operatorname{sn}(K, k)=1$.

[It will be seen in § 22·302 that this definition of K is equivalent to the definition as $\frac{1}{2}\pi\vartheta_3{}^2$ in § 21·61.]

It is obvious that cn $K = 0$ and dn $K = \pm k'$; to fix the ambiguity in sign, suppose $0 < k < 1$, and trace the change in $(1 - k^2 t^2)^{\frac{1}{2}}$ as t increases from 0 to 1; since this expression is initially unity and as neither of its branch points (at $t = \pm k^{-1}$) is encountered, the final value of the expression is positive, and so it is $+ k'$; and therefore, since dn K is a continuous function of k, its value is always $+ k'$.

The elliptic functions of K are thus given by the formulae

$$\text{sn } K = 1, \quad \text{cn } K = 0, \quad \text{dn } K = k'.$$

22·301. *The expression of K in terms of k.*

In the integral defining K, write $t = \sin \phi$, and we have at once

$$K = \int_0^{\frac{1}{2}\pi} (1 - k^2 \sin^2 \phi)^{-\frac{1}{2}} \, d\phi.$$

When $|k| < 1$, the integrand may be expanded in a series of powers of k, the series converging uniformly with regard to ϕ (by § 3·34, since $\sin^{2n} \phi \leqslant 1$); integrating term-by-term (§ 4·7), we at once get

$$K = \tfrac{1}{2} \pi F\left(\tfrac{1}{2}, \ \tfrac{1}{2}; \ 1; \ k^2\right) = \tfrac{1}{2} \pi F\left(\tfrac{1}{2}, \ \tfrac{1}{2}; \ 1; \ c\right),$$

where $c = k^2$. By the theory of analytic continuation, this result holds for all values of c when a cut is made from 1 to $+\infty$ in the c-plane, since both the integrand and the hypergeometric function are one-valued and analytic in the cut plane.

Example. Shew that

$$\frac{d}{dk}\left(kk'^2 \frac{dK}{dk}\right) = kK.$$

(Legendre, *Fonctions Elliptiques*, I. (1825), p. 62.)

22·302. *The equivalence of the definitions of K.*

Taking $u = \tfrac{1}{2} \pi \vartheta_3^2$ in § 21·61, we see at once that sn $(\tfrac{1}{2}\pi \vartheta_3^2) = 1$ and so cn $(\tfrac{1}{2}\pi \vartheta_3^2) = 0$. Consequently, $1 - \text{sn } u$ has a *double* zero at $\tfrac{1}{2}\pi \vartheta_3^2$. Therefore, since the number of poles of sn u in the cell with corners 0, $2\pi \vartheta_3^2$, $\pi(\tau+1)\vartheta_3^2$, $\pi(\tau-1)\vartheta_3^2$ is two, it follows from § 20·13 that the *only* zeros of $1 - \text{sn } u$ are at the points $u = \tfrac{1}{2}\pi(4m+1+2n\tau)\vartheta_3^2$, where m and n are integers. Therefore, with the definition of § 22·3,

$$K = \tfrac{1}{2}\pi(4m+1+2n\tau)\vartheta_3^2.$$

Now take τ to be a pure imaginary, so that $0 < k < 1$, and K is real; and we have $n = 0$, so that

$$\tfrac{1}{2}\pi(4m+1)\vartheta_3^2 = \int_0^{\frac{1}{2}\pi} (1 - k^2 \sin^2 \phi)^{-\frac{1}{2}} \, d\phi,$$

where m is a positive integer or zero; it is obviously not a negative integer.

If m is a positive integer, since $\int_0^a (1 - k^2 \sin^2 \phi)^{-\frac{1}{2}} \, d\phi$ is a continuous function of a and so passes through all values between 0 and K as a increases from 0 to $\tfrac{1}{2}\pi$, we can find a value of a *less* than $\tfrac{1}{2}\pi$, such that

$$K/(4m+1) = \tfrac{1}{2}\pi \vartheta_3^2 = \int_0^a (1 - k^2 \sin^2 \phi)^{-\frac{1}{2}} \, d\phi \ ;$$

and so $\text{sn }(\tfrac{1}{2}\pi \vartheta_3^2) = \sin a < 1,$

which is untrue, since $\text{sn }(\tfrac{1}{2}\pi \vartheta_3^2) = 1.$

Therefore m *must be zero*, that is to say we have

$$K = \tfrac{1}{2}\pi \vartheta_3^2.$$

But both K and $\tfrac{1}{2}\pi\vartheta_3^2$ are analytic functions of k when the c-plane is cut from 1 to $+\infty$, and so, by the theory of analytic continuation, this result, proved when $0 < k < 1$, persists throughout the cut plane.

The equivalence of the definitions of K has therefore been established.

Example 1. By considering the integral

$$\int_0^{(1+)} (1-t^2)^{-\frac{1}{2}} (1-k^2 t^2)^{-\frac{1}{2}} \, dt,$$

shew that $\operatorname{sn} 2K = 0$.

Example 2. Prove that

$$\operatorname{sn} \tfrac{1}{2}K = (1+k')^{-\frac{1}{2}}, \quad \operatorname{cn} \tfrac{1}{2}K = k'^{\frac{1}{2}}(1+k')^{-\frac{1}{2}}, \quad \operatorname{dn} \tfrac{1}{2}K = k'^{\frac{1}{2}}.$$

[Notice that when $u = \tfrac{1}{2}K$, $\operatorname{cn} 2u = 0$. The simplest way of determining the signs to be attached to the various radicals is to make $k \to 0$, $k' \to 1$, and then $\operatorname{sn} u$, $\operatorname{cn} u$, $\operatorname{dn} u$ degenerate into $\sin u$, $\cos u$, 1.]

Example 3. Prove, by means of the theory of Theta-functions, that

$$\operatorname{cs} \tfrac{1}{2}K = \operatorname{dn} \tfrac{1}{2}K = k'^{\frac{1}{2}}.$$

22·31. *The periodic properties (associated with K) of the Jacobian elliptic functions.*

The intimate connexion of K with periodic properties of the functions $\operatorname{sn} u$, $\operatorname{cn} u$, $\operatorname{dn} u$, which may be anticipated from the periodic properties of Theta-functions associated with $\tfrac{1}{2}\pi$, will now be demonstrated directly from the addition-theorem.

By § 22·2, we have

$$\operatorname{sn}(u+K) = \frac{\operatorname{sn} u \operatorname{cn} K \operatorname{dn} K + \operatorname{sn} K \operatorname{cn} u \operatorname{dn} u}{1 - k^2 \operatorname{sn}^2 u \operatorname{sn}^2 K} = \operatorname{cd} u.$$

In like manner, from § 22·21,

$$\operatorname{cn}(u+K) = -k' \operatorname{sd} u, \quad \operatorname{dn}(u+K) = k' \operatorname{nd} u.$$

Hence

$$\operatorname{sn}(u+2K) = \frac{\operatorname{cn}(u+K)}{\operatorname{dn}(u+K)} = -\frac{k' \operatorname{sd} u}{k' \operatorname{nd} u} = -\operatorname{sn} u,$$

and, similarly, $\operatorname{cn}(u+2K) = -\operatorname{cn} u$, $\quad \operatorname{dn}(u+2K) = \operatorname{dn} u$.

Finally, $\quad \operatorname{sn}(u+4K) = -\operatorname{sn}(u+2K) = \operatorname{sn} u$, $\quad \operatorname{cn}(u+4K) = \operatorname{cn} u$.

Thus $4K$ is a period of each of the functions $\operatorname{sn} u$, $\operatorname{cn} u$, *while* $\operatorname{dn} u$ *has the smaller period $2K$.*

Example 1. Obtain the results

$$\operatorname{sn}(u+K) = \operatorname{cd} u, \quad \operatorname{cn}(u+K) = -k' \operatorname{sd} u, \quad \operatorname{dn}(u+K) = k' \operatorname{nd} u,$$

directly from the definitions of $\operatorname{sn} u$, $\operatorname{cn} u$, $\operatorname{dn} u$ as quotients of Theta-functions.

Example 2. Shew that $\qquad \operatorname{cs} u \operatorname{cs}(K-u) = k'.$

22·32.   *The constant K′.*

We shall denote the integral

$$\int_0^1 (1-t^2)^{-\frac{1}{2}} (1-k'^2 t^2)^{-\frac{1}{2}} \, dt$$

by the symbol K', so that K' is the same function of $k'^2 \,(= c')$ as K is of $k^2 \,(= c)$; and so

$$K' = \tfrac{1}{2}\pi F\left(\tfrac{1}{2},\ \tfrac{1}{2};\ 1;\ k'^2\right),$$

when the c'-plane is cut from 1 to $+\infty$, i.e. when the c-plane is cut from 0 to $-\infty$.

To shew that this definition of K' is equivalent to the definition of § 21·61, we observe that if $\tau\tau' = -1$, K is the *one-valued* function of k^2, in the cut plane, defined by the equations

$$K = \tfrac{1}{2}\pi\vartheta_3^2(0 \mid \tau), \quad k^2 = \vartheta_2^4(0 \mid \tau) \div \vartheta_3^4(0 \mid \tau),$$

while, with the definition of § 21·51,

$$K' = \tfrac{1}{2}\pi\vartheta_3^2(0 \mid \tau'), \quad k'^2 = \vartheta_2^4(0 \mid \tau') \div \vartheta_3^4(0 \mid \tau'),$$

so that K' must be the same function of k'^2 as K is of k^2; and this is consistent with the integral definition of K' as

$$\int_0^1 (1-t^2)^{-\frac{1}{2}} (1-k'^2 t^2)^{-\frac{1}{2}} \, dt.$$

It will now be shewn that, if the c-plane be cut from 0 to $-\infty$ and from 1 to $+\infty$, then, in the cut plane, K' may be defined by the equation

$$K' = \int_1^{1/k} (s^2-1)^{-\frac{1}{2}} (1-k^2 s^2)^{-\frac{1}{2}} \, ds.$$

First suppose that $0 < k < 1$, so that $0 < k' < 1$, and then the integrals concerned are real.   In the integral

$$\int_0^1 (1-t^2)^{-\frac{1}{2}} (1-k'^2 t^2)^{-\frac{1}{2}} \, dt$$

make the substitution

$$s = (1-k'^2 t^2)^{-\frac{1}{2}},$$

which gives

$$(s^2-1)^{\frac{1}{2}} = k't(1-k'^2 t^2)^{-\frac{1}{2}}, \quad (1-k^2 s^2)^{\frac{1}{2}} = k'(1-t^2)^{\frac{1}{2}}(1-k'^2 t^2)^{-\frac{1}{2}},$$

$$\frac{ds}{dt} = \frac{k'^2 t}{(1-k'^2 t^2)^{\frac{3}{2}}},$$

it being understood that the positive value of each radical is to be taken. On substitution, we at once get the result stated, namely that

$$K' = \int_1^{1/k} (s^2-1)^{-\frac{1}{2}} (1-k^2 s^2)^{-\frac{1}{2}} \, ds,$$

provided that $0 < k < 1$; the result has next to be extended to complex values of k.

Consider $\qquad\qquad \int_0^{1/k} (1-t^2)^{-\frac{1}{2}} (1-k^2t^2)^{-\frac{1}{2}}\, dt,$

the path of integration passing above the point 1, and not crossing the imaginary axis*. The path may be taken to be the straight lines joining 0 to $1-\delta$ and $1+\delta$ to k^{-1} together with a semicircle of (small) radius δ above the real axis. If $(1-t^2)^{\frac{1}{2}}$ and $(1-k^2t^2)^{\frac{1}{2}}$ reduce to $+1$ at $t=0$ the value of the former at $1+\delta$ is $e^{-\frac{1}{2}\pi i}\delta^{\frac{1}{2}}(2+\delta)^{\frac{1}{2}} = -i(t^2-1)^{\frac{1}{2}}$, where each radical is positive; while the value of the latter at $t=1$ is $+k'$ when k is real, and hence by the theory of analytic continuation it is always $+k'$.

Make $\delta \to 0$, and the integral round the semicircle tends to zero like $\delta^{\frac{1}{2}}$; and so

$$\int_0^{1/k} (1-t^2)^{-\frac{1}{2}}(1-k^2t^2)^{-\frac{1}{2}}\, dt = K + i\int_1^{1/k} (t^2-1)^{-\frac{1}{2}}(1-k^2t^2)^{-\frac{1}{2}}\, dt.$$

Now $\qquad \int_0^{1/k} (1-t^2)^{-\frac{1}{2}}(1-k^2t^2)^{-\frac{1}{2}}\, dt = \int_0^1 (k^2-u^2)^{-\frac{1}{2}}(1-u^2)^{-\frac{1}{2}}\, du,$

which† is analytic throughout the cut plane, while K is analytic throughout the cut plane.

Hence $\qquad\qquad \int_1^{1/k} (t^2-1)^{-\frac{1}{2}}(1-k^2t^2)^{-\frac{1}{2}}\, dt$

is analytic throughout the cut plane, and as it is equal to the analytic function K' when $0 < k < 1$, the equality persists throughout the cut plane; that is to say

$$K' = \int_1^{1/k} (t^2-1)^{-\frac{1}{2}}(1-k^2t^2)^{-\frac{1}{2}}\, dt,$$

when the c-plane is cut from 0 to $-\infty$ and from 1 to $+\infty$.

Since $\qquad\qquad K + iK' = \int_0^{1/k} (1-t^2)^{-\frac{1}{2}}(1-k^2t^2)^{-\frac{1}{2}}\, dt,$

we have $\qquad\qquad \operatorname{sn}(K+iK') = 1/k, \quad \operatorname{dn}(K+iK')=0;$

while the value of $\operatorname{cn}(K+iK')$ is the value of $(1-t^2)^{\frac{1}{2}}$ when t has followed the prescribed path to the point $1/k$, and so its value is $-ik'/k$, *not* $+ik'/k$.

Example 1. Shew that

$$\frac{1}{2}\int_0^1 \{t(1-t)(1-k^2t)\}^{-\frac{1}{2}}\, dt = \frac{1}{2}\int_{1/k^2}^\infty \{t(t-1)(k^2t-1)\}^{-\frac{1}{2}}\, dt = K,$$

$$\frac{1}{2}\int_{-\infty}^0 \{-t(1-t)(1-k^2t)\}^{-\frac{1}{2}}\, dt = \frac{1}{2}\int_1^{1/k^2} \{t(t-1)(1-k^2t)\}^{-\frac{1}{2}}\, dt = K'.$$

Example 2. Shew that K' satisfies the same linear differential equation as K (§ 22·301 example).

22·33. *The periodic properties‡ (associated with $K+iK'$) of the Jacobian elliptic functions.*

If we make use of the three equations

$$\operatorname{sn}(K+iK') = k^{-1}, \quad \operatorname{cn}(K+iK') = -ik'/k, \quad \operatorname{dn}(K+iK')=0,$$

---

* $R(k) > 0$ because $|\arg c| < \pi$.

† The path of integration passes above the point $u=k$.

‡ The double periodicity of $\operatorname{sn} u$ may be inferred from dynamical considerations. See Whittaker, *Analytical Dynamics* (1917), § 44.

we get at once, from the addition-theorems for sn u, cn u, dn u, the following results :

$$\operatorname{sn}(u + K + iK') = \frac{\operatorname{sn} u \operatorname{cn}(K + iK') \operatorname{dn}(K + iK') + \operatorname{sn}(K + iK') \operatorname{cn} u \operatorname{dn} u}{1 - k^2 \operatorname{sn}^2 u \operatorname{sn}^2(K + iK')}$$

$$= k^{-1} \operatorname{dc} u,$$

and similarly
$$\operatorname{cn}(u + K + iK') = - ik'k^{-1} \operatorname{nc} u,$$
$$\operatorname{dn}(u + K + iK') = ik' \operatorname{sc} u.$$

By repeated applications of these formulae we have

$$\begin{cases} \operatorname{sn}(u + 2K + 2iK') = - \operatorname{sn} u, \\ \operatorname{cn}(u + 2K + 2iK') = \operatorname{cn} u, \\ \operatorname{dn}(u + 2K + 2iK') = - \operatorname{dn} u, \end{cases} \quad \begin{cases} \operatorname{sn}(u + 4K + 4iK') = \operatorname{sn} u, \\ \operatorname{cn}(u + 4K + 4iK') = \operatorname{cn} u, \\ \operatorname{dn}(u + 4K + 4iK') = \operatorname{dn} u. \end{cases}$$

Hence the functions sn u *and* dn u *have period* $4K + 4iK'$, *while* cn u *has the smaller period* $2K + 2iK'$.

$22\!\cdot\!34$. *The periodic properties (associated with iK') of the Jacobian elliptic functions.*

By the addition-theorem we have
$$\operatorname{sn}(u + iK') = \operatorname{sn}(u - K + K + iK')$$
$$= k^{-1} \operatorname{dc}(u - K)$$
$$= k^{-1} \operatorname{ns} u.$$

Similarly we find the equations
$$\operatorname{cn}(u + iK') = - ik^{-1} \operatorname{ds} u,$$
$$\operatorname{dn}(u + iK') = - i \operatorname{cs} u.$$

By repeated applications of these formulae we have

$$\begin{cases} \operatorname{sn}(u + 2iK') = \operatorname{sn} u, \\ \operatorname{cn}(u + 2iK') = - \operatorname{cn} u, \\ \operatorname{dn}(u + 2iK') = - \operatorname{dn} u, \end{cases} \quad \begin{cases} \operatorname{sn}(u + 4iK') = \operatorname{sn} u, \\ \operatorname{cn}(u + 4iK') = \operatorname{cn} u, \\ \operatorname{dn}(u + 4iK') = \operatorname{dn} u. \end{cases}$$

Hence the functions cn u *and* dn u *have period* $4iK'$, *while* sn u *has the smaller period* $2iK'$.

Example. Obtain the formulae
$$\operatorname{sn}(u + 2mK + 2niK') = (-)^m \operatorname{sn} u,$$
$$\operatorname{cn}(u + 2mK + 2niK') = (-)^{m+n} \operatorname{cn} u,$$
$$\operatorname{dn}(u + 2mK + 2niK') = (-)^n \operatorname{dn} u.$$

$22\!\cdot\!341$. *The behaviour of the Jacobian elliptic functions near the origin and near iK'.*

We have
$$\frac{d}{du} \operatorname{sn} u = \operatorname{cn} u \operatorname{dn} u, \quad \frac{d^3}{du^3} \operatorname{sn} u = 4k^2 \operatorname{sn}^2 u \operatorname{cn} u \operatorname{dn} u - \operatorname{cn} u \operatorname{dn} u (\operatorname{dn}^2 u + k^2 \operatorname{cn}^2 u).$$

Hence, by Maclaurin's theorem, we have, for small values of $|u|$,

$$\operatorname{sn} u = u - \frac{1}{6}(1 + k^2) u^3 + O(u^5),$$

on using the fact that sn u is an *odd* function.

In like manner

$$\operatorname{cn} u = 1 - \frac{1}{2} u^2 + O(u^4),$$

$$\operatorname{dn} u = 1 - \frac{1}{2} k^2 u^2 + O(u^4).$$

It follows that

$$\operatorname{sn} (u + iK') = k^{-1} \operatorname{ns} u$$

$$= \frac{1}{ku} \left\{ 1 - \frac{1}{6}(1 + k^2) u^2 + O(u^4) \right\}^{-1}$$

$$= \frac{1}{ku} + \frac{1 + k^2}{6k} u + O(u^3);$$

and similarly

$$\operatorname{cn} (u + iK') = \frac{-i}{ku} + \frac{2k^2 - 1}{6k} iu + O(u^3),$$

$$\operatorname{dn} (u + iK') = -\frac{i}{u} + \frac{2 - k^2}{6} iu + O(u^3).$$

It follows that at the point iK' the functions sn v, cn v, dn v *have simple poles with residues* k^{-1}, $-ik^{-1}$, $-i$ *respectively.*

Example. Obtain the residues of sn u, cn u, dn u at iK' by the theory of Theta-functions.

22·35. *General description of the functions* sn u, cn u, dn u.

The foregoing investigations of the functions sn u, cn u and dn u may be summarised in the following terms:

(I) The function sn u is a doubly-periodic function of u with periods $4K$, $2iK'$. It is analytic except at the points congruent to iK' or to $2K + iK'$ (mod. $4K$, $2iK'$); these points are simple poles, the residues at the first set all being k^{-1} and the residues at the second set all being $-k^{-1}$; and the function has a simple zero at all points congruent to 0 (mod. $2K$, $2iK'$).

It may be observed that sn u is the only function of u satisfying this description; for if $\phi(u)$ were another such function, sn $u - \phi(u)$ would have no singularities and would be a doubly-periodic function; hence (§ 20·12) it would be a constant, and this constant vanishes, as may be seen by putting $u = 0$; so that $\phi(u) \equiv$ sn u.

When $0 < k^2 < 1$, it is obvious that K and K' are real, and sn u is real for real values of u and is a pure imaginary when u is a pure imaginary.

(II) The function cn u is a doubly-periodic function of u with periods $4K$ and $2K + 2iK'$. It is analytic except at points congruent to iK' or to $2K + iK'$ (mod. $4K$, $2K + 2iK'$); these points are simple poles, the residues at the first set being $-ik^{-1}$, and the residues at the second set being ik^{-1}; and the function has a simple zero at all points congruent to K (mod. $2K, 2iK'$).

(III) The function $\mathrm{dn}\,u$ is a doubly-periodic function of u with periods $2K$ and $4iK'$. It is analytic except at points congruent to iK' or to $3iK'$ (mod. $2K, 4iK'$); these points are simple poles, the residues at the first set being $-i$, and the residues at the second set being i; and the function has a simple zero at all points congruent to $K + iK'$ (mod. $2K, 2iK'$).

[To see that the functions have no zeros or poles other than those just specified, recourse must be had to their definitions in terms of Theta-functions.]

22·351. *The connexion between Weierstrassian and Jacobian elliptic functions.*

If e_1, e_2, e_3 be any three distinct numbers whose sum is zero, and if we write

$$y = e_3 + \frac{e_1 - e_3}{\mathrm{sn}^2\,(\lambda u, k)},$$

we have

$$\left(\frac{dy}{du}\right)^2 = 4\,(e_1 - e_3)^2\,\lambda^2\,\mathrm{ns}^2\,\lambda u\,\mathrm{cs}^2\,\lambda u\,\mathrm{ds}^2\,\lambda u$$

$$= 4\,(e_1 - e_3)^2\,\lambda^2\,\mathrm{ns}^2\,\lambda u\,(\mathrm{ns}^2\,\lambda u - 1)\,(\mathrm{ns}^2\,\lambda u - k^2)$$

$$= 4\lambda^2\,(e_1 - e_3)^{-1}\,(y - e_3)\,(y - e_1)\,\{y - k^2\,(e_1 - e_3) - e_3\}.$$

Hence, if $\lambda^2 = e_1 - e_3$ and $k^2 = (e_2 - e_3)/(e_1 - e_3)$, then y satisfies the equation*

$$\left(\frac{dy}{du}\right)^2 = 4y^3 - g_2 y - g_3,$$

and so

$$e_3 + (e_1 - e_3)\,\mathrm{ns}^2\left\{u\,(e_1 - e_3)^{\frac{1}{2}},\ \sqrt{\frac{e_2 - e_3}{e_1 - e_3}}\right\} = \wp\,(u + a;\ g_2, g_3),$$

where a is a constant. Making $u \to 0$, we see that a is a period, and so

$$\wp\,(u;\ g_2, g_3) = e_3 + (e_1 - e_3)\,\mathrm{ns}^2\{u\,(e_1 - e_3)^{\frac{1}{2}}\},$$

the Jacobian elliptic function having its modulus given by the equation

$$k^2 = \frac{e_2 - e_3}{e_1 - e_3}.$$

22·4. *Jacobi's imaginary transformation†.*

The result of § 21·51, which gave a transformation from Theta-functions with parameter τ to Theta-functions with parameter $\tau' = -1/\tau$, naturally produces a transformation of Jacobian elliptic functions; this transformation is expressed by the equations

$$\mathrm{sn}\,(iu, k) = i\,\mathrm{sc}\,(u, k'), \quad \mathrm{cn}\,(iu, k) = \mathrm{nc}\,(u, k'), \quad \mathrm{dn}\,(iu, k) = \mathrm{dc}\,(u, k').$$

Suppose, for simplicity, that $0 < c < 1$ and $y > 0$; let

$$\int_0^{iy} (1 - t^2)^{-\frac{1}{2}}\,(1 - k^2 t^2)^{-\frac{1}{2}}\,dt = iu,$$

so that

$$iy = \mathrm{sn}\,(iu, k);$$

take the path of integration to be a straight line, and we have

$$\mathrm{cn}\,(iu, k) = (1 + y^2)^{\frac{1}{2}}, \quad \mathrm{dn}\,(iu, k) = (1 + k^2 y^2)^{\frac{1}{2}}.$$

* The values of g_2 and g_3 are, as usual, $-\frac{1}{4}\Sigma e_2 e_3$ and $\frac{1}{4}e_1 e_2 e_3$.

† *Fundamenta Nova*, pp. 34, 35. Abel (*Journal für Math.* II. (1827), p. 104) derives the double periodicity of elliptic functions from this result. Cf. a letter of Jan. 12, 1828, from Jacobi to Legendre [Jacobi, *Ges. Werke*, I. (1881), p. 402].

Now put $y = \eta/(1-\eta^2)^{\frac{1}{2}}$, where $0 < \eta < 1$, so that the range of values of t is from 0 to $i\eta/(1-\eta^2)^{\frac{1}{2}}$, and hence, if $t = it_1/(1-t_1^2)^{\frac{1}{2}}$, the range of values of t_1 is from 0 to η.

Then $dt = i(1-t_1^2)^{-\frac{3}{2}} i \, dt_1,$ $(1-t^2)^{\frac{1}{2}} = (1-t_1^2)^{-\frac{1}{2}},$

$$1 - k^2 t^2 = (1 - k'^2 t_1^2)^{-\frac{1}{2}} (1 - t_1^2)^{-\frac{1}{2}},$$

and we have $iu = \int_0^\eta (1-t_1^2)^{-\frac{1}{2}} (1-k'^2 t_1^2)^{-\frac{1}{2}} i \, dt_1,$

so that $\eta = \operatorname{sn}(u, k')$

and therefore $y = \operatorname{sc}(u, k')$

We have thus obtained the result that

$$\operatorname{sn}(iu, k) = i \operatorname{sc}(u, k').$$

Also $\operatorname{cn}(iu, k) = (1+y^2)^{\frac{1}{2}} = (1-\eta^2)^{-\frac{1}{2}} = \operatorname{nc}(u, k'),$

and $\operatorname{dn}(iu, k) = (1 - k^2 y^2)^{\frac{1}{2}} = (1 - k'^2 \eta^2)^{\frac{1}{2}} (1-\eta^2)^{-\frac{1}{2}} = \operatorname{dc}(u, k').$

Now $\operatorname{sn}(iu, k)$ and $i \operatorname{sc}(u, k')$ are one-valued functions of u and k (in the cut c-plane) with isolated poles. Hence by the theory of analytic continuation the results proved for real values of u and k hold for general complex values of u and k.

22·41.   *Proof of Jacobi's imaginary transformation by the aid of Theta-functions.*

The results just obtained may be proved very simply by the aid of Theta-functions.   Thus, from § 21·61,

$$\operatorname{sn}(iu, k) = \frac{\vartheta_3(0 \mid \tau)}{\vartheta_2(0 \mid \tau)} \frac{\vartheta_1(iz \mid \tau)}{\vartheta_4(iz \mid \tau)},$$

where $z = u/\vartheta_3^2(0 \mid \tau),$

and so, by § 21·51, $\operatorname{sn}(iu, k) = \frac{\vartheta_3(0 \mid \tau')}{\vartheta_4(0 \mid \tau')} \cdot \frac{-i\vartheta_1(iz\tau' \mid \tau')}{\vartheta_2(iz\tau' \mid \tau')}$

$$= -i \operatorname{sc}(v, k'),$$

where $v = iz\tau' \vartheta_3^2(0 \mid \tau') = iz\tau' \cdot (-i\tau) \vartheta_3^2(0 \mid \tau) = -u,$

so that, finally, $\operatorname{sn}(iu, k) = i \operatorname{sc}(u, k').$

Example 1.   Prove that $\operatorname{cn}(iu, k) = \operatorname{nc}(u, k'),$ $\operatorname{dn}(iu, k) = \operatorname{dc}(u, k')$ by the aid of Theta-functions.

Example 2.   Shew that

$$\operatorname{sn}(\tfrac{1}{2} iK', k) = i \operatorname{sc}(\tfrac{1}{2} K', k') = ik^{-\frac{1}{2}},$$

$$\operatorname{cn}(\tfrac{1}{2} iK', k) = (1+k)^{\frac{1}{2}} k^{-\frac{1}{2}}, \quad \operatorname{dn}(\tfrac{1}{2} iK', k) = (1+k)^{\frac{1}{2}}.$$

[There is great difficulty in determining the signs of $\operatorname{sn} \tfrac{1}{2} iK',$ $\operatorname{cn} \tfrac{1}{2} iK',$ $\operatorname{dn} \tfrac{1}{2} iK',$ if any method other than Jacobi's transformation is used.]

Example 3. Shew that

$$\operatorname{sn} \tfrac{1}{2}(K+iK') = \frac{(1+k)^{\frac{1}{2}} + i(1-k)^{\frac{1}{2}}}{\sqrt{(2k)}}, \quad \operatorname{cn} \tfrac{1}{2}(K+iK') = \frac{(1-i)\sqrt{k'}}{\sqrt{(2k)}},$$

$$\operatorname{dn} \tfrac{1}{2}(K+iK') = \frac{k'^{\frac{1}{2}}\{(1+k')^{\frac{1}{2}} - i(1-k')^{\frac{1}{2}}\}}{\sqrt{2}}.$$

Example 4. If $0 < k < 1$ and if θ be the modular angle, shew that

$$\operatorname{sn} \tfrac{1}{2}(K+iK') = e^{\frac{1}{4}\pi i - \frac{1}{2}i\theta} \sqrt{(\operatorname{cosec} \theta)}, \quad \operatorname{cn} \tfrac{1}{2}(K+iK') = e^{-\frac{1}{4}\pi i} \sqrt{(\cot \theta)},$$

$$\operatorname{dn} \tfrac{1}{2}(K+iK') = e^{-\frac{1}{2}i\theta} \sqrt{(\cos \theta)}.$$

(Glaisher.)

$22\cdot42$. *Landen's transformation*.*

We shall now obtain the formula

$$\int_0^{\phi_1} (1 - k_1^2 \sin^2 \theta_1)^{-\frac{1}{2}} d\theta_1 = (1 + k') \int_0^{\phi} (1 - k^2 \sin^2 \theta)^{-\frac{1}{2}} d\theta,$$

where $\qquad \sin \phi_1 = (1 + k') \sin \phi \cos \phi (1 - k^2 \sin^2 \phi)^{-\frac{1}{2}}$

and $\qquad\qquad k_1 = (1 - k')/(1 + k')$.

This formula, of which Landen was the discoverer, may be expressed by means of Jacobian elliptic functions in the form

$$\operatorname{sn} \{(1 + k') u, k_1\} = (1 + k') \operatorname{sn}(u, k) \operatorname{cd}(u, k),$$

on writing $\qquad\qquad \phi = \operatorname{am} u, \quad \phi_1 = \operatorname{am} u_1.$

To obtain this result, we make use of the equations of § $21\cdot52$, namely

$$\frac{\vartheta_3(z \mid \tau) \vartheta_4(z \mid \tau)}{\vartheta_4(2z \mid 2\tau)} = \frac{\vartheta_2(z \mid \tau) \vartheta_1(z \mid \tau)}{\vartheta_1(2z \mid 2\tau)} = \frac{\vartheta_3(0 \mid \tau) \vartheta_4(0 \mid \tau)}{\vartheta_4(0 \mid 2\tau)}.$$

Write† $\tau_1 = 2\tau$, and let k_1, Λ, Λ' be the modulus and quarter-periods formed with parameter τ_1; then the equation

$$\frac{\vartheta_1(z \mid \tau) \vartheta_2(z \mid \tau)}{\vartheta_3(z \mid \tau) \vartheta_4(z \mid \tau)} = \frac{\vartheta_1(2z \mid \tau_1)}{\vartheta_4(2z \mid \tau_1)}$$

may obviously be written

$$k \operatorname{sn}(2Kz/\pi, k) \operatorname{cd}(2Kz/\pi, k) = k_1^{\frac{1}{2}} \operatorname{sn}(4\Lambda z/\pi, k_1) \quad \ldots\ldots\ldots(A).$$

To determine k_1 in terms of k, put $z = \tfrac{1}{4}\pi$, and we immediately get

$$k/(1 + k') = k_1^{\frac{1}{2}},$$

which gives, on squaring, $k_1 = (1 - k')/(1 + k')$, as stated above.

To determine Λ, divide equation (A) by z, and then make $z \to 0$; and we get

$$2Kk = 4k_1^{\frac{1}{2}} \Lambda,$$

so that $\qquad\qquad\qquad \Lambda = \tfrac{1}{2}(1 + k') K.$

---

* *Phil. Trans. of the Royal Soc.* LXV. (1775), p. 285.

† It will be supposed that $|R(\tau)| < \frac{1}{2}$, to avoid difficulties of sign which arise if $R(\tau_1)$ does not lie between ± 1. This condition is satisfied when $0 < k < 1$, for τ is then a pure imaginary.

Hence, writing u in place of $2Kz/\pi$, we at once get from (A)

$$(1+k')\,\mathrm{sn}\,(u,\,k)\,\mathrm{cd}\,(u,\,k) = \mathrm{sn}\,\{(1+k')\,u,\,k_1\},$$

since
$$4\Lambda z/\pi = 2\Lambda u/K = (1+k')\,u\,;$$

so that Landen's result has been completely proved.

Example 1. Shew that $\Lambda'/\Lambda = 2K'/K$, and thence that $\Lambda' = (1+k')\,K'$.

Example 2. Shew that

$$\mathrm{cn}\,\{(1+k')\,u,\,k_1\} = \{1-(1+k')\,\mathrm{sn}^2\,(u,\,k)\}\,\mathrm{nd}\,(u,\,k),$$
$$\mathrm{dn}\,\{(1+k')\,u,\,k_1\} = \{k'+(1-k')\,\mathrm{cn}^2\,(u,\,k)\}\,\mathrm{nd}\,(u,\,k).$$

Example 3. Shew that

$$\mathrm{dn}\,(u,\,k) = (1-k')\,\mathrm{cn}\,\{(1+k')\,u,\,k_1\} + (1+k')\,\mathrm{dn}\,\{(1+k')\,u,\,k_1\},$$

where
$$k = 2k_1^{\frac{1}{2}}/(1+k_1).$$

22·421. *Transformations of elliptic functions.*

The formula of Landen is a particular case of what is known as a transformation of elliptic functions; a transformation consists in the expression of elliptic functions with parameter τ in terms of those with parameter $(a+b\tau)/(c+d\tau)$, where a, b, c, d are integers. We have had another transformation in which $a = -1$, $b=0$, $c=0$, $d=1$, namely Jacobi's imaginary transformation. For the general theory of transformations, which is outside the range of this book, the reader is referred to Jacobi, *Fundamenta Nova*, to Klein, *Vorlesungen über die Theorie der elliptischen Modulfunktionen* (edited by Fricke), and to Cayley, *Elliptic Functions* (London, 1895).

Example. By considering the transformation $\tau_2 = \tau \pm 1$, shew, by the method of § 22·42, that

$$\mathrm{sn}\,(k'u,\,k_2) = k'\,\mathrm{sd}\,(u,\,k),$$

where $k_2 = \pm ik/k'$, and the upper or lower sign is taken according as $R(\tau) < 0$ or $R(\tau) > 0$; and obtain formulae for $\mathrm{cn}\,(k'u,\,k_2)$ and $\mathrm{dn}\,(k'u,\,k_2)$.

22·5. *Infinite products for the Jacobian elliptic functions*[*].

The products for the Theta-functions, obtained in § 21·3, at once yield products for the Jacobian elliptic functions; writing $u = 2Kx/\pi$, we obviously have, from § 22·11, formulae (A), (B) and (C),

$$\mathrm{sn}\,u = 2q^{\frac{1}{4}}k^{-\frac{1}{2}}\sin x\prod_{n=1}^{\infty}\left\{\frac{1-2q^{2n}\cos 2x + q^{4n}}{1-2q^{2n-1}\cos 2x + q^{4n-2}}\right\},$$

$$\mathrm{cn}\,u = 2q^{\frac{1}{4}}k'^{\frac{1}{2}}k^{-\frac{1}{2}}\cos x\prod_{n=1}^{\infty}\left\{\frac{1+2q^{2n}\cos 2x + q^{4n}}{1-2q^{2n-1}\cos 2x + q^{4n-2}}\right\},$$

$$\mathrm{dn}\,u = k'^{\frac{1}{2}}\prod_{n=1}^{\infty}\left\{\frac{1+2q^{2n-1}\cos 2x + q^{4n-2}}{1-2q^{2n-1}\cos 2x + q^{4n-2}}\right\}.$$

From these results the products for the nine reciprocals and quotients can be written down.

There are twenty-four other formulae which may be obtained in the following manner: From the duplication-formulae (§ 22·21 example 5) we have

$$\frac{1-\mathrm{cn}\,u}{\mathrm{sn}\,u} = \mathrm{sn}\,\tfrac{1}{2}u\,\mathrm{dc}\,\tfrac{1}{2}u, \qquad \frac{1+\mathrm{dn}\,u}{\mathrm{sn}\,u} = \mathrm{ds}\,\tfrac{1}{2}u\,\mathrm{nc}\,\tfrac{1}{2}u, \qquad \frac{\mathrm{dn}\,u+\mathrm{cn}\,u}{\mathrm{sn}\,u} = \mathrm{cn}\,\tfrac{1}{2}u\,\mathrm{ds}\,\tfrac{1}{2}u.$$

* *Fundamenta Nova*, pp. 84–115.

Take the first of these, and use the products for $\operatorname{sn} \tfrac{1}{2} u$, $\operatorname{cn} \tfrac{1}{2} u$, $\operatorname{dn} \tfrac{1}{2} u$; we get

$$\frac{1 - \operatorname{cn} u}{\operatorname{sn} u} = \frac{1 - \cos x}{\sin x} \prod_{n=1}^{\infty} \left\{ \frac{1 - 2 (-q)^n \cos x + q^{2n}}{1 + 2 (-q)^n \cos x + q^{2n}} \right\},$$

on combining the various products.

Write $u + K$ for u, $x + \tfrac{1}{2} \pi$ for x, and we have

$$\frac{\operatorname{dn} u + k' \operatorname{sn} u}{\operatorname{cn} u} = \frac{1 + \sin x}{\cos x} \prod_{n=1}^{\infty} \left\{ \frac{1 + 2 (-q)^n \sin x + q^{2n}}{1 - 2 (-q)^n \sin x + q^{2n}} \right\}.$$

Writing $u + iK'$ for u in these formulae we have

$$k \operatorname{sn} u + i \operatorname{dn} u = i \prod_{n=1}^{\infty} \left\{ \frac{1 + 2i (-)^n q^{n-\frac{1}{2}} \sin x - q^{2n-1}}{1 - 2i (-)^n q^{n-\frac{1}{2}} \sin x - q^{2n-1}} \right\},$$

and the expression for $k \operatorname{cd} u + ik' \operatorname{nd} u$ is obtained by writing $\cos x$ for $\sin x$ in this product.

From the identities $(1 - \operatorname{cn} u)(1 + \operatorname{cn} u) \equiv \operatorname{sn}^2 u$, $(k \operatorname{sn} u + i \operatorname{dn} u)(k \operatorname{sn} u - i \operatorname{dn} u) \equiv 1$, etc., we at once get four other formulae, making eight in all; the other sixteen follow in the same way from the expressions for $\operatorname{ds} \tfrac{1}{2} u \operatorname{nc} \tfrac{1}{2} u$ and $\operatorname{cn} \tfrac{1}{2} u \operatorname{ds} \tfrac{1}{2} u$. The reader may obtain these as an example, noting specially the following:

$$\operatorname{sn} u + i \operatorname{cn} u = i e^{-ix} \prod_{n=1}^{\infty} \left\{ \frac{(1 - q^{4n-3} e^{2ix})(1 - q^{4n-1} e^{-2ix})}{(1 - q^{4n-1} e^{2ix})(1 - q^{4n-3} e^{-2ix})} \right\}.$$

Example 1.   Shew that

$$\operatorname{dn} \tfrac{1}{2} (K + iK') = k'^{\frac{1}{2}} \prod_{n=1}^{\infty} \left\{ \frac{(1 + iq^{2n-\frac{1}{2}})(1 - iq^{2n-\frac{3}{2}})}{(1 - iq^{2n-\frac{1}{2}})(1 + iq^{2n-\frac{3}{2}})} \right\}$$

$$= k'^{\frac{1}{2}} \prod_{n=0}^{\infty} \left\{ \frac{1 - (-)^n iq^{n+\frac{1}{2}}}{1 + (-)^n iq^{n+\frac{1}{2}}} \right\}.$$

Example 2.   Deduce from example 1 and from § 22·41 example 4, that, if θ be the modular angle, then

$$e^{-\frac{1}{2} i\theta} = \prod_{n=0}^{\infty} \left\{ \frac{1 - (-)^n iq^{n+\frac{1}{2}}}{1 + (-)^n iq^{n+\frac{1}{2}}} \right\},$$

and thence, by taking logarithms, obtain Jacobi's result

$$\tfrac{1}{4} \theta = \sum_{n=0}^{\infty} (-)^n \arctan q^{n+\frac{1}{2}} = \arctan \sqrt{q} - \arctan \sqrt{q^3} + \arctan \sqrt{q^5} - \ldots,$$

'quae inter formulas elegantissimas censeri debet.'. (*Fund. Nova*, p. 108.)

Example 3.   By expanding each term in the equation

$$\log \operatorname{sn} u = \log (2q^{\frac{1}{4}}) - \tfrac{1}{2} \log k + \log \sin x + \sum_{n=1}^{\infty} \{ \log (1 - q^{2n} e^{2ix})$$

$$+ \log (1 - q^{2n} e^{-2ix}) - \log (1 - q^{2n-1} e^{2ix}) - \log (1 - q^{2n-1} e^{-2ix}) \}$$

in powers of $e^{\pm 2ix}$, and rearranging the resulting double series, shew that

$$\log \operatorname{sn} u = \log (2q^{\frac{1}{4}}) - \tfrac{1}{2} \log k + \log \sin x + \sum_{m=1}^{\infty} \frac{2q^m \cos 2mx}{m (1 + q^m)},$$

when $| I (z) | < \tfrac{1}{2} \pi I (\tau)$.

Obtain similar series for $\log \operatorname{cn} u$, $\log \operatorname{dn} u$.

(Jacobi, *Fundamenta Nova*, p. 99.)

Example 4.   Deduce from example 3 that

$$\int_0^K \log \operatorname{sn} u \, du = - \tfrac{1}{4} \pi K' - \tfrac{1}{2} K \log k.$$

(Glaisher, *Proc. Royal Soc.* XXIX.)

22·6. *Fourier series for the Jacobian elliptic functions*.*

If $u \equiv 2Kx/\pi$, $\operatorname{sn} u$ is an odd periodic function of x (with period 2π), which obviously satisfies Dirichlet's conditions (§ 9·2) for real values of x; and therefore (§ 9·22) we may expand $\operatorname{sn} u$ as a Fourier sine-series in sines of multiples of x, thus

$$\operatorname{sn} u = \sum_{n=1}^{\infty} b_n \sin nx,$$

the expansion being valid for all real values of x. It is easily seen that the coefficients b_n are given by the formula

$$\pi i b_n = \int_{-\pi}^{\pi} \operatorname{sn} u \cdot \exp(nix) \, dx.$$

To evaluate this integral, consider $\int \operatorname{sn} u \cdot \exp(nix) \, dx$ taken round the parallelogram whose corners are $-\pi$, π, $\pi\tau$, $-2\pi + \pi\tau$.

From the periodic properties of $\operatorname{sn} u$ and $\exp(nix)$, we see that $\int_{\pi}^{\pi\tau}$ cancels $\int_{-2\pi+\pi\tau}^{-\pi}$; and so, since $-\pi + \frac{1}{2}\pi\tau$ and $\frac{1}{2}\pi\tau$ are the only poles of the integrand (*qua* function of x) inside the contour, with residues†

$$-k^{-1}\left(\tfrac{1}{2}\,\pi/K\right)\exp\left(-ni\pi + \tfrac{1}{2}n\pi i\tau\right)$$

and

$$k^{-1}\left(\tfrac{1}{2}\,\pi/K\right)\exp\left(\tfrac{1}{2}n\pi i\tau\right)$$

respectively, we have

$$\left\{\int_{-\pi}^{\pi} - \int_{-2\pi+\pi\tau}^{\pi\tau}\right\} \operatorname{sn} u \cdot \exp(nix)\,dx = \frac{\pi^2 i}{Kk} q^{\frac{1}{2}n}\{1 - (-)^n\}.$$

Writing $x - \pi + \pi\tau$ for x in the second integral, we get

$$\{1 + (-)^n q^n\}\int_{-\pi}^{\pi}\operatorname{sn} u \cdot \exp(nix)\,dx = \frac{\pi^2 i}{Kk} q^{\frac{1}{2}n}\{1 - (-)^n\}.$$

Hence, when n is even, $b_n = 0$; but when n is odd.

$$b_n = \frac{2\pi}{Kk}\frac{q^{\frac{1}{2}n}}{1 - q^n}.$$

Consequently

$$\operatorname{sn} u = \frac{2\pi}{Kk}\left\{\frac{q^{\frac{1}{2}}\sin x}{1-q} + \frac{q^{\frac{3}{2}}\sin 3x}{1-q^3} + \frac{q^{\frac{5}{2}}\sin 5x}{1-q^5} + \ldots\right\},$$

when x is real; but the right-hand side of this equation is analytic when $q^{\frac{1}{2}n}\exp(nix)$ and $q^{\frac{1}{2}n}\exp(-nix)$ both tend to zero as $n \to \infty$, and the left-hand side is analytic except at the poles of $\operatorname{sn} u$.

---

* These results are substantially due to Jacobi, *Fundamenta Nova*, p. 101.

† The factor $\frac{1}{2}\pi/K$ has to be inserted because we are dealing with $\operatorname{sn}(2Kx/\pi)$.

Hence both sides are analytic in the strip (in the plane of the complex variable x) which is defined by the inequality $|I(x)| < \frac{1}{2}\pi I(\tau)$.

And so, by the theory of analytic continuation, we have the result

$$\operatorname{sn} u = \frac{2\pi}{Kk} \sum_{n=0}^{\infty} \frac{q^{n+\frac{1}{2}} \sin(2n+1)x}{1 - q^{2n+1}},$$

(where $u = 2Kx/\pi$), valid throughout the strip $|I(x)| < \frac{1}{2}\pi I(\tau)$.

Example 1.   Shew that, if $u = 2Kx/\pi$, then

$$\operatorname{cn} u = \frac{2\pi}{Kk} \sum_{n=0}^{\infty} \frac{q^{n+\frac{1}{2}} \cos(2n+1)x}{1 + q^{2n-1}}, \qquad \operatorname{dn} u = \frac{\pi}{2K} + \frac{2\pi}{K} \sum_{n=1}^{\infty} \frac{q^n \cos 2nx}{1 + q^{2n}},$$

$$\operatorname{am} u = \int_0^u \operatorname{dn} t \, dt = x + \sum_{n=1}^{\infty} \frac{2q^n \sin 2nx}{n(1 + q^{2n})},$$

these results being valid when $|I(x)| < \frac{1}{2}\pi I(\tau)$.

Example 2.   By writing $x + \frac{1}{2}\pi$ for x in results already obtained, shew that, if
$$u = 2Kx/\pi \quad \text{and} \quad |I(x)| < \frac{1}{2}\pi I(\tau),$$

then $$\operatorname{cd} u = \frac{2\pi}{Kk} \sum_{n=0}^{\infty} \frac{(-)^n q^{n+\frac{1}{2}} \cos(2n+1)x}{1 - q^{2n+1}}, \qquad \operatorname{sd} u = \frac{2\pi}{Kkk'} \sum_{n=0}^{\infty} \frac{(-)^n q^{n+\frac{1}{2}} \sin(2n+1)x}{1 + q^{2n+1}},$$

$$\operatorname{nd} u = \frac{\pi}{2Kk'} + \frac{2\pi}{Kk'} \sum_{n=1}^{\infty} \frac{(-)^n q^n \cos 2nx}{1 + q^{2n}}.$$

22·61.   *Fourier series for reciprocals of Jacobian elliptic functions.*

In the result of § 22·6, write $u + iK'$ for u and consequently $x + \frac{1}{2}\pi\tau$ for x; then we see that, if $0 > I(x) > -\pi I(\tau)$,

$$\operatorname{sn}(u + iK') = \frac{2\pi}{Kk} \sum_{n=0}^{\infty} \frac{q^{n+\frac{1}{2}} \sin(2n+1)(x + \frac{1}{2}\pi\tau)}{1 - q^{2n+1}},$$

and so (§ 22·34)

$$\operatorname{ns} u = (-i\pi/K) \sum_{n=0}^{\infty} q^{n+\frac{1}{2}} \{ q^{n+\frac{1}{2}} e^{(2n+1)ix} - q^{-n-\frac{1}{2}} e^{-(2n+1)ix} \} / (1 - q^{2n+1})$$

$$= (-i\pi/K) \sum_{n=0}^{\infty} \{ 2iq^{2n+1} \sin(2n+1)x + (1 - q^{-2n-1}) e^{-(2n+1)ix} \} / (1 - q^{2n+1})$$

$$= \frac{2\pi}{K} \sum_{n=0}^{\infty} \frac{q^{2n+1} \sin(2n+1)x}{1 - q^{2n+1}} - \frac{i\pi}{K} \sum_{n=0}^{\infty} e^{-(2n+1)ix}.$$

That is to say

$$\operatorname{ns} u = \frac{\pi}{2K} \operatorname{cosec} x + \frac{2\pi}{K} \sum_{n=0}^{\infty} \frac{q^{2n+1} \sin(2n+1)x}{1 - q^{2n+1}}.$$

But, apart from isolated poles at the points $x = n\pi$, each side of this equation is an analytic function of x in the strip in which
$$\pi I(\tau) > I(x) > -\pi I(\tau):$$
—a strip double the width of that in which the equation has been proved to be true; and so, by the theory of analytic continuation, this expansion for $\operatorname{ns} u$ is valid throughout the wider strip, except at the points $x = n\pi$.

Example.   Obtain the following expansions, valid throughout the strip $|I(x)| < \pi I(\tau)$ except at the poles of the first term on the right-hand sides of the respective expansions:

$$\operatorname{ds} u = \frac{\pi}{2K} \operatorname{cosec} x - \frac{2\pi}{K} \sum_{n=0}^{\infty} \frac{q^{2n+1} \sin(2n+1)x}{1+q^{2n+1}},$$

$$\operatorname{cs} u = \frac{\pi}{2K} \cot x \quad - \frac{2\pi}{K} \sum_{n=1}^{\infty} \frac{q^{2n} \sin 2nx}{1+q^{2n}},$$

$$\operatorname{dc} u = \frac{\pi}{2K} \sec x \quad + \frac{2\pi}{K} \sum_{n=0}^{\infty} \frac{(-)^n q^{2n+1} \cos(2n+1)x}{1-q^{2n+1}},$$

$$\operatorname{nc} u = \frac{\pi}{2Kk'} \sec x \quad - \frac{2\pi}{Kk'} \sum_{n=0}^{\infty} \frac{(-)^n q^{2n+1} \cos(2n+1)x}{1+q^{2n+1}},$$

$$\operatorname{sc} u = \frac{\pi}{2Kk'} \tan x \quad + \frac{2\pi}{Kk'} \sum_{n=1}^{\infty} \frac{(-)^n q^{2n} \sin 2nx}{1+q^{2n}}.$$

22·7.   *Elliptic integrals.*

An integral of the form $\int R(w, x)\, dx$, where R denotes a rational function of w and x, and w^2 *is a* QUARTIC, *or* CUBIC *function of* x (without repeated factors), is called an *elliptic integral* *.

[NOTE.   Elliptic integrals are of considerable historical importance, owing to the fact that a very large number of important properties of such integrals were discovered by Euler and Legendre before it was realised that the *inverses* of certain standard types of such integrals, rather than the integrals themselves, should be regarded as fundamental functions of analysis.

The first mathematician to deal with elliptic *functions* as opposed to elliptic *integrals* was Gauss (§ 22·8), but the first results published were by Abel† and Jacobi‡.

The results obtained by Abel were brought to the notice of Legendre by Jacobi immediately after the publication by Legendre of the *Traité des fonctions elliptiques*.   In the supplement (tome III. (1828), p. 1), Legendre comments on their discoveries in the following terms: "À peine mon ouvrage avait-il vu le jour, à peine son titre pouvait-il être connu des savans étrangers, que j'appris, avec autant d'étonnement que de satisfaction, que deux jeunes géomètres, MM. *Jacobi* (C.-G.-J.) de Koenigsberg et *Abel* de Christiania, avaient réussi, par leurs travaux particuliers, à perfectionner considérablement la théorie des fonctions elliptiques dans ses points les plus élevés."

An interesting correspondence between Legendre and Jacobi was printed in *Journal für Math.* LXXX. (1875), pp. 205–279; in one of the letters Legendre refers to the claim of Gauss to have made in 1809 many of the discoveries published by Jacobi and Abel.   The validity of this claim was established by Schering (see Gauss, *Werke*, III. (1876), pp. 493, 494), though the researches of Gauss (*Werke*, III. pp. 404–460) remained unpublished until after his death.]

We shall now give a brief outline of the important theorem that every elliptic integral can be evaluated by the aid of Theta-functions, combined

---

* Strictly speaking, it is only called an elliptic integral when it cannot be integrated by means of the elementary functions, and consequently involves one of the three kinds of elliptic integrals introduced in § 22·72.

† *Journal für Math.* II. (1827), pp. 101–196.

‡ Jacobi announced his discovery in two letters (dated June 13, 1827 and August 2, 1827) to Schumacher, who published extracts from them in *Astr. Nach.* VI. (No. 123) in September 1827— the month in which Abel's memoir appeared.

with the elementary functions of analysis; it has already been seen (§ 20·6) that this process can be carried out in the special case of $\int w^{-1} dx$, since the Weierstrassian elliptic functions can easily be expressed in terms of Theta-functions and their derivates (§ 21·73).

[The most important case practically is that in which R is a real function of x and w, which are themselves real on the path of integration; it will be shewn how, in such circumstances, the integral may be expressed in a real form.]

Since $R(w, x)$ is a *rational* function of w and x we may write

$$R(w, x) \equiv P(w, x)/Q(w, x),$$

where P and Q denote polynomials in w and x; then we have

$$R(w, x) \equiv \frac{wP(w, x) Q(-w, x)}{wQ(w, x) Q(-w, x)}.$$

Now $Q(w, x) Q(-w, x)$ is a *rational function of w^2 and x*, since it is unaffected by changing the sign of w; it is therefore expressible as a rational function of x.

If now we multiply out $wP(w, x) Q(-w, x)$ and substitute for w^2 in terms of x wherever it occurs in the expression, we ultimately reduce it to a polynomial in x and w, the polynomial being *linear in w*. We thus have an identity of the form

$$R(w, x) \equiv \{R_1(x) + wR_2(x)\}/w,$$

by reason of the expression for w^2 as a quartic in x; where R_1 and R_2 denote rational functions of x.

Now $\int R_2(x)\, dx$ can be evaluated by means of elementary functions only*; so the problem is reduced to that of evaluating $\int w^{-1} R_1(x)\, dx$. To carry out this process it is necessary to obtain a canonical expression for w^2, which we now proceed to do.

22·71. *The expression of a quartic as the product of sums of squares.*

It will now be shewn that *any quartic (or cubic†) in x (with no repeated factors) can be expressed in the form*

$$\{A_1(x-\alpha)^2 + B_1(x-\beta)^2\} \{A_2(x-\alpha)^2 + B_2(x-\beta)^2\},$$

where, if the coefficients in the quartic are real, $A_1, B_1, A_2, B_2, \alpha, \beta$ are all real.

---

* The integration of *rational* functions of one variable is discussed in text-books on Integral Calculus.

† In the following analysis, a cubic may be regarded as a quartic in which the coefficient of x^4 vanishes.

To obtain this result, we observe that any quartic can be expressed in the form $S_1 S_2$ where S_1, S_2 are quadratic in x, say*

$$S_1 \equiv a_1 x^2 + 2b_1 x + c_1, \quad S_2 \equiv a_2 x^2 + 2b_2 x + c_2.$$

Now, λ being a constant, $S_1 - \lambda S_2$ will be a perfect square in x if

$$(a_1 - \lambda a_2)(c_1 - \lambda c_2) - (b_1 - \lambda b_2)^2 = 0.$$

Let the roots of this equation be λ_1, λ_2; then, by hypothesis, numbers α, β exist such that

$$S_1 - \lambda_1 S_2 \equiv (a_1 - \lambda_1 a_2)(x - \alpha)^2, \quad S_1 - \lambda_2 S_2 \equiv (a_1 - \lambda_2 a_2)(x - \beta)^2;$$

on solving these as equations in S_1, S_2, we obviously get results of the form

$$S_1 \equiv A_1 (x - \alpha)^2 + B_1 (x - \beta)^2, \quad S_2 \equiv A_2 (x - \alpha)^2 + B_2 (x - \beta)^2,$$

and the required reduction of the quartic has been effected.

[NOTE. If the quartic is real and has two or four complex factors, let S_1 have complex factors; then λ_1 and λ_2 are real and distinct since

$$(a_1 - \lambda a_2)(c_1 - \lambda c_2) - (b_1 - \lambda b_2)^2$$

is positive when $\lambda = 0$ and negative† when $\lambda = a_1/a_2$.

When S_1 and S_2 have real factors, say $(x - \xi_1)(x - \xi_1')$, $(x - \xi_2)(x - \xi_2')$, the condition that λ_1 and λ_2 should be real is easily found to be

$$(\xi_1 - \xi_2)(\xi_1' - \xi_2)(\xi_1 - \xi_2')(\xi_1' - \xi_2') > 0,$$

a condition which is satisfied when the zeros of S_1 and those of S_2 do not interlace; this was, of course, the reason for choosing the factors S_1 and S_2 of the quartic in such a way that their zeros do not interlace.]

22·72. *The three kinds of elliptic integrals.*

Let α, β be determined by the rule just obtained in § 22·71, and, in the integral $\int w^{-1} R_1(x)\, dx$, take a new variable t defined by the equation‡

$$t = (x - \alpha)/(x - \beta);$$

we then have $$\dfrac{dx}{w} = \pm \dfrac{(\alpha - \beta)^{-1} dt}{\{(A_1 t^2 + B_1)(A_2 t^2 + B_2)\}^{\frac{1}{2}}}.$$

---

* If the coefficients in the quartic are real, the factorisation can be carried out so that the coefficients in S_1 and S_2 are real. In the special case of the quartic having four real linear factors, these factors should be associated in pairs (to give S_1 and S_2) in such a way that the roots of one pair do not interlace the roots of the other pair; the reason for this will be seen in the note at the end of the section.

† Unless $a_1 : a_2 = b_1 : b_2$, in which case

$$S_1 \equiv a_1 (x - \alpha)^2 + B_1, \quad S_2 \equiv a_2 (x - \alpha)^2 + B_2.$$

‡ It is rather remarkable that Jacobi did not realise the existence of this homographic substitution; in his reduction he employed a quadratic substitution, equivalent to the result of applying a Landen transformation to the elliptic functions which we shall introduce.

If we write $R_1(x)$ in the form $\pm(\alpha - \beta) R_3(t)$, where R_3 is rational, we get

$$\int \frac{R_1(x)\,dx}{w} = \int \frac{R_3(t)\,dt}{\{(A_1 t^2 + B_1)(A_2 t^2 + B_2)\}^{\frac{1}{2}}}.$$

Now $R_3(t) + R_3(-t) = 2R_4(t^2)$, $R_3(t) - R_3(-t) = 2t R_5(t^2)$,

where R_4 and R_5 are rational functions of t^2, and so

$$R_3(t) = R_4(t^2) + t R_5(t^2).$$

But $$\int \{(A_1 t^2 + B_1)(A_2 t^2 + B_2)\}^{-\frac{1}{2}} t R_5(t^2)\,dt$$

can be evaluated in terms of elementary functions by taking t^2 as a new variable*; so that, if we put $R_4(t^2)$ into partial fractions, the problem of integrating $\int R(w, x)\,dx$ has been reduced to the integration of integrals of the following types:

$$\int t^{2m} \{(A_1 t^2 + B_1)(A_2 t^2 + B_2)\}^{-\frac{1}{2}}\,dt,$$

$$\int (1 + N t^2)^{-m} \{(A_1 t^2 + B_1)(A_2 t^2 + B_2)\}^{-\frac{1}{2}}\,dt;$$

in the former of these m is an integer, in the latter m is a positive integer and $N \neq 0$.

By differentiating expressions of the form

$$t^{2m-1} \{(A_1 t^2 + B_1)(A_2 t^2 + B_2)\}^{\frac{1}{2}}, \quad t(1 + N t^2)^{1-m} \{(A_1 t^2 + B_1)(A_2 t^2 + B_2)\}^{\frac{1}{2}},$$

it is easy to obtain reduction formulae by means of which the above integrals can be expressed in terms of one of the three canonical forms:

(i) $\int \{(A_1 t^2 + B_1)(A_2 t^2 + B_2)\}^{-\frac{1}{2}}\,dt,$

(ii) $\int t^2 \{(A_1 t^2 + B_1)(A_2 t^2 + B_2)\}^{-\frac{1}{2}}\,dt,$

(iii) $\int (1 + N t^2)^{-1} \{(A_1 t^2 + B_1)(A_2 t^2 + B_2)\}^{-\frac{1}{2}}\,dt.$

These integrals were called by Legendre† *elliptic integrals of the first, second and third kinds*, respectively.

The elliptic integral of the first kind presents no difficulty, as it can be integrated at once by a substitution based on the integral formulae of §§ 22·121, 22·122; thus, if A_1, B_1, A_2, B_2 are all positive and $A_2 B_1 > A_1 B_2$, we write

$$A_1^{\frac{1}{2}} t = B_1^{\frac{1}{2}} \operatorname{cs}(u, k). \qquad [k'^2 = (A_1 B_2)/(A_2 B_1).]$$

---

* See, e.g., Hardy, *Integration of Functions of a single Variable* (Camb. Math. Tracts, No. 2).
† *Exercices de Calcul Intégral*, I. (Paris, 1811), p. 19.

Example 1. Verify that, in the case of *real* integrals, the following scheme gives all possible essentially different arrangements of sign, and determine the appropriate substitutions necessary to evaluate the corresponding integrals.

A_1	+	+	−	+	+	−
B_1	+	−	+	−	−	+
A_2	+	+	+	+	−	−
B_2	+	+	+	−	+	+

Example 2. Shew that

$$\int \operatorname{sn} u \, du = \frac{1}{2k} \log \frac{1 - k \operatorname{cd} u}{1 + k \operatorname{cd} u}, \qquad \int \operatorname{cn} u \, du = k^{-1} \arctan \left(k \operatorname{sd} u\right),$$

$$\int \operatorname{dn} u \, du = \operatorname{am} u, \qquad \int \operatorname{sc} u \, du = \frac{1}{2k'} \log \frac{\operatorname{dn} u + k'}{\operatorname{dn} u - k'},$$

$$\int \operatorname{ds} u \, du = \frac{1}{2} \log \frac{1 - \operatorname{cn} u}{1 + \operatorname{cn} u}, \qquad \int \operatorname{dc} u \, du = \frac{1}{2} \log \frac{1 + \operatorname{sn} u}{1 - \operatorname{sn} u},$$

and obtain six similar formulae by writing $u + K$ for u.

(Glaisher.)

Example 3. Prove, by differentiation, the equivalence of the following twelve expressions :

$$u - k^2 \int \operatorname{sn}^2 u \, du, \qquad\qquad k'^2 u + k^2 \int \operatorname{cn}^2 u \, du,$$

$$\int \operatorname{dn}^2 u \, du, \qquad\qquad u - \operatorname{dn} u \operatorname{cs} u - \int \operatorname{ns}^2 u \, du,$$

$$k'^2 u + \operatorname{dn} u \operatorname{sc} u - k'^2 \int \operatorname{nc}^2 u \, du, \qquad k^2 \operatorname{sn} u \operatorname{cd} u + k'^2 \int \operatorname{nd}^2 u \, du,$$

$$\operatorname{dn} u \operatorname{sc} u - k'^2 \int \operatorname{sc}^2 u \, du, \qquad k'^2 u + k^2 \operatorname{sn} u \operatorname{cd} u + k^2 k'^2 \int \operatorname{sd}^2 u \, du,$$

$$u + k^2 \operatorname{sn} u \operatorname{cd} u - k^2 \int \operatorname{cd}^2 u \, du, \qquad - \operatorname{dn} u \operatorname{cs} u - \int \operatorname{cs}^2 u \, du,$$

$$k'^2 u - \operatorname{dn} u \operatorname{cs} u - \int \operatorname{ds}^2 u \, du, \qquad u + \operatorname{dn} u \operatorname{sc} u - \int \operatorname{dc}^2 u \, du.$$

Example 4. Shew that

$$\frac{d^2 \operatorname{sn}^n u}{du^2} = n \left(n - 1\right) \operatorname{sn}^{n-2} u - n^2 \left(1 + k^2\right) \operatorname{sn}^n u + n \left(n + 1\right) k^2 \operatorname{sn}^{n+2} u,$$

and obtain eleven similar formulae for the second differential coefficients of $\operatorname{cn}^n u$, $\operatorname{dn}^n u$, ... $\operatorname{nd}^n u$. What is the connexion between these formulae and the reduction formula for $\int t^n \left\{\left(A_1 t^2 + B_1\right)\left(A_2 t^2 + B_2\right)\right\}^{-\frac{1}{2}} dt$?

(Jacobi ; and Glaisher, *Messenger*, XI.)

Example 5. By means of § 20·6 shew that, if a and β are positive,

$$\int_{-a}^{a} \left\{\left(a^2 - x^2\right)\left(x^2 + \beta^2\right)\right\}^{-\frac{1}{2}} dx = \int_{e_1}^{\infty} \left(4s^3 - g_2 s - g_3\right)^{-\frac{1}{2}} ds,$$

where e_1 is the real root of the cubic and

$$g_2 = \tfrac{1}{12} \left(a^2 - \beta^2\right)^2 - a^2 \beta^2, \quad g_3 = - \left(a^2 - \beta^2\right) \left\{\left(a^2 - \beta^2\right)^2 + 36 a^2 \beta^2\right\}/216 ;$$

and prove that, if $g_2 = 0$, then a and β are given by the equations

$$a^2 - \beta^2 = - 3 \left(2 g_3\right)^{\frac{1}{3}}, \quad a^2 + \beta^2 = 2 \sqrt{3} . \, | \, 2 g_3 |^{\frac{1}{3}}.$$

Example 6. Deduce from example 5, combined with the integral formula for cn u, that, if g_3 is positive,

$$\int_{e_1}^{\infty}(4s^3-g_3)^{-\frac{1}{2}}\,ds=2\,(a^2+\beta^2)^{-\frac{1}{2}}\,K, \qquad \int_{-e_1}^{\infty}(4s^3+g_3)^{-\frac{1}{2}}\,ds=2\,(a^2+\beta^2)^{-\frac{1}{2}}\,K',$$

where $a^2=(\sqrt{3}-\frac{3}{2})\,(2g_3)^{\frac{1}{3}}$, $\beta^2=(\sqrt{3}+\frac{3}{2})\,(2g_3)^{\frac{1}{3}}$, and the modulus is $a\,(a^2+\beta^2)^{-\frac{1}{2}}$.

22·73. *The elliptic integral of the second kind. The function* [*] $E\,(u)$.

To reduce an integral of the type

$$\int t^2\,\{(A_1t^2+B_1)\,(A_2t^2+B_2)\}^{-\frac{1}{2}}\,dt,$$

we employ the same elliptic function substitution as in the case of that elliptic integral of the first kind which has the same expression under the radical.   We are thus led to one of the twelve integrals

$$\int\mathrm{sn}^2u\,du, \qquad \int\mathrm{cn}^2u\,du,\ \dots \int\mathrm{nd}^2u\,du.$$

By § 22·72 example 3, these are all expressible in terms of u, elliptic functions of u and $\int\mathrm{dn}^2u\,du$; it is convenient to regard

$$E\,(u)\equiv\int_0^u\mathrm{dn}^2u\,du$$

as the fundamental elliptic integral of the second kind, in terms of which all others can be expressed; when the modulus has to be emphasized, we write $E\,(u,k)$ in place of $E\,(u)$.

We observe that

$$\frac{dE\,(u)}{du}=\mathrm{dn}^2u, \qquad E\,(0)=0.$$

Further, since dn^2u is an even function with double poles at the points $2mK+(2n+1)iK$, the residue at each pole being zero, it is easy to see that $E\,(u)$ is an odd one-valued[†] function of u with simple poles at the poles of dn u.

It will now be shewn that $E\,(u)$ may be expressed in terms of Theta-functions; the most convenient type to employ is the function $\Theta\,(u)$.

Consider

$$\frac{d}{du}\left\{\frac{\Theta'\,(u)}{\Theta\,(u)}\right\};$$

it is a doubly-periodic function of u with double poles at the zeros of $\Theta\,(u)$, i.e. at the poles of dn u, and so, if A be a suitably chosen constant,

$$\mathrm{dn}^2u-A\,\frac{d}{du}\left\{\frac{\Theta'\,(u)}{\Theta\,(u)}\right\}$$

---

[*] This notation was introduced by Jacobi, *Journal für Math.* IV. (1829), p. 373 [*Ges. Werke*, I. (1881), p. 299].   In the *Fundamenta Nova*, he wrote $E\,(\mathrm{am}\,u)$ where we write $E\,(u)$.

[†] Since the residues of dn^2u are zero, the integral defining $E\,(u)$ is independent of the path chosen (§ 6·1).

is a doubly-periodic function of u, with periods $2K$, $2iK'$, with only a single simple pole in any cell. It is therefore a constant; this constant is usually written in the form E/K. To determine the constant A, we observe that the principal part of $\mathrm{dn}^2 u$ at iK' is $-(u-iK')^{-2}$, by § 22·341; and the residue of $\Theta'(u)/\Theta(u)$ at this pole is unity, so the principal part of $\dfrac{d}{du}\left\{\dfrac{\Theta'(u)}{\Theta(u)}\right\}$ is $-(u-iK')^{-2}$. Hence $A=1$, so

$$\mathrm{dn}^2 u = \frac{d}{du}\left\{\frac{\Theta'(u)}{\Theta(u)}\right\} + \frac{E}{K}.$$

Integrating and observing that $\Theta'(0)=0$, we get

$$E(u) = \Theta'(u)/\Theta(u) + uE/K.$$

Since $\Theta'(K)=0$, we have $E(K)=E$; hence

$$E = \int_0^K \mathrm{dn}^2 u\, du = \int_0^{\frac{1}{2}\pi}(1-k^2\sin^2\phi)^{\frac{1}{2}}d\phi = \tfrac{1}{2}\pi F\left(-\tfrac{1}{2}, \tfrac{1}{2}; 1; k^2\right).$$

It is usual (cf. § 22·3) to call K and E the *complete* elliptic integrals of the first and second kinds. Tables of them *qua* functions of the modular angle are given by Legendre, *Fonctions Elliptiques*, II.

Example 1. Shew that $E(u+2nK)=E(u)+2nE$, where n is any integer.

Example 2. By expressing $\Theta(u)$ in terms of the function $\vartheta_4(\tfrac{1}{2}\pi u/K)$, and expanding about the point $u=iK'$, shew that

$$E = \tfrac{1}{3}\left\{2 - k^2 - \vartheta_1'''/(\vartheta_3^4\vartheta_1')\right\}K.$$

22·731. *The Zeta-function* $Z(u)$.

The function $E(u)$ is not periodic in either $2K$ or in $2iK'$, but, associated with these periods, it has additive constants $2E$, $\{2iK'E - \pi i\}/K$; it is convenient to have a function of the same general type as $E(u)$ which is singly-periodic, and such a function is

$$Z(u) \equiv \Theta'(u)/\Theta(u);$$

from this definition, we have*

$$Z(u) = E(u) - uE/K, \qquad \Theta(u) = \Theta(0)\exp\left\{\int_0^u Z(t)\,dt\right\}.$$

22·732. *The addition-formulae for* $E(u)$ *and* $Z(u)$.

Consider the expression

$$\frac{\Theta'(u+v)}{\Theta(u+v)} - \frac{\Theta'(u)}{\Theta(u)} - \frac{\Theta'(v)}{\Theta(v)} + k^2 \,\mathrm{sn}\,u\,\mathrm{sn}\,v\,\mathrm{sn}(u+v)$$

---

* The integral in the expression for $\Theta(u)$ is not one-valued as $Z(t)$ has residue 1 at its poles; but the difference of the integrals taken along any two paths with the same end points is $2n\pi i$ where n is the number of poles enclosed, and the exponential of the integral is therefore one-valued, as it should be, since $\Theta(u)$ is one-valued.

qua function of u. It is doubly-periodic* (periods $2K$ and $2iK'$) with simple poles congruent to iK' and to $iK' - v$; the residue of the first two terms at iK' is -1, and the residue of $\operatorname{sn} u \operatorname{sn} v \operatorname{sn} (u + v)$ is $k^{-1} \operatorname{sn} v \operatorname{sn} (iK' + v) = k^{-2}$.

Hence the function is doubly-periodic and has no poles at points congruent to iK' or (similarly) at points congruent to $iK' - v$. By Liouville's theorem, it is therefore a constant, and, putting $u = 0$, we see that the constant is zero.

Hence we have the addition-formulae

$$Z (u) + Z (v) - Z (u + v) = k^2 \operatorname{sn} u \operatorname{sn} v \operatorname{sn} (u + v),$$
$$E (u) + E (v) - E (u + v) = k^2 \operatorname{sn} u \operatorname{sn} v \operatorname{sn} (u + v).$$

[NOTE. Since $Z(u)$ and $E(u)$ are not doubly-periodic, it is possible to prove that no *algebraic* relation can exist connecting them with $\operatorname{sn} u$, $\operatorname{cn} u$ and $\operatorname{dn} u$, so these are not *addition-theorems* in the strict sense†.]

22·733. *Jacobi's imaginary transformation‡ of* $Z(u)$.

From § 21·51 it is fairly evident that there must be a transformation of Jacobi's type for the function $Z(u)$. To obtain it, we translate the formula

$$\vartheta_2 (ix \mid \tau) = (- i\tau)^{\frac{1}{2}} \exp (- i\tau' x^2/\pi) . \vartheta_4 (ix\tau' \mid \tau')$$

into Jacobi's earlier notation, when it becomes

$$H (iu + K, k) = (- i\tau)^{\frac{1}{2}} \exp \left(\frac{\pi u^2}{4KK'} \right) \Theta (u, k'),$$

and hence

$$\operatorname{cn} (iu, k) = (- i\tau)^{\frac{1}{2}} \exp \left(\frac{\pi u^2}{4KK'} \right) \frac{\vartheta_4 (0 \mid \tau)}{\vartheta_2 (0 \mid \tau)} \frac{\Theta (u, k')}{\Theta (iu, k)}.$$

Taking the logarithmic differential of each side, we get, on making use of § 22·4,

$$Z (iu, k) = i \operatorname{dn} (u, k') \operatorname{sc} (u, k') - iZ (u, k') - \pi iu/(2KK').$$

22·734. *Jacobi's imaginary transformation of* $E(u)$.

It is convenient to obtain the transformation of $E (u)$ directly from the integral definition; we have

$$E (iu, k) = \int_0^{iu} \operatorname{dn}^2 (t, k) \, dt = \int_0^u \operatorname{dn}^2 (it', k) \, i dt'$$

$$= i \int_0^u \operatorname{dc}^2 (t', k') \, dt',$$

on writing $t = it'$ and making use of § 22·4.

---

* $2iK'$ is a period since the additive constants for the first two terms cancel.

† A theorem due to Weierstrass states that an analytic function, $f(z)$, possessing an addition-theorem in the strict sense must be either

        (i)   an algebraic function of z,

or   (ii)   an algebraic function of $\exp (\pi iz/\omega)$,

or   (iii) an algebraic function of $\wp (z \mid \omega_1, \omega_2)$;

where ω, ω_1, ω_2 are suitably chosen constants. See Forsyth, *Theory of Functions* (1918), Ch. XIII.

‡ *Fundamenta Nova*, p. 161.

Hence, from § 22·72 example 3, we have

$$E(iu, k) = i\left\{u + dn(u, k') sc(u, k') - \int_0^u dn^2(t', k') dt'\right\},$$

and so $\qquad E(iu, k) = iu + i\, dn(u, k')\, sc(u, k') - iE(u, k').$

This is the transformation stated.

It is convenient to write E' to denote the same function of k' as E is of k, i.e. $E' = E(K', k')$, so that

$$E(2iK', k) = 2i(K' - E').$$

22·735. *Legendre's relation*.

From the transformations of $E(u)$ and $Z(u)$ just obtained, it is possible to derive a remarkable relation connecting the two kinds of complete elliptic integrals, namely

$$EK' + E'K - KK' = \tfrac{1}{2}\pi.$$

For we have, by the transformations of §§ 22·733, 22·734,

$$E(iu, k) - Z(iu, k) = iu - i\{E(u, k') - Z(u, k')\} + \pi iu/(2KK'),$$

and on making use of the connexion between the functions $E(u, k)$ and $Z(u, k)$, this gives

$$iuE/K = iu - i\{uE'/K'\} + \pi iu/(2KK').$$

Since we may take $u \neq 0$, the result stated follows at once from this equation; it is the analogue of the relation $\eta_1\omega_2 - \eta_2\omega_1 = \tfrac{1}{2}\pi i$ which arose in the Weierstrassian theory (§ 20·411).

Example 1. Shew that

$$E(u + K) - E(u) = E - k^2 sn\, u\, cd\, u.$$

Example 2. Shew that

$$E(2u + 2iK') = E(2u) + 2i(K' - E').$$

Example 3. Deduce from example 2 that

$$E(u + iK') = \tfrac{1}{2}E(2u + 2iK') + \tfrac{1}{2}k^2 sn^2(u + iK') sn(2u + 2iK')$$
$$= E(u) + cn\, u\, ds\, u + i(K' - E').$$

Example 4. Shew that

$$E(u + K + iK') = E(u) - sn\, u\, dc\, u + E + i(K' - E').$$

Example 5. Obtain the expansions, valid when $|I(x)| < \tfrac{1}{2}\pi I(\tau)$,

$$(kK)^2 sn^2 u = K^2 - KE - 2\pi^2 \sum_{n=1}^{\infty} \frac{nq^n \cos 2nx}{1 - q^{2n}}, \qquad KZ(u) = 2\pi \sum_{n=1}^{\infty} \frac{q^n \sin 2nx}{1 - q^{2n}}.$$

(Jacobi.)

* *Exercices de Calcul Intégral*, I. (1811), p. 61. For a geometrical proof see Glaisher, *Messenger*, IV. (1874), pp. 95–96.

22·736. *Properties of the complete elliptic integrals, regarded as functions of the modulus.*

If, in the formulae $E = \int_0^{\frac{1}{2}\pi} (1 - k^2 \sin^2 \phi)^{\frac{1}{2}} d\phi$, we differentiate under the sign of integration (§ 4·2), we have

$$\frac{dE}{dk} = -\int_0^{\frac{1}{2}\pi} k \sin^2 \phi \, (1 - k^2 \sin^2 \phi)^{-\frac{1}{2}} d\phi = \frac{E - K}{k}.$$

Treating the formula for K in the same manner, we have

$$\frac{dK}{dk} = \int_0^{\frac{1}{2}\pi} k \sin^2 \phi \, (1 - k^2 \sin^2 \phi)^{-\frac{3}{2}} d\phi = k \int_0^K \mathrm{sd}^2 u \, du$$

$$= \frac{1}{kk'^2} \left\{ \int_0^K \mathrm{dn}^2 u \, du - \left[k'^2 u \right]_0^K \right\},$$

by § 22·72 example 3; so that

$$\frac{dK}{dk} = \frac{E}{kk'^2} - \frac{K}{k}.$$

If we write $k^2 = c$, $k'^2 = c'$, these results assume the forms

$$2 \frac{dE}{dc} = \frac{E - K}{c}, \qquad 2 \frac{dK}{dc} = \frac{E - Kc'}{cc'}.$$

Example 1. Shew that

$$2 \frac{dE'}{dc} = \frac{K' - E'}{c'}, \qquad 2 \frac{dK'}{dc} = \frac{cK' - E'}{cc'}.$$

Example 2. Shew, by differentiation with regard to c, that $EK' + E'K - KK'$ is constant.

Example 3. Shew that K and K' are solutions of

$$\frac{d}{dk} \left\{ kk'^2 \frac{du}{dk} \right\} = ku,$$

and that E and $E' - K'$ are solutions of

$$k'^2 \frac{d}{dk} \left(k \frac{du}{dk} \right) + ku = 0. \qquad \text{(Legendre.)}$$

22·737. *The values of the complete elliptic integrals for small values of k.*

From the integral definitions of E and K it is easy to see, by expanding in powers of k, that

$$\lim_{k \to 0} K = \lim_{k \to 0} E = \tfrac{1}{2}\pi, \qquad \lim_{k \to 0} (K - E)/k^2 = \tfrac{1}{4}\pi.$$

In like manner, $\qquad \lim_{k \to 0} E' = \int_0^{\frac{1}{2}\pi} \cos \phi \, d\phi = 1.$

It is not possible to determine $\lim_{k \to 0} K'$ in the same way because $(1 - k'^2 \sin^2 \phi)^{-\frac{1}{2}}$ is discontinuous at $\phi = 0$, $k = 0$; but it follows from example 21 of Chapter XIV (p. 299) that, when $|\arg k| < \pi$,

$$\lim_{k \to 0} \{ K' - \log (4/k) \} = 0.$$

This result is also deducible from the formulae $2iK' = \pi\tau\vartheta_3{}^2$, $k = \vartheta_2{}^2/\vartheta_3{}^2$, by making $q \to 0$; or it may be proved for real values of k by the following elementary method:

By § 22·32, $K' = \int_k^1 (t^2 - k^2)^{-\frac{1}{2}} (1 - t^2)^{-\frac{1}{2}} dt$; now, when $k < t < \sqrt{k}$, $(1 - t^2)$ lies between 1 and $1 - k$; and, when $\sqrt{k} < t < 1$, $(t^2 - k^2)/t^2$ lies between 1 and $1 - k$. Therefore K' lies between

$$\int_k^{\sqrt{k}} (t^2 - k^2)^{-\frac{1}{2}} dt + \int_{\sqrt{k}}^1 t^{-1} (1 - t^2)^{-\frac{1}{2}} dt$$

and

$$(1 - k)^{-\frac{1}{2}} \left\{ \int_k^{\sqrt{k}} (t^2 - k^2)^{-\frac{1}{2}} dt + \int_{\sqrt{k}}^1 t^{-1} (1 - t^2)^{-\frac{1}{2}} dt \right\};$$

and therefore

$$K' = (1 - \theta k)^{-\frac{1}{2}} \left\{ \log \frac{\sqrt{k} + \sqrt{(k - k^2)}}{k} - \log \frac{\sqrt{k}}{1 + \sqrt{(1 - k)}} \right\}$$

$$= (1 - \theta k)^{-\frac{1}{2}} [2 \log \{1 + \sqrt{(1 - k)}\} - \log k],$$

where $0 \leqslant \theta \leqslant 1$.

Now

$$\lim_{k \to 0} [2 (1 - \theta k)^{-\frac{1}{2}} \log \{1 + \sqrt{(1 - k)}\} - \log 4] = 0,$$

$$\lim_{k \to 0} \{1 - (1 - \theta k)^{-\frac{1}{2}}\} \log k = 0,$$

and therefore

$$\lim_{k \to 0} \{K' - \log (4/k)\} = 0,$$

which is the required result.

Example. Deduce Legendre's relation from § 22·736 example 2, by making $k \to 0$.

22·74. *The elliptic integral of the third kind*[*].

To evaluate an integral of the type

$$\int (1 + Nt^2)^{-1} \{(A_1 t^2 + B_1)(A_2 t^2 + B_2)\}^{-\frac{1}{2}} dt$$

in terms of known functions, we make the substitution made in the corresponding integrals of the first and second kinds (§§ 22·72, 22·73). The integral is thereby reduced to

$$\int \frac{\alpha + \beta \operatorname{sn}^2 u}{1 + \nu \operatorname{sn}^2 u} du = \alpha u + (\beta - \alpha\nu) \int \frac{\operatorname{sn}^2 u}{1 + \nu \operatorname{sn}^2 u} du,$$

where α, β, ν are constants; if $\nu = 0$, -1, ∞ or $-k^2$ the integral can be expressed in terms of integrals of the first and second kinds; for other values of ν we determine the *parameter* a by the equation $\nu = -k^2 \operatorname{sn}^2 a$, and then it is evidently permissible to take as the fundamental integral of the third kind

$$\Pi (u, a) = \int_0^u \frac{k^2 \operatorname{sn} a \operatorname{cn} a \operatorname{dn} a \operatorname{sn}^2 u}{1 - k^2 \operatorname{sn}^2 a \operatorname{sn}^2 u} du.$$

To express this in terms of Theta-functions, we observe that the integrand may be written in the form

$$\tfrac{1}{2} k^2 \operatorname{sn} u \operatorname{sn} a \{\operatorname{sn} (u + a) + \operatorname{sn} (u - a)\} = \tfrac{1}{2} \{Z (u - a) - Z (u + a) + 2Z (a)\},$$

---

* Legendre, *Exercices de Calcul Intégral*, I. (1811), p. 17; *Fonctions Elliptiques*, I. (1825), pp. 14–18, 74, 75; Jacobi, *Fundamenta Nova* (1829), pp. 137–172; we employ Jacobi's notation, not Legendre's.

by the addition-theorem for the Zeta-function; making use of the formula $Z(u) = \Theta'(u)/\Theta(u)$, we at once get

$$\Pi(u, a) = \tfrac{1}{2} \log \frac{\Theta(u-a)}{\Theta(u+a)} + u Z(a),$$

a result which shews that $\Pi(u, a)$ is a many-valued function of u with logarithmic singularities at the zeros of $\Theta(u \pm a)$.

Example 1.   Obtain the addition-formula*

$$\Pi(u, a) + \Pi(v, a) - \Pi(u+v, a) = \tfrac{1}{2} \log \frac{\Theta(u+v+a)\,\Theta(u-a)\,\Theta(v-a)}{\Theta(u+v-a)\,\Theta(u+a)\,\Theta(v+a)}$$

$$= \tfrac{1}{2} \log \frac{1 - k^2 \operatorname{sn} a \operatorname{sn} u \operatorname{sn} v \operatorname{sn}(u+v-a)}{1 + k^2 \operatorname{sn} a \operatorname{sn} u \operatorname{sn} v \operatorname{sn}(u+v+a)}.$$

(Legendre.)

(Take $x : y : z : w = u : v : \pm a : u+v \pm a$ in Jacobi's fundamental formula

$$[4] + [1] = [4]' + [1]'.)$$

Example 2.   Shew that

$$\Pi(u, a) - \Pi(a, u) = u Z(a) - a Z(u).$$

(Legendre and Jacobi.)

[This is known as the formula for interchange of argument and parameter.]

Example 3.   Shew that

$$\Pi(u, a) + \Pi(u, b) - \Pi(u, a+b) = \tfrac{1}{2} \log \frac{1 - k^2 \operatorname{sn} a \operatorname{sn} b \operatorname{sn} u \operatorname{sn}(a+b-u)}{1 + k^2 \operatorname{sn} a \operatorname{sn} b \operatorname{sn} u \operatorname{sn}(a+b+u)}$$

$$+ u k^2 \operatorname{sn} a \operatorname{sn} b \operatorname{sn}(a+b).$$

(Jacobi.)

[This is known as the formula for addition of parameters.]

Example 4.   Shew that

$$\Pi(iu, ia+K, k) = \Pi(u, a+K', k').$$

(Jacobi.)

Example 5.   Shew that

$$\Pi(u+v, a+b) + \Pi(u-v, a-b) - 2\Pi(u, a) - 2\Pi(v, b)$$

$$= - k^2 \operatorname{sn} a \operatorname{sn} b . \{(u+v) \operatorname{sn}(a+b) - (u-v) \operatorname{sn}(a-b)\} + \tfrac{1}{2} \log \frac{1 - k^2 \operatorname{sn}^2(u-a)\operatorname{sn}^2(v-b)}{1 + k^2 \operatorname{sn}^2(u+a)\operatorname{sn}^2(v+b)},$$

and obtain special forms of this result by putting v or b equal to zero.   (Jacobi.)

22·741.   *A dynamical application of the elliptic integral of the third kind.*

It is evident from the expression for $\Pi(u, a)$ in terms of Theta-functions that if u, a, k are real, the *average* rate of increase of $\Pi(u, a)$ as u increases is $Z(a)$, since $\Theta(u \pm a)$ is periodic with respect to the real period $2K$.

This result determines the mean precession about the invariable line in the motion of a rigid body relative to its centre of gravity under forces whose resultant passes through its centre of gravity. It is evident that, for purposes of computation, a result of this nature is preferable to the corresponding result in terms of Sigma-functions and Weierstrassian Zeta-functions, for the reasons that the Theta-functions have a specially simple behaviour with respect to their real period—the period which is of importance in Applied Mathematics—and that the q-series are much better adapted for computation than the product by which the Sigma-function is most simply defined.

---

* No fewer than 96 forms have been obtained for the expression on the right. See Glaisher, *Messenger*, x. (1881), p. 124.

22·8. *The lemniscate functions.*

The integral $\int_0^x (1-t^4)^{-\frac{1}{2}}\,dt$ occurs in the problem of rectifying the arc of the lemniscate*; if the integral be denoted by ϕ, we shall express the relation between ϕ and x by writing† $x = \sin \operatorname{lemn} \phi$.

In like manner, if

$$\phi_1 = \int_x^1 (1-t^4)^{-\frac{1}{2}}\,dt, \qquad \tfrac{1}{2}\varpi = \int_0^1 (1-t^4)^{-\frac{1}{2}}\,dt,$$

we write

$$x = \cos \operatorname{lemn} \phi_1,$$

and we have the relation

$$\sin \operatorname{lemn} \phi = \cos \operatorname{lemn}\left(\tfrac{1}{2}\varpi - \phi\right).$$

These *lemniscate functions*, which were the first functions‡ defined by the inversion of an integral, can easily be expressed in terms of elliptic functions with modulus $1/\sqrt{2}$; for, from the formula (§ 22·122 example)

$$u = \int_0^{\operatorname{sd} u} \{(1-k'^2 y^2)(1+k^2 y^2)\}^{-\frac{1}{2}}\,dy,$$

it is easy to see (on writing $y = t\sqrt{2}$) that

$$\sin \operatorname{lemn} \phi = 2^{-\frac{1}{2}}\operatorname{sd}(\phi\sqrt{2},\,1/\sqrt{2});$$

similarly,

$$\cos \operatorname{lemn} \phi = \operatorname{cn}(\phi\sqrt{2},\,1/\sqrt{2}).$$

Further, $\tfrac{1}{2}\varpi$ is the smallest positive value of ϕ for which

$$\operatorname{cn}(\phi\sqrt{2},\,1/\sqrt{2}) = 0,$$

so that

$$\varpi = \sqrt{2}K_0,$$

the suffix attached to the complete elliptic integral denoting that it is formed with the particular modulus $1/\sqrt{2}$.

This result renders it possible to express K_0 in terms of Gamma-functions, thus

$$K_0 = 2^{\frac{1}{2}}\int_0^1 (1-t^4)^{-\frac{1}{2}}\,dt = 2^{-\frac{3}{2}}\int_0^1 u^{-\frac{3}{4}}(1-u)^{-\frac{1}{2}}\,du$$

$$= 2^{-\frac{3}{2}}\,\Gamma\left(\tfrac{1}{4}\right)\Gamma\left(\tfrac{1}{2}\right)/\Gamma\left(\tfrac{3}{4}\right) = \tfrac{1}{4}\pi^{-\frac{1}{2}}\{\Gamma\left(\tfrac{1}{4}\right)\}^2,$$

a result first obtained by Legendre§.

Since $k = k'$ when $k = 1/\sqrt{2}$, it follows that $K_0 = K_0'$, and so $q_0 = e^{-\pi}$.

* The equation of the lemniscate being $r^2 = a^2 \cos 2\theta$, it is easy to derive the equation $\left(\dfrac{ds}{dr}\right)^2 = \dfrac{a^4}{a^4 - r^4}$ from the formula $\left(\dfrac{ds}{dr}\right)^2 = 1 + \left(\dfrac{r\,d\theta}{dr}\right)^2$.

† Gauss wrote sl and cl for sin lemn and cos lemn, *Werke*, III. (1876), p. 493.

‡ Gauss, *Werke*, III. (1876), p. 404. The idea of investigating the functions occurred to Gauss on January 8, 1797.

§ *Exercices de Calcul Intégral*, I. (Paris, 1811), p. 209. The value of K_0 is $1·85407468...,$ where $\varpi = 2·62205756....$

Example 1.   Express K_0 in terms of Gamma-functions by using Kummer's formula (see Chapter XIV, example 12, p. 298).

Example 2.   By writing $t = (1 - u^2)^{\frac{1}{2}}$ in the formula

$$E_0 = \int_0^1 (1 - \tfrac{1}{2}t^2)^{\frac{1}{2}} (1 - t^2)^{-\frac{1}{2}} dt,$$

shew that

$$2^{\frac{1}{2}} E_0 = \int_0^1 (1 - u^4)^{-\frac{1}{2}} du + \int_0^1 u^2 (1 - u^4)^{-\frac{1}{2}} du,$$

and deduce that

$$2E_0 - K_0 = 2\pi^{\frac{3}{2}} \{\Gamma(\tfrac{1}{4})\}^{-2}.$$

Example 3.   Deduce Legendre's relation (§ 22·735) from example 2 combined with § 22·736 example 2.

Example 4.   Shew that

$$\sin \operatorname{lemn}^2 \phi = \frac{1 - \cos \operatorname{lemn}^2 \phi}{1 + \cos \operatorname{lemn}^2 \phi}.$$

22·81.   *The values of K and K' for special values of k.*

It has been seen that, when $k = 1/\sqrt{2}$, K can be evaluated in terms of Gamma-functions, and $K = K'$; this is a special case of a general theorem* that, whenever

$$\frac{K'}{K} = \frac{a + b\sqrt{n}}{c + d\sqrt{n}},$$

where a, b, c, d, n are integers, k is a root of an algebraic equation with integral coefficients.

This theorem is based on the theory of the transformation of elliptic functions and is beyond the scope of this book; but there are three distinct cases in which k, K, K' all have fairly simple values, namely

$$\text{(I)} \qquad k = \sqrt{2} - 1, \qquad K' = K\sqrt{2},$$
$$\text{(II)} \qquad k = \sin \tfrac{1}{12}\pi, \qquad K' = K\sqrt{3},$$
$$\text{(III)} \qquad k = \tan^2 \tfrac{1}{8}\pi, \qquad K' = 2K.$$

Of these we shall give a brief investigation†.

(I)   *The quarter-periods with the modulus* $\sqrt{2} - 1$.

Landen's transformation gives a relation between elliptic functions with any modulus k and those with modulus $k_1 = (1 - k')/(1 + k')$; and the quarter-periods Λ, Λ' associated with the modulus k_1 satisfy the relation $\Lambda'/\Lambda = 2K'/K$.

If we choose k so that $k_1 = k'$, then $\Lambda = K'$ and $k_1' = k$ so that $\Lambda' = K$; and the relation $\Lambda'/\Lambda = 2K'/K$ gives $\Lambda'^2 = 2\Lambda^2$.

Therefore the quarter-periods Λ, Λ' associated with the modulus k_1 given by the equation $k_1 = (1 - k_1)/(1 + k_1)$ are such that $\Lambda' = \pm \Lambda\sqrt{2}$; i.e. if $k_1 = \sqrt{2} - 1$, then $\Lambda' = \Lambda\sqrt{2}$ (since Λ, Λ' obviously are both positive).

(II)   *The quarter-periods associated with the modulus* $\sin \tfrac{1}{12}\pi$.

The case of $k = \sin \tfrac{1}{12}\pi$ was discussed by Legendre‡; he obtained the remarkable result that, with this value of k,

$$K' = K\sqrt{3}.$$

---

* Abel, *Journal für Math.* III. p. 184 [*Oeuvres*, I. (1881), p. 377].

† For some similar formulae of a less simple nature, see Kronecker, *Berliner Sitzungsberichte*, 1857, 1862.

‡ *Exercices de Calcul Intégral*, I. (1811), pp. 59, 210; *Fonctions Elliptiques*, I. (1825), pp. 59, 60.

This result follows from the relation between definite integrals

$$\int_{-\infty}^{1} (1-x^3)^{-\frac{1}{2}} dx = \sqrt{3} \int_{1}^{\infty} (x^3-1)^{-\frac{1}{2}} dx.$$

To obtain this relation, consider $\int (1-z^3)^{-\frac{1}{3}} dz$ taken round the contour formed by the part of the real axis (indented at $z=1$ by an arc of radius R^{-1}) joining the points 0 and R, the line joining $Re^{\frac{2}{3}\pi i}$ to 0 and the arc of radius R joining the points R and $Re^{\frac{2}{3}\pi i}$; as $R \to \infty$, the integral round the arc tends to zero, as does the integral round the indentation, and so, by Cauchy's theorem,

$$\int_{0}^{1} (1-x^3)^{-\frac{1}{3}} dx + i\int_{1}^{\infty} (x^3-1)^{-\frac{1}{3}} dx + e^{\frac{2}{3}\pi i}\int_{\infty}^{0} (1+x^3)^{-\frac{1}{3}} dx = 0,$$

on writing x and $xe^{\frac{2}{3}\pi i}$ respectively for z on the two straight lines.

Writing

$$\int_{0}^{1} (1-x^3)^{-\frac{1}{3}} dx = I_1, \quad \int_{1}^{\infty} (x^3-1)^{-\frac{1}{3}} dx = I_2, \quad \int_{0}^{\infty} (1+x^3)^{-\frac{1}{3}} dx = \int_{-\infty}^{0} (1-x^3)^{-\frac{1}{3}} dx = I_3,$$

we have

$$I_1 + iI_2 = \tfrac{1}{2}(1 + i\sqrt{3}) I_3;$$

so, equating real and imaginary parts,

$$I_1 = \tfrac{1}{2}I_3, \quad I_2 = \tfrac{1}{2}I_3\sqrt{3},$$

and therefore

$$I_1 + I_3 - I_2\sqrt{3} = \tfrac{1}{2}I_3 + I_3 - \tfrac{3}{2}I_3 = 0,$$

which is the relation stated*.

Now, by § 22·72 example 6,

$$I_2 = 4(a^2+\beta^2)^{-\frac{1}{2}} K, \quad I_1 + I_3 = 4(a^2+\beta^2)^{-\frac{1}{2}} K',$$

where the modulus is $a(a^2+\beta^2)^{-\frac{1}{2}}$ and

$$a^2 = 2\sqrt{3} - 3, \quad \beta^2 = 2\sqrt{3} + 3,$$

so that

$$k^2 = \tfrac{1}{4}(2-\sqrt{3}) = \sin^2 \tfrac{1}{12}\pi.$$

We therefore have

$$3^{-\frac{1}{4}} \cdot 2K = 3^{-\frac{3}{4}} \cdot 2K' = I_2 = 3^{\frac{1}{2}} I_1$$

$$= 3^{-\frac{1}{2}} \int_{0}^{1} t^{-\frac{2}{3}} (1-t)^{-\frac{1}{2}} dt = \tfrac{1}{3}\pi^{\frac{1}{2}} \Gamma\left(\tfrac{1}{6}\right)/\Gamma\left(\tfrac{2}{3}\right),$$

when the modulus k is $\sin \tfrac{1}{12}\pi$.

(III) *The quarter-periods with the modulus* $\tan^2 \tfrac{1}{8}\pi$.

If, in Landen's transformation (§ 22·42), we take $k = 1/\sqrt{2}$, we have $\Lambda'/\Lambda = 2K'/K = 2$; now this value of k gives

$$k_1 = \frac{\sqrt{2}-1}{\sqrt{2}+1} = \tan^2 \tfrac{1}{8}\pi;$$

and the corresponding quarter-periods Λ, Λ' are $\tfrac{1}{2}(1+2^{-\frac{1}{2}}) K_0$ and $(1+2^{-\frac{1}{2}}) K_0$.

Example 1. Discuss the quarter-periods when k has the values $(2\sqrt{2}-2)^{\frac{1}{2}}$, $\sin \tfrac{5}{12}\pi$, and $2^{\frac{5}{4}}(\sqrt{2}-1)$.

---

* Another method of obtaining the relation is to express I_1, I_2, I_3 in terms of Gamma-functions by writing $t^{\frac{1}{3}}$, $t^{-\frac{1}{3}}$, $(t^{-1}-1)^{\frac{1}{3}}$ respectively for x in the integrals by which I_1, I_2, I_3 are defined.

Example 2.   Shew that

$$2^{\frac{1}{4}} e^{-\frac{1}{24}\pi} = \prod_{n=0}^{\infty} (1 + e^{-(2n+1)\pi}), \quad 3^{\frac{1}{4}} e^{-\frac{1}{18}\pi\sqrt{3}} = \prod_{n=1}^{\infty} (1 - e^{-2n\pi/\sqrt{3}}).$$

(Glaisher, Messenger, v.)

Example 3.   Express the coordinates of any point on the curve $y^2 = x^3 - 1$ in the form

$$x = 1 + \frac{3^{\frac{1}{2}}(1 - \operatorname{cn} u)}{1 + \operatorname{cn} u}, \quad y = \frac{2 \cdot 3^{\frac{3}{4}} \operatorname{sn} u \operatorname{dn} u}{(1 + \operatorname{cn} u)^2},$$

where the modulus of the elliptic functions is $\sin \frac{1}{12}\pi$, and shew that $\dfrac{dx}{du} = 3^{-\frac{1}{4}} y$.

By considering $\displaystyle\int_1^\infty y^{-1} dx = 3^{-\frac{1}{4}} \int_0^{2K} du$, evaluate K in terms of Gamma-functions when $k = \sin \frac{1}{12}\pi$.

Example 4.   Shew that, when $y^2 = x^3 - 1$,

$$\int_1^\infty y^{-3} (x-1)^2 dx = \left[-\frac{2}{3} y^{-1} (1 - x^{-1})^2 \right]_1^\infty + \frac{4}{3} \int_1^\infty (x^{-2} y^{-1} - x^{-3} y^{-1}) \, dx;$$

and thence, by using example 3 and expressing the last integral in terms of Gamma-functions by the substitution $x = t^{-\frac{1}{3}}$, obtain the formula of Legendre (*Calcul Intégral*, p. 60) connecting the first and second complete elliptic integrals with modulus $\sin \frac{1}{12}\pi$:

$$\frac{\pi}{4\sqrt{3}} = K \left\{ E - \frac{\sqrt{3} + 1}{2\sqrt{3}} K \right\}.$$

Example 5.   By expressing the coordinates of any point on the curve $Y^2 = 1 - X^3$ in the form

$$X = 1 - \frac{3^{\frac{1}{2}}(1 - \operatorname{cn} v)}{1 + \operatorname{cn} v}, \quad Y = \frac{2 \cdot 3^{\frac{3}{4}} \operatorname{sn} v \operatorname{dn} v}{(1 + \operatorname{cn} v)^2},$$

in which the modulus of the elliptic functions is $\sin \frac{5}{12}\pi$, and evaluating

$$\left\{ \int_{-\infty}^0 + \int_0^1 \right\} Y^{-3} (1 - X)^2 dX$$

in terms of Gamma-functions, obtain Legendre's result that*, when $k = \sin \frac{1}{12}\pi$,

$$\frac{\pi\sqrt{3}}{4} = K' \left\{ E' - \frac{\sqrt{3} - 1}{2\sqrt{3}} K' \right\}.$$

22·82.   *A geometrical illustration of the functions* sn u, cn u, dn u.

A geometrical representation of Jacobian elliptic functions with $k = 1/\sqrt{2}$ is afforded by the arc of the lemniscate, as has been seen in § 22·8; to represent the Jacobian functions with any modulus k $(0 < k < 1)$, we may make use of a *curve described on a sphere*, known as *Seiffert's spherical spiral*†.

Take a sphere of radius unity with centre at the origin, and let the cylindrical polar coordinates of any point on it be (ρ, ϕ, z), so that the arc of a curve traced on the sphere is given by the formula ‡

$$(ds)^2 = \rho^2 (d\phi)^2 + (1 - \rho^2)^{-1} (d\rho)^2.$$

* It is interesting to observe that, when Legendre had proved by differentiation that $EK' + E'K - KK'$ is constant, he used the results of examples 4 and 5 to determine the constant, before using the methods of § 22·8 example 3 and of § 22·737.

† Seiffert, *Ueber eine neue geometrische Einführung in die Theorie der elliptischen Funktionen* (Charlottenburg, 1896).

‡ This is an obvious transformation of the formula $(ds)^2 = (d\rho)^2 + \rho^2 (d\phi)^2 + (dz)^2$ when ρ and z are connected by the relation $\rho^2 + z^2 = 1$.

Seiffert's spiral is defined by the equation

$$\phi = ks,$$

where s is the arc measured from the pole of the sphere (i.e. the point where the axis of z meets the sphere) and k is a positive constant, less than unity*.

For this curve we have

$$(ds)^2 (1 - k^2 \rho^2) = (1 - \rho^2)^{-1} (d\rho)^2,$$

and so, since s and ρ vanish together,

$$\rho = \operatorname{sn} (s, k).$$

The cylindrical polar coordinates of any point on the curve expressed in terms of the arc measured from the pole are therefore

$$(\rho, \phi, z) = (\operatorname{sn} s, ks, \operatorname{cn} s);$$

and dn s is easily seen to be the cosine of the angle at which the curve cuts the meridian. Hence it may be seen that, if K be the arc of the curve from the pole to the equator, then sn s and cn s have period $4K$, while dn s has period $2K$.

REFERENCES.

A. M. Legendre, *Traité des Fonctions Elliptiques* (Paris, 1825–1828).

C. G. J. Jacobi, *Fundamenta Nova Theoriae Functionum Ellipticarum* (Königsberg, 1829).

J. Tannery et J. Molk, *Fonctions Elliptiques* (Paris, 1893–1902).

A. Cayley, *Elliptic Functions* (London, 1895).

P. F. Verhulst, *Traité élémentaire des fonctions elliptiques* (Brussels, 1841).

A. Enneper, *Elliptische Funktionen*, Zweite Auflage von F. Müller (Halle, 1890).

Miscellaneous Examples.

1. Shew that one of the values of

$$\left\{ \left(\frac{\operatorname{dn} u + \operatorname{cn} u}{1 + \operatorname{cn} u} \right)^{\frac{1}{2}} + \left(\frac{\operatorname{dn} u - \operatorname{cn} u}{1 - \operatorname{cn} u} \right)^{\frac{1}{2}} \right\} \left\{ \left(\frac{1 - \operatorname{sn} u}{\operatorname{dn} u - k' \operatorname{sn} u} \right)^{\frac{1}{2}} + \left(\frac{1 + \operatorname{sn} u}{\operatorname{dn} u + k' \operatorname{sn} u} \right)^{\frac{1}{2}} \right\}$$

is $2 (1 + k')$. (Math. Trip. 1904.)

2. If $x + iy = \operatorname{sn}^2 (u + iv)$ and $x - iy = \operatorname{sn}^2 (u - iv)$, shew that

$$\{(x - 1)^2 + y^2\}^{\frac{1}{2}} = (x^2 + y^2)^{\frac{1}{2}} \operatorname{dn} 2u + \operatorname{cn} 2u.$$

(Math. Trip. 1911.)

3. Shew that

$$\{1 \pm \operatorname{cn} (u + v)\} \{1 \pm \operatorname{cn} (u - v)\} = \frac{(\operatorname{cn} u \pm \operatorname{cn} v)^2}{1 - k^2 \operatorname{sn}^2 u \operatorname{sn}^2 v}.$$

4. Shew that

$$1 + \operatorname{cn} (u + v) \operatorname{cn} (u - v) = \frac{\operatorname{cn}^2 u + \operatorname{cn}^2 v}{1 - k^2 \operatorname{sn}^2 u \operatorname{sn}^2 v}.$$

(Jacobi.)

* If $k > 1$, the curve is imaginary.

5. Express $\dfrac{1+\operatorname{cn}(u+v)\operatorname{cn}(u-v)}{1+\operatorname{dn}(u+v)\operatorname{dn}(u-v)}$ as a function of $\operatorname{sn}^2 u + \operatorname{sn}^2 v$.

(Math. Trip. 1909.)

6. Shew that

$$\operatorname{sn}(u-v)\operatorname{dn}(u+v)=\frac{\operatorname{sn} u \operatorname{dn} u \operatorname{cn} v - \operatorname{sn} v \operatorname{dn} v \operatorname{cn} u}{1-k^2 \operatorname{sn}^2 u \operatorname{sn}^2 v}.$$

(Jacobi.)

7. Shew that

$$\{1-(1+k')\operatorname{sn} u \operatorname{sn}(u+K)\}\{1-(1-k')\operatorname{sn} u \operatorname{sn}(u+K)\}=\{\operatorname{sn}(u+K)-\operatorname{sn} u\}^2.$$

(Math. Trip. 1914.)

8. Shew that

$$\operatorname{sn}\left(u+\tfrac{1}{2}K\right)=(1+k')^{-\frac{1}{2}}\frac{k' \operatorname{sn} u + \operatorname{cn} u \operatorname{dn} u}{1-(1-k')\operatorname{sn}^2 u},$$

$$\operatorname{sn}\left(u+\tfrac{1}{2}iK'\right)=k^{-\frac{1}{2}}\frac{(1+k)\operatorname{sn} u + i \operatorname{cn} u \operatorname{dn} u}{1+k \operatorname{sn}^2 u}.$$

9. Shew that

$$\sin\{\operatorname{am}(u+v)+\operatorname{am}(u-v)\}=\frac{2 \operatorname{sn} u \operatorname{cn} u \operatorname{dn} v}{1-k^2 \operatorname{sn}^2 u \operatorname{sn}^2 v},$$

$$\cos\{\operatorname{am}(u+v)-\operatorname{am}(u-v)\}=\frac{\operatorname{cn}^2 v - \operatorname{sn}^2 v \operatorname{dn}^2 u}{1-k^2 \operatorname{sn}^2 u \operatorname{sn}^2 v}.$$

(Jacobi.)

10. Shew that

$$\operatorname{dn}(u+v)\operatorname{dn}(u-v)=\frac{\operatorname{ds}^2 u \operatorname{ds}^2 v + k^2 k'^2}{\operatorname{ns}^2 u \operatorname{ns}^2 v - k^2},$$

and hence express

$$\left[\frac{\wp(u+v)-e_2}{\wp(u+v)-e_3}\cdot\frac{\wp(u-v)-e_2}{\wp(u-v)-e_3}\right]^{\frac{1}{2}}$$

as a rational function of $\wp(u)$ and $\wp(v)$. (Trinity, 1903.)

11. From the formulae for $\operatorname{cn}(2K-u)$ and $\operatorname{dn}(2K-u)$ combined with the formulae for $1+\operatorname{cn} 2u$ and $1+\operatorname{dn} 2u$, shew that

$$(1-\operatorname{cn}\tfrac{2}{3}K)(1+\operatorname{dn}\tfrac{2}{3}K)=1.$$ (Trinity, 1906.)

12. With notation similar to that of § 22·2, shew that

$$\frac{c_1 d_2 - c_2 d_1}{s_1 - s_2}=\frac{\operatorname{cn}(u_1+u_2)-\operatorname{dn}(u_1+u_2)}{\operatorname{sn}(u_1+u_2)};$$

and deduce that, if $u_1+u_2+u_3+u_4=2K$, then

$$(c_1 d_2 - c_2 d_1)(c_3 d_4 - c_4 d_3)=k'^2(s_1-s_2)(s_3-s_4).$$

(Trinity, 1906.)

13. Shew that, if $u+v+w=0$, then

$$1-\operatorname{dn}^2 u - \operatorname{dn}^2 v - \operatorname{dn}^2 w + 2 \operatorname{dn} u \operatorname{dn} v \operatorname{dn} w=k^4 \operatorname{sn}^2 u \operatorname{sn}^2 v \operatorname{sn}^2 w.$$

(Math. Trip. 1907.)

14. By Liouville's theorem or otherwise, shew that

$$\operatorname{dn} u \operatorname{dn}(u+w) - \operatorname{dn} v \operatorname{dn}(v+w)=k^2\{\operatorname{sn} v \operatorname{cn} u \operatorname{sn}(v+w)\operatorname{cn}(u+w)$$
$$-\operatorname{sn} u \operatorname{cn} v \operatorname{sn}(u+w)\operatorname{cn}(v+w)\}.$$

(Math. Trip. 1910.)

15. Shew that

$$\Sigma \operatorname{cn} u_2 \operatorname{cn} u_3 \operatorname{sn}(u_2-u_3)\operatorname{dn} u_1 + \operatorname{sn}(u_2-u_3)\operatorname{sn}(u_3-u_1)\operatorname{sn}(u_1-u_2)\operatorname{dn} u_1 \operatorname{dn} u_2 \operatorname{dn} u_3=0,$$

the summation applying to the suffices 1, 2, 3. (Math. Trip. 1894.)

W. M. A.

34

16. Obtain the formulae
$$\operatorname{sn} 3u = A/D, \quad \operatorname{cn} 3u = B/D, \quad \operatorname{dn} 3u = C/D,$$
where
$$A = 3s - 4(1 + k^2) s^3 + 6k^2 s^5 - k^4 s^9,$$
$$B = c\{1 - 4s^2 + 6k^2 s^4 - 4k^4 s^6 + k^4 s^8\},$$
$$C = d\{1 - 4k^2 s^2 + 6k^2 s^4 - 4k^2 s^6 + k^4 s^8\},$$
$$D = 1 - 6k^2 s^4 + 4k^2(1 + k^2) s^6 - 3k^4 s^8,$$
and
$$s = \operatorname{sn} u, \quad c = \operatorname{cn} u, \quad d = \operatorname{dn} u.$$

17. Shew that
$$\frac{1 - \operatorname{dn} 3u}{1 + \operatorname{dn} 3u} = \left(\frac{1 - \operatorname{dn} u}{1 + \operatorname{dn} u}\right)\left(\frac{1 + a_1 \operatorname{dn} u + a_2 \operatorname{dn}^2 u + a_3 \operatorname{dn}^3 u + a_4 \operatorname{dn}^4 u}{1 - a_1 \operatorname{dn} u + a_2 \operatorname{dn}^2 u - a_3 \operatorname{dn}^3 u + a_4 \operatorname{dn}^4 u}\right)^2,$$
where a_1, a_2, a_3, a_4 are constants to be determined. (Trinity, 1912.)

18. If
$$P(u) = \left(\frac{1 + \operatorname{dn} 3u}{1 + \operatorname{dn} u}\right)^{\frac{1}{2}},$$
shew that
$$\frac{P(u) + P(u + 2iK')}{P(u) - P(u + 2iK')} = -\frac{\operatorname{sn} 2u \operatorname{cn} u}{\operatorname{cn} 2u \operatorname{sn} u}.$$

Determine the poles and zeros of $P(u)$ and the first term in the expansion of the function about each pole and zero. (Math. Trip. 1908.)

19. Shew that
$$\operatorname{sn}(u_1 + u_2 + u_3) = A/D, \quad \operatorname{cn}(u_1 + u_2 + u_3) = B/D, \quad \operatorname{dn}(u_1 + u_2 + u_3) = C/D,$$
where
$$A = s_1 s_2 s_3 \{-1 - k^2 + 2k^2 \Sigma s_1^2 - (k^2 + k^4) \Sigma s_2^2 s_3^2 + 2k^4 s_1^2 s_2^2 s_3^2\}$$
$$+ \Sigma \{s_1 c_2 c_3 d_2 d_3 (1 + 2k^2 s_2^2 s_3^2 - k^2 \Sigma s_2^2 s_3^2)\},$$
$$B = c_1 c_2 c_3 \{1 - k^2 \Sigma s_2^2 s_3^2 + 2k^4 s_1^2 s_2^2 s_3^2\}$$
$$+ \Sigma \{c_1 s_2 s_3 d_2 d_3 (-1 + 2k^2 s_2^2 s_3^2 + 2k^2 s_1^2 - k^2 \Sigma s_2^2 s_3^2)\},$$
$$C = d_1 d_2 d_3 \{1 - k^2 \Sigma s_2^2 s_3^2 + 2k^2 s_1^2 s_2^2 s_3^2\}$$
$$+ k^2 \Sigma \{d_1 s_2 s_3 c_2 c_3 (-1 + 2k^2 s_2^2 s_3^2 + 2s_1^2 - k^2 \Sigma s_2^2 s_3^2)\},$$
$$D = 1 - 2k^2 \Sigma s_2^2 s_3^2 + 4(k^2 + k^4) s_1^2 s_2^2 s_3^2 - 2k^4 s_1^2 s_2^2 s_3^2 \Sigma s_1^2 + k^4 \Sigma s_2^4 s_3^4,$$
and the summations refer to the suffices 1, 2, 3. (Glaisher, *Messenger*, XI.)

20. Shew that
$$\operatorname{sn}(u_1 + u_2 + u_3) = A'/D', \quad \operatorname{cn}(u_1 + u_2 + u_3) = B'/D', \quad \operatorname{dn}(u_1 + u_2 + u_3) = C'/D',$$
where
$$A' = \Sigma s_1 c_2 c_3 d_2 d_3 - s_1 s_2 s_3 (1 + k^2 - k^2 \Sigma s_1^2 + k^4 s_1^2 s_2^2 s_3^2),$$
$$B' = c_1 c_2 c_3 (1 - k^4 s_1^2 s_2^2 s_3^2) - d_1 d_2 d_3 \Sigma s_2 s_3 c_1 d_1,$$
$$C' = d_1 d_2 d_3 (1 - k^2 s_1^2 s_2^2 s_3^2) - k^2 c_1 c_2 c_3 \Sigma s_2 s_3 c_1 d_1,$$
$$D' = 1 - k^2 \Sigma s_2^2 s_3^2 + (k^2 + k^4) s_1^2 s_2^2 s_3^2 - k^2 s_1 s_2 s_3 \Sigma s_1 c_2 c_3 d_2 d_3.$$
(Cayley, *Journal für Math.* XLI.)

21. By applying Abel's method (§ 20·312) to the intersections of the twisted curve $x^2 + y^2 = 1$, $z^2 + k^2 x^2 = 1$ with the variable plane $lx + my + nz = 1$, shew that, if
$$u_1 + u_2 + u_3 + u_4 = 0,$$
then
$$\begin{vmatrix} s_1 & c_1 & d_1 & 1 \\ s_2 & c_2 & d_2 & 1 \\ s_3 & c_3 & d_3 & 1 \\ s_4 & c_4 & d_4 & 1 \end{vmatrix} = 0.$$

Obtain this result also from the equation
$$(s_2 - s_1)(c_3 d_4 - c_4 d_3) + (s_4 - s_3)(c_1 d_2 - c_2 d_1) = 0,$$
which may be proved by the method of example 12.
(Cayley, *Messenger*, XIV.)

22. Shew that
$$(s_4{}^2 - s_3{}^2)(c_1{}^2 d_2{}^2 - c_2{}^2 d_1{}^2) = (s_2{}^2 - s_1{}^2)(c_3{}^2 d_4{}^2 - c_4{}^2 d_3{}^2),$$
by expressing each side in terms of s_1, s_2, s_3, s_4; and deduce from example 21 that, if
$$u_1 + u_2 + u_3 + u_4 = 0,$$
then
$$s_4 c_1 d_2 + s_3 c_2 d_1 + s_2 c_3 d_4 + s_1 c_4 d_3 = 0,$$
$$s_4 c_2 d_1 + s_3 c_1 d_2 + s_2 c_4 d_3 + s_1 c_3 d_4 = 0.$$

(Forsyth, *Messenger*, XIV.)

23. Deduce from Jacobi's fundamental Theta-function formulae that, if
$$u_1 + u_2 + u_3 + u_4 = 0,$$
then
$$k'^2 - k^2 k'^2 s_1 s_2 s_3 s_4 + k^2 c_1 c_2 c_3 c_4 - d_1 d_2 d_3 d_4 = 0.$$

(Gudermann, *Journal für Math.* XVIII.)

24. Deduce from Jacobi's fundamental Theta-function formulae that, if
$$u_1 + u_2 + u_3 + u_4 = 0,$$
then
$$k^2 (s_1 s_2 c_3 c_4 - c_1 c_2 s_3 s_4) - d_1 d_2 + d_3 d_4 = 0,$$
$$k'^2 (s_1 s_2 - s_3 s_4) + d_1 d_2 c_3 c_4 - c_1 c_2 d_3 d_4 = 0,$$
$$s_1 s_2 d_3 d_4 - d_1 d_2 s_3 s_4 + c_3 c_4 - c_1 c_2 = 0.$$

(H. J. S. Smith, *Proc. London Math. Soc.* (1), X.)

25. If $u_1 + u_2 + u_3 + u_4 = 0$, shew that the cross-ratio of sn u_1, sn u_2, sn u_3, sn u_4 is equal to the cross-ratio of sn $(u_1 + K)$, sn $(u_2 + K)$, sn $(u_3 + K)$, sn $(u_4 + K)$.

(Math. Trip. 1905.)

26. Shew that
$$\begin{vmatrix} \operatorname{sn}^2(u+v) & \operatorname{sn}(u+v)\operatorname{sn}(u-v) & \operatorname{sn}^2(u-v) \\ \operatorname{cn}^2(u+v) & \operatorname{cn}(u+v)\operatorname{cn}(u-v) & \operatorname{cn}^2(u-v) \\ \operatorname{dn}^2(u+v) & \operatorname{dn}(u+v)\operatorname{dn}(u-v) & \operatorname{dn}^2(u-v) \end{vmatrix} = -\frac{8k'^2 s_1 s_3{}^3 c_1 c_2 d_1 d_2}{(1 - k^2 s_1{}^2 s_2{}^2)^3}.$$

(Math. Trip. 1913.)

27. Find all systems of values of u and v for which $\operatorname{sn}^2(u+iv)$ is real when u and v are real and $0 < k^2 < 1$.

(Math. Trip. 1901.)

28. If $k' = \frac{1}{4}(a^{-1} - a)^2$, where $0 < a < 1$, shew that
$$\operatorname{sn}^2 \tfrac{1}{4} K = \frac{4a^3}{(1 + a^2)(1 + 2a - a^2)},$$
and that $\operatorname{sn}^2 \tfrac{3}{4} K$ is obtained by writing $- a^{-1}$ for a in this expression.

(Math. Trip. 1902.)

29. If the values of cn z, which are such that cn $3z = a$, are c_1, c_2, ... c_9, shew that
$$3k^4 \prod_{r=1}^{9} c_r + k'^4 \sum_{r=1}^{9} c_r = 0.$$

(Math. Trip. 1899.)

30. If
$$\frac{a + \operatorname{sn}(u+v)}{a + \operatorname{sn}(u-v)} = \frac{b + \operatorname{cn}(u+v)}{b + \operatorname{cn}(u-v)} = \frac{c + \operatorname{dn}(u+v)}{c + \operatorname{dn}(u-v)},$$
and if none of sn v, cn u, dn u, $1 - k^2 \operatorname{sn}^2 u \operatorname{sn}^2 v$ vanishes, shew that u is given by the equation
$$k^2 (k'^2 a^2 + b^2 - c^2) \operatorname{sn}^2 u = k'^2 + k^2 b^2 - c^2.$$

(King's, 1900.)

34—2

31. Shew that

$$1 - \operatorname{sn}(2Kx/\pi) = (1 - \sin x) \prod_{n=1}^{\infty} \left\{ \frac{(1 - q^{2n-1})^2}{(1 + q^{2n})^2} \frac{(1 - 2q^n \sin x + q^{2n})^2}{(1 - 2q^{2n-1} \cos 2x + q^{4n-2})} \right\}.$$

(Math. Trip. 1912.)

32. Shew that

$$\frac{1 - \operatorname{sn}(2Kx/\pi)}{\{\operatorname{dn}(2Kx/\pi) - k' \operatorname{sn}(2Kx/\pi)\}^{\frac{1}{2}}} = \prod_{n=1}^{\infty} \left\{ \frac{1 - 2q^{2n-1} \sin x + q^{4n-2}}{1 + 2q^{2n-1} \sin x + q^{4n-2}} \right\}.$$

(Math. Trip. 1904.)

33. Shew that if k be so small that k^4 may be neglected, then

$$\operatorname{sn} u = \sin u - \tfrac{1}{4} k^2 \cos u \,.\, (u - \sin u \cos u),$$

for small values of u. (Trinity, 1904.)

34. Shew that, if $|I(x)| < \tfrac{1}{2} \pi I(\tau)$, then

$$\log \operatorname{cn}(2Kx/\pi) = \log \cos x - \sum_{n=1}^{\infty} \frac{4q^n \sin^2 nx}{n\{1 + (-q)^n\}}.$$

(Math. Trip. 1907.)

[Integrate the Fourier series for $\operatorname{sn}(2Kx/\pi) \operatorname{dc}(2Kx/\pi)$.]

35. Shew that

$$\int_0^{\frac{1}{2}K} \frac{1 - k^2 \operatorname{sn}^4 u}{\operatorname{cn}^2 u \operatorname{dn}^2 u} \, du = \{(1 + k')^{\frac{1}{2}} - 1\}/k'^{\frac{3}{2}}.$$

(Math. Trip. 1906.)

[Express the integrand in terms of functions of $2u$.]

36. Shew that

$$\int \frac{\operatorname{cn} v \, du}{\operatorname{sn} v - \operatorname{sn} u} = \log \frac{\vartheta_1\left(\tfrac{1}{2}x + \tfrac{1}{2}y - \tfrac{1}{2}\pi\right) \vartheta_1\left(\tfrac{1}{2}x + \tfrac{1}{2}y - \tfrac{1}{2}\pi - \tfrac{1}{2}\pi\tau\right)}{\vartheta_1\left(\tfrac{1}{2}x - \tfrac{1}{2}y\right) \vartheta_1\left(\tfrac{1}{2}x - \tfrac{1}{2}y - \tfrac{1}{2}\pi\tau\right)} - x \frac{\vartheta_1'\left(y + \tfrac{1}{2}\pi\tau\right)}{\vartheta_1\left(y + \tfrac{1}{2}\pi\tau\right)},$$

where $2Kx = \pi u$, $2Ky = \pi v$. (Math. Trip. 1912.)

37. Shew that

$$(1 + k') k'^2 \int_0^K \frac{\operatorname{sn}^3 u \, du}{(1 + \operatorname{cu} u) \operatorname{dn}^2 u} = 1.$$

(Math. Trip. 1903.)

38. Shew that

$$k \int_{a-\beta}^{a+\beta} \operatorname{sn} u \, du = \log \frac{1 + k \operatorname{sn} a \operatorname{sn} \beta}{1 - k \operatorname{sn} a \operatorname{sn} \beta}.$$

(St John's, 1914.)

39. By integrating $\int e^{2iz} \operatorname{dn} u \operatorname{cs} u \, dz$ round a rectangle whose corners are $\pm \tfrac{1}{2}\pi$, $\pm \tfrac{1}{2}\pi + \infty i$ (where $2Kz = \pi u$) and then integrating by parts, shew that, if $0 < k^2 < 1$, then

$$\int_0^K \cos(\pi u/K) \log \operatorname{sn} u \, du = \tfrac{1}{2} K \tanh\left(\tfrac{1}{2}\pi i\tau\right).$$

(Math. Trip. 1902.)

40. Shew that K and Λ' satisfy the equation

$$c(1 - c) \frac{d^2 u}{dc^2} + (1 - 2c) \frac{du}{dc} - \tfrac{1}{4} u = 0,$$

where $c = k^2$; and deduce that they satisfy Legendre's equation for functions of degree $-\tfrac{1}{2}$ with argument $1 - 2k^2$.

41. Express the coordinates of any point on the curve $x^3 + y^3 = 1$ in the form

$$x = \frac{2 \cdot 3^{\frac{1}{4}} \operatorname{sn} u \operatorname{dn} u - (1 - \operatorname{cn} u)^2}{2 \cdot 3^{\frac{1}{4}} \operatorname{sn} u \operatorname{dn} u + (1 - \operatorname{cn} u)^2}, \quad y = \frac{2^{\frac{1}{6}} \cos \frac{1}{12}\pi \,(1 - \operatorname{cn} u)\,\{1 + \tan \frac{1}{12}\pi \operatorname{cn} u\}}{2 \cdot 3^{\frac{1}{4}} \operatorname{sn} u \operatorname{dn} u + (1 - \operatorname{cn} u)^2},$$

the modulus of the elliptic functions being $\sin \frac{1}{12}\pi$; and shew that

$$\int_x^1 (1 - x^3)^{-\frac{2}{3}} dx = \int_0^y (1 - y^3)^{-\frac{2}{3}} dy = 2^{-\frac{2}{3}} \cdot 3^{\frac{1}{4}} u.$$

Shew further that the sum of the parameters of three collinear points on the cubic is a period.

[See Richelot, *Journal für Math.* IX. (1832), pp. 407–408 and Cayley, *Proc. Camb. Phil. Soc.* IV. (1883), pp. 106–109. A uniformising variable for the general cubic in the canonical form $X^3 + Y^3 + Z^3 + 6m\,XYZ = 0$ has been obtained by Bobek, *Einleitung in die Theorie der elliptischen Funktionen* (Leipzig, 1884), p. 251. Dixon (*Quarterly Journal*, XXIV. (1890), pp. 167–233) has developed the theory of elliptic functions by taking the equivalent curve $x^3 + y^3 - 3axy = 1$ as fundamental, instead of the curve

$$y^2 = (1 - x^2)(1 - k^2 x^2).]$$

42. Express $\displaystyle\int_0^2 \{(2x - x^2)(4x^2 + 9)\}^{-\frac{1}{2}} dx$ in terms of a complete elliptic integral of the first kind with a real modulus. (Math. Trip. 1911.)

43. If $\displaystyle u = \int_x^\infty \{(t + 1)(t^2 + t + 1)\}^{-\frac{1}{2}} dt,$

express x in terms of Jacobian elliptic functions of u with a real modulus.

(Math. Trip. 1899.)

44. If . $\displaystyle u = \int_0^x (1 + t^2 - 2t^4)^{-\frac{1}{2}} dt,$

express x in terms of u by means of either Jacobian or Weierstrassian elliptic functions.

(Math. Trip. 1914.)

45. Shew that

$$e^{-\pi} + e^{-9\pi} + e^{-25\pi} + \ldots = \frac{(2^{\frac{1}{4}} - 1)\,\Gamma(\frac{1}{4})}{2^{\frac{11}{4}} \pi^{\frac{3}{4}}}.$$

(Trinity, 1881.)

46. When $a > x > \beta > \gamma$, reduce the integrals

$$\int_x^a \{(a - t)(t - \beta)(t - \gamma)\}^{-\frac{1}{2}} dt, \quad \int_\beta^x \{(a - t)(t - \beta)(t - \gamma)\}^{-\frac{1}{2}} dt$$

by the substitutions

$$x - \gamma = (a - \gamma)\operatorname{dn}^2 u, \quad x - \gamma = (\beta - \gamma)\operatorname{nd}^2 v$$

respectively, where $k^2 = (a - \beta)/(a - \gamma)$.

Deduce that, if $u + v = K$, then

$$1 - \operatorname{sn}^2 u - \operatorname{sn}^2 v + k^2 \operatorname{sn}^2 u \operatorname{sn}^2 v = 0.$$

By the substitution $y = (a - t)(t - \beta)/(t - \gamma)$ applied to the above integral taken between the limits β and a, obtain the Gaussian form of Landen's transformation,

$$\int_0^{\frac{1}{2}\pi} (a_1^2 \cos^2 \theta + b_1^2 \sin^2 \theta)^{-\frac{1}{2}} d\theta = \int_0^{\frac{1}{2}\pi} (a^2 \cos^2 \theta + b^2 \sin^2 \theta)^{-\frac{1}{2}} d\theta,$$

where a_1, b_1 are the arithmetic and geometric means between a and b.

(Gauss, *Werke*, III. p. 352; Math. Trip. 1895.)

47. Shew that
$$\operatorname{sc} u = -k'^{-1}\{\zeta(u-K)-\zeta(u-K-2iK')-\zeta(2iK')\},$$
where the Zeta-functions are formed with periods $2\omega_1,\ 2\omega_2=2K,\ 4iK'$.

(Math. Trip. 1903.)

48. Shew that $E - k'^2 K$ satisfies the equation
$$4cc'\frac{d^2u}{dc^2}=u,$$
where $c=k^2$, and obtain the primitive of this equation.   (Math. Trip. 1911.)

49. Shew that
$$n\int_0^1 k^n K'\,dk = (n-1)\int_0^1 k^{n-2}E'\,dk,$$
$$(n+2)\int_0^1 k^n E'\,dk = (n+1)\int_0^1 k^n K'\,dk.$$

(Trinity, 1906.)

50. If
$$u = \frac{1}{2}\int_0^x \{t(1-t)(1-ct)\}^{-\frac{1}{2}}dt,$$
shew that
$$c(c-1)\frac{d^2u}{dc^2}+(2c-1)\frac{du}{dc}+\frac{1}{4}u = \frac{1}{4}\left\{\frac{x(1-x)}{(1-cx)^3}\right\}^{\frac{1}{2}}.$$

(Trinity, 1896.)

51. Shew that the primitive of
$$\frac{du}{dk}+\frac{u^2}{k}+\frac{k}{1-k^2}=0$$
is
$$u = \frac{A(E-K)+A'E'}{AE+A'(E'-K')},$$
where $A,\ A'$ are constants.   (Math. Trip. 1906.)

52. Deduce from the addition-formula for $E(u)$ that, if
$$u_1+u_2+u_3+u_4=0,$$
then
$$(\operatorname{sn} u_1\operatorname{sn} u_2 - \operatorname{sn} u_3\operatorname{sn} u_4)\operatorname{sn}(u_1+u_2)$$
is unaltered by any permutation of suffices.   (Math. Trip. 1910.)

53. Shew that
$$E(3u)-3E(u) = \frac{-8k^2 s^3 c^3 d^3}{1-6k^2 s^4+4(k^2+k^4)s^6-3k^4 s^8}.$$

(Math. Trip. 1913.)

54. Shew that
$$3k^4\int_0^{2K}u\operatorname{cd}^4 u\,du = 2K\{(2+k^2)K-2(1+k^2)E\}.$$
[Write $u=K+v$.]   (Math. Trip. 1904.)

55. By considering the curves $y^2=x(1-x)(1-k^2x),\ y=l+mx+nx^2$, shew that, if $u_1+u_2+u_3+u_4=0$, then
$$E(u_1)+E(u_2)+E(u_3)+E(u_4) = k\left\{\sum_{r=1}^4 s_r^2 + 2c_1c_2c_3c_4 - 2s_1s_2s_3s_4 - 2\right\}^{\frac{1}{2}}.$$

(Math. Trip. 1908.)

56. By the method of example 21, obtain the following seven expressions for $E(u_1)+E(u_2)+E(u_3)+E(u_4)$ when $u_1+u_2+u_3+u_4=0$:

$$\frac{-k^2 s_1s_2s_3s_4}{1+k^2 s_1s_2s_3s_4}\sum_{r=1}^4 c_r d_r/s_r,\qquad \frac{k^2 d_1d_2d_3d_4}{k'^2+d_1d_2d_3d_4}\sum_{r=1}^4 s_r c_r/d_r,\qquad \frac{k^2 c_1c_2c_3c_4}{k^2 c_1c_2c_3c_4-k'^2}\sum_{r=1}^4 s_r d_r/c_r,$$

$$\frac{k^2 s_1s_2s_3s_4 d_1d_2d_3d_4}{k^2 k'^2 s_1s_2s_3s_4-d_1d_2d_3d_4}\sum_{r=1}^4 c_r/(s_r d_r),\qquad \frac{-k^2 c_1c_2c_3c_4 d_1d_2d_3d_4}{d_1d_2d_3d_4+k^2 c_1c_2c_3c_4}\sum_{r=1}^4 s_r/(c_r d_r),$$

$$\frac{k^2 s_1s_2s_3s_4+c_1c_2c_3c_4}{c_1c_2c_3c_4+k'^2 s_1s_2s_3s_4}\sum_{r=1}^4 d_r/(s_r c_r),$$

$$-k^2\{(s_1s_2s_3s_4)^{-1}+(c_1c_2c_3c_4)^{-1}+k^4(d_1d_2d_3d_4)^{-1}\}^{-1}\sum_{r=1}^4 1/(s_r c_r d_r).$$

(Forsyth, *Messenger*, xv.)

57. Shew that

$$\left(\frac{2K}{\pi}\right)^2 \mathrm{ns}^2\left(\frac{2Kx}{\pi}\right) = \operatorname{cosec}^2 x + \frac{4K(K-E)}{\pi^2} - 8 \sum_{n=1}^{\infty} \frac{nq^{2n}\cos 2nx}{1-q^{2n}},$$

when $|I(x)| < \pi I(\tau)$; and, by differentiation, deduce that

$$6\left(\frac{2K}{\pi}\right)^4 \mathrm{ns}^4\left(\frac{2Kx}{\pi}\right) = 6\operatorname{cosec}^4 x + 4\left[(1+k^2)\left(\frac{2K}{\pi}\right)^2 - 1\right]\operatorname{cosec}^2 x$$

$$+ 64(1+k^2)\frac{K^3(K-E)}{\pi^4} - 2k^2\left(\frac{2K}{\pi}\right)^4$$

$$- 32\sum_{n=1}^{\infty} n\left[(1+k^2)\left(\frac{2K}{\pi}\right)^2 - n^2\right]\frac{q^{2n}\cos 2nx}{1-q^{2n}}.$$

Shew also that, when $|I(x)| < \frac{1}{2}\pi I(\tau)$,

$$\mathrm{sn}^3\left(\frac{2Kx}{\pi}\right) = \sum_{n=0}^{\infty}\left\{\frac{1+k^2}{2k^3} - \frac{(2n+1)^2}{2k^3}\left(\frac{\pi}{2K}\right)^2\right\}\frac{2\pi q^{n+\frac{1}{2}}\sin(2n+1)x}{K(1-q^{2n+1})}.$$

(Jacobi.)

58. Shew that, if a be the semi-major axis of an ellipse whose eccentricity is $\sin\frac{1}{12}\pi$, the perimeter of the ellipse is

$$a\left(\frac{\pi}{\sqrt{3}}\right)^{\frac{1}{2}}\left\{\left(1+\frac{1}{\sqrt{3}}\right)\frac{\Gamma\left(\frac{1}{3}\right)}{\Gamma\left(\frac{5}{6}\right)} + \frac{2\Gamma\left(\frac{5}{6}\right)}{\Gamma\left(\frac{1}{3}\right)}\right\}.$$

(Ramanujan, *Quarterly Journal*, XLV.)

59. Deduce from example 19 of Chapter XXI that

$$k^2\,\mathrm{cn}^3\,2u = \frac{-k'^2 + \mathrm{dn}^3\,u\,\mathrm{dn}\,3u}{1+k^2\,\mathrm{sn}^3\,u\,\mathrm{sn}\,3u}, \qquad \mathrm{dn}^3\,2u = \frac{k'^2 + k^2\,\mathrm{cn}^3\,u\,\mathrm{cn}\,3u}{1+k^2\,\mathrm{sn}^3\,u\,\mathrm{sn}\,3u}.$$

(Trinity, 1882.)

60. From the formula $\mathrm{sd}(iu, k) = i\,\mathrm{sd}(u, k')$ deduce that

$$\frac{1}{K}\sum_{n=0}^{\infty}\frac{(-)^n q^{n+\frac{1}{2}}}{1+q^{2n+1}}\sinh\left(\frac{(n+\frac{1}{2})\pi u}{K}\right) = \frac{1}{K'}\sum_{n=0}^{\infty}\frac{(-)^n q_1^{n+\frac{1}{2}}}{1+q_1^{2n+1}}\sin\left(\frac{(n+\frac{1}{2})\pi u}{K'}\right),$$

where

$$q = \exp(-\pi K'/K), \qquad q_1 = \exp(-\pi K/K'),$$

and u lies inside the parallelogram whose vertices are

$$\pm iK \pm K'.$$

By integrating from u to K', from 0 to u and again from u to K', prove that

$$\frac{\pi^3}{64}(K'^2 - K^2 - u^2) + K^2\sum_{n=0}^{\infty}\frac{(-)^n q^{n+\frac{1}{2}}}{(2n+1)^3(1+q^{2n+1})}\cosh\left(\frac{(n+\frac{1}{2})\pi u}{K}\right)$$

$$= K'^2\sum_{n=0}^{\infty}\frac{(-)^n q_1^{n+\frac{1}{2}}}{(2n+1)^3(1+q_1^{2n+1})}\cos\left(\frac{(n+\frac{1}{2})\pi u}{K'}\right).$$

[A formula which may be derived from this by writing $u = \xi + i\eta$, where ξ and η are real, and equating imaginary parts on either side of the equation was obtained by Thomson and Tait, *Natural Philosophy*, II. (1883), p. 249, but they failed to observe that their formula was nothing but a consequence of Jacobi's imaginary transformation. The formula was suggested to Thomson and Tait by the solution of a problem in the theory of Elasticity.]

CHAPTER XXIII

ELLIPSOIDAL HARMONICS AND LAMÉ'S EQUATION

23·1. *The definition of ellipsoidal harmonics.*

It has been seen earlier in this work (§ 18·4) that solutions of Laplace's equation, which are analytic near the origin and which are appropriate for the discussion of physical problems connected with a sphere, may be conveniently expressed as linear combinations of functions of the type

$$r^n P_n (\cos \theta), \qquad r^n P_n^m (\cos \theta) {\cos \atop \sin} m\phi,$$

where n and m are positive integers (zero included).

When $P_n (\cos \theta)$ is resolved into a product of factors which are linear in $\cos^2 \theta$ (multiplied by $\cos \theta$ when n is odd), we see that, if $\cos \theta$ is replaced by z/r, then the zonal harmonic $r^n P_n (\cos \theta)$ is expressible as a product of factors which are linear in x^2, y^2 and z^2, the whole being multiplied by z when n is odd. The tesseral harmonics are similarly resoluble into factors which are linear in x^2, y^2 and z^2 multiplied by one of the eight products 1, x, y, z, yz, zx, xy, xyz.

The surfaces on which any given zonal or tesseral harmonic vanishes are surfaces on which either θ or ϕ has some constant value, so that they are circular cones or planes, the coordinate planes being included in certain cases.

When we deal with physical problems connected with ellipsoids, the structure of spheres, cones and planes associated with polar coordinates is replaced by a structure of confocal quadrics. The property of spherical harmonics which has just been explained suggests the construction of a set of harmonics which shall vanish on certain members of the confocal system.

Such harmonics are known as *ellipsoidal* harmonics; they were studied by Lamé[*] in the early part of the nineteenth century by means of confocal coordinates. The expressions for ellipsoidal harmonics in terms of Cartesian coordinates were obtained many years later by W. D. Niven[†], and the following account of their construction is based on his researches.

The fundamental ellipsoid is taken to be

$$\frac{x^2}{a^2} + \frac{y^2}{b^2} + \frac{z^2}{c^2} = 1,$$

and any confocal quadric is

$$\frac{x^2}{a^2 + \theta} + \frac{y^2}{b^2 + \theta} + \frac{z^2}{c^2 + \theta} = 1,$$

[*] *Journal de Math.* IV. (1839), pp. 100–125, 126–163.
[†] *Phil. Trans.* 182 A (1892), pp. 231–278.

where θ is a constant. It will be necessary to consider sets of such quadrics, and it conduces to brevity to write

$$\frac{x^2}{a^2+\theta_p}+\frac{y^2}{b^2+\theta_p}+\frac{z^2}{c^2+\theta_p}-1 \equiv \Theta_p, \qquad \frac{x^2}{a^2+\theta_p}+\frac{y^2}{b^2+\theta_p}+\frac{z^2}{c^2+\theta_p} \equiv K_p.$$

The equation of any member of the set is then

$$\Theta_p = 0.$$

The analysis is made more definite by taking the x-axis as the longest axis of the fundamental ellipsoid and the z-axis as the shortest, so that $a>b>c$.

$23\cdot2$. *The four species of ellipsoidal harmonics.*

A consideration of the expressions for spherical harmonics in factors indicates that there are four possible species of ellipsoidal harmonics to be investigated. These are included in the scheme

$$\left\{ \begin{array}{cccc} & x, & yz, & \\ 1, & y, & zx, & xyz \\ & z, & xy, & \end{array} \right\} \Theta_1 \Theta_2 \dots \Theta_m,$$

where one or other of the expressions in $\{\ \}$ is to multiply the product $\Theta_1 \Theta_2 \dots \Theta_m$.

If we write for brevity

$$\Theta_1 \Theta_2 \dots \Theta_m = \Pi\,(\Theta),$$

any harmonic of the form $\Pi\,(\Theta)$ will be called *an ellipsoidal harmonic of the first species.* A harmonic of any of the three forms* $x\Pi\,(\Theta)$, $y\Pi\,(\Theta)$, $z\Pi\,(\Theta)$ will be called *an ellipsoidal harmonic of the second species.* A harmonic of any of the three forms* $yz\Pi\,(\Theta)$, $zx\Pi\,(\Theta)$, $xy\Pi\,(\Theta)$ will be called *an ellipsoidal harmonic of the third species.* And a harmonic of the form $xyz\Pi\,(\Theta)$ will be called *an ellipsoidal harmonic of the fourth species.*

The terms of highest degree in these species of harmonics are of degrees $2m$, $2m+1$, $2m+2$, $2m+3$ respectively. It will appear subsequently (§ $23\cdot26$) that $2n+1$ linearly independent harmonics of degree n can be constructed, and hence that the terms of degree n in these harmonics form a fundamental system (§ $18\cdot3$) of harmonics of degree n.

We now proceed to explain in detail how to construct harmonics of the first species and to give a general account of the construction of harmonics of the other three species. The reader should have no difficulty in filling up the *lacunae* in this account with the aid of the corresponding analysis given in the case of functions of the first species.

---

* The three forms will be distinguished by being described as different *types* of the species.

23·21. *The construction of ellipsoidal harmonics of the first species.*

As a simple case let us first consider the harmonics of the first species which are of the second degree. Such a harmonic must be simply of the form Θ_1.

Now the effect of applying Laplace's operator, namely

$$\frac{\partial^2}{\partial x^2} + \frac{\partial^2}{\partial y^2} + \frac{\partial^2}{\partial z^2} \quad \text{to} \quad \frac{x^2}{a^2 + \theta_1} + \frac{y^2}{b^2 + \theta_1} + \frac{z^2}{c^2 + \theta_1} - 1$$

is

$$\frac{2}{a^2 + \theta_1} + \frac{2}{b^2 + \theta_1} + \frac{2}{c^2 + \theta_1},$$

and so Θ_1 is a harmonic if θ_1 is a root of the quadratic equation

$$(\theta + b^2)(\theta + c^2) + (\theta + c^2)(\theta + a^2) + (\theta + a^2)(\theta + b^2) = 0.$$

This quadratic has one root between $-c^2$ and $-b^2$ and another between $-b^2$ and $-a^2$. Its roots are therefore unequal, and, by giving θ_1 the value of each root in turn, we obtain two* ellipsoidal harmonics of the first species of the second degree.

Next consider the general product $\Theta_1\Theta_2 \ldots \Theta_m$; this product will be denoted by $\Pi(\Theta)$ and it will be supposed that it has no repeated factors—a supposition which will be justified later (§ 23·43).

If we temporarily regard $\Theta_1, \Theta_2, \ldots \Theta_m$ as a set of auxiliary variables, the ordinary formula of partial differentiation gives

$$\frac{\partial \Pi(\Theta)}{\partial x} = \sum_{p=1}^{m} \frac{\partial \Pi(\Theta)}{\partial \Theta_p} \frac{\partial \Theta_p}{\partial x} = \sum_{p=1}^{m} \frac{\partial \Pi(\Theta)}{\partial \Theta_p} \cdot \frac{2x}{a^2 + \theta_p},$$

and, if we differentiate again,

$$\frac{\partial^2 \Pi(\Theta)}{\partial x^2} = \sum_{p=1}^{m} \frac{\partial \Pi(\Theta)}{\partial \Theta_p} \cdot \frac{2}{a^2 + \theta_p} + \sum_{p \neq q} \frac{\partial^2 \Pi(\Theta)}{\partial \Theta_p \partial \Theta_q} \cdot \frac{8x^2}{(a^2 + \theta_p)(a^2 + \theta_q)},$$

where the last summation extends over all *unequal* pairs of the integers $1, 2, \ldots m$. The terms for which $p = q$ may be omitted because none of the expressions $\Theta_1, \Theta_2, \ldots \Theta_m$ enters into $\Pi(\Theta)$ to a degree higher than the first.

It follows that the result of applying Laplace's operator to $\Pi(\Theta)$ is

$$\sum_{p=1}^{m} \frac{\partial \Pi(\Theta)}{\partial \Theta_p} \left\{ \frac{2}{a^2 + \theta_p} + \frac{2}{b^2 + \theta_p} + \frac{2}{c^2 + \theta_p} \right\}$$

$$+ \sum_{p \neq q} \frac{\partial^2 \Pi(\Theta)}{\partial \Theta_p \partial \Theta_q} \left\{ \frac{8x^2}{(a^2 + \theta_p)(a^2 + \theta_q)} + \frac{8y^2}{(b^2 + \theta_p)(b^2 + \theta_q)} + \frac{8z^2}{(c^2 + \theta_p)(c^2 + \theta_q)} \right\}.$$

Now

$$\sum_{\substack{(x, y, z) \\ (a, b, c)}} \frac{x^2}{(a^2 + \theta_p)(a^2 + \theta_q)} = \frac{\Theta_p - \Theta_q}{\theta_q - \theta_p};$$

* The complete set of 5 ellipsoidal harmonics of the second degree is composed of these two together with the three harmonics yz, zx, xy, which are of the third species.

and $\partial\Pi(\Theta)/\partial\Theta_p$ consists of the product $\Pi(\Theta)$ with the factor Θ_p omitted, while $\partial^2\Pi(\Theta)/\partial\Theta_p\partial\Theta_q$ consists of the product $\Pi(\Theta)$ with the factors Θ_p and Θ_q omitted. That is to say

$$\Theta_p\frac{\partial^2\Pi(\Theta)}{\partial\Theta_p\partial\Theta_q}=\frac{\partial\Pi(\Theta)}{\partial\Theta_q},\quad \Theta_q\frac{\partial^2\Pi(\Theta)}{\partial\Theta_p\partial\Theta_q}=\frac{\partial\Pi(\Theta)}{\partial\Theta_p}.$$

If we make these substitutions, we see that

$$\left[\frac{\partial^2}{\partial x^2}+\frac{\partial^2}{\partial y^2}+\frac{\partial^2}{\partial z^2}\right]\Pi(\Theta)$$

may be written in the form

$$\sum_{p=1}^{m}\frac{\partial\Pi(\Theta)}{\partial\Theta_p}\left\{\frac{2}{a^2+\theta_p}+\frac{2}{b^2+\theta_p}+\frac{2}{c^2+\theta_p}+\sum_{q=1}^{m}{}'\frac{8}{\theta_p-\theta_q}\right\},$$

the prime indicating that the term for which $q=p$ has to be omitted from the summation.

If $\Pi(\Theta)$ is to be a harmonic it is annihilated by Laplace's operator; and it will certainly be so annihilated if it is possible to choose $\theta_1, \theta_2, \dots \theta_m$ so that each of the equations

$$\frac{1}{a^2+\theta_p}+\frac{1}{b^2+\theta_p}+\frac{1}{c^2+\theta_p}+\sum{}'\frac{4}{\theta_p-\theta_q}=0$$

is satisfied, where p takes the values $1, 2, \dots m$.

Now let θ be a variable and let $\Lambda_1(\theta)$ denote the polynomial of degree m in θ

$$\prod_{q=1}^{m}(\theta-\theta_q).$$

If $\Lambda_1{}'(\theta)$ denotes $d\Lambda_1(\theta)/d\theta$, then, by direct differentiation, it is seen that $\Lambda_1{}'(\theta)$ is equal to the sum of all products of $\theta-\theta_1, \theta-\theta_2, \dots \theta-\theta_m$, $m-1$ at a time, and $\Lambda_1{}''(\theta)$ is twice the sum of all products of the same expressions, $m-2$ at a time.

Hence, if θ be given the special value θ_p, the quotient $\Lambda_1{}''(\theta_p)/\Lambda_1{}'(\theta_p)$ becomes equal to twice the sum of the reciprocals of $\theta_p-\theta_1, \theta_p-\theta_2, \dots \theta_p-\theta_m$, (the expression $\theta_p-\theta_p$ being omitted).

Consequently the set of equations derived from the hypothesis that $\prod_{p=1}^{m}(\Theta_p)$ is a harmonic shews that the expression

$$\frac{1}{a^2+\theta}+\frac{1}{b^2+\theta}+\frac{1}{c^2+\theta}+\frac{2\Lambda_1{}''(\theta)}{\Lambda_1{}'(\theta)}$$

vanishes whenever θ has any of the special values $\theta_1, \theta_2, \dots \theta_m$.

Hence the expression

$$(a^2+\theta)(b^2+\theta)(c^2+\theta)\Lambda_1{}''(\theta)+\frac{1}{2}\left\{\sum_{a,\,b,\,c}(b^2+\theta)(c^2+\theta)\right\}\Lambda_1{}'(\theta)$$

is a polynomial in θ which vanishes when θ has any of the values $\theta_1, \theta_2, \ldots, \theta_m$, and so it has $\theta - \theta_1, \theta - \theta_2, \ldots, \theta - \theta_m$ as factors. Now this polynomial is of degree $m + 1$ in θ and the coefficient of θ^{m+1} is $m(m + \frac{1}{2})$. Since m of the factors are known, the remaining factor must be of the form

$$m(m + \tfrac{1}{2})\,\theta + \tfrac{1}{4}C,$$

where C is a constant which will be determined subsequently.

We have therefore shewn that

$$(a^2 + \theta)(b^2 + \theta)(c^2 + \theta)\,\Lambda_1''(\theta) + \frac{1}{2}\left\{\sum_{a,b,c}(b^2 + \theta)(c^3 + \theta)\right\}\Lambda_1'(\theta)$$
$$= \{m(m + \tfrac{1}{2})\,\theta + \tfrac{1}{4}C\}\,\Lambda_1(\theta).$$

That is to say, any ellipsoidal harmonic of the first species of (even) degree n is expressible in the form

$$\prod_{p=1}^{\frac{1}{2}n}\left\{\frac{x^2}{a^2 + \theta_p} + \frac{y^2}{b^2 + \theta_p} + \frac{z^2}{c^2 + \theta_p} - 1\right\}$$

where $\theta_1, \theta_2, \ldots, \theta_{\frac{1}{2}n}$ are the zeros of a polynomial $\Lambda_1(\theta)$ of degree $\frac{1}{2}n$; and this polynomial must be a solution of a differential equation of the type

$$4\sqrt{\{(a^2 + \theta)(b^2 + \theta)(c^2 + \theta)\}}\,\frac{d}{d\theta}\left[\sqrt{\{(a^2 + \theta)(b^2 + \theta)(c^2 + \theta)\}}\,\frac{d\Lambda_1(\theta)}{d\theta}\right]$$
$$= \{n(n + 1)\,\theta + C\}\,\Lambda_1(\theta).$$

This equation is known as *Lamé's differential equation*. It will be investigated in considerable detail in §§ 23·4–23·81, and in the course of the investigation it will be shewn that (I) there are precisely $\frac{1}{2}n + 1$ different real values of C for which the equation has a solution which is a polynomial in θ of degree $\frac{1}{2}n$, and (II) these polynomials have no repeated factors.

The analysis of this section may then be reversed step by step to establish the existence of $\frac{1}{2}n + 1$ ellipsoidal harmonics of the first species of (even) degree n, and the elementary theory of the harmonics of the first species will then be complete.

The corresponding results for harmonics of the second, third and fourth species will now be indicated briefly, the notation already introduced being adhered to so far as possible.

23·22. *Ellipsoidal harmonics of the second species.*

We take $x\prod_{p=1}^{m}(\Theta_p)$ as a typical harmonic of the second species of degree $2m + 1$. The result of applying Laplace's operator to it is

$$x\left[\sum_{p=1}^{m}\frac{\partial\Pi(\Theta)}{\partial\Theta_p}\left\{\frac{6}{a^2 + \theta_p} + \frac{2}{b^2 + \theta_p} + \frac{2}{c^2 + \theta_p}\right\}\right.$$
$$\left.+ \sum_{p\neq q}\frac{\partial^2\Pi(\Theta)}{\partial\Theta_p\partial\Theta_q}\left\{\frac{8x^2}{(a^2 + \theta_p)(a^2 + \theta_q)} + \frac{8y^2}{(b^2 + \theta_p)(b^2 + \theta_q)} + \frac{8z^2}{(c^2 + \theta_p)(c^2 + \theta_q)}\right\}\right],$$

and this has to vanish. Consequently, if

$$\Lambda_2(\theta) \equiv \prod_{q=1}^{m} (\theta - \theta_q),$$

we find, by the reasoning of § 23·21, that $\Lambda_2(\theta)$ is a solution of the differential equation

$$(a^2 + \theta)(b^2 + \theta)(c^2 + \theta) \Lambda_2''(\theta)$$
$$+ \tfrac{1}{2}\{3(b^2 + \theta)(c^2 + \theta) + (c^2 + \theta)(a^2 + \theta) + (a^2 + \theta)(b^2 + \theta)\} \Lambda_2'(\theta)$$
$$= \{m(m + \tfrac{3}{2})\theta + \tfrac{1}{4}C_2\} \Lambda_2(\theta),$$

where C_2 is a constant to be determined.

If now we write $\Lambda_2(\theta) \equiv \Lambda(\theta)/\sqrt{(a^2 + \theta)}$, we find that $\Lambda(\theta)$ is a solution of the differential equation

$$4\sqrt{\{(a^2 + \theta)(b^2 + \theta)(c^2 + \theta)\}} \frac{d}{d\theta}\left[\sqrt{\{(a^2 + \theta)(b^2 + \theta)(c^2 + \theta)\}} \frac{d\Lambda(\theta)}{d\theta}\right]$$
$$= \{(2m + 1)(2m + 2)\theta + C\} \Lambda(\theta),$$

where $$C = C_2 + b^2 + c^2.$$

It will be observed that the last differential equation is of the same type as the equation derived in § 23·21, the constant n being still equal to the degree of the harmonic, which, in the case now under consideration, is $2m + 1$.

Hence the discussion of harmonics of the second species is reduced to the discussion of solutions of Lamé's differential equation. In the case of harmonics of the first type the solutions are required to be polynomials in θ multiplied by $\sqrt{(a^2 + \theta)}$; the corresponding factors for harmonics of the second and third types are $\sqrt{(b^2 + \theta)}$ and $\sqrt{(c^2 + \theta)}$ respectively. It will be shewn subsequently that precisely $m + 1$ values of C can be associated with each of the three types, so that, in all, $3m + 3$ harmonics of the second species of degree $2m + 1$ are obtained.

23·23. *Ellipsoidal harmonics of the third species.*

We take $yz \prod_{p=1}^{m} (\Theta_p)$ as a typical harmonic of the third species of degree $2m + 2$. The result of applying Laplace's operator to it is

$$yz\left[\sum_{p=1}^{m} \frac{\partial \Pi(\Theta)}{\partial \Theta_p}\left\{\frac{2}{a^2 + \theta_p} + \frac{6}{b^2 + \theta_p} + \frac{6}{c^2 + \theta_p}\right\}\right.$$
$$\left. + \sum_{p \neq q} \frac{\partial^2 \Pi(\Theta)}{\partial \Theta_p \partial \Theta_q}\left\{\frac{8x^2}{(a^2 + \theta_p)(a^2 + \theta_q)} + \frac{8y^2}{(b^2 + \theta_p)(b^2 + \theta_q)} + \frac{8z^2}{(c^2 + \theta_p)(c^2 + \theta_q)}\right\}\right],$$

and this has to vanish. Consequently, if

$$\Lambda_3(\theta) \equiv \prod_{q=1}^{m} (\theta - \theta_q),$$

we find, by the reasoning of § 23·21, that $\Lambda_3(\theta)$ is a solution of the differential equation

$$(a^2 + \theta)(b^2 + \theta)(c^2 + \theta)\Lambda_3''(\theta)$$
$$+ \tfrac{1}{2}\{(b^2 + \theta)(c^2 + \theta) + 3(c^2 + \theta)(a^2 + \theta) + 3(a^2 + \theta)(b^2 + \theta)\}\Lambda_3'(\theta)$$
$$= \{m(m + \tfrac{5}{2})\theta + \tfrac{1}{4}C_3\}\Lambda_3(\theta),$$

where C_3 is a constant to be determined.

If now we write $\quad \Lambda_3(\theta) \equiv \Lambda(\theta)/\sqrt{\{(b^2 + \theta)(c^2 + \theta)\}}$,

we find that $\Lambda(\theta)$ is a solution of the differential equation

$$4\sqrt{\{(a^2 + \theta)(b^2 + \theta)(c^2 + \theta)\}}\frac{d}{d\theta}\left[\sqrt{\{(a^2 + \theta)(b^2 + \theta)(c^2 + \theta)\}}\frac{d\Lambda(\theta)}{d\theta}\right]$$
$$= \{(2m + 2)(2m + 3)\theta + C\}\Lambda(\theta),$$

where $\quad\quad\quad\quad\quad\quad\quad\quad C = C_3 + 4a^2 + b^2 + c^2.$

It will be observed that the last equation is of the same type as .the equation derived in § 23·21, the constant n being still equal to the degree of the harmonic, which, in the case now under consideration, is $2m + 2$.

Hence the discussion of harmonics of the third species is reduced to the discussion of solutions of Lamé's differential equation. In the case of harmonics of the first type, the solutions are required to be polynomials in θ multiplied by $\sqrt{\{(b^2 + \theta)(c^2 + \theta)\}}$; the corresponding factors for harmonics of the second and third types are $\sqrt{\{(c^2 + \theta)(a^2 + \theta)\}}$ and $\sqrt{\{(a^2 + \theta)(b^2 + \theta)\}}$ respectively. It will be shewn subsequently that precisely $m + 1$ values of C can be associated with each of the three types, so that, in all, $3m + 3$ harmonics of the third species of degree $2m + 2$ are obtained.

23·24. *Ellipsoidal harmonics of the fourth species.*

The harmonic of the fourth species of degree $2m + 3$ is expressible in the form $xyz \prod\limits_{p=1}^{m}(\Theta_p)$. The result of applying Laplace's operator to it is

$$xyz\left[\sum_{p=1}^{m}\frac{\partial\Pi(\Theta)}{\partial\Theta_p}\left\{\frac{6}{a^2 + \theta_p} + \frac{6}{b^2 + \theta_p} + \frac{6}{c^2 + \theta_p}\right\}\right.$$
$$\left.+ \sum_{p\neq q}\frac{\partial^2\Pi(\Theta)}{\partial\Theta_p\partial\Theta_q}\left\{\frac{8x^2}{(a^2 + \theta_p)(a^2 + \theta_q)} + \frac{8y^2}{(b^2 + \theta_p)(b^2 + \theta_q)} + \frac{8z^2}{(c^2 + \theta_p)(c^2 + \theta_q)}\right\}\right],$$

and this has to vanish. Consequently, if

$$\Lambda_4(\theta) \equiv \prod_{q=1}^{m}(\theta - \theta_q),$$

we find by the reasoning of § 23·21 that $\Lambda_4(\theta)$ is a solution of the equation

$$(a^2 + \theta)(b^2 + \theta)(c^2 + \theta)\Lambda_4''(\theta) + \frac{3}{2}\left\{\sum_{a,\,b,\,c}(b^2 + \theta)(c^2 + \theta)\right\}\Lambda_4'(\theta)$$
$$= \{m(m + \tfrac{7}{2})\theta + \tfrac{1}{4}C_4\}\Lambda_4(\theta),$$

where C_4 is a constant to be determined.

If now we write

$$\Lambda_4(\theta) \equiv \Lambda(\theta)/\sqrt{\{(a^2+\theta)(b^2+\theta)(c^2+\theta)\}},$$

we find that $\Lambda(\theta)$ is a solution of the differential equation

$$4\sqrt{\{(a^2+\theta)(b^2+\theta)(c^2+\theta)\}}\,\frac{d}{d\theta}\left[\sqrt{\{(a^2+\theta)(b^2+\theta)(c^2+\theta)\}}\,\frac{d\Lambda(\theta)}{d\theta}\right]$$
$$= \{(2m+3)(2m+4)\,\theta + C\}\,\Lambda(\theta),$$

where $\qquad\qquad C = C_4 + 4\,(a^2 + b^2 + c^2).$

It will be observed that the last equation is of the same type as the equation derived in § 23·21, the constant n being still equal to the degree of the harmonic which, in the case now under consideration, is $2m + 3$.

Hence the discussion of harmonics of the fourth species is reduced to the discussion of solutions of Lamé's differential equation. The solutions are required to be polynomials in θ multiplied by $\sqrt{\{(a^2+\theta)(b^2+\theta)(c^2+\theta)\}}$. It will be shewn subsequently that precisely $m + 1$ values of C can be associated with solutions of this type, so that $m + 1$ harmonics of the fourth species of degree $2m + 3$ are obtained.

23·25. *Niven's expressions for ellipsoidal harmonics in terms of homogeneous harmonics.*

If $G_n(x, y, z)$ denotes any of the harmonics of degree n which have just been tentatively constructed, then $G_n(x, y, z)$ consists of a finite number of terms of degrees n, $n - 2$, $n - 4$, ... in x, y, z. If $H_n(x, y, z)$ denotes the aggregate of terms of degree n, it follows from the homogeneity of Laplace's operator that $H_n(x, y, z)$ is itself a solution of Laplace's equation, and it may obviously be obtained from $G_n(x, y, z)$ by replacing the factors Θ_p, which occur in the expression of $G_n(x, y, z)$ as a product, by the factors K_p.

It has been shewn by Niven (*loc. cit.*, pp. 243–245) that $G_n(x, y, z)$ may be derived from $H_n(x, y, z)$ by applying to the latter function the differential operator

$$1 - \frac{D^2}{2\,(2n-1)} + \frac{D^4}{2\,.\,4\,.\,(2n-1)(2n-3)} - \frac{D^6}{2\,.\,4\,.\,6\,(2n-1)(2n-3)(2n-5)} + \dots,$$

where D^2 stands for

$$a^2\frac{\partial^2}{\partial x^2} + b^2\frac{\partial^2}{\partial y^2} + c^2\frac{\partial^2}{\partial z^2};$$

and terms containing powers of D higher than the nth may be omitted from the operator.

We shall now give a proof of this result for any harmonic of the first species*.

---

* The proofs for harmonics of the other three species are left to the reader as examples. A proof applicable to functions of all four species has been given by Hobson, *Proc. London Math. Soc.* xxiv. (1893), pp. 60–64. In constructing the proof given in the text, several modifications have been made in Niven's proof.

For such harmonics the degree is even and we write

$$G_n(x, y, z) = \prod_{p=1}^{\frac{1}{2}n} \Theta_p = \prod_{p=1}^{\frac{1}{2}n} (K_p - 1)$$

$$= S_n - S_{n-2} + S_{n-4} - \ldots,$$

where $S_n, S_{n-2}, S_{n-4}, \ldots$ are homogeneous functions of degrees $n, n-2, n-4, \ldots,$ respectively, and

$$S_n = H_n(x, y, z) = \prod_{p=1}^{\frac{1}{2}n} K_p.$$

The function S_{n-2r} is evidently the sum of the products of $K_1, K_2, \ldots K_{\frac{1}{2}n}$ taken $\frac{1}{2}n - r$ at a time.

If $K_1, K_2, \ldots K_{\frac{1}{2}n}$ be regarded as an auxiliary system of variables, then, by the ordinary formula of partial differentiation

$$\frac{\partial S_{n-2r}}{\partial x} = \sum_{p=1}^{\frac{1}{2}n} \frac{\partial S_{n-2r}}{\partial K_p} \frac{\partial K_p}{\partial x}$$

$$= \sum_{p=1}^{\frac{1}{2}n} \frac{\partial S_{n-2r}}{\partial K_p} \cdot \frac{2x}{a^2 + \theta_p};$$

and, if we differentiate again,

$$\frac{\partial^2 S_{n-2r}}{\partial x^2} = \sum_{p=1}^{\frac{1}{2}n} \frac{\partial S_{n-2r}}{\partial K_p} \frac{2}{a^2 + \theta_p} + \sum_{p \neq q} \frac{\partial^2 S_{n-2r}}{\partial K_p \partial K_q} \frac{8x^2}{(a^2 + \theta_p)(a^2 + \theta_q)}.$$

The terms in $\partial^2 S_{n-2r}/\partial K_p{}^2$ can be omitted because each of the functions K_p does not occur in S_{n-2r} to a degree higher than the first.

It follows that

$$D^2 S_{n-2r} = \sum_{p=1}^{\frac{1}{2}n} \frac{\partial S_{n-2r}}{\partial K_p} \left\{ \frac{2a^2}{a^2 + \theta_p} + \frac{2b^2}{b^2 + \theta_p} + \frac{2c^2}{c^2 + \theta_p} \right\}$$

$$+ \sum_{p \neq q} \frac{\partial^2 S_{n-2r}}{\partial K_p \partial K_q} \left\{ \frac{8a^2 x^2}{(a^2 + \theta_p)(a^2 + \theta_q)} + \frac{8b^2 y^2}{(b^2 + \theta_p)(b^2 + \theta_q)} + \frac{8c^2 z^2}{(c^2 + \theta_p)(c^2 + \theta_q)} \right\}.$$

It will now be shewn that the expression on the right is a constant multiple of S_{n-2r-2}.

We first observe that

$$\sum_{\substack{(x, y, z) \\ (a, b, c)}} \frac{a^2 x^2}{(a^2 + \theta_p)(a^2 + \theta_q)} = \frac{\theta_p K_p - \theta_q K_q}{\theta_p - \theta_q}$$

and that, by the differential equation of § 23·21,

$$\sum_{a, b, c} \frac{a^2}{a^2 + \theta_p} = 3 - \theta_p \sum_{a, b, c} \frac{1}{a^2 + \theta_p}$$

$$= 3 + \theta_p \sum_{q=1}^{\frac{1}{2}n} {}' \frac{4}{\theta_p - \theta_q},$$

so that

$$D^2 S_{n-2r} = 6 \sum_{p=1}^{\frac{1}{2}n} \frac{\partial S_{n-2r}}{\partial K_p} + 8 \sum_{p=1}^{\frac{1}{2}n} \theta_p \frac{\partial S_{n-2r}}{\partial K_p} \left\{ \sum_{q=1}^{\frac{1}{2}n}{}' \frac{1}{\theta_p - \theta_q} \right\}$$

$$+ 8 \sum_{p \neq q} \frac{\partial^2 S_{n-2r}}{\partial K_p \partial K_q} \cdot \frac{\theta_p K_p - \theta_q K_q}{\theta_p - \theta_q}.$$

Now $\partial S_{n-2r}/\partial K_p$ is the sum of the products of the expressions K_1, K_2, ... $K_{\frac{1}{2}n}$ (K_p being omitted) taken $\frac{1}{2}n - r - 1$ at a time; and $K_q \partial^2 S_{n-2r}/\partial K_p \partial K_q$ consists of those terms of this sum which contain K_q as a factor.

Hence

$$\frac{\partial S_{n-2r}}{\partial K_p} - K_q \frac{\partial^2 S_{n-2r}}{\partial K_p \partial K_q}$$

is equal to the sum of the products of the expressions K_1, K_2, ... $K_{\frac{1}{2}n}$, (K_p and K_q both being omitted) taken $\frac{1}{2}n - r - 1$ at a time; and therefore, by symmetry, we have

$$\frac{\partial S_{n-2r}}{\partial K_p} - K_q \frac{\partial^2 S_{n-2r}}{\partial K_p \partial K_q} = \frac{\partial S_{n-2r}}{\partial K_q} - K_p \frac{\partial^2 S_{n-2r}}{\partial K_p \partial K_q},$$

so that

$$\frac{\partial^2 S_{n-2r}}{\partial K_p \partial K_q} = \left\{ \frac{\partial S_{n-2r}}{\partial K_p} - \frac{\partial S_{n-2r}}{\partial K_q} \right\} \Big/ (K_q - K_p).$$

On substituting by this formula for the second differential coefficients, it is found that

$$D^2 S_{n-2r} = \sum_{p=1}^{\frac{1}{2}n} \frac{\partial S_{n-2r}}{\partial K_p} \left[6 + 8 \theta_p \sum_{q=1}^{\frac{1}{2}n}{}' \frac{1}{\theta_p - \theta_q} - 8 \sum_{q=1}^{\frac{1}{2}n}{}' \frac{\theta_p K_p - \theta_q K_q}{(\theta_p - \theta_q)(K_p - K_q)} \right]$$

$$= \sum_{p=1}^{\frac{1}{2}n} \frac{\partial S_{n-2r}}{\partial K_p} \left[6 - 8 \sum_{q=1}^{\frac{1}{2}n}{}' \frac{K_q}{K_p - K_q} \right]$$

$$= (4n - 2) \sum_{p=1}^{\frac{1}{2}n} \frac{\partial S_{n-2r}}{\partial K_p} - 8 \sum_{p \neq q} \left\{ K_p \frac{\partial S_{n-2r}}{\partial K_p} - K_q \frac{\partial S_{n-2r}}{\partial K_q} \right\} \Big/ (K_p - K_q).$$

Now we may write S_{n-2r} in the form

$$\bar{S}_{n-2r} + K_p \bar{S}_{n-2r-2} + K_q \bar{S}_{n-2r-2} + K_p K_q \bar{S}_{n-2r-4},$$

where $\bar{S}_{2m}$ denotes the sum of the products of the expressions K_1, K_2, ... $K_{\frac{1}{2}n}$ (K_p and K_q both being omitted) taken m at a time; and we then see that

$$K_p \frac{\partial S_{n-2r}}{\partial K_p} - K_q \frac{\partial S_{n-2r}}{\partial K_q} = (K_p - K_q) \bar{S}_{n-2r-2}.$$

Hence

$$D^2 S_{n-2r} = (4n - 2) \sum_{p=1}^{\frac{1}{2}n} \frac{\partial S_{n-2r}}{\partial K_p} - 8 \sum_{p \neq q} \bar{S}_{n-2r-2}.$$

Now it is clear that the expression on the right is a homogeneous symmetric function of K_1, K_2, ... $K_{\frac{1}{2}n}$ of degree $\frac{1}{2}n - r - 1$, and it contains no power of any of the expressions K_1, K_2, ... $K_{\frac{1}{2}n}$ to a degree higher than the first. It is therefore a multiple of S_{n-2r-2}. To determine the multiple we observe that when S_{n-2r-2} is written out at length it contains ${}_{\frac{1}{2}n}C_{r+1}$ terms while the number of terms in

$$(4n-2) \sum_{p=1}^{\frac{1}{2}n} \frac{\partial S_{n-2r}}{\partial K_p} - 8 \sum_{p \neq q} \bar{S}_{n-2r-2}$$

is
$$\tfrac{1}{2}n(4n-2) \cdot {}_{\frac{1}{2}n-1}C_r - 8 \cdot {}_{\frac{1}{2}n}C_2 \cdot {}_{\frac{1}{2}n-2}C_{r-1}.$$

The multiple is consequently

$$\frac{\tfrac{1}{2}n(4n-2) \cdot {}_{\frac{1}{2}n-1}C_r - 8 \cdot {}_{\frac{1}{2}n}C_2 \cdot {}_{\frac{1}{2}n-2}C_{r-1}}{{}_{\frac{1}{2}n}C_{r+1}},$$

and this is equal to $(2r+2)(2n-2r-1)$.

It has consequently been proved that

$$D^2 S_{n-2r} = (2r+2)(2n-2r-1) S_{n-2r-2}.$$

It follows at once by induction that

$$S_{n-2r} = \frac{D^{2r} S_n}{2 \cdot 4 \ldots 2r \cdot (2n-1)(2n-3) \ldots (2n-2r+1)},$$

and the formula

$$G_n(x, y, z) = \left[\sum_{r=0}^{\frac{1}{2}n} \frac{(-)^r D^{2r}}{2 \cdot 4 \ldots 2r \cdot (2n-1)(2n-3) \ldots (2n-2r+1)} \right] H_n(x, y, z)$$

is now obvious when $G_n(x, y, z)$ is an ellipsoidal harmonic of the first species.

Example 1.   Prove Niven's formula when $G_n(x, y, z)$ is an ellipsoidal harmonic of the second, third or fourth species.

Example 2.   Obtain the symbolic formula

$$G_n(x, y, z) = \Gamma(\tfrac{1}{2}-n) \cdot (\tfrac{1}{2}D)^{n+\frac{1}{2}} I_{-n-\frac{1}{2}}(D) \cdot H_n(x, y, z).$$

23·26.   *Ellipsoidal harmonics of degree n.*

The results obtained and stated in §§ 23·21–23·24 shew that when n is even, there are $\frac{1}{2}n+1$ harmonics of the first species and $\frac{3}{2}n$ harmonics of the third species; when n is odd there are $\frac{3}{2}(n+1)$ harmonics of the second species and $\frac{1}{2}(n-1)$ harmonics of the fourth species, so that, in either case, there are $2n+1$ harmonics in all.   It follows from § 18·3 that, if the terms of degree n in these harmonics are linearly independent, they form a fundamental system of harmonics of degree n; and any homogeneous harmonic of degree n is expressible as a linear combination of the homogeneous harmonics which are obtained by selecting the terms of degree n from the $2n+1$ ellipsoidal harmonics.

In order to prove the results concerning the number of harmonics of degree n and to establish their linear independence, it is necessary to make an intensive study of Lamé's equation; but before we pursue this investigation we shall study the construction of ellipsoidal harmonics in terms of confocal coordinates.

These expressions for ellipsoidal harmonics are of historical importance in view of Lamé's investigations, but the expressions which have just been obtained by Niven's method are, in some respects, more suitable for physical applications.

For applications of ellipsoidal harmonics to the investigation of the Figure of the Earth, and for the reduction of the harmonics to forms adapted for numerical computation, the reader is referred to the memoir by G. H. Darwin, *Phil. Trans.* 197 A (1901), pp. 461–537.

23·3. *Confocal coordinates.*

If (X, Y, Z) denote current coordinates in three-dimensional space, and if a, b, c are positive $(a > b > c)$, the equation

$$\frac{X^2}{a^2} + \frac{Y^2}{b^2} + \frac{Z^2}{c^2} = 1$$

represents an ellipsoid; the equation of any confocal quadric is

$$\frac{X^2}{a^2 + \theta} + \frac{Y^2}{b^2 + \theta} + \frac{Z^2}{c^2 + \theta} = 1,$$

and θ is called the *parameter* of this quadric.

The quadric passes through a particular point (x, y, z) if θ is chosen so that

$$\frac{x^2}{a^2 + \theta} + \frac{y^2}{b^2 + \theta} + \frac{z^2}{c^2 + \theta} = 1.$$

Whether θ satisfies this equation or not, it is convenient to write

$$1 - \frac{x^2}{a^2 + \theta} - \frac{y^2}{b^2 + \theta} - \frac{z^2}{c^2 + \theta} \equiv \frac{f(\theta)}{(a^2 + \theta)(b^2 + \theta)(c^2 + \theta)},$$

and, since $f(\theta)$ is a cubic function of θ, it is clear that, in general, three quadrics of the confocal system pass through any particular point (x, y, z).

To determine the species of these three quadrics, we construct the following Table:

θ	$f(\theta)$
$-\infty$	$-\infty$
$-a^2$	$-x^2 (a^2 - b^2)(a^2 - c^2)$
$-b^2$	$y^2 (a^2 - b^2)(b^2 - c^2)$
$-c^2$	$-z^2 (a^2 - c^2)(b^2 - c^2)$
$+\infty$	$+\infty$

It is evident from this Table that the equation $f(\theta) = 0$ has three real roots λ, μ, ν, and if they are arranged so that $\lambda > \mu > \nu$, then

$$\lambda > -c^2 > \mu > -b^2 > \nu > -a^2;$$

and also $\qquad\qquad f(\theta) \equiv (\theta - \lambda)(\theta - \mu)(\theta - \nu).$

From the values of λ, μ, ν it is clear that the surfaces, on which θ has the respective values λ, μ, ν, are an ellipsoid, an hyperboloid of one sheet and an hyperboloid of two sheets.

Now take the identity in θ,

$$1 - \frac{x^2}{a^2+\theta} - \frac{y^2}{b^2+\theta} - \frac{z^2}{c^2+\theta} \equiv \frac{(\theta-\lambda)(\theta-\mu)(\theta-\nu)}{(a^2+\theta)(b^2+\theta)(c^2+\theta)},$$

and multiply it, in turn, by $a^2+\theta$, $b^2+\theta$, $c^2+\theta$; and after so doing, replace θ by $-a^2$, $-b^2$, $-c^2$ respectively. It is thus found that

$$x^2 = \frac{(a^2+\lambda)(a^2+\mu)(a^2+\nu)}{(a^2-b^2)(a^2-c^2)},$$

$$y^2 = -\frac{(b^2+\lambda)(b^2+\mu)(b^2+\nu)}{(a^2-b^2)(b^2-c^2)},$$

$$z^2 = \frac{(c^2+\lambda)(c^2+\mu)(c^2+\nu)}{(a^2-c^2)(b^2-c^2)}.$$

From these equations it is clear that, if (x, y, z) be any point of space and if λ, μ, ν denote the parameters of the quadrics confocal with

$$\frac{X^2}{a^2} + \frac{Y^2}{b^2} + \frac{Z^2}{c^2} = 1$$

which pass through the point, then (x^2, y^2, z^2) are uniquely determinate in terms of (λ, μ, ν) and *vice versa*.

The parameters (λ, μ, ν) are called the *confocal coordinates* of the point (x, y, z) relative to the fundamental ellipsoid

$$\frac{X^2}{a^2} + \frac{Y^2}{b^2} + \frac{Z^2}{c^2} = 1.$$

It is easy to shew that confocal coordinates form an orthogonal system; for consider the direction cosines of the tangent to the curve of intersection of the surfaces (μ) and (ν); these direction cosines are proportional to

$$\left(\frac{\partial x}{\partial \lambda}, \quad \frac{\partial y}{\partial \lambda}, \quad \frac{\partial z}{\partial \lambda} \right),$$

and since $\quad \frac{\partial x}{\partial \lambda}\frac{\partial x}{\partial \mu} + \frac{\partial y}{\partial \lambda}\frac{\partial y}{\partial \mu} + \frac{\partial z}{\partial \lambda}\frac{\partial z}{\partial \mu} = \frac{1}{4} \sum_{a,\,b,\,c} \frac{a^2+\nu}{(a^2-b^2)(a^2-c^2)} = 0,$

it is evident that the directions

$$\left(\frac{\partial x}{\partial \lambda}, \quad \frac{\partial y}{\partial \lambda}, \quad \frac{\partial z}{\partial \lambda} \right), \quad \left(\frac{\partial x}{\partial \mu}, \quad \frac{\partial y}{\partial \mu}, \quad \frac{\partial z}{\partial \mu} \right)$$

are perpendicular; and, similarly, each of these directions is perpendicular to

$$\left(\frac{\partial x}{\partial \nu}, \quad \frac{\partial y}{\partial \nu}, \quad \frac{\partial z}{\partial \nu} \right).$$

It has therefore been shewn that the three systems of surfaces, on which λ, μ, ν respectively are constant, form a triply orthogonal system.

Hence the square of the line-element, namely

$$(\delta x)^2 + (\delta y)^2 + (\delta z)^2,$$

is expressible in the form

$$(H_1 \delta\lambda)^2 + (H_2 \delta\mu)^2 + (H_3 \delta\nu)^2,$$

where
$$H_1{}^2 = \left(\frac{\partial x}{\partial \lambda}\right)^2 + \left(\frac{\partial y}{\partial \lambda}\right)^2 + \left(\frac{\partial z}{\partial \lambda}\right)^2,$$

with similar expressions in μ and ν for $H_2{}^2$ and $H_3{}^2$.

To evaluate $H_1{}^2$ in terms of (λ, μ, ν), observe that
$$H_1{}^2 = \frac{1}{4x^2}\left(\frac{\partial x^2}{\partial \lambda}\right)^2 + \frac{1}{4y^2}\left(\frac{\partial y^2}{\partial \lambda}\right)^2 + \frac{1}{4z^2}\left(\frac{\partial z^2}{\partial \lambda}\right)^2$$
$$= \tfrac{1}{4} \sum_{a,\,b,\,c} \frac{(a^2 + \mu)(a^2 + \nu)}{(a^2 + \lambda)(a^2 - b^2)(a^2 - c^2)}.$$

But, if we express
$$\frac{(\lambda - \mu)(\lambda - \nu)}{(a^2 + \lambda)(b^2 + \lambda)(c^2 + \lambda)},$$

qua function of λ, as a sum of partial fractions, we see that it is precisely equal to
$$\sum_{a,\,b,\,c} \frac{(a^2 + \mu)(a^2 + \nu)}{(a^2 + \lambda)(a^2 - b^2)(a^2 - c^2)},$$

and consequently
$$H_1{}^2 = \frac{(\lambda - \mu)(\lambda - \nu)}{4(a^2 + \lambda)(b^2 + \lambda)(c^2 + \lambda)}.$$

The values of $H_2{}^2$ and $H_3{}^2$ are obtained from this expression by cyclical interchanges of (λ, μ, ν).

Formulae equivalent to those of this section were obtained by Lamé, *Journal de Math.* II. (1837), pp. 147–183.

Example 1.   With the notation of this section, shew that
$$x^2 + y^2 + z^2 = a^2 + b^2 + c^2 + \lambda + \mu + \nu.$$

Example 2.   Shew that
$$4H_1{}^2 = \frac{x^2}{(a^2 + \lambda)^2} + \frac{y^2}{(b^2 + \lambda)^2} + \frac{z^2}{(c^2 + \lambda)^2}.$$

23·31.   *Uniformising variables associated with confocal coordinates.*

It has been seen in § 23·3 that when the Cartesian coordinates (x, y, z) are expressed in terms of the confocal coordinates (λ, μ, ν), the expressions so obtained are not one-valued functions of (λ, μ, ν).   To avoid the inconvenience thereby produced, we express (λ, μ, ν) in terms of three new variables (u, v, w) respectively by writing
$$\wp(u) = \lambda + \tfrac{1}{3}(a^2 + b^2 + c^2),$$
$$\wp(v) = \mu + \tfrac{1}{3}(a^2 + b^2 + c^2),$$
$$\wp(w) = \nu + \tfrac{1}{3}(a^2 + b^2 + c^2),$$

the invariants g_2 and g_3 of the Weierstrassian elliptic functions being defined by the identity
$$4(a^2 + \lambda)(b^2 + \lambda)(c^2 + \lambda) \equiv 4\wp^3(u) - g_2\wp(u) - g_3.$$

The discriminant associated with the elliptic functions (cf. § 20·33, example 3) is

$$16 \, (a^2 - b^2)^2 \, (b^2 - c^2)^2 \, (c^2 - a^2)^2,$$

and so it is positive; and, therefore[*], of the periods $2\omega_1$, $2\omega_2$ and $2\omega_3$, $2\omega_1$ is positive while $2\omega_3$ is a pure imaginary; and $2\omega_2$ has its real part negative, since $\omega_1 + \omega_2 + \omega_3 = 0$; the imaginary part of ω_2 is positive since $I \, (\omega_2/\omega_1) > 0$.

In these circumstances $e_1 > e_2 > e_3$, and so we have

$$3e_1 = a^2 + b^2 - 2c^2, \quad 3e_2 = c^2 + a^2 - 2b^2, \quad 3e_3 = b^2 + c^2 - 2a^2.$$

Next we express (x, y, z) in terms of (u, v, w); we have

$$
\begin{aligned}
x^2 &= \frac{(a^2 + \lambda)\,(a^2 + \mu)\,(a^2 + \nu)}{(a^2 - b^2)\,(a^2 - c^2)} \\
&= \frac{\{\wp\,(u) - e_3\}\,\{\wp\,(v) - e_3\}\,\{\wp\,(w) - e_3\}}{(e_1 - e_3)\,(e_2 - e_3)} \\
&= \frac{\sigma_3{}^2\,(u)\,\sigma_3{}^2\,(v)\,\sigma_3{}^2\,(w)}{\sigma^2\,(u)\,\sigma^2\,(v)\,\sigma^2\,(w)} \cdot \frac{\sigma^2\,(\omega_1)\,\sigma^2\,(\omega_2)}{\sigma_3{}^2\,(\omega_1)\,\sigma_3{}^2\,(\omega_2)},
\end{aligned}
$$

by § 20·53, example 4. Therefore, by § 20·421, we have

$$x = \pm \, e^{-\eta_3 \omega_3} \sigma^2\,(\omega_3) \, \frac{\sigma_3\,(u)\,\sigma_3\,(v)\,\sigma_3\,(w)}{\sigma\,(u)\,\sigma\,(v)\,\sigma\,(w)},$$

and similarly

$$y = \pm \, e^{-\eta_2 \omega_2} \sigma^2\,(\omega_2) \, \frac{\sigma_2\,(u)\,\sigma_2\,(v)\,\sigma_2\,(w)}{\sigma\,(u)\,\sigma\,(v)\,\sigma\,(w)}$$

$$z = \pm \, e^{-\eta_1 \omega_1} \sigma^2\,(\omega_1) \, \frac{\sigma_1\,(u)\,\sigma_1\,(v)\,\sigma_1\,(w)}{\sigma\,(u)\,\sigma\,(v)\,\sigma\,(w)}.$$

The effect of increasing each of u, v, w by $2\omega_3$ is to change the sign of the expression given for x while the expressions for y and z remain unaltered; and similar statements hold for increases by $2\omega_2$ and $2\omega_1$; and again each of the three expressions is changed in sign by changing the signs of u, v, w.

Hence, if the upper signs be taken in the ambiguities, there is a unique correspondence between all sets of values of (x, y, z), real or complex, and all the sets of values of (u, v, w) whose three representative points lie in any given cell.

The uniformisation is consequently effected by taking

$$
\begin{cases}
x = e^{-\eta_3 \omega_3} \sigma^2\,(\omega_3) \, \dfrac{\sigma_3\,(u)\,\sigma_3\,(v)\,\sigma_3\,(w)}{\sigma\,(u)\,\sigma\,(v)\,\sigma\,(w)}, \\[2ex]
y = e^{-\eta_2 \omega_2} \sigma^2\,(\omega_2) \, \dfrac{\sigma_2\,(u)\,\sigma_2\,(v)\,\sigma_2\,(w)}{\sigma\,(u)\,\sigma\,(v)\,\sigma\,(w)}, \\[2ex]
z = e^{-\eta_1 \omega_1} \sigma^2\,(\omega_1) \, \dfrac{\sigma_1\,(u)\,\sigma_1\,(v)\,\sigma_1\,(w)}{\sigma\,(u)\,\sigma\,(v)\,\sigma\,(w)}.
\end{cases}
$$

Formulae which differ from these only by the interchange of the suffixes 1 and 3 were given by Halphen, *Fonctions Elliptiques*, II. (1888), p. 459.

[*] Cf. § 20·32, example 1.

23·32. *Laplace's equation referred to confocal coordinates.*

It has been shewn by Lamé and by W. Thomson* that Laplace's equation when referred to *any* system of orthogonal coordinates (λ, μ, ν) assumes the form

$$\frac{\partial}{\partial \lambda}\left\{\frac{H_2 H_3}{H_1} \cdot \frac{\partial V}{\partial \lambda}\right\} + \frac{\partial}{\partial \mu}\left\{\frac{H_3 H_1}{H_2} \cdot \frac{\partial V}{\partial \mu}\right\} + \frac{\partial}{\partial \nu}\left\{\frac{H_1 H_2}{H_3} \cdot \frac{\partial V}{\partial \nu}\right\} = 0,$$

where (H_1, H_2, H_3) are to be determined from the consideration that

$$(H_1 \delta\lambda)^2 + (H_2 \delta\mu)^2 + (H_3 \delta\nu)^2$$

is to be the square of the line-element. Although W. Thomson's proof of this result, based on arguments of a physical character, is extremely simple, all the analytical proofs are either very long or else severely compressed.

It has, however, been shewn by Lamé† that, in the special case in which (λ, μ, ν) represent confocal coordinates, Laplace's equation assumes a simple form obtainable without elaborate analysis; when the uniformising variables (u, v, w) of § 23·31 are adopted as coordinates, the form of Laplace's equation becomes still simpler.

By straightforward differentiation it may be proved that, when *any* three independent functions (λ, μ, ν) of (x, y, z) are taken as independent variables, then

$$\frac{\partial^2 V}{\partial x^2} + \frac{\partial^2 V}{\partial y^2} + \frac{\partial^2 V}{\partial z^2}$$

transforms into

$$\sum_{\lambda, \mu, \nu}\left[\left(\frac{\partial\lambda}{\partial x}\right)^2 + \left(\frac{\partial\lambda}{\partial y}\right)^2 + \left(\frac{\partial\lambda}{\partial z}\right)^2\right]\frac{\partial^2 V}{\partial\lambda^2}$$

$$+ 2\sum_{\lambda, \mu, \nu}\left[\frac{\partial\mu}{\partial x}\frac{\partial\nu}{\partial x} + \frac{\partial\mu}{\partial y}\frac{\partial\nu}{\partial y} + \frac{\partial\mu}{\partial z}\frac{\partial\nu}{\partial z}\right]\frac{\partial^2 V}{\partial\mu\,\partial\nu}$$

$$+ \sum_{\lambda, \mu, \nu}\left[\frac{\partial^2\lambda}{\partial x^2} + \frac{\partial^2\lambda}{\partial y^2} + \frac{\partial^2\lambda}{\partial z^2}\right]\frac{\partial V}{\partial\lambda}.$$

In order to reduce this expression, we observe that λ satisfies the equation

$$\frac{x^2}{a^2 + \lambda} + \frac{y^2}{b^2 + \lambda} + \frac{z^2}{c^2 + \lambda} = 1,$$

and so, by differentiation with x, y, z as independent variables,

$$\frac{2x}{a^2 + \lambda} - \left\{\frac{x^2}{(a^2 + \lambda)^2} + \frac{y^2}{(b^2 + \lambda)^2} + \frac{z^2}{(c^2 + \lambda)^2}\right\}\frac{\partial\lambda}{\partial x} = 0,$$

$$\frac{2}{a^2 + \lambda} - \frac{4x}{(a^2 + \lambda)^2}\frac{\partial\lambda}{\partial x} + 2\left\{\frac{x^2}{(a^2 + \lambda)^3} + \frac{y^2}{(b^2 + \lambda)^3} + \frac{z^2}{(c^2 + \lambda)^3}\right\}\left(\frac{\partial\lambda}{\partial x}\right)^2$$

$$- \left\{\frac{x^2}{(a^2 + \lambda)^2} + \frac{y^2}{(b^2 + \lambda)^2} + \frac{z^2}{(c^2 + \lambda)^2}\right\}\frac{\partial^2\lambda}{\partial x^2} = 0.$$

* Cf. the footnote on p. 401.
† *Journal de Math.* IV. (1839), pp. 133–136.

Hence
$$\frac{2x}{a^2+\lambda} = 4H_1^2 \frac{\partial \lambda}{\partial x},$$

$$\frac{2}{a^2+\lambda} - \frac{2x^2}{(a^2+\lambda)^3 H_1^2} + \frac{x^2}{2H_1^4(a^2+\lambda)^2} \sum_{\substack{(x,\,y,\,z)\\(a,\,b,\,c)}} \frac{x^2}{(a^2+\lambda)^3} = 4H_1^2 \frac{\partial^2 \lambda}{\partial x^2},$$

with similar equations in μ, ν and y, z.

From equations of the first type it is seen that the coefficient of $\frac{\partial^2 V}{\partial \lambda^2}$ is $\frac{1}{H_1^2}$ and the coefficient of $\frac{\partial^2 V}{\partial \mu \partial \nu}$ is zero; and if we add up equations of the second type obtained by interchanging x, y, z cyclically, it is found that

$$4H_1^2 \left\{ \frac{\partial^2 \lambda}{\partial x^2} + \frac{\partial^2 \lambda}{\partial y^2} + \frac{\partial^2 \lambda}{\partial z^2} \right\} = \sum_{a,\,b,\,c} \frac{2}{a^2+\lambda},$$

with similar equations in μ and ν.

If, for brevity, we write

$$\sqrt{\{(a^2+\lambda)(b^2+\lambda)(c^2+\lambda)\}} \equiv \Delta_\lambda,$$

with similar meanings for Δ_μ and Δ_ν, we see that

$$\frac{\partial^2 \lambda}{\partial x^2} + \frac{\partial^2 \lambda}{\partial y^2} + \frac{\partial^2 \lambda}{\partial z^2} = \frac{\Delta_\lambda^2}{(\lambda-\mu)(\lambda-\nu)} \left\{ \frac{2}{a^2+\lambda} + \frac{2}{b^2+\lambda} + \frac{2}{c^2+\lambda} \right\}$$

$$= \frac{4\Delta_\lambda}{(\lambda-\mu)(\lambda-\nu)} \frac{d\Delta_\lambda}{d\lambda},$$

and so Laplace's equation assumes the form

$$\sum_{\lambda,\,\mu,\,\nu} \frac{4}{(\lambda-\mu)(\lambda-\nu)} \left[\Delta_\lambda^2 \frac{\partial^2 V}{\partial \lambda^2} + \Delta_\lambda \frac{d\Delta_\lambda}{d\lambda} \frac{\partial V}{\partial \lambda} \right] = 0,$$

that is to say

$$(\mu-\nu)\Delta_\lambda \frac{\partial}{\partial \lambda} \left\{ \Delta_\lambda \frac{\partial V}{\partial \lambda} \right\} + (\nu-\lambda)\Delta_\mu \frac{\partial}{\partial \mu} \left\{ \Delta_\mu \frac{\partial V}{\partial \mu} \right\} + (\lambda-\mu)\Delta_\nu \frac{\partial}{\partial \nu} \left\{ \Delta_\nu \frac{\partial V}{\partial \nu} \right\} = 0.$$

The equivalent equation with (u, v, w) as independent variables is simply

$$\{\wp(v) - \wp(w)\} \frac{\partial^2 V}{\partial u^2} + \{\wp(w) - \wp(u)\} \frac{\partial^2 V}{\partial v^2} + \{\wp(u) - \wp(v)\} \frac{\partial^2 V}{\partial w^2} = 0,$$

or, more briefly,

$$(\mu-\nu) \frac{\partial^2 V}{\partial u^2} + (\nu-\lambda) \frac{\partial^2 V}{\partial v^2} + (\lambda-\mu) \frac{\partial^2 V}{\partial w^2} = 0.$$

The last three equations will be regarded as canonical forms of Laplace's equation in the subsequent analysis.

23·33. *Ellipsoidal harmonics referred to confocal coordinates.*

When Niven's function Θ_p, defined as

$$\frac{x^2}{a^2+\theta_p} + \frac{y^2}{b^2+\theta_p} + \frac{z^2}{c^2+\theta_p} - 1,$$

is expressed in terms of the confocal coordinates (λ, μ, ν) of the point (x, y, z), it assumes the form

$$-\frac{(\lambda - \theta_p)(\mu - \theta_p)(\nu - \theta_p)}{(a^2 + \theta_p)(b^2 + \theta_p)(c^2 + \theta_p)},$$

and consequently, when constant factors of the form

$$-(a^2 + \theta_p)(b^2 + \theta_p)(c^2 + \theta_p)$$

are omitted, ellipsoidal harmonics assume the form

$$\begin{Bmatrix} & x, & yz \\ 1, & y, & zx, & xyz \\ & z, & xy \end{Bmatrix} \prod_{p=1}^{m}(\lambda - \theta_p) \prod_{p=1}^{m}(\mu - \theta_p) \prod_{p=1}^{m}(\nu - \theta_p).$$

If now we replace x, y, z by their values in terms of λ, μ, ν, we see that *any ellipsoidal harmonic is expressible in the form of a constant multiple of* ΛMN, where Λ is a function of λ only, and M and N are the same functions of μ and ν respectively as Λ is of λ. Further Λ is a polynomial of degree m in λ multiplied, in the case of harmonics of the second, third or fourth species, by one, two or three of the expressions $\sqrt{(a^2 + \lambda)}$, $\sqrt{(b^2 + \lambda)}$, $\sqrt{(c^2 + \lambda)}$.

Since the polynomial involved in Λ is $\prod_{p=1}^{m}(\lambda - \theta_p)$, it follows from a consideration of §§ 23·21–23·24 that Λ is a solution of Lamé's differential equation

$$4\sqrt{\{(a^2 + \lambda)(b^2 + \lambda)(c^2 + \lambda)\}} \frac{d}{d\lambda}\left[\sqrt{\{(a^2 + \lambda)(b^2 + \lambda)(c^2 + \lambda)\}}\frac{d\Lambda}{d\lambda}\right]$$
$$= \{n(n+1)\lambda + C\}\Lambda,$$

where n is the degree of the harmonic in (x, y, z).

This result may also be attained from a consideration of solutions of Laplace's equation which are of the type*

$$V = \Lambda MN,$$

where Λ, M, N are functions only of λ, μ, ν respectively.

For if we substitute this expression in Laplace's equation, as transformed in § 23·32, on division by V, we find that

$$\frac{\wp(v) - \wp(w)}{\Lambda}\frac{d^2\Lambda}{du^2} + \frac{\wp(w) - \wp(u)}{M}\frac{d^2M}{dv^2} + \frac{\wp(u) - \wp(v)}{N}\frac{d^2N}{dw^2} = 0.$$

The last two terms, *qua* functions of u, are linear functions of $\wp(u)$, and so $\frac{1}{\Lambda}\frac{d^2\Lambda}{du^2}$ must be a linear function of $\wp(u)$; since it is independent of the coordinates v and w, we have

$$\frac{1}{\Lambda}\frac{d^2\Lambda}{du^2} = \{K\wp(u) + B\},$$

where K and B are constants.

* A harmonic which is the product of three functions, each of which depends on one coordinate only, is sometimes called a *normal solution* of Laplace's equation. Thus normal solutions with polar coordinates are (§ 18·31)

$$r^n P_n{}^m(\cos\theta) \begin{matrix}\cos \\ \sin\end{matrix} m\phi.$$

If we make this substitution in the differential equation, we get a linear function of $\wp(u)$ equated (identically) to zero, and so the coefficients in this linear function must vanish; that is to say

$$K\{\wp(v) - \wp(w)\} - \frac{1}{M}\frac{d^2M}{dv^2} + \frac{1}{N}\frac{d^2N}{dw^2} = 0,$$

$$B\{\wp(v) - \wp(w)\} + \frac{\wp(w)}{M}\frac{d^2M}{dv^2} - \frac{\wp(v)}{N}\frac{d^2N}{dw^2} = 0,$$

and on solving these with the observation that $\wp(v) - \wp(w)$ is not identically zero, we obtain the three equations

$$\frac{d^2\Lambda}{du^2} = \{K\wp(u) + B\}\,\Lambda,$$

$$\frac{d^2M}{dv^2} = \{K\wp(v) + B\}\,M,$$

$$\frac{d^2N}{dw^2} = \{K\wp(w) + B\}\,N.$$

When λ is taken as independent variable, the first equation becomes

$$4\Delta_\lambda\frac{d}{d\lambda}\left\{\Delta_\lambda\frac{d\Lambda}{d\lambda}\right\} = \{K\lambda + B + \tfrac{1}{3}K(a^2 + b^2 + c^2)\}\,\Lambda,$$

and this is the equation already obtained for Λ, the degree n of the harmonic being given by the formula

$$n(n+1) = K.$$

We have now progressed so far with the study of ellipsoidal harmonics as is convenient without making use of properties of Lamé's equation.

We now proceed to the detailed consideration of this equation.

23·4. *Various forms of Lamé's differential equation.*

We have already encountered two forms of Lamé's equation, namely

$$4\Delta_\lambda\frac{d}{d\lambda}\left\{\Delta_\lambda\frac{d\Lambda}{d\lambda}\right\} = \{n(n+1)\lambda + C\}\,\Lambda,$$

and this may also be written

$$\frac{d^2\Lambda}{d\lambda^2} + \left\{\frac{\tfrac{1}{2}}{a^2+\lambda} + \frac{\tfrac{1}{2}}{b^2+\lambda} + \frac{\tfrac{1}{2}}{c^2+\lambda}\right\}\frac{d\Lambda}{d\lambda} = \frac{\{n(n+1)\lambda + C\}\,\Lambda}{4(a^2+\lambda)(b^2+\lambda)(c^2+\lambda)},$$

which may be termed the algebraic form; and

$$\frac{d^2\Lambda}{du^2} = \{n(n+1)\wp(u) + B\}\,\Lambda,$$

which, since it contains the Weierstrassian elliptic function $\wp(u)$, may be termed the Weierstrassian form; the constants B and C are connected by the relation

$$B + \tfrac{1}{3}n(n+1)(a^2 + b^2 + c^2) = C.$$

If we take $\wp(u)$ as a new variable, which will be called ξ, we obtain the slightly modified algebraic form (cf. § 10·6)

$$\frac{d^2\Lambda}{d\xi^2} + \left\{ \frac{\frac{1}{2}}{\xi - e_1} + \frac{\frac{1}{2}}{\xi - e_2} + \frac{\frac{1}{2}}{\xi - e_3} \right\} \frac{d\Lambda}{d\xi} = \frac{\{n(n+1)\xi + B\}\Lambda}{4(\xi - e_1)(\xi - e_2)(\xi - e_3)}.$$

This differential equation has singularities at e_1, e_2, e_3 at which the exponents are $0, \frac{1}{2}$ in each case; and a singularity at infinity, at which the exponents are $-\frac{1}{2}n, \frac{1}{2}(n+1)$.

The Weierstrassian form of the equation has been studied by Halphen, *Fonctions Elliptiques*, II. (Paris, 1888), pp. 457–531.

The algebraic forms have been studied by Stieltjes, *Acta Math.* VI. (1885), pp. 321–326, Klein, *Vorlesungen über lineare Differentielgleichungen* (lithographed, Göttingen, 1894), and Bôcher, *Über die Reihenentwickelungen der Potentialtheorie* (Leipzig, 1894).

The more general differential equation with four arbitrary singularities at which the exponents are arbitrary (save that the sum of all the exponents at all the singularities is 2) has been discussed by Heun, *Math. Ann.* XXXIII. (1889), pp. 161–179; the gain in generality by taking the singularities arbitrary is only apparent, because by a homographic change of the independent variable one of them can be transferred to the point at infinity, and then a change of origin is sufficient to make the sum of the complex coordinates of the three finite singularities equal to zero.

Another important form of Lamé's equation is obtained by using the notation of Jacobian elliptic functions; if we write

$$z_1 = u\sqrt{(e_1 - e_3)},$$

the Weierstrassian form becomes

$$\frac{d^2\Lambda}{dz_1^2} = \left[n(n+1)\left\{ \frac{e_3}{e_1 - e_3} + \mathrm{ns}^2 z_1 \right\} + \frac{B}{e_1 - e_3} \right] \Lambda,$$

and putting $z_1 = \alpha - iK'$, where $2iK'$ is the imaginary period of $\mathrm{sn}\, z_1$, we obtain the simple form

$$\frac{d^2\Lambda}{d\alpha^2} = \{ n(n+1) k^2 \mathrm{sn}^2 \alpha + A \} \Lambda,$$

where A is a constant connected with B by the relation

$$B + e_3 n(n+1) = A(e_1 - e_3).$$

The Jacobian form has been studied by Hermite, *Sur quelques applications des fonctions elliptiques, Comptes Rendus*, LXXXV. (1877), published separately, Paris, 1885.

In studying the properties of Lamé's equation, it is best not to use one form only, but to take the form best fitted for the purpose in hand. For practical applications the Jacobian form, leading to the Theta functions, is the most suitable. For obtaining the properties of the solutions of the equation, the best form to use is, in general, the second algebraic form, though in some problems analysis is simpler with the Weierstrassian form.

23·41. *Solutions in series of Lamé's equation.*

Let us now assume a solution of Lamé's equation, which may be written

$$4(\xi - e_1)(\xi - e_2)(\xi - e_3)\frac{d^2\Lambda}{d\xi^2} + (6\xi^2 - \tfrac{1}{2}g_2)\frac{d\Lambda}{d\xi} - \{n(n+1)\xi + B\}\Lambda = 0,$$

in the form

$$\Lambda = \sum_{r=0}^{\infty} b_r (\xi - e_2)^{\frac{1}{2}n - r}.$$

The series on the right, if it is a solution, will converge (§ 10·31) for sufficiently small values of $|\xi - e_2|$; but our object will be not the discussion of the convergence but the choice of B in such a way that the series may terminate, so that considerations of convergence will be superfluous.

The result of substituting this series for Λ on the left-hand side of the differential equation and arranging the result in powers of $\xi - e_2$ is minus the series

$$4\sum_{r=0}^{\infty}(\xi - e_2)^{\frac{1}{2}n - r + 1}\left[r(n - r + \tfrac{1}{2})b_r - \{3e_2(\tfrac{1}{2}n - r + 1)^2 - \tfrac{1}{4}n(n+1)e_2 - \tfrac{1}{4}B\}b_{r-1}\right.$$
$$\left. + (e_1 - e_2)(e_2 - e_3)(\tfrac{1}{2}n - r + 2)(\tfrac{1}{2}n - r + \tfrac{3}{2})b_{r-2}\right],$$

in which the coefficients b_r with negative suffixes are to be taken to be zero.

Hence, if the series is to be a solution, the relation connecting successive coefficients is

$$r(n - r + \tfrac{1}{2})b_r = \{3e_2(\tfrac{1}{2}n - r + 1)^2 - \tfrac{1}{4}n(n+1)e_2 - \tfrac{1}{4}B\}b_{r-1}$$
$$- (e_1 - e_2)(e_2 - e_3)(\tfrac{1}{2}n - r + 2)(\tfrac{1}{2}n - r + \tfrac{3}{2})b_{r-2},$$

and
$$(n - \tfrac{1}{2})b_1 = \{\tfrac{3}{4}n^2e_2 - \tfrac{1}{4}n(n+1)e_2 - \tfrac{1}{4}B\}b_0.$$

If we take $b_0 = 1$, as we may do without loss of generality, the coefficients b_r are seen to be functions of B with the following properties:

(i) b_r is a polynomial in B of degree r.

(ii) The sign of the coefficient of B^r in b_r is that of $(-)^r$, provided that $r \leqslant n$; the actual coefficient of B^r is

$$\frac{(-)^r}{2.4\ldots 2r(2n-1)(2n-3)\ldots(2n - 2r + 1)}.$$

(iii) If e_1, e_2, e_3 and B are real and $e_1 > e_2 > e_3$, then, if $b_{r-1} = 0$, the values of b_r and b_{r-2} are opposite in sign, provided that $r < \tfrac{1}{2}(n+3)$ and $r < n$.

Now suppose that n is even and that we choose B in such a way that

$$b_{\frac{1}{2}n + 1} = 0.$$

If this choice is made, the recurrence formula shews that

$$b_{\frac{1}{2}n + 2} = 0,$$

by putting $r = \frac{1}{2}n + 2$ in the formula in question; and if both $b_{\frac{1}{2}n+1}$ and $b_{\frac{1}{2}n+2}$ are zero *the subsequent recurrence formulae are satisfied by taking*

$$b_{\frac{1}{2}n+3} = b_{\frac{1}{2}n+4} = \ldots = 0.$$

Hence the condition that Lamé's equation should have a solution which is a polynomial in ξ is that B should be a root of a certain algebraic equation of degree $\frac{1}{2}n + 1$, when n is even.

When n is odd, we take $b_{\frac{1}{2}(n+1)}$ to vanish and then $b_{\frac{1}{2}(n+3)}$ also vanishes, and so do the subsequent coefficients; so that the condition, when n is odd, is that B should be a root of a certain algebraic equation of degree $\frac{1}{2}(n+1)$.

It is easy to shew that, when $e_1 > e_2 > e_3$, these algebraic equations have all their roots real. For the properties (ii) and (iii) shew that, *qua* functions of B, the expressions $b_0, b_1, b_2, \ldots b_r$ form a set of Sturm's functions* when $r < \frac{1}{2}(n+3)$, and so the equation

$$b_{\frac{1}{2}n+1} = 0 \quad \text{or} \quad b_{\frac{1}{2}(n+1)} = 0$$

has all its roots real† and unequal.

Hence, when the constants e_1, e_2, e_3 are real (which is the case of practical importance, as was seen in § 23·31), there are $\frac{1}{2}n + 1$ real and distinct values of B for which Lamé's equation has a solution of the type

$$\sum_{r=0}^{\frac{1}{2}n} b_r (\xi - e_2)^{\frac{1}{2}n - r}$$

when n is even; and there are $\frac{1}{2}(n+1)$ real and distinct values of B for which Lamé's equation has a solution of the type

$$\sum_{r=0}^{\frac{1}{2}(n-1)} b_r (\xi - e_2)^{\frac{1}{2}n - r}$$

when n is odd.

When the constants e_1, e_2, e_3 are *not* all real, it is possible for the equation satisfied by B to have equal roots; the solutions of Lamé's equation in such cases have been discussed by Cohn in a Königsberg dissertation (1888).

Example 1. Discuss solutions of Lamé's equation of the types

$$\text{(i)} \quad (\xi - e_1)^{\frac{1}{2}} \sum_{r=0}^{\infty} b_r{}' (\xi - e_2)^{\frac{1}{2}n - r - \frac{1}{2}},$$

$$\text{(ii)} \quad (\xi - e_3)^{\frac{1}{2}} \sum_{r=0}^{\infty} b_r{}'' (\xi - e_2)^{\frac{1}{2}n - r - \frac{1}{2}},$$

$$\text{(iii)} \quad (\xi - e_1)^{\frac{1}{2}} (\xi - e_3)^{\frac{1}{2}} \sum_{r=0}^{\infty} b_r{}''' (\xi - e_2)^{\frac{1}{2}n - r - 1},$$

---

* *Mém. présentés par les Savans Étrangers*, vi. (1835), pp. 271–318.

† This procedure is due to Liouville, *Journal de Math.* xi. (1846), p. 221.

obtaining the recurrence relations

(i) $r \left(n - r + \tfrac{1}{2} \right) b_r' = \{ 3 e_2 \left(\tfrac{1}{2} n - r + \tfrac{1}{2} \right)^2 + \left(e_2 - e_3 \right) \left(\tfrac{1}{2} n - r + \tfrac{3}{4} \right) - \tfrac{1}{4} n \left(n + 1 \right) e_2 - \tfrac{1}{4} B \} \, b'_{r-1}$
$$- \left(e_1 - e_2 \right) \left(e_2 - e_3 \right) \left(\tfrac{1}{2} n - r + \tfrac{3}{2} \right) \left(\tfrac{1}{2} n - r + 1 \right) b'_{r-2},$$

(ii) $r \left(n - r + \tfrac{1}{2} \right) b_r'' = \{ 3 e_2 \left(\tfrac{1}{2} n - r + \tfrac{1}{2} \right)^2 - \left(e_1 - e_2 \right) \left(\tfrac{1}{2} n - r + \tfrac{3}{4} \right) - \tfrac{1}{4} n \left(n + 1 \right) e_2 - \tfrac{1}{4} B \} \, b''_{r-1}$
$$- \left(e_1 - e_2 \right) \left(e_2 - e_3 \right) \left(\tfrac{1}{2} n - r + \tfrac{3}{2} \right) \left(\tfrac{1}{2} n - r + 1 \right) b''_{r-2},$$

(iii) $r \left(n - r + \tfrac{1}{2} \right) b_r''' = \{ 3 e_2 \left(\tfrac{1}{2} n - r + \tfrac{1}{2} \right)^2 - \tfrac{1}{4} e_2 \left(n^2 + n + 1 \right) - \tfrac{1}{4} B \} \, b'''_{r-1}$
$$- \left(e_1 - e_2 \right) \left(e_2 - e_3 \right) \left(\tfrac{1}{2} n - r + 1 \right) \left(\tfrac{1}{2} n - r + \tfrac{1}{2} \right) b'''_{r-2}.$$

Example 2.   With the notation of example 1 shew that the numbers of real distinct values of B for which Lamé's equation is satisfied by terminating series of the several species are

(i) $\tfrac{1}{2} (n-1)$ or $\tfrac{1}{2} (n-2)$;   (ii) $\tfrac{1}{2} (n-1)$ or $\tfrac{1}{2} (n-2)$;   (iii) $\tfrac{1}{2} (n-2)$ or $\tfrac{1}{2} (n-3)$.

23·42.   *The definition of Lamé functions.*

When we collect the results which have been obtained in § 23·41, it is clear that, given the equation

$$\frac{d^2 \Lambda}{du^2} = \left[n \left(n + 1 \right) \wp \left(u \right) + B \right] \Lambda,$$

n being a positive integer, there are $2n + 1$ values of B for which the equation has a solution of one or other of the four species described in §§ 23·21–23·24.

If, when such a solution is expanded in descending powers of ξ, the coefficient of the leading term $\xi^{\frac{1}{2}n}$ is taken to be unity, as was done in § 23·41, the function so obtained is called a *Lamé function of degree n, of the first kind,* of the first (second, third or fourth) species.   The $2n + 1$ functions so obtained are denoted by the symbol

$$E_n{}^m \left(\xi \right) ; \qquad \left(m = 1, 2, \ldots 2n + 1 \right).$$

and, when we have to deal with only one such function, it may be denoted by the symbol

$$E_n \left(\xi \right).$$

Tables of the expressions representing Lamé functions for $n = 1, 2, \ldots 10$ have been compiled by Guerritore, *Giornale di Mat.* (2) XVI. (1909), pp. 164–172.

Example 1.   Obtain the five Lamé functions of degree 2, namely

$$\lambda + \tfrac{1}{3} \Sigma a^2 \pm \tfrac{1}{3} \sqrt{\left\{ \Sigma a^4 - \Sigma b^2 c^2 \right\}},$$

$$\sqrt{\left(\lambda + b^2 \right)} \sqrt{\left(\lambda + c^2 \right)}, \quad \sqrt{\left(\lambda + c^2 \right)} \sqrt{\left(\lambda + a^2 \right)}, \quad \sqrt{\left(\lambda + a^2 \right)} \sqrt{\left(\lambda + b^2 \right)}.$$

Example 2.   Obtain the seven Lamé functions of degree 3, namely

$$\sqrt{\left\{ \left(\lambda + a^2 \right) \left(\lambda + b^2 \right) \left(\lambda + c^2 \right) \right\}},$$

and six functions obtained by interchanges of a, b, c in the expressions

$$\sqrt{\left(\lambda + a^2 \right)} \cdot \left[\lambda + \tfrac{1}{3} \left(a^2 + 2 b^2 + 2 c^2 \right) \pm \tfrac{1}{3} \sqrt{\left\{ a^4 + 4 b^4 + 4 c^4 - 7 b^2 c^2 - c^2 a^2 - a^2 b^2 \right\}} \right].$$

23·43.   *The non-repetition of factors in Lamé functions.*

It will now be shewn that all the rational linear factors of $E_n{}^m \left(\xi \right)$ are *unequal.*   This result follows most simply from the differential equation which $E_n{}^m \left(\xi \right)$ satisfies; for, if $\xi - \xi_1$ be any factor of $E_n{}^m \left(\xi \right)$, where ξ_1 is not one of the numbers e_1, e_2 or e_3, then ξ_1 is a regular point of the equation (§ 10·3), and any solution of the equation which, when expanded in powers of $\xi - \xi_1$, does not begin with a term in $(\xi - \xi_1)^0$ or $(\xi - \xi_1)^1$ must be identically zero.

Again, if ξ_1 were one of the numbers e_1, e_2 or e_3, the indicial equation appropriate to ξ_1 would have the roots 0 and $\frac{1}{2}$, and so the expansion of $E_n{}^m(\xi)$ in ascending powers of ξ_1 would begin with a term in $(\xi - \xi_1)^0$ or $(\xi - \xi_1)^{\frac{1}{2}}$.

Hence, in no circumstances has $E_n{}^m(\xi)$, qua function of ξ, a repeated factor.

The determination of the numbers θ_1, θ_2, ... θ_m introduced in §§ 23·21–23·24 may now be regarded as complete; for it has been seen that solutions of Lamé's equation can be constructed with non-repeated factors, and the values of θ_1, θ_2, ... which correspond to the roots of $E_n{}^m(\xi) = 0$ satisfy the equations which are requisite to ensure that Niven's products are solutions of Laplace's equation.

It still remains to be shewn that the $2n + 1$ ellipsoidal harmonics constructed in this way form a fundamental system of solutions of degree n of Laplace's equation.

23·44. *The linear independence of Lamé functions.*

It will now be shewn that the $2n + 1$ Lamé functions $E_n{}^m(\xi)$ which are of degree n are linearly independent, that is to say that no linear relation can exist which connects them identically for general values of ξ.

In the first place, if such a linear relation existed in which functions of different species were involved, it is obvious that by suitable changes of signs of the radicals $\sqrt{(\xi - e_1)}$, $\sqrt{(\xi - e_2)}$, $\sqrt{(\xi - e_3)}$ we could obtain other relations which, on being combined by addition or subtraction with the original relation, would give rise to two (or more) linear relations each of which involved functions restricted not merely to be of the same species but also of the same type.

Let one of these latter relations, if it exists, be

$$\Sigma a_m E_n{}^m(\xi) \equiv 0 \qquad (a_m \neq 0)$$

and let this relation involve r of the functions.

Operate on this identity $r - 1$ times with the operator

$$\frac{d^2}{du^2} - n(n+1)\xi.$$

The results of the successive operations are

$$\Sigma a_m (B_n{}^m)^s E_n{}^m(\xi) \equiv 0 \qquad (s = 1, 2, \dots r - 1),$$

where $B_n{}^m$ is the particular value of B which is associated with $E_n{}^m(\xi)$.

Eliminate $a_1, a_2, \ldots a_r$ from the r equations now obtained; and it is found that

$$\begin{vmatrix} 1 & , & 1 & , & 1, & \ldots & 1 \\ B_n{}^1 & , & B_n{}^2 & , & B_n{}^3, & \ldots & B_n{}^r \\ \hdotsfor{7} \\ (B_n{}^1)^{r-1}, & (B_n{}^2)^{r-1}, & & \ldots\ldots & (B_n{}^r)^{r-1} \end{vmatrix} = 0.$$

Now the only factors of the determinant on the left are differences of the numbers $B_n{}^m$, and these differences cannot vanish, by § 23·41. Hence the determinant cannot vanish and so the postulated relation does not exist.

The linear independence of the $2n+1$ Lamé functions of degree n is therefore established.

23·45. *The linear independence of ellipsoidal harmonics.*

Let $G_n{}^m(x, y, z)$ be the ellipsoidal harmonic of degree n associated with $E_n{}^m(\xi)$, and let $H_n{}^m(x, y, z)$ be the corresponding homogeneous harmonic.

It is now easy to shew that not only are the $2n+1$ harmonics of the type $G_n{}^m(x, y, z)$ linearly independent, but also the $2n+1$ harmonics of the type $H_n{}^m(x, y, z)$ are linearly independent.

In the first place, if a linear relation existed between harmonics of the type $G_n{}^m(x, y, z)$, then, when we expressed these harmonics in terms of confocal coordinates (λ, μ, ν), we should obtain a linear relation between Lamé functions of the type $E_n{}^m(\xi)$ where $\xi = \lambda + \frac{1}{3}(a^2 + b^2 + c^2)$, and it has been seen that no such relation exists.

Again, if a linear relation existed between homogeneous harmonics of the type $H_n{}^m(x, y, z)$, by operating on the relation with Niven's operator (§ 23·25),

$$1 - \frac{D^2}{2(2n-1)} + \frac{D^4}{2.4(2n-1)(2n-3)} - \cdots,$$

we should obtain a linear relation connecting functions of the type $G_n{}^m(x, y, z)$, and since it has just been seen that no such relation exists, it follows that the homogeneous harmonics of degree n are linearly independent.

23·46. *Stieltjes' theorem on the zeros of Lamé functions.*

It has been seen that any Lamé function of degree n is expressible in the form

$$(\theta + a^2)^{\kappa_1}(\theta + b^2)^{\kappa_2}(\theta + c^2)^{\kappa_3} . \prod_{p=1}^{m}(\theta - \theta_p),$$

where $\kappa_1, \kappa_2, \kappa_3$ are equal to 0 or $\frac{1}{2}$ and the numbers $\theta_1, \theta_2, \ldots \theta_m$ are real and unequal both to each other and to $-a^2, -b^2, -c^2$; and $\frac{1}{2}n = m + \kappa_1 + \kappa_2 + \kappa_3$. When $\kappa_1, \kappa_2, \kappa_3$ are given the number of Lamé functions of this degree and type is $m + 1$.

The remarkable result has been proved by Stieltjes* that these $m+1$ functions can be arranged in order in such a way that the rth function of the set has $r-1$ of its zeros† between $-a^2$ and $-b^2$ and the remaining $m-r+1$ of its zeros between $-b^2$ and $-c^2$, and, incidentally, that, for *all* the $m+1$ functions, $\theta_1, \theta_2, \ldots \theta_m$ lie between $-a^2$ and $-c^2$.

To prove this result, let $\phi_1, \phi_2, \ldots \phi_m$ be any real variables such that

$$\begin{cases} -a^2 \leqslant \phi_p \leqslant -b^2, & (p = 1, 2, \ldots r-1) \\ -b^2 \leqslant \phi_p \leqslant -c^2, & (p = r, r+1, \ldots m) \end{cases}$$

and consider the product

$$\Pi = \prod_{p=1}^{m} \left[\left|(\phi_p + a^2)\right|^{\kappa_1 + \frac{1}{4}} \cdot \left|(\phi_p + b^2)\right|^{\kappa_2 + \frac{1}{4}} \cdot \left|(\phi_p + c^2)\right|^{\kappa_3 + \frac{1}{4}} \right] \prod_{p \neq q} \left|(\phi_p - \phi_q)\right|.$$

This product is zero when all the variables ϕ_p have their least values and also when all have their greatest values; when the variables ϕ_p are unequal both to each other and to $-a^2, -b^2, -c^2$, then Π is positive and it is obviously a continuous bounded function of the variables.

Hence there is a set of values of the variables for which Π attains its upper bound, which is positive and not zero (cf. § 3·62).

For this set of values of the variables the conditions for a maximum give

$$\frac{\partial \log \Pi}{\partial \phi_1} = \frac{\partial \log \Pi}{\partial \phi_2} = \ldots = 0,$$

that is to say

$$\frac{\kappa_1 + \frac{1}{4}}{\phi_p + a^2} + \frac{\kappa_2 + \frac{1}{4}}{\phi_p + b^2} + \frac{\kappa_3 + \frac{1}{4}}{\phi_p + c^2} + \sum_{q=1}^{m}{'} \frac{1}{\phi_p - \phi_q} = 0,$$

where p assumes in turn the values $1, 2, \ldots m$.

Now this system of equations is precisely the system by which $\theta_1, \theta_2, \ldots \theta_p$ are determined (cf. §§ 23·21–23·24); and *so the system of equations determining $\theta_1, \theta_2, \ldots \theta_m$ has a solution for which*

$$\begin{cases} -a^2 < \theta_p < -b^2, & (p = 1, 2, \ldots r-1) \\ -b^2 < \theta_p < -c^2. & (p = r, r+1, \ldots m) \end{cases}$$

Hence, if r has any of the values $1, 2, \ldots m+1$, a Lamé function exists with $r-1$ of its zeros between $-a^2$ and $-b^2$ and the remaining $m-r+1$ zeros between $-b^2$ and $-c^2$.

Since there are $m+1$ Lamé functions of the specified type, they are all obtained when r is given in turn the values $1, 2, \ldots m+1$; and this is the theorem due to Stieltjes.

---

* *Acta Mathematica*, VI. (1885), pp. 321–326.

† The zeros $-a^2, -b^2, -c^2$ are to be omitted from this enumeration, $\theta_1, \theta_2, \ldots \theta_m$ only being taken into account.

An interesting statical interpretation of the theorem was given by Stieltjes, namely that if $m+3$ particles which attract one another according to the law of the inverse distance are placed on a line, and three of these particles, whose masses are $\kappa_1+\frac{1}{4}$, $\kappa_2+\frac{1}{4}$, $\kappa_3+\frac{1}{4}$, are fixed at points with coordinates $-a^2$, $-b^2$, $-c^2$, the remainder being of unit mass and free to move on the line, then $\log \Pi$ is the gravitational potential of the system; and the positions of equilibrium of the system are those in which the coordinates of the moveable particles are θ_1, θ_2, ... θ_m, i.e. the values of θ for which a certain one of the Lamé functions of degree $2(m+\kappa_1+\kappa_2+\kappa_3)$ vanishes.

Example. Discuss the positions of the zeros of polynomials which satisfy an equation of the type

$$\frac{d^2\Lambda}{d\theta^2} + \sum_{r=1}^{s} \frac{1-a_s}{\theta-a_s} \frac{d\Lambda}{d\theta} + \frac{\phi_{r-2}(\theta)}{\prod\limits_{s=1}^{r}(\theta-a_s)} \Lambda = 0,$$

where $\phi_{r-2}(\theta)$ is a polynomial of degree $r-2$ in θ in which the coefficient of θ^{r-2} is

$$-m\{m+r-1- \sum_{s=1}^{r} a_s\},$$

m being a positive integer, and the remaining coefficients in $\phi_{r-2}(\theta)$ are determined from the consideration that the equation has a polynomial solution.

(Stieltjes.)

23·47. *Lamé functions of the second kind.*

The functions $E_n{}^m(\xi)$, hitherto discussed, are known as Lamé functions of the *first kind*. It is easy to verify that an independent solution of Lamé's equation

$$\frac{d^2\Lambda}{du^2} = \{n(n+1)\xi + B_n{}^m\}\Lambda$$

is the function $F_n{}^m(\xi)$ defined by the equation*

$$F_n{}^m(\xi) = (2n+1)E_n{}^m(\xi)\int_0^u \frac{du}{\{E_n{}^m(\xi)\}^2},$$

and $F_n{}^m(\xi)$ is termed a Lamé function of the *second kind*.

From this formula it is clear that, near $u=0$,

$$F_n{}^m(\xi) = (2n+1)u^{-n}\{1+O(u)\}\int_0^u u^{2n}\{1+O(u)\}\,du = u^{n+1}\{1+O(u)\},$$

and we obviously have

$$E_n{}^m(\xi) = u^{-n}\{1+O(u)\}.$$

It is clear from these results that $F_n{}^m(\xi)$ can never be a Lamé function of the first kind, *and so there is no value of $B_n{}^m$ for which Lamé's equation is satisfied by two Lamé functions of the first kind of different species or types.*

It is possible to obtain an expression for $F_n{}^m(\xi)$ which is free from quadratures, analogous to Christoffel's formula for $Q_n(z)$, given on p. 333, example 29. We shall give the analysis in the case when $E_n{}^m(\xi)$ is of the first species. The only irreducible poles of $1/\{E_n{}^m(\xi)\}^2$, *qua* function of u, are at a set of points u_1, u_2, ... u_n which are none of them periods or half periods.

* This definition of the function $F_n{}^m(\xi)$ is due to Heine, *Journal für Math.* xxix. (1845), p. 194.

Near any one of these points we have an expansion of the form

$$E_n{}^m (\xi) = k_1 (u - u_r) + k_2 (u - u_r)^2 + k_3 (u - u_r)^3 + \ldots,$$

and, by substitution of this series in the differential equation, it is found that k_2 is zero.

Hence the principal part of $1/\{E_n{}^m (\xi)\}^2$ near u_r is

$$\frac{1}{k_1{}^2 (u - u_r)^2},$$

and the residue is zero.

Hence we can find constants A_r such that

$$\{E_n{}^m (\xi)\}^{-2} - \sum_{r=1}^{n} A_r \wp (u - u_r)$$

has no poles at any points congruent to any of the points u_r; it is therefore a constant A, by Liouville's theorem, since it is a doubly periodic function of u.

Hence　　　$$\int_0^u \frac{du}{\{E_n{}^m (\xi)\}^2} = Au - \sum_{r=1}^{n} A_r \{\zeta (u - u_r) + \zeta (u_r)\}.$$

Now the points u_r can be grouped in pairs whose sum is zero, since $E_n{}^m (\xi)$ is an even function of u.

If we take $u_{n-r} = - u_{r+1}$, we have

$$\int_0^u \frac{du}{\{E_n{}^m (\xi)\}^2} = Au - \sum_{r=1}^{\frac{1}{2}n} A_r \{\zeta (u - u_r) + \zeta (u + u_r)\}$$

$$= Au - 2\zeta (u) \sum_{r=1}^{\frac{1}{2}n} A_r - \sum_{r=1}^{\frac{1}{2}n} \frac{A_r \wp' (u)}{\wp (u) - \wp (u_r)},$$

and therefore

$$F_n{}^m (\xi) = (2n + 1) \{Au - 2\zeta (u) \sum_{r=1}^{\frac{1}{2}n} A_r\} E_n{}^m (\xi) + \wp' (u) w_{\frac{1}{2}n - 1} (\xi),$$

where $w_{\frac{1}{2}n - 1} (\xi)$ is a polynomial in ξ of degree $\frac{1}{2}n - 1$.

Example. Obtain formulae analogous to this expression for $F_n{}^m (\xi)$ when $E_n{}^m (\xi)$ is of the second, third or fourth species.

23·5. *Lamé's equation in association with Jacobian elliptic functions.*

All the results which have so far been obtained in connexion with Lamé functions of course have their analogues in the notation of Jacobian elliptic functions, and, in the hands of Hermite (cf. § 23·71), the use of Jacobian elliptic functions in the discussion of generalisations of Lamé's equation has produced extremely interesting results.

Unfortunately it is not possible to use Jacobian elliptic functions in which all the variables involved are real, without a loss of symmetry.

36—2

The symmetrical formulae may be obtained by taking new variables α, β, γ defined by the equations

$$\begin{cases} \alpha = iK' + u \sqrt{(e_1 - e_3)}, \\ \beta = iK' + v \sqrt{(e_1 - e_3)}, \\ \gamma = iK' + w \sqrt{(e_1 - e_3)}, \end{cases}$$

and then the formulae of § 23·31 are equivalent to

$$\begin{cases} x = \quad k^2 \sqrt{(a^2 - c^2)} . \operatorname{sn} \alpha \operatorname{sn} \beta \operatorname{sn} \gamma, \\ y = -\, (k^2/k') \sqrt{(a^2 - c^2)} . \operatorname{cn} \alpha \operatorname{cn} \beta \operatorname{cn} \gamma, \\ z = \quad (i/k') \sqrt{(a^2 - c^2)} . \operatorname{dn} \alpha \operatorname{dn} \beta \operatorname{dn} \gamma, \end{cases}$$

the modulus of the elliptic functions being

$$\sqrt{\left(\frac{a^2 - b^2}{a^2 - c^2} \right)}.$$

The equation of the quadric of the confocal system on which α is constant is

$$\frac{X^2}{(a^2 - b^2) \operatorname{sn}^2 \alpha} - \frac{Y^2}{(a^2 - b^2) \operatorname{cn}^2 \alpha} - \frac{Z^2}{(a^2 - c^2) \operatorname{dn}^2 \alpha} = 1.$$

This is an ellipsoid if α lies between iK' and $K + iK'$; the quadric on which β is constant is an hyperboloid of one sheet if β lies between $K + iK'$ and K; and the quadric on which γ is constant is an hyperboloid of two sheets if γ lies between 0 and K; and with this determination of (α, β, γ) the point (x, y, z) lies in the positive octant.

It has already been seen (§ 23·4) that, with this notation, Lamé's equation assumes the form

$$\frac{d^2 \Lambda}{d\alpha^2} = \{ n(n+1) k^2 \operatorname{sn}^2 \alpha + A \} \Lambda,$$

and the solutions expressible as periodic functions of α will be called* $E_n{}^m(\alpha)$. The first species of Lamé function is then a polynomial in $\operatorname{sn}^2 \alpha$, and generally the species may be defined by a scheme analogous to that of § 23·2,

$$\left\{ \begin{array}{llll} & \operatorname{sn} \alpha, & \operatorname{cn} \alpha \operatorname{dn} \alpha, & \\ 1, & \operatorname{cn} \alpha, & \operatorname{dn} \alpha \operatorname{sn} \alpha, & \operatorname{sn} \alpha \operatorname{cn} \alpha \operatorname{dn} \alpha \\ & \operatorname{dn} \alpha, & \operatorname{sn} \alpha \operatorname{cn} \alpha, & \end{array} \right\} \prod_p (\operatorname{sn}^2 \alpha - \operatorname{sn}^2 \alpha_p).$$

23·6. *The integral equation satisfied by Lamé functions of the first and second species*†.

We shall now shew that, if $E_n{}^m(\alpha)$ is any Lamé function of the first species (n being even) or of the second species (n being odd) with $\operatorname{sn} \alpha$ as a

---

* There is no risk of confusing these with the corresponding functions $E_n{}^m(\xi)$.

† This integral equation and the corresponding formulae of § 23·62 associated with ellipsoidal harmonics were given by Whittaker, *Proc. London Math. Soc.* (2) xiv. (1915), pp. 260–268. Proofs of the formulae involving functions of the third and fourth species have not been previously published.

factor, then $E_n{}^m(\alpha)$ is a solution of the integral equation

$$E_n{}^m(\alpha) = \lambda \int_{-2K}^{2K} P_n(k\operatorname{sn}\alpha\operatorname{sn}\theta)\, E_n{}^m(\theta)\, d\theta\,;$$

where λ is one of the 'characteristic numbers' (§ 11·23).

To establish this result we need the lemma that $P_n(k\operatorname{sn}\alpha\operatorname{sn}\theta)$ is annihilated by the partial differential operator

$$\frac{\partial^2}{\partial\alpha^2} - \frac{\partial^2}{\partial\theta^2} - n(n+1)\,k^2(\operatorname{sn}^2\alpha - \operatorname{sn}^2\theta).$$

To prove the lemma, observe that, when μ is written for brevity in place of $k\operatorname{sn}\alpha\operatorname{sn}\theta$, we have

$$\left\{\frac{\partial^2}{\partial\alpha^2} - \frac{\partial^2}{\partial\theta^2}\right\} P_n(k\operatorname{sn}\alpha\operatorname{sn}\theta)$$

$$= k^2\left\{\operatorname{cn}^2\alpha\operatorname{dn}^2\alpha\operatorname{sn}^2\theta - \operatorname{cn}^2\theta\operatorname{dn}^2\theta\operatorname{sn}^2\alpha\right\} P_n{}''(\mu)$$

$$+ 2k^3\operatorname{sn}\alpha\operatorname{sn}\theta\,(\operatorname{sn}^2\alpha - \operatorname{sn}^2\theta)\,P_n{}'(\mu)$$

$$= k^2(\operatorname{sn}^2\alpha - \operatorname{sn}^2\theta)\left[(\mu^2-1)\,P_n{}''(\mu) + 2\mu P_n{}'(\mu)\right]$$

$$= k^2(\operatorname{sn}^2\alpha - \operatorname{sn}^2\theta)\,n(n+1)\,P_n(\mu),$$

when we use Legendre's differential equation (§ 15·13). And the lemma is established.

The result of applying the operator

$$\frac{\partial^2}{\partial\alpha^2} - n(n+1)\,k^2\operatorname{sn}^2\alpha - A_n{}^m$$

to the integral

$$\int_{-2K}^{2K} P_n(k\operatorname{sn}\alpha\operatorname{sn}\theta)\, E_n{}^m(\theta)\, d\theta$$

is now seen to be

$$\int_{-2K}^{2K} \left\{\frac{\partial^2}{\partial\alpha^2} - n(n+1)\,k^2\operatorname{sn}^2\alpha - A_n{}^m\right\} P_n(k\operatorname{sn}\alpha\operatorname{sn}\theta)\, E_n{}^m(\theta)\, d\theta$$

$$= \int_{-2K}^{2K} \left[\left\{\frac{\partial^2}{\partial\theta^2} - n(n+1)\,k^2\operatorname{sn}^2\theta - A_n{}^m\right\} P_n(k\operatorname{sn}\alpha\operatorname{sn}\theta)\right] E_n{}^m(\theta)\, d\theta,$$

and when we integrate twice by parts this becomes

$$\left[\frac{\partial P_n(k\operatorname{sn}\alpha\operatorname{sn}\theta)}{\partial\theta} E_n{}^m(\theta) - P_n(k\operatorname{sn}\alpha\operatorname{sn}\theta)\frac{dE_n{}^m(\theta)}{d\theta}\right]_{-2K}^{2K}$$

$$+ \int_{-2K}^{2K} P_n(k\operatorname{sn}\alpha\operatorname{sn}\theta)\left\{\frac{d^2}{d\theta^2} - n(n+1)\,k^2\operatorname{sn}^2\theta - A_n{}^m\right\} E_n{}^m(\theta)\,.\,d\theta = 0.$$

Hence it follows that the integral

$$\int_{-2K}^{2K} P_n(k\operatorname{sn}\alpha\operatorname{sn}\theta)\, E_n{}^m(\theta)\, d\theta$$

is annihilated by the operator

$$\frac{d^2}{d\alpha^2} - n(n+1)\,k^2\operatorname{sn}^2\alpha - A_n{}^m,$$

and it is evidently a polynomial of degree n in $\operatorname{sn}^2 \alpha$. Since Lamé's equation has only one integral of this type*, it follows that the integral is a multiple of $E_n{}^m(\alpha)$ if it is not zero; and the result is established.

It appears that *every* characteristic number associated with the equation

$$f(a) = \lambda \int_{-2K}^{2K} P_n(k \operatorname{sn} a \operatorname{sn} \theta) f(\theta)$$

yields a solution of Lamé's equation; cf. Ince, *Proc. Royal Soc. Edin.* XLII. (1922), pp. 43–53.

Example 1. Shew that the nucleus of an integral equation satisfied by Lamé functions of the first species (n being even) or of the second species (n being odd) with $\operatorname{cn} a$ as a factor, may be taken to be

$$P_n\left(\frac{ik}{k'} \operatorname{cn} a \operatorname{cn} \theta\right).$$

Example 2. Shew that the nucleus of an integral equation satisfied by Lamé functions of the first species (n being even) or of the second species (n being odd) with $\operatorname{dn} a$ as a factor, may be taken to be

$$P_n\left(\frac{1}{k'} \operatorname{dn} a \operatorname{dn} \theta\right).$$

23·61. *The integral equation satisfied by Lamé functions of the third and fourth species.*

The theorem analogous to that of § 23·6, in the case of Lamé functions of the third and fourth species, is that any Lamé function of the fourth species (n being odd) or of the third species (n being even) with $\operatorname{cn} \alpha \operatorname{dn} \alpha$ as a factor, satisfies the integral equation

$$E_n{}^m(\alpha) = \lambda \int_{-2K}^{2K} \operatorname{cn} \alpha \operatorname{dn} \alpha \operatorname{cn} \theta \operatorname{dn} \theta P_n''(k \operatorname{sn} \alpha \operatorname{sn} \theta) E_n{}^m(\theta)\, d\theta.$$

The preliminary lemma is that the nucleus

$$\operatorname{cn} \alpha \operatorname{dn} \alpha \operatorname{cn} \theta \operatorname{dn} \theta P_n''(k \operatorname{sn} \alpha \operatorname{sn} \theta),$$

like the nucleus of § 23·6, is annihilated by the operator

$$\frac{\partial^2}{\partial \alpha^2} - \frac{\partial^2}{\partial \theta^2} - n(n+1) k^2 (\operatorname{sn}^2 \alpha - \operatorname{sn}^2 \theta).$$

To verify the lemma observe that

$$\frac{\partial^2}{\partial \alpha^2}\{\operatorname{cn} \alpha \operatorname{dn} \alpha P_n''(k \operatorname{sn} \alpha \operatorname{sn} \theta)\}$$

$$= k^2 \operatorname{cn}^3 \alpha \operatorname{dn}^3 \alpha \operatorname{sn}^2 \theta P_n{}^{iv}(\mu) - 3k \operatorname{sn} \alpha \operatorname{cn} \alpha \operatorname{dn} \alpha \operatorname{sn} \theta (\operatorname{dn}^2 \alpha + k^2 \operatorname{cn}^2 \alpha) P_n'''(\mu)$$
$$- \operatorname{cn} \alpha \operatorname{dn} \alpha (\operatorname{dn}^2 \alpha + k^2 \operatorname{cn}^2 \alpha - 4k^2 \operatorname{sn}^2 \alpha) P_n''(\mu),$$

and so

$$\left\{\frac{\partial^2}{\partial \alpha^2} - \frac{\partial^2}{\partial \theta^2}\right\} . \{\operatorname{cn} \alpha \operatorname{dn} \alpha \operatorname{cn} \theta \operatorname{dn} \theta P_n''(k \operatorname{sn} \alpha \operatorname{sn} \theta)\}$$

$$= k \operatorname{cn} \alpha \operatorname{dn} \alpha \operatorname{cn} \theta \operatorname{dn} \theta (\operatorname{sn}^2 \alpha - \operatorname{sn}^2 \theta)\{(\mu^2 - 1) P_n{}^{iv}(\mu) + 6\mu P_n'''(\mu) + 6P_n''(\mu)\}$$

$$= k^2 \operatorname{cn} \alpha \operatorname{dn} \alpha \operatorname{cn} \theta \operatorname{dn} \theta (\operatorname{sn}^2 \alpha - \operatorname{sn}^2 \theta) \frac{d^3}{d\mu^3}\{(\mu^2 - 1) P_n'(\mu)\}$$

$$= k^2 n(n+1) \operatorname{cn} \alpha \operatorname{dn} \alpha \operatorname{cn} \theta \operatorname{dn} \theta (\operatorname{sn}^2 \alpha - \operatorname{sn}^2 \theta) P_n''(\mu),$$

---

* The other solution when expanded in descending powers of $\operatorname{sn} a$ begins with a term in $(\operatorname{sn} a)^{-n-1}$.

and the lemma is established. The proof that $E_n{}^m(\alpha)$ satisfies the integral equation now follows precisely as in the case of the integral equation of § 23·6.

Example 1. Shew that the nucleus of an integral equation which is satisfied by Lamé functions of the fourth species (n being odd) or of the third species (n being even) with $\operatorname{sn}a\,\operatorname{dn}a$ as a factor, may be taken to be

$$\operatorname{sn}a\,\operatorname{dn}a\,\operatorname{sn}\theta\,\operatorname{dn}\theta\,P_n{}''\left(\frac{ik}{k'}\operatorname{cn}a\,\operatorname{cn}\theta\right).$$

Example 2. Shew that the nucleus of an integral equation which is satisfied by Lamé functions of the fourth species (n being odd) or of the third species (n being even) with $\operatorname{sn}a\,\operatorname{cn}a$ as a factor, may be taken to be

$$\operatorname{sn}a\,\operatorname{cn}a\,\operatorname{sn}\theta\,\operatorname{cn}\theta\,P_n{}''\left(\frac{1}{k'}\operatorname{dn}a\,\operatorname{dn}\theta\right).$$

Example 3. Obtain the following three integral equations satisfied by Lamé functions of the fourth species (n being odd) and of the third species (n being even):

$$\text{(i)}\qquad k^2\operatorname{sn}^2a\,E_n{}^m(a)=\lambda\operatorname{cn}a\,\operatorname{dn}a\int_{-2K}^{2K}P_n(k\operatorname{sn}a\,\operatorname{sn}\theta)\frac{d}{d\theta}\left\{\frac{1}{\operatorname{cn}\theta\,\operatorname{dn}\theta}\frac{dE_n{}^m(\theta)}{d\theta}\right\}d\theta,$$

$$\text{(ii)}\quad -k^2\operatorname{cn}^2a\,E_n{}^m(a)=\lambda k'^2\operatorname{sn}a\,\operatorname{dn}a\int_{-2K}^{2K}P_n\left(\frac{ik}{k'}\operatorname{cn}a\,\operatorname{cn}\theta\right)\frac{d}{d\theta}\left\{\frac{1}{\operatorname{sn}\theta\,\operatorname{dn}\theta}\frac{dE_n{}^m(\theta)}{d\theta}\right\}d\theta,$$

$$\text{(iii)}\quad k^2\operatorname{dn}^2a\,E_n{}^m(a)=\lambda k'^2\operatorname{sn}a\,\operatorname{cn}a\int_{-2K}^{2K}P_n\left(\frac{1}{k'}\operatorname{dn}a\,\operatorname{dn}\theta\right)\frac{d}{d\theta}\left\{\frac{1}{\operatorname{sn}\theta\,\operatorname{cn}\theta}\frac{dE_n{}^m(\theta)}{d\theta}\right\}d\theta;$$

in the case of functions of even order, the functions of the different types each satisfy one of these equations only.

23·62. *Integral formulae for ellipsoidal harmonics.*

The integral equations just considered make it possible to obtain elegant representations of the ellipsoidal harmonic $G_n{}^m(x,y,z)$ and of the corresponding homogeneous harmonic $H_n{}^m(x,y,z)$ in terms of definite integrals.

From the general equation formula of § 18·3, it is evident that $H_n{}^m(x,y,z)$ is expressible in the form

$$H_n{}^m(x,y,z)=\int_{-\pi}^{\pi}(x\cos t+y\sin t+iz)^n f(t)\,dt,$$

where $f(t)$ is a periodic function to be determined.

Now the result of applying Niven's operator D^2 to $(x\cos t+y\sin t+iz)^n$ is

$$n(n-1)(a^2\cos^2 t+b^2\sin^2 t-c^2)(x\cos t+y\sin t+iz)^{n-2},$$

and so, by Niven's formula (§ 23·25) we find that $G_n{}^m(x,y,z)$ is expressible in the form

$$G_n{}^m(x,y,z)=\int_{-\pi}^{\pi}\left\{\mathfrak{A}^n-\frac{n(n-1)}{2(2n-1)}\mathfrak{A}^{n-2}\mathfrak{B}^2\right.$$
$$\left.+\frac{n(n-1)(n-2)(n-3)}{2\,.\,4\,(2n-1)(2n-3)}\mathfrak{A}^{n-4}\mathfrak{B}^4-\ldots\right\}f(t)\,dt,$$

where
$$\mathfrak{A} \equiv x \cos t + y \sin t + iz,$$
$$\mathfrak{B} \equiv \sqrt{\{(a^2 - c^2) \cos^2 t + (b^2 - c^2) \sin^2 t\}},$$

so that

$$G_n{}^m (x, y, z) = \frac{2^n \cdot (n!)^2}{(2n)!} \int_{-\pi}^{\pi} \mathfrak{B}^n P_n \left(\frac{x \cos t + y \sin t + iz}{\sqrt{\{(a^2 - c^2) \cos^2 t + (b^2 - c^2) \sin^2 t\}}} \right) f(t) \, dt.$$

Now write $\sin t \equiv \operatorname{cd} \theta$, the modulus of the elliptic functions being, as usual, given by the equation

$$k^2 = \frac{a^2 - b^2}{a^2 - c^2}.$$

The new limits of integration are $-3K$ and K, but they may be replaced by $-2K$ and $2K$ on account of the periodicity of the integrand.

It is thus found that

$$G_n{}^m (x, y, z) = \int_{-2K}^{2K} P_n \left(\frac{k' x \operatorname{sn} \theta + y \operatorname{cn} \theta + iz \operatorname{dn} \theta}{\sqrt{(b^2 - c^2)}} \right) \phi(\theta) \, d\theta,$$

where $\phi(\theta)$ is a periodic function of θ, independent of x, y, z, which is, as yet, to be determined.

If we express the ellipsoidal harmonic as the product of three Lamé functions, with the aid of the formulae of § 23·5 we find that

$$E_n{}^m (\alpha) E_n{}^m (\beta) E_n{}^m (\gamma) = C \int_{-2K}^{2K} P_n (\mu) \phi(\theta) \, d\theta,$$

where C is a known constant and

$$\mu \equiv k^2 \operatorname{sn} \alpha \operatorname{sn} \beta \operatorname{sn} \gamma \operatorname{sn} \theta - (k^2/k'^2) \operatorname{cn} \alpha \operatorname{cn} \beta \operatorname{cn} \gamma \operatorname{cn} \theta$$
$$- (1/k'^2) \operatorname{dn} \alpha \operatorname{dn} \beta \operatorname{dn} \gamma \operatorname{dn} \theta.$$

If the ellipsoidal harmonic is of the first species or of the second species and first type, we now give β and γ the special values

$$\beta = K, \quad \gamma = K + iK',$$

and we see that

$$C \int_{-2K}^{2K} P_n (k \operatorname{sn} \alpha \operatorname{sn} \theta) \phi(\theta) \, d\theta$$

is a solution of Lamé's equation, and so, by § 23·6, $\phi(\theta)$ is a solution of Lamé's equation *which can be no other* than a multiple of* $E_n{}^m (\theta)$.

Hence it follows that

$$G_n{}^m (x, y, z) = \lambda \int_{-2K}^{2K} P_n \left(\frac{k' x \operatorname{sn} \theta + y \operatorname{cn} \theta + iz \operatorname{dn} \theta}{\sqrt{(b^2 - c^2)}} \right) E_n{}^m (\theta) \, d\theta,$$

where λ is a constant.

---

* If $\phi(\theta)$ involved the second solution, the integral would not converge.

If $G_n{}^m(x, y, z)$ be of the second species and of the second or third type we put

$$\beta = 0, \quad \gamma = K + iK',$$

or

$$\beta = 0, \quad \gamma = K$$

respectively, and we obtain anew the same formula.

It thus follows that if $G_n{}^m(x, y, z)$ be any ellipsoidal harmonic of the first or second species, then

$$G_n{}^m(x, y, z) = \lambda \int_{-2K}^{2K} P_n(\mu)\, E_n{}^m(\theta)\, d\theta,$$

$$H_n{}^m(x, y, z) = \lambda \cdot \frac{(2n)!}{2^n (n!)^2 (b^2 - c^2)^{\frac{1}{2}n}} \int_{-\pi}^{\pi} (k'x\operatorname{sn}\theta + y\operatorname{cn}\theta + iz\operatorname{dn}\theta)^n\, E_n{}^m(\theta)\, d\theta,$$

where

$$\mu \equiv (k'x\operatorname{sn}\theta + y\operatorname{cn}\theta + iz\operatorname{dn}\theta)/\sqrt{(b^2 - c^2)}.$$

23·63. *Integral formulae for ellipsoidal harmonics of the third and fourth species.*

In order to obtain integral expressions for harmonics of the third and fourth species, we turn to the equation of § 23·62, namely

$$E_n{}^m(\alpha)\, E_n{}^m(\beta)\, E_n{}^m(\gamma) = C \int_{-2K}^{2K} P_n(\mu)\, \phi(\theta)\, d\theta,$$

where

$$\mu \equiv k^2\operatorname{sn}\alpha\operatorname{sn}\beta\operatorname{sn}\gamma\operatorname{sn}\theta - (k^2/k'^2)\operatorname{cn}\alpha\operatorname{cn}\beta\operatorname{cn}\gamma\operatorname{cn}\theta - (1/k'^2)\operatorname{dn}\alpha\operatorname{dn}\beta\operatorname{dn}\gamma\operatorname{dn}\theta;$$

this equation is satisfied by harmonics of *any* species.

Suppose now that $E_n{}^m(\alpha)$ is of the fourth species or of the first type of the third species so that it has $\operatorname{cn}\alpha\operatorname{dn}\alpha$ as a factor.

We next differentiate the equation with respect to β and γ, and then put $\beta = K$, $\gamma = K + iK'$.

It is thus found that

$$E_n{}^m(\alpha) \left[\frac{d}{d\beta} E_n{}^m(\beta) \right]_{\beta = K} \left[\frac{d}{d\gamma} E_n{}^m(\gamma) \right]_{\gamma = K+iK'}$$

$$= C \int_{-2K}^{2K} \left[\frac{\partial^2 P_n(\mu)}{\partial\beta\,\partial\gamma} \right]_{(\beta = K,\ \gamma = K+iK')} \phi(\theta)\, d\theta.$$

Now

$$\left[\frac{\partial P_n(\mu)}{\partial\gamma} \right]_{\gamma = K+iK'} = -(i/k')\operatorname{dn}\alpha\operatorname{dn}\beta\operatorname{dn}\theta\, P_n'(\mu),$$

so that

$$\left[\frac{\partial^2 P_n(\mu)}{\partial\beta\,\partial\gamma} \right]_{(\beta = K,\ \gamma = K+iK')} = -k\operatorname{cn}\alpha\operatorname{dn}\alpha\operatorname{cn}\theta\operatorname{dn}\theta\, P_n''(k\operatorname{sn}\alpha\operatorname{sn}\theta).$$

Hence

$$\int_{-2K}^{2K} \operatorname{cn}\alpha\operatorname{dn}\alpha\operatorname{cn}\theta\operatorname{dn}\theta\, P_n''(k\operatorname{sn}\alpha\operatorname{sn}\theta)\, \phi(\theta)\, d\theta$$

is a solution of Lamé's equation with $\operatorname{cn}\alpha\operatorname{dn}\alpha$ as a factor; and so, by § 23·61, $\phi(\theta)$ *can be none other than a constant multiple of* $E_n{}^m(\alpha)$.

We have thus found that the equation

$$G_n{}^m(x, y, z) = \lambda \int_{-2K}^{2K} P_n(\mu)\, E_n{}^m(\theta)\, d\theta$$

is satisfied by any ellipsoidal harmonic which has $\operatorname{cn} \alpha \operatorname{dn} \alpha$ as a factor; the corresponding formula for the homogeneous harmonic is

$$H_n{}^m(x, y, z) = \lambda\, \frac{(2n)!}{2^n (n!)^2 (b^2 - c^2)^{\frac{1}{2}n}} \int_{-2K}^{2K} (k'\, x \operatorname{sn}\theta + y \operatorname{cn}\theta + iz \operatorname{dn}\theta)^n\, E_n{}^m(\theta)\, d\theta.$$

Example. Shew that the equation of this section is satisfied by the ellipsoidal harmonics which have $\operatorname{sn} a \operatorname{dn} a$ or $\operatorname{sn} a \operatorname{cn} a$ as a factor.

23·7. *Generalisations of Lamé's equation.*

Two obvious generalisations of Lamé's equation at once suggest themselves. In the first, the constant B has not one of the characteristic values $B_n{}^m$, for which a solution is expressible as an algebraic function of $\wp(u)$; and in the second, the degree n is no longer supposed to be an integer. The first generalisation has been fully dealt with by Hermite[*] and Halphen[†], but the only case of the second which has received any attention is that in which n is half of an odd integer; this has been discussed by Brioschi[‡], Halphen[§] and Crawford[||].

We shall now examine the solution of the equation

$$\frac{d^2 \Lambda}{du^2} = \{n(n+1)\wp(u) + B\}\,\Lambda,$$

where B is arbitrary and n is a positive integer, by the method of Lindemann-Stieltjes already explained in connexion with Mathieu's equation (§§ 19·5–19·52).

The product of any pair of solutions of this equation is a solution of

$$\frac{d^3 X}{du^3} - 4\{n(n+1)\wp(u) + B\}\frac{dX}{du} - 2n(n+1)\wp'(u) X = 0,$$

by § 19·52. The algebraic form of this equation is

$$4(\xi - e_1)(\xi - e_2)(\xi - e_3)\frac{d^3 X}{d\xi^3} + 3(6\xi^2 - \tfrac{1}{2}g_2)\frac{d^2 X}{d\xi^2}$$

$$- 4\{(n^2 + n - 3)\xi + B\}\frac{dX}{d\xi} - 2n(n+1) X = 0.$$

If a solution of this in descending powers of $\xi - e_2$ be taken to be

$$X = \sum_{r=0}^{\infty} c_r (\xi - e_2)^{n-r}, \qquad (c_0 = 1)$$

* *Comptes Rendus*, LXXXV. (1877), pp. 689–695, 728–732, 821–826.
† *Fonctions Elliptiques*, II. (Paris, 1888), pp. 494–502.
‡ *Comptes Rendus*, LXXXVI. (1878), pp. 313–315.
§ *Fonctions Elliptiques*, II. (Paris, 1888), pp. 471–473.
|| *Quarterly Journal*, XXVII. (1895), pp. 93–98.

the recurrence formula for the coefficients c_r is

$$4r \left(n - r + \tfrac{1}{2}\right)(2n - r + 1)\, c_r$$
$$= (n - r + 1)\{12e_2\,(n - r)\,(n - r + 2) - 4e_2\,(n^2 + n - 3) - 4B\}\, c_{r-1}$$
$$- 2\,(n - r + 1)\,(n - r + 2)\,(e_1 - e_2)\,(e_2 - e_3)\,(2n - 2r + 3)\, c_{r-2}.$$

Write $r = n + 1$, and it is seen that $c_{n+1} = 0$; then write $r = n + 2$ and $c_{n+2} = 0$; and the recurrence formulae with $r > n + 2$ are all satisfied by taking

$$c_{n+3} = c_{n+4} = \ldots = 0.$$

Hence Lamé's generalised equation always has two solutions whose product is of the form

$$\sum_{r=0}^{n} c_r\,(\xi - e_2)^{n-r}.$$

This polynomial may be written in the form

$$\prod_{r=1}^{n} \{\wp(u) - \wp(a_r)\},$$

where $a_1, a_2, \ldots a_n$ are, as yet, undetermined as to their signs; and the two solutions of Lamé's equation will be called Λ_1, Λ_2.

Two cases arise, (I) when Λ_1/Λ_2 is constant, (II) when Λ_1/Λ_2 is not constant.

(I) The first case is easily disposed of; for unless the polynomial

$$\prod_{r=1}^{n} \{\xi - \wp(a_r)\}$$

is a perfect square in ξ, multiplied possibly by expressions of the type $\xi - e_1$, $\xi - e_2$, $\xi - e_3$, then the algebraic form of Lamé's equation has an indicial equation, one of whose roots is $\tfrac{1}{2}$, at one or more of the points $\xi = \wp(a_r)$; and this is not the case (§ 23·43).

Hence the polynomial must be a square multiplied possibly by one or more of $\xi - e_1$, $\xi - e_2$, $\xi - e_3$, and then Λ_1 is a Lamé function, so that B has one of the characteristic values $B_n{}^m$; and this is the case which has been discussed at length in §§ 23·1–23·47.

(II) In the second case we have (§ 19·53)

$$\Lambda_1 \frac{d\Lambda_2}{du} - \Lambda_2 \frac{d\Lambda_1}{du} = 2\mathfrak{C},$$

where $\mathfrak{C}$ is a constant which is not zero. Then

$$\begin{cases} \dfrac{d \log \Lambda_2}{du} - \dfrac{d \log \Lambda_1}{du} = \dfrac{2\mathfrak{C}}{X}, \\[2mm] \dfrac{d \log \Lambda_2}{du} + \dfrac{d \log \Lambda_1}{du} = \dfrac{1}{X}\dfrac{dX}{du}, \end{cases}$$

so that $\qquad \dfrac{d \log \Lambda_1}{du} = \dfrac{1}{2X}\dfrac{dX}{du} - \dfrac{\mathfrak{C}}{X}, \qquad \dfrac{d \log \Lambda_2}{du} = \dfrac{1}{2X}\dfrac{dX}{du} + \dfrac{\mathfrak{C}}{X}.$

On integration, we see that we may take

$$\Lambda_1 = \sqrt{X} \exp\left\{-\mathfrak{C}\int \frac{du}{X}\right\}.$$

Again, if we differentiate the equation

$$\frac{1}{\Lambda_1}\frac{d\Lambda_1}{du} = \frac{1}{2X}\frac{dX}{du} - \frac{\mathfrak{C}}{X},$$

we find that

$$\frac{1}{\Lambda_1}\frac{d^2\Lambda_1}{du^2} - \left\{\frac{1}{\Lambda_1}\frac{d\Lambda_1}{du}\right\}^2 = \frac{1}{2X}\frac{d^2X}{du^2} - \frac{1}{2X^2}\left(\frac{dX}{du}\right)^2 + \frac{\mathfrak{C}}{X^2}\frac{dX}{du},$$

and hence, with the aid of Lamé's equation, we obtain the interesting formula

$$n(n+1)\wp(u) + B = \frac{1}{2X}\frac{d^2X}{du^2} - \left(\frac{1}{2X}\frac{dX}{du}\right)^2 + \frac{\mathfrak{C}^2}{X^2}.$$

If now $\xi_r \equiv \wp(a_r)$, we find from this formula (when multiplied by X^2), that, if u be given the special value a_r, then

$$\left(\frac{dX}{d\xi}\right)^2_{\xi=\xi_r} = \frac{4\mathfrak{C}^2}{\wp'^2(a_r)}.$$

We now fix the signs of $a_1, a_2, \ldots a_n$ by taking

$$\left(\frac{dX}{d\xi}\right)_{\xi=\xi_r} = \frac{2\mathfrak{C}}{+\wp'(a_r)}.$$

And then, if we put $2\mathfrak{C}/X$, *qua* function of ξ, into partial fractions, it is seen that

$$\frac{2\mathfrak{C}}{X} = \sum_{r=1}^{n}\frac{\wp'(a_r)}{\xi-\wp(a_r)} = \sum_{r=1}^{n}\{\zeta(u-a_r) - \zeta(u+a_r) + 2\zeta(a_r)\},$$

and therefore

$$\Lambda_1 = \left[\prod_{r=1}^{n}\{\wp(u) - \wp(a_r)\}\right]^{\frac{1}{2}}$$

$$\times \exp\left[\frac{1}{2}\sum_{r=1}^{n}\{\log\sigma(a_r+u) - \log\sigma(a_r-u) - 2u\zeta(a_r)\}\right],$$

whence it follows that (§ 20·53, example 1)

$$\Lambda_1 = \prod_{r=1}^{n}\left\{\frac{\sigma(a_r+u)}{\sigma(u)\sigma(a_r)}\right\}\exp\left\{-u\sum_{r=1}^{n}\zeta(a_r)\right\},$$

and

$$\Lambda_2 = \prod_{r=1}^{n}\left\{\frac{\sigma(a_r-u)}{\sigma(u)\sigma(a_r)}\right\}\exp\left\{u\sum_{r=1}^{n}\zeta(a_r)\right\}.$$

The complete solution has therefore been obtained for arbitrary values of the constant B.

23·71. *The Jacobian form of the generalised Lamé equation.*

We shall now construct the solution of the equation

$$\frac{d^2\Lambda}{d\alpha^2} = \{n(n+1)k^2 \operatorname{sn}^2\alpha + A\}\Lambda,$$

for general values of A, in a form resembling that of § 23·6.

The solution which corresponds to that of § 23·6 is seen to be*

$$\Lambda = \prod_{r=1}^{n} \left\{\frac{H(\alpha + \alpha_r)}{\Theta(\alpha)}\right\} e^{\rho\alpha},$$

where $\rho, \alpha_1, \alpha_2, \ldots \alpha_n$ are constants to be determined.

On differentiating this equation it is seen that

$$\frac{1}{\Lambda}\frac{d\Lambda}{d\alpha} = \sum_{r=1}^{n} \left\{\frac{H'(\alpha + \alpha_r)}{H(\alpha + \alpha_r)} - \frac{\Theta'(\alpha)}{\Theta(\alpha)}\right\} + \rho$$

$$= \sum_{r=1}^{n} \{Z(\alpha + \alpha_r + iK') - Z(\alpha)\} + \rho + \tfrac{1}{2}n\pi i/K,$$

so that $\quad \dfrac{1}{\Lambda}\dfrac{d^2\Lambda}{d\alpha^2} - \left\{\dfrac{1}{\Lambda}\dfrac{d\Lambda}{d\alpha}\right\}^2 = \sum\limits_{r=1}^{n} \{\operatorname{dn}^2(\alpha + \alpha_r + iK') - \operatorname{dn}^2\alpha\},$

and therefore, since Λ is a solution of Lamé's equation, the constants $\rho, \alpha_1, \alpha_2, \ldots \alpha_n$ are to be determined from the consideration that the equation

$$n(n+1)k^2 \operatorname{sn}^2\alpha + A = \sum_{r=1}^{n} \{\operatorname{dn}^2(\alpha + \alpha_r + iK') - \operatorname{dn}^2\alpha\}$$

$$+ \left[\sum_{r=1}^{n} \{Z(\alpha + \alpha_r + iK') - Z(\alpha)\} + \rho + \tfrac{1}{2}n\pi i/K\right]^2$$

is to be an identity; that is to say

$$n^2 k^2 \operatorname{sn}^2\alpha + n + A + \sum_{r=1}^{n} \operatorname{cs}^2(\alpha + \alpha_r)$$

$$\equiv \left[\sum_{r=1}^{n} \{Z(\alpha + \alpha_r + iK') - Z(\alpha)\} + \rho + \tfrac{1}{2}n\pi i/K\right]^2.$$

Now both sides of the proposed identity are doubly periodic functions of α with periods $2K$, $2iK'$, and their singularities are double poles at points congruent to $-iK'$, $-\alpha_1$, $-\alpha_2$, $\ldots -\alpha_n$; the dominant terms near $-iK'$ and $-\alpha_r$ are respectively

$$\frac{n^2}{(\alpha + iK')^2}, \quad -\frac{1}{(\alpha + \alpha_r)^2}$$

in the case of each of the expressions under consideration.

The residues of the expression on the left are all zero and so, if we choose $\rho, \alpha_1, \alpha_2, \ldots \alpha_n$ so that the residues of the expression on the right are zero,

* This solution was published in 1872 in Hermite's lithographed notes of his lectures delivered at the École polytechnique.

it will follow from Liouville's theorem that the two expressions differ by a constant which can be made to vanish by proper choice of A.

We thus obtain $n + 2$ equations connecting ρ, α_1, α_2, ... α_n with A, but these equations are not all independent.

It is easy to prove that, near $-\alpha_r$,

$$\sum_{r=1}^{n} \{Z(\alpha + \alpha_r + iK') - Z(\alpha)\} + \rho + \tfrac{1}{2}n\pi i/K$$

$$= \frac{1}{\alpha + \alpha_r} + \sum_{p=1}^{n}{}' Z(\alpha_p - \alpha_r + iK') + nZ(\alpha_r) + \rho + \tfrac{1}{2}(n-1)\pi i/K + O(\alpha + \alpha_r),$$

where the prime denotes that the term for which $p = r$ is omitted; and, near $-iK'$,

$$\sum_{r=1}^{n} \{Z(\alpha + \alpha_r + iK') - Z(\alpha)\} + \rho + \tfrac{1}{2}n\pi i/K$$

$$= -\frac{n}{\alpha + iK} + \sum_{r=1}^{n} Z(\alpha_r) + \rho + O(\alpha + iK').$$

Hence the residues of

$$\left[\sum_{r=1}^{n} \{Z(\alpha + \alpha_r + iK') - Z(\alpha)\} + \rho + \tfrac{1}{2}n\pi i/K \right]^2$$

will all vanish if ρ, α_1, α_2, ... α_n are chosen so that the equations

$$\begin{cases} \sum_{p=1}^{n}{}' Z(\alpha_p - \alpha_r + iK') + nZ(\alpha_r) + \rho + \tfrac{1}{2}(n-1)\pi i/K = 0, \\[2mm] \sum_{r=1}^{n} \dot{Z}(\alpha_r) + \rho = 0 \end{cases}$$

are all satisfied.

The last equation merely gives the value of ρ, namely

$$- \sum_{r=1}^{n} Z(\alpha_r),$$

and, when we substitute this value in the first system, we find that

$$\sum_{p=1}^{n}{}' [Z(\alpha_p - \alpha_r + iK') + Z(\alpha_r) - Z(\alpha_p) + \tfrac{1}{2}\pi i/K] = 0,$$

where $r = 1, 2, ... n$. By § 22·735, example 2, the sum of the left-hand sides of these equations is zero, so they are equivalent to $n - 1$ equations at most; and, when α_1, α_2, ... α_n have any values which satisfy them, the difference

$$\left[n^2 k^2 \operatorname{sn}^2 \alpha + n + A + \sum_{r=1}^{n} \operatorname{cs}^2 (\alpha + \alpha_r) \right]$$

$$- \left[\sum_{r=1}^{n} \{Z(\alpha + \alpha_r + iK') - Z(\alpha) - Z(\alpha_r) + \tfrac{1}{2}\pi i/K\} \right]^2$$

is constant.   By taking $\alpha = 0$, it is seen that the constant is zero if

$$n + A + \sum_{r=1}^{n} \operatorname{cs}^2 \alpha_r = \left[\sum_{r=1}^{n} \left\{ Z \left(\alpha_r + iK' \right) - Z \left(\alpha_r \right) + \tfrac{1}{2} \pi i / K \right\} \right]^2,$$

i.e. if

$$\left\{ \sum_{r=1}^{n} \operatorname{cn} \alpha_r \operatorname{ds} \alpha_r \right\}^2 - \sum_{r=1}^{n} \operatorname{ns}^2 \alpha_r = A.$$

We now reduce the system of n equations; with the notation of § 22·2, if functions of a_p, a_r be denoted by the suffixes 1 and 2, it is easy to see that

$$Z \left(a_p - a_r + iK' \right) + Z \left(a_r \right) - Z \left(a_p \right) + \tfrac{1}{2} \pi i / K$$

$$= Z \left(a_p - a_r + iK' \right) + Z \left(a_r \right) - Z \left(a_p + iK' \right) + c_1 d_1 / s_1$$

$$= k^2 \operatorname{sn} \left(a_p + iK' \right) \operatorname{sn} a_r \operatorname{sn} \left(a_p + iK' - a_r \right) + c_1 d_1 / s_1$$

$$= \frac{s_2}{s_1 \operatorname{sn} \left(a_p - a_r \right)} + \frac{c_1 d_1}{s_1}$$

$$= \frac{s_2 \left(s_1 c_2 d_2 + s_2 c_1 d_1 \right) + c_1 d_1 \left(s_1{}^2 - s_2{}^2 \right)}{s_1 \left(s_1{}^2 - s_2{}^2 \right)}$$

$$= \frac{s_1 c_1 d_1 + s_2 c_2 d_2}{s_1{}^2 - s_2{}^2}.$$

Consequently a solution of Lamé's equation

$$\frac{d^2 \Lambda}{d\alpha^2} = \left\{ n \left(n + 1 \right) k^2 \operatorname{sn}^2 \alpha + A \right\} \Lambda$$

is

$$\Lambda = \prod_{r=1}^{n} \left[\frac{H \left(\alpha + \alpha_r \right)}{\Theta \left(\alpha \right)} \exp \left\{ - \alpha Z \left(\alpha_r \right) \right\} \right],$$

provided that $\alpha_1, \alpha_2, \ldots \alpha_n$ be chosen to satisfy the n independent equations comprised in the system

$$\begin{cases} \sum_{p=1}^{n}{}' \dfrac{\operatorname{sn} \alpha_p \operatorname{cn} \alpha_p \operatorname{dn} \alpha_p + \operatorname{sn} \alpha_r \operatorname{cn} \alpha_r \operatorname{dn} \alpha_r}{\operatorname{sn}^2 \alpha_p - \operatorname{sn}^2 \alpha_r} = 0, \\[2mm] \left[\sum_{r=1}^{n} \operatorname{cn} \alpha_r \operatorname{ds} \alpha_r \right]^2 - \sum_{r=1}^{n} \operatorname{ns}^2 \alpha_r = A ; \end{cases}$$

and if this solution of Lamé's equation is not doubly periodic, a second solution is

$$\prod_{r=1}^{n} \left[\frac{H \left(\alpha - \alpha_r \right)}{\Theta \left(\alpha \right)} \exp \left\{ \alpha Z \left(\alpha_r \right) \right\} \right] = 0.$$

The existence of a solution of the system of $n + 1$ equations follows from § 23·7.

REFERENCES.

G. Lamé, *Journal de Math.* II. (1837), pp. 147–188; IV. (1839), pp. 100–125, 126–163, 351–385; VIII. (1843), pp. 397–434.   *Leçons sur les fonctions inverses des transcendantes et les surfaces isothermes* (Paris, 1857).   *Leçons sur les coordonnées curvilignes* (Paris, 1859).

E. Heine, *Journal für Math.* XXIX. (1845), pp. 185–208.   *Theorie der Kugelfunctionen*, II. (Berlin, 1880).

C. Hermite, *Comptes Rendus*, LXXXV. (1877), pp. 689–695, 728–732, 821–826 ; *Ann. di Mat.* (2) IX. (1878), pp. 21–24.   *Oeuvres Mathématiques* (Paris, 1905–1917).

G. H. Halphen, *Fonctions Elliptiques*, II. (Paris, 1888).

F. Lindemann, *Math. Ann.* XIX. (1882), pp. 323–386.

K. Heun, *Math. Ann.* XXXIII. (1889), pp. 161–179, 180–196.

L. Crawford, *Quarterly Journal*, XXVII. (1895), pp. 93–98; XXIX. (1898), pp. 196–201.

W. D. Niven, *Phil. Trans. of the Royal Society*, 182 A (1891), pp. 231–278.

A. Cayley, *Phil. Trans. of the Royal Society*, 165 (1875), pp. 675–774.

G. H. Darwin, *Phil. Trans. of the Royal Society*, 197 A (1901), pp. 461–557; 198 A (1901), pp. 301–331.

Miscellaneous Examples.

1. Obtain the formula

$$G_n(x, y, z) = \frac{2^n \cdot n}{(2n)!} \int_0^\infty D^{2n} P_n\left(\frac{u}{D}\right) e^{-u} du \cdot H_n(x, y, z).$$

(Niven, *Phil. Trans.* 182 A (1891), p. 245.)

2. Shew that

$$H_n\left(\frac{\partial}{\partial x}, \frac{\partial}{\partial y}, \frac{\partial}{\partial z}\right) \frac{1}{\sqrt{(x^2+y^2+z^2)}} = \frac{(-)^n \cdot (2n)!}{2^n \cdot n!} \frac{H_n(x, y, z)}{(x^2+y^2+z^2)^{n+\frac{1}{2}}}.$$

(Hobson, *Proc. London Math. Soc.* XXIV.)

3. Shew that the 'external ellipsoidal harmonic' $F_n^m(\xi) E_n^m(\eta) E_n^m(\zeta)$ is a constant multiple of

$$H_n\left(\frac{\partial}{\partial x}, \frac{\partial}{\partial y}, \frac{\partial}{\partial z}\right)\left(1 + \frac{D^2}{2 \cdot (2n+3)} + \frac{D^4}{2 \cdot 4 (2n+3)(2n+5)} + \ldots\right) \frac{1}{\sqrt{(x^2+y^2+z^2)}}.$$

(Niven; and Hobson, *Proc. London Math. Soc.* XXIV.)

4. Discuss the confluent form of Lamé's equation when the invariants g_2 and g_3 of the Weierstrassian elliptic function are made to tend to zero; express the solution in terms of Bessel functions.

(Haentzschel, *Zeitschrift für Math. und Phys.* XXXI.)

5. If v denotes $\dfrac{H(a+\mu)}{\Theta(a)} \exp[\{\lambda - Z(\mu)\} a]$, where λ and μ are constants, shew that Lamé's equation has a solution which is expressible as a linear combination of

$$\frac{d^{n-1}v}{da^{n-1}}, \quad \frac{d^{n-3}v}{da^{n-3}}, \quad \frac{d^{n-5}v}{da^{n-5}}, \ldots,$$

where λ^2 and $\operatorname{sn}^2\mu$ are algebraic functions of the constant A.

(Hermite.)

6. Obtain solutions of

$$\frac{1}{w} \frac{d^2w}{dz^2} = 12k^2 \operatorname{sn}^2 z - 4(1+k^2) \pm 5\sqrt{(1-k^2+k^4)}.$$

(Stenberg, *Acta Math.* X.)

7. Discuss the solution of the equation

$$z(z-1)(z-a)\frac{d^2y}{dz^2} + [(a+\beta+1)z^2 - \{a+\beta-\delta+1+(\gamma+\delta)a\}z + a\gamma]\frac{dy}{dz} + a\beta(z-q)y = 0$$

in the form of the series

$$1 + a\beta \sum_{n=1}^\infty \frac{G_n(q)(z/a)^n}{n! \gamma(\gamma+1)\ldots(\gamma+n)},$$

where $G_1(q) = q$, $G_2(q) = a\beta q^2 + \{(a+\beta-\delta+1)+(\gamma+\delta)a\}q - a\gamma,$

$$G_{n+1}(q) = [n\{(a+\beta-\delta+n)+(\gamma+\delta+n-1)a\}+a\beta q] G_n(q)$$
$$- (a+n-1)(\beta+n-1)(\gamma+n-1) na G_{n-1}(q).$$

(Heun, *Math. Ann.* XXXIII.)

8. Shew that the exponents at the singularities 0, 1, a, ∞ of Heun's equation are

$$(0, 1-\gamma), \quad (0, 1-\delta), \quad (0, 1-\epsilon), \quad (a, \beta),$$

where
$$\gamma+\delta+\epsilon=a+\beta+1.$$

(Heun, *Math. Ann.* XXXIII.)

9. Obtain the following group of variables for Heun's equation, corresponding to the group

$$z, \quad 1-z, \quad \frac{1}{z}, \quad \frac{1}{1-z}, \quad \frac{z}{z-1}, \quad \frac{z-1}{z},$$

for the hypergeometric equation:

$$z, \quad 1-z, \quad \frac{1}{z}, \quad \frac{1}{1-z}, \quad \frac{z}{z-1}, \quad \frac{z-1}{z},$$

$$\frac{z}{a}, \quad \frac{a-z}{a}, \quad \frac{a}{z}, \quad \frac{a}{a-z}, \quad \frac{z}{z-a}, \quad \frac{z-a}{z},$$

$$\frac{z-a}{1-a}, \quad \frac{z-1}{a-1}, \quad \frac{1-a}{z-a}, \quad \frac{a-1}{z-1}, \quad \frac{z-a}{z-1}, \quad \frac{z-1}{z-a},$$

$$\frac{z-a}{a(z-1)}, \quad \frac{(a-1)z}{a(z-1)}, \quad \frac{a(z-1)}{z-a}, \quad \frac{a(z-1)}{(a-1)z}, \quad \frac{z-a}{(1-a)z}, \quad \frac{(1-a)z}{z-a}.$$

(Heun, *Math. Ann.* XXXIII.)

10. If the series of example 7 be called

$$F(a, q; a, \beta, \gamma, \delta; z),$$

obtain 192 solutions of the differential equation in the form of powers of z, $z-1$ and $z-a$ multiplied by functions of the type F.

[Heun gives 48 of these solutions.]

11. If $u=2v$, shew that Lamé's equation

$$\frac{d^2\Lambda}{du^2} = \{n(n+1)\wp(u)+B\}\Lambda$$

may be transformed into

$$\frac{d^2L}{dv^2} - 2n\frac{\wp''(v)}{\wp'(v)}\frac{dL}{dv} + 4\{n(2n-1)\wp(v)-B\}L=0,$$

by the substitution

$$\Lambda=\{\wp'(v)\}^{-n}L.$$

12. If $\zeta=\wp(v)$, shew that a formal solution of the equation of example 11 is

$$L=\sum_{r=0}^{\infty} b_r(\zeta-e_2)^{a-r},$$

provided that
$$(a-2n)(a-n+\tfrac{1}{2})=0$$
and that

$$4(a-r-2n)(a-r-n+\tfrac{1}{2})b_r + [12e_2(a-r+1)(a-r-2n+1)+4e_2n(2n-1)-4B]b_{r-1}$$
$$- 4(e_1-e_2)(e_2-e_3)(a-r+2)(a-r-n+\tfrac{3}{2})b_{r-2}=0.$$

(Brioschi, *Comptes Rendus*, LXXXVI. (1878), pp. 313–315 and Halphen.)

13. Shew that, if n is half of an odd positive integer, a solution of the equation of example 11 expressible in finite form is

$$L=\sum_{r=0}^{n-\frac{1}{2}} b_r(\zeta-e_2)^{2n-r},$$

provided that

$$4r(n-r+\tfrac{1}{2})\,b_r + [12e_2(2n-r+1)(r-1) - 4e_2 n(2n-1) + 4B]\,b_{r-1}$$

$$+ 4(e_1-e_2)(e_2-e_3)(2n-r+2)(n-r+\tfrac{3}{2})\,b_{r-2} = 0,$$

and B is so determined that $\qquad\qquad b_{n+\frac{1}{2}} = 0.$

(Brioschi and Halphen.)

14.   Shew that, if n is half of an odd integer, a solution of the equation of example 11 expressible in finite form is

$$L' = \sum_{p=0}^{n-\frac{1}{2}} b_p{}' (\zeta - e_2)^{n-p-\frac{1}{2}},$$

provided that

$$4p(n+p+\tfrac{1}{2})\,b_p{}' - [12e_2(n-p+\tfrac{1}{2})(n+p-\tfrac{1}{2}) - 4e_2 n(2n-1) + 4B]\,b'_{p-1}$$

$$+ 4(e_1-e_2)(e_2-e_3)(n-p+\tfrac{3}{2})(p-1)\,b'_{p-2} = 0$$

and $b'_{n+\frac{1}{2}} = 0$ is the equation which determines B.

(Crawford.)

15.   With the notation of examples 13 and 14 shew that, if

$$b_p{}' = (-)^p (e_1 - e_2)^p (e_2 - e_3)^p\, c_{n-p-\frac{1}{2}},$$

the equations which determine $c_0, c_1, \ldots c_{n-\frac{1}{2}}$ are identical with those which determine $b_0, b_1, \ldots b_{n-\frac{1}{2}}$; and deduce that, if one of the solutions of Lamé's equation (in which n is half of an odd integer) is expressible as an algebraic function of $\wp(v)$, so also is the other.

(Crawford.)

16.   Prove that the values of B determined in example 13 are real when e_1, e_2 and e_3 are real.

17.   Shew that the complete solution of

$$\frac{1}{\Lambda} \frac{d^2\Lambda}{du^2} = \tfrac{3}{4}\wp(u)$$

is

$$\Lambda = \{\wp'(\tfrac{1}{2}u)\}^{-\frac{1}{2}} \{A\wp(\tfrac{1}{2}u) + B\},$$

where A and B are arbitrary constants.

(Halphen, *Mém. par divers savants*, XXVIII. (i), (1880), p. 105.)

18.   Shew that the complete solution of

$$\frac{1}{\Lambda} \frac{d^2\Lambda}{da^2} = \tfrac{3}{4}k^2 \operatorname{sn}^2 a - \tfrac{1}{4}(1+k^2)$$

is

$$\Lambda = \{\operatorname{sn}\tfrac{1}{2}(C-a)\operatorname{cn}\tfrac{1}{2}(C-a)\operatorname{dn}\tfrac{1}{2}(C-a)\}^{-\frac{1}{2}}\{A + B\operatorname{sn}^2\tfrac{1}{2}(C-a)\},$$

where A and B are arbitrary constants and $C = 2K + iK'$.

(Jamet, *Comptes Rendus*, CXI.)

APPENDIX

THE ELEMENTARY TRANSCENDENTAL FUNCTIONS

A·1. *On certain results assumed in Chapters I–IV.*

It was convenient, in the first four chapters of this work, to assume some of the properties of the elementary transcendental functions, namely the exponential, logarithmic and circular functions ; it was also convenient to make use of a number of results which the reader would be prepared to accept intuitively by reason of his familiarity with the geometrical representation of complex numbers by means of points in a plane.

To take two instances, (i) it was assumed (§ 2·7) that $\lim (\exp z) = \exp (\lim z)$, and (ii) the geometrical concept of an angle in the Argand diagram made it appear plausible that the argument of a complex number was a many-valued function, possessing the property that any two of its values differed by an integer multiple of 2π.

The assumption of results of the first type was clearly illogical ; it was also illogical to base arithmetical results on geometrical reasoning. For, in order to put the foundations of geometry on a satisfactory basis, it is not only desirable to employ the axioms of arithmetic, but it is also necessary to utilise a further set of axioms of a more definitely geometrical character, concerning properties of points, straight lines and planes*. And, further, the arithmetical theory of the logarithm of a complex number appears to be a necessary preliminary to the development of a logical theory of angles.

Apart from this, it seems unsatisfactory to the aesthetic taste of the mathematician to employ one branch of mathematics as an essential constituent in the structure of another ; particularly when the former has, to some extent, a material basis whereas the latter is of a purely abstract nature†.

The reasons for pursuing the somewhat illogical and unaesthetic procedure, adopted in the earlier part of this work, were, firstly, that the properties of the elementary transcendental functions were required gradually in the course of Chapter II, and it seemed undesirable that the course of a general development of the various infinite processes should be frequently interrupted in order to prove theorems (with which the reader was, in all probability, already familiar) concerning a single particular function ; and, secondly, that (in connexion with the assumption of results based on geometrical considerations) a purely arithmetical mode of development of Chapters I–IV, deriving no help or illustrations from geometrical processes, would have very greatly increased the difficulties of the reader unacquainted with the methods and the spirit of the analyst.

---

* It is not our object to give any account of the foundations of geometry in this work. They are investigated by various writers, such as Whitehead, *Axioms of Projective Geometry* (Cambridge Math. Tracts, no. 4, 1906) and Mathews, *Projective Geometry* (London, 1914). A perusal of Chapters I, XX, XXII and XXV of the latter work will convince the reader that it is even more laborious to develop geometry in a logical manner, from the minimum number of axioms, than it is to evolve the theory of the circular functions by purely analytical methods. A complete account of the elements both of arithmetic and of geometry has been given by Whitehead and Russell, *Principia Mathematica* (1910–1913).

† Cf. Merz, *History of European Thought in the Nineteenth Century*, II. (London, 1903), pp. 631 (note 2) and 707 (note 1), where a letter from Weierstrass to Schwarz is quoted. See also Sylvester, *Phil. Mag.* (5), II. (1876), p. 307 [*Math. Papers*, III. (1909), p. 50].

A·11. *Summary of the Appendix.*

The general course of the Appendix is as follows:

In §§ A·2–A·22, the exponential function is defined by a power series. From this definition, combined with results contained in Chapter II, are derived the elementary properties (apart from the periodic properties) of this function. It is then easy to deduce corresponding properties of logarithms of positive numbers (§§ A·3–A·33).

Next, the sine and cosine are defined by power series from which follows the connexion of these functions with the exponential function. A brief sketch of the manner in which the formulae of elementary trigonometry may be derived is then given (§§ A·4–A·42).

The results thus obtained render it possible to discuss the periodicity of the exponential and circular functions by *purely arithmetical methods* (§§ A·5, A·51).

In §§ A·52–A·522, we consider, substantially, the continuity of the inverse circular functions. When these functions have been investigated, the theory of logarithms of complex numbers (§ A·6) presents no further difficulty.

Finally, in § A·7, it is shewn that an angle, defined in a purely analytical manner, possesses properties which are consistent with the ordinary concept of an angle, based on our experience of the material world.

It will be obvious to the reader that we do not profess to give a complete account of the elementary transcendental functions, but we have confined ourselves to a brief sketch of the logical foundations of the theory*. The developments have been given by writers of various treatises, such as Hobson, *Plane Trigonometry*; Hardy, *A course of Pure Mathematics*; and Bromwich, *Theory of Infinite Series.*

A·12. *A logical order of development of the elements of Analysis.*

The reader will find it instructive to read Chapters I–IV and the Appendix a second time in the following order:

Chapter I (omitting† all of § 1·5 except the first two paragraphs).

Chapter II to the end of § 2·61 (omitting the examples in §§ 2·31–2·61).

Chapter III to the end of § 3·34 and §§ 3·5–3·73.

The Appendix, §§ A·2–A·6 (omitting §§ A·32, A·33).

Chapter II, the examples of §§ 2·31–2·61.

Chapter III, §§ 3·341–3·4.

Chapter IV, inserting §§ A·32, A·33, A·7 after § 4·13.

Chapter II, §§ 2·7–2·82.

He should try thus to convince himself that (in that order) it is possible to elaborate a purely arithmetical development of the subject, in which the graphic and familiar language of geometry‡ is to be regarded as merely conventional.

---

* In writing the Appendix, frequent reference has been made to the article on Algebraic Analysis in the *Encyklopädie der Math. Wissenschaften* by Pringsheim and Faber, to the same article translated and revised by Molk for the *Encyclopédie des Sciences Math.*, and to Tannery, *Introduction à la Théorie des Fonctions d'une Variable* (Paris, 1904).

† The properties of the argument (or phase) of a complex number are not required in the text before Chapter V.

‡ E.g. 'a point' for 'an ordered number-pair,' 'the circle of unit radius with centre at the origin' for 'the set of ordered number-pairs (x, y) which satisfy the condition $x^2 + y^2 = 1$,' 'the points of a straight line' for 'the set of ordered number-pairs (x, y) which satisfy a relation of the type $Ax + By + C = 0$,' and so on

A·2. *The exponential function* exp z.

The exponential function, of a complex variable z, is defined by the series[*]

$$\exp z = 1 + \frac{z}{1!} + \frac{z^2}{2!} + \frac{z^3}{3!} + \ldots = 1 + \sum_{n=1}^{\infty} \frac{z^n}{n!}.$$

This series converges absolutely for all values of z (real and complex) by D'Alembert's ratio test (§ 2·36) since $\lim_{n \to \infty} |(z/n)| = 0 < 1$; so the definition is valid for all values of z.

Further, the series converges uniformly throughout any bounded domain of values of z; for, if the domain be such that $|z| \leqslant R$ when z is in the domain, then

$$|(z^n/n!)| \leqslant R^n/n!,$$

and the uniformity of the convergence is a consequence of the test of Weierstrass (§ 3·34), by reason of the convergence of the series $1 + \sum_{n=1}^{\infty} (R^n/n!)$, in which the terms are independent of z.

Moreover, since, for any fixed value of n, $z^n/n!$ is a continuous function of z, it follows from § 3·32 that the exponential function is continuous for all values of z; and hence (cf. § 3·2), if z be a variable which tends to the limit ζ, we have

$$\lim_{z \to \zeta} \exp z = \exp \zeta.$$

A·21. *The addition-theorem for the exponential function, and its consequences.*

From Cauchy's theorem on multiplication of absolutely convergent series (§ 2·53), it follows that[†]

$$(\exp z_1)(\exp z_2) = \left(1 + \frac{z_1}{1!} + \frac{z_1^2}{2!} + \ldots\right)\left(1 + \frac{z_2}{1!} + \frac{z_2^2}{2!} + \ldots\right)$$

$$= 1 + \frac{z_1 + z_2}{1!} + \frac{z_1^2 + 2z_1 z_2 + z_2^2}{2!} + \ldots$$

$$= \exp(z_1 + z_2),$$

so that $\exp(z_1 + z_2)$ can be expressed in terms of exponential functions of z_1 and of z_2 by the formula

$$\exp(z_1 + z_2) = (\exp z_1)(\exp z_2).$$

This result is known as the *addition-theorem* for the exponential function. From it, we see by induction that

$$(\exp z_1)(\exp z_2) \ldots (\exp z_n) = \exp(z_1 + z_2 + \ldots + z_n),$$

and, in particular,

$$\{\exp z\}\{\exp(-z)\} = \exp 0 = 1.$$

From the last equation, it is apparent that there is no value of z for which $\exp z = 0$; for, if there were such a value of z, since $\exp(-z)$ would exist for this value of z, we should have $0 = 1$.

It also follows that, when x is real, $\exp x > 0$; for, from the series definition, $\exp x \geqslant 1$ when $x \geqslant 0$; and, when $x \leqslant 0$, $\exp x = 1/\exp(-x) > 0$.

---

[*] It was formerly customary to define $\exp z$ as $\lim_{n \to \infty} \left(1 + \frac{z}{n}\right)^n$, cf. Cauchy, *Cours d'Analyse*, I. p. 167. Cauchy (*ibid.* pp. 168, 309) also derived the properties of the function from the series, but his investigation when z is not rational is incomplete. See also Schlömilch, *Handbuch der alg. Analysis* (1889), pp. 29, 178, 246. Hardy has pointed out (*Math. Gazette*, III. p. 284) that the limit definition has many disadvantages.

[†] The reader will at once verify that the general term in the product series is

$$(z_1^n + {}_nC_1 z_1^{n-1} z_2 + {}_nC_2 z_1^{n-2} z_2^2 + \ldots + z_2^n)/n! = (z_1 + z_2)^n/n!.$$

Further, $\exp x$ is an *increasing* function of the real variable x; for, if $k>0$,

$$\exp(x+k) - \exp x = \exp x \cdot \{\exp k - 1\} > 0,$$

because $\exp x > 0$ and $\exp k > 1$.

Also, since $\qquad\qquad \{\exp h - 1\}/h = 1 + (h/2!) + (h^2/3!) + \ldots,$

and the series on the right is seen (by the methods of § A·2) to be continuous for all values of h, we have

$$\lim_{h \to 0} \{\exp h - 1\}/h = 1,$$

and so $\qquad\qquad \dfrac{d \exp z}{dz} = \lim_{h \to 0} \dfrac{\exp(z+h) - \exp z}{h} = \exp z.$

A·22. *Various properties of the exponential function.*

Returning to the formula $(\exp z_1)(\exp z_2) \ldots (\exp z_n) = \exp(z_1 + z_2 + \ldots + z_n)$, we see that, when n is a positive integer,

$$(\exp z)^n = \exp(nz),$$

and $\qquad\qquad (\exp z)^{-n} = 1/(\exp z)^n = 1/\exp(nz) = \exp(-nz).$

In particular, taking $z=1$ and writing e in place of $\exp 1 = 2{\cdot}71828\ldots$, we see that, when m is an integer, positive or negative,

$$e^m = \exp m = 1 + (m/1!) + (m^2/2!) + \ldots.$$

Also, if μ be any rational number $(=p/q,$ where p and q are integers, q being positive)

$$(\exp \mu)^q = \exp \mu q = \exp p = e^p,$$

so that the qth power of $\exp \mu$ is e^p; that is to say, $\exp \mu$ is a value of $e^{p/q} = e^\mu$, and it is obviously (§ A·21) the real positive value.

If x be an irrational-real number (defined by a section in which a_1 and a_2 are typical members of the L-class and the R-class respectively), the *irrational* power e^x is most simply *defined* as $\exp x$; we thus have, for all real values of x, rational and irrational,

$$e^x = 1 + \frac{x}{1!} + \frac{x^2}{2!} + \ldots,$$

an equation first given by Newton*.

It is, therefore, legitimate to write e^x for $\exp x$ when x is real, and it is customary to write e^z for $\exp z$ when z is complex. The function e^z (which, of course, must not be regarded as being a power of e), thus defined, is subject to the ordinary laws of indices, viz.

$$e^z \cdot e^\zeta = e^{z+\zeta}, \quad e^{-z} = 1/e^z.$$

[NOTE. Tannery, *Leçons d'Algèbre et d'Analyse* (1906), I. p. 45, practically defines e^x, when x is irrational, as the *only* number X such that $e^{a_1} \leqslant X \leqslant e^{a_2}$, for every a_1 and a_2. From the definition we have given it is easily seen that such a *unique* number exists. For $\exp x (=X)$ satisfies the inequality, and if $X' (\neq X)$ also did so, then

$$\exp a_2 - \exp a_1 = e^{a_2} - e^{a_1} \geqslant |X' - X|,$$

so that, since the exponential function is continuous, $a_2 - a_1$ cannot be chosen arbitrarily small, and so (a_1, a_2) does not define a section.]

---

* *De Analysi per aequat. num. term. inf.* (written before 1669, but not published till 1711); it was also given both by Newton and by Leibniz in letters to Oldenburg in 1676; it was first published by Wallis in 1685 in his *Treatise on Algebra*, p. 343. The equation when x is irrational was explicitly stated by Schlömilch, *Handbuch der alg. Analysis* (1889), p. 182.

A·3.   *Logarithms of positive numbers*.*

It has been seen (§§ A·2, A·21) that, when x is real, $\exp x$ is a positive continuous increasing function of x, and obviously $\exp x \to +\infty$ as $x \to +\infty$, while

$$\exp x = 1/\exp(-x) \to 0 \text{ as } x \to -\infty.$$

If, then, a be any positive number, it follows from § 3·63 that the equation in x,

$$\exp x = a,$$

has one real root and only one. This root (which is, of course, a function of a) will be written† $\mathrm{Log}_e\, a$ or simply $\mathrm{Log}\, a$; it is called the *Logarithm of the positive number* a.

Since a one-one correspondence has been established between x and a, and since a is an increasing function of x, x must be an increasing function of a; that is to say, the Logarithm is an increasing function.

Example.   Deduce from § A·21 that $\mathrm{Log}\, a + \mathrm{Log}\, b = \mathrm{Log}\, ab$.

A·31.   *The continuity of the Logarithm.*

It will now be shewn that, when a is positive, $\mathrm{Log}\, a$ is a continuous function of a.

Let

$$\mathrm{Log}\, a = x, \quad \mathrm{Log}\,(a+h) = x+k,$$

so that

$$e^x = a, \quad e^{x+k} = a+h, \quad 1+(h/a) = e^k.$$

First suppose that $h > 0$, so that $k > 0$, and then

$$1 + (h/a) = 1 + k + \tfrac{1}{2}k^2 + \ldots > 1 + k,$$

and so

$$0 < k < h/a,$$

that is to say

$$0 < \mathrm{Log}\,(a+h) - \mathrm{Log}\, a < h/a.$$

Hence, h being positive, $\mathrm{Log}\,(a+h) - \mathrm{Log}\, a$ can be made arbitrarily small by taking h sufficiently small.

Next, suppose that $h < 0$, so that $k < 0$, and then $a/(a+h) = e^{-k}$.

Hence (taking $0 < -h < \tfrac{1}{2}a$, as is obviously permissible) we get

$$a/(a+h) = 1 + (-k) + \tfrac{1}{2}k^2 + \ldots > 1 - k,$$

and so

$$-k < -1 + a/(a+h) = -h/(a+h) < -2h/a.$$

Therefore, whether h be positive or negative, if ϵ be an arbitrary positive number and if $|h|$ be taken less than both $\tfrac{1}{2}a$ and $\tfrac{1}{2}a\epsilon$, we have

$$|\mathrm{Log}\,(a+h) - \mathrm{Log}\, a| < \epsilon,$$

and so the condition for continuity (§ 3·2) is satisfied.

A·32.   *Differentiation of the Logarithm.*

Retaining the notation of § A·31, we see, from results there proved, that, if $h \to 0$ (a being fixed), then also $k \to 0$. Therefore, when $a > 0$,

$$\frac{d\,\mathrm{Log}\, a}{da} = \lim_{k \to 0} \frac{k}{e^{x+k} - e^x} = \frac{1}{e^x} = \frac{1}{a}.$$

Since $\mathrm{Log}\, 1 = 0$, we have, by § 4·13 example 3,

$$\mathrm{Log}\, a = \int_1^a t^{-1}\, dt.$$

---

* Many mathematicians define the Logarithm by the integral formula given in § A·32. The reader should consult a memoir by Hurwitz (*Math. Ann.* LXX. (1911), pp. 33–47) on the foundations of the theory of the logarithm.

† This is in agreement with the notation of most text-books, in which Log denotes the principal value (see § A·6) of the logarithm of a complex number.

A·33. *The expansion of* Log $(1+a)$ *in powers of* a.

From § A·32 we have

$$\text{Log}\,(1+a)=\int_0^a (1+t)^{-1}\,dt$$

$$=\int_0^a \{1-t+t^2-\ldots+(-)^{n-1}t^{n-1}+(-)^n t^n (1+t)^{-1}\}\,dt$$

$$=a-\tfrac{1}{2}a^2+\tfrac{1}{3}a^3-\ldots+(-)^{n-1}\frac{1}{n}a^n+R_n,$$

where

$$R_n=(-)^n\int_0^a t^n (1+t)^{-1}\,dt.$$

Now, if $-1<a<1$, we have

$$|R_n|\leqslant \int_0^{|a|} t^n (1-|a|)^{-1}\,dt$$

$$=|a|^{n+1}\{(n+1)(1-|a|)\}^{-1}$$

$$\to 0 \text{ as } n\to\infty.$$

Hence, when $-1<a<1$, Log $(1+a)$ can be expanded into the convergent series *

$$\text{Log}\,(1+a)=a-\tfrac{1}{2}a^2+\tfrac{1}{3}a^3-\ldots=\sum_{n=1}^{\infty}(-)^{n-1}a^n/n.$$

If $a=+1$,

$$|R_n|=\int_0^1 t^n (1+t)^{-1}\,dt<\int_0^1 t^n\,dt=(n+1)^{-1}\to 0 \text{ as } n\to\infty,$$

so the expansion is valid when $a=+1$; it is not valid when $a=-1$.

Example. Shew that
$$\lim_{n\to\infty}\left(1+\frac{1}{n}\right)^n=e.$$

[We have
$$\lim_{n\to\infty} n\log\left(1+\frac{1}{n}\right)=\lim_{n\to\infty}\left(1-\frac{1}{2n}+\frac{1}{3n^2}-\ldots\right)$$
$$=1,$$

and the result required follows from the result of § A·2 that $\lim_{z\to\zeta} e^z=e^{\zeta}$.]

A·4. *The definition of the sine and cosine.*

The functions† $\sin z$ and $\cos z$ are defined analytically by means of power series, thus

$$\sin z=z-\frac{z^3}{3!}+\frac{z^5}{5!}-\ldots=\sum_{n=0}^{\infty}\frac{(-)^n z^{2n+1}}{(2n+1)!},$$

$$\cos z=1-\frac{z^2}{2!}+\frac{z^4}{4!}-\ldots=1+\sum_{n=1}^{\infty}\frac{(-)^n z^{2n}}{(2n)!};$$

these series converge absolutely for all values of z (real and complex) by § 2·36, and so the definitions are valid for all values of z.

On comparing these series with the exponential series, it is apparent that the sine and cosine are not essentially new functions, but they can be expressed in terms of exponential functions by the equations ‡

$$2i\sin z=\exp\,(iz)-\exp\,(-iz),\quad 2\cos z=\exp\,(iz)+\exp\,(-iz).$$

* This method of obtaining the Logarithmic expansion is, in effect, due to Wallis, *Phil. Trans.* II. (1668), p. 754.

† These series were given by Newton, *De Analysi...* (1711), see § A·22 footnote. The other trigonometrical functions are defined in the manner with which the reader is familiar, as quotients and reciprocals of sines and cosines.

‡ These equations were derived by Euler [they were given in a letter to Johann Bernoulli in 1740 and published in the *Hist. Acad. Berlin.* v. (1749), p. 279] from the geometrical definitions of the sine and cosine, upon which the theory of the circular functions was then universally based.

It is obvious that $\sin z$ and $\cos z$ are odd and even functions of z respectively ; that is to say

$$\sin(-z) = -\sin z, \quad \cos(-z) = \cos z.$$

A·41. *The fundamental properties of* $\sin z$ *and* $\cos z$.

It may be proved, just as in the case of the exponential function (§ A·2), that the series for $\sin z$ and $\cos z$ converge uniformly in any bounded domain of values of z, and consequently that $\sin z$ and $\cos z$ are continuous functions of z for all values of z.

Further, it may be proved in a similar manner that the series

$$1 - \frac{z^2}{3!} + \frac{z^4}{5!} - \cdots$$

defines a continuous function of z for all values of z, and, in particular, this function is continuous at $z=0$, and so it follows that

$$\lim_{z \to 0} (z^{-1} \sin z) = 1.$$

A·42. *The addition-theorems for* $\sin z$ *and* $\cos z$.

By using Euler's equations (§ A·4), it is easy to prove from properties of the exponential function that

$$\sin(z_1 + z_2) = \sin z_1 \cos z_2 + \cos z_1 \sin z_2$$

and

$$\cos(z_1 + z_2) = \cos z_1 \cos z_2 - \sin z_1 \sin z_2 ;$$

these results are known as *the addition-theorems* for $\sin z$ and $\cos z$.

It may also be proved, by using Euler's equations, that

$$\sin^2 z + \cos^2 z = 1.$$

By means of this result, $\sin(z_1 + z_2)$ can be expressed as an algebraic function of $\sin z_1$ and $\sin z_2$, while $\cos(z_1 + z_2)$ can similarly be expressed as an algebraic function of $\cos z_1$ and $\cos z_2$; so the addition-formulae may be regarded as addition-theorems in the strict sense (cf. §§ 20·3, 22·732 note).

By differentiating Euler's equations, it is obvious that

$$\frac{d \sin z}{dz} = \cos z, \qquad \frac{d \cos z}{dz} = -\sin z.$$

Example. Shew that

$$\sin 2z = 2 \sin z \cos z, \quad \cos 2z = 2 \cos^2 z - 1 ;$$

these results are known as the duplication-formulae.

A·5. *The periodicity of the exponential function.*

If z_1 and z_2 are such that $\exp z_1 = \exp z_2$, then, multiplying both sides of the equation by $\exp(-z_2)$, we get $\exp(z_1 - z_2) = 1$; and writing γ for $z_1 - z_2$, we see that, for all values of z and all integral values of n,

$$\exp(z + n\gamma) = \exp z \cdot (\exp \gamma)^n = \exp z.$$

The exponential function is then said *to have period* γ, since the effect of increasing z by γ, or by an integral multiple thereof, does not affect the value of the function.

It will now be shewn that such numbers γ (other than zero) actually exist, and that *all* the numbers γ, possessing the property just described, are comprised in the expression

$$2n\pi i, \qquad\qquad (n = \pm 1, \ \pm 2, \ \pm 3, \ \ldots)$$

where π is a certain positive number* which happens to be greater than $2\sqrt{2}$ and less than 4.

---

* The fact that π is an irrational number, whose value is $3\cdot14159\ldots$, is irrelevant to the present investigation. For an account of attempts at determining the value of π, concluding with a proof of the theorem that π satisfies no algebraic equation with rational coefficients, see Hobson's monograph *Squaring the Circle* (1913).

A·51. *The solution of the equation* $\exp \gamma = 1$.

Let $\gamma = a + i\beta$, where a and β are real; then the problem of solving the equation $\exp \gamma = 1$ is identical with that of solving the equation

$$\exp a . \exp i\beta = 1.$$

Comparing the real and imaginary parts of each side of this equation, we have

$$\exp a . \cos \beta = 1, \quad \exp a . \sin \beta = 0.$$

Squaring and adding these equations, and using the identity $\cos^2 \beta + \sin^2 \beta \equiv 1$, we get

$$\exp 2a = 1.$$

Now if a were positive, $\exp 2a$ would be greater than 1, and if a were negative, $\exp 2a$ would be less than 1; *and so the only possible value for a is zero*.

It follows that $\qquad \cos \beta = 1, \quad \sin \beta = 0.$

Now the equation $\sin \beta = 0$ is a necessary consequence of the equation $\cos \beta = 1$, on account of the identity $\cos^2 \beta + \sin^2 \beta \equiv 1$. It is therefore sufficient to consider solutions (if such solutions exist) of the equation $\cos \beta = 1$.

Instead, however, of considering the equation $\cos \beta = 1$, it is more convenient to consider the equation * $\cos x = 0$.

It will now be shewn that the equation $\cos x = 0$ has one root, and only one, lying between 0 and 2, and that this root exceeds $\sqrt{2}$; to prove these statements, we make use of the following considerations:

(I) The function $\cos x$ is certainly continuous in the range $0 \leqslant x \leqslant 2$.

(II) When $0 \leqslant x \leqslant \sqrt{2}$, we have †

$$1 - \frac{x^2}{2!} \geqslant 0, \qquad \frac{x^4}{4!} - \frac{x^6}{6!} \geqslant 0, \qquad \frac{x^8}{8!} - \frac{x^{10}}{10!} \geqslant 0, ...,$$

and so, when $0 \leqslant x \leqslant \sqrt{2}$, $\cos x > 0$.

(III) The value of $\cos 2$ is

$$1 - 2 + \tfrac{2}{3} - \frac{2^6}{720}\left(1 - \frac{4}{7.8}\right) - \frac{2^{10}}{10!}\left(1 - \frac{4}{11.12}\right) - ... = -\tfrac{1}{3} - ... < 0.$$

(IV) When $0 < x \leqslant 2$,

$$\frac{\sin x}{x} = \left(1 - \frac{x^2}{6}\right) + \frac{x^4}{120}\left(1 - \frac{x^2}{6.7}\right) + ... > 1 - \frac{x^2}{6} \geqslant \tfrac{1}{3},$$

and so, when $0 \leqslant x \leqslant 2$, $\sin x \geqslant \tfrac{1}{3}x$.

It follows from (II) and (III) combined with the results of (I) and of § 3·63 that the equation $\cos x = 0$ has *at least* one root in the range $\sqrt{2} < x < 2$, and it has no root in the range $0 \leqslant x \leqslant \sqrt{2}$.

Further, there is *not more than* one root in the range $\sqrt{2} < x < 2$; for, suppose that there were two, x_1 and x_2 $(x_2 > x_1)$; then $0 < x_2 - x_1 < 2 - \sqrt{2} < 1$, and

$$\sin (x_2 - x_1) = \sin x_2 \cos x_1 - \sin x_1 \cos x_2 = 0,$$

and this is incompatible with (IV) which shews that $\sin (x_2 - x_1) \geqslant \tfrac{1}{3}(x_2 - x_1)$.

The equation $\cos x = 0$ *therefore has one and only one root lying between 0 and 2.* This root lies between $\sqrt{2}$ and 2, and it is called $\tfrac{1}{2}\pi$; and, as stated in the footnote to § A·5, its actual value happens to be $1 \cdot 57079....$

* If $\cos x = 0$, it is an immediate consequence of the duplication-formulae that $\cos 2x = -1$ and thence that $\cos 4x = 1$, so, if x is a solution of $\cos x = 0$, $4x$ is a solution of $\cos \beta = 1$.

† The symbol $\geqslant$ may be replaced by $>$ except when $x = \sqrt{2}$ in the first place where it occurs, and except when $x = 0$ in the other places.

From the addition-formulae, it may be proved at once by induction that

$$\cos n\pi = (-1)^n, \quad \sin n\pi = 0,$$

where n is any integer.

In particular, $\cos 2n\pi = 1$, where n is any integer.

Moreover, there is no value of β, other than those values which are of the form $2n\pi$, for which $\cos \beta = 1$; for if there were such a value, it must be real[*], and so we can choose the integer m so that

$$-\pi \leqslant 2m\pi - \beta < \pi.$$

We then have

$$\sin |m\pi - \tfrac{1}{2}\beta| = \pm \sin(m\pi - \tfrac{1}{2}\beta) \doteq \pm \sin \tfrac{1}{2}\beta = \pm 2^{-\frac{1}{2}}(1 - \cos \beta)^{\frac{1}{2}} = 0,$$

and this is inconsistent[†] with $\sin |m\pi - \tfrac{1}{2}\beta| \geqslant \tfrac{1}{3} |m\pi - \tfrac{1}{2}\beta|$ unless $\beta = 2m\pi$.

Consequently the numbers $2n\pi$, $(n = 0, \pm 1, \pm 2, \ldots)$, and no others, have their cosines equal to unity.

It follows that a positive number π exists such that $\exp z$ *has period $2\pi i$ and that $\exp z$ has no period fundamentally distinct from $2\pi i$.*

The formulae of elementary trigonometry concerning the periodicity of the circular functions, with which the reader is already acquainted, can now be proved by analytical methods without any difficulty.

Example 1. Shew that $\sin \tfrac{1}{2}\pi$ is equal to 1, not to -1.

Example 2. Shew that $\tan x > x$ when $0 < x < \tfrac{1}{2}\pi$.

[For $\cos x > 0$ and

$$\sin x - x \cos x = \sum_{n=1}^{\infty} \frac{x^{4n-1}}{(4n-1)!} \left\{ 4n - 2 - \frac{x^2}{4n+1} \right\};$$

and every term in the series is positive.]

Example 3. Shew that $1 - \dfrac{x^2}{2} + \dfrac{x^4}{24} - \dfrac{x^6}{720}$ is positive when $x = \dfrac{25}{16}$, and that $1 - \dfrac{x^2}{2} + \dfrac{x^4}{24}$

vanishes when $x = (6 - 2\sqrt{3})^{\frac{1}{2}} = 1.5924\ldots$; and deduce that[‡]

$$3.125 < \pi < 3.185.$$

A·52. *The solution of a pair of trigonometrical equations.*

Let λ, μ be a pair of real numbers such that $\lambda^2 + \mu^2 = 1$.

Then, if $\lambda \neq -1$, the equations

$$\cos x = \lambda, \quad \sin x = \mu$$

have an infinity of solutions of which one and only one lies between[§] $-\pi$ and π.

First, let λ and μ be not negative; then (§ 3·63) the equation $\cos x = \lambda$ has at least one solution x_1 such that $0 \leqslant x_1 \leqslant \tfrac{1}{2}\pi$, since $\cos 0 = 1$, $\cos \tfrac{1}{2}\pi = 0$. The equation has not two solutions in this range, for if x_1 and x_2 were distinct solutions we could prove (cf. § A·51) that $\sin(x_1 - x_2) = 0$, and this would contradict § A·51 (IV), since

$$0 < |x_2 - x_1| \leqslant \tfrac{1}{2}\pi < 2.$$

Further, $\sin x_1 = +\sqrt{(1 - \cos^2 x_1)} = +\sqrt{(1 - \lambda^2)} = \mu$, so x_1 is a solution of *both* equations.

---

[*] The equation $\cos \beta = 1$ implies that $\exp i\beta = 1$, and we have seen that this equation has no complex roots.

[†] The inequality is true by (IV) since $0 \leqslant |m\pi - \tfrac{1}{2}\beta| \leqslant \tfrac{1}{2}\pi < 2$.

[‡] See De Morgan, *A Budget of Paradoxes* (London, 1872), pp. 316 *et seq.*, for reasons for proving that $\pi > 3\tfrac{1}{8}$.

[§] If $\lambda = -1$, $\pm\pi$ are solutions and there are no others in the range $(-\pi, \pi)$.

The equations have no solutions in the ranges $(-\pi, 0)$ and $(\tfrac{1}{2}\pi, \pi)$ since, in these ranges, either $\sin x$ or $\cos x$ is negative. Thus the equations have one solution, and only one, in the range $(-\pi, \pi)$.

If λ or μ (or both) is negative, we may investigate the equations in a similar manner; the details are left to the reader.

It is obvious that, if x_1 is a solution of the equations, so also is $x_1 + 2n\pi$, where n is any integer, and therefore the equations have an infinity of real solutions.

A·521. *The principal solution of the trigonometrical equations.*

The unique solution of the equations $\cos x = \lambda$, $\sin x = \mu$ (where $\lambda^2 + \mu^2 = 1$) which lies between $-\pi$ and π is called the *principal solution**, and any other solution differs from it by an integer multiple of 2π.

The *principal value†* *of the argument* of a complex number $z\ (\neq 0)$ can now be defined analytically as the principal solution of the equations
$$|z|\cos\phi = R(z), \quad |z|\sin\phi = I(z),$$
and then, if
$$z = |z| \cdot (\cos\theta + i\sin\theta),$$
we must have $\theta = \phi + 2n\pi$, and θ is called *a value of the argument* of z, and is written $\arg z$ (cf. § 1·5).

A·522. *The continuity of the argument of a complex variable.*

It will now be shewn that it is possible to choose such a value of the argument $\theta(z)$, of a complex variable z, that it is a continuous function of z, provided that z does not pass through the value zero.

Let z_0 be a given value of z and let θ_0 be any value of its argument; then, to prove that $\theta(z)$ is continuous at z_0, it is sufficient to shew that a number θ_1 exists such that $\theta_1 = \arg z_1$ and that $|\theta_1 - \theta_0|$ can be made less than an arbitrary positive number ϵ by giving $|z_1 - z_0|$ any value less than some positive number η.

Let
$$z_0 = x_0 + iy_0, \quad z_1 = x_1 + iy_1.$$

Also let $|z_1 - z_0|$ be chosen to be so small that the following inequalities are satisfied ‡ :

(I)　$|x_1 - x_0| < \tfrac{1}{2}|x_0|$, provided that $x_0 \neq 0$,

(II)　$|y_1 - y_0| < \tfrac{1}{2}|y_0|$, provided that $y_0 \neq 0$,

(III)　$|x_1 - x_0| < \tfrac{1}{4}\epsilon|z_0|$, $\quad |y_1 - y_0| < \tfrac{1}{4}\epsilon|z_0|$.

From (I) and (II) it follows that $x_0 x_1$ and $y_0 y_1$ are not negative, and
$$x_0 x_1 \geq \tfrac{1}{2}x_0^2, \quad y_0 y_1 \geq \tfrac{1}{2}y_0^2,$$
so that
$$x_0 x_1 + y_0 y_1 \geq \tfrac{1}{2}|z_0|^2.$$

Now let that value of θ_1 be taken which differs from θ_0 by less than π; then, since x_0 and x_1 have not opposite signs and y_0 and y_1 have not opposite signs§, it follows from the solution of the equations of § A·52 that θ_1 and θ_0 *differ by less than* $\tfrac{1}{2}\pi$.

Now
$$\tan(\theta_1 - \theta_0) = \frac{x_0 y_1 - x_1 y_0}{x_0 x_1 + y_0 y_1},$$

---

* If $\lambda = -1$, we take $+\pi$ as the principal solution; cf. p. 9.

† The term *principal value* was introduced in 1845 by Björling; see the *Archiv der Math. und Phys.* IX. (1847), p. 408.

‡ (I) or (II) respectively is simply to be suppressed in the case when (i) $x_0 = 0$, or when (ii) $y_0 = 0$.

§ The geometrical interpretation of these conditions is merely that z_0 and z_1 are not in different quadrants of the plane.

and so (§ A·51 example 2),

$$|\theta_1-\theta_0|\leqslant\frac{|x_0y_1-x_1y_0|}{x_0x_1+y_0y_1}$$

$$=\frac{|x_0(y_1-y_0)-y_0(x_1-x_0)|}{x_0x_1+y_0y_1}$$

$$\leqslant 2|z_0|^{-2}\{|x_0|.|y_1-y_0|+|y_0|.|x_1-x_0|\}.$$

But $|x_0|\leqslant|z_0|$ and also $|y_0|\leqslant|z_0|$; therefore

$$|\theta_1-\theta_0|\leqslant 2|z_0|^{-1}\{|y_1-y_0|+|x_1-x_0|\}<\epsilon.$$

Further, if we take $|z_1-z_0|$ less than $\frac{1}{2}|x_0|$, (if $x_0\neq 0$) and $\frac{1}{2}|y_0|$, (if $y_0\neq 0$) and $\frac{1}{4}\epsilon|z_0|$, the inequalities (I), (II), (III) above are satisfied; so that, if η be the smallest of the three numbers* $\frac{1}{2}|x_0|,\frac{1}{2}|y_0|,\frac{1}{4}\epsilon|z_0|$, by taking $|z_1-z_0|<\eta$, we have $|\theta_1-\theta_0|<\epsilon$; and this is the condition that $\theta(z)$ should be a continuous function of the complex variable z.

A·6. *Logarithms of complex numbers.*

The number ζ is said to be a *logarithm* of z if $z=e^\zeta$.

To solve this equation in ζ, write $\zeta=\xi+i\eta$, where ξ and η are real; and then we have

$$z=e^\xi(\cos\eta+i\sin\eta).$$

Taking the modulus of each side, we see that $|z|=e^\xi$, so that (§ A·3), $\xi=\mathrm{Log}|z|$; and then

$$z=|z|\cdot(\cos\eta+i\sin\eta),$$

so that η must be a value of $\arg z$.

The logarithm of a complex number is consequently a many-valued function, and it can be expressed in terms of more elementary functions by the equation

$$\log z=\mathrm{Log}|z|+i\arg z.$$

The continuity of $\log z$ (when $z\neq 0$) follows from § A·31 and § A·522, since $|z|$ is a continuous function of z.

The differential coefficient of any particular branch of $\log z$ (§ 5·7) may be determined as in § A·32; and the expansion of § A·33 may be established for $\log(1+a)$ when $|a|<1$.

Corollary. If a^z be defined to mean $e^{z\log a}$, a^z is a continuous function of z and of a when $a\neq 0$.

A·7. *The analytical definition of an angle.*

Let z_1, z_2, z_3 be three complex numbers represented by the points P_1, P_2, P_3 in the Argand diagram. Then the angle between the lines (§ A·12, footnote) P_1P_2 and P_1P_3 is defined to be any value of $\arg(z_3-z_1)-\arg(z_2-z_1)$.

It will now be shewn† that the area (defined as an integral), which is bounded by two radii of a given circle and the arc of the circle terminated by the radii, is proportional to one of the values of the angle between the radii, so that an angle (in the analytical sense) possesses the property which is given at the beginning of all text-books on Trigonometry‡.

* If any of these numbers is zero, it is to be omitted.

† The proof here given applies only to acute angles; the reader should have no difficulty in extending the result to angles greater than $\frac{1}{2}\pi$, and to the case when OX is not one of the bounding radii.

‡ Euclid's definition of an angle does not, in itself, afford a *measure* of an angle; it is shewn in treatises on Trigonometry (cf. Hobson, *Plane Trigonometry* (1918), Ch. I) that an angle is measured by twice the area of the sector which the angle cuts off from a unit circle whose centre is at the vertex of the angle.

Let $(x_1,\ y_1)$ be any point (both of whose coordinates are positive) of the circle $x^2 + y^2 = a^2 \, (a > 0)$. Let θ be the principal value of $\arg(x_1 + iy_1)$, so that $0 < \theta < \tfrac{1}{2}\pi$. Then the area bounded by OX and the line joining $(0,\ 0)$ to $(x_1,\ y_1)$ and the arc of the circle joining $(x_1,\ y_1)$ to $(a,\ 0)$ is $\displaystyle\int_0^a f(x)\,dx$, where*

$$f(x) = x \tan\theta \qquad (0 \leqslant x \leqslant a\cos\theta),$$

$$f(x) = (a^2 - x^2)^{\frac{1}{2}} \qquad (a\cos\theta \leqslant x \leqslant a),$$

if an area be defined as meaning a suitably chosen integral (cf. p. 61).

It remains to be proved that $\displaystyle\int_0^a f(x)\,dx$ is proportional to θ.

Now
$$\int_0^a f(x)\,dx = \int_0^{a\cos\theta} x\tan\theta\,dx + \int_{a\cos\theta}^a (a^2 - x^2)^{\frac{1}{2}}\,dx$$

$$= \tfrac{1}{2}a^2 \sin\theta\cos\theta + \tfrac{1}{2}\int_{a\cos\theta}^a \left\{ a^2(a^2 - x^2)^{-\frac{1}{2}} + \frac{d}{dx}\,x(a^2 - x^2)^{\frac{1}{2}} \right\} dx$$

$$= \tfrac{1}{2}a^2 \int_{a\cos\theta}^a (a^2 - x^2)^{-\frac{1}{2}}\,dx$$

$$= \tfrac{1}{2}a^2 \left\{ \int_0^1 (1 - t^2)^{-\frac{1}{2}}\,dt - \int_0^{\cos\theta} (1 - t^2)^{-\frac{1}{2}}\,dt \right\}$$

$$= \tfrac{1}{2}a^2 \{\tfrac{1}{2}\pi - (\tfrac{1}{2}\pi - \theta)\} = \tfrac{1}{2}a^2\theta,$$

on writing $x = at$ and using the example worked out on p. 64.

That is to say, the area of the sector is proportional to the angle of the sector. To this extent, we have shewn that the popular conception of an angle is consistent with the analytical definition.

* The reader will easily see the geometrical interpretation of the integral by drawing a figure.

LIST OF AUTHORS QUOTED

[The numbers refer to the pages. Initials which are rarely used are given in italics]

GENERAL INDEX

[The numbers refer to the pages. References to theorems contained in a few of the more important examples are given by numbers in italics]

Modified Heine-Borel theorem, 53

Modular angle, 492; function, 481, (equation connected with) 482; -surface, 41

Modulus, 430; of a complex number, 8; of Jacobian elliptic functions, 479, 492, (complementary) 479, 493; periods of elliptic functions regarded as functions of the, 484, 498, 499, 501, 521

Monogenic, 83; distinguished from analytic, 99

Monotonic, 57

Morera's theorem (converse of Cauchy's theorem), 87, *110*

Motions of lunar perigee and node, 406

M-test for uniformity of convergence, 49

Multiplication formula for $\Gamma(z)$, 240; for the Sigma-function, *460*

Multiplication of absolutely convergent series, 29; of asymptotic expansions, 152; of convergent series (Abel's theorem), 58, *59*

Multipliers of Theta-functions, 463

Murphy's formulae for Legendre functions and polynomials, 311, *312*

Neumann's definition of Bessel functions of the second kind, 372; expansions in series of Legendre and Bessel functions, 322, 374; (F. E. Neumann's) integral for the Legendre function of the second kind, 320; method of solving integral equations, 221

Neumann's function $[O_n(z)]$, 374; differential equation satisfied by, *385*; expansion of, 374; expansion of functions in series of, 376, *384*; integral for, 375; integral properties of, *385*; recurrence formulae for, *375*

Non-uniform convergence, 44; and discontinuity, 47

Normal functions, 224

Normal solutions of Laplace's equation, 553

Notations, for Bessel functions, 356, 372, 373; for Legendre functions, 325, 326; for quotients and reciprocals of elliptic functions, 494, *498*; for Theta-functions, 464, 479, 487

Nucleus of an integral equation, 213; symmetric, 223, 228

Numbers, 3–10 (Chapter I); basic, 462; Bernoulli's, 125; Cauchy's, 379; characteristic, 219, (reality of) 226; complex, 6; irrational, 6; irrational-real, 5; pairs of, 6; rational, 3, 4; rational-real, 5; real, 5

Odd functions, 115, 166; of Mathieu, $[se_n(z, q)]$, 407

Open, 44

Order (O and o), 11; of Bernoullian polynomials, 126; of Bessel functions, 356; of elliptic functions, 432; of Legendre functions, 324; of Mathieu functions, 410; of poles of a function, 102; of terms in a series, 25; of the factors of a product, 33; of zeros of a function, 94

Ordinary discontinuity, 42

Ordinary point of a linear differential equation, 194

Orthogonal coordinates, 394; functions, 224

Oscillation, 11

Parabolic cylinder functions $[D_n(z)]$, 347; contour integral for, 349; differential equation for, 204, *209*, 347; expansion in a power series, 347; expansion of a function as a series of, 351; general asymptotic expansion of, 348; inequalities satisfied by, *354*; integral equation satisfied by, *231*; integral properties, 350; integrals involving, *353*; integrals representing, *353*; properties when n is an integer, 350, *353, 354*; recurrence formulae, 350; relations between different kinds of $[D_n(z)$ and $D_{-n-1}(\pm iz)]$, 348; zeros of, 354. *See also* **Weber's equation**

Parallelogram of periods, 430

Parameter, change of (method of solving Mathieu's equation), 424; connected with Theta-functions, 463, 464; of a point on a curve, 442, *496, 497, 527, 530, 533*; of members of confocal systems of quadrics, 547; of third kind of elliptic integral, 522; thermometric, 405

Parseval's theorem, 182

Partial differential equations, property of, 390, *391*. *See also* **Linear differential equations**

Partition function, 462

Parts, real and imaginary, 9

Pearson's function $[\varpi_{n, m}(z)]$, *353*

P-equation, Riemann's, 206, 337; connexion with the hypergeometric equation, 208, 283; solutions of, 283, 291, (relations between) 294; transformations of, 207

Periodic coefficients, equations with (Floquet's theory of), 412

Periodic functions, integrals involving, 112, 256. *See also* **Fourier series** *and* **Doubly periodic functions**